AQUATIC PHYCOMYCETES

P. A. Dangeard, 1862-1947

A. Scherffel, 1865-1939

F. W. Zopf, 1846-1909

M. Cornu, 1843-1901

AQUATIC PHYCOMYCETES

by

FREDERICK K. SPARROW, Jr.

Second Revised Edition

ANN ARBOR • THE UNIVERSITY OF MICHIGAN PRESS

Second Revised Edition, 1960
Library of Congress Catalog Card No. 59-11269
Published in the United States of America by
The University of Michigan Press and simultaneously
in Toronto, Canada, by Ambassador Books, Ltd.

University of Michigan Studies
Scientific Series
Volume XV

Printed in The Netherlands
By E. J. Brill, Leiden

To

NAN GABLER SPARROW

PREFACE TO THE FIRST EDITION

IN THE more than two and one-half decades which have ensued since the completion of publication of Minden's treatment of the lower, primarily aquatic, groups of Phycomycetes in *Kryptogamenflora der Mark Brandenburg*, considerable new material has been accumulated about these curious and oftentimes very unplantlike organisms. The later researches, added to those of the earlier period of activity, which might well be considered to have terminated with Minden's contributions to the field, have resulted in the bringing to light of a rather rich and certainly a remarkably diverse flora composed of a hitherto unsuspected number of species. New types of sexuality and life histories have been discovered, and much has been learned of the nuclear phenomena; methods of cultivation have been evolved and other material of general biological interest made available. Coker (1923) has provided an invaluable aid to the student of the Saprolegniaceae in his monograph of that family. Furthermore, the aquatic as well as the amphibious and terrestrial species of the important genus *Pythium* have been dealt with in recent years by Miss Matthews (1931). Since the authoritative monographs of Coker and Miss Matthews are in English and of relatively late date and, in addition, since they deal with well-defined compact groups the reader is referred directly to them. There remains, however, a not inconsiderable number of organisms that have not been touched upon by either of these authors or by students of special groups (Kanouse, 1927; Indoh, 1940; and others), including in particular the large and notoriously difficult order of the Chytridiales.

The present volume is intended to give an account of the Phycomycetes, other than the Saprolegniaceae and *Pythium*, that occur in fresh and marine waters. Any biological treatise that attempts to circumscribe organisms primarily on the basis of their habitat inevitably encounters difficulties. These have not been overcome here. In general, groups whose members are predominantly inhabitants of terrestrial host plants, for example *Synchytrium* and *Physoderma*, are not dealt with, although it is evident from their structure, reproduction, and development that they might conceivably be regarded as aquatic fungi adapted for entering and occupying a special type of habitat, the living cytoplasm of their phanerogamic hosts.

It is inevitable that a book requiring some years of preparation, as this one has, should suffer to a degree from lack of uniformity, due oftentimes to a changing point of view on the part of the author. An attempt has been made, however, to be consistent in most matters, particularly in the diagnoses of genera and species. Although the classification departs from that generally used, it is believed that the taxonomic treatment is essentially a conservative one. If any doubt exists as to the distinctiveness of a species, it has not been placed in synonymy. This seems a justifiable course considering the relatively few accounts thus far published of most of these fungi and, in many groups, our as yet primitive methods of studying them. If a suitable English diagnosis is available, it has been quoted directly. Occasionally such diagnoses have been slightly modified in the interests of conciseness or in order to include additional pertinent information. Unless a specific description is accompanied by citation of a collection made by me, it has been compiled. After each specific description the substrata, collectors, and place of collection are given, together with the citation of accounts and figures in the literature. A question mark preceding the name of the substratum indicates doubt as to the identity of the *fungus*; a question mark after this name implies doubt as to the identity of the *substratum*. Needless to say, preciseness in the citation of "countries" has sometimes suffered from events of the times. Austria, Czechoslovakia, and East Prussia are here included under "Germany." Scherffel's collections made largely before the first World War are given simply as in "Hungary." When matters of international suzerainty become more static than at present, these locality names can be amended. Species considered imperfectly known are preceded by a question mark, those rejected, by an asterisk. Very recent material is interpolated wherever possible. The figures should be considered in conjunction with the text to which they apply and which they are intended to supplement.

A few specimens are cited; the following abbreviations denote the location of the material:

B.M. British Museum (N.H.), London
F. Farlow Herbarium, Harvard University
L. Herbarium of D. H. Linder, Harvard University
S. Sparrow collection.

It is probable that no book of this nature ever appears without the friendly support and active cooperation of various persons and institutions. Particularly is this true of the present work in all its phases.

The preparation of the manuscript was immeasurably facilitated by grants from the Faculty Research Fund and the Horace H. Rackham Fund. Its publication was made possible by appropriations by the Board of Regents of the University of Michigan.

The laborious task of preparing reproductions of illustrations from other authors has for the most part been done by Richard Higgins and Frances Gracey. Permission to use these illustrations has been generously given wherever the authors could be reached; the sources have been acknowledged in each instance. Professor H. Munro Fox, editor of *Biological Reviews*, has kindly allowed the reproduction of Figure 1,[1] which is taken from that journal. James McCranie has generously contributed certain figures on the cytology of *Allomyces*, and V. M. Cutter, Jr., that of *Rozella allomycis*. If no acknowledgment is made, the illustration is an original one prepared for this book. I am indebted to Professor Sarah Bach-Wiig, of Smith College, for the portrait of Dangeard, to the botany department of Michigan State College for that of Zopf, and to Doctor O. Gram, of Copenhagen, for that of Petersen.[2]

To Miss Grace Potter, assistant editor of scholarly publications of the University of Michigan, I should like to express my very great appreciation for her painstaking editing and careful supervision of the manuscript while in the process of publication. To Nan Gabler Sparrow, I am greatly indebted for help in reading proof and for her ready and able assistance in the preparing of this and other manuscripts for publication.

[1] Figure 3 in this edition.   [2] Omitted in this edition.

Because of the almost total lack of herbarium specimens of aquatic Phycomycetes and the paucity of significant data to be derived from such specimens as are available, the would-be monographer of these fungi has, perforce, to seek out his material in nature and to study it in the laboratory in the living state. That a large number of aquatic Phycomycetes have been so studied in preparation for this book has been made possible to a considerable degree by the tenure of National Research Council fellowships in the Biological Sciences and by the hospitality of the directors of many laboratories and institutions. It is a pleasure at this time to express my appreciation to Professor L. M. Massey, chairman, and H. H. Whetzel, acting chairman, of the Department of Plant Pathology, Cornell University; the late Professor Sir Albert Seward, formerly professor of botany, The Botany School, Cambridge University; Professor Knud Jessen, director of the Plante-anatomiske Laboratorium, University of Copenhagen; the director of the Universitetets Havbiologiske Laboratorium, Fredrikshavn, Jutland; Sir Edwin Butler, F. R. S., sometime director of the Imperial Mycological Institute, Kew; John Ramsbottom, F. L. S., Keeper of Botany, the British Museum (N.H.); the late Doctor Reginald Harris, formerly director of the Cold Spring Harbor Biological Laboratory; Professor H. B. Bigelow, lately director of the Woods Hole Oceanographic Institution. I am greatly indebted to my colleagues, Professors H. H. Bartlett, chairman of the Department of Botany, W. R. Taylor, and L. E. Wehmeyer, for advice solicited from time to time. D. H. Linder, S. A. Waksman, H. M. Fitzpatrick, and Ralph Emerson have all contributed in one way or another to the furtherance of this volume. Miss Hilda Harris, librarian of the Farlow Library, Harvard University, and Miss A. C. Atwood, botanical bibliographer of the Bureau of Plant Industry, have been of the greatest assistance in bibliographical matters.

I am deeply indebted to Professor E. B. Mains, director of the University of Michigan Herbarium, for his painstaking reading of the entire manuscript, for valuable suggestions, and for helpful criticism and advice. Professor J. N. Couch, of the University of North Carolina, kindly read critically the introductory material of the orders and made certain suggestions.

My sincere appreciation is expressed at this time to F. T. Brooks, F.R.S., professor of botany, Cambridge University, and to Docent Doctor H. E. Petersen, of the University of Copenhagen, for their active sponsorship of my researches and their continuing interest.

Finally, it is a genuine pleasure to acknowledge my great and lasting indebtedness to Professor W. H. Weston, Jr., of Harvard University, who, by his stimulating guidance and his love for and profound knowledge of aquatic Phycomycetes, first aroused my interest in these most curious organisms.

F. K. S., JR.

ANN ARBOR, MICHIGAN
December, 1940

PREFACE TO THE SECOND EDITION

THE second edition of *Aquatic Phycomycetes* has been extended to include: (1) descriptions of those species of *Pythium* (in key form) and of *Phytophthora* that are known to exist in nature as "water molds"; (2) of genera of the Saprolegniaceae and citations of new taxa described since Coker (1923) and Coker and Matthews (1937); and (3) of the few desmid parasites belonging to the genus *Ancylistes* of the Entomophthorales. A further addition is the inclusion of the names and citations of species of *Physoderma* parasitic on marsh and aquatic vascular plants. [1] With respect to the Plasmodiophorales, full descriptions are given of those species parasitic in aquatic cryptogams. As in *Physoderma*, citations only are included of plasmodiophoraceous species in aquatic and marsh vascular plants. In both groups there is so much need of careful morphological, life history and host range studies that to present these species otherwise at this time seems meaningless.

The treatment and arrangement of the descriptions of most of the fungi included here do not differ appreciably from those explained in the Preface of the first edition. An effort has been made to assemble

---

[1] Subsequent to 1950.

descriptions of all taxa published since then. Arbitrarily, the date limit of January 1, 1955, was established, at which time the contents were in a sense "set." Literature subsequent to that date, however, has not been omitted, but in most instances (such small groups as the Monoblepharidales excepted) no provision is made in the keys and body of the text for new taxa and results of more recent investigations. Those taxa published since the deadline date, usually through 1957, are given under the heading of "Recently Described Taxa" at the end of the descriptions of valid species. By means of footnotes, every effort has been made, even in the final page proof, to incorporate references to new investigations. For more ready reference, the format of the "List of Substrata" has been revised. No attempts have been made to tackle the nomenclatorial problems of hosts, and the binomials are usually those given by the particular investigator.

If any doubt exists as to the distinctiveness of the taxon, it has not been placed in synonymy but separated by rules from the description of the form to which it is related. Thus, the reader can make his own decision in the matter. Duplication of pertinent facts throughout is usually intentional since it is not expected that the volume will be read as a whole but, rather, will be consulted at random as the need arises.

Changes in locality names from the first edition are as follows: Great Britain substituted for England; Austria and Czechoslovakia no longer included under Germany.

I am indebted to various persons in the preparation of this edition. First and foremost I wish to express my thanks to the Dean and Executive Board of the Horace H. Rackham School of Graduate Studies of the University of Michigan for their financial aid and warm support of this entire project from the preparation of the manuscript through the issuance of the volume.

J. N. Couch has kindly scrutinized the treatment of the Saprolegniaceae and has supplied revised descriptions of the Coelomomycetaceae. J. T. Middleton went over the key to *Pythium* and then generously consented to the adoption of his style of presenting it; Grace Waterhouse made suggestions with respect to *Phytophthora* as did Ralph Emerson for the chapter on the Blastocladiales. Their comments and suggestions are here gratefully acknowledged. The responsibility for any shortcomings in these groups, however, is mine. H. H. Bartlett, as before, has supplied the Latin descriptions of new taxa, for which I am indebted to him. J. S. Karling has graciously given permission to quote certain descriptions from his considerable publications on the Phycomycetes. The portrait of Aladár Scherffel was obtained through the good offices of Olga Sebestyén of the Hungarian Institute for Biological Research at Tihany.

The preparation of the manuscript and drawings was greatly facilitated by the efforts of Margaret Barr Bigelow. Marilyn Everett Wilson and Martha Jane Stockard were of much help in the preparation of copy and in proofreading. To all these I wish to express my thanks.

F. K. S., Jr.

Ann Arbor, Michigan
March, 1959

CONTENTS

xv

ILLUSTRATIONS

INTRODUCTION

A NY truly comprehensive account of the interrelated and delicately balanced society of plants and animals existing in waters should consider all the entities, great and small, which form a part of it. As is well known, green plants by their photosynthetic activities add new materials in organic form to their environment and hence contribute in a positive way to this society. Organisms lacking chlorophyll must, for the most part, depend ultimately upon the synthesizers for their existence. Yet such nonproducers are not to be regarded as mere impoverishers of the food supply, for they may perform useful and, indeed, necessary functions in the reduction, reworking, and transformation of organic materials, and, as Bigelow (1931) in referring to the activities of marine bacteria has well put it, in the keeping in "action of the cycle of matter through its organic and inorganic stages." By far the greatest number of plants lacking chlorophyll belong in the fungi, a group which, though primarily terrestrial, has a number of aquatic representatives. The latter are for the most part Phycomycetes ("algal fungi"), although the Myxomycetes, Ascomycetes, Basidiomycetes, and Fungi Imperfecti all contain water-living forms. Species of *Labyrinthula*, for example, ordinarily regarded as Myxomycetes, have been reported not only from fresh but from marine waters, where certain ones undoubtedly cause destruction of eelgrass (Renn, 1936; Young, 1943). Ascomycetes and numerous Fungi Imperfecti, hitherto unknown, have been described in recent years from water (for example, by Ingold, 1951, 1954, 1955). No doubt many others await discovery. Of the Basidiomycetes, at least two genera of smuts, *Doassansia* and *Burrillia*, have members which attack aquatic vascular plants (Fischer, 1953).

The Phycomycetes are ordinarily considered the most primitive of the true fungi. As a whole, they include a wide diversity of forms, some showing definite relationships to the flagellates, others closely resembling colorless algae, and still others being true molds. The vegetative

1

body (thallus) may be unspecialized and entirely converted into a reproductive organ, or it may bear tapering rhizoids, or be mycelial and very extensive. In any event, the outstanding characteristic of the thallus is a tendency to be nonseptate and, in most groups, multinucleate, cross walls being laid down in vigorously growing material only to delimit the reproductive organs. The unit of nonsexual reproduction, the spore, is borne in a sporangium, and, in the aquatic and semi-aquatic orders, is provided with a single posterior flagellum, a single anterior flagellum, or two laterally or terminally attached ones. Sexual reproduction is accomplished in one great group, the "Zygomycetes," by conjugation of the tips of two mycelial branches, which results in the formation of a thick-walled zygospore; only nonmotile spores are formed. In the other group, generally spoken of collectively in the older literature as the "Oömycetes" (to which many students assign the forms treated in the present work), there is great diversity in the method of sexual reproduction and, as in the green algae, all gradations from isogamous planogametic to oögamous aplanogametic types occur. Moreover, the character of the sexual reproduction is not necessarily linked with the degree of thallus development. Thus planogametes (isogamous) are found in the endobiotic holocarpic genus *Olpidium*, a form with a simple thallus, and planogametes (anisogamous) in *Allomyces*, a eucarpic form with a well-developed mycelium. On the other hand, in *Sapromyces*, a member of the Leptomitales, although the thallus resembles that of *Allomyces*, sexual reproduction is by oögamy of a high type and, in general, involves, as in the better-known genera *Saprolegnia* and *Achlya*, the formation of an oösphere contained in an oögonium and of an antheridium. Fertilization in *Sapromyces* is accomplished by the transference of antheridial material into the oögonium through a specialized tube produced by the male gametangium, and a single thick-walled oöspore is formed from the fertilized egg. This type of sexual reproduction is characteristic of the higher aquatic and semiaquatic orders. Other variations occur, but these are sufficient to illustrate the diversity found in the Oomycetes.

The Phycomycetes comprise the following orders, which are here grouped in three series.[1]

Chytridiales
Blastocladiales
Monoblepharidales
Hyphochytriales   } Zoosporic; aquatic
Plasmodiophorales
Saprolegniales
Leptomitales
Lagenidiales

Peronosporales   } Zoosporic or "conidial"; terrestrial except for the Pythiaceae which are amphibious

Mucorales   } Conidial; terrestrial except for *Ancylistes* of
Entomophthorales   } the Entomophthorales

The zoosporic aquatic series, with which we are primarily concerned, is composed of fungi which live as saprophytes or parasites on various plants and animals or their parts, in water, or in damp soil. In this field, however, as elsewhere in biology, no hard and fast distinction can be drawn between aquatic, amphibious, and terrestrial organisms. The many and diverse soil-inhabiting zoosporic types isolated in recent years are all clearly related to and usually congeneric with purely aquatic forms and have no doubt only secondarily invaded land. Another even more striking instance of what may be termed "adaptive radiation," is to be seen in *Ancylistes*, a member of a conidial, terrestrial order (the Entomophthorales), which occurs as a parasite of desmids, a group of strictly aquatic algae. Also, there is found in the elegant series of aquatic, amphibious, and terrestrial fungi belonging to the Peronosporales, at least one genus, *Phytophthora*, that is well known both to plant pathologists and to students of aquatic fungi. The present volume does not,

[1] This arrangement was for the most part suggested by Professor W. H. Weston of Harvard University. It does not include the Zoopagales, a group (tentatively brought together by Bessey, 1950) of predaceous fungi of uncertain affinities which prey upon soil- and water-inhabiting animals.

however, deal with any group (such as *Synchytrium*, *Physoderma*,[1] and so on) whose members are exclusively inhabitants of vascular plants.

PHYLOGENY AND RELATIONSHIPS

The relationships and particularly the phylogeny of the fungi decsribed here have always had a peculiar fascination for the speculative mycologist. Lengthy accounts have appeared almost since the beginning of the investigations on aquatic Phycomycetes, each purporting to show beyond question that these fungi are derived from algae by loss of chlorophyll, or from higher fungi by the degenerative effects of parasitism, or from simpler flagellate or monad ancestry (for a full discussion in English of these theories see Atkinson, 1909b; Petersen, 1910; Cavers, 1915; Cook, 1928; Gaumann and Dodge, 1928; Fitzpatrick, 1930). As might be expected of any discussions on the phylogeny of organisms so little known as these, all such accounts suffer from the serious defect of being based on scanty and, too frequently, inaccurate information.[2] No investigator of these fungi pursues his studies for long before he comes to appreciate the enormous lacunae in our present knowledge of them. It seems useless, therefore, to add another chapter at this time to the already superabundant literature on the subject.

One paper on phylogeny should, however, be read carefully, in the original, by those interested in the lower Phycomycetes —"Endophytische Phycomyceten-Parasiten der Bacillariaceen und einige neue Monadinen. Ein Beitrag zur Phylogenie der Oomyceten (Schröter)" by A. Scherffel (1925a). The conclusions of this distinguished Hungarian investigator are of highest importance since they result from first-hand study, over many years, of flagellates, algae, and aquatic Phycomycetes. Very briefly, Scherffel considers that the aquatic Phycomycetes are made up of two distinct series, the "Chytridineen" and the "Saprolegniineen-Peronosporineen." These he believes to have arisen from differ-

---

[1] A description of the genus *Physoderma* and brief mention of the family Physodermataceae, with which it is coextensive, is given on pp. 482-483. For reasons stated there, no treatment of the species is attempted at this time.

[2] See, for instance, Schussnig (1949), in which the Myrioblepharidinae, based on *Myrioblepharis* (a mixture of a protozoan and pythiaceous fungus), is considered a group under the Archimycetes (see p. 742).

ent monad ancestors, the first from a uniflagellate type, the second from a biflagellate, and to have undergone independent development. Other features are correlated with the flagellation of the zoospore. Within the "Saprolegniineen-Peronosporineen" series two subseries are distinguished, the "Saprolegniineae" and "Pythium-Peronosporineae," which have probably arisen from an archetype similar to *Ectrogella*. Although the Monoblepharidales are recognized as distinct in origin and development from both of these series, and are probably related to the Blastocladiales, their ancestry is in doubt. For further details and for specific evidence refuting the theories of algal origin of the chytrids, or their origin from higher fungi, the reader is referred to the paper cited above. The present author is thoroughly in accord with the main features of Scherffel's ideas on phylogeny, since they seem best to fit the facts as now known. It can be added, however, that, as a result of discoveries subsequent to the publication of Scherffel's work, the Monoblepharidales appear to be unquestionably related to the chytrids and might be thought of as a terminal group of the "Chytridineen" series. As Scherffel intimated, the Blastocladiales show undoubted relationships to the chytrids on the one hand, and to the Monoblepharidales on the other.

It is believed that the interpretation of the Chytridiales given here, a modification of Scherffel's, has resulted in the recognition of a compact interrelated group of organisms. Elimination from it of numerous fungi with similar thallus structure but with very different reproductive bodies (for example, the Hyphochytriales, the Olpidiopsidaceae, and so on) has not only made the group a more homogeneous natural one but has also reëstablished it in its original sense (Sparrow, 1935b). The transference of the simple biflagellate chytrid-like fungi to orders with which they appear to have greater affinities than with the Chytridiales, has brought about a more natural arrangement of all the lower Phycomycetes. Although the classification would appear to rest primarily on the flagellation of the zoospore, other characters correlated with this are found in the great majority of species, as Scherffel (1925a) pointed out. In the chytrid series the frequently radially symmetrical zoospore is posteriorly uniflagellate; its plasma is homogeneous, almost or completely free of granules, and bears a single conspicuous, often large, oil globule. These spores are monoplanetic (monomorphic) and they usually undergo a short rest period, or pause, immediately after emergence from the sporangium. Their movement, as Cohn (1853) long ago pointed out, is highly erratic, frequently being a hopping punctuated by periods of amoeboid creeping and changes of shape. Other features of the group were noted by Scherffel. Among them are the gleaming cytoplasm and the resting spores formed by direct transformation—either sexually or asexually—of a cell (the spore usually not resting within a "mother cell" or container).

Characteristic of the members of the "Saprolegniineen-Peronosporineen" series are the biflagellate, bilaterally symmetrical zoospore, the more granular cytoplasm, and a resting spore borne within the lumen of a larger container. The secondary zoospore is somewhat kidney-like or grape-seed-like in shape and bears a shallow longitudinal groove from which two nearly equal, oppositely directed flagella arise. The plasma, in contrast to that of the chytrid zoospore, is granular, no large single globule being formed. The swimming spores appear to lack the capacity for pronounced amoeboid movement. Scherffel considered the vacuolar phenomena occurring in the sporangium during formation of the zoospores in the "Saprolegniineen-Peronosporineen" series to be a further distinction between the two groups, but cytological work (Karling, 1937b; Hillegas, 1940) has not substantiated this difference.

Within the Chytridiales, as here delimited, two series of forms are recognized, the Inoperculatae and the Operculatae, whose members frequently parallel each other in their methods of development and in their thallus structure (Sparrow, 1935b). In the first of these series, the Inoperculatae, the zoosporangium opens upon the dissolution of the discharge papilla, forming on the sporangium wall or at the tip of the discharge tube a pore for the liberation of the zoospores. In the second, the Operculatae, this pore is formed after the circumscissile dehiscence of a well-defined operculum or cap. The cap is a definite specialized morphological structure and not merely a torn-off portion of the sporangium wall or tip of the discharge tube.[1] Furthermore, the type of discharge is constant in a population of a given fungus and in the sporangia subsequently formed by its zoospores. The further interrelationships of members of the Chytridiales are indicated by the

[1] For a discussion of the "endooperculum", see p. 63.

constitution of the families and subfamilies and are chiefly based on methods of development and thallus structure.

The Hyphochytriales at present are considered an isolated group of problematical affinities, whose members have, perhaps, evolved from anteriorly rather than posteriorly uniflagellate monads. In spite of their close resemblance in body plan to the chytrids, they are not believed closely allied to them. Of the orders Blastocladiales, Monoblepharidales, Saprolegniales, Leptomitales, and Peronosporales, each appears to be composed of clearly related fungi. Whether or not the Lagenidiales as here defined will prove to be a natural group must await the test of time. The same may be said of our present concept of the Entomophthorales (*Ancylistes*). Until adequate studies have been made of the zoospores and the life cycles of a number of the species, little can be said concerning the interrelationships within the Plasmodiophorales. Indeed, this also holds true for their alliance to the Phycomycetes as a whole. [1]

THE ZOOSPORE

The now universal acceptance of the significance of the structure of the zoospore in determining the relationships of aquatic Phycomycetes makes it essential at this point to give consideration to the different types that are thus far known. More details concerning these spores will be found under the respective orders.

Five principal types of swarmers are distinguished in the zoosporic series, viz.: (1) posteriorly uniflagellate, (2) anteriorly uniflagellate, (3) unequally ("heterokont") biflagellate, (4) anteriorly biflagellate ("primary"), and (5) laterally biflagellate ("secondary"). In general they may be characterized as follows:

1. The posteriorly uniflagellate zoospore is typical of the orders Chytridiales, Blastocladiales, and Monoblepharidales. In the Chytri-

---

[1] It is becoming increasingly clear that the "Phycomycetes" as now constituted is an artificial grouping of coenocytic fungi, which embraces among its aquatic members (exclusive of *Ancylistes*) at least four distinct lines of descent: (1) the Chytridiales-Blastocladiales-Monoblepharidales, (2) the Hyphochytriales, (3) the Plasmodiophorales, (4) the Saprolegniales-Leptomitales-Lagenidiales-Peronosporales. The last-named galaxy probably has some forms derived from coenocytic algae. See Sparrow, in *Mycologia*, 50 : 797. 1958 (1959.)

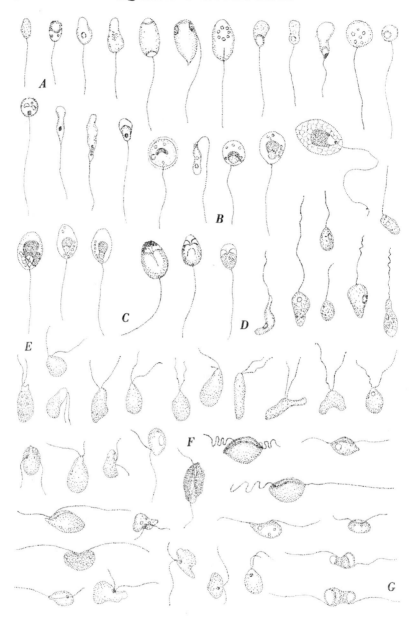

FIG. 1. Zoospore types

diales (Fig. 1 A-B, p. 8) the body of the spore is usually, but not always, radially symmetrical, and in most species contains a highly refractive "oil globule" and, sometimes, minute granules as well. The posterior flagellum may vary in length, depending upon the species, but is at least twice the diameter of the body and usually longer. In the Blastocladiales (Fig. 1 B-C), the body tends to be bilaterally symmetrical and lacks the conspicuous globule of the chytrid spore. There is, moreover, a somewhat central, hemispherical nuclear cap frequently visible, and sometimes (but usually only to be seen after staining) a tear-shaped "side body." The flagellum is always quite long. The Monoblepharidales (Fig. 1 C-D) also possess a posteriorly uniflagellate type of zoospore which, while it lacks a globule as does that of the Blastocladiales, usually has an anterior granule or collection of granules which projects forward as the spore is in motion.

2. The anteriorly uniflagellate zoospore that is found in the few fungi making up the Hyphochytriales (Fig. 1 D-E) has been variously described as obpyriform, pyriform, clavate, oval and somewhat flattened, oblong, spherical, or ovoid. One conspicuous or several small refractive globules or granules may be present in the body. At the anterior end of the spore a flagellum of varying length is attached.

3. The unequally biflagellate "heterokont" zoospore is typical of the Plasmodiophorales (Fig. 1 G, the left five spores in lowermost line) and is said to have a spherical or an oval body. In some instances the flagella are described as apically attached and oppositely disposed with the shorter one anteriorly directed; in others they are simply termed "anterior" (short) and "posterior" (long). Both flagella terminate in a whiplash (Fig. 2 L, p. 12).

The peculiar situation, noted below, that prevails in the order Saprolegniales, in which both the remaining types of spores or their homo-

---

Explanation of Figure 1

A–D. Posteriorly uniflagellate: *A–B*, Chytridiales; *B–C*, Blastocladiales; *C–D*, Monoblepharidales. *D–E*. Anteriorly uniflagellate: Hyphochytriales. *E–F*. Anteriorly biflagellate primary zoospores: Saprolegniales. *F–G*. Laterally biflagellate zoospores: Saprolegniales, Leptomitales, Lagenidiales, and Plasmodiophorales.

(From various authors, freehand. Read from left to right; letters limit the various types).

logues are formed (sometimes by a single fungus), is remarkable.

4. The anteriorly biflagellate "primary" type of saprolegniaceous zoospore (Fig. 1 E-F) has a somewhat narrowly pyriform body and its two flagella are apically or slightly subapically attached. Although these flagella have usually been said to be anteriorly directed in motion and of about equal length, they are, at least in some cases, disposed oppositely and are slightly unequal, the shorter one being anteriorly directed.

5. The secondary zoospore in the Saprolegniales (Fig. 1 F, first seven) has been characterized as "bean-shaped," "kidney-shaped," "grape-seed-like," and so on. The flagella, which arise from a shallow groove on the body, are about equal in length and are oppositely disposed. Such a type of spore is also to be found in the Leptomitales, the Lagenidiales (at least in the filamentous types), and the Peronosporales. Other but somewhat differently shaped biflagellate spores have been figured, particularly in holocarpic forms (Fig. 1 G and the two above). Owing to their small size, however, they are frequently difficult to delineate.

In recent years considerable work has been done with the aid of modern microscopic techniques and equipment on the structure of these various types of zoospores, particularly on their flagella and on their movement. The finer structure of the flagella has been carefully worked out by Couch (1941). Using Vlk's (1939) procedure, dark-field illumination, and special stains, he determined that the posteriorly flagellum of the Chytridiales, Blastocladiales, and Monoblepharidales (Fig. 2 A-G, p. 12), with few exceptions, consists of a long, relatively thick rod which narrows abruptly at its tip to a delicate prolongation of variable length. In the living state this tailpiece, or whiplash, is ordinarily invisible in many forms, but in others it may be seen when the zoospore is quiescent or comes to a temporary stop. Some spores, however, appear to lack it altogether. There is evidence that the tailpiece may be an extension of the more fluid endoplasmic core of the flagellum.

Manton, Clarke, Greenwood, and Flint (1952) made a study with an electron microscope of the posteriorly uniflagellate zoospores of *Allomyces* (Blastocladiales) and *Olpidium* (Chytridiales) which further explains flagellar structure of the whiplash type. In *Allomyces*, under magnifications of × 10,000, a wide translucent sheath may be seen surrounding a central axis. Faint longitudinal striations are detected in both axis and tip. When the flagellum is dismembered it disintegrates into eleven longitudinal strands, including a central pair; both sheath and whiplash have vanished. The presence of coarse dark bands crossing the fibrils in the basal part of the flagellum suggests the retention of some material which binds the fibrils together in the living spore. In *Olpidium brassicae* fibrillar disintegration also reveals the presence of eleven strands, including a central pair. In this instance, however, a smokelike prolongation extending beyond the apparent end of each strand is visible. This has been conjectured to be the remains of the whiplash. If so, the whiplash is composed of the same eleven strands. In the *Olpidium* zoospore there was no conspicuous sheath.[1]

Zoospores of the anteriorly uniflagellate type (Fig. 2 H) characteristic of the Hyphochytriales and exemplified by *Rhizidiomyces apophysatus* (p. 754), have a very different flagellar structure. In these, according to Couch (1941), the flagellum bears along its length a series of fine, short, lateral threads arranged either in two opposite rows or spirally or irregularly. This "tinsel" or "Flimmer" type is also typical of the anterior flagellum of a biflagellate zoospore (Fig. 2 M).

The zoospores of the laterally biflagellate type (Fig. 2 J-K, M) formed by the "Saprolegniineen—Peronosporineen" series (including the Lagenidiales) are essentially alike in flagellar structure. With respect to the primary zoospores of *Saprolegnia*, commonly referred to as "anteriorly biflagellate," Couch (1941) noted that, although the almost equal flagella are indeed attached near the anterior end, one is directed backwards and is of the whiplash type, whereas the other is directed forward and is of the tinsel type (Fig. 2 I). In the second swimming stage ("secondary zoospore") the anterior flagellum is distinctly shorter than it was on the primary spore and its tinsel hairs are more conspicuous. The longer posterior flagellum is of the usual whiplash type (Fig. 2 M).

[1] See also Koch (1956) for further details of the structure of the flagellar apparatus of the chytrid zoospore as revealed by the electron microscope. Among other things, he finds the fibrils of the flagellum to be composed of parallel subfibrils, the whole surrounded by a membrane of spiral substructure. The whiplash is a prolongation of the central thinner pair of fibrils, which extend beyond the decreasingly numerous peripheral ones. Koch also gives evidence for the presence in the body of the chytrid zoospore of a second, vestigial blepharoplast. This suggests (to him) a possible biflagellate ancestry for the group. See also Koch (1958) for details of internal structure of chytrid zoospore with light microscopy.

Further details of the structure of the flagella of the primary and secondary zoospores of *Saprolegnia* have been given by Manton, *et al.* (1951, 1952). Those investigators found that the anteriorly directed flagellum in both the primary and secondary spores has tinsel hairs arranged in two rows, each hair ending in a thin delicate point. The fibrillar axis is covered by a wide transparent sheath and a similar sheath surrounds that of the fibrillar axis of the smooth, whiplash posterior flagellum.

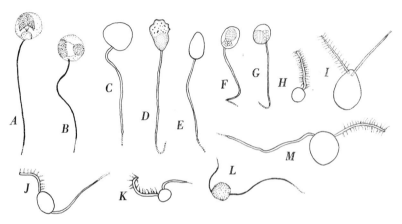

FIG. 2. Flagellar types

A–G. Zoospores of the Chytridiales, Monoblepharidales, and Blastocladiales; stained to show whiplash type of posterior flagellum. *H.* Zoospore of *Rhizidiomyces* showing tinsel type of anterior flagellum of Hyphochytriales. *I.* Primary zoospore of Saprolegniales, showing anterior tinsel and posterior whiplash flagella. *J–K.* Biflagellate secondary zoospore of *Lagenidium* and *Olpidiopsis* of the Lagenidiales, showing anterior tinsel and posterior whiplash flagella. *L.* Biflagellate zoospore of Plasmodiophorales showing flagella, both of the whiplash type. *M.* Biflagellate secondary zoospore of *Achlya*.
(From Couch, 1941; Koch, 1951; and Goldie-Smith, 1954).

Both types of flagella disintegrate into eleven fibrillar strands, but in the posterior one, which dismembers less easily, there are clear indications, as in *Allomyces*, of a transverse cementing material. These authors interpret the massive sheath surrounding the fibrillar axis as a homogeneous secretion rather than a tubular structure. There is some evidence for believing that the sheath, at least in the posterior flagellum of the secondary spore, is flattened and finlike in life with an internal framework of fine hairs. If this is true, it would, along with the greater length, explain the more powerful swimming action of the secondary zoospore as compared with the primary one. An essentially similar type of flagellar structure on the secondary zoospore of *Phytophthora* has been reported by Ferris (1954).

The cysts formed by the biflagellate primary zoospores have curious double-headed processes, which strongly resemble miniature boat hooks, scattered over the surface (Manton, *et al.*, 1951). Meier and Webster (1954) found that the cysts' formed by the motile primary spores of *Saprolegnia* and *Isoachlya* are essentially smooth-walled, although some bear tufts of radiating hairs that are believed by them to be the remains of flagella. Those of the secondary swarmers, however, have the stalked double-headed hooks. In *Protoachlya*, *Achlya*, and *Brevilegnia* neither type of cyst bore hooks and in *Dictyuchus sterile* the cysts of the secondary spores bore large spiny projections. The latter two investigators believe that more extensive study of cysts may show them to be of value in determining relationships within the family. Incidentally, their findings confirm Rothert's (1894) as to the fate of the flagella of the secondary zoospore; namely, they are shed. The flagella of the primary zoospore are, however, resorbed save for the tufts of radiating hairs previously alluded to. These are, in fact, the Flimmer-like hairs of the flagellum.

The movements of the various types of zoospores were extensively studied by Couch (1941) with the aid of dark-field illumination. He found that those of the posteriorly uniflagellate type are propelled by the transmission of waves through the flagellum in one plane and in one direction with respect to the spore. A spore may swim (1) in a wide circular orbit; (2) in a straight line, either rotating or not rotating on its axis; or (3) in a spiral path and rotating on its axis. If the spore rotates on its axis the flagellum presents an alternating single and double image, the single image when it undulates in a plane vertical to the observer, the double when it undulates in a plane which is horizontal or diagonal to him. Further information on the movement of the chytrid swarmer is given on page 60.

With respect to the anteriorly uniflagellate type of zoospore that occurs in the Hyphochytriales, Couch raises the question: how is it possible for the undulatory movement of an anteriorly directed flagellum to *pull* the spore forward, when in the Chytridiales, in which it is posteriorly directed, it *pushes* the spore ahead? The answer is that, in general, in the anterior type (represented by *Rhizidiomyces* of the Hyphochytriales) undulations are propagated just back of the tip, travel toward the body of the spore, and pull it forward. In the posterior type the tip does not undulate but, rather, waves start near the base of the flagellum and travel toward the tip and push it forward. According to Couch, the anterior type of spore is able to reverse its path and swim for a short distance with the flagellum directed backwards. In such instances he surmises wave propagation is from spore body to flagellar tip.[1] Karling (1943) in describing zoospore movement in the marine *Anisolpidium ectocarpii* says that in it the single flagellum extends straight forward and appears to be almost stationary save for the anterior portion which whips rapidly back and forth. This distal lashing propels the spore forward rapidly and evenly, the movement being interspersed by sudden stops and changes of direction. He records no undulations of the whole flagellum as noted by Couch in *Rhizidiomyces*, another member of the same order.

The primary biflagellate zoospore of *Saprolegnia* (Couch, 1941) has two subapically attached flagella which, when the spore is moving, are oppositely directed. These spores, which Couch found to be poor swimmers, exhibit two main methods of locomotion: (1) They may swim slowly and awkwardly in broad spirals while rotating on their axes, in which case, although the anterior is the more active, both flagella produce an alternating single and double image under dark-field illumination, indicating that each undulates in only one plane with respect to the zoospore; (2) the spore may move in a narrow circle making about a one-half turn on its axis as it completes a circle, with both flagella active but the anterior one always the more vigorous. Occasionally, one or the other flagellum is missing. If the posteriorly directed one is lost the zoospore swims smoothly, without rotating on its axis or describing a spiral path, but if the anterior one, the spore travels a very irregular

[1] Such a reversal of spore movement has also been noted, under certain conditions, by Gaertner (1954a) in a member of the chytrid genus *Phlyctochytrium*.

spiral path, turning on its axis, the whole movement being more awkward and irregular than in normal spores.

The secondary biflagellate zoospore of *Saprolegnia*, which emerges from the cyst formed by the primary one, is in contrast to it an extremely vigorous and more durable swimmer. The reason for this may be the fin-like construction of the posterior flagellum mentioned earlier (Manton, *et al.*, 1951). Both the anterior and the (longer) posterior flagellum present alternating double and single images but, since they do not undulate in the same plane, the two do not show like images at the same time. The spore swims in a spiral path, rotating on its own axis, the flagella presenting at one time single, at other times double images. As Couch points out, these observations, indicating that both flagella are active, are at variance with the generally accepted idea that the posterior flagellum is dragged passively along behind and functions mainly as a rudder. This passive appearance is in reality due to the fact that at such times the flagellum is undulating in a plane vertical to the observer. Further studies on zoospore motility, using phase and other types of equipment, will undoubtedly be productive and supplement the pioneering studies of Couch.

Schussnig (1949) applied the terms "monokont" and (because the single flagellum is posterior) "opisthokont" to the chytridiaceous swarmer. That of the Hyphochytriales he called "akrokont." The kidney-shaped bilaterally symmetrical secondary swarmer of the Lagenidiales–Saprolegniales–Peronosporales series he designated "subakrokont," if the flagella are subapical, and "pleurokont," if they are laterally attached in the groove. Whether these and other of his terms will convey a clearer picture of the zoospore than those in present usage seems questionable. His lengthy discussion of zoospore morphology and its bearing on origin and relationships contains, however, many stimulating passages.

A bilaterally symmetrical, dorsiventrally flattened zoospore with a laterally attached, posteriorly directed flagellum was reported by Geitler (1942) to be characteristic of *Zygorhizidium verrucosum*. Schussnig points out that it is strikingly different from the radially symmetrical "opisthokont" of other chytrid spores, and he even advocates erection of a new genus to accommodate the fungus. Laterally attached, posterior flagella have, however, been reported in other chytrids, namely in

Olpidiomorpha, where they are nearly apical (Fig. 12 J, p. 124), and in *Pleotrachelus wildemani* (Ingold, 1952). Furthermore, all chytrid zoospores are not radially symmetrical.

OCCURRENCE

Aquatic Phycomycetes occur on a wide variety of substrata, principally in fresh but also, although to lesser extent, in marine waters. Probably the only limiting factors are inimical physical conditions and lack of suitable substrata. Members of the Chytridiales are found as saprophytes or parasites on many diverse hosts. These hosts include algae, other aquatic fungi, aquatic and terrestrial herbaceous angiosperms, the spores of vascular plants, and vegetable debris; also, the eggs, embryos, and adults of microscopic animals, the empty chitinous integuments of aquatic insects, and keratinized substances, such as snake-skin casts and (especially) hair. Since other chitinous materials and kinds of keratin, when used as bait, retrieve many fungi from the aquatic habitat, they most certainly must be utilized by them under natural conditions. The Hyphochytriales are similar to the Chytridiales in occurrence. The Blastocladiales, Saprolegniales, Leptomitales, and Pythiaceae (Peronosporales) are predominantly saprophytes, although a few species of the Saprolegniales and Pythiaceae are parasitic on aquatic and terrestrial plants and on aquatic animals. Among the substrata utilized by the fresh-water saprophytes belonging to these orders are twigs, rosaceous fruits, and cadavers of fish and insects. The Monoblepharidales are usually found on sunken twigs or fruits in cool water, although several species of *Monoblepharella*, a member of this order, have, on the contrary, been isolated on hempseed from tropical soils. The Plasmodiophorales are all obligate parasites of other aquatic fungi and of terrestrial and aquatic (both fresh-water and marine) angiosperms. The Lagenidiales are primarily parasitic and usually live on fresh-water algae, fresh-water Phycomycetes, and microscopic animals. However, one family, the Sirolpidiaceae of this order, includes facultative parasites of certain marine algae and invertebrates. Members of the one genus (*Ancylistes*) of the order Entomophthorales that is treated here are parasites of desmids.

The great majority of the aquatic Phycomycetes are found in fresh waters, but the Chytridiales, Saprolegniales, Hyphochytriales, Plasmodiophorales, Lagenidiales, and the Peronosporales have marine representatives. Too little is as yet known about marine Phycomycetes to make any generalizations about their occurrence. Most of those thus far discovered belong to the Saprolegniales and the Lagenidiales. They are for the most part chiefly chytrid-like forms living in algae. A few are members of the uniflagellate groups but the presence of these in the sea is apparently rare in comparison with their occurrence in fresh water.

The work of Sörgel (1941), of Harder (1939b, 1948, 1954), and of Harder's students Remy (1948), Reinboldt (1951), and Gaertner (1954b, c) makes it abundantly clear that true chytrids are as common in soils as are the saprolegniaceous and pythiaceous forms earlier noted by Butler (1907), Harvey (1925, 1927, 1928), and others. It quickly becomes apparent to anyone investigating soil Phycomycetes that species of such genera as *Rhizophlyctis* and *Pythium* are well-nigh ubiquitous. In West Indian soils, Sörgel (1941) noted that species of these two genera, as well as of *Nowakowskiella* and various mucors, were the chief constituents of the phycomycetous flora; other species constituted less than 20 per cent. Soil from plots in contact with man or domestic animals had more fungi than that from undisturbed regions, and moist sites were more favorable than dry. A small area might support many different kinds of Phycomycetes and depth played no essential role in limiting the fungous content of the soil. Furthermore, distribution throughout an area was fairly uniform.

Harder[1] (1948) collected soils in Germany from various types of habitats, such as shores, ditches, woods, roads, fields, gardens, pastures, meadows, and uncultivated land, and recorded the frequency of occurrence of certain genera of Phycomycetes. As Sörgel had observed for the West Indies, *Nowakowskiella* and *Rhizophlyctis* headed the list and disturbed land had the richest flora. Remy (1948) also worked with German soils. She found the two genera mentioned, together with *Rhizophydium*, were most frequent. Only three of her 144 samples were completely free of phycomycetous fungi. Disturbed land and moist habitats again proved most prolific and loam was more favored than sand. Her work revealed no particular relationship between frequency of occurrence and soil acidity. Remy also noted that some of the com-

[1] See also Harder and Uebelmesser in *Arch. f. Mikrobiol.*, 31 : 82. 1958.

mon soil Phycomycetes were recoverable from the dry soil samples eight years after collection.

Similarly, Reinboldt (1951) made a series of studies, again on German soils, and found species of *Rhizophlyctis* and *Nowakowskiella*, "*Phlyctochytrium n. sp.*," four species of *Rhizophydium*, and one of *Chytridium* to be most numerous. Analysis of her samples, from 0.5 meter quadrats, indicated that these soil Phycomycetes were not uniformly distributed but, rather, tended to form pockets or nests. Moreover, in summer, soil moisture rather than soil temperature proved the more potent factor in determining the numbers of individuals (as of *Rhizophlyctis*, for example) present. From her extensive work on the effect of excretory products of angiosperm roots in the rhizosphere, Reinboldt concluded that Phycomycetes, like other microorganisms, are influenced by these substances. A paper of Gaertner's (1954b) includes data on frequency of occurrence, numbers in relation to different habitats, and other biological aspects.

In special water and soil types, as from brackish localities (Höhnk, 1939, *et seq.*)[1] and remote coral atolls (Sparrow, 1948), phycomycetous fungi have also been obtained. Höhnk (1939, 1952b, c) isolated from brackish sites species of *Pythiogeton*, *Phytophthora* ("*Pythiomorpha*"), saprolegnians, and species of *Pythium*. Harder and Uebelmesser (1955) and Uebelmesser (1956) have recorded true chytrids from seashore and strongly alkaline (desert) soils.

HYDROBIOLOGICAL ASPECTS

Recent studies have underlined the limnological importance of the fresh-water aquatic Phycomycetes. Their position in this respect, as compared with that of the bacteria, was well stated by Weston (1941) when he wrote: "It is in their parasitism that these fungi attain a significance in limnology far surpassing that of the water bacteria; for but few of the latter are destructively parasitic on aquatic animals and practically none on plants. In contrast there is abundant evidence for the sweeping statement that not one of the groups of organisms important in inland waters escapes some measure of loss from the attacks of aquatic fungi." Similarly, in commenting on the limnological role of these fungi, Welch (1952) concluded "that aquatic fungi exercise an important influence on biological productivity."

[1] See Scholz (*Arch. f. Mikrobiol.*, 30 : 119. 1958).

Just how significant these parasites are in the fresh-water habitat has been made abundantly clear by the researches of Canter (1946-53) and Canter and Lund (1948, 1951, 1953). Their investigations of certain English lakes indicate not only the widespread presence of chytridiaceous parasites but their occurrence in sufficient numbers to exert a destructive influence on populations of phytoplankters (see "The Chytrid Epidemic," p. 105).

Although the aquatic Phycomycetes of flowing waters have been little investigated, there is no reason to believe that they will differ from those in other fresh-water habitats. In one of the few such studies undertaken, Waterhouse (1942) detected a seasonal rhythm of saprophytic forms in an English river. The molds appeared in September or October, rose to a maximum in December, January, and February, and disappeared in summer. A species of *Pythium* was the only phycomycete that was recovered throughout the year. The disappearance of the fungi in summer is considered most likely to result from the rise in temperature, falling water level, and decrease in hydrogen-ion concentration. Other factors or combination of factors, such as percentage of sewage effluent present, and the weather may also be influences. Moreover, the sporadic appearance of some species may be due to their transport from higher reaches. Waterhouse concluded that, although the flora of a river was less rich than that of a pond, it was more varied and not so static. Since her study, Harvey (1952) has examined, in a preliminary fashion, the role of aquatic fungi in stream sanitation and their relation to the processes of natural purification.

Although it is not so well known, epidemics may be produced by certain aquatic Phycomycetes in marine hosts.[1] Of marine organisms affected, the stalked littoral diatoms, such as *Licmophora*, seem most susceptible to invasion by Phycomycetes. In species of that genus losses of 50 to 88 per cent of the population have been reported (Petersen, 1905; Sparrow, 1936b; Höhnk, 1939; Aleem, 1950d, 1953). Attacks by *Olpidium laguncula* on the alga *Dumontia incrassata* have had a marked effect upon its periodicity (S. M. Lodge, in Aleem, 1953) and on the Isle of Man, for example, two particular populations of it were wiped

[1] See Vishniac (1955a, 1956) and Johnson (1957b) for a discussion and descriptions of marine Phycomycetes.

out by incursion of the fungus. An epidemic in the bisporangia of the red alga *Seirospora* in the Mediterranean caused by *Petersenia lobata* was recorded by J. and G. Feldmann (1940). In this instance, the host plant reproduces by other means as well, hence, the balance of the population was little disturbed. On the other hand, in an attack on the epiphytic red alga *Falkenbergia* by a species of *Olpidiopsis* more than 70 per cent of the essential apical cells of the host were invaded, and *Trailliella* was similarly parasitized (Aleem, 1952b). Since sporulation of these last two algae occurs for only a brief period (they are sterile the rest of the time), heavy infection may and probably does seriously affect their population and limit their distribution. Aleem (*op. cit.*) discusses the whole problem of phycomycete epidemics as it relates to the marine habitat. He furnishes some evidence for the existence of resistant races and host specificity. Incidentally, he (1952a) has also recorded a fresh-water species of algal parasite (*Myzocytium proliferum*) as causing epidemics in *Spirogyra* living in brackish water (salinity, 9.6-10.1 per cent).[1]

In ecological observations made on certain marine fungal parasites of algae from the west coast of Sweden and from the Mediterranean, Aleem (1953) discovered that these fungi occur in both shallow and deep water. Their absence in the littoral region was in most cases, he found, due to the absence of the host plant. Some species will tolerate a wide range of temperature and salt concentration—the diatom parasite *Ectrogella perforans*, for example, might occur in waters that varied from 14.6 to 38 per cent in salinity and at temperatures that ranged from 5° to 30° C. Aleem noted a similar adaptability in *Pontisma lagenidioides*, an inhabitant of the red alga *Ceramium*. Earlier, Höhnk (1939) had observed the opposite at Kiel in that the distribution of seven Phycomycetes he studied was influenced markedly by salt concentrations. At salinities lower than 16.8 per cent three of his marine species dropped out; with increasing salinity zoospore formation was inhibited and the production of gemmae favored in an unnamed species of *Saprolegnia*. Among the factors favoring the spread of parasitic marine fungi in a host population, that Höhnk noted, are crowding of

[1] Earlier, Stoll (1936) had isolated species of *Achlya, Saprolegnia, Aphanomyces*, and *Pythium* from brackish water.

the hosts and their growth in sheltered, more or less polluted habitats. The latter point is most certainly true, for in this writer's experience marine Phycomycetes are most often encountered in algae from distinctly polluted waters.

Geographic Distribution

From the knowledge now available, it is apparent that members of the lower Phycomycetes are world-wide in geographic distribution. A comparison of the floras of western Europe and eastern North America, the regions in which these fungi have received most attention, reveals no proven striking cases of endemism. Scattered accounts from more remote localities, as Australia, Pacific atolls, and the arctic, all confirm their ubiquity.

Information concerning geographic distribution was greatly increased by Emerson's (1941) work on *Allomyces* and by Gaertner's (1954b) extensive investigations of soils from Africa, Sweden, and Spitsbergen. The latter investigator's 287 soil samples from Egypt, North Africa, West Africa, Equatorial East Africa, and Southeast and South Africa yielded over sixty different forms. Members of the genera *Rhizophydium, Pythium, Rhizophlyctis, Phlyctochytrium,* and *Olpidium* were most abundant.

Harder [1] (1954) extended his studies to embrace the distribution of forms in arctic regions. Other than this there are only fragmentary reports of the existence of Phycomycetes in far northerly latitudes, notably those given in Linder (1947) and Gaertner (1954b) and in the earlier studies of Petersen (1905). Harder (*op. cit.*) examined sixty-eight soil samples from Swedish Lapland (Abisko), north of the Arctic Circle, and six from Spitsbergen. In Lapland, in natural soils in the alpine zone (650—1412 m.) only four different species were recovered, whereas in the birch zone lower down, six were found. Samples from Spitsbergen yielded but two distinct species. These results led Harder to observe that as one progresses northward from the Equator to the North Pole the number of genera, as well as the frequency of the occurrence of their respective species, appears to decline.

Collection

The supposed rarity of many of the aquatic Phycomycetes appears

[1] See also Harder and Gallwitz-Uebelmesser in *Arch. f. Mikrobiol.*, 32:115. 1959.

to be due largely to a lack of knowledge of proper methods of collection. It must be admitted, however, that some are, in fact, of very infrequent occurrence.

In nature the aquatic Chytridiales utilize a variety of substrata, namely, algae, other aquatic Phycomycetes, decaying plant debris, microscopic animals and their eggs, and exuviae or empty integuments of aquatic insects.

Several methods are used in obtaining chytrid inhabitants of fresh-water algae. The first of these is by the microscopic examination of large amounts of material immediately after collection. This is a labori-ous process, but it is necessary for those forms which are unusually sensitive to environmental conditions and which are unable to with-stand change. Another method is to place the material (small mats of filamentous algae, scum of *Euglena*, and the like) immediately after collection in shallow dishes of water in diffuse light, care being taken to avoid overcrowding. Frequently, these conditions favor the devel-opment of fungi, and in a few days a variety of chytrids often appears. Still another and, perhaps, the most successful method is to set up a gross culture of a fairly hardy alga, such as *Cladophora*, and place in it bits of boiled algae, pollen, and herbaceous stems. After a few days such "baits" frequently yield interesting fungi. The algae on which chytrids are most often found are members of the Zygnematales (Con-jugatae), Oedogoniales, and Cladophorales (particularly *Cladophora*). Usually both living and dead plants of *Nitella* and *Chara* harbor a chytrid flora. Chytridiaceous fungi are frequent on filamentous water molds, such as *Achlya* and *Saprolegnia*, in old gross water cultures. Bits of plant debris from aquatic, soil (terrestrial), or bog sites occasion-ally yield chytrids upon direct microscopic investigation. A surer meth-od, however, is to prepare gross water cultures with such debris or soil cultures,[1] into which are put as bait small pieces of soft stem tissues, such as corn or grass culms, bits of leaves of *Elodea* or *Acorus*, or root tips. Care should always be taken to maintain a proper balance between the amount of organic debris and the volume of water, so as to prevent fouling of the culture. Most gross cultures of algae and debris support

---

[1] Soil cultures from cultivated land have a higher frequency of occurrence of fungi and yield more varied forms than those from "natural" soils, see p. 17.

a population of microscopic animals, usually rotifers and nematodes. The adults and their eggs should be watched for evidences of parasitic organisms, and all dead animals should be examined carefully for traces of fungi. The layer of scum formed on the sides of the culture jar at the water line is a particularly favorable place to find them. One of the most curious and productive habitats for chytrids is the empty cases (integuments or exuviae) of aquatic insects such as caddis flies, mayflies, midges, and the like.[1] After the insect emerges from the water and sheds its skin this integument is frequently washed back into the water. Within it no doubt persist the remnants of the molting fluid, which are attractive to the zoospores of certain chytrids. These fungi soon establish themselves within the integument and may flourish there in great abundance for a few days, after which they either disappear or form resting spores and become quiescent. It is possible that the material of the integument itself is utilized by the chytrids, but this does not seem probable in view of the rarity of their occurrence in integuments which have obviously been in the water for a long period. The collection of the exuviae offers no difficulty if they are searched for in early spring among stands of emergent phanerogams such as *Scirpus* or *Juncus* in shallow water.

Of late, many new chytrids have been discovered through the use as bait of such substances of animal origin as purified shrimp chitin and various forms of keratin (snake-skin casts, defatted hair and skin, horn shavings, and the like). Materials of vegetable origin, as unwater-proofed cellophane, have been similarly utilized. These baits tend to attract chitinophilic, keratinophilic, and cellulolytic fungi which are not ordinarily found.

Members of the Blastocladiales occur for the most part in two very different habitats. The most widespread genus of this order, *Blastocladia*, is primarily an inhabitant of submerged twigs and rosaceous fruits. On these it forms white, generally rather crisp and granulated hemispherical pustules of densely compacted plants. The collection of fruit- and twig-inhabiting fungi is relatively simple. Such substrata can be searched for at a likely aquatic site, but a surer method is to place

---

[1] Although dragonfly exuviae are excellent habitats for chytrids, they are too large and too opaque for good observation of the fungi.

twigs of ash or birch, or apples, pears, or the like in a galvanized perforated metal container or closed test-tube basket, or one of wire
screening, and submerge it—well concealed and anchored—in a favorable locality. After a month or more the material can be brought
back to the laboratory in a jar or in very wet paper, the surrounding
slime (which should be examined for pythiaceous fungi) washed off,
and samples made of various pustules and filamentous fungi. This
material should be worked intensively immediately after collection,
since the changing environmental conditions generally induce quick
zoospore production. Samples of minute pustules as well as of the
larger ones should be made, for the former are not always merely immature plants of larger species but often belong to totally different
ones. Submerged fruits and twigs are a prolific source of other fungi
as well as of *Blastocladia*. For example, *Macrochytrium*, a chytrid,
Gonapodya and *Monoblepharis*, members of the Monoblepharidales,
and *Apodachlya*, *Rhipidium*, *Sapromyces*, *Araiospora*, and *Mindeniella*
of the Leptomitales, and *Phytophthora* of the Peronosporales have all
been reported from these substrata.

The other habitat in which members of the Blastocladiales occur
is soil. Although species of *Allomyces*, the commonest terricolous
form, are occasionally found in standing water, they have been isolated most often from either permanently or periodically wet soil.
In the preparation of water cultures with soil samples battery jars
full of water are sterilized. After the water has cooled, the soil (about
one or two tablespoonfuls are sufficient) is dumped in and the culture
baited with an appropriate substratum. Boiled split hempseed or cadavers of fruit flies are the baits most frequently used. In the isolation
of *Allomyces* it appears almost essential that a large volume of water
cover the sunken bait.

The highly specialized parasites of mosquito larvae belonging to the
Coelomomycetaceae are, of course, to be looked for wherever the hosts
occur. Temporary pools support different forms from the ones in permanent bodies of water. The Catenariaceae are essentially similar to
the aquatic chytrids in their habitat (see p. 650).

Like the closely related Blastocladiales, the members of the Monoblepharidales have been collected from standing water and from soil.

Species of *Gonapodya* may be found on submerged twigs and fruits. *Monoblepharis* occurs for the most part on old undecorticated sunken twigs, particularly of birch and ash, in clear, often cool, water. If a few such twigs are placed in battery jars of pure water and kept at about 11° C., the growth of *Monoblepharis* is particularly favored. The fungus may form dense pustules or a complex of delicate hyphae covering the whole twig. *Monoblepharella* has, thus far, been recovered primarily from tropical soils, where it often occurs with *Allomyces* (see above). It grows readily on hempseed bait.

Those members of the Plasmodiophorales which are parasitic on aquatic Phycomycetes are sometimes found in old gross water cultures. The fungi parasitic on aquatic phanerogams produce (with the exception of *Ligniera*) conspicuous hypertrophy of the host, a fact which aids in the recognition and collection of infected material.

The simpler members of the Saprolegniales (Ectrogellaceae, Thraustochytriaceae) occur on fresh-water and marine algae. Species of *Ectrogella* often develop in Petri dishes of fresh-water diatomaceous scum left in a cool light place in the laboratory for a few days. One marine form, *E. perforans*, is very common on marine species of *Licmophora*, a stalked diatom epiphytic on littoral seaweeds. Parasitic marine forms such as *Eurychasma* and *Eurychasmidium* are local; the former, for example, has been found by the writer to occur in the Kattegat only on the phaeophycean *Striaria* growing on a clay bottom. The rhodophycean *Ceramium* infected by *Eurychasmidium* may frequently be detected by the presence on it of numerous short, abnormal, lateral branches. *Thraustochytrium proliferum* has been collected on disintegrating plants of the green alga *Bryopsis* and on the rhodophycean *Ceramium diaphanum*. It is usually found on material in shallow dishes into which fresh sea water is allowed to drip constantly. Saprophytic species of the Saprolegniaceae occur on bits of substrata of both plant and animal origin. The cadavers of insects or their larvae, dead fish, twigs, flowers, fruits, and so on, are all favorable sources of food. Split boiled seed of hemp (*Cannabis sativa*) is now extensively used as bait as well as for the maintenance of these fungi in gross water cultures. It has proved an exceedingly favorable medium, with the distinct advantage of being less likely to become fouled by bacteria and protozoa than are flies, grubs, and the like. A number of interesting fungi belonging to the Saprolegniaceae have been isolated from the soil (Harvey, 1925, *et al.*) by methods similar to those described by Butler (1907) for the collection of species of *Pythium*. In contrast to the technique noted above for the isolation of *Allomyces*, here only a thin layer of water covers the soil and the bait is allowed to float on the surface of the water as well as to rest in direct contact with the earth. Since a few of these fungi lack a motile stage, actual contact of some of the bait with the soil is essential.

The Leptomitales occur primarily as inhabitants of fruits and twigs. The methods of collection outlined for members of the Blastocladiales in a similar habitat apply here as well. *Leptomitus* has been most frequently found in water polluted by decaying organic material, such as that in the outlets of drains, sugar-beet factories, and the like.

Olpidiopsis, the commonest member of the Lagenidiales, often appears in gross water cultures of saprolegniaceous Phycomycetes. The three predominantly marine genera, *Petersenia*, *Sirolpidium*, and *Pontisma* often develop in algae which have been in a tank of running sea water for from several days to a week. *Sirolpidium* occurring in *Bryopsis* frequently causes blackened areas on the frond which are recognizable to the naked eye. Its greatest development, however, takes place after it has remained under laboratory conditions for a few days. Species of *Myzocytium* and *Lagenidium* are infrequently collected. Algal mats, particularly those composed of Conjugatae, must be systematically examined microscopically for the presence of these fungi.

The species of the Pythiaceae considered here are, for the most part, saprophytes of fruits and twigs, occurring with such forms as *Rhipidium*, *Gonapodya*, and so on. *Zoophagus*, however, has usually been found ramifying between filaments of green algae, or among plants of the Characeae.

The only genus of the Entomophthorales treated, namely, *Ancylistes*, occurs exclusively as a parasite of desmids and should be looked for in sites supporting growths of these algae.

Isolation and Culture [1]

Many of the species of fungi discussed in the present work can be

---

[1] See the important paper by Emerson (*Mycologia*, 50 : 589. 1958) on cultivation and preparation of Phycomycetes for class use.

isolated by ordinary methods and cultivated on a variety of prepared solidified media. Particularly is this true of members of the Pythiaceae, Saprolegniaceae, and Blastocladiales. By far the greater number, however, have not been isolated in unifungal culture or induced to grow on artificial media. The evidence that has slowly accumulated shows very definitely that many of them are capable of living under conditions of the laboratory. Opportunity exists, therefore, for wider investigation of their nutritional requirements and the like. Meanwhile, knowledge is being steadily added to this field; see Emerson (1950) and Cantino (1950, 1955) for a résumé of the newer literature on the subject.

If one is dealing with the rarer water molds, Emerson's (*op. cit.*) comprehensive summary of methods to use in obtaining pure cultures and maintaining them should be consulted. An excerpt from his paper is given below.

At least four important points ought to be borne in mind in making initial isolations of water fungi. The organism may tolerate only a rather narrow range of hydrogen ion concentration; aside from mineral constituents, it will require a supply of nutrients including a source of nitrogen, a source of carbon, and very possibly a source of growth factors; its zoospores may easily be injured or killed if the total osmotic concentration of the medium is high; and, finally, it may itself produce metabolic products which accumulate and rapidly become toxic, thus inhibiting growth and necessitating early transfer....

In those instances where no specific information is available regarding the nutritional requirements of a fungus, the various natural media, which have so long been used by mycologists, are still extremely useful, since they can be expected to supply adequate amounts of all the organic nutrients which might ordinarily be required. Such standardized products as the corn meal agar and prune agar of the Difco Laboratories give transparent preparations that permit detailed microscopic observation of zoospores and germlings. Semisynthetic media, provided with yeast extract, beef extract, or peptone, and some generally available carbohydrate like glucose, also serve well ... When gross enrichment cultures, like those previously mentioned, have given definite indication of some of the nutritional characteristics of an organism, more selective media can often be used to advantage. Thus, Stanier [1942] and Whiffen [1941b] both employed mineral-glucose or mineral-cellulose media in isolating cellulolytic chytrids.

Some of the water fungi, as might be expected, seem unable to tolerate high osmotic concentrations, and media containing relatively small amounts of salts and nutrients are certainly advisable for initial isolations. Dilute media also induce more rapid spreading of the filamentous forms, often allow normal zoospore emergence, and tend to reduce the rate of multiplication of bacterial contaminants.

A striking illustration of the importance of watching for toxic metabolic products was revealed in the work of Emerson & Cantino [1948] on *Blastocladia*. This organism produces acidic products so rapidly from glucose that the pH of the medium close to the colonies drops quickly below the lower limit of tolerance, and transfers have to be made every few days in order to maintain viable material on agar. That these observations are of more than isolated significance became clear recently when the writer found that *Rhipidium* and *Sapromyces* are also strong acid producers which require frequent transfer when they are cultured on agar media. Cantino [1949b] has just reported that *Pythiogeton* too forms acids when carbohydrates are metabolized.

While the development of methods for the isolation and cultivation of chytrids has been receiving increasing attention, it should be noted that Zopf (1887) long ago pointed out that some chytrids could be isolated from water on fern spores or pollen grains. The bait could be dropped into a large sample of pond water (one liter or more) and watched for fungi. By transferring to sterile water, with a sterile needle, a pollen grain having a single ripe sporangium and adding new pollen grains a unifungal culture could be established. Since this sporangium was formed from a single zoospore, the culture started from it, if no other plants were present on the pollen grain, was the equivalent of a single-spore culture. This method has been used with success by Couch (1939a) and his students in developing unifungal cultures of a number of chytrids. Couch has found pollen of *Liquidambar* a particularly favorable substratum for this work. Unifungal cultures have been reported by other investigators. Minden (1902) briefly records the isolation and cultivation on plum (or prune) gelatine of an unnamed member of the Rhizidiaceae, but he does not indicate whether or not the cultures were free from bacteria. Sparrow (1931c) isolated filaments of *Spirogyra* infected with *Cladochytrium replicatum* and after washing them thoroughly in sterile water, planted them in dishes of maize agar. The fungus spread out from the algal thread into the medium. Because of the chytrid's slow rate of growth, however, it could not be freed of bacteria. Other chytrids have been secured in unifungal (but not always pure) culture by various investigators, notably Karling (1937a, *et seq.*),

Berdan (1939), Haskins (1939), Ward (1939), and others. Whether these reports refer to bacteria-free unifungal cultures is not always made clear.

Couch (1939a) cites several methods which have been particularly effective in securing unifungal (but not bacteria-free) cultures from materials such as decaying grass leaves infested with various chytrids. He describes these in (1)—(4) below:

(1) Isolation in water of a single sporangium or (2) isolation on agar of a single sporangium; (3) isolation of spores from a single sporangium on slide; (4) isolation of single spore in a capillary tube or (5) isolation of single spore on agar or (6) isolation of a single thread or several threads on agar.

With method (1) the procedure may be as follows: Place leaf with chytrids in a drop of water in a Petri dish and in another drop of water about one cm. away in the same dish put a new piece of sterile leaf. Then under a wide field binocular dissecting microscope ($\times 40$—$\times 100$) with sharp, smooth, steel needles dissect out a small piece of leaf to which only one sporangium is attached. Transfer this to a small drop of water in the same dish and examine under compound microscope to be sure only one sporangium and no spores are present. The fragment of leaf with the sporangium may now be transferred to the fresh piece of leaf. All transfers up to this stage are made from drop to drop in the same dish, because if the delicate chytrid were transferred from one dish to another, it might dry up in the operation. After the chytrid sporangium is on the large, moist leaf, the latter is transferred to a drop of charcoal water in a fresh sterile dish and other drops of water are added to the floor and ceiling of the dish to prevent desiccation. In this operation many of the single sporangia are injured in transfer. Hence it is advisable to make large numbers of transfers.

If one is lucky, each isolated sporangium will form zoospores which will infect the new leaf, thus establishing the chytrid in pure culture save for the presence of bacteria.

The above technic is useful only if the sporangia are large. A more useful technic (2), particularly with small sporangia, and where several species are mixed and are discharging spores simultaneously, is as follows. An infected leaf is transferred after washing to the surface of a 3 % agar plate .... The desired chytrid sporangium is now dissected out from the leaf tissue and dragged along on the surface of the agar to free it from spores, bacteria, etc. After examining under the compound microscope to make sure that only one chytrid sporangium is now present, it is cut out with a little cube of agar and transferred to a fresh Petri dish in a drop of water with a fresh piece of leaf, other drops of water being added to the bottom of the dish to prevent desiccation. This is a very useful technic because it enables one to transfer nothing but the sporangium and its rhizoids. We have used a slight modification of this method by tearing the leaf tissue apart on the surface of the agar and spreading it out. If water is present, some of the sporangia may discharge their spores on the surface of the agar. The spores may then germinate in contact with the leaf, sending their rhizoids into the agar. It is possible then to remove the leaf, wash the surface of the agar with water from the wash bottle and then to dissect out one sporangium from the agar surface.

If the rhizoidal system is very complex and the spores of other fungi abundant, the method just described may be unsatisfactory, in which case the following method (3) is useful. A single sporangium about ready to discharge spores is isolated by method 1 or 2 and put on a sterile slide in a drop of water and kept under observation so that one may determine just when the spores emerge. The moment this happens some of the spores are drawn up in a capillary tube and blown out in a drop of water with a piece of sterile leaf in a fresh Petri dish. If ordinary care is used one may secure cultures by this technic descended from a few spores. It is possible so to perfect this method that one can, with a little practice and skill, make single spore cultures. This may be done as follows: (4) By using a very fine capillary tube and picking up only a few spores, then diluting the spores by mixing in another drop of water and so on by further dilutions, it is possible finally to get only one or two spores in the capillary tube. If the tube were clean to begin with, it may be examined on the surface of the Petri dish to determine how many spores it contains. If only one spore is present, the tube is then transferred to a drop of water containing a piece of leaf. If it contains two or even several spores, it is possible to break the tube in such a way that one can separate a single spore from the others.

The securing of bacteria-free cultures of chytrids on artificial media is difficult, owing primarily to the slow rate of growth of the rhizoidal system and, in many species, to the monocentric nature of the thallus. Couch's methods 5 and 6 (below) refer to the preparation of bacteria-free cultures:

So far we have developed two methods for doing this. The easier, if the spores will germinate on agar, is by the isolation of a single spore on agar (5). After much experimenting with spore germination on nutrient agars, we have found several which are useful in this work.

1. Plain agar 3 % (the agar shreds should be washed over night in several changes of water to free from trash).

2. Agar No. 12 (Leitner's agar) 2 % agar and 0.004 % peptone (meat).

3. Agar No. 13 (Foust's agar) 2 % agar and 0.15 % maltose and 0.004 % peptone (meat).

4. Corn meal agar (use 2-4 heaping teaspoons full to 1 litre water, depending upon strength desired. Heat gently in water bath, temperature about 60°, 1 hour. Filter. Add water to make 1 litre. Agar 2 %).

The spores seem to germinate better on plain agar or agar with very small amounts of nutrient material. Before taking time to spread the spores carefully on agar it is worth while to drop a few on the medium used to determine whether or not the spores go to pieces or settle down and encyst. Naturally, if the spores are plasmolized by the nutrient agar it is a waste of time to go further with that particular medium. Spores to be isolated should be as free from bacteria as possible. Hence, it is well to isolate one or a few sporangia about to discharge spores in a drop of water on a sterile slide. However, where only a few spores are available it is possible to pick them up with a platinum loop or a small pipette directly from the original dish. The essential part of this technic is to spread the spores so well on the surface of the agar that some of the spores will be completely separated from the bacteria and other organisms. A successful spreading requires a firm agar (2-3 % agar) and a steady hand. The spores are picked up with a platinum loop and the loop dragged along the surface of the plate in a straight line. Several east-west lines may be made and then another group of north-south ones. It is unnecessary to mark these lines for the bacterial colonies will make the lines quite evident. If the laboratory is clean and free from spores of *Penicillium*, etc., it is possible to do this spreading with the uncovered dish on the table. However, if the air is dusty, the dish should be held at an angle with the agar surface down. If the spores germinate at all they will germinate within 12 to 24 hours or in even less time. After 12 hours the plate should be examined under the binocular dissecting microscope ($\times$ 40 — $\times$ 100). If the spores have been properly spread, one may now cut out a tiny block of agar with a single sporangium descended from a single spore. The cutting out operation requires a very fine tool. For this we use a tiny chisel made by sharpening down a steel needle under the microscope. Individual sporangia may be transferred to a drop of water in a sterile Petri dish on a piece of leaf. Such a culture descended from a single spore may be kept free from bacteria for a few generations in water cultures. In some chytrids the sporangia mature and discharge their spores on agar. It is possible, though exceedingly tedious, to keep such cultures pure, growing on agar and free from bacteria. The labor involved, however, is excessive and we have carried such cultures on agar for only a few generations.

In some of the polycentric chytrids as *Cladochytrium replicatum* the spores germinated on agar to produce a distinct mycelium. It is therefore possible to isolate this species by cutting out a single thread or several threads. This method (6), however, is useless with the monocentric chytrids.

Stanier (1942) developed methods for isolating and culturing *Rhizophlyctis rosea*. He outlined them as follows:

The present isolation of *Rhizophlyctis rosea* was greatly facilitated by the fact that it first appeared in a highly selective enrichment culture. The enrichment medium—prepared in an attempt to isolate cellulose-decomposing myxobacteria—consisted of a mineral agar plate covered with a round of filter paper, which was inoculated with compost and incubated at 28° C. After four days the filter paper had become entirely covered with a bright pink growth. Microscopic examination showed the presence of large numbers of typically chytridiaceous thalli. The culture was maintained in crude form for several weeks by repeated streaking of pieces of attacked filter paper on fresh plates, but such treatment did little to reduce the large number of contaminating organisms originally present, and it became clear that other methods of purification would have to be adopted.

When a piece of filter paper heavily invested with mature thalli was placed in water, spore discharge occurred almost simultaneously from numerous zoosporangia after a period of from 20 minutes to half an hour. This phenomenon suggested a convenient method of purification. Large pieces of attacked filter paper were removed from a gross culture and put in the bottoms of test tubes containing 10-15 cc. of sterile tap water, where they were left undisturbed until after spore discharge had begun. Since the zoospores move more rapidly than bacteria and are in addition strongly aerotactic, they soon accumulated in large numbers in the upper layers, accompanied by only a few bacteria. At this stage, microscopically controlled, loopsful of the surface water were removed (care being taken to avoid agitation of the tube) and streaked on mineral dextrose agar plates, which were incubated at 28° C. After 24 hours the plates were examined under a dissecting microscope; numerous small thalli were seen interspersed among the bacterial colonies. The positions of uncontaminated thalli well separated from bacterial colonies were marked on the bottoms of the plates with India ink, and the cultures reincubated until spore discharge had taken place (this took on the average an additional 12-36 hours at 28° C.). At the time of discharge a small amount of liquid was exuded from the zoosporangia but rapidly reabsorbed by the agar, after which the spores lay motionless in small fields surrounding the empty spore cases.... Under the dissecting microscope a mass of such spores was picked up on a sterile needle, transferred to a drop of sterile water on another mineral dextrose agar plate, mixed with the water and streaked. With proper precautions, the air contamination incidental to manipulating an open plate under the microscope is negligible; thus the second plates yielded either pure cultures or else cultures whose further purification presented no difficulties. One point concerning the isolation technique deserves special mention. For both the first and second streakings it is highly desirable, if not essential, to use *well-dried* agar plates, so that after inoculation no water remains on their surfaces. If this is not done, isolation of the chytrid may be impossible due to the rapid spreading of motile bacteria always present in the enrichment cultures.

In order to make perfectly sure of the purity of cultures, zoospores from the first plate showing no bacterial colonies were streaked once more as previously described, and only from these latter plates was material taken for pure culture slants. In addition, the purity of stock cultures was checked at frequent intervals by microscopic examination.

The synthetic medium on which Stanier (1942) cultivated *Rhizophlyctis rosea* was composed of a mineral base (1.0 gm. K_2HPO_4, 1.0 gm. $(NH_4)_2SO_4$, 0.2 gm. $MgSO_4$, 0.1 gm. NaCl, 0.1 gm. $CaCl_2$. 0.02 gm. $FeCl_3$, 1000 ml. tap water, pH adjusted to 7.0-7.2) to which cellulose in the form of lens paper, filter paper, or precipitated filter paper and 0.5 per cent glucose were added as carbon sources. This medium could be solidified by the addition of 1.5 per cent agar. Stock cultures were maintained on mineral-glucose agar slants or in tubes of liquid mineral base with strips of filter paper partly immersed. Transfers were accomplished simply by flooding agar slants less than a week old with water and streaking the resultant zoospore suspension on agar. If older cultures or cellulose media were used, pieces of agar or cellulose were removed and placed in sterile water blanks.

According to Emerson (1950) sixteen different chytrids have been cultivated in pure culture, and more have been reported since his paper (Crasemann, 1954; Gaertner, 1954a-d; Koch, 1957) appeared.

Pure cultures[1] of several chytrids were obtained by Whiffen (1941b). She separated sporangia growing in unifungal culture on various natural substrata and transferred them by means of a capillary pipette to 3 per cent plain agar. Here they were freed of remaining debris with glass dissecting needles and carried to a plate of 0.5 per cent plain agar. After zoospore discharge the spores swam about in the weak agar, from which they (with any remaining bacteria) were picked up in a fine-pointed dilution tube containing 1 cc. of sterile water. Drops of this mixture were then allowed to run over the surface of a plate of 0.5 per cent agar, upon which some spores free of bacteria subsequently formed young plants. These could then be transferred to nutrient media.

Whiffen cultivated her material on the following nutrient agar media: (1) 600 mg. maltose, 40 mg. meat peptone, 3 gm. agar, and 500 cc.

[1] See Koch (1957) for a method of securing pure cultures of chytrids.

mineral-salt solution; (2) 2.5 gm. dextrose, 0.5 gm. ammonium nitrate, 500 cc. mineral-salt solution, and 3 gm. agar; (3) 0.5 gm. ammonium nitrate, 50 cc. cellulose suspension containing about 0.5 gm. of cellulose, 3 gm. agar, and 450 cc. mineral-salt solution. The cellulose used in (3) was precipitated with sulfuric acid. The mineral-salt solution consisted of the following: 0.3 gm. K_2HPO_4, 0.2 gm. KH_2PO_4, 0.2 gm. $MgSO_4.7H_2O$, 0.1 gm. NaCl, 0.1 gm. $CaCl_2.3H_2O$, 0.01 gm. $FeCl_2.4H_2O$, 0.001 gm. $ZnSO_4.7H_2O$, and 1000 cc. of distilled water. The pH of the mineral-salt solution was adjusted to 7.2 by the addition of N/20 NaOH. She found certain differences among the fungi she studied with respect to their capacity to live on these media.

Two-membered cultures, that is the host and its endophytic parasite, have been reported by Emerson (1950) for the chytrids *Rozella achlyae* and *R. allomycis.*

Whether or not certain so-called "chitinophilic" and "keratinophilic" chytrids are confined to chitin and keratin, respectively, in nature seems unlikely in view of the findings of Antikajian (1949) and Ajello (1948b). Antikajian dealt with *Asterophlyctis sarcoptoides*, an inhabitant of insect exuviae, and Ajello (1948b) recovered *Polychytrium aggregatum* from soil by means of chitinous bait. Both these fungi grew well on a medium composed of 1.0 per cent dextrose, 0.1 per cent Difco yeast extract, 0.1 per cent Bacto-peptone, and 2.0 per cent agar.

Among the members of the Blastocladiales considerable work on isolation and culture has been accomplished. Butler and Humphries (1932) secured outgrowths of *Catenaria anguillulae*, a filamentous form, from infected liver-fluke eggs and obtained growth from zoospores, when the latter were placed in fluke-ova extract and flaked egg albumen. Growth of zoospores also occurred in this medium when agar (0.25 per cent) was added to it. Couch (1945a) also cultivated this fungus in pure culture. He used liver extract–liver paste agar without sugars. *Allomyces*, which is a filamentous form with indeterminate hyphal growth, presents no special problems. It has long been isolated and under cultivation. With such coenocytic forms as *Blastocladia* and *Blastocladiella*, however, both of which have a determinate or restricted growth, special difficulties arise because of the lack of hyphae in any significant amount. Handling of *Blastocladia* is further complicated by the formation in culture of large amounts of toxic metabolic products.

Emerson and Cantino (1948) have described their isolation of *Blastocladia pringsheimii* and *B. ramosa*, species common in nature on rosaceous fruits where they form dense pustules of plants mixed with swarms of bacteria, as follows:

(1) Wash the fruit for several minutes under a strong stream of tap water to displace as much debris and slime as possible. Many of the looser, superficial masses of bacteria are effectively removed in this manner, while the plants of *Blastocladia*, being firmly attached by well-developed basal rhizoids, are not dislodged or appreciably injured. (2) Pick off three or four healthy pustules and place them in a Petri dish of sterile water. (3) Using small needles under a wide-field dissecting microscope, tease apart one or two of the pustules bearing the largest number of mature healthy zoosporangia. Individual plants, sporangium-bearing branches, and even dislodged but intact sporangia can be separated in this way, and at the same time clouds or adhering masses of bacteria are released from between the fungal hyphae. (4) With fine needle-tweezers, transfer several of the plant-fragments bearing uninjured zoosporangia to a second, smaller (ca. 5 cm. diameter) Petri dish containing sterile water. With the mirror of the dissecting microscope adjusted to give a partial dark field or Tyndall-effect, the largest swarms of bacteria can readily be detected and avoided while portions of the fungus bearing a minimum of contaminants are removed. If intact sporangia have become detached, they can be picked up in the capillary stream of a sterile micropipette and likewise transferred to another dish of sterile water. If necessary the washing process can be repeated two or three times until the material appears relatively free from bacteria. (5) The plant-fragments and sporangia are now allowed to remain until the discharge of zoospores begins ... The material should be examined every few minutes to detect the emergence of spores at the earliest opportunity.(6) At this stage it is worth while to plate out some of the spores directly without further handling, since adequate separation from bacteria may already have been achieved. In most instances, however, it is necessary to wash the spores through one or two dishes of sterile water. The zoospores of *Blastocladia* are about 10 μ in diameter, and single ones can be readily detected with a high power dissecting microscope giving a magnification of at least 60 ×, especially if the lighting is adjusted as described above in item 4. With a sterile Pasteur-pipette, made of soft glass and pulled out into a microcapillary at the tip (20-50 μ internal bore), zoospores, singly or in groups, can easily be picked up in the capillary stream which develops when the pipette is placed in water. If the mouth of a small capillary is situated opposite the discharge pore of a large sporangium, it is possible in the space of a few seconds to

collect a hundred or more zoospores. They are contained in such a small amount of water that the number of bacteria included is small if the initial preparation is relatively clean. These spores can be deposited in another small dish of sterile water and with another pipette can be picked up singly or in twos or threes and transferred to agar plates. (7) The agar used [corn-meal, prune] for initial isolations should be as transparent as possible and poured in thin layers, not over 2 or 3 mm. thick, in Petri dishes. It is allowed to dry for a day or two until all surface-moisture has disappeared. Four or five drops of sterile water, large enough to spread out to a diameter of several millimeters, are then distributed separately on the agar surface. Before this water has been absorbed into the agar, washed zoospores are transferred in small numbers to the drops on the agar plate. The site of each inoculation is marked on the bottom of the Petri dish. A few minutes later, by turning the plate upside down and examining it microscopically, the zoospores can be detected, swimming about in the remaining surface-film of water or already rounded and quiescent. (8) Germination takes place within 24 hr. at room temperature, and by 48 hr. little germlings can be found with well-developed rhizoidal systems and swollen hyphal tubes.... As soon as discrete colonies of bacteria appear, and if they are not too numerous or close to the fungus germlings, the latter, embedded in little pieces of agar, can be lifted out with needle-tweezers and transplanted to fresh agar plates. Sometimes the washing is so effective that there are no contaminating bacterial colonies and the growth is pure from the start.

The formula for the basic glucose-yeast medium that Emerson and Cantino used in their cultivation and physiological studies of *Blastocladia pringsheimii* is given below.

Salts — $K_2 HPO_4$, 0.1 %; $MgSO_4.7H_2O$, 0.02 %; NaCl, 0.01 %; $CaCl_2$.$2H_2O$, 0.01 %; $FeCl_3.6H_2O$, 0.002 %. Glucose — 0.3 %. Powdered yeast extract (Difco) — 0.1 %. pH, adjusted with sterile $M/15$ phosphoric acid and $M/10$ sodium hydroxide to 6.5.

Owing to excessive acid formation, healthy growth in culture was maintained only when alkali was added. By keeping the pH of the medium near the starting level viable material for transplants was derived from such cultures up to seven weeks after their inoculation.

Stüben (1939), Harder and Sörgel (1938), and Cantino (1951a) have all grown various species of *Blastocladiella* in pure culture.

Of the Monoblepharidales, *Monoblepharella* offers no particular problems of cultivation of the vegetative phase on various media, but no reproductive organs have ever been formed under these circumstances. *Gonapodya*, although more troublesome than *Monoblepharella*, can be readily cultivated on glucose–yeast (Emerson, 1950, and R. M. Johns, comm.). One would expect published records of the cultivation of *Monoblepharis* to be numerous, because of its relatively profuse mycelial growth. They seem confined,[1] however, to those of Emerson (1950), who reports the growth of *M. polymorpha* and *M. sphaerica* in pure culture on agar containing 0.5 per cent tryptone.

Of the few known members of the Hyphochytriales, only three have been cultivated, namely, *Rhizidiomyces apophysatus* by Whiffen (1941b), *R. bivellatus* by Nabel (1939), and *Hyphochytrium catenoides* by Karling (1939b) and others.

Save for Couch's (1939a) account of obtaining pure two-membered[2] cultures of *Woronina polycystis*, none of the endophytic obligate parasites of the Plasmodiophorales has been recorded in cultivation.

Of the Leptomitales, Minden (1916) records the growth of *Rhipidium interruptum* in dextrose and peptone solutions, malt gelatin, and the like. Minden cultured *Araiospora spinosa* on plum-decoction gelatin and in malt and bouillon broth, but not until recently has his feat been duplicated, despite repeated attempts (see Kanouse, 1927). Thus, Emerson (1950) records the successful cultivation of *Rhipidium americanum* on glucose-yeast medium. Species of *Leptomitus* (Schade, 1940; Schade and Thimann, 1940), *Apodachlya* (Gilpin, 1954), and *Sapromyces* (Bishop, 1940; Emerson, 1950) have all been obtained in pure culture.

Few of the Lagenidiales have been brought into culture. *Lagenidium giganteum*, however, has been grown bacteria-free on various laboratory media by Couch (1935b) as has also a species of *Myzocytium* by this same investigator (1939a). A species of *Sirolpidium*, parasitic on marine clams, has been grown in culture by Vishniac (1955b).

Although the higher members of the Saprolegniales[3] have nearly all been cultured, the minuteness and the simple nature of the thalli in the Ectrogellaceae and the Thraustochytriaceae make them exceed-

---

[1] Perrott (comm.) reports growing certain larger species in pure agar cultures.

[2] That is, the host with its endophytic parasite. Two-membered cultures have also been reported by Emerson (1950) for the chytrids *Rozella achlyae* and *R. allomycis*.

[3] See Goldie-Smith (1956b) on maintenance of stock cultures.

ingly difficult forms to propagate. *Thraustochytrium proliferum*, a marine species saprophytic on *Bryopsis*, has recently been secured in pure culture by Reischer and Watson (in Vishniac, 1955b).

Of the Peronosporales considered, Cantino (1949b) has repeated the success, previously achieved by Ito and Nagai (1931) and Drechsler (1932), of raising *Pythiogeton* in pure culture. He also made a study of its physiology. Recently, Prowse (1954b) reported the rotifer-capturing *Zoophagus insidians* in pure culture for the first time.

PRESERVATION

The most useful method in preserving aquatic Phycomycetes so as to make them readily available for examination is by the preparation of permanent mounts. Water mounts of material are mordanted with a weak solution of acetic acid; they are then washed and eosin in 10 per cent glycerin solution is run under the cover glass. After the solution has concentrated to pure glycerin and eosin, the slide is sealed with a cement. Instead of glycerin and eosin, Amann's (lactophenol) mounting medium, to which either acid fuchsin or cotton blue has been added, makes an excellent preservative. When tightly sealed such preparations last for many years. In dealing with minute forms such as chytrids on algae, in which the material may frequently be very scanty, either the infected substratum may be isolated on another slide and preserved or the whole lot of material may be preserved on the slide and the region where the infected filament lies encircled with India ink.

A. F. Bartsch, of the University of Wisconsin, has kindly outlined, in a personal communication, a method he has used with excellent results on material of *Blyttiomyces spinulosus*, a parasite of the zygospores of *Spirogyra*. His procedure may be summarized as follows: The material is fixed in a small vial in formalin-acetic acid alcohol (glacial acetic acid, 5 cc.; commercial formalin, 5 cc.; 50 per cent ethyl alcohol, 90 cc.) for three days. It is then washed by adding small amounts of water to the vial, shaking slightly, and pouring off the fluid. This is continued until the odor of the acetic acid is gone. The water is now poured off again and a solution of 0.5 per cent iron alum is added. After twelve hours the iron alum is washed out with three changes of water. About seven drops of 1 per cent haematoxylin in 95 per cent alcohol is then added to 10 cc. of water and poured over the material, which is allowed to stain for three days, after which it is washed in tap water (alkaline) several times. Next it is destained in 2 per cent iron alum, a sample being watched under the microscope until the destaining is satisfactory, when the iron-alum solution is poured off and the material is washed in six changes of water and placed in 10 per cent glycerin in an open Petri dish. After the glycerin has become concentrated the alga is mounted in glycerin jelly on a slide, a round cover glass is added, and the whole is sealed with balsam.

Another method found useful by Bartsch for fungi infecting plankton algae (but not filamentous algae) is to mount directly in Zirkle's fluid[1] and after a half hour to ring the preparation with balsam.

Large amounts of material, previously fixed and killed, may be preserved in 70 per cent alcohol to which a small amount of glycerin has been added. H. E. Petersen, of the University of Copenhagen, has pointed out that formalin solutions are not good preservatives for chytrids, since the rhizoids of the fungi do not keep well.

The precise methods necessary for the preparation of material for cytological studies may be found in the papers dealing with this aspect of the aquatic Phycomycetes (see discussions of the cytology of the different orders in the text).

KEY TO THE ORDERS OF THE AQUATIC PHYCOMYCETES [2]

Forming free-swimming zoospores.
> Zoospores posteriorly uniflagellate, formed inside the sporangium
>> Thallus either lacking a vegetative system and converted as a whole into reproductive structures (holocarpic) or with a specialized rhizoidal vegetative system (eucarpic) and one (monocentric) or more (polycentric) reproductive struc-

---

[1] Zirkle's fluid may be prepared as follows:

Glacial acetic acid	45 cc.
Water	55 cc.
Glycerin	5 or 10 cc.
Gelatin (powdered)	10 gms.
Fe Cl$_3$	0.02 gms.
Carmine	to saturation

Stir the gelatin with water until it forms a paste. Then add glycerin, acetic acid, iron salt, and carmine in order. Boil one minute and filter.

[2] Note that this and certain of the other keys are not dichotomous.

tures; zoospore usually bearing a single conspicuous oil globule, germination monopolar .... CHYTRIDIALES, p. 42
Thallus nearly always differentiated into a well-developed vegetative system, often hypha-like, on which are borne numerous reproductive organs; zoospore without a conspicuous
globule, germination bipolar
Thallus usually having a well-defined basal cell anchored in the
substratum by a system of tapering rhizoids; resting
structure an asexually formed thick-walled often punctate resting spore; sexual reproduction by means of isogamous or anisogamous planogametes; alternation of
generations present in some species
BLASTOCLADIALES, p. 604
Thallus without a well-defined basal cell; composed of delicate
much-branched hyphae; resting structure an öospore;
sexual reproduction oögamous, the male gamete always
free-swimming, the female devoid of a flagellum
MONOBLEPHARIDALES, p. 696
Zoospores anteriorly uniflagellate, usually formed outside or
inside the sporangium .... HYPHOCHYTRIALES, p. 743
Zoospores (at least the secondary ones) with two oppositely directed flagella, formed either inside or outside the sporangium
Zoospores with a very short anterior flagellum and a long posterior one; thallus wholly endobiotic, holocarpic, forming a
zoosporangium or a sorus of zoosporangia or resting spores
PLASMODIOPHORALES, p. 768
Zoospores with two flagella of approximately equal length,
which are oppositely directed in the secondary zoospores;
thallus endobiotic and holocarpic or eucarpic and both
intra- and extramatrical; sexual reproduction oögamous
Zoospores always cleaved out within the sporangium, diplanetic, the primary zoospore motile or encysting immediately after discharge, or completely suppressed (i.e. only
secondary zoospores formed)
Thallus holocarpic or eucarpic; the hyphae in eucarpic
forms without constrictions or cellulin plugs, not arising from a well-defined basal cell; oögonium with one
or more eggs .... SAPROLEGNIALES, p. 792
Thallus eucarpic; the hyphae bearing constrictions accompanied by cellulin plugs, usually arising from a more or
less well defined basal cell anchored in the substratum; oögonium (with the exception of *Apodachlyella*)
with a single egg .... LEPTOMITALES, p. 852

Zoospores cleaved out either within the sporangium or partly
or wholly formed outside the sporangium, where they are
usually surrounded by a more or less evanescent vesicle;
motile spore always [1] of the secondary type

Primarily aquatic; the thallus holocarpic, endobiotic,
either unicellular or consisting at maturity of a series of
unbranched or rarely branched segments of slight
extent; zoosporangia persistent ...... LAGENIDIALES, p. 904

Primarily terrestrial; thallus eucarpic, mycelial, and usually
both intra- and extramatrical; zoosporangia persistent
or deciduous (conidia)   PERONOSPORALES, p. 1012

Forming conidia which are forcibly shot off from the tip of a conidiophore .... ENTOMOPHTHORALES, p. 1061

---

[1] Scherffel (1925a) has reported primary flagellated zoospores in *Olpidiopsis
oedogoniarum.*

UNIFLAGELLATAE

CHYTRIDIALES

THE discovery of the fungous nature of the aquatic chytrids and their recognition as a taxonomic entity are due for the most part to the researches of Alexander Braun. It is clear that as early as 1846 Braun (1856a: 22) had observed chytrids on the fresh-water algae *Hydrodictyon* and *Stigeoclonium* and was aware of their parasitic role. In his *Betrachtungen über die Erscheinung der Verjüngung in der Natur* (1851), he formally established the genus *Chytridium* with one species, *C. olla*, which was parasitic on the oögonia of *Oedogonium*. To be sure, there were descriptions in the literature prior to Braun's paper of organisms now known to be true chytrids (species of *Synchytrium*, *Physoderma*, and *Micromyces*), but their affinities and, indeed, in some instances, their parasitic nature were not understood. Gross (1851), in connection with a curious account of supposed polymorphism and metamorphism in lower plants and animals, described and figured a chytrid identifiable with *Polyphagus euglenae*. Thwaites (1846-47), Shadbolt (1852), and other early algologists gave the term "asterospheres" to spiny spheres found by them in vegetative cells of Conjugatae. As late as 1860 Pringsheim interpreted the zoospores of an endobiotic chytrid (now known as *Pringsheimiella*) parasitic on a sterile *Achlya* as the antherozoids of the host, and other examples might be cited. With the publication of Braun's classic series of papers on *Chytridium* (1855a, 1855b, 1856a, 1856b), the small group became well established and their true nature generally recognized.

Included in Braun's *Chytridium* was one supposed chytrid, *C. saprolegniae*, whose zoospores were not observed and which probably was not related to his other species. It came to be identified with fungi which were observed by Nägeli (1846), Cienkowski (1855), and Cohn (1853, as *Peronium aciculare*) and which were all probably species of *Olpidiopsis*. Subsequently a number of other one-celled aquatic fungi resembling superficially Braun's species of *Chytridium*, but differing, as did *C. saprolegniae* (Cornu, 1872a), in the number of flagella on the zoospore, were gradually added to the group. As a result, the "chytrids" soon became a dumping ground for all aquatic Phycomycetes of simple body plan.

In 1864 de Bary and Woronin recognized the chytrids as constituting a family made up of the genera *Chytridium*, *Rhizidium*, and *Synchytrium*. Cohn (1879: 279) made the group coequal with the Saprolegniales and Peronosporales and it has usually been so regarded by most students of the Phycomycetes. In the well-known monograph by Fischer (1892), however, the Chytridiales are combined with the Ancylistales (now the Lagenidiales) to form the Archimycetes, coequal with the Zygomycetes and Oomycetes. This merging of the two groups has been followed by few subsequent workers, but the term "Archimycetes" has been retained by some and applied to various combinations of lower fungi. Sparrow (1935b) restricted the order to forms with posteriorly uniflagellate zoospores and later (1942; 1943) removed from the old group similar fungi with anteriorly uniflagellate zoospores to the Hyphochytriaceae, regarded as a family of uncertain affinities. Karling (1943) assembled such anteriorly uniflagellate types in a new order Anisochytridiales, which in the present publication is designated the Hyphochytriales (p. 743).

The minute and often bizarre fungi belonging to the Chytridiales occur predominantly in fresh waters, although, as earlier indicated, a few live in the ocean and many more in soils in terrestrial or semi-terrestrial habitats. In fresh water they most often appear on algae, other aquatic Phycomycetes, spores and decaying parts of higher plants, on microscopic animals and their eggs, in the empty exuviae of certain aquatic insects, and on keratinous, chitinous, and cellulosic materials from which they have been taken by baiting. Of the relatively few marine species now known nearly all have been discovered on seaweeds; one as yet little-understood marine form has been recorded from the ductless kidney of ascidians. Some are obligate parasites of phanerogams. Chytridiaceous fungi have been found wherever they have been searched for by trained observers and are probably worldwide in their distribution. At present the best-known areas are western

Europe and eastern North America, the regions where most of the investigations on these fungi have been undertaken.

The most striking characteristics of the chytrids are their simple body plan, their vegetative system of strongly tapering rhizoids, and their posteriorly uniflagellate zoospores, which often exhibit a hopping motion and which contain a highly refractive oil globule. The purely vegetative part of the thallus, if formed, is ordinarily inconspicuous because of its tenuity, but nonetheless it may be exceedingly wide - spread and profusely branched. Only one reproductive structure is produced on the thallus in the majority of these fungi; its rudiment is for the most part clearly differentiated from the less obvious vegetative system, and when reproductive activity is culminated the whole plant body usually disintegrates. In certain chytrids, however, more than one center of thallus organization is formed, some or all of which may ultimately be converted into reproductive organs.

DEVELOPMENT AND MORPHOLOGY

THE THALLUS

Establishment and Development

Considerable differences exist among the chytrids with respect to their relation to the substratum. In some the thallus may be formed completely within the substratum (endobiotic). In others it is partly on the outer surface (epibiotic) and partly within, the two components being separated by the wall of the substratum. In this situation the outer part (which frequently becomes the reproductive organ) and the inner (the nutrient-gathering system) are joined by a narrow tube formed from the penetration tube of the infecting zoospore. In a third type of relationship the reproductive rudiment and the bulk of the rhizoidal system radiating from it lie free in the water among the sources of nutrition, only the tips of the rhizoids penetrating the nutrient material (interbiotic).

It is difficult to make any generalizations in regard to the establishment and development of the thallus in the Chytridiales, since its members often differ so widely in these respects. Taken as a whole, however, certain principal types may for practical purposes be recog-

nized, to each of which may appropriately be applied the genus name
of the fungus which most nearly exemplifies it, that is, (1) *Olpidi-*
um type, (2) *Entophlyctis* type, (3) *Chytridium* type, and (4) *Rhizidium*
type. Other well-marked types may also be discerned, but they either
are regarded as variations or elaborations of those already named or
are so unique and occur in so few forms as to merit individual attention.
This arbitrary grouping is to be considered in no other light than that
of convenience. In the present state of our knowledge of the chytrids
it is impossible to make any sweeping statements concerning the deri-
vations and interrelationships of developmental types. It is apparent,
however, in taking the lower aquatic Phycomycetes as a whole, that
certain of these types occur not only in both the operculate and the
inoperculate chytrids but in other orders as well. Thus the *Olpidium*
type is found in the Chytridiales (*Olpidium, Endochytrium oophilum*),
the Anisolpidiaceae of the Hyphochytriales (*Latrostium*), the Saprolegniales (*Ectrogella*), and the Lagenidiales (*Olpidiopsis, Sirolpidium,*
Lagenidium oophilum, and so on). The failure to recognize the fact
that parallel body types have arisen independently in these different
groups has greatly confused and retarded significant studies on the
taxonomy and phylogeny of the lower aquatic Phycomycetes (Sparrow,
1933a, 1935b).

In the first three of the developmental types about to be described
actual entry of the fungous protoplasm into the substratum (a process
first observed by Kloss, 1856a) is accomplished by means of a tenuous
tube produced by the encysted zoospore. This tube, perhaps aided by
enzyme action, penetrates the wall of the substratum and either conveys a part of the contents of the spore into the interior or retains the
contents, its tip then elongating and laying down the rudiments of the
vegetative system. In the fourth or *Rhizidium* type only the distal parts
of the rhizoids emanating from the encysted spore probably make
contact with and enter the substratum.

1. *Olpidium type.*—After the tip of the penetration tube in this type
has reached the lumen of the host cell the contents of the encysted zoospore are conveyed to the inside (Fig. 3 A, p. 48). Here the naked mass
is surrounded by a pellicle, which soon becomes a discrete wall. With

growth the young thallus may assume a spherical or ellipsoidal shape and in parasitic forms be carried away, perhaps by cytoplasmic movements of the host, from the open tip of the penetration tube. This tube, as well as its attendant epibiotic cyst, usually disintegrates and takes no further part in the developmental cycle. Inside, the young thallus absorbs materials over its whole surface and increases steadily in size. No specialized vegetative parts are formed, and at maturity the body, which is completely within the substratum (endobiotic), becomes converted as a whole into a reproductive structure (holocarpic). The zoospores in the sporangia of endobiotic types are conveyed to the outside by a more or less well developed discharge tube, the tip of which is extramatrical. Such a type of development is characteristic of the Olpidiaceae. It is elaborated in the Achlyogetonaceae, in which family the thallus is cylindrical, and at maturity becomes segmented into a linear series of sporangia. Another variation is found in the Synchytriaceae, in which sorus formation takes place.

2. *Entophlyctis type.*—In the *Entophlyctis* type (Fig. 3 B, p. 48), the endobiotic tip of the penetration tube remains filamentous, elongates as it drains the cyst of its contents, and lays down within the substratum the main axes of the branching rhizoidal system. The elements of the vegetative system just beneath the substratum wall then expand to form the rudiment of the reproductive structure. In the majority of the fungi exhibiting this sequence of development the empty cyst and the penetration tube disintegrate and play no further part. Thus the incipient reproductive structure arises secondarily[1] by expansion of those elements of the vegetative system immediately beneath the wall of the substratum, often including portions of the primary branches. Both vegetative and reproductive parts are, therefore, developed endobiotically. The zoospores reach the outside medium by the formation of a discharge tube, as in the previous type.

Since here, as is not true of the *Olpidium* type, structures of a purely vegetative nature (the rhizoids) are formed, as well as a reproductive rudiment, this and succeeding types of thalli are said to be "eucarpic," that is, they are differentiated into sterile and fertile portions. If, as

[1] Observations on the development of *Endochytrium operculatum* by Hillegas (1940: 9) indicate that the rudiment may sometimes be formed first.

in the majority of eucarpic types, only a single reproductive rudiment is developed on the thallus, the thallus is said to be "monocentric," whereas if more than one is formed (as in *Cladochytrium*), it is termed "polycentric" (Karling, 1932). The rhizoids of all eucarpic thalli are probably conveying materials back to the enlarging reproductive rudiment at all times during their elongation into the substratum, except when they are first being established. When extension of the rhizoids ceases the residue of materials within them is soon drained into the future reproductive body, which is then delimited by septa from the now empty vegetative system.

Variations and elaborations of the *Entophlyctis* type may be found among both operculate and inoperculate chytrids. Indeed, the *Chytridium* type itself may be regarded as one of these variations. Since it occurs with great frequency, however, it is kept separate here. No attempt is made to decide whether the endobiotic or the epibiotic center of thallus organization is the more primitive, or whether one has been derived from the other.

3. *Chytridium type.*—The early stages of the *Chytridium* type (Fig. 3 C, p. 48) resemble those of the *Entophlyctis* type. After establishment within the substratum, however, the rhizoids continue to elongate and soon convey materials back through the penetration tube to the persistent epibiotic cyst of the infecting zoospore. As a result, the cyst expands and ultimately becomes the rudiment of the reproductive structure within which all the contents of the vegetative system have been concentrated. This system is then separated from the fertile portion by a cross wall. Although the contents of the cyst are probably partly depleted during the early stages of establishment and growth of the rhizoids, materials soon begin to flow in the opposite direction, and cause the expansion of the reproductive rudiment.

The type of development that occurs in *Phlyctochytrium* and apophysate species of *Chytridium* might be considered here a variation of the *Chytridium* type, although, as has been mentioned, there is equal reason for supposing it to be allied to that found in *Entophlyctis*. In *Phlyctochytrium spp.* and *Chytridium lagenaria*, for example, an endobiotic subsporangial apophysis is formed which probably always arises as a secondary enlargement of the proximal portion of the already

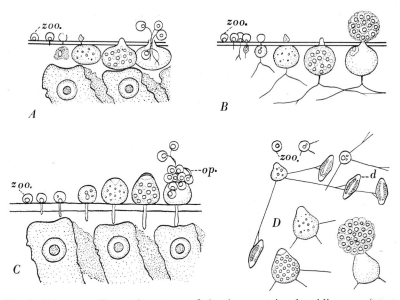

Fɪɢ. 3. Diagrams illustrating types of development in chytridiaceous fungʐ

A. Olpidium type: At extreme left an encysted zoospore (*zoo.*) is resting on outer surface of wall of a *Spirogyra* cell; second cyst has produced a pene-tration tube through which, as shown in third cyst, the contents have been discharged into the host; thallus is enlarging in fourth figure, has become a mature sporangium in the fifth, and is discharging its zoospores in the sixth. *B. Entophlyctis* type: At extreme left a zoospore (*zoo.*) has encysted on outer surface of wall of an algal cell; second cyst has produced a penetration tube; the third has formed the beginnings of the rhizoidal system; the fourth shows the swelling which will become the reproductive rudiment forming on the very young rhizoidal system; fifth and sixth figures illustrate the further development of the rhizoidal system and of the reproductive rudiment, which has become, in seventh figure, a mature sporangium bearing a discharge tube; last figure on the right shows discharge of the zoospores. *C. Chytridium* type: At extreme left a zoospore (*zoo.*) has encysted on outer surface of wall of a *Spirogyra* cell; second cyst has formed a peglike penetration tube, which, in third cyst, has further elongated; contents of cyst remain outside for the most part and, as materials are conveyed to the cyst from the host, its body enlarges, as indicated in third, fourth, and fifth figures, and eventually be-comes transformed into a sporangium; in operculate chytrids a well-defined cap or operculum (*op.*) is dehisced, allowing for discharge of the zoospores, whereas in inoperculate chytrids the apex of the sporangium or discharge tube merely deliquesces, as shown in *A, B,* and *D. D. Rhizidium* type: In this

established rudiments of the rhizoidal system. The cyst and the germ tube, however, unlike those in *Entophlyctis* (except *E. bulligera*), remain functional, and, as the endobiotic vegetative system becomes more extensive, materials are carried back to the epibiotic part (Sparrow, 1936a; Karling, 1937c). As a result, the cyst expands, receives the contents of both rhizoids and apophysis, and eventually becomes transformed into a reproductive organ. This alternating intra- and extramatrical habit of development has been termed "endo-exogenous" by Karling (1936a), who considers it an especial characteristic of apophysate chytrids. Since, however, there is necessarily a period during the early stages of penetration and establishment of the rhizoids of all epibiotic types during which material is being sent from the cyst into the rhizoids developing in the substratum and none is returned, one should merely say, perhaps, that in these apophysate types this reversal is simply more evident and more striking.

4. *Rhizidium type.*—In the *Rhizidium* type (Fig. 3 D, p. 48) the zoospore comes to rest in the water (or, in exuviae-inhabiting forms, for example, within the hollow substratum) and, after losing its flagellum and encysting, produces one or more rhizoids which radiate from the body. These rhizoids come into contact with and penetrate the substratum. If the fungus is developing in insect exuviae it is possible that the whole surface of the thallus is absorptive. After the rhizoids become established they continue to develop, and materials are conveyed back into the spore body. As a consequence, this structure enlarges and forms the rudiment of either the reproductive organ or, in some genera, the prosporangium. Typically the fertile part of the thallus is not intimately related to the substratum (that is, it is interbiotic),

type the zoospore (*zoo.*) usually encysts free in the water, as in upper left figure; it then forms one or more rhizoidal outgrowths from its body, as in second and third cysts to the right; the cyst expands as material is carried to it by the rhizoids from one or more host cells (*d*), as is clear in succeeding figures, and is eventually converted into a zoosporangium, which, as shown at lower right, discharges its zoospores. All the fungi in Figure 3 illustrate monocentric chytrids, i.e. those in which only one center of reproductive activity (zoosporangium or resting spore) is formed on a single thallus; in the polycentric chytrid more than one reproductive organ is produced. (Sparrow, 1935a)

although occasionally, as in *Polyphagus euglenae* and *Obelidium*, it may be so. In the majority of genera exhibiting the *Rhizidium* type of development the thallus is monocentric. It is probable that when the development of such polycentric genera as *Physocladia*, *Nowakowskiella*, *Megachytrium*, *Zygochytrium*, *Tetrachytrium*, and the like, is more fully understood, they too will be found to be of the *Rhizidium* type.

In concluding any account of development in the chytrids it should be pointed out that much observational and experimental work still needs to be done before it can be determined just how static the types really are, however distinctive they may appear under natural conditions.

When the developmental types discussed above were first proposed (Sparrow, 1935a, 1943), Whiffen (1944) took exception to their recognition in spite of emphasis given the fact that they are practical arbitrary groups only and should be so considered. She felt that sufficient was already known to be able to lay the foundation for a natural system based on types of development within the Chytridiales. To this end, she suggested recognition of two groups and five types among the eucarpic, monocentric chytrids. Group I contained those forms in which the encysted zoospore is functional; Group II, those in which the encysted zoospore is not functional and the zoosporangium or prosporangium develops from the germ tube. Her scheme is quoted below

Group I

Type 1. The encysted zoospore enlarges into a sporangium, as in *Rhizophydium* or *Rhizidium*.

Type 2. The encysted zoospore enlarges into a prosporangium from which the zoosporangium develops as in *Polyphagus*.

Type 3. A swelling of the germ tube gives rise to a prosporangium [1] that contributes to the subsequent enlargement of the encysted zoospore into a zoosporangium as in *Chytridium lagenaria* (the endo-exogenous type of development described by Karling, 1936[a].

[1] Note that Whiffen's use of the term "prosporangium" includes not only the enlarged body of the zoospore out of which at maturity grows a sporangium, but also the structure (termed herein an "apophysis" or "subsporangial swelling"). which forms at the tip of the germ tube of the zoospore within the substratum,

GROUP II

Type 4. The zoosporangium develops from an enlargement of the germ tube as in *Entophlyctis*.

Type 5. The zoosporangium develops from a prosporangium which originates as an enlargement of the germ tube as in *Diplophlyctis*.

Whether Whiffen's types accomplish some degree of natural grouping is problematical, particularly in view of the many variations in types of development recorded in recent years (see, for example, Antikajian, 1949; Karling, 1949d, f; Haskins, 1948; and the discussion under *Diplophlyctis*, p. 384). Data derived from pure cultures in artificial media are beginning to accumulate and they may or may not throw light on just what is fundamental here. Until further evidence is forthcoming it seems wiser not to make any final decisions. In the meantime, to continue to be of some practical assistance to those who have material from the field before them and who are not concerned as yet with theoretical matters, the admittedly somewhat artificial system of the first edition of the *Aquatic Phycomycetes* is maintained.

Structure of the Thallus

The thallus of the chytrid consists of at least one center of reproductive activity and, with the exception of the Olpidiaceae, Achlyogetonaceae, and Synchytriaceae, of a more or less well-developed nutrient-gathering system (Fig. 3 B, p. 48). In the three families of holocarpic chytrids just mentioned the absorption of materials doubtless occurs over the entire surface of the thallus, which is then converted as a whole into a reproductive organ (Fig. 3A). The remaining eucarpic chytrids are for the most part "rhizoidal," that is, the purely vegetative part of the thallus consists of unbranched or branched, distinctly tapering threads or "rhizoids," which are frequently of great delicacy (Fig. 27 A, p. 428). By repeated branching the surface over which, presumably, active absorption of materials occurs is enormously enlarged. In species which form an apophysis (Fig. 19 H-I, p. 318) this surface is still further increased. There is no direct evidence, however, to show that all the endobiotic parts of a chytrid are active in the absorption of materials from the substratum. Sometimes the vegetative system, instead of being rhizoidal, either is cylindrical and blunt-tipped

(Fig. 3 C) or it is bulbous, coralloid, or composed of short stubby digitations. Such structures are often referred to as "haustoria." In other chytrids, as in *Coenomyces* and *Megachytrium*, the vegetative part is distinctly hypha-like, resembling in this respect the mycelium of the higher fungi. All of these, however, are exceptions to the prevailing rule that the eucarpic chytrids are rhizoidal.

The polycentric thallus[1] is usually far more extensive than the monocentric and is characterized by the formation on it of new centers of thallus organization (Karling, 1932). They are either swellings, which sometimes develop into reproductive structures, or fusiform or ellipsoidal, often septate, purely vegetative "turbinate cells" or "spindle organs" (Fig. 30 I, p. 474). Various conjectures regarding their function have been proposed. It is possible that they serve either to increase the active absorptive surface or, if they become converted wholly or in part into a reproductive structure, to collect materials for the reproductive rudiment. In *Physoderma* (*Urophlyctis*), an obligate parasite in the tissues of certain phanerogams, similar (but not identical) turbinate cells have been definitely shown to function as vegetative centers from which, after tangential septation, new parts of the extensive thallus originate (Jones and Drechsler, 1920). A like role is assigned them by Karling (1931b, 1932), who points out that, in *Cladochytrium*, as the thallus extends its growth, these enlargements serve as successive centers for reduplication or replication of the growing vegetative system.

In most genera of both monocentric and polycentric chytrids the rhizoids are profusely branched. Elongation and further branching may give rise to an extensive vegetative system with an enormous absorptive surface. Branching of the main axes is usually in dichotomous fashion, the diverticula frequently emerging at wide angles. This dichotomy is usually retained in the secondary branches, although there is a marked tendency here toward unequal development of the resulting elements. Thus one secondary branch may remain relatively broad and continue as a main axis, while the other may taper suddenly and terminate its growth. This inequality often brings about the characteristic zigzagging course taken by the main axis as it continues to grow. The

---

[1] Karling (1932) called the polycentric thallus a "rhizomycelium," a term which, though useful, carries too great a phylogenetic implication.

individual components of the rhizoidal system may be slightly undulate or unusually straight for long distances. When passing through the walls of the substratum they are sometimes strongly constricted.

Certain chytrids have developed special types of vegetative systems, some of which have been previously mentioned. One of the most curious is the highly flexible extramatrical stalk formed by the diatom parasite *Chytridium versatile*. By its flexibility this needle-like structure which elevates the sporangium above the frustule of the host enables the ob-pyriform sporangium to bend back as the diatom goes between or pushes against bits of debris commonly present in its environment. After the obstruction is passed the sporangium snaps back to its orig-inal upright position (Scherffel, 1926a; Sparrow, 1933a). In genera such as *Rhizosiphon, Aphanistis, Megachytrium, Zygochytrium, Tetra-chytrium,* and *Coenomyces* the vegetative part of the thallus is more or less isodiametric and blunt-tipped, assuming as a result a distinctly hypha-like aspect (Fig. 37 A, p. 598). In *Aphanistis* and *Coenomyces* transverse septa are formed. Although these hypha-like filaments strongly resemble those of the higher fungi it is probable that they have no phylogenetic significance and are simply similar vegetative devices occurring in wholly unrelated organisms. Thus they have been repeated in the posteriorly uniflagellate series (*Megachytrium* and others), the anteriorly uniflagellate series (*Hyphochytrium*), and the nonchytridiaceous laterally biflagellate series (*Lagenidium, Pythium,* and the like).

The walls of the chytrid thallus rarely give a well-marked cellulose reaction with ordinary reagents. Cellulose has, however, been demon-strated in certain species, notably in *Rhizophydium* by Zopf (1887), *Pringsheimiella* by Couch (1939b), and *Rhizophlyctis* by Ward (1939). Following methods used by Nabel (1939), Ajello (1948a) demonstrated the presence of chitosan in the walls of *Polychytrium*, as had the former investigator in several other chytrids. Haskins (1948), working with *Rhizophlyctis*, found that the outer and inner walls of zoosporangia differed in their reaction to zinc chloriodide, the outer were yellowish or unstained, the inner, mauve-purple, indicating cellulose. If cellulose is universally present in the chytrids, either the usual methods of dem-onstrating it are not effective or it is masked, as in the Monoblepharidales, by some accessory substance. (See Nabel [1939] for a discussion of the occurrence of chitin and cellulose in the lower fungi.)

In the active vegetative stage the cytoplasm of the chytrid presents a typically lustrous gleaming aspect, and is further characterized by the presence within it of vacuoles, refractive, probably fatty, masses, and minute globules. As the thallus matures changes occur in the cytoplasm. In that of *Obelidium mucronatum*, for example, the globule of the zoospore persists in the homogeneous protoplasm for a time after germination. Eventually it disintegrates, conspicuous vacuoles appear, and the protoplasm of the reproductive rudiment assumes a watery aspect. With the enlargement of the thallus there follows a stage in which the protoplasm is densely and uniformly granular. Minute refractive droplets, sometimes in rings, then make their appearance and, accompanied by a gradual "clearing" of the whole protoplasm, coalesce to form regularly spaced conspicuous refractive globules. During the densely granular stage the delicate rhizoids are completely drained of their contents and septa are laid down cutting off the sterile and fertile parts of the thallus. Little can be observed of the contents of the rhizoids other than vacuoles in a finely granular matrix and occasional fatty globules.

In most chytrids the cytoplasm and its globules are colorless. In *Polyphagus euglenae, Siphonaria variabilis, Rhizoclosmatium aurantiacum, Cladochytrium replicatum, Zygochytrium*, and others, however, in the later stages of maturation, the protoplasm becomes shot through with minute golden or reddish-orange globules. It is these droplets which eventually fuse at maturity to form the regularly spaced colored globules, one in each zoospore. Though in the species cited the pigmented material is found in the globules of the zoospores, in certain others it is retained in the cytoplasm. Sorokin (1874a) found the blue coloration of the cytoplasm of *Tetrachytrium* to be homogeneously dispersed throughout, even after the zoospores were formed. On the other hand, Zopf (1892) noted that the brilliant orange hue of the vegetative stage of *Pleotrachelus fulgens* was only temporary, for at maturity the zoospores were colorless. He was probably correct in stating that this coloration was due to the ingested carotene material of the host (*Pilobolus*).

The size of the thallus and, in particular, of the reproductive rudiment formed on it, though falling within certain well-defined limits, is undoubtedly modified somewhat by prevailing external conditions. Of these the most important are probably the availability and nature of food and, in endophytic forms, restrictions of space imposed by the substratum. Competition between individuals of the same or other species may result in the cutting down of both space and nutriment.

REPRODUCTION

Nonsexual Reproduction

In practically all chytrids nonsexual reproduction is accomplished by means of posteriorly uniflagellate zoospores produced in a sporangium which is formed in most instances from the reproductive rudiment of the thallus.

Cleavage of the zoospores.—After the accumulation of protoplasm in the reproductive rudiment and after the sequence of changes previously described the zoospores are delimited. These are usually completely formed, apparently always within the sporangium, by cleavage of the contents into uninucleated segments of similar size. Although delimitation of the spore origins has been described almost uniformly as simultaneous, certain observations show beyond question that it is progressive, at least in some species (see "Cytology," p. 85). In *Septolpidium lineare* (Sparrow, 1936a), a parasite of diatoms which forms a tubular thallus, progressive cleavage has been observed in living material, not only in the division of the contents into zoospores, but in the formation of the sporangia themselves. Cytological studies of zoospore formation in the polycentric endobiotic *Cladochytrium replicatum* (Karling, 1937b) also reveal a progressive rather than a simultaneous division into zoospores. In sporangia of this fungus, in which the contents are homogeneously distributed throughout, cleavage furrows first appear on the periphery of the mass and extend inward as radial, often somewhat curved arms. The furrows for the most part delimit uninucleate segments. Occasionally, however, bi- and trinucleate segments may first be formed. These, by the subsequent production of secondary furrows, are ultimately divided into uninucleate "spore initials." The contents of certain sporangia, instead of being uniformly distributed, are disposed around a large vacuole. Such a disposition has been noted in several other chytrids, notably in *Rhizosiphon crassum* (Scherffel, 1926a). In *Cladochytrium replicatum* cleavage furrows appear to originate on the periphery of the vacuole and progress outward as broad wedge-shaped radial arms. Very rarely both methods of cleavage occur in the same sporangium. After delimitation the spore initials become somewhat swollen, possibly because of the intake of water. At this time the contours of the pentagonal, hexagonal, or somewhat cuneiform segments become nearly but not completely obliterated, and the sporangium appears to have just undergone simultaneous division into polyhedral segments. Because of this Karling suggests that the accounts of simultaneous division recorded in the literature are due to the observers' failure to note the early phases, which are actually progressive. The fact that in living material it is usually difficult to follow the process of segmentation has no doubt led to the conflicting accounts of cytokinesis in the chytrids. Cytological observations of this process on other representatives of the order confirm it as being progressive (Antikajian, 1949; Ajello, 1948a; J. M. Roberts, 1948; etc.).

Obviously the number of zoospores formed in a sporangium is dependent upon the size of the individual spore and of the sporangium. The motile zoospores of a species appear to be relatively constant in size, although most of them are too minute to enable one to obtain any significant measurements. For example, though plants of *Chytridium lagenaria* when growing on different types of algae ranged from 8 to 29 μ in diameter, the zoospores constantly remained 5 μ (Sparrow, 1936a). On the other hand, the size of the sporangium, as just indicated, may vary considerably in a single species. The factors which influence this are not known with certainty. Nature of the substratum, available space, competition, size of the cell of the substratum (in monophagous types), and available nutriment have all been suggested, however, as possible determinants. In a preliminary study of *Chytridium lagenaria* (Sparrow, *op. cit.*) striking variations in the size of sporangia were noted on three different algae, *Rhizoclonium*, *Spirogyra*, and a slender species of *Oedogonium*. Such variations were not, however, coördinated with differences in size of the algal cell on which the thallus was developing. Though the largest sporangia were formed on the alga having the largest cells (*Rhizoclonium*), the smallest were not formed on that with the smallest cells (*Oedogonium*), but, rather, on *Spirogyra*. Evidently in this instance the type of nutrient material or its availability to the fungus was a factor. A similar lack of constant correlation between the size of the sporangia and the cell of the substratum has been observed in other chytrids, notably in *Endochytrium operculatum* (Karling, 1937a). In this fungus mature almost spherical sporangia ranged from 5 to 140 μ and pyriform ones from 5 by 7 to 60 by 150 μ. Though range in size was to a certain extent proportional to the diameter of the cell of the substratum, small sporangia might be found in large cells or vice versa. *E. operculatum* also demonstrates the variation in the number of zoospores which may be produced by individual sporangia of the same species. Fewer than twenty were found in small sporangia, whereas thousands were estimated to be present in the largest. Haskins (1939) has estimated that up to 70,000 zoospores are formed in large sporangia of "*Rhizophlyctis petersenii.*"

Discharge of the zoospores.—In inoperculate chytrids there are formed one or more discharge papillae on the sporangium, some time previous to the cleavage of the zoospores. In certain species these may make their appearance when the thallus is relatively immature. In *Siphonaria variabilis*, to cite an extreme example, the papilla is clearly visible as one of the first-formed elements of the young thallus (Sparrow, 1937a). The degree of development of the papilla varies considerably among the different species. In *Obelidium mucronatum* if a papilla is present at all it must be very slightly developed, since it is not visible at ordinary magnifications on the mature plant (Sparrow, 1938d). In *Rhizophydium sphaerotheca* (Zopf, 1887), *Rhizosiphon crassum* (Scherffel, 1926a), and *Phlyctochytrium chaetiferum* (Karling, 1937c), on the other hand, the papilla is a pronounced and prominent structure. In most of the epibiotic chytrids it protrudes directly from the wall of the sporangium. In others it is slightly elevated, and in *Rhizophydium ampullaceum* (Sorokin, 1874b) it is formed at the tip of a tubular prolongation. The endophytic chytrids for the most part produce a more or less well-developed tube which penetrates the wall of the substratum and forms the papilla at its tip. Thus a passageway is made available through which the zoospores are conveyed to the outside medium. This tube may be short, as in *Olpidium vampyrellae* (Scherffel, 1926a) and *Diplophlyctis laevis* (Sparrow, 1939a), or may attain a considerable length, particularly if it is not so oriented as to gain immediate contact with the wall of the substratum. Its length may vary strikingly in a single species. Usually, endophytic types produce only one. *Pleotrachelus fulgens* (Zopf, 1884) offers a notable exception, however, in that it typically forms many such structures (Fig. 12 E, p. 124). Indeed, it is on this basis that the genus is separated from the predominantly one-tubed *Olpidium*, which it otherwise resembles.

The discharge papilla is characterized by its contents and its strongly arched contour. The contents are ordinarily clear and highly refractive and of an apparently viscid material. At the moment of discharge they may frequently be observed to ooze out into the medium ahead of the emerging zoospores. Just beneath this peripheral zone a clear, less refractive region may often be seen, the concave base of which is in contact with the plasma of the zoospores. At the moment of discharge, however, these two zones appear to become quickly confluent. Whether the materials of the two regions are derived from the wall or from the protoplasm of the sporangium it is difficult to say. In species in which a pronounced zonation is apparent, it is possible that the outer, refractive layer is derived from the wall, the inner, from the contents. Upon dissolution of the papilla a discharge pore is formed through which the zoospores emerge (Fig. 23 E-H, p. 385).

Couch (1932) observed in *Rhizophydium couchii* a somewhat different method of discharge-pore formation. In this multiporous species there are formed on the wall from one to five small rounded thin areas. The internal pressure of the expanding spore mass within the sporangium causes the wall to bulge out at these thin spots, which results in the development of blunt papillae. A similar situation has been described by Zopf (1887) as well as by Gaertner (1954c) and many others.

In some forms (*Rhizosiphon crassum* Scherffel, 1926b; *Rhizophlyctis spp.*) the wall material of the apex of the tube disappears before discharge, leaving the contents separated from the outside medium by a thin membrane, which may thicken. In certain sporangia of *Diplo-*

phlyctis laevis (Sparrow, 1939a) the outer wall of the tip of the short tube likewise disappears before discharge. Here, however, a well-defined papilla remains on the surface of the mass of zoospores. This circumstance might be considered evidence for the cytoplasmic origin of the papilla.

Little can be said with certainty concerning the external factors which induce the discharge of the mature sporangia. Under some conditions they will remain mature but undischarged for relatively long periods, whereas under others they may evacuate their zoospores as soon as they are formed. In general, however, sudden changes in environmental conditions may precipitate sporulation, as in the algae. Thus if sporangia are transferred into fresh clean oxygenated water from the quiet water in which they have matured and which presumably contains various metabolic products accumulated during the vegetative phase of the fungus, discharge can frequently be brought about (Couch, 1939a). Changes in temperature, though most often noted in the literature in connection with the inducing of sporulation in biflagellate Phycomycetes (Coker, 1923), no doubt act in a similar fashion here. There seems to be a certain periodicity in the sporangial discharge of *Phlyctochytrium hallii* and *P. biporosum* (Couch, 1932), since sporangia of these species have been observed to release their zoospores usually in the late afternoon or evening.

Even less is known of the processes within the sporangium that cause the discharge of the zoospores. Possibly, the intake of water by the mass of mature spores creates a pressure too great for the modified material of the papilla to resist. If this hypothesis is correct, however, the permeability of the sporangium wall to water must vary, since in undisturbed water mature sporangia often remain undischarged for days or even weeks. In the blastocladiaceous fungus *Allomyces*, Ritchie (1947) found that the sporangium at the time of discharge had lost 22 per cent of its original volume, this presumably by excretion of water. In sporangia of *Phlyctochytrium biporosum* about to discharge, Couch (1932) observed that, after a period of slight motion, the spore initials become quiescent and clear narrow spaces appear between them. This results in a flattening out of those spores next to the wall, as though pressure is being applied to them. Simultaneously, the sporangium swells until the wall gives way and discharge of zoospores is begun. While the first spores are ejaculated by internal pressure from within the sporangium, this force soon diminishes in intensity and the remainder of the swarmers assume individual motility and creep or swim out. Aside from pressure, another factor influencing discharge may be an increasing solubility in water, as the sporangium matures, of the material of the papilla. Then, too, sometimes the zoospores themselves initiate motility within the sporangium and their activity may have an effect on spore discharge. Whatever the cause or causes, the first zoospores ejected appear, as a rule, to be pushed out; the later ones, particularly in large sporangia, either creep out amoeboidly or swim out by flagellar action.

The precise method and the time of formation of the flagellum of the zoospore are not known. Karling (1937b) and Hillegas (1940), who have made perhaps the most extensive cytological study of chytrids, merely state that it is formed while the zoospores are in the sporangium. In many species, for example in *Rhizophydium goniosporum* (Scherffel, 1925b; Sparrow, 1936a), *Phlyctochytrium planicorne, P. bullatum,* and *P. dentiferum,* the fully formed flagellum may be clearly seen trailing behind the body of the spore as it emerges. Scherffel (1926a) believes that in *Chytridium schenkii* the flagellum of the spore is formed after discharge, during the resting period at the orifice of the sporangium. This is denied, however, by Couch (1938b) for the closely allied *C. oedogonii,* in which, as well as in *R. carpophilum,* the flagellum is coiled in "watch-spring" fashion around the body of the emerged spore and during the rest period merely falls away from the body, straightens, and eventually assumes its activity. This disposition of the flagellum has been noted in other chytrids also (for example, *C. nodulosum, C. schenkii* [Sparrow, 1932b, 1933a]).

The behavior of the emerged zoospores is probably dependent to some degree upon conditions prevailing in the medium at the time of discharge. Under what appear to be excellent conditions they emerge from the sporangium en masse, without flagellar action, and form a motionless group at the sporangial orifice (Fig. 35 D, p. 583). Here they remain quiescent for a varying period, apparently imbedded in a matrix of mucus or "slime" (Nowakowski, 1876a), which slowly dissolves in the water and liberates them. They then assume flagellar action and swim away either at once or after undergoing a period of collective swarming at or near the orifice of the discharge pore (*Asterophlyctis*, *Siphonaria*, *Rhizidium mycophilum*). Whether the slime is formed from the substance of the papilla alone or from the inner wall of the sporangium or from material between the spore origins (Nowakowski, *op. cit.*) is not known. Observations on certain operculate forms, such as *Nowakowskiella elegans* (Sparrow, 1933a) and *Endochytrium operculatum* (Karling, 1937a), indicate that at least part of it is of papillary origin. The formation of a vesicle into which the spores pass upon discharge has been recorded by several workers (Zopf, 1884; Sparrow, 1931c, 1936a, 1937a; Karling, 1937c, 1945c; Antikajian, 1949; and others). Owing to the minuteness of the structures involved, however, and the tenuousness of such membranes, these observations require abundant confirmation.

A word might be said concerning the remarkable collective swarming which has been noted in certain instances among both inoperculate and operculate species. This phenomenon is perhaps most typical of the small group of chytrids inhabiting insect exuviae (Sparrow, 1937a; Karling, 1945c; Antikajian, 1949). In *Asterophlyctis* and *Siphonaria* the emerged spores remain for a short time in a motionless cluster at the basal orifice. Then a few on the periphery of the mass initiate individual motion, which ordinarily starts as a slight trembling of each spore body. This increases in intensity and culminates in a violent lashing of the spore from side to side. In a short time all are in motion, and the group becomes a writhing mass of tugging individuals endeavoring to pull their flagella free from some apparently confining substance. After a few minutes of this wild activity, during which the contour of the struggling group may become very elongated, occasional spores dart from the mass. These are quickly followed by others, until all have dispersed. In the new species *Rhizidium chitinophilum* Sparrow (p. 412) the spore behavior is even more extraordinary. After discharge the spores form a compact subspherical mass. Soon they fall apart, and in about a minute each assumes individual movement. Instead of darting away, however, the writhing mass moves about 10 μ or more from the orifice and assumes a broadly reniform shape. After several minutes, during which the spores continue to swarm violently and with incredible speed, the shape of the mass changes and becomes broadly sagittate. Finally a few spores dart from the apex of one of the lobes and are soon followed by the remainder, which escape by the same route or from the tip of the opposite lobe. In this type of discharge the spores appear to be beating against a vesicular structure that confines them until they have undergone a period of preliminary "test" swarming.

The significance of this collective swarming, which has been noted in other chytrids as well, notably in *Chytriomyces*, is not clear unless it is connected with the final fashioning of the flagella. It is possible that these are only partly formed at the time of zoospore emergence and may require further maturation before the spore can cope successfully with the outside medium.

True operculate chytrids differ from the inoperculate in possessing a more or less convex cap which surmounts the discharge papilla. The operculum is a definite and constant morphological structure in species in which it is formed. For example, all sporangia on the polycentric thallus of *Nowakowskiella* are operculate, and plants grown from zoospores of this plant will have sporangia which in turn are operculate. There has not as yet been discovered a species of chytrid in which sporangial discharge is at one time inoperculate, at another time operculate.

The operculum is formed of wall material and in epibiotic and interbiotic species is from a portion of the wall of the zoospore cyst (Haskins, 1948; Berdan, 1942; and others). At the moment of discharge it is dehisced and either thrown aside or carried up by the mass of emerging zoospores (Fig. 35 B-D, p. 583). Often, as in *Endochytrium ramosum* and *Chytridium perniciosum* (Sparrow, 1933a, c), it appears to be attached hingelike to the orifice. It may be smoothly contoured like a watch glass, with varying degrees of convexity, or may have on its outer surface a pronounced apiculus or umbo. Although in some species (for example, *C. sphaerocarpum*) it is so thin-walled as almost to escape detection, in others it is large and thick-walled, often appearing solid and very conspicuous (as in *C. perniciosum, C. olla*). The presence or the absence of an operculum is of great taxonomic importance. Since, unfortunately, one cannot foretell with certainty whether an undischarged sporangium will turn out to be operculate or inoperculate, the witnessing of the escape of the zoospores is absolutely essential to proper identification.

In recent years the term "endooperculum" has been applied by a few workers to a structure whose origin differs from that of a true operculum. As indicated previously (p. 58), in some chytrids, notably those with a prominent discharge papilla, a membrane may form over the face of the protoplasm in the base of the tube. In sporangia quiescent for a period after maturity this membrane may thicken and become rigid and even umbonate. Such structures have been observed in a number of chytrids belonging to different genera, both inoperculate and operculate. It is not, however, produced by all sporangia in all cultures. Certain species and strains seem more prone to form it than others. That it does form sometimes has been attested to by competent observers of these fungi.

Considerable taxonomic stress has been laid on this secondarily developed protective coating for the contents in more or less quiescent sporangia by Johanson (1944). As a result, she segregated species of *Rhizophlyctis* that form it into a distinct genus, which she named *Karlingia* (see *Karlingiomyces*, p. 559). Haskins (1948), however, subsequently made an extensive study of many strains of the species that Johanson designated the type of "*Karlingia*," the ubiquitous *R. rosea* de Bary and Woronin. He discovered that in some of these strains zoospore discharge often took place before there was any evidence of an endooperculum. His observations confirm our own studies on this species with respect to variability in endooperculum formation. Note, too, that in discussing another chytrid, *Diplophlyctis sexualis* Haskins (*op. cit.*) comments:

Our species in rapidly growing cultures, dehisces in a normal inoperculate manner and occasionally after extrusion of a gelatinous plug, but in older stagnating cultures, after the deliquescence of the gelatinous tip of the exit-tube has occurred, the membrane between the protoplasmic contents of the sporangium and the external medium thickens. This membrane may thicken so as to form an endo-operculum-like structure, which at subsequent dehiscence of the sporangium may merely rupture or may be forced out as a cap as described for *Nephrochytrium amazonensis* (Karling, 1944 [e]).

On the basis of Haskin's observations, our own on such species as *Nowakowskiella macrospora* Karling, and accounts of the process in *Karlingiomyces* (*Karlingia*) *granulatus*, we conclude that endooperculation can occur in any chytrid, under certain environmental conditions, particularly with age. Moreover, Hanson (1945a: 438), in a discussion of relationships of certain chytridiaceous fungi, states that she considers the endooperculum a "generically invalid" character.

With respect to *Karlingiomyces* (*Karlingia*) *granulatus* and *Nowakowskiella macrospora*, described as having both a true operculum and an endooperculum, Haskins (1948) says that these "require further study to determine the composition of the exo-operculum [true operculum] as it exists in these forms. If it is of the same substance as the inner wall, then the condition is at one of the extremes of endo-operculation. If it is truly an exo-operculum in composition and origin, as well as appearance and function, then it is a form for which allowances must be made in any scheme of classification." In the few cases in which Haskins observed exooperculation and endooperculation in the same plant, he believes that the apparent exooperculum was not, in fact, derived from the original sporangium wall and, hence, was not a true operculum.

We agree with Haskins (*op. cit.*) when he states:

The term [operculum] should be reserved for a very definite and discrete structure, an actual portion of the original sporangial wall, which, because of a thinning and weakening of a circumscissile linear region of that wall, lifts off or hinges as a cap or lid upon dehiscence of the sporangium.... The condition where the sporangium is actually inoperculate, but a secondary structure is formed across the base of the discharge tube or in it, may be conveniently termed 'endo-operculate,' remembering its closer association with the inoperculate rather than the operculate condition.

Internal proliferation of the sporangium by a renewal of growth and expansion of the nucleated apex of the rhizoidal stalk which grows up through the base of the previously formed, now empty, sporangium has been observed in both monocentric (for example, *Loborhiza* and *Phlyctochytrium proliferum*) (Fig. 19, J, p. 318) and, more commonly, in polycentric chytrids (*Cladochytrium*, *Nowakowskiella* [Fig. 35 H-I, p. 583], *Polychytrium*, and *Physocladia*). It also occurs in the monocentric epibiotic phase of certain species of *Physoderma* (Büsgen, 1887; Clinton, 1902; Sparrow, 1934a, 1946).

Structure and behavior of the zoospore.—The zoospore of the chytrid (see also "Zoospore," p. 7; Fig. 1 A-B, p. 8) is a highly characteristic structure, its internal organization being so remarkably uniform throughout the group that an experienced observer of these fungi can recognize it even when it is free-swimming among aquatic debris. The body, which appears to have no well-defined wall, is ordinarily spherical or somewhat ovoid, usually with the broader end posterior. In certain forms, however, it is obovoid (*Rhizophlyctis mastigotrichis*), cylindrical with rounded ends (*Polyphagus euglenae*), or rodlike (*Rhizophydium goniosporum*). The plasma of the body is generally somewhat lustrous and is homogeneous or bears a few minute refractive granules or contains a globule. A nucleus and a nuclear cap may sometimes be detected, but as a rule these are invisible in the living zoospore. The most conspicuous element in the body is the large refractive globule, which may lie near or at the center (centric) or, more often, near the periphery (eccentric). Occasionally, as in *Rhizophlyctis mastigotrichis*, it is basal. The globule is extremely minute in some species, but in others it occupies approximately two thirds of the whole body. A few exceptions to this characteristic internal organization are found. Thus in *Olpidium vampyrellae* (Scherffel, 1926a) no globule is formed, whereas in *Cladochytrium granulatum*, for example, zoospores with several globules are produced. In general the type of organization of the zoospore remains relatively constant in a given species. [1]

Various conjectures have been made in the past as to the nature and function of the globule in the zoospore of the chytrid. Early investigators supposed it to be the nucleus, but, probably because of its fatty appearance, soon abandoned this view. Indeed, A. Braun (1856a) himself suggested that it might be oleaginous, and it has since been most commonly referred to as an "oil globule." Microchemical tests by Karling (1937b) indicate that the globule of the zoospore of *Cladochytrium replicatum* is of a more complex nature. Hillegas (1940) has reported similar findings in *Endochytrium operculatum* and Antikajian (1949) reports it in *Asterophlyctis sarcoptoides* to be of fat and some other accessory substance.

[1] See Koch (1958) for a detailed study of the chytrid zoospore by light microscopy.

It seems logical to suppose, considering the efficiency of oil as a concentrated source of energy, that the globule provides the material necessary for the activity of the flagellum, and, after encystment, for the production of the penetration tube and the very young thallus. By this means food is assured the developing plant until such time as contact with nutrient materials in the substratum has been established. Indeed, early in the formation of the thallus the globule ordinarily fragments and, possibly owing to the resultant increase in surface, is soon absorbed into the cytoplasm.

The posteriorly directed flagellum is apparently attached to the rear of the body in all forms except *Olpidiomorpha* (Scherffel, 1926b), *Zygorhizidium verrucosum* Geitler (1942), and *Pleotrachelus wildemani* Ingold (1952), in which it is subapical. For further details concerning flagella, see "Zoospore," p. 7.

The type of movement exhibited by the chytrid zoospore may be either free-swimming or amoeboid, a fact early noted by Schenk (1858b). During swimming the motion may be extremely erratic, the zoospore sometimes hopping and at other times gliding steadily for a while then suddenly going into a series of short convulsive springs. The hopping or dancing type of movement has been considered highly characteristic of the chytrid zoospore, particularly by Scherffel (1925a, 1926b, etc.), but, like the amoeboid type, it is not found in all species. Often the movement may consist solely of extremely rapid darting with frequent pauses and changes of direction; at other times it is a smooth even gliding, accompanied by a gentle rocking or an occasional rotation of the body. During sudden pauses the body may undergo remarkable amoeboid changes of shape and become strongly vacuolate. It then creeps around for varying periods on bits of substrata, its passive flagellum trailing behind. No ingestion of solid materials during such periods has ever been convincingly described. In resuming the swimming type of movement the body of the zoospore all at once becomes rounded, the flagellum vibrates again, and the spore darts off.

The duration of the period of motility of the free-swimming zoospore no doubt depends upon the species of chytrid, the vitality of the individual spore, and the conditions prevailing in the medium at the time. The amount of oxygen, the temperature, and freeness from noxious materials are probably of first importance. Under conditions necessary for observation, from three to four hours is usually a maximum period of swarming, although this is not always true. In one remarkable instance (Braun, 1856a) the zoospores of *Rhizophydium decipiens* continued swarming within the sporangium for one hundred and eight hours.

Not all chytrids possess zoospores capable of pronounced and prolonged motility. Couch (1935a) has reported the flagellated spores of *Phlyctidium anatropum* to be incapable of active swimming. After discharge they merely creep about amoeboidly over objects in the medium, and the flagellum never becomes active. A somewhat similar condition has been noted by Karling (1938c) in *Chytridium aggregatum*. In this fungus the failure of the zoospores to assume motility after emergence from the sporangium results in the characteristic development of clusters of thalli on the surface of the substratum. In *Amoebochytrium*, *Sporophlyctis rostrata*, and *Sporophlyctidium* the spore apparently fails to form a flagellum. In *Amoebochytrium* it shows pronounced amoeboid motion, but in the others it either germinates directly in the sporangium (*Sporophlyctis*) or after discharge floats about in the medium (*Sporophlyctidium*) and is termed an "aplanospore."

Tactic response of the chytrid zoospores to certain external stimuli has been observed. In *Rhizidium vorax* (Strasburger, 1878) and *Polyphagus euglenae* (Nowakowski, in Strasburger, *op. cit.*; Wager, 1913) they are positively phototactic. Since both of these fungi are parasitic upon motile green algae, the value of this physiological adaptation is readily apparent. The mechanism of the response is not as yet understood. It has been suggested by Wager that in *Polyphagus* the close proximity of the golden globule of the zoospore to the nucleus may indicate that it is a photoreceptive organ. He conjectures that light rays absorbed by it could cause local changes which, perhaps through the mediation of the nucleus, might exert a directive influence on the free-swimming zoospore. This may possibly be the explanation in *Polyphagus* and certain terrestrial chytrids (Kusano, 1930a), especially since photoreceptive organs are ordinarily pigmented. It would not explain, however, the phototactic response of the zoospore of *Rhizidium vorax*, which has a colorless globule. Furthermore, there are certain well-known chytrids with pigmented globules in their zoospores in which no phototactic response has ever been noted (*Cladochytrium replicatum, Rhizoclosmatium aurantiacum, Siphonaria variabilis,* and so on).

Müller (1911) has observed that the zoospores of *Rhizophydium pollinis-pini* and of *R. sphaerotheca* are positively chemotactic to genuine protein. The latter fungus also shows a positive response to the products of regressive protein metamorphosis and allied N compounds. The reactions of the swarmers were always greatly inhibited by poisonous materials in the atmosphere and by the lack of oxygen. H and OH ions exerted a negative effect. Similarly, Kusano (1932) has found the swarmers of *Olpidium trifolii* and *O. viciae* to be positively chemotactic to juices of their respective phanerogamic hosts. The active substances here were potassium compounds.

It seems probable, then, even from the limited information now available, that the zoospore is greatly aided in seeking out available sources of food in nature by its tactic responses to external stimuli.

Germination of the zoospore.—After the period of swarming the zoospore comes to rest and encysts. During this process the flagellum either contracts and is absorbed into the body or, sometimes, apparently drops off; its precise fate is difficult to follow. At the disappearance of the flagellum the spore body is surrounded by a delicate but rigid wall. Further development of the encysted zoospore is dependent upon the proximity of the substratum. If the source of food cannot be reached the spore may degenerate at once or after the formation of a rudimentary rhizoidal system. A curious fusion of zoospores of *Chytridium lagenaria* in drops of water lacking food has been noted (Sparrow, 1936a). Some of the motile spores settled down in contact with quiescent or even with germinated spores. The contents of the contacting and, by now, encysted spore then flowed into the other one. The receptive body subsequently enlarged, and there ensued during the next five days a remarkable development of the rhizoidal system. This was of far greater extent and complexity than that formed by single germinated spores in the same medium. Such unconjugated spores gave rise to only a feebly developed rhizoidal system and disintegrated within twelve hours. It seems probable that this fusion was an attempt by the chytrid to rejuvenate and prolong its vegetative activity under poor nutritional conditions, with the purpose of ultimately reaching a suitable substratum. In connection with these purely morphological observations on vegetative "rejuvenation" by means of the fusion of two protoplasts it is of interest to quote the remarks of Wager (1913) concerning the so-called "double fusion" in *Polyphagus* (see also "Sexual Reproduction," p. 75): "The double fusion which takes place in the life-cycle of *Polyphagus* is clearly bound up with this dual function of the nucleus, the chromidial fusion in the zygote promoting vegetative growth, whilst the nuclear fusion in the sporangium precedes the formation of the spores. The importation of two nuclei into the zygote appears therefore to be primarily for the purpose of increasing its vegetative activity...."

The emergence of a motile swarmer from a cyst has been observed in *Achlyogeton* and, possibly, in *Phlyctidium* (Atkinson, 1894).

Sexual Reproduction

Although much has been learned about the chytrids, particularly in recent years, the sexual reproduction of most species is still unknown; in some chytrids, indeed, such reproduction is suspected to be entirely lacking. It has been established, however, that sexuality when it does exist is of an extremely varied character. In all well-authenticated occurrences the zygote becomes transformed into a resting spore, which upon germination produces swarmers. From this fact it is probable that the thalli are haploid and that, as in many of the algae, the sexually formed resting spore represents the only diploid structure in the life cycle.

Among the inoperculate chytrids as in certain species of *Olpidium*, which are parasitic upon terrestrial phanerogams (Kusano, 1912, 1929) the fusion of isogamous (like) planogametes (swimming gametes) has been observed (Fig. 4 A, p. 72). After this fusion the biflagellate zygote encysts on the surface of the host, penetrates it, and forms endobiotically a thick-walled resting spore. Among the alga-inhabiting members of the Olpidiaceae no sexual process has as yet been convincingly demonstrated. Observations on certain terrestrial chytrids belonging to the genus *Synchytrium* (Curtis, 1921; Kusano, 1930a) show unquestionably that fusion of isoplanogametes precedes resting-spore formation. There is strong but not conclusive evidence (Couch, 1931) that a similar type of sexuality also occurs in *Micromyces longispinosis*, an algal parasite belonging to the same family (Synchytriaceae).

Sexuality has been noted in several members of the Phlyctidiaceae. Gimesi (1924) stated that in *Phlyctidium eudorinae* the resting spore is formed after terminal or lateral fusion of two isogamous gametes, one of which has previously come to rest and germinated and the other has become encysted on it. Hanson (1944a) shows a similar type of sexuality is present in *Loborhiza* (Fig. 4 U, p. 72). In resting-spore formation in *Dangeardia mammillata*, Canter (1946) found that union typically occurs between a large flask-shaped thallus ("female"), similar in appearance to a zoosporangium, and a small one ("male"), resembling a young undeveloped sporangium. The germ tube of the male, which rarely branches, makes contact with the swollen base of the female. In some instances males were lacking, in which case the resting spores apparently developed parthenogenetically. In several species of *Rhizophydium* a sexual process of a somewhat different nature has been reported (Scherffel, 1925b; Couch, 1932, 1935a; Sparrow, 1933c, 1936a, 1939a; Canter, 1950a). In certain species, as *R. goniosporum*, *R. ephippium*, *R. planktonicum*, *R. sphaerocystidis*, and *R. hyalobryonis*, the male gamete (rarely two) attaches itself directly to the larger, epibiotic, receptive thallus, which is already established on the host. Communication is made between the two, and the contents of the small encysted male pass into the thallus. There is no loss of identity of the two gametangia, and after the receptive structure, which now contains the two gametes, becomes transformed into a thick-walled resting spore, the empty cyst of the male remains adherent to it. Indications are that sometimes, at least, the receptive thallus may undergo considerable enlargement before contact with the male is made. At other times like-sized swarmers settle down in pairs on the surface of the host and establish themselves. One of them apparently enlarges at a greater rate than the other, receives the contents of the smaller one, and becomes transformed into the resting spore. In *R. couchii* (Couch, 1932; Sparrow, 1933c) the swarmers which give rise to the gametangia are at first identical in size and shape (Fig. 4 G, p. 72). After a period of swarming they come to rest on the surface of the alga in groups of four to ten or more. Each of two adjacent encysted swarmers produces an endobiotic rhizoidal system. The epibiotic part of one thallus now enlarges rapidly and continues to extend its rhizoidal system, but the other apparently ceases to grow. Within the larger thallus at the point of contact can be observed a short refractive tube seemingly formed by the male gametangium (Fig. 4 H). The entire contents of this gametangium, with the exception of a small globule, is then discharged through the tube into the larger plant, which continues to grow and is ultimately transformed into a thick-walled resting spore to which the empty cyst of the male gametangium, generally torn from its rhizoidal system, remains adherent (Fig. 4 I). In *R. ovatum* (Couch, 1935a) and at times in *R. granulosporum* (Scherffel, 1925b; Sparrow, 1939a, Fig. 4 J–O), the swarmer which will then give rise to the male gametangium comes to rest on the algal cell and forms a rudimentary rhizoidal system. A second, like-sized swarmer then attaches itself to the upper part of this gametangium (Fig. 4 B). The second spore, however, never makes contact with the host and never forms a vegetative system. Eventually it receives the contents of the other gametangium and enlarges to form the resting body. In *R. ovatum*, in which the sequence of development has been carefully followed, both gametangia enlarge at the expense of the host, materials being obtained by the rhizoidal system of the epibiotic male for both it and the more distal receptive thallus. The latter enlarges at a much greater rate and eventually receives the contents of the male thallus through a broad opening formed in the walls at the place of contact. It then becomes converted into a thick-walled smooth resting spore (Fig. 4 C–F). A cytological examination of this process shows the gametangia to be uninucleate and reveals that with the merging of the gametes the nuclei as well as the cytoplasm fuse. A thickened wall is then laid down around the zygote, which is supported at the apex of the thin-walled male gametangium. A variation of this process is seen in *R. anomalum* (Canter, 1950a), in which the contributing thallus develops until it resembles an early stage in sporangial growth. A zoospore then attaches itself to the base of the male thallus and eventually receives the contents of the latter.

It is clear that in certain species of the large genus *Rhizophydium* a sexual act precedes the formation of the resting spore. Many phases

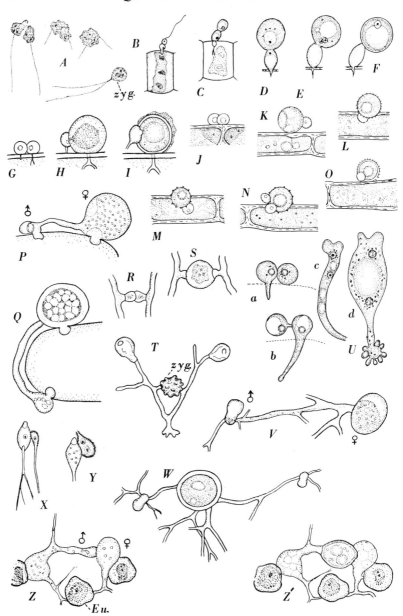

Fig. 4. Sexuality in the Chytridiales

Explanation of Figure 4

A. Stages in conjugation of isogamous planogametes of *Olpidium trifolii* Schroeter (*zyg.*, motile biflagellate zygote). *B–F. Rhizophydium ovatum* Couch on *Stigeoclonium*, stages in development of zygote: *B*, flagellated gamete making contact with young gametangial plant; *C–D*, gametangia enlarged and stained to show nuclei; *E*, entrance of gamete of basal gametangium into distal one; *F*, mature zygote with fusion nucleus and thickened wall. *G–I. Rhizophydium couchii*, Sparrow on *Spirogyra sp.*, stages in development of zygote: *G*, two very young gametangia on outer surface of algal wall, with beginnings of rhizoidal systems; *H*, large receptive gametangium to which is attached small male gametangium; a fertilization tube is clearly visible; *I*, mature zygote with thickened wall, to which is attached empty male gametangium. *J–O. Rhizophydium granulosporum* Scherffel on *Tribonema*: *J*, two very young gametangia on outer surface of algal wall, one with rudimentary rhizoidal system; *K*, immature zygote with adherent male gametangium; *L*, more mature zygote bearing echinulations on wall; only the male gametangium appears to have made contact with host; *M*, similar to preceding but with more peglike spines; *N*, immature zygote showing polyandrous condition; *O*, mature thick-walled zygote; both gametangia have here made contact with host wall. *P–Q. Zygorhizidium willei* Löwenthal on *Cylindrocystis*: *P*, large female gametangium and small male gametangium on surface of host cell, connected by a conjugation tube produced by the male; *Q*, mature thick-walled zygote with male gametangium and tube still attached. *R–T. Zygochytrium aurantiacum* Sorokin: *R*, early stage in conjugation of lateral branches; gametangia are delimited by cross walls; *S*, immature zygote; *T*, rough thick-walled mature zygote (*zyg.*); two empty sporangia are shown at tips of branches. *U, Loborhiza metzneri* Hanson on daughter colonies of *Volvox*: *a*, two young gametangia on gelatinous sheath of host colony; *b*, receptive gametangium forming rhizoidal system, male producing conjugation tube; *c*, stained receptive thallus showing two gamete nuclei separated by refractive globule; *d*, binucleate developing resting spore. *V–W. Siphonaria variabilis* H. E. Petersen in exuviae: *V*, large, female gametangium receiving contents of smaller male through an anastomosed rhizoid; *W*, mature thick-walled zygote to which are attached two empty male gametangia. *X–Y. Sporophlyctis rostrata* Serbinow on *Draparnaldia*: *X*, uninucleate gametangia attached laterally; *Y*, binucleate spiny-walled zygote. *Z–Z′. Polyphagus laevis* Bartsch on *Euglena* (*Eu.*): *Z*, male and female thalli attached by conjugation tube formed by male; *Z′*, later stage of same, showing mature thick-walled zygote which has been formed in distal part of conjugation tube from contents of the two gametangia.

(*A*, Kusano, 1929; *B–F*, Couch, 1935a; *G–I*, Sparrow, 1933c; *J–O*, Sparrow, 1939a; *P–Q*, Löwenthal, 1905; *R–T*, Sorokin, 1874a, 1883; *U*, Hanson, 1944a; *V–W*, Sparrow, 1943; *X–Y*, Serbinow, 1907; *Z–Z′*, Sparrow, 1943)

of this process need further amplification. Thus, in none of the observed occurrences is it certain that the swarmer which may form the gametangium is not also capable, if contact is not established with another swarmer, of becoming transformed into a zoosporangium, that is, whether it may not be potentially both a zoospore and a gamete. Furthermore, it is not known if the gametes are formed in special gametangia or if from the first they are sexually differentiated as male and female. It is of course possible that in some species a situation similar to that in *Synchytrium fulgens* (Kusano, 1930a) prevails. In this chytrid the sex of the gametes is not fixed, the active ones behaving as males and the quiescent or germinated ones as females. Since unfused swarmers may function nonsexually to produce a thallus, Kusano feels that they should be regarded as gametes undergoing parthenogenetic development rather than as zoospores. That is, in *S. fulgens* no zoospores are formed, only gametes capable of either sexual fusion or parthenogenetic development. The sexuality of *Rhizophydium* appears to be a step removed from the isogamous planogametic type found in *Olpidium* and closer to the condition in *S. fulgens* in that at least one of the gametes (and sometimes both) is generally nonmotile when contact is established and fusion occurs. It differs from both *Olpidium* and *S. fulgens* in that the swarmers themselves do not fuse. Rather, they give rise after encystment to bodies which contain the gametic material, that is, to gametangia at least one of which has developed a vegetative system and is an immature thallus. Furthermore, even after fusion of the gametes has occurred, the two gametangia remain distinct structures, the one eventually becoming the resting spore, the other, the adherent cyst.

Ledingham (1936) has reported evidence of the occurrence in *Rhizophydium graminis*, a parasite on the roots of certain grasses, of another type of sexuality. In this fungus anastomosis of the rhizoids has been detected, although the actual fusion of the gametes was not witnessed. The same investigator has also reported that fusion of zoospores takes place in *R. graminis*, but he does not describe the fate of these fused swarmers.

Evidence for a sexual process in *Diplophlyctis intestina* involving rhizoidal anastomosis of immature thalli was presented by Sparrow

(1936d). More recently, Haskins (1950) has shown that an essentially similar process precedes resting-spore formation in *D. sexualis*.

Of considerable interest too is the discovery of sexuality by Canter (1951) in the little-known genus *Rhizosiphon*. Here, an isogamous fusion takes place in which the gametes make contact directly, or laterally by means of a short tube. One gamete only has contact with the host and that by means of a single rhizoid. Although the process as recorded is based upon scanty observations, from the figures and description it appears that one gamete first produces an unbranched germ tube, part of which is extramatrical, and is then joined with the other gamete. The bodies of both remain distinct. The resting spore is endobiotic and from its size must have undergone a period of vegetative growth within the host cell.

Sexuality has also been observed in the Rhizidiaceae. Here, too, the gametic material fuses in elements of one or the other gametangium and is never set free in the medium. Furthermore, in all well-authenticated occurrences the gametangia themselves were more or less mature thalli, often of markedly different size.

The sexual reproduction in the rhizidiaceous genus *Polyphagus* is perhaps the best-known example of this process among the chytrids. The classic investigations of Nowakowski (1876b) on *Polyphagus* showed that one thallus put out a tube which made contact with another (Fig. 4 Z, p. 72).[1] In the distal part of this tube the contents (gametes) of both thalli accumulated. The zygote, subterminal in the tube, then became invested with a thick wall and underwent a period of rest (Fig. 4 Z'). At germination it produced a zoosporangium. Although the tube-producing thallus in *P. euglenae* is frequently smaller than the other one and is ordinarily referred to as the male, in many individuals there is little or no difference between the two. Indeed, in some instances the male may be the larger. Cytological investigations of this sexual process (Wager, 1899a, 1913; Dangeard, 1900-1901c) show that the two gametes are uninucleate. Wager observed that the male nucleus is the smaller and that it, with the cytoplasm, passes first into the swollen tip of the tube (Fig. 5 G, p. 80). The female gamete thereupon enters and the two nuclei make contact but do not fuse (Fig. 5 H). The smaller enlarges until it equals the female nucleus in size, and the two move

[1] Illustrations are of *P. laevis*.

apart to opposite sides of the cell, which is now surrounded by a thick spiny wall. Considerable chromatin is extruded from the nuclei, and as a result they become smaller and show less affinity for stains. The extruded, deep-staining material eventually becomes massed in the center of the cell. At the time of germination the resting spore functions as a prosporangium. There is protruded from its ruptured wall a sphere which increases in size as the contents of the spore emerge into it. The two nuclei pass out into the sporangium (Fig. 5 I) and there fuse (Fig. 5 J). The fusion nucleus then multiplies to form the nuclei of the zoospores, which are eventually cleaved out from the contents. Although meiosis was not observed it has been supposed to occur at the first division of the fusion nucleus in the sporangium formed by the resting spore (Fig. 5 K). On this hypothesis and proceeding from the fact that in Nowakowski's cultures nearly equal numbers of male and female thalli were formed, Kniep (1928) has proposed that the fungus is dioecious and that the zoospores are sexually differentiated. He suggests (*op. cit.*) the following developmental cycle:

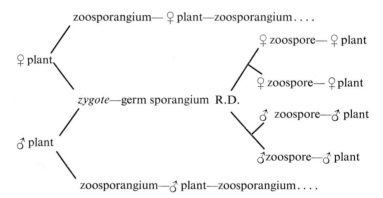

Bartsch (1945) noted that in *Polyphagus laevis* the zygote was always formed terminally in the conjugation tube and, hence, at maturity was directly adnate to the female thallus (Fig. 4 Z').

In the closely related *Sporophlyctis rostrata*, fusion of two uninucleate thalli of equal size takes place (Serbinow, 1907) (Fig. 4 X, p. 72). One thallus receives the contents of the other through a pore. The distal part of the receptive thallus is then transformed into a thick-walled spiny resting spore (Fig. 4 Y), and fusion of the nuclei follows. The curious sexual reproduction in *Rhizoclosmatium* and *Siphonaria* involves passage of gametic material through anastomosed rhizoids. *Siphonaria* is, however, the only one in which the passage of gametic material and subsequent fusion have actually been seen (Petersen, 1903; Sparrow, 1937a; Karling, 1945d). Because of the tenuousness of the parts in members of other genera observations on such processes are difficult even at high magnifications. In *Siphonaria variabilis* two (sometimes three) thalli of unequal size make contact by the fusion of elements of their rhizoidal systems. The contents of the smaller plant migrate into the larger one (Fig. 4 V), which then lays down a thick wall around the reproductive rudiment and becomes a resting spore (Fig. 4 W). Many times active contact of the two thalli appears to be accomplished solely by the efforts of the receptive thallus. The rhizoids of this plant seem to seek out the other thallus and, often, instead of fusing with some element of the vegetative system, make direct contact with the main body. Whether or not the two types of thalli develop from swarmers formed in the same sporangium is not known. It has been frequently observed in *Siphonaria*, however, that sporangia of two very different size classes are produced.

In *Siphonaria petersenii* (Karling, 1945d), the male thallus is recognizable by a single apical spine which usually forms on it (Fig. 26 D, p. 422). Variation in the degree of development of the male's rhizoidal system is evident. Sometimes rhizoids are absent and the male body either makes direct contact with the female or is joined to it by a broad tube. Similar variation in the spatial relations of the two conjugants occurs in *S. sparrowii*. In this species, however, as in *S. variabilis*, no structural differences are found in the two types of thalli. Fusion of the protoplasts through anastomosed rhizoids or a long conjugation tube is very common in *S. sparrowii*. Furthermore, as many as six male thalli may be connected to one resting spore. Since fusions in *Siphonaria* always resulted in resting-spore formation. Karling (*op. cit.*) considers them to be syngamous rather than merely vegetative even though karyogamy has not as yet been observed. Karling presents two theoretical life-cycle diagrams based (1) on the very probable supposition that karyogamy takes place shortly after plasmogamy and that meiosis occurs at the first division of the diploid nucleus during germination of the zygote, and sex genotypically determined, making sporangia and conjugating thalli haplonts, and (2) on meiosis occurring at germination of zygote but sex phenotypically segregated at close of sporangial and zoosporic period.

In *Rhizidium windermerense,* Canter (1950c) states that contact is made between two encysted zoospores (sexual thalli) by means of fine threads ("conjugation tubes") which they produce. These meet at their tips and a swelling is formed at their junction which is the incipient resting spore. The contents of both thalli pass into the developing zygote, which increases in size, and a well-developed rhizoidal system is then formed. Because of the small size of the conjugating thalli, it is evident the zygotic plant functions vegetatively for a time.

Among the operculate chytrids sexual reproduction has been reported with certainty in *Chytridium* and *Zygorhizidium* of the Chytridiaceae and in *Zygochytrium* of the Megachytriaceae. It may possibly occur also in *Tetrachytrium* (see pp. 599, 601) of the latter family. In *Zygorhizidium* (Löwenthal, 1905; Scherffel, 1925b; Canter, 1950c) epibiotic thalli of different sizes are formed on the algal cell. Each of the smaller thalli produces a tube which makes contact with the lateral wall of a larger plant and fuses with it (Fig. 4 P, p. 72). The contents of the small ("male") thallus are then conveyed into the larger ("female"), which subsequently becomes transformed into a thick-walled resting spore (Fig. 4 Q). It is probable that upon germination this resting structure produces zoospores. A cytological examination of *Zygorhizidium* by Löwenthal revealed that the two gametangia were uninucleate. The female possessed a relatively large centrally disposed nucleus imbedded in the fatty cytoplasm. That of the male was distinctly smaller. After migration of all or nearly all of the male gametic material a wall was formed which separated the tube from the zygote. Plasmogamy took place at once, but the two nuclei remained separate even after the formation of the thick wall of the resting spore. It is possible that fusion occurs at germination.

Certain aspects of the sexuality of *Zygorhizidium* are puzzling. From the accounts of both Löwenthal and Scherffel two kinds of sporangia are produced, large, "typical," ones about 15 μ in diameter and "dwarf" ones 4–5.4 μ in diameter. The latter are considered to be "male" thalli which either have not succeeded in making contact with a receptive plant after forming a conjugation tube or have at once been transformed into sporangia. A further distinction between such sporangia and typical ones, according to Scherffel, is the lack of rhizoids on the endobiotic knob and the failure to produce bending of the host cell. In some specimens at least the "dwarfs" attained nearly the size of the usual sporangia (see Löwenthal, 1905: figs. 17 and 26). Presumably both nonsexual and sexual individuals have been derived from ordinary zoospores which came from sporangia of typical size. The question arises, then, whether environmental conditions determine the subsequent nature of the thallus formed by the zoospore (nonsexual sporangium or gametangium), or whether there are inherent differences in the swarmers which are produced at the germination of the resting spore. In favor of the former interpretation is the fact (observed by both Löwenthal and Scherffel) that dwarf thalli on which a conjugation tube has already developed may function as sporangia. Since both nonsexual and sexual structures are formed at the same time and since a cytological examination shows that sporangia and receptive thalli of the same size differ in their nuclear condition, the former being multinucleate, the latter uninucleate, the evidence is not conclusive.

A type of sexuality which resembles that seen in certain species of *Rhizophydium* was found in *Chytridium sexuale* by Koch (1951). A swarmer comes to rest on the host wall (*Vaucheria*), encysts, and introduces into the alga a germ tube which expands into an apophysis. The epibiotic spore cyst then enlarges and elongates and, while this is yet relatively undeveloped, a motile male gamete encysts on the thallus surface and empties its contents through a short germ tube into the young plant. The combined protoplasts migrate into the endobiotic apophysis, which increases in size and is converted into a resting spore. No structural differences were observed between the zoospores which formed receptive thalli and those which functioned as males. Indeed, whether a thallus became a zoosporangium or a receptive plant seemed entirely dependent upon whether or not engagement with a male cell took place; however, Koch indicated there was no proof of this.

The authenticity of Sorokin's (1874a) account of the sexual process

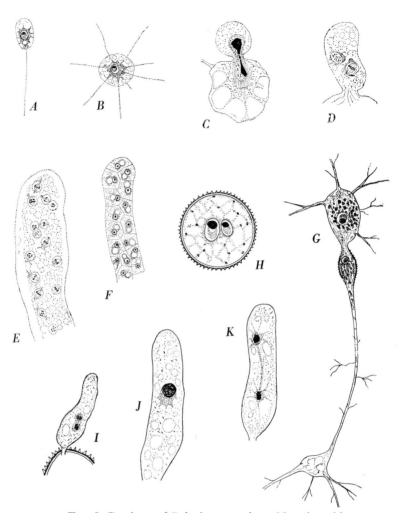

FIG. 5. Cytology of *Polyphagus euglenae* Nowakowski

A. Zoospore with nucleus and basal oil droplet; both oil droplet and nucleus are surrounded by dark-staining chromidial material. *B*. Young thallus with single nucleus surrounded by chromidial material; delicate rhizoids radiate from periphery of body. *C*. Single nucleus of large prosporangium passing into smaller, developing sporangium; large nucleolus has been much constricted in passing through the opening. *D*. Two nuclei in process of division in young sporangium; extruded chromatin lies on periphery of

in *Zygochytrium* has long been doubted, as has, indeed, the existence of the genus itself. The type of conjugation appears to be no more aberrant, however, than that found in *Siphonaria* or *Polyphagus*, except that the polycentric *Zygochytrium* is monoecious. According to Sorokin, two short lateral opposing outgrowths are formed, one on each of the main branches of the thallus. The tips of these outgrowths, after fusing, enlarge and, as in a species of *Mucor*, become delimited as like-sized gametangia (Fig. 4 R, p. 72). The contents of the two gametangia then fuse (Fig. 4 S), and from the resulting zygote is formed a thick-walled rough resting spore (Fig. 4 T), which, upon germination, produces in turn a hypha-like structure.

In *Tetrachytrium* fusion of isogamous posteriorly uniflagellate swarmers takes place. The biflagellate zygote does not become transformed into a resting structure, but germinates at once to form a new plant. The behavior of the zygote is so remarkable in *Tetrachytrium*, as compared with all other chytrids, that Sorokin's observations should probably here be regarded with a certain degree of skepticism (Fig. 38 I–M, p. 600).

Couch (1939b) has presented strong but not conclusive evidence that heterothallism occurs in *Pringsheimiella dioica* and *Rhizophlyctis rosea*. In *Pringsheimiella*, an obligate parasite of *Achlya*, isolated strains

---

each nucleus; spindle is intranuclear. *E.* Portion of sporangium showing nuclei in process of simultaneous division; at poles of some spindles are kinoplasmic masses with radiating striae. *F.* Part of sporangium in which zoospores have been delimited; each nucleus bears an oil globule adjacent to it; both globule and nucleus are surrounded by dark-staining chromidial material. *G.* Two conjugating thalli; male nucleus has already passed into enlarged spiny thick-walled tip of conjugation tube, and larger, female nucleus is about to do so. *H.* Spiny resting spore with the two gamete nuclei lying side by side; smaller, male nucleus soon becomes equal in size to female; later both become smaller, owing to extrusion of chromidia into cytoplasm; deep-stained chromidial material is scattered throughout cytoplasm. *I.* Developing sporangium, formed at germination of resting spore; the two gamete nuclei have migrated into sporangium and are close together, probably fusing. *J.* Sporangium formed at germination of resting spore; the two gamete nuclei are now fused. *K.* Division of large fusion nucleus into two nuclei in sporangium formed by germinating resting spore.

(Wager, 1913)

when grown alone gave rise only to zoosporangia. When certain strains were paired, however, either with or without actual contact of the hyphae of their respective hosts, abundant resting spores were formed. The type of sexuality involved has evidently not as yet been discovered. With respect to the saprophytic *R. rosea* the following situation has been observed. Plants of all but one collection were found incapable of forming resting spores. This one collection, however, produced them in abundance. Individual sporangia from it were isolated in separate dishes of sterile water baited with appropriate substrata. Of the twenty monosporangial cultures thus started four showed growth of new plants. In none were resting spores ever formed. When all possible crosses had been made between the four available strains it was found that whenever a certain strain was paired with the others resting spores were produced. It was concluded from this that three of the four strains were of the same "sex," and that the fourth was of the opposite "sex." As in *Pringsheimiella*, the type of sexuality was not determined.

In his summary on sexuality in the chytrids, Emerson (1950) has this to say concerning sex determination:

Suggestions regarding possible instances of genotypic sex determination have been made by various investigators and schemes, such as that recently proposed by Karling [1945d] for *Siphonaria* have been drawn up, but, to the writer's knowledge, there is not yet a single well-established example in the chytrids of a differentiation of sexes clearly attributable to segregation of genetic factors at the time of meiosis in the life cycle. In view of the widespread and very general occurrence of hermaphroditism and phenotypic sex determination in the higher aquatic fungi, and the very few instances in which a genetic difference between the sexes is indicated, perhaps we should not expect to find more than scattered examples of genotypic sex determination in the lower forms.

The Resting Spore

The resting spore or "resting sporangium" may be produced either sexually, from the zygote, as previously indicated, or, more often, asexually, from a modified reproductive rudiment or prosporangium or from an apophysis. With the exception of *Chytridium* and such genera as *Blyttiomyces*, the asexually developed resting spore is formed either outside or inside the substratum, according to the position of the sporangium. Outstanding features are its thickened wall and its guttulate contents (Fig. 4 I, Q, Z', p. 72). This stout durable wall undoubtedly serves during the rest period to protect the living contents from the harmful, or lethal, effects of unfavorable factors in the environment.

The thallus bearing the asexually formed spore is often indistinguishable at first from that which bears the zoosporangium. As it matures, however, certain distinctive features become evident. For example, the rhizoidal system of monocentric forms is frequently less well developed than that of zoosporangial plants. The contents, particularly those of the reproductive rudiment, become highly oleaginous. After the incipient resting spore has attained its maximum size and has received the protoplasm of the rhizoids, its wall begins to thicken. Coincidently, the many small globules coalesce, until at maturity a single or, less often, several large ones are formed. The remainder of the contents appears strongly condensed and sometimes may consist of only a relatively thin peripheral layer around the centric or eccentric globule. Since in the formation of the resting spore the contents do not permanently contract, the mature structure usually completely fills its container.

The wall may be smooth or variously ornamented, colorless or pale yellow to dark brown. In certain smooth-walled types, as for example *Rhizophydium fallax* (Scherffel, 1925b), *R. couchii* (Couch, 1932), and *Chytridium olla* (de Bary, 1884), it is clearly differentiated into an outer and an inner layer. In these species the outer wall probably represents the wall of the container; the inner, the wall laid down by the accumulated contents of the rudiment. In *C. lagenaria* (Karling, 1936a), *R. ovatum* (Couch, 1935a), and others the wall is described as consisting of only one layer, and is evidently simply the centripetally thickened wall of the container. Spines, blunt knobs, lobes, undulations, or rays are the most common types of ornamentation. In rough-walled resting spores two distinct layers may generally be discerned, an inner smooth thin one and an outer thicker one which bears the characteristic ornamentation. In the case of the roughened wall of *Nowakowskiella ramosa*, however, J. Roberts (1948) indicates that the ornamentation arises from an inner layer. In the imperfectly known *Chytridium characii* (Scherffel, *op. cit.*) the outer wall is thick and warty, and clearly prismatic in optical section, as it is in the resting spore of *Blastocladia*, whereas the inner wall is thin and solid. Other curious types of ornamentation are described by Scherffel (*op. cit.*). The origin of the peculiar zones of gelatinous material surrounding the resting spores and sporangia in *Rhizophydium coronum* (p. 251) is unknown. Hanson (1945b) suggested that they may be a protoplasmic exudate which is passed through the wall to the outside.

The precise method by which ornamentation on the resting spore is produced is not well understood. In *Rhizophydium asterosporum* (Scherffel, 1925b) the incipient and as yet thin-walled resting body forms protrusions which become filled, as the spore matures, with solid refractive often stratified material. In those species of *Rozella* that have a spiny-walled resting spore (Cornu, 1872a; Foust, 1937) the echinulations are described as originating in a clear zone which envelops the densely granular main body. In *Rozella allomycis* (Foust, *op. cit.*) minute granules appear in the clear enveloping material and align themselves at right angles to the spore wall. They then fuse linearly to form the tenuous spines (Fig. 14 A, p. 179).

Germination of the resting spores has been observed among representatives of a number of different genera. The factors which induce it are not known with any preciseness. Generally, as in *Rhizidium mycophilum* (Nowakowski, 1876a) and *Polyphagus euglenae* (Nowakowski, 1876b; Wager, 1913), a rest period of a month or more appears necessary. Resting spores of *Rhizophydium ovatum* (Couch, 1935a) and *Rhizophydium sp.* (Karling, 1939c), however, may undergo germination in from two to five days after their formation, only a short period of dormancy being required. In by far the majority of instances in which germination has been witnessed the resting structure functioned as a prosporangium (*Polyphagus*, *Entophlyctis*, *Endochytrium*, *Diplophlyctis*, *Megachytrium*, *Chytridium*, *Siphonaria*, *Rhizophydium*, and others). In so doing either the wall of the spore cracked or a pore was formed through which the contents emerged, surrounded by a thin membrane. This structure was converted into a zoosporangium attached to the now empty resting body and discharged its zoospores in the same fashion as the zoosporangium formed on the thallus, that is, either operculately or inoperculately (Fig. 23 C, p. 385; Fig. 25 G,

p. 411). Each zoospore gives rise to a new thallus. Direct transformation of the resting spore into a zoosporangium rather than a prosporangium has been occasionally described, notably in *Rhizophydium messanensis* (Morini, 1896), *Rhizophydium transversum* (Dangeard, 1900–1901e), *Rhizophydium ovatum* (Couch, *op. cit.*), *Diplophlyctis intestina* (Zopf, 1884), and *Cladochytrium replicatum* (Karling, 1935).[1]

The so-called "cyst" formed in *Polyphagus euglenae* (Dangeard, 1900–1901c; Wager, 1913) is perhaps to be regarded as a less specialized type of resting spore. It is produced simply by the thickening of the wall of the prosporangium and upon germination functions in turn as a typical thin-walled prosporangium.

CYTOLOGY

While knowledge of the cytology of the aquatic chytrids is increasing, it is still fragmentary. The most complete accounts are those dealing with the interbiotic monocentric *Polyphagus euglenae* (Wager, 1899a, 1913; Dangeard, 1900–1901c), the endobiotic polycentric *Cladochytrium replicatum* (Karling, 1937b), and the endobiotic monocentric *Endochytrium operculatum* (Hillegas, 1940). Since these studies, cytological investigations of certain phases of other types have appeared. In the treatment below the older accounts are given precedence, the more recent are discussed on pages (92–104) that follow.

Both Wager and Dangeard were in essential agreement as to the nuclear behavior in *Polyphagus euglenae*, details of the sexual stage of which have been described above (see "Sexual Reproduction," p. 75). From Wager's account, the thallus is one-celled and has in the rudiment of the prosporangium a single more or less spherical nucleus (Fig. 5 B, p. 80). In the resting state this nucleus exhibits a central region of lightly stained meshwork connected by delicate radiating threads to the nuclear membrane. A deeply stained arc-shaped cap lying at one side contains all the chromatin material. Surrounding the nucleus is a coarse, densely granular network having a strong affinity for chromatin stains. Deeply staining knots which occur on this reticulum also give a chromatin reaction and are considered to have something to do with oil formation. Whether the precise origin of this so-

[1] See, however, Karling, *Torreya*, 41: 108. 1941.

called "chromidial" net is cytoplasmic or nuclear is not known. It first appears during the later stages in zoospore formation in the sporangium, is present in the young thallus, and passes, finally, along with the nucleus, into the new sporangium, where it becomes dispersed in the cytoplasm. During development chromatin is constantly extruded from the nucleus. After migrating from the mature prosporangium into the enlarging sporangium (Fig. 5 C) the nucleus divides mitotically. The daughter nuclei then continue to divide simultaneously (Fig. 5 D–E) until, in large sporangia, several hundred have been formed. In the mitotic process an intranuclear spindle is formed, on which at the metaphase from ten to twelve minute chromosomes can be observed. Only a small amount of chromatin is used in the production of the chromosomes, the remainder forming a layer on the inner periphery of the nuclear membrane. This layer is visible during the prophases and is ultimately set free in the cytoplasm, where it is used in the growth of the developing sporangium. Soon after the spindle becomes evident the nuclear membrane disappears at the poles, allowing them to protrude slightly into the cytoplasm. The remainder of the nuclear membrane then contracts. Centrosome-like bodies are visible at the poles of the spindles at this stage. Upon the separation of the daughter nuclei the nuclear membrane vanishes and the peripheral chromatin mass contracts to form a more or less globular body in the cytoplasm. The chromosomes then become aggregated at the periphery of the new daughter nuclei in contact with a light-staining network which forms the bulk of each new nucleus. Delicate strands persist for a time between the daughter nuclei, but finally disappear.

Nuclear divisions are completed before cytokinesis is initiated. Cleavage lines separating irregular, uninucleated, polyhedral segments of the cytoplasm then make their appearance. In each of the segments the small oil droplets dispersed in the cytoplasm fuse to form a large globule which is in close contact with the nucleus (Fig. 5 F, p. 80). The deep-staining chromidial mass then appears around both nucleus and globule. At this stage the cleavage planes disappear for a time, to reappear again shortly before discharge. The nucleus of the zoospore is almost centrally located, in close proximity to the globule; the surrounding chromidial mass extends to the point of attachment of the flagellum (Fig. 5 A). Cytological details of the sexual process have already been given (see under "Sexual Reproduction," p. 75).

In the endophytic polycentric *Cladochytrium replicatum* (Karling, 1937b) the infecting zoospore has a large central nucleus (Fig. 6 A, p. 88). Within it is a small nucleolus and, outside the nuclear membrane, a large deeply stained nuclear cap of uncertain origin and composition, similar to that in *Blastocladia*, *Allomyces*, and *Monoblepharis*. Faint cytoplasmic strands connect the nucleus to the posterior flagellum. After encystment a penetration tube is formed, through which the nucleus and possibly the nuclear cap as well, if this has not already disassociated, pass into the substratum (Fig. 6 B–C). In some individuals the tip of the tube expands at once to form the first turbinate cell, or spindle organ, into which the primary nucleus migrates. In others formation of the first spindle organ may sometimes be delayed until the now strongly elongated nucleus has reached the tip of the tube. Recently migrated nuclei are readily recognized by their distinctly pyriform shape (Fig. 6 D). In them the chromatin forms a faint reticulum and the deeply stained nucleolus is disposed in a broad flat transverse ring around the inner periphery of the narrower end. One or several rhizoids then emerge from the surface of the primary spindle organ and eventually form at their tips *new* spindle organs. As the primary swelling increases in size the nucleus divides mitotically, with the formation of an intranuclear spindle. During such division the nucleolus persists as a laterally placed, dark-staining, generally arc-shaped structure. Cytokinesis follows, and the spindle organ becomes two-celled. The more distal nucleus subsequently migrates into the secondary rhizoid and eventually comes to lie in the new spindle organ. Sometimes both nuclei migrate from the primary spindle organ before the formation of the septum. The mature thallus thus "replicated" is multinucleate, with the nuclei present (save when migrating) only in the spindle organs and rudiments of the reproductive structures. In the rhizoids the cytoplasm is strongly vacuolate and bears, at irregular intervals, deeply staining granules of unknown composition.

The resting nucleus of the thallus is large and spherical, oval, or citriform. Lying to one side near the inner wall of the nuclear membrane is a conspicuous disclike, oval, or bandlike nucleolus entirely similar

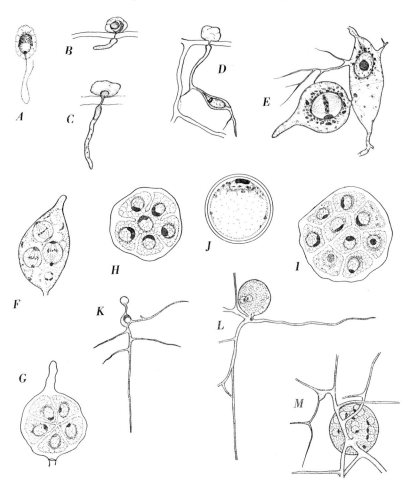

FIG. 6. Cytology of *Cladochytrium replicatum* and *Endochytrium operculatum*

A–J. Cladochytrium replicatum Karling: *A*, zoospore, showing deep-stained nuclear cap over anterior part of nucleus; at opposite pole of nucleus is a small nucleole from which a delicate strand runs to point of attachment of posterior flagellum; *B*, early stage in germination of an encysted spore lying on surface of substratum; *C*, later stage in germination, showing nucleus migrating into germ tube formed within substratum; *D*, pear-shaped primary nucleus resting in first-formed spindle organ; *E*, two-celled spindle organ from one cell of which a zoosporangium is developing; nucleus of zoosporangium is in process of division; persistent nucleole lies within nuclear mem-to the "chromatin cap" described by Wager (1913) in *Polyphagus*. In addition, a well-defined chromatin reticulum is present and is particularly abundant near the nuclear membrane. The reticulum consists of chromatin granules, net knots, and irregular bodies distributed on a linin framework. The two structures, nucleolus and reticulum, are distinct from each other in appearance, position, and staining properties, a fact which Karling (1937b) believes to argue against the theories of the nucleolar origin of the chromatin. In the spindle organs and the young zoosporangia the nuclei are frequently surrounded by deeply staining granules of unknown origin and nature, strikingly like the "chromidial" material Wager describes in *Polyphagus*. The position of this material makes it impossible to determine with absolute certainty whether or not centrosomes and astral rays are formed.

Various prophase stages have been described by Karling (1937b), to whose paper the reader is referred for further details. It is sufficient to say that the chromatin making up the chromosomes in *Cladochytrium replicatum* does not seem to originate from material extruded or discharged from the nucleolus, as it does in certain terrestrial chytrids (Curtis, 1921; Kusano, 1930a, 1930b; and others), but solely from the contracted chromatin reticulum. The reticulum, though oriented on the nucleolus, is distinct and separated from it. There are from six to nine chromosomes, the small size of these structures making precise determination of the number difficult. Some reason exists for believing that the division spindle arises from the linin, although the evidence for this is as yet meager. At the time of its formation the nuclear membrane is still very apparent and distinct. The poles of the spindle are

brane (lower side); *F*, longitudinal section of developing zoosporangium in which the three visible nuclei are in equatorial-plate stage of division; *G–I*, sporangia with partly and completely cleaved contents; in *I* masses of densely basophilic granules surround nuclei; *J*, mature resting spore with flattened nucleus lying just beneath wall. *K–M. Endochytrium operculatum* (de Wild.) Karling: *K*, young thallus with nucleus in rudiment of endobiotic sporangium; *L*, thallus with two nuclei in sporangial rudiment; what may possibly be extranuclear material is seen at point of attachment of rhizoidal system to sporangial rudiment; *M*, portion of thallus with multinucleate rudiment of zoosporangium; no nuclei were found in the rhizoids.

(*A–J*, Karling, 1937b; *K–M*, Hillegas, 1940)

centered on two disc-shaped bodies lying on the nuclear membrane. In the metaphase the chromosomes form a crowded ring around the periphery of the equator, the nucleolus persisting as a crescent-shaped dark-staining body at the side of the spindle (Fig. 6 E, p. 88). Actual separation of the individual chromosomes has not been observed, but in the early anaphase the groups of daughter chromosomes form two somewhat flattened loops. Later these turn into more flattened crescentic bands at the poles. The spindle then elongates and penetrates the nuclear membrane, which disappears except at the equatorial region, where it persists for a time. The nucleolus is now liberated into the cytoplasm, where it may remain for a long period before disintegrating and being absorbed. Definite polar radiations appear in the cytoplasm around the chromosome groups. Evidence at present indicates that in the telophase each of the chromosome masses somehow becomes surrounded by a membrane. From each nucleolus-like body the reticulum of the new nucleus then takes its origin. There is nothing to show that the chromosome mass fragments into successively smaller and ultimately dispersed bodies. It is believed that the nucleolus of the new nucleus consists of the residue of the chromosome mass remaining after the reticulum is formed.

Cytokinesis, which occurs after division of the nucleus, appears to be independent of the activity of the achromatic spindle. Actual wall formation in the spindle organs (turbinate cells) is initiated by a peripheral furrow, which progresses centripetally in the equatorial region. A thin membrane, continuous with the cell wall, extends inward.

The rudiment of the sporangium is uninucleate (Fig. 6 E), the nucleus being surrounded (as in *Polyphagus*) by deep-staining material. The number of nuclei is increased by repeated simultaneous mitotic divisions like those occurring in the spindle organs, and, coincidently, the size of the individual nuclei decreases (Fig. 6 F). The spore origins are cut out by a process of progressive cleavage around the individual nuclei (Fig. 6 G–I). No cytological observations on the nuclear behavior in proliferated sporangia are recorded. The thick-walled asexually formed resting spores (Fig. 6 J) are predominantly uninucleate, although occasional binucleate ones occur.

A cytological investigation by Hillegas (1940) of the monocentric endobiotic *Endochytrium operculatum*, which has an *Entophlyctis* type of development, has revealed the following situation: The infecting zoospore differs in no essential features of its internal organization from that of *Cladochytrium replicatum*. After encystment a germ tube is formed which branches and eventually expands locally to produce the incipient zoosporangium. The nucleus, apparently with the nuclear cap persisting, migrates into the germ tube and comes to lie in the sporangial rudiment (Fig. 6 K, p. 88). Initiation of expansion of the axis to form the rudiment is seemingly not dependent upon the presence of the nucleus in the region, since swelling may take place before nuclear migration. Atypical, binucleate, young thalli are occasionally produced. After the establishment of the nucleated reproductive rudiment and rhizoidal system within the substratum a period of thallus growth ensues which continues until maturity is reached. Meanwhile, the single nucleus, which in the zoospore was less than 2 μ in diameter, enlarges to 3.5–5 μ, without appreciable alteration in its internal structure. The resting nucleus in the young thallus is essentially like that of *C. replicatum* except that at first no chromatin reticulum can be distinguished. Occasionally, a well-defined nuclear cap is present. While the thallus is expanding, materials are carried back to the reproductive rudiment by the rhizoids. The nucleus, however, remains at all times within the rudiment and just prior to division enlarges to approximately three times its original size. The resting and early prophase stages differ in no respect from those of *C. replicatum*. Nuclear division in the developing sporangium is simultaneous. The spindles are intranuclear, variously oriented, and bear at their poles densely staining conical structures. The latter are considered by Hillegas to function as centrosomes, since prominent astral rays are frequently found radiating from them. The chromosomes were differentiated before the appearance of the achromatic spindle, but because of their small size their number could not be determined. During the metaphase and succeeding division stages the ring-shaped nucleolus persists, although its size and shape may differ in various nuclei. In the anaphase stages the poles of the spindle protrude through the nuclear membrane.

By successive simultaneous divisions numerous nuclei are formed in the reproductive rudiment; none of them, however, migrates into the rhizoids (Fig. 6 L–M, p. 88). The vegetative system, therefore, is at all stages in its development devoid of nuclei. Progressive cleavage of the contents of the rudiment into zoospores is initiated soon after the protoplasm has become finely granular and homogeneous. The cleavage furrows extend centripetally from the periphery of the contents as well as centrifugally from clefts originating in the mid-region. Apparently there is no central vacuole. The conspicuous nuclear cap of the zoospore appears some time after the initial stages of cleavage. There is evidence to show that it is wholly of chondriosomal origin. No details of the formation of the flagella or operculum have, presumably, been observed in fixed and stained material.

The resting spore is asexually formed on a thallus similar to that which produces the zoosporangium. The single nucleus (occasionally two) lies in the enlarged rudiment and is surrounded by small heavily staining granules similar to those in the resting spores of *Polyphagus euglenae* and *Cladochytrium replicatum*. The wall of the mature resting spore consists of an outer thick layer, a thinner middle layer (mesospore), and an innermost thin membranous endospore. The outer wall may occasionally be smooth, but typically it is strongly roughened. During its formation a broad envelope of hyaline gelatinous material of unknown origin surrounds the whole spore. This material shrinks during maturation and becomes transformed at first into broad warts and eventually into lobed processes. Whether these lobes are the result of the infolding of the hyaline material or of outgrowths from the resting spore into the hyaline zone is not known. The wall material, which in the course of its development gave a negative reaction for cellulose, becomes yellowish and opaque. At germination the resting spore functions as a prosporangium. Division of the nucleus, which is mitotic, appears to occur only in the zoosporangium. This structure in most instances rests directly on the empty case of the resting spore, although occasionally it may be produced at the tip of a long tube.

Among the newer cytological observations published, those of Antikajian (1949) on the inoperculate monocentric chytrid *Asterophlyctis sarcoptoides* (p. 434), a rhizidiaceous form living in insect exuviae, are the most complete. She reports that the young apophysate thallus is uninucleate (Fig. 7 A–B, p. 94), and that the nucleus increases in size relative to the growth of the incipient sporangium (Fig. 7 C), so that it may attain a diameter of up to 10.7 μ. Although the primary nucleus does not divide until the sporangium has reached mature size, its first division is quickly followed by others, all of which are intranuclear and synchronous. Average nuclear diameter decreases with each successive mitosis. While cytological details from her work are given below, for full particulars her publication should be consulted.

The nucleolus is central, spherical, and about 2 μ in diameter. In some instances the chromatin is collected around the nucleolus, but in well-fixed sections it was more or less evenly distributed. Progressive prophase changes (Fig. 7 D) result in a thickening and shortening of the chromonemata, which are often oriented on the nucleolus; their exact number could not be determined. There was no evidence of pairing as one might expect if the nuclei were diploid. At late prophase the chromosomes lie in the equatorial region with the nucleolus still present but an intranuclear spindle not yet apparent. In certain nuclei, rudiments of the spindle were seen prior to the arrangement of the chromosomes on the equatorial plate, but nothing further of their origin could be determined.

In the equatorial-plate stages the spindle is broad at the center but tapers sharply at the poles. In several preparations a deep-staining granule was seen at the spindle pole, but, as Karling (1937b) noted for *Cladochytrium replicatum*, such granules cannot often be distinguished from others in the cytoplasm. Hence, it is not certain whether these bodies were actually centrosomes.

Since chromosome number is important in determining presence or absence of sexuality, special attention was paid to this aspect in both sporangia and resting spores but no conclusion was reached. The chromosomes form a dense irregular band across the spindle (Fig. 7 E), an uneven ring in polar view (Fig. 7 H). The density and their minute size made accurate count impossible. In some preparations the equatorial ring appears to consist of from four to six, in others (polar views of anaphase stages) of five chromosomes (Fig. 7 I).

At anaphase the nucleolus no longer stained easily, but two smaller spherical nucleole-like, ruby-red bodies were evident in the nucleus, presumably nucleoli formed *de novo* at late anaphase. In *Asterophlyctis*

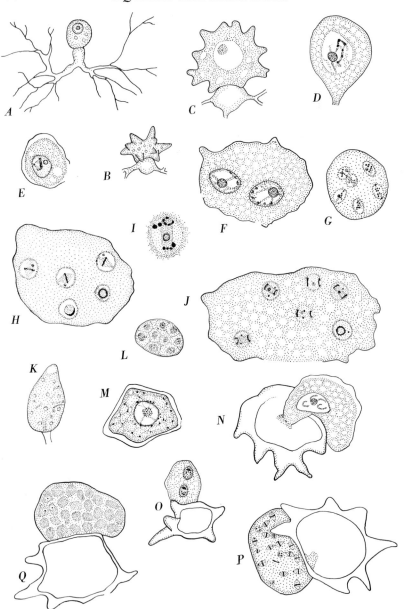

FIG. 7. Cytology of *Asterophlyctis sarcoptoides*

sarcoptoides the nuclear membrane begins to disappear at the poles at anaphase but remains present longer in the equatorial region. No stages of telophasic reconstruction of nuclei were observed.

After repeated nuclear divisions (Fig. 7 F–J) the sporangial contents underwent cleavage independent of the activity of the division spindles. In living material the stages preceding this process were accompanied by an increase in the number of certain small refractive globules and just prior to cleavage these aggregated to form the larger definitive globules of the zoospores. Following this aggregation the contents divided.

Progressive cleavage, with the furrows more common at the periphery than in the interior, then took place (Fig. 7 K), and resulted in the development of many uninucleate segments.

Although no evidence of them was seen either before or during cleavage, nuclear caps were present in the fully delimited zoospore initials (Fig. 7 L). In some germinating zoospores traces of the cap were observable; others had no sign of it, suggesting that its material disperses during germination.

With respect to germination of the uninucleate resting spore (Fig. 7 M–Q), which functions as a prosporangium, Antikajian comments that nuclear division does not occur within the resting spore proper. Rather, the nucleus passes out of the spore into the germ sporangium during germination and remains undivided as the sporangium develops. Then follows a series of successive and synchronous divisions, whereby

---

Explanation of Figure 7

A–B. Young thalli developing from zoospore cyst. *C*. Young sporangium showing large primary nucleus. *D*. Early prophase of primary nucleus. *E*. Metaphase of primary nucleus. *F*. Binucleate sporangium. *G*. Late prophases in multinucleate sporangium. *H*. Metaphases of sporangial nuclei. *I*. Anaphase nucleus showing chromosomes and nucleoli. *J*. Anaphase nuclei in sporangium. *K*. Sporangium showing cleavage of contents. *L*. Sporangium with fixed and stained zoospores. *M*. Uninucleate resting spore. *N*. Germinating resting spore with prophase nucleus. *O*. Binucleate germinating resting spore. *P*. Polar and profile views of metaphases in sporangium of germinating resting spore. *Q*. Mature sporangium from germinated resting spore.

(Antikajian, 1949)

the sporangium becomes multinucleate. Subsequently, uninucleate segments are progressively cleaved out of the protoplasm.

In addition to that on *Asterophlyctis* some fragmentary cytological data on a few other inoperculate monocentric chytrids are available. Hanson (1944a) found in *Loborhiza metzneri* (see p. 227), a parasite of *Volvox*, that the nucleus of the epibiotic infecting spore migrates late from its cyst into the developing endobiotic sporangium. She gives no details but, from her figures, the nucleus then apparently multiplies while the rudimentary sporangium is still somewhat cylindrical and unexpanded. Sexual reproduction is by conjugation of an immature receptive thallus and a swarmer which comes to rest upon it. The two nuclei can be clearly followed during the development which ensues, and the resting spore near maturity bears a single, presumably fusion, nucleus.

Hanson (1946b) also discusses certain details of the cytology of *Phlyctorhiza endogena* (see p. 392). In this inhabitant of the basement membrane of mosquito integuments, the rudiment of the sporangium remains uninucleate until fairly well developed, but as it enlarges the nucleus also increases in size and soon multiplies. Rarely, when the sporangium approaches maturity, may secondary vesiculations of the rhizoids produce new centers of reproduction, into which, it is believed, nuclei migrate from the main body.

Karling (1946d) figured, but did not describe, some cytological aspects of *Rhizophydium keratinophilum* (p. 265). Here, the immature sporangium is uninucleate with the nucleus located, as in other monocentric chytrids, in the developing reproductive rudiment. When mature size is attained, the nucleus appears to undergo a series of synchronous intranuclear divisions, with the daughter nuclei decreasing in size, as in *Asterophlyctis*. For the most part, the resting spores are binucleate, which suggests that they may be gametic in origin and dikaryotic. Occasional ones have more than two nuclei.

The cytological development of *Rhizophydium coronum* (p. 251) was followed by Hanson (1945b). The young incipient sporangium is uninucleate (Fig. 8 F) and usually remains so until the sporangium reaches maximum size. As the reproductive rudiment grows, its nucleus nearly doubles in size. Densely staining granules occur not only on the periphery of the nucleus but also in other regions of the cytoplasm, an indication, perhaps, that not all these bodies originated from the nucleus. Prophase stages, which resemble those in *Cladochytrium replicatum* and *Endochytrium operculatum*, are recognizable. During early

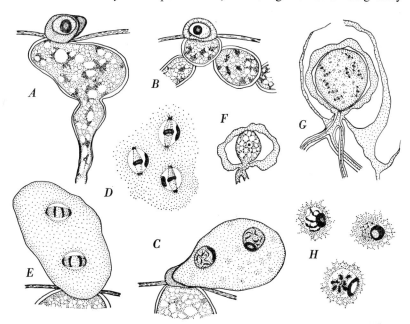

Fig. 8. Cytology of *Catenochytridium laterale* and *Rhizophydium coronum*

A–E. Catenochytridium laterale Hanson: *A–B*, enlarged primary nucleus in the zoospore cyst and catenulate rhizoidal system; *C*, prophases of second nuclear division; *D*, metaphases; *E*, anaphases of the second nuclear division in zoosporangium. *F–H. Rhizophydium coronum* Hanson: *F*, uninucleate incipient sporangium; *G*, sporangium with nuclei in metaphase; *H*, prophase figures showing reticulum and chromosomes oriented on the ringlike nucleolus.
(*A–E*, Hanson, 1946a; *F–H*, Hanson, 1945b)

prophase the chromatic reticulum is oriented on the nucleolus (Fig. 8 H). In later prophase the nuclear reticulum differentiates into elongate nodular chromosomes, which may or may not be associated with the nucleolus. Chromosomes appear to number between six and eight.

The nucleolus is variable in appearance and possibly changes in shape during prophase; it ultimately becomes a ring-shaped structure. Nuclear division is mitotic and synchronous, and the division spindle is intranuclear (Fig. 8 G). In the equatorial-plate stage it is narrow and spindle-shaped, with its poles terminating in minute dense bodies from which faint cytoplasmic strands radiate. The chromosomes are not clearly distinguishable as discrete bodies, but, rather, form a crowded nodular band across the equator. The nucleolus persists during division, lying very close to the equatorial band of chromosomes but separate from them. The resting spore is uninucleate and, upon germination, functions as a prosporangium—no cytological information is available on this phase.

With respect to the operculate monocentric chytrids, the data at hand come chiefly from Hanson's (1946a) work on the apophysate epibiotic species *Catenochytridium laterale* (p. 558). In this form, because of the strongly developed endobiotic apophysis, the secondary apophyses, and the catenulations on the rhizoidal system, as well as the "endo-exogeneous" method of development, the nuclear condition of the thallus is of unusual interest (Fig. 8 A–E, p. 97). In the case of *Chytridium lagenaria*, Karling (1936a) earlier had postulated that the original zoospore nucleus might migrate into the developing endobiotic apophysis, there to multiply during endogenous growth, and, further, that the resulting daughter nuclei then passed out with the protoplasm, during the exogenous growth of the zoospore cyst, into the mature sporangium. According to Hanson, *Catenochytridium laterale* and *C. carolinianum* have types of development similar to *Chytridium lagenaria*. She says that the nucleus in both *Catenochytridium laterale* and *C. carolinianum* remains in the extramatrical zoospore cyst during the development and maturation of the rhizoidal system and apophysis (Fig. 8 A–B). With zoosporangial development in both species the nucleus increases in size and, while the incipient zoosporangia enlarge, the primary nuclei divide. Nuclear division in both forms is mitotic, intranuclear, and synchronous. At metaphase, the nucleolus of *Catenochytridium laterale* is very prominent (Fig. 8 D), but that of *C. carolinianum* is either lacking or reduced. Further observations are essential before it can be established whether the nucleolus is really absent or is merely more reduced at metaphase in *C. carolinianum* than in *C. laterale*. No individual separate chromosomes were recognized at the equatorial-plate stage in *C. laterale*, but in *C. carolinianum* they were seen as irregular lumps in the equatorial-ring and anaphase groups.

J. Roberts (1948) studied the cytology of two species of the polycentric operculate genus *Nowakowskiella*, *N. ramosa* (p. 586) and ?*N. profusa* (p. 585). In *N. ramosa*, the stained zoospore bears a prominent nuclear cap over the nucleus. A blepharoplast and a rhizoplast are associated with the flagellum. When the zoospore comes to rest the nuclear cap presumably dissociates to form the deposit of large granules around the nuclear membrane which, in some instances, radiates out to the periphery of the spore body. A clear space adjacent to the nucleus no doubt represents the position of the prominent oil globule in the living spore. The nucleus proper contains a central nucleolus and a fine reticulum. At germination of the zoospore a primary swelling or spindle organ develops after the first dichotomy of the rhizoids. The nucleus may remain in the spore case until the primary swelling appears or it may pass into the unswollen tube which then enlarges around it. If it stays within the spore cyst, the nucleus may divide there and the daughter nuclei pass out individually into the primary swelling. Subsequent growth produces further branches and nucleated swellings but no cross walls.

Numerous flexuous, isodiametric or irregular filaments, usually extramatrical, arise from the sides or ends of the vegetative swellings or develop between them. The filaments branch richly and elongate; fusiform swellings of even contour are usual in their proximal third. As many as six nuclei are common in these enlargements, but they are for the most part absent in the narrow lateral branches. Irregularly swollen filaments or those lacking swellings contain nuclei scattered throughout their length.

The flexuous extramatrical filaments bear the terminal or intercalary sporangia. In their early stages the sporangia appear as somewhat elongate fusiform swellings filled with granular cytoplasm and having a single nucleus about 2 μ in diameter. The tapering portion of the enlargement which will become the subsporangial swelling has one or more nuclei. Several large nuclei appear in the sporangial rudiment as it expands but it is not known whether they have been derived from the first nucleus or have migrated there. As the rudiment continues to enlarge and become more globose, it contains more nuclei and in the center there is an aggregation of deeply staining granules. When the sporangium is mature, the filament bearing it is usually devoid of nuclei save for the swollen subsporangial region which is nucleated. In intercalary sporangia, concomitant vegetative elements on either side are similarly nucleated.

As maturation of the sporangium continues, the central, deeply staining mass disintegrates and becomes a densely granular reticulum which spreads throughout the swelling. The sporangial nuclei are aligned on the strands of this reticulum, some elements of which apparently assist in the formation of the basal cross wall. At this time, too, the sporangial wall thickens and the discharge papilla begins to form. The granules of the reticulum disperse and the cytoplasm becomes uniformly granular, except just beneath the papilla, a region which seems devoid of stainable cytoplasm. The peripheral sporangial wall thickens and the arched operculum appears as a lightly stained dome, thicker in the center and tapering off toward the edges. Where the operculum is attached to the rest of the sporangium the wall does not thicken but remains as a thin ring, obviously the region of dehiscence. By the time the operculum is fully developed, the basal cross wall has thickened to the same degree as the wall of the sporangium.

The cytoplasm now begins to be furrowed by elongate vacuoles which extend centripetally from the periphery. Other vacuoles progress laterally until each nucleus is surrounded by a mass of cytoplasm. As deep-staining material collects around each nucleus to form a large nuclear cap, the remainder of the cytoplasm in the cleaved-out masses becomes clearer. These masses then swell so as to obscure the spore origins and the nuclear caps become more compact. The nucleolus is visible in the center of the nucleus before as well as after aggregation of the granules making up the cap, evidence, Roberts believes, that it is not concerned with nuclear-cap formation. His observations support Karling's (1937b) contention that the nuclear cap is extranuclear in origin and may represent food material utilized during spore germination.

Nuclear behavior in *Nowakowskiella ramosa* differs from that in *Cladochytrium replicatum, Endochytrium operculatum,* and *Catenochytridium laterale,* described earlier, in that there is no appreciable increase in nuclear size before division and there are repeated divisions during enlargement of the incipient sporangium both before and after the formation of the sporangial cross wall. Furthermore, although nuclear division in a single sporangium is simultaneous, it is not absolutely synchronous.

The formation of the resting spore from the pseudoparenchyma is a striking characteristic of *Nowakowskiella ramosa.* The process was followed cytologically by J. Roberts. Nucleated cells of the pseudoparenchyma produce short clavate projections. The tips of these become filled with granular cytoplasm as they enlarge. After becoming somewhat spherical, the nucleus from the pseudoparenchyma cell migrates into the incipient resting spore, which is then cut off by a cross wall. The now centrally disposed nucleus is surrounded by a loosely packed mass of granules from which radiate strands to the periphery. The evenly dispersed oil droplets of the contents finally coalesce into about eight globules. A similar subsequent coalescence of the granules takes place. The cytoplasm itself remains reticulate. After the internal structure of the resting spore becomes stabilized, a striated, thickened inner wall is laid down beneath the original one. No further stages were observed of the mature resting spore.

The development and nuclear history of ?*Nowakowskiella profusa,* the other species of the genus investigated by Roberts, offers few significant variations from that of *N. ramosa,* save that in it no pseudoparenchyma or resting spores were formed.

In the polycentric inoperculate *Polychytrium aggregatum* (p. 478), a strongly chitinophilic form, Ajello (1948a) was able to follow the nuclear behavior clearly (Fig. 9). His findings revealed that the zoospore possesses a conspicuous nuclear cap closely affixed to the nucleus. This structure is formed by the coalescence of granular particles which lie in the immediate vicinity of the nucleus but which could not be definitely identified as mitochondrial in origin. The nucleus of the encysted zoospore (Fig. 9 A, p. 102) is spherical or slightly oval, averages 3.2 µ in diameter, and contains a deeply staining nucleolus and a

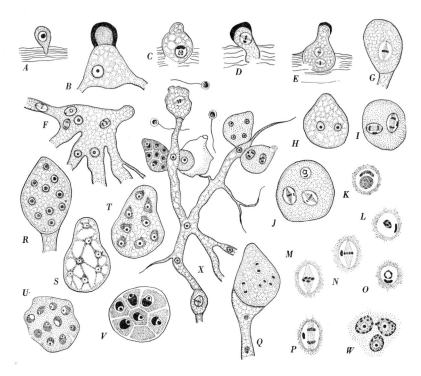

FIG. 9. Cytology of *Polychytrium aggregatum* Ajello

A. Early stage in the germination of a zoospore. *B*. Young thallus with persistent zoospore cyst and broad branched germ tube. *C*. Late prophase stage of nucleus in zoospore cyst. *D*. Metaphase of germinating zoospore nucleus, with thickened wall of zoospore cyst. *E*. Metaphases in second nuclear division in a young thallus. *F*. Multinucleate young thallus showing nonsynchronous nuclear division. *G*. Metaphase of the primary nucleus in a young sporangium. *H*. Binucleate zoosporangium. *I*. Anaphases of second nuclear division. *J*. Trinucleate sporangium with metaphase nuclei, one metaphase plate in polar view. *K*. Early prophase nucleus showing ill-defined densely stained reticulum shrunken together and crescent-shaped nucleolus. *L*. Late prophase stage showing formation of chromosomes. *M*. Very late prophase stage with chromosomes approaching the equator of the spindle. *N*. Metaphase nucleus with five or six chromosomes forming a band on equator of spindle. *O*. Metaphase plate (polar view) showing chromosomes arranged in a ring and lateral nucleolus close to nuclear membrane. *P*. Anaphase stage with elongated

faintly staining, poorly defined reticulum. Nuclear division takes place first within the thick-walled zoospore cyst (Fig. 9 B–D) and the daughter nuclei migrate into the growing germ tube (Fig. 9 E–F).

At prophase, the nucleus contains a lens-shaped, deeply staining nucleolus and several discrete bodies which may possibly be regarded as an early stage in chromosome formation. At metaphase (Fig. 9 E–G), the chromosomes form a dense band on the intranuclear spindle which, in polar view, appears as a ring on the equator (Fig. 9 F). Individual chromosomes are difficult to recognize because the chromatin is compact and the nucleus small. No centrosomes were seen nor was there any evidence of astral-ray formation. Nuclear divisions in the germinating zoospores, developing thalli, and rhizomycelium are not synchronous (Fig. 9 F), in contrast to those in the developing sporangia which are synchronous.

The sporangia originate as swellings on the broader parts of the thallus, either alone or in groups. A single nucleus migrates into each swelling, which is then cut off by a cross wall from the thallus. In the incipient zoosporangium, division of the primary nucleus is immediate and is not preceded by a preliminary enlargement. Sporangial mitosis is synchronous (Fig. 9 I–J), as in all other chytrids thus far investigated and contrasts with the nonsynchronous nuclear division in the Blastocladiales. The resting nucleus contains a dense spherical nucleolus and a weakly staining chromatin network. During prophase, chromatic strands (Fig. 9 K) develop which later contract to form the chromosomes (Fig. 9 L–M). Equatorial-plate stages (Fig. 9 G, J) show intranuclear spindles which are rather broad at the center and taper at the poles. The origin of the spindle remains obscure. At

spindle. *Q.* Feulgen-stained sporangium showing Feulgen-positive anaphase chromosome masses, nucleoli unstained. *R.* Multinucleate sporangium. *S.* Multinucleate sporangium showing aggregation of chromatic particles about the nuclei. *T.* Coalescence of basophilic granules about the sporangial nuclei. *U.* Beginnings of progressive cleavage in a sporangium, nuclear caps fully formed. *V.* Polygonal zoospore initials in sporangium following cleavage, nuclear caps fully formed. *W.* Enlarged group of zoospore initials showing granules surrounding nuclei. *X.* Part of a thallus showing organization and cytology of the vegetative system (composite drawing).

(All from Ajello, 1948a)

metaphase the chromosomes usually form a dense equatorial band, which sometimes appears to be composed of several discrete bodies (Fig. 9 J, N). Polar views of the equatorial plate apparently reveal the presence of five or six chromosomes (Fig. 9 J, O); their exact number was impossible to determine.

During mitosis the nucleolus as indicated earlier is usually lens-shaped, lies close to the nuclear membrane, and persists throughout metaphase and anaphase (Fig. 9 I, J, N, P). Nucleus and spindle elongate during anaphase and at telophase the nuclear membrane is no longer clear as a distinct structure.

Cleavage furrows separating the developing zoospores progress centripetally from the periphery and by their extension and branching eventually cleave out the uninucleate zoospores (Fig. 9, H, Q–X). After zoospore discharge sporangial proliferation is common, the new sporangium arising from an ingrowing of protoplasm with a single nucleus from the concomitant vegetative system.

PARASITISM

Before their true nature was understood chytridiaceous fungi were often taken by early investigators to be the reproductive structures of the aquatic organisms on which they were living. For example, references are found in the early literature to the formation of zoospores by desmids (Archer, 1860), of antherozoids by saprolegnians (Pringsheim, 1860), and of sperms in its eggs by the animal *Nais* (Carter, 1858). Similar misinterpretations might be cited regarding marine organisms (Wright, 1879b). As knowledge of Braun's monograph (1856a) became more general, however, the extraneous nature of the chytridiaceous interloper was recognized.

Early observers of these fungi generally assumed that when a chytrid was found on dead or dying algal cells it was the primary causal agent. Rosen (1887) soon pointed out, however, in connection with a study of *Phlyctochytrium zygnematis*, that the zoospores of this fungus most often came to rest on obviously dead cells of *Zygnema* or on green filaments which, because of unfavorable environmental conditions, were fast becoming moribund. This saprophytic tendency of chytridiaceous fungi was later emphasized by Serbinow (1907), who, from studies of a number of different chytrid parasites of algae, concluded that many of them were at most only facultative parasites. Serbinow's views have received support from numerous subsequent observations, and it is probable that they hold true for a large number of the Phlyctidiaceae and Chytridiaceae. Certain members of these families appear, however, to be truly parasitic and have never been induced to live saprophytically.

The Chytrid Epidemic

One feature of the chytrids which has been noted by many students of the group is the evanescent nature of their occurrence. Many instances (Cohn, 1853; Zopf, 1888; Dangeard, 1889b; Wager, 1913; Reynolds, 1940, and others) are on record of the sudden appearance of these fungi in ponds, as well as in the restricted habitat of the laboratory. Once established, they enjoy a brief period of rapid multiplication, which is followed by a decline, often involving the formation of resting spores, and ultimately by total disappearance. The rapid rate of establishment and the intensity of the epidemic are no doubt due to the virulence of the fungus, as well as to the degree of host-plant susceptibility, which in turn may possibly be strongly influenced by environmental factors. Random samples of collections of algae brought into the laboratory and examined for chytrids may show little or no evidence of their presence. It is a common experience, however, to find that this material, if left in the laboratory (which is generally warmer than the natural habitat) under conditions which allow for a maximum oxygen supply, will within a few days become infested with various chytrids. At the time of the first examination the invaders may have been present in the water as zoospores, resting spores, or inconspicuous immature thalli. The sudden change in the environment no doubt works to the advantage of the fungi and to the disadvantage of the algae.

The reason for the brief period of rapid multiplication of chytrid individuals once they are established under favorable conditions is readily understandable, as Nowakowski (1876b) long ago indicated for *Polyphagus euglenae*. The progress of an epidemic of this chytrid can be easily followed in the laboratory. Under favorable conditions a single zoospore, possibly originating in the sporangium formed by a germinating resting spore, will come to rest, germinate, and eventually produce a sporangium within which develop perhaps twenty zoospores. If after the swarmers are liberated only half of them—probably a very low figure—ultimately give rise to new thalli, the first nonsexual generation will have been multiplied tenfold within a short time. At least part of these new thalli will produce new plants and new zoosporangia, and thus enormously increase the number of units capable of causing new infections. Furthermore, in such a form as *Polyphagus*, the effect of this multiplication of individuals on the attacked algae is intensified by the fact that the thalli are strongly polyphagous, each of the tips of the numerous profusely branched and widely spread elements of the rhizoidal system being potentially capable of penetrating a different *Euglena*. In this way the original zoospore has produced a tremendous number of structures able to seek out and infect new host cells, itself and each of its progeny being capable, by means of rhizoids, of invading up to fifty or more *Euglena* individuals. The optimum rate of multiplication does not last long, no doubt being gradually diminished by various adverse factors in the environment, chief of which are probably the shrinking food supply, decrease of oxygen, increase of CO_2, increase of by-products of metabolism, and competition. Natural enemies of the fungus, such as Protozoa which consume the zoospores, develop in the culture, and there appears to be a resistance to attack on the part of a certain percentage of potential host cells. All these factors, as well as others, combine to produce a decline in the number of new parasites. It is during this period that resting-spore formation often occurs, usually followed by the complete disappearance of the chytrid. Those individuals of the host which have survived the epidemic may then reoccupy the culture, or it may be taken over by other, different, algae. Attempts to maintain these parasitic chytrids in gross cultures are usually unsuccessful, and it even seems that they cannot be induced to reappear, once the epidemic has subsided.

With respect to chytrid epidemics in nature, Canter (1946–51) and Canter and Lund in recent years have gathered information in the English Lake District concerning the parasites of phytoplankters (see Figs. 10–11 pp. 108, 110) and their influence on the phytoplankton popu-

lation cycle. Many chytrids of various genera occur in significant numbers on these plankton algae. In a series of three papers Canter and Lund
(1948, 1951, 1953) give a survey, from the limnological point of view,
of (1) the fluctuation in numbers of the important diatom *Asterionella*
in relation to fungal epidemics; (2) the incidence of parasitism of diatoms by chytridiaceous fungi; and (3) the interaction between parasitism and other factors determining the growth of the diatoms.

A good example of their observations (Canter and Lund, 1948)
is the account of the parasitism of *Asterionella formosa* by *Rhizophydium planktonicum* (Fig. 10 H, I). *Asterionella* is the dominant diatom
over a considerable part of the year in Lake Windermere and has a
large spring and a small autumn maximum, 12,000 and 400 cells per
ml., respectively.

The effect of *Rhizophydium planktonicum* on the periodicity of
Asterionella was observed in a section of the lake, Esthwaite Water,
a somewhat silted eutrophic area, the plankton population of which
is dominated by Myxophyceae and diatoms. Canter and Lund report
on two epidemics which took place in the late summer to early spring
period; that is, between the renewal in *Asterionella* of fall growth,
after the summer minimum, to the beginning of its spring growth period. The data concerning the 1946 epidemic are given below:

In 1946, the autumn growth period of *Asterionella* began between
September 24 and October 1. Numbers of *Rhizophydium* remained
low until October 28, when 10 per cent of the 322 live *Asterionella*
cells per ml. were infected. On November 2, infection was 26 per cent;
Asterionella cells, 390 per ml. Two days later (November 4) infection
was 2 per cent lower and the cell number was virtually unchanged
(388). On November 8, 26 per cent of the cells were parasitized whose
number had now declined to 266 per ml. From then on to November
26, both host cells and infection decreased (*Asterionella* to 45 per ml.;
Rhizophydium to less than 1 per cent infection). The final fall in *Asterionella* numbers may be attributed in part to mechanical depletion
due to the rapid rise in lake level (between November 18 to 26) and in
part, although no data are available, to dilution from vertical mixing
as a result of final and complete loss of temperature stratification.

Variation in number of diatom cells per colony was correlated mark-

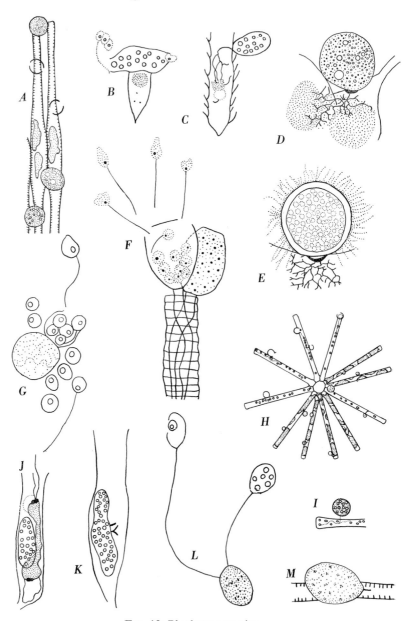

FIG. 10. Plankton parasites

edly with the course of the epidemic. At the start of the autumn growth period the cell count for each colony rose from 6.4 to over 8 and then declined slightly, but only to the still high level of 7.5. By November 14, however, it had fallen very low, to 4.6. With the end of the *Rhizophydium* epidemic and the onset of flood conditions this average rose rapidly. Thus, here and also in the epidemics of 1945, 1947, and 1948, a rise in fungus count was followed by a fall not only in number of *Asterionella* cells but in cell-per-colony average. This decline lasted until the end of the period or as long as the lake level remained low. Throughout the period the concentrations of nitrates, phosphates, and silica were suitable for active growth of *Asterionella*. In 1947 a similar epidemic occurred in the same period and under closely similar conditions, but it was of shorter duration and the maximum infection (38 per cent of the *Asterionella* cells) was higher.,

Although similar epidemics were recorded on other parts of the lake and at other times in the three years observed, none occurred during the main part of the spring-growth period possibly because of the host's fast growth. Furthermore, only once was there an instance of an epidemic after the *Asterionella* maximum and even this one took place before the typical catastrophic fall in numbers of live cells began. Canter

---

Explanation of Figure 10

A. *Rhizophydium fragilariae* Canter, mature and discharged sporangia on a filament of *Fragilaria sp.* B. *Rhizophydium ephippium* Canter, discharging sporangium on *Stylosphaeridium stipitatum.* C. *Rhizophydium hyalobryonis* Canter, sporangium on *Hyalobryon mucicola.* D–E. *Rhizophydium difficile* Canter: D, immature sporangium; E, resting spore with mucilaginous envelopment; both on *Staurastrum faculiferum.* F. *Rhizophydium megarrhizum* Sparrow, immature and discharging sporangium on *Oscillatoria sp.* (del. Ingold). G. *Rhizophydium uniguttulatum* Canter, discharging sporangium in *Gemellicystis neglecta.* H–I. *Rhizophydium planktonicum* Canter: H, thalli and discharged sporangia; I, mature sporangium, both on *Asterionella sp.* J–K. *Rhizophydium oblongum* Canter: J, a mature sporangium; K, another, showing rhizoidal system, both on *Dinobryon sp.* L. *Rhizophydium fulgens* Canter, mature and discharged sporangium on *Gemellicystis neglecta.* M. *Chytridium versatile* Scherffel, sporangium on *Fragilaria crotonensis.*

(A–B, Canter, 1950c; C, Canter, 1951; D–E, Canter, 1954; F, Canter and Lund, 1951; G, Canter, 1954; H–I, Canter and Lund, 1948; J–K, Canter, 1954; L, Canter, 1951; M, Canter, 1950c).

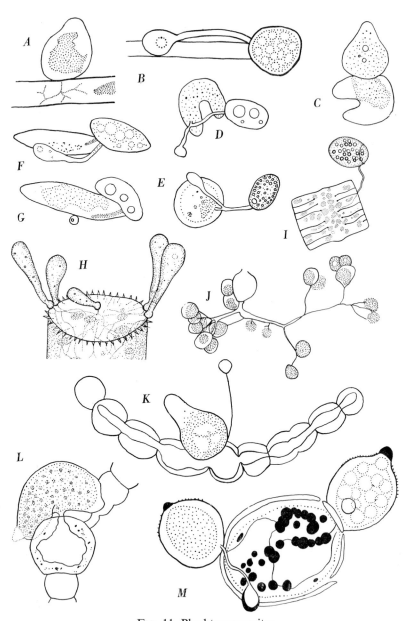

Fig. 11. Plankton parasites

and Lund believe that they have strong, if indirect, evidence that *Rhizophydium planktonicum* is not a saprophyte, merely attacking dead or moribund cells, but a true parasite.

Canter and Lund (1948) also point out that one can follow the natural sequence of an epidemic by an analysis of the stage of development of each fungal cell, whether it is encysted zoospore, sporangium, empty sporangium, or resting spore. Early in an epidemic, encysted zoospores which are about to or are just penetrating the diatom host, predominate. At this stage the alga is little affected and, even though a high percentage of infection exists, the host population does not decrease. When, for unknown reasons, the period of active parasite multiplication comes to an end, the number of zoospores decreases, but that of the sporangia resulting from the infective units produced during multiplication continues to increase. In the final stage, when very few zoospores or sporangia remain to accomplish further infection, the number of empty sporangia reaches a maximum, whereas the count of algal cells falls sharply. Although the influences governing the formation of the parasite's resting spores are not known, the appear-

---

Explanation of Figure 11

A–B. Zygorhizidium planktonicum Canter: *A*, young sporangium with rhizoidal system; *B*, resting spore with small, conjugating male plant; on *Asterionella formosa. C–E. Zygorhizidium parvum* Canter: *C*, sporangium; *D*, resting spore with small conjugating male plant; *E*, another; on *Kirchneriella. F–G. Zygorhizidium parallelosede* Canter: *F*, immature resting spore with small conjugating male plant; *G*, immature sporangium; on *Ankistrodesmus sp. H. Podochytrium cornutum* Sparrow, developing sporangia on *Stephanodiscus niagarae. I. Chytriomyces tabellariae* (C. Schröter) Canter, mature operculate sporangium on *Tabellaria flocculosa. J. Rhizidium windermerense* Canter, empty sporangium showing broad rhizoidal axes; on *Gemellicystis neglecta. K. Rhizosiphon crassum* Scherffel, nearly mature sporangium with persistent cyst and germ tube of zoospore; on *Anabaena sp. L. Rhizosiphon anabaenae* (Rodhe and Skuja) Canter, sporangium on heterocyst of *Anabaena sphaerica. M. ? Rhizosiphon akinetum* Canter, two sporangia, the younger with persistent zoospore cyst and germ tube; on akinetes of *Anabaena affinis* var. *intermedia.*

(*A–B*, Canter and Lund, 1953; *C–E*, Canter, 1950c; *F–G*, Canter, 1954; *H*, Sparrow, 1951; *I*, Canter, 1949a; *J*, Canter, 1950c; *K–L*, Canter, 1951; *M*, Canter, 1954)

ance of the spores always corresponds with a period of intense parasitic activity and their number builds up to a maximum near the close of an epidemic. Since *Asterionella*, whenever collected, is rarely free of the sporangial or zoospore-cyst stage, the authors conjecture that it is the germination of the resting spores in abundance which initiates the full-scale epidemic. Actually, however, no one is sure just what factor or group of factors is primarily responsible. Temperature, light, lake level, dissolved substances, antibiotics, abundance of host cells, predators, and the possibility that zoospores from germinated sexually formed resting spores possess unusual vigor and infective capacity all have been considered. Evidence in regard to any one of them is inconclusive.

Although Canter and Lund pose many unsolved problems, they do give us the first clear-cut picture and analysis of a chytrid epidemic, open a new approach to the study of Phycomycetes, and demonstrate beyond question that these organisms are significant factors in the cycle of disintegration in an aquatic environment.

Saprophytism and Facultative Parasitism

A great number of chytrids apparently lead a purely saprophytic existence. These forms occur wherever appropriate substrata are available in the natural habitat. Moreover, they readily appear when gross laboratory cultures containing vegetable trash from an aquatic site are baited with a variety of organic materials. During the temperate seasons such fungi are probably constantly at work in the submerged decaying parts of plants and animals.

There have also been reported a relatively large number of species which seem capable of living either as saprophytes or parasites (see especially Serbinow, 1907). Unfortunately, it is far easier to demonstrate that a chytrid may live as a saprophyte than it is to prove unquestionably that it can attack a living healthy organism. Saprophytism may be shown, for example, by the simple expedient of boiling the prospective substratum until it is killed and then placing it in a culture dish in which the chytrid is growing. If the fungus attacks this material there is no question of its ability to utilize a dead substratum as a source of food. On the other hand, living microscopic organisms subjected to inoculation experiments must necessarily be taken from their natural environment and placed under more or less restricted and controlled conditions, where the results can be observed. Hence such experiments are handicapped from the beginning, and the significance of the results is definitely limited. It is difficult to judge in successfully induced infection under laboratory conditions whether the virulence of the parasite or the weakened condition of the host made the invasion possible. As has been previously mentioned, changes of environment in all probability bring about changes in the susceptibility of the host. This was early pointed out by Dangeard (1889b), who emphasized that anything which caused impoverishment of the host plant, such as alterations in the properties of the cellulose wall, known to occur under conditions of culture, favored the development of parasites. It should be recognized in situations where conflicting evidence regarding the parasitism or saprophytism of a species arises that almost never would two investigators be observing the same strain of host and fungus under exactly the same environmental conditions. In this connection, the results of inoculation studies by Johnson (1955a), discussed below, are extremely pertinent.

Host Specificity

It is commonly found in a mixed collection of algae that only one species of host has been attacked by a particular chytrid. In spite of this, there is little direct evidence to support the view that many of the aquatic chytrids are confined to a single host species or genus. Generalizations in this respect have, however, but slight significance, since relatively little data have thus far been accumulated. A few well-marked instances of apparent host specificity may be cited: Species of *Micromyces* have thus far been found only on conjugates; *Chytridium olla*, with one exception, has been noted only on the oögonia and eggs of *Oedogonium*; *Polyphagus euglenae* primarily attacks quiescent or encysted *Euglena*, although it has also been reported on *Chlamydomonas*; *P. parasiticus* is confined to *Tribonema bombycina*; *Rhizophydium laterale*, to *Ulothrix*; *Blyttiomyces spinulosus*, to the zygotes and zygospores of *Spirogyra*; *Podochytrium clavatum*, *R. fusus*, and *Chytridium versatile* to various diatoms. These are all species which exhibit well-defined distinctive structural features and which do not depend upon the nature of their host for their specific identity. On the other hand, species of *Rozella* and *Olpidium*, which also have apparent host specificities, are poorly defined morphologically, and many of them have been separated from already described species chiefly on the basis of the host. Little or no evidence exists in most instances to support this segregation.

Inoculation experiments conducted by Johnson (1955a) using *Rozella achlyae*, an olpidiaceous form originally discovered parasitizing a species of *Dictyuchus*, demonstrate that this fungus is capable of infecting two species of *Achlya* as well as a second species of *Dictyuchus*. His success in this respect is important for it indicates a wider host range for a single species than has generally been believed to be true. Earlier, Karling (1942a) had reported a *Rozella* in *Cladochytrium* that parasitizes three species each of *Cladochytrium* and *Nowakowskiella* but does not infect certain monocentric chytrids. Two other species of *Rozella* that he studied, however, were found to be confined to their respective hosts.

Effect of Chytrid on Host Cell

Parasitic chytrids differ in their destructive effect on the invaded host cell. Almost always, except perhaps in the case of protozoans attacked by certain species of *Sphaerita* and said to extrude the fungus, the cell is ultimately killed. Braun (1856a: 71) noted that whereas chytrid infection produced the death of a one-celled alga, it usually killed only the infected cell in multicellular forms. Filaments of multicelled *Ulothrix zonata* parasitized by *Phlyctidium laterale* were exceptions. In organisms attacked by *Sphaerita* and *Nucleophaga* (Dangeard, 1889b, 1894–95b) actual death may be delayed for a considerable period after infection, usually until the sporulation of the parasite. It has also been observed that motile chlamydomonads attacked by *Rhizophydium transversum* may continue to swim about while the thallus of the invader is maturing, and succumb completely only at the time of sporulation of the chytrid.

By reason of their simple body plan, semitransparency, color, and well-defined internal organization, the reaction of green algae to attack by chytrids can frequently be followed with comparative ease. Careful observations on the early stages in the infection of the host have been recorded by several investigators, notably Scherffel and Couch. Scherffel (1925b) records that the first visible reaction of *Tribonema* cells attacked by *Chytridium confervae* was the concentration of plasma at the point of entrance of the infection tube. The host nucleus was displaced from its central position in the cell and moved to the point of infection. Secretion of wall material then occurred in an attempt to stop the further incursion of the parasite. It was this displacement which suggested to Scherffel the possibility that the nucleus may have a definite role in the formation of the wall material. Couch (1932) has described the reactions of the protoplast of *Spirogyra* to the growing rhizoids of the epibiotic *Rhizophydium couchii*. Where several young thalli were being formed at one point on the host a violent rotation of the cytoplasm of the alga was apparent, and suggested an attempt to ward off the invading rhizoids. As a result of this activity on the part of the host abnormal development of the rhizoids sometimes ensued. Certain of these rotating cytoplasmic streams communicated directly with the pyrenoids, a fact considered of some significance since it is the stored food material of these pyrenoids which is utilized by the developing fungus. As the course of the infection proceeded, the pyrenoids were destroyed, their starch was hydrolized, and the cytoplasmic membrane along with the chloroplasts became contracted and concentrated around the region of the rhizoids. Ultimately disintegration of the whole contents took place.

At times the host is stimulated to abnormal growth, a fact first noted by Braun (1856a: 72) in regard to the swelling of *Stigeoclonium* cells infected by *Rhizophydium mammillatum*. Cells of *Zygogonium* infected by *Micromyces zygogonii* (Dangeard, 1889b) show a pronounced swelling of the wall. As the fungus develops the deformed chloroplasts shrink, while the hypertrophy of the wall becomes more pronounced. Eventually the whole contents are consumed, and the reproductive body of the chytrid lies in the distended cell. Infected cells of other conjugates attacked by species of *Micromyces* may at times be bent, swollen, or even burst. Canter (1949c) has indicated that species of *Micromyces* do not always cause hypertrophy of their algal hosts.

An interesting feature of *Micromyces*, and one repeatedly noted, is the strong attraction of the young thallus for the host nucleus. Couch (1931) has intimated the value of this tendency to the fungus, which, by thus achieving a central position in the host cell, is enabled to make contact with the cytoplasmic strands of the alga. Since these are attached to the pyrenoids, the fungus is in an advantageous position for utilizing the reserve food. The young thallus apparently reaches the nucleus either by its own slight amoeboid motion or by cytoplasmic currents of the host. Possibly a tactic response to nucleic acids aids it in making contact with the nucleus. In *Spirogyra* cells attacked by *Micromyces* contraction, disintegration, and discoloration of the chloroplasts gradually take place, and eventually the entire contents are reduced to a granular, often brownish mass within which is imbedded the reproductive structure (prosorus or resting spore) of the chytrid.

In diatoms infected with such epibiotic forms as *Chytridium perniciosum* and *Rhizophydium fusus* the changes brought about by the invading rhizoids are well marked. Soon after infection the chromatophores lose their golden-brown color and tend to become yellow green to green. The cytoplasmic membrane contracts somewhat, and the yellow-green chloroplasts become dislocated and eventually fragment. At maturity of the fungus there frequently remain in the frustule only a few chestnut-brown refractive granules.

Perhaps the most unusual and vivid color changes produced by a chytrid are those resulting from infection of *Filarszkya*, a blue-green alga, by *Rhizosiphon crassum* (Scherffel, 1926a). No appreciable change is noted in the infected host cell until the thallus of the fungus is 5–6 μ in diameter. The infected cell as well as adjacent ones then turns deep wine-red, as if the chytrid were producing a poisonous substance which was diffusing through the filament and causing the death of the cells. As the fungous thallus enlarges and the broad absorbing organ invades more and more of the filament, the cross walls are broken down, and new cells become discolored and filled with a clear red-violet or bluish liquid. By this time, the cells first infected, whose contents have by now been partly or almost wholly exhausted, have turned bright orange and contain light orange-brown granules of unassimilated substances. The algal cytoplasm is ultimately consumed save for some residual material, which appears as a series of equidistant broad bands around the absorbing organ of the chytrid.

Wager (1913) described the sequence of changes occurring in *Euglena* parasitized by *Polyphagus euglenae*. He observed that discoloration of the chloroplasts occurs soon after infection, the bright green changing to yellow or yellow green. The chloroplast gradually disappears and is replaced by a clump of rusty-red granules. Coincidently with these changes the protoplasm is absorbed, the paramylum grains are broken up, and the granules of the red eye spot are disassociated. The nucleus and cell membrane persist for a time, but the former is gradually absorbed, and after several days the wall disappears, releasing the reddish residual material into the water.

Chytrids are often found parasitizing other aquatic Phycomycetes in old water cultures. If endobiotic, as are species of *Rozella*, the hyphae of the host are commonly stimulated to form conspicuous ellipsoidal, spherical, or saclike enlargements. These are frequently isolated from the rest of the hyphae by cross walls apparently produced by the host. Reproductive organs, sporangia, for example, when attacked by such endobiotic parasites retain their general configuration but are usually somewhat enlarged. The protoplasm of infected regions is often strongly vacuolate, or it may contain numerous bodies of fatty material.

Resistance of Algae to Infection by Chytrids

There is no marked evidence to show that healthy algae attacked by chytrids possess varying degrees of immunity. It is frequently observed, however, both in nature and in gross cultures, that during the progress of an epidemic certain individuals of a species remain uninvaded. Whether this is due to inherent factors within the alga (general health, vigor, state of the cellulose wall, and so on) or to external conditions is not known.

The attempt of some algae to ward off attack by chytrids by what might be termed "mechanical means," that is, by "protective plugs" of wall material, has been observed in numerous instances. This curious method of defense was early noted by Braun (1856a) in *Ulothrix zonata* attacked by *Phlyctidium laterale* and has since been found in other members of the Chlorophyceae and in Heterokontae, as well as in the phycomycete *Allomyces* (Scherffel, 1925b; Dangeard, 1937; Foust, 1937; Couch, 1938b; Sparrow, 1939a; Karling, 1948c). Certain flowering plants react in a similar manner when attacked by chytrid zoospores (see especially Kusano, 1936). The formation and functioning of these protective plugs or calluses have been described at some length by Dangeard in vigorous individuals of *Closterium ehrenbergii* attacked by *Phlyctochytrium desmidiacearum*. In this instance the zoospore of the chytrid, after encysting on the surface of the host, produced a delicate tube which penetrated the algal wall in its effort to make contact with the living cytoplasmic membrane. In the short period during which penetration was taking place the host had responded to the incursion by the formation of a sheath of wall material which surrounded the infection tube. As the latter elongated, the sheath too became extended, at all times insulating, as it were, the fungus from the living cytoplasm of the alga. During this process of elongation the chytrid germling was necessarily using up its own food supply in an effort to reach the nutritive contents of the alga. The chytrid, with no nourishment forthcoming and its own supply exhausted by the tube formation, was literally "starved out." But Dangeard also noted that when host cells were growing under unfavorable conditions or when they had been weakened by the attacks of other parasites they lacked this capacity for callus formation and succumbed in great numbers to the chytrid.

Hyperparasitism

Instances of one chytrid parasitizing another have been reported by various investigators. Serbinow (1907) recorded the invasion of the prosporangia of *Saccomyces* by another chytrid, called by him "*Phlyctidium dangeardii*." No endobiotic system was found and it is possible that he was dealing with a species of *Rozella* parasitic in the sporangium rather than the prosporangium of the host. Sporangia of the marine species *Rhizophydium discinctum* and *Chytridium polysiphoniae* have been found to be attacked by other chytrids, the first by *Pleotrachelus paradoxus* (H. E. Petersen, 1905) and the second by *Rozella marina* (Sparrow, 1936b). Similarly, sporangia of the fresh-water *Rhizophydium goniosporum* and *Phlyctidium bumilleriae* have been invaded by *Rhizophydium parasitans* (Scherffel, 1925b) and *Septosperma anomala* (Couch, 1932), respectively. Prosporangia of *Polyphagus euglenae* have been known to be attacked by a species of *Rozella* (*R. polyphagi* Sparrow, 1936a). The incidence of hyperparasitism among the chytrids has been reviewed by Karling (1942a). He points out its relative rarity. Since his first report was published, however, a number of additional instances have been observed (Karling, 1944f; 1946a; 1946d; 1948b; 1949d; Sparrow, 1948; Willoughby, 1956).

SYSTEMATIC ACCOUNT

CHYTRIDIALES

MICROSCOPIC parasitic or saprophytic primarily aquatic fungi of simple body plan, the thallus either endobiotic, without specialized vegetative structures and converted as a whole (holocarpic) into one or more reproductive organs, or epi-, endo-, or interbiotic or extramatrical and differentiated into a more or less extensive unbranched or branched, generally nonseptate rhizoidal (rarely tubular and septate) vegetative system at least the tips of which in interbiotic and extramatrical forms are endobiotic, and one (monocentric) or more (polycentric) reproductive organs (eucarpic); contents refractive with glistening globules and minute granules, walls occasionally giving a cellulose reaction; zoosporangia discharging after the deliquescence or rupturing of one or more papillae (inoperculate) or after the dehiscence of an operculum (operculate), zoospores generally formed within the sporangium, posteriorly uniflagellate (flagella lacking in several genera), usually bearing a conspicuous oil globule, movement hopping or swimming or amoeboid, encysting before penetration; resting spore thick-walled, generally filling its container, often with a large globule, asexually formed or sexually after fusion of isogamous planogametes or anisogamous aplanogametes borne in thalloid gametangia, upon germination functioning as a zoosporangium or prosporangium.

Occurring on a wide variety of fresh-water algae; also on fresh-water fungi, pollen grains, decaying plant tissues, and microscopic animals. A few are found in marine waters on marine algae. Some species of otherwise primarily aquatic genera, as well as species of *Synchytrium* and *Physoderma* (including *Urophlyctis*), occur as obligate parasites of terrestrial and aquatic vascular plants. The order as defined here is restricted to "chytrids" with posteriorly uniflagellate zoospores formed in the sporangium. There are recognizable within the group two parallel series in which specialization of the thallus has achieved equal complexity; in one the sporangium opens by the deliquescence or rupturing of the tip of the discharge tube (Inoperculatae), in the other, by the dehiscence of a very definite and discrete operculum (Operculatae).

KEY TO THE FAMILIES OF THE CHYTRIDIALES

Sporangium opening by the deliquescence or rupturing of one or
more papillae .... Series INOPERCULATAE, [1] p. 121
   Thallus holocarpic, without specialized vegetative structures,
   endobiotic
      Thallus forming a single sporangium ...... OLPIDIACEAE, p. 121
      Thallus forming more than one sporangium
         Thallus converted into a linear series of sporangia
               ACHLYOGETONACEAE, p. 182
         Thallus converted into a prosorus or sorus surrounded by
         a common soral membrane ...... SYNCHYTRIACEAE, p. 190
   Thallus eucarpic, i.e. differentiated into a vegetative system and
   reproductive organs, monocentric or polycentric, epi- and
   endobiotic, endobiotic, interbiotic, or extramatrical
      Thallus always monocentric
         Thallus epi- and endobiotic, or entirely endobiotic, repro-
            ductive organ epi- or endobiotic .. PHLYCTIDIACEAE, p. 207
         Thallus interbiotic; sporangium, prosporangium, or resting
            spore formed from the enlarged body of the encysted
            zoospore ......................RHIZIDIACEAE, p. 403

[1] Whiffen (1944) does not consider inoperculate and operculate sporangial discharge to be of fundamental importance above generic level. Rather, she prefers as indicated earlier (p. 50) to group the monocentric chytrids on the basis of whether the sporangium develops from the encysted zoospore body or from its tube. The writer does not accept this view, particularly since recent work has shown much variation in types of development within one fungus, whereas not a single authentic instance of a chytrid being both inoperculate and operculate has been recorded. See Willoughby, *Trans. Brit. Mycol. Soc.*, 41:309. 1958, for support of this viewpoint.

Thallus, at least in some phases, polycentric
  Sporangia and resting spores formed on the same endobiotic
    polycentric thallus .... CLADOCHYTRIACEAE, p. 460
  [Sporangia and resting spores formed on separate thalli;
    sporangia epibiotic, thallus monocentric; resting
    spores endobiotic, thallus polycentric PHYSODERMATACEAE] [1]
Sporangium opening by the dehiscence of an operculum
                              Series OPERCULATAE, p. 486
  Thallus monocentric, epi- and endobiotic, or endobiotic
                              CHYTRIDIACEAE, p. 486
  Thallus polycentric, completely endobiotic, or endobiotic and
    extramatrical .... MEGACHYTRIACEAE, p. 580

INOPERCULATAE

OLPIDIACEAE

Thallus endobiotic, holocarpic, without a specialized vegetative system, converted as a whole into a single inoperculate sporangium or a resting spore; zoospores formed in the sporangium, posteriorly uniflagellate, generally with a single globule; sexuality, where known, by fusion of posteriorly uniflagellate planogametes, the zygote after penetration forming an endobiotic resting spore which upon germination functions as a zoosporangium.

A large primarily aquatic family, the members of which are found as parasites and saprophytes of fresh-water algae, fresh-water and marine Phycomycetes, microscopic animals, and plant spores. Several species are also known as parasites of flowering plants, notably *Olpidium brassicae* (Woronin) Dang. (see Woronin, 1878: 557), *O. viciae* Kusano (1912), *O. trifolii* Schroeter (see Kusano, 1929), *O. agrostidis* Sampson (1932).

Undoubted instances of a sexual act preceding resting-spore formation have been found by Kusano in *Olpidium viciae* and *O. trifolii* and by Sawada (1922) in *O. bothriospermii* (see *Olpidium*, p. 128).

KEY TO THE GENERA OF THE OLPIDIACEAE

Zoospore with the flagellum subapically attached, the body bearing
    an anterior ring of refractive granules .... OLPIDIOMORPHA, p. 122

[1] See page 483.

Zoospore with the flagellum posteriorly attached (except in *Sphaerita*),
the body generally bearing a single prominent globule
  Sporangium never filling the host cell, with a very short discharge
  papilla or devoid of a specialized discharge apparatus; the
  wall simply bursting at maturity; parasitic in Euglenophyceae or amoebae
    Parasitic in the nuclei of amoebae .... NUCLEOPHAGA, p. 123
    Parasitic in the protoplasm of Euglenophyceae and amoebae
                                                      SPHAERITA, p. 125
  Sporangium either not filling or filling the host cell, with one or
  more well-defined discharge tubes; parasitic in algae, fungi,
  or microscopic animals
    Sporangium more or less ovoid, spherical, or tubular, never
    completely filling the host cell or losing its individuality
      Sporangium with one (rarely more) discharge tube
        Sporangia generally scattered; resting spore not lying
          loosely in a container .... OLPIDIUM, p. 128
        Sporangia formed in dense clusters; resting spore lying
          loosely in a container .... PRINGSHEIMIELLA, p. 157
      Sporangium predominantly with numerous discharge tubes
                                              PLEOTRACHELUS, p. 158
    Sporangium more or less completely filling the host cell and
    assuming its shape
      Sporangium nearly filling the host cell; its walls, however,
      never completely fusing with those of the host
                                              PLASMOPHAGUS, p. 164
      Sporangium completely filling the reproductive organ or
      hypertrophied part of the host; the walls of host and
      parasite fused, at least laterally.......... ROZELLA, p. 165

OLPIDIOMORPHA SCHERFFEL

Arch. Protistenk., 54: 515. 1926
(Fig. 12 J, p. 124)

Thallus endobiotic, holocarpic, resembling *Olpidium*; contents refractive, with glistening irregular lumps but without fat globules; sporangium inoperculate, with a single discharge tube; zoospores formed
within the sporangium, emerging upon the dissolution of the tip of
the discharge tube, with a single trailing lateral subapically attached
flagellum, the body containing an anterior ring of refractive granules;
resting spore not observed.

Differing from *Olpidium* in the structure of the zoospore and, to a lesser degree, in the lack of the characteristic chytridiaceous fat globules in the contents of the developing sporangium.

OLPIDIOMORPHA PSEUDOSPORAE Scherffel

Arch. Protistenk., 54: 515, pl. 28, figs. 7-8. 1926

Sporangium more or less spherical or broadly ovoid, 8–14 μ in diameter, with a single long slender discharge tube 3 μ in diameter, wall thin, smooth, colorless; zoospores ovoid, 3–4 μ long by 2 μ in diameter, slightly attenuated posteriorly, plasma dense, homogeneous, with an anterior circlet of strongly refractive granules and a small lateral basal vacuole, flagellum from four to five times as long as body, emerging individually and at once swimming away, movement smooth, gliding in a zigzag line; resting spores not observed.

In zoocyst of *Pseudospora leptoderma*, living in *Vaucheria sp.*, HUNGARY.

NUCLEOPHAGA DANGEARD

Le Botaniste, 4: 214, 1894-95

(Fig. 12 A, p. 124)

Thallus endobiotic, within the nucleus of the host, holocarpic; sporangium inoperculate, formed from the walled thallus, filling the nuclear cavity, spores simultaneously formed, set free upon the disintegration of the host body.

A genus of uncertain relationships.

NUCLEOPHAGA AMOEBAE Dangeard

Le Botaniste, 4: 214, figs. 1-5. 1894-95.

From one to five sporangia in the hypertrophied nucleus of the amoeba; spores spherical, up to one hundred in a sporangium.

In *Amoeba verrucosa*, FRANCE.

Since the vegetative body of the organism did not ingest the solid particles of the host, Dangeard considered *Nucleophaga amoebae* a chytrid allied to *Sphaerita*. The vital activities of the host were not affected until the time of sporulation of the parasite. The host then disintegrated, allowing the spores to be dispersed.

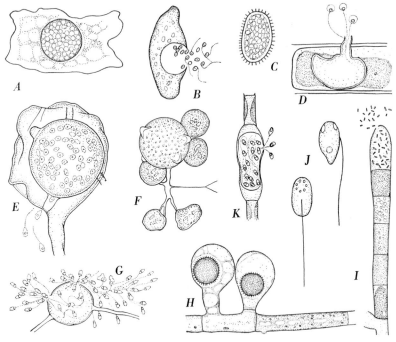

FIG. 12. Olpidiaceae

A. Nucleophaga amoebae Dangeard in *Amoeba*, mature sporangium in nucleus of *A. verrucosa*. *B–C. Sphaerita dangeardii* Chatton and Brodsky in *Euglena*: *B*, sporangium discharging its spores to outside of host; *C*, thick-walled spiny resting spore. *D.* Sporangium of *Olpidium endogenum* (Braun) Schroeter in cell of *Zygnema*, with last of zoospores just emerging. *E. Pleotrachelus fulgens* Zopf in *Pilobolus*, discharging sporangium. *F–G. Rozella polyphagi* Sparrow in prosporangium of *Polyphagus euglenae*: *F*, mature sporangium, with several discharge papillae, completely filling parasitized prosporangium of host; *G*, discharge of zoospores. *H–I. Rozella septigena* Cornu in hyphae of *Achlya* and *Saprolegnia*: *H*, resting spores in swollen lateral hyphal outgrowths of *Saprolegnia spiralis*; at right is young zoosporangium of parasite with a discharge papilla; around left-hand resting spore the hyaline region, within which spines are formed, still persists; *I*, portion of hypha of *Achlya polyandra*, showing sporangia of *Rozella septigena* in various stages of development; in lowest segment wall of parasite has not yet fused with that of host; at the tip the sporangium is discharging its zoospores; in third cell from the top the strongly vacuolate stage of the protoplasm is shown. *J. Olpidiomorpha pseudosporae* Scherffel, zoospores, showing

A *Nucleophaga sp.* has also been reported by Scherffel (1902a) in *Zygnema*. Numerous records occur in the extensive protozoological literature (see Sassuchin, 1934; Brumpt and Lavier, 1935).

Doflein (1907) has described motile bodies in a parasite of *Amoeba* which conjugate to form biflagellate zygotes. There is no real evidence that they belong to Dangeard's fungus, particularly since the flagellum is said to be anterior.

SPHAERITA DANGEARD

Bull. Soc. Bot. France, 33: 241. 1886; Ann. Sci. Nat. Bot.,
VII, 4: 277. 1886
(Fig. 12 B-C, p. 124)

Thallus parasitic in the cytoplasm of Rhizopoda and Euglenophyceae, endobiotic, holocarpic, walled, without specialized vegetative structures, forming the rudiment of the sporangium; sporangium inoperculate, spherical, ellipsoidal or fusiform, usually liberated from the host at maturity, discharging its zoospores by a splitting of the wall or by the formation of a discharge papilla; zoospores uniflagellate, the flagellum anteriorly attached but directed posteriorly; resting spores not known with certainty.

Species of *Sphaerita* are all parasitic in the cytoplasm of the host, on which they may often exert little effect, at least until the sporulation of the parasite, when death may ensue.

Dangeard (1933) indicated that in view of the fact that *Sphaerita dangeardii*, a species parasitic in *Euglena*, has been more adequately studied than his *S. endogena*, he would designate it, if this did not violate the rules of nomenclature, as the type of the genus. He felt that further investigations of *S. endogena*, in Rhizopoda, might indicate that it should be segregated in a genus of its own. It might be pointed out that under Article 66 of the *International Code for Botanical Nomenclature* the specific name *endogena* should be discarded as a *nomen confusum*.

---

subapical attachment of flagellum and anterior refractive granules. *K. Plasmophagus oedogoniorum* de Wildeman, discharging sporangium in *Tribonema*.

(*A*, Dangeard, 1894-95b; *B–C*, Dangeard, 1889b; *D*, *F–G*, Sparrow, 1936a; *E*, Zopf, 1884; *H–I*, Cornu, 1872a; *J*, Scherffel, 1926b; *K*, Sparrow, 1933c)

Dangeard (1933) also states that the spiny resting spores described (1889b: 46) for *Sphaerita endogena* in *Euglena* may actually belong to *S. dangeardii* and that the conjugation of zoospores observed (1889b: 49, pl. 3, fig. 8), later ascribed to incomplete segmentation, was indeed a sexual process similar to that found in *Olpidium viciae*. In his earlier researches Dangeard did not recognize that at least two different parasites might be present in the *Euglena*, one with uniflagellate zoospores (*Sphaerita*) and another with biflagellate zoospores (*Pseudosphaerita*). This, together with the fact that data were often obtained from fixed material, has led to much confusion in distinguishing what structures belong to a particular fungus. The following treatment is probably only partly successful in unraveling the tangle, since new observations alone can solve it. Many references to "*Sphaerita*" may be found in protozoological literature, but little can be got from them since they ordinarily refer only to fixed and stained material. See also *Pseudosphaerita*, page 961.

SPHAERITA DANGEARDII Chatton and Brodsky
Arch. Protistenk., 17: 8. 1909
(Fig. 12 B-C, p. 124)

Sphaerita endogena Dangeard, pro parte (in *Euglena*), Ann. Sci. Nat. Bot., VII, 4:277, pl. 12, figs. 14-21. 1886.

Sporangium spherical or somewhat ellipsoidal, extremely thin-walled, sometimes with two oppositely placed short discharge papillae; zoospores spherical or ovoid, 1.5–2 μ in diameter, resting for a short time after discharge, movement hopping or slightly amoeboid; resting spore (?) ovoid, 12 μ long by 8 μ in diameter, with a brownish spiny wall, upon germination forming a discharge papilla and functioning as a zoosporangium.,

Parasitic in *Euglena spp.*, Dangeard (*loc. cit.*; 1889b: 46, pl. 2, figs. 11–19, pl. 3, figs. 1–2), FRANCE; *Euglena sp.*, Constantineanu (1901: 370), RUMANIA; *Euglena sp.*, Serbinow (1907: 154, pl. 5, figs. 4–8), RUSSIA; *Euglena viridis*, Valkanov (1931a: 361), BULGARIA.

No statement was made by Dangeard (1933) as to whether the *Sphaerita* in *Phacus* and *Trachelomonas* is to be considered to belong here or in *S. endogena*. Whether or not the smooth-walled resting spores described in the 1886 paper belong here is apparently not known.

IMPERFECTLY KNOWN SPECIES OF SPHAERITA

? SPHAERITA ENDOGENA Dangeard
Pro parte (in Rhizopoda), Ann. Sci. Nat. Bot., VII, 4: 277, pl. 12,
figs. 22-36. 1886

Sporangia single or in groups, spherical or somewhat elongate,
5–20 μ in diameter, the spores when mature appearing as mulberry-
like masses, expelled from the host at maturity and liberated by rupturing of the wall, apparently without flagella; resting stage not observed.

Parasitic in Rhizopoda, *Nuclearia simplex*, and *Heterophrys dispersa*,
Dangeard (*loc. cit.*), *Amoeba limax*, Chatton and Brodsky (1909: 3,
figs. 1–3), FRANCE; *Nuclearia simplex*, Constantineanu (1901: 370),
RUMANIA.

Records of the occurrence of *Sphaerita endogena* and other "species"
in parasitic amoebae are frequent in protozoological literature.

Chatton and Brodsky have emphasized that characteristically the
very young thallus has an eccentric nucleus apparently without a
membrane. Their studies on fixed and stained material indicated that
the thallus is surrounded at all times by a wall, that the nuclei divide
simultaneously, and that the spores are formed by condensation of
the cytoplasm around each of the nuclei. Secretion of a thin wall
follows. The spores were liberated simply by the rupturing of the
wall, no special discharge pore being formed. These investigators
noted, as did Dangeard, that the liberated spores of *Sphaerita endogena* parasitizing Rhizopoda lacked motility. Dangeard later (1933)
emphasized this point as indicative of a possible specific and perhaps
even generic difference between *S. endogena* and the parasite of *Euglena* (*S. dangeardii*).

? SPHAERITA TRACHELOMONADIS Skvortzow
Arch. Protistenk., 57: 205, fig. 2. 1927

Sporangium broadly ellipsoidal, with broad rounded ends, 20–29 μ
long by 18–20 μ in diameter, wall thin, smooth; zoospores not observed; resting spore spherical, with a thick brownish spiny wall.

In the lorica of *Trachelomonas teres* var. *glabra, T. swirenkoi,* Manchuria.

Observations on the flagellation of the zoospores will be necessary
before it can be said whether this is a species of *Sphaerita* or *Pseudosphaerita.*

? Sphaerita sp.

Karling (1941a) listed an unnamed species of this genus in *Euglena*
in the United States. A *Sphaerita sp.* has also been reported from Czechoslovakia as parasitic in *Gonyostomum semen* (Chloromonadineae) by
Fott (1952).

OLPIDIUM (Braun) Rabenhorst

Flora Europaea algarum, 3: 288. 1868 (sensu recent. Schroeter.
Kryptogamenfl. Schlesien, 3 (1): 180. 1885)

(Figs. 12 D, p. 124; 4 A, p. 72)

Chytridium, subgen. *Olpidium* Braun, Abhandl. Berlin Akad., 1855: 75.
1856.
Cyphidium Magnus, Wissensch. Meeresunters. Abt. Kiel, 2-3: 77. 1875.
Olpidiella Lagerheim, Journ. de Botanique, 2: 438. 1888.
Endolpidium de Wildeman, Ann. Soc. Belge Micro (Mém.), 18: 153. 1894.

Thallus soon becoming walled, endobiotic, holocarpic, without rhizoids, not entirely filling the cell of the substratum, forming either a
sporangium or a resting spore; sporangium inoperculate, predominantly spherical or ellipsoidal, smooth-walled, usually forming a single
discharge tube (sometimes several) of variable length, the tip, at
least, extramatrical; zoospores formed within the sporangium, posteriorly uniflagellate, usually with a single globule, discharged through
a pore formed upon the deliquescence or rupturing of the tip of
the discharge tube; resting spore thick-walled, generally with a large
globule, borne like the sporangium, formed in some instances (all?)
from a planozygote produced by the fusion of isogamous planogametes,
upon germination forming zoospores.

The genus includes forms parasitic primarily in fresh-water algae,
flowering plants, spores, moss protonema (Petersen, 1910; Skvortzow,
1927), and aquatic microscopic animals.

Braun's subgenus, raised to generic rank by Rabenhorst, included

Olpidium apiculatum (*Entophlyctis*), *O. endogenum*, and *O. saprolegniae* (*Olpidiopsis*). Rabenhorst emphasized the inoperculate sporangium and the presence of a discharge tube as characters common to all the species regardless of their relation to the substratum. Hence *Rhizophydium ampullaceum* even though epibiotic fell within these limits and was included in the genus. Schroeter (1885: 180) established *Olpidium* as it is here understood and it has so been maintained by subsequent monographers, that is, as a genus confined to endobiotic holocarpic chytrids without rhizoids and with one, or occasionally several, discharge tubes. His assertion that the zoospore was anteriorly flagellate is incorrect, however, and probably rests on Fisch's observations on "*O. lemnae*" (now ?*Reessia lemnae*, see p. 765). Because of this character in Schroeter's description of the genus Lagerheim (*loc. cit.*) was led to establish *Olpidiella* for forms with posteriorly uniflagellate zoospores.

Endolpidium hormisciae de Wildeman (1894) in *Hormiscia zonata* in France differs from species of *Olpidium* only in forming a short discharge tube which does not penetrate the algal wall and in producing hypertrophy of the host wall. The zoospores and resting spores were not observed.

Cyphidium was established by Magnus (*loc. cit.*) as a subgenus of *Chytridium* for *Olpidium*-like forms in which the sporangium rests between the wall and the protoplasm of the host. No combinations, however, were made. (See remarks under *O. zygnemicola*, p. 134). Petersen (1910: 504, footnote) applied the generic name *Oligostomum* to "*Olpidium*-shaped marine forms with uniflagellated zoospores and with a limited number of channels for the zoospores (several *Pleotrachelus* forms)." His description is too inadequate and too vague to be tenable, and no species is named which would typify the genus. *Asterocystis* de Wildeman (1893a: 21), erected for an *Olpidium*-like parasite in the roots of terrestrial flowering plants, has been discussed by Karling (1937d).

A genus *Gamolpidium* (*G. nitidis*) is mentioned by Constantineanu (1901) as having been established by Vladescu (1892).

Sexuality has been demonstrated to occur in several species of *Olpidium* parasitic in certain flowering plants (Kusano, 1912, 1929), namely, *O. viciae* and *O. trifolii*. Cytological evidence for its occurrence in *O. agrostidis* has also been presented by Miss Sampson (1932). It has not been convincingly described in any of the purely aquatic species.

In *Olpidium viciae*, Kusano observed that the swarmers copulated in pairs (Fig. 4 A, p. 72,) the zygote then infecting the host and producing within it a resting spore. Swarmers which did not copulate eventually penetrated the host, where each formed a sporangium. A more critical investigation by Kusano of sexuality as it exists in *O. trifolii* seems to indicate that sister gametes from the same gametangium are usually incapable of fusing with one another to form a planozygote. He concludes, therefore, that the fungus is dioecious but has a tendency toward monoecism. Another feature of the behavior of the gametes in *O. trifolii* was their aggregation at certain places in the medium. This aggregation was found to have a definite influence in promoting conjugation. Kusano suggests that the groups of nearly stationary gametes, undergoing amoeboid changes of shape, exert an attractive action upon free-swimming ones and thus induce fusion. In both species gametes discharged from recently formed gametangia were not so apt to conjugate as those from somewhat older ones.

In the following analytical key to the species considerable use is made of differences in substrata. In all probability this is not sound, and future work is very likely to reveal that a single species may occur in a variety of substrata. Since the basic morphological plan of an *Olpidium* is very simple there exists little chance for wide variation in this respect. Features such as the length of the discharge tube and the relative position of the fungus and the plasma of the substratum impressed the earlier investigators, but these are now known to be of little taxonomic value.

KEY TO THE SPECIES OF OLPIDIUM [1]

In plants
    In Chlorophyceae; sporangium variable in shape;
        zoospores formed in the sporangium
      Sporangium ellipsoidal, spherical, subspherical,
        pyriform, or ovoid

[1] Note that this key is not completely dichotomous.

Sporangium subspherical or broadly ellipsoidal, its long axis
parallel with that of the algal cell; discharge tube arising
from the middle of the sporangium, thus appearing
lateral, with a pronounced endobiotic swelling; in Conjugatae .... O. ENDOGENUM, p. 132
Sporangium spherical, ellipsoidal, ovoid, or pyriform, endobiotic part of the apical discharge tube isodiametric; in
various green algae
  Sporangium spherical, ellipsoidal, or ovoid, resting spore
  smooth-walled
    Sporangium spherical, discharge tube not projecting
    beyond outer surface of the algal wall; in *Zygnema*
                           O. ZYGNEMICOLA, p. 134
    Sporangium spherical, ellipsoidal, ovoid, or occasion-
    ally somewhat pyriform, discharge tube project-
    ing more or less beyond wall
      Discharge tube strongly constricted when passing
      through host wall, expanded locally on outer
      surface and extending extramatrically; in zygo-
      spores of *Spirogyra* ...... O. ROSTRIFERUM, p. 134
      Discharge tube isodiametric, extending for varying
      distances beyond algal wall
        In vegetative cells of various green algae
                      O. ENTOPHYTUM, p. 135
        In oöspores of *Sphaeroplea* ... O. SPHAEROPLEAE, p. 137
  Sporangium pyriform, with a short sessile discharge tube,
  resting spore spiny; in *Hyalotheca* O. HYALOTHECAE, p. 137
Sporangium tubular or saclike; in desmids
  Sporangium swollen and short sausage-like or saclike, con-
  stricted in the mid-region .... O. SACCATUM, p. 138
  Sporangium a complex of branched tubes, without con-
  strictions .... O. UTRICULIFORME, p. 139
In Euglenophyceae; sporangium spherical; zoospores formed in
an extruded vesicle as well as in the sporangium
                      O. EUGLENAE, p. 139
In diatoms; sporangium spherical, 3.4-5.5 μ in diameter, opening
by a pore; in *Hantzschia* .... O. HANTZSCHIAE, p. 140
In plant spores
  In pollen grains; sporangium spherical or ovoid; discharge
  tube short or long
  Sporangium spherical, generally with a short broad discharge
  tube; zoospores spherical, 4-5 μ in diameter; penetration
  tube often persistent on the smooth-walled resting spore
                    O. PENDULUM, p. 140

Sporangium spherical or ovoid, discharge tube narrow, often prolonged extramatrically; penetration tube not persistent on the spherical or ellipsoidal resting spore .... O. LUXURIANS, p. 142

In rust spores; sporangium spherical or somewhat angular; discharge tube short or only a papilla ... O. UREDINIS, p. 142

In aquatic Phycomycetes

In resting spores of *Allomyces*; sporangium often with a broad, long, exit tube; zoospores oval, elongate or slightly curved with four to nine refractive globules ... O. ALLOMYCETOS, p. 143

In thalli, sporangia, and resting spores of *Rhizophlyctis*; exit tube not prolonged; zoospores spherical, lacking globules .... O. RHIZOPHLYCTIDIS, p. 144

[In moss protenoma .... O. PROTONEMAE [1]]

In animals

In eggs and adults of rotifers

Sporangium spherical, ovoid, ellipsoidal or irregularly saccate; zoospores spherical; resting spore lying loosely in a spherical structure

Zoospores with a single globule .... O. GREGARIUM, p. 144

Zoospores with numerous globules and a 38-45 μ long flagellum .... O. GRANULATUM, p. 145

Sporangium predominantly pyriform, ovoid or subspherical; zoospores oblong, with a short (12-14 μ) flagellum and one or two lateral, elongate, refractive bodies .... O. ROTIFERUM, p. 146

In zoocysts of *Vampyrella*

Sporangium spherical or broadly ovoid; zoospore without a large refractive globule .... O. VAMPYRELLAE, p. 146

Sporangium ovoid, somewhat irregular, or, if several in a cell, somewhat tubular; zoospore with a minute eccentric globule .... O. PSEUDOSPOREARUM, p. 146

In adult nematodes .... O. NEMATODEAE, p. 147

OLPIDIUM ENDOGENUM (Braun) Schroeter

Kryptogamenfl. Schlesien, 3 (1): 180. 1885.

(Fig. 12 D, p. 124)

Chytridium endogenum Braun, pro parte, Monatsber. Berlin Akad., 1855: 384; Abhandl. Berlin Akad., 1855:60, pl. 5, fig. 21. 1856 (not the forms in *Vaucheria* and *Spirogyra*); Monatsber. Berlin Akad., 1856: 588.

Chytridium intestinum Braun, Monatsber. Berlin Akad., 1856: 589. Non *C. intestinum* Schenk.

[1] Not considered in the present work.

Sporangium spherical or ovoid, discharge tube narrow, often prolonged extramatrically; penetration tube not persistent on the spherical or ellipsoidal resting spore
O. LUXURIANS, p. 142
In rust spores; sporangium spherical or somewhat angular; discharge tube short or only a papilla ... O. UREDINIS, p. 142
In aquatic Phycomycetes
In resting spores of *Allomyces*; sporangium often with a broad, long, exit tube; zoospores oval, elongate or slightly curved with four to nine refractive globules ... O. ALLOMYCETOS, p. 143
In thalli, sporangia, and resting spores of *Rhizophlyctis*; exit tube not prolonged; zoospores spherical, lacking globules
O. RHIZOPHLYCTIDIS, p. 144
[In moss protenoma .... O. PROTONEMAE [1]]
In animals
In eggs and adults of rotifers
Sporangium spherical, ovoid, ellipsoidal or irregularly saccate; zoospores spherical; resting spore lying loosely in a spherical structure
Zoospores with a single globule .... O. GREGARIUM, p. 144
Zoospores with numerous globules and a 38-45 μ long flagellum .... O. GRANULATUM, p. 145
Sporangium predominantly pyriform, ovoid or subspherical; zoospores oblong, with a short (12-14 μ) flagellum and one or two lateral, elongate, refractive bodies
O. ROTIFERUM, p. 146
In zoocysts of *Vampyrella*
Sporangium spherical or broadly ovoid; zoospore without a large refractive globule .... O. VAMPYRELLAE, p. 146
Sporangium ovoid, somewhat irregular, or, if several in a cell, somewhat tubular; zoospore with a minute eccentric globule .... O. PSEUDOSPOREARUM, p. 146
In adult nematodes .... O. NEMATODEAE, p. 147

OLPIDIUM ENDOGENUM (Braun) Schroeter

Kryptogamenfl. Schlesien, 3 (1): 180. 1885.
(Fig. 12 D, p. 124)

Chytridium endogenum Braun, pro parte, Monatsber. Berlin Akad., 1855: 384; Abhandl. Berlin Akad., 1855:60, pl. 5, fig. 21. 1856 (not the forms in *Vaucheria* and *Spirogyra*); Monatsber. Berlin Akad., 1856: 588.
Chytridium intestinum Braun, Monatsber. Berlin Akad., 1856: 589. Non *C. intestinum* Schenk.

[1] Not considered in the present work.

Olpidium intestinum (Braun) Rabenhorst, Flora Europaea algarum, 3: 283. 1868.
Olpidiella endogena (Braun) Lagerheim, Journ. de Botanique, 2: 438. 1888.

Sporangium strongly subspherical or broadly ellipsoidal, occasionally spherical, up to 35 μ in diameter, its longer axis parallel with that of the alga, wall smooth, slightly thickened, colorless, discharge tube long, 5 μ in diameter, arising from the middle or end of the sporangium, narrowly cylindrical, with a pronounced swelling (6.6–11 μ in diameter) where it meets the inner face of the algal wall, extending for a variable distance extramatrically and terminating in a funnel-like apex; zoospores spherical, 3 μ in diameter, with a colorless globule; resting spore spherical, ellipsoidal, or somewhat pyriform, 15 μ in diameter, wall smooth, colorless, of two layers, the outer thicker than the inner, contents with a large oil globule, germination not observed.

Parasitic in *Closterium, Pleurotaenium, Cosmarium, Penium, Euastrum, Tetmemorus, Micrasterias*, etc., Braun (*loc. cit.*), de Bary, Pringsheim (in Braun, 1855a: 384), Schroeter (1885: 180), Cejp (1933a: 2, pl. 1, figs. 1–3), Schulz (1922: 147, figs. 85b, 86–90; 1923: 179, fig. 3), GERMANY; *Closterium lunula*, Archer (1860: 215, pl. 11, fig. 5), GREAT BRITAIN; *Spirogyra majuscula*, Loscos (in Rabenhorst, 1868: 283), SPAIN; *Closterium lunula, Closterium sp.*, Sorokin (1874b: 4, pl. 1, figs. 1–5; 1883: 31, fig. 35), RUSSIA; *Closterium sp.*, Dangeard (1886a: 285), desmids, de Brébisson (1856: 150), FRANCE; *Cosmarium pachydermum*, Skvortzow (1925: 429), MANCHURIA; *Penium margaritaceum* (F. slide No. 2701), *Closterium ralfsii* var. *hybridum* (F. slide No. 2703), Linder (1947: 242), CANADIAN EASTERN ARCTIC; *Closterium sp.*, Wolle (1887: 203), *Pleurotaenium sp., Cosmarium sp.*, Sparrow and Barr (1955: 553), UNITED STATES; *Cosmarium depressum* var. *achondrum*, Skuja (1948: 379, pl. 39, fig. 8), SWEDEN; *Closterium sp.*, Litvinow (1953: 76), LATVIA; *Closterium, Penium, Tetmemorus, Cosmarium*, Kobayasi and Ookubo (1954b: 572, fig. 14), JAPAN.

Sorokin (1876: 63, pl. 3, fig. 1) placed in this species a fungus with an ellipsoidal sporangium bearing a cylindrical isodiametric curved discharge tube. It occurred in great numbers in eelworms, where it was the first of a series of parasites causing an epidemic in his cultures.

The sporangia were closely packed in linear series. As Fischer (1892: 24) has suggested, this may in reality be a species of *Myzocytium* or, but less likely, of *Catenaria*.

Gwynne-Vaughan and Barnes (1937: fig. 11) and Sparrow (1936a: 427, pl. 14, fig. 1) figured a fungus on filamentous Conjugatae in England which has ellipsoidal sporangia, as does the present species, but differs from it in having a short stout discharge tube only slightly inflated basally. Future studies of *Olpidium endogenum* may allow the inclusion of this variety.

Karling (1941b: 108) has reported this desmid parasite from the United States in pollen grains of *Pinus*. No details are given.

The fungus in *Cylindrocystis brebissonii* with cylindrical to bottle-like sporangia, 18–42 μ long by 11–14 μ broad with a terminal discharge tube 6–10 μ by 4 μ and an endobiotic swelling, found by Fott (1950: 8, figs. 15–18) in Czechoslovakia, is probably, as he indicates, distinct from *O. endogenum*. It has certain affinities with *O. tuba* Sorok. and *O. immersum* Sorok.

OLPIDIUM ZYGNEMICOLA Magnus

Verhandl. Bot. Vereins Prov. Brandenburg, 26: 79. 1885

Sporangium formed between the wall and the contents of the alga, resting directly on the protoplasm, spherical, colorless, smooth-walled, with a discharge tube which does not project beyond the outer wall of the alga; zoospores uniflagellate; resting spore within the host contents, spherical, with a faintly mottled thick smooth wall and a large oil globule, germination not observed.

In *Zygnema sp.*, GERMANY.

The location of the sporangium between the wall and the protoplasm of the alga is by itself of little significance as a character in maintaining this species distinct from *Olpidium entophytum*. All gradations in position are often found in an algal cell heavily infected with a species of *Olpidium*.

OLPIDIUM ROSTRIFERUM Tokunaga

Trans. Sapporo Nat. Hist. Soc., 13: 80, pl. 5, fig. 11. 1933

Sporangia spherical to ovoid, 14.4–25.2 μ in diameter, singly or from two to five in a zygospore of the host, wall smooth, discharge tube single, up to 70 μ in length, 3–4.2 μ in diameter, strongly constricted when passing through the wall of the zygote and expanded locally (up to 6 μ) on its outer surface, extending for a variable distance outside the gametangium wall; zoospores spherical, about 3.6 μ in diameter, with a single flagellum; resting spore spherical or ellipsoidal, 16.8–24 μ in diameter, from one to three in a zygote, with a smooth golden-yellow wall 1.6 μ thick, contents with a large central globule, germination not observed. (Modified from Tokunaga.)

In zygospores of *Spirogyra jurgensii,* JAPAN.

OLPIDIUM ENTOPHYTUM (Braun) Rabenhorst

(Fig. 13 A, p. 136)

Chytridum entophytum Braun, Monatsber. Berlin Akad., 1856: 589.

Flora Europaea algarum, 3: 283. 1868

Sporangium spherical, ellipsoidal, ovoid, or somewhat pyriform, 5.7–27.7 μ in diameter, wall thin, smooth, colorless, discharge tube (rarely two) isodiametric throughout, variable in length, up to 14.8 μ long by 3–5.7 μ in diameter; zoospores spherical, 3–5 μ in diameter, with a colorless globule and a long flagellum, forming a temporary, motionless mass at the orifice of the discharge tube; resting spore spherical or ellipsoidal and 11–22.5 μ broad by 18.5–29.6 μ long, wall smooth, thick, colorless, contents dense, germination not observed.

In *Vaucheria globifera* (*salina*?), de Bary (in Braun, *loc. cit.*), *Spirogyra, Vaucheria,* Kloss (in Braun, *loc. cit.*), *V. geminata, V. sessilis,* Schenk (1858a: 237), *Cladophora glomerata, Vaucheria sp.,* Schroeter (1885: 181), GERMANY; *Vaucheria,* Dangeard (1886a: 286, pl. 14, fig. 11), *Cladophora sp.,* de Wildeman (1895c: 215), FRANCE; *Desmidium swartzii,* de Wildeman (1893b: 49, pl. 7, fig. 4), BELGIUM; *Vaucheria sp.,* Constantineanu (1901: 370), RUMANIA; *Spirogyra sp.,* Skvortzow (1925: 428), MANCHURIA; *Spirogyra communis, Aegagropila sauteri,* Tokunaga (1933b: 79, pl. 5, figs. 1–3), JAPAN; *Spirogyra sp.,* Sparrow (1933c: 515), oöspores of *Oedogonium sp., Bulbochaete sp.,* Sparrow and Barr (1955: 553), UNITED STATES; *Cladophora sp.,* Sparrow (1936a: 427, pl. 14, fig. 6), GREAT BRITAIN; zygote of *Oedogonium sp.,* Shen and Siang (1948: 180), CHINA; *Gloeocystis bacillus,* Skuja (1948: 379, pl. 39, figs. 5–7), SWEDEN; *Cladophora sp.*, Litvinow (1953: 75), LAT-VIA; *Closterium*, Kobayashi and Ookubo (1954b: 573, fig. 15), JAPAN; *Spirogyra sp.*, Lacy (1955: 209), INDIA.

All forms with a spherical, ellipsoidal, ovoid, or somewhat pyri-

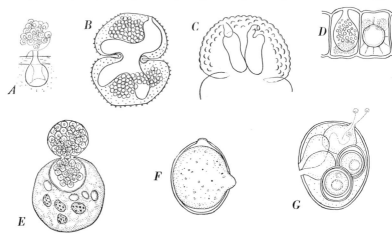

FIG. 13. *Olpidium*

A. Olpidium entophytum (Braun) Rabenhorst, discharged sporangium in *Cladophora*. *B. Olpidium utriculiforme* Scherffel, empty sporangium in *Cosmarium*. *C. Olpidium saccatum* Sorokin, empty sporangia in semicell of *Cosmarium*. *D. Olpidium hyalothecae* Scherffel, zoosporangium and spiny resting spore in cells of *Hyalotheca*. *E. Olpidium euglenae* Dangeard, discharging sporangium in *Euglena* cyst. *F–G. Olpidium gregarium* (Nowak.) Schroeter in rotifer eggs: *F*, single sporangium with discharge papilla protruding through wall of egg case; *G*, empty and discharging sporangia and resting spores.

(*A, F–G*, Sparrow, 1936a; *B–C*, Scherffel, 1926a; *D*, after Scherffel, 1926a; *E*, Dangeard, 1894-95b)

form sporangium and an isodiametric discharge tube of variable length which inhabit green algae are included in this species. Cross-inoculation experiments may in the future show the species as now understood to be a collective one.

The fungus on *Aegagrophila* reported by Tokunaga (1933b: 79), tentatively placed here, forms sporangia ranging from 19.2–62.4 µ in diameter; the discharge tube is broad, attaining a diameter of 9.6 µ.

Olpidium entophytum (?) var. *intermedium* Constantineanu
Revue Gén. Bot., 13: 371, fig. 75. 1901

Sporangium either spherical and 20–30 μ in diameter or elongate and 30–33 μ in diameter, wall thin, smooth, colorless, with a strongly projecting somewhat irregular or undulate discharge tube 108–114 μ long by 6–8 μ in diameter; zoospores and resting spore not observed.

In rotifer eggs, RUMANIA.

If the zoospores of this fungus are found to resemble those of *Olpidium gregarium* it is probably a tenable variety of that species. As was suggested by Constantineanu, it also resembles *O. macrosporum* Nowak. and may be referable to it. That only a single sporangium was formed in Nowakowski's species, whereas from five to twenty were present in var. *intermedium*, is not considered significant.

OLPIDIUM SPHAEROPLEAE Tokunaga
Trans. Sapporo Nat. Hist. Soc., 13: 81, pl. 5, figs. 9-10. 1933

Sporangia spherical, mostly solitary in the oöspores of the host, which they fill at maturity, 12–24 μ in diameter, with a single short cylindrical discharge tube; zoospores ellipsoidal to ovoidal, about 4.8 by 2.4 μ, uniflagellate; one resting spore, very rarely two, in the oöspores of the host, spherical, 11.4–12.6 μ (mostly 12 μ) in diameter, with a smooth slightly golden wall 1 μ thick, contents with a large globule, germination not observed.

In oöspores of *Sphaeroplea annulina*, JAPAN.

The sporangia of this species resemble those of *Rozella* in their tendency to fill the oöspore of the host.

OLPIDIUM HYALOTHECAE Scherffel
Arch. Protistenk., 54: 200, pl. 9, figs. 62-63. 1926
(Fig. 13 D, p. 136)

Sporangia pyriform, with a smooth colorless thin wall, one or two, rarely three, occupying the greater part of the host cell, 6.5–19 μ in diameter and 9–28 μ long, forming a short discharge tube which grows to the outer surface of the host cell; zoospores spherical, 3–4 μ in diameter, with a single basal oil droplet and a long delicate posterior flagellum, motion hopping; resting spore spherical, 8–12 μ in diameter with a thickened wall the outer surface of which bears a few straight faintly refractive rodlike spines, germination not observed.

On *Hyalotheca dissiliens*, *H. mucosa*, Scherffel (*loc. cit.*), HUNGARY; *H. dissiliens*, Canter (1949b: 22, fig. 1 a, 2), GREAT BRITAIN; *Desmidium swartzii*, Sparrow and Barr (1955: 553), UNITED STATES.

OLPIDIUM SACCATUM Sorokin

Arch. Bot. Nord France, 2: 30, fig. 33 a-d. 1883 (separate) [1]
(Fig. 13 C, p. 136)

Sporangium swollen and short sausage- or saclike, smooth, thin-walled, constricted in the mid-region, with a somewhat conical end resting against the inner surface of the host cell and by means of a circular pore opening at the level of the outer host wall to the outside at maturity, or, if the sporangium body does not directly make contact with the wall, forming a short, or rarely elongate and bent, sharply defined cylindrical discharge tube the open apex of which is just level with the outer surface of the host wall but never extends beyond it; zoospores minute, typically chytridiaceous with the characteristic oil droplet; resting spore apparently asexually formed by contraction of the protoplasm of the thallus, nearly spherical or somewhat pyriform, colorless, 11–16 μ in diameter, mostly 14–15 μ high by 16 μ in diameter, wall about 2 μ thick, the outer layer appearing dark and of double contour, the inner faintly refractive contents with a densely crowded group of strongly refractive (oil?) coarse granules or with a single large fat droplet, the spore lying in the spherical widened end of the thin-walled tube, from which it is separated by a cross wall, germination not known.

In desmids, Sorokin (*loc. cit.*), ASIATIC RUSSIA; *Cosmarium sp.*, de Wildeman (1893b: 50, pl. 6, figs. 17–25), BELGIUM; *Staurastrum sp.*, *Cosmarium sp.*, coll. Massart, de Wildeman (1896b: 46, pl. 3, figs. 29–32), NORWAY, FRANCE; *Cosmarium botrytis*, *Cosmarium sp.*, Scherffel (1926a: 210, pl. 10, figs. 80–83), HUNGARY; *Micrasterias truncata*,

---

[1] See also Sorokin, *Revue Mycologique*, 11: 136, pl. 79, figs. 86-89. 1889.

Kobayashi and Ookubo (1954b: 573, fig. 16), JAPAN; *Cosmarium sp.*, Sparrow and Barr (1955: 554), UNITED STATES.

Fischer and others after him consider the distinctive constriction characteristic of this species to be brought about by conditions imposed upon the sporangium by the shape of the host cell. Scherffel, however, has found such constricted sporangia lying wholly within one semicell of the desmid. Furthermore, the posteriorly uniflagellate zoospores observed by Scherffel throw doubt on the possibility that his fungus could have been a depauperate species of the laterally biflagellate genus *Myzocytium* (see p. 973) rather than the present species *Olpidium saccatum*, which it resembles, moreover, in all other respects.

OLPIDIUM UTRICULIFORME Scherffel
Arch. Protistenk., 54: 213, pl. 10, figs. 84-87. 1926
(Fig. 13 B, p. 136)

Sporangium usually occupying both algal semicells, irregular, tube-like, a simple sac or with a bulging outgrowth or several broad finger-like branches, in large host cells becoming extensive, much branched and consisting of elements up to 550 μ long by 11–20 μ wide, wall thick, smooth, colorless, forming a single sessile discharge pore; zoospores very numerous, spherical, 2.4–2.8 μ in diameter with a conspicuous oil globule and a 14–19 μ long flagellum, movement a smooth gliding or amoeboid; resting spores not observed.

In desmids, *Cosmarium botrytis*, Scherffel (*loc. cit.*), HUNGARY; *Closterium lunula, C. costatum, C. dianeae*, Canter (1949b: 25, figs. 1 b–3, 3–5, Pl. 5), GREAT BRITAIN; *Euastrum bidentatum* (Whelden No. 140), *Cosmarium conspersum, C. undulatum* var. *minutum*, *Cosmarium sp.* (F. slide No. 2707), (Whelden Nos. 23, 84), Linder (1947: 242), CANADIAN EASTERN ARCTIC.

OLPIDIUM EUGLENAE Dangeard
Le Botaniste, 4: 248, fig. 10 A-F. 1894-1895
(Fig. 13 E, p. 136)

Sporangium spherical, with a slightly thickened colorless smooth wall, lying eccentrically and loosely in the host cell; zoospores spherical, with a small centric yellow-orange globule and a long posterior flagellum, formed in the sporangium as well as in an extramatrical vesicle which is extruded through a wide sessile pore to the outside of the host cell, escaping upon the dissolution of the vesicle, movement hopping; resting spore not observed.

Parasitic in *Euglena sp.*, FRANCE (rare).

The species differs from other members of the genus in the method of formation of the zoospores. Further observations may indicate that it should be segregated from *Olpidium*. At maturity the sporangium opens by a sessile pore to the outside of the host and there forms a sac equal to or exceeding the endobiotic part in size. The protoplasm of both parts is then quickly divided into zoospores. In this unusual instance the endobiotic part functions both as a prosporangium and a sporangium. From Dangeard's Figure B it is also apparent that sometimes at least the globules of the spores are already organized before extrusion of the vesicle.

OLPIDIUM HANTZSCHIAE Skvortzow

Arch. Protistenk., 51: 430, text figs. 3-4. 1925

Sporangia spherical, from nine to twenty-seven in the abnormally swollen host cell, 3.4–5.5 μ in diameter, without projecting discharge papilla or tube, opening by a pore; zoospores at first spherical, then egg-shaped, with a colorless oil droplet and a long flagellum, 3.4 μ long by 1.5–1.7 μ in diameter; resting spore spherical, 5–6 μ in diameter, with dense plasma and a smooth wall, germination not observed.

In *Hantzschia amphioxys*, MANCHURIA.

In its small size, lack of a discharge tube, and general habit the organism strongly resembles a flagellate, particularly *Aphelidium*.

OLPIDIUM PENDULUM Zopf

A. Schenk, Handbuch d. Bot. .. , 4: 555, fig. 66 (1-5). 1890

Sporangia spherical, with a slightly thickened smooth wall, up to twelve in a host cell, up to 30 μ in diameter and with a short broad discharge tube when occurring singly, smaller and with a long narrow discharge tube when there are several in a cell; zoospores spherical,

4–5 μ in diameter, with a small colorless basal globule and a long flagellum, movement lively; resting spore spherical, with a smooth thick wall and a large globule, infection tube often persistent, appearing as an appendage, germination not observed.

In pine pollen, Zopf (*loc. cit.*), GERMANY; (?) pollen, Voronichin (1920: 9), RUSSIA; pollen of *Pinus ponderosa*, Graff (1928: 158) pine pollen, Sparrow (1952d: 759), UNITED STATES; pine pollen, Gaertner (1954b: 20), EGYPT, NORTHWEST AFRICA, WEST AFRICA, EQUATORIAL EAST AFRICA, SOUTH AFRICA; Gaertner (*op. cit.*, p. 40), SWEDEN, SPITSBERGEN.

? *Olpidium maritimum* Höhnk and Aleem

Veröff. Inst. Meeresforsch. Bremerhaven, 2: 227, figs. 1-7. 1953

Sporangium spherical, 12.6–21.6 μ in diameter, with smooth, thin wall and simple discharge tube up to 12 μ long by 4–5 μ wide which protrudes slightly from the substratum; zoospores numerous, oval or subspherical, 2.7–4.05 by 1.9–3 μ, with a basal globule and posterior flagellum emerging at first in a mass; resting spore spherical, with a large oil globule, wall smooth, 1.2–2.7 μ thick, upon germination forming a discharge tube and zoospores.

In pollen grains, in brackish soil, GERMANY.

Whether this species is distinguishable from *Olpidium pendulum* is questionable. Its zoospores are not significantly smaller, although they are ovoid instead of spherical. Other differences such as slightly projecting discharge tube and lack of a persistent infection tube do not seem of specific rank.

Zoospore production was optimal in water of 13 per cent salt content. It was also good in distilled water. In view of Aleem's (1952a) report that *Lagenidium entophytum*, *Myzocytium proliferum*, and *Rhizophydium couchii* all can live in saline waters, perhaps we are dealing here with a similarly adaptive *Olpidium pendulum*.

OLPIDIUM LUXURIANS (Tomaschek) Fischer

Rabenhorst. Kryptogamen-Fl., 1 (4): 29. 1892

Chytridium luxurians Tomaschek, Sitzungsber. Acad. Wiss. Wien (Math.-Nat. Cl.), 78: 204, figs. 1, 3-4, 6-11. (1878) 1879.

Diplochytrium sp., ibid., p. 198.

Chytridium pollinis-typhae forma *latifoliae, ibid.*, p. 203.

Olpidium diplochytrium (Tomaschek) Schroeter, Kryptogamenfl. Schlesien, 3 (1): 181. 1885.

Olpidiella diplochytrium Lagerheim, Journ. de Botanique, 2: 439. 1888

Sporangia spherical or ovoid, up to thirty in a pollen grain, of different sizes, up to 40 μ in diameter, wall smooth, colorless, discharge tube narrow, often somewhat curved and prolonged outside the substratum; zoospores somewhat elongate, with rounded apex and narrow end, 2 μ in diameter, movement even or undulate, swimming; resting spore spherical or somewhat ellipsoidal, 20 μ in diameter, with a thin smooth wall and a large oil globule, resting in a larger, thick-walled structure 24 μ in diameter, upon germination forming zoospores.

In pollen of *Pinus, Taxus, Lilium, Typha, Cannabis*, etc., Tomaschek (*loc. cit.*), AUSTRIA; *Pinus*, Schroeter (1885: 181), pollen, Minden (1915: 240), GERMANY; *Picea excelsa* pollen, Rostrup (1896: 126), Petersen (1910: 554, fig. 25a), DENMARK; *Pinus koraiensis*, Skvortzow (1927: 206), MANCHURIA; pine pollen, Gaertner (1954b: 20), EGYPT, NORTHWEST AFRICA, WEST AFRICA, SOUTH AFRICA; Gaertner (*op. cit.*, p. 40), SWEDEN.

The resting spores usually germinated after the disintegration of the pollen grain.

OLPIDIUM UREDINIS (Lagerh.) Fischer

Rabenhorst. Kryptogamen-Fl., 1 (4): 30. 1892

Olpidiella uredinis Lagerheim, Journ. de Botanique, 2: 438, pl. 10, figs. 1-15. 1888.

Sporangia spherical when occurring singly, or angular and smaller when there is more than one in the host cell, 26 μ in diameter, with a delicate hyaline or subhyaline smooth wall, forming a short discharge tube which pierces the wall, or only a papilla; zoospores ellipsoidal, posteriorly uniflagellate, with a single globule, 3-4 μ in diameter; resting spore endobiotic, globose, with a thick colorless smooth wall, 16 μ in diameter, contents colorless, with a large oil globule.

In uredospores of *Puccinia airae*, *P. violae*, and *P. rhamni*, but not capable of infecting uredospores of certain other rusts, GERMANY.

OLPIDIUM ALLOMYCETOS Karling

Amer. J. Bot., 35: 508, figs. 1-32. 1948

"Sporangia single to numerous in host cell, hyaline, smooth, spherical (8–38 μ), oval (10 × 16–20 × 30 μ), pyriform (8 × 15–24 × 33 μ), or occasionally angular with one short or long exit tube, 5 to 10 μ broad by 9 to 220 μ long. Zoospores, oval (4 × 5.5 μ) elongate (3.6 × 6.4 μ) slightly curved, with 4–9 refractive globules; flagellum 14–16 μ long. Resting spores partly or completely filling a hyaline vesicle, smooth, hyaline, spherical (6–30 μ), oval (1 × 14–18 × 27 μ) or slightly angular, containing numerous refractive granules or globules; forming zoospores directly upon germination" (Karling, *loc. cit.*).

Parasitic in *Allomyces anomalus*, and by inoculation in *A. arbuscula*, *A. javanicus*, *A. cystogenes*, *A. moniliformis*, *Rhizophlyctis* (*Karlingia*) *rosea*, and in rotifer eggs, Karling (*loc. cit.*), UNITED STATES; *A. arbuscula*, Sparrow (1952a: 35), CUBA.

Karling was able to infect thalli of *Rhizophlyctis* (*Karlingia*) and rotifer eggs by using zoospores of the *Allomyces* parasite, a most remarkable range of hosts.

The species is of particular interest since it appears to be only the second aquatic species in which germination of the resting spore has been observed. In undergoing germination a localized area of the resting spore becomes resorbed and ruptures. A broad discharge tube, sometimes almost equal to the diameter of the spore gradually develops. This structure penetrates the wall of the host cell and extends as a somewhat contorted tube of irregular diameter and up to 120 μ in length. If growth is inhibited by the host wall, a globular vesicular sporangium-like structure is formed. Zoospores of the same size, shape, and behavior as those produced by the sporangia are discharged and these directly infect resting spores of *Allomyces*. There were no evidences of sexuality.

OLPIDIUM RHIZOPHLYCTIDIS Sparrow

Mycologia, 40: 449, figs. 7, 8, 12, 14, 18, 19. 1948

Sporangia spherical or ellipsoidal, 25–50 μ long by 12–45 μ in diameter, hyaline, smooth-walled, with a single discharge tube which protrudes through the host wall; zoospores numerous, spherical, about 2 μ in diameter, without a conspicuous globule, posteriorly uniflagellate, movement an erratic hopping interspersed with periods of swimming; resting spore spherical, 12–20 μ in diameter, faintly brown, apparently asexually formed, with a smooth wall about 2 μ thick, contents with a large fat droplet, germination not observed.

Parasitic in thalli, sporangia, and resting spores of *Rhizophlyctis spp.*, Bikini, Eniwetok, and Rongelap atolls, MARSHALL ISLANDS, Sparrow (*loc. cit.*); Sparrow (1952a: 35), CUBA.

OLPIDIUM GREGARIUM (Nowak.) Schroeter

Kryptogamenfl. Schlesien, 3 (1): 182. 1885
(Fig. 13 F-G, p. 136)

Chytridium gregarium Nowakowski, in Cohn, Beitr. Biol. Pflanzen, 2: 77, pl. 4, fig. 2. 1876.

Sporangia spherical, ovoid, ellipsoidal, or irregularly saclike, the spherical ones 30–70 μ in diameter, the ovoid and ellipsoidal ones 18–35 μ long by 17–32 μ in diameter, with a single short broad papilla 7–10 μ in diameter which protrudes through the wall of the egg, wall thin or slightly thickened, smooth, colorless; zoospores spherical, 2.5–4 μ in diameter, with a single eccentric refractive globule and a long flagellum, emerging through a pore formed at the tip of a nearly sessile or slightly protruding discharge tube and either forming a temporary compact mass surrounded by a quickly evanescent slime film or swimming directly away, movement swimming and amoeboid; resting spore sometimes lying loosely in a spherical containing structure, spherical, brownish, thick-walled, the wall up to 6 μ thick, smooth or with faint striations, 15–20 μ in diameter, containing a large globule, germination not observed.

Parasitic on rotifer eggs, Nowakowski (*loc. cit.*), E. J. Butler (1907: 136, pl. 8, figs. 13–18), coll. (?) Hieronymus, Schroeter (1885: 182), GERMANY; eggs of *Brachionus sp.*, adults of *Euchlanis sp.*, Tokunaga

(1933b: 79, pl. 5, figs. 4–7), JAPAN; Sparrow (1936a: 427, pl. 14, figs. 2–4), GREAT BRITAIN; Petersen (1910: 554), Sparrow (*loc. cit.*), DENMARK; Karling (1941b: 108 [? adults]; 1948c: 508), rotifer eggs (?), Sparrow and Barr (1955: 554), UNITED STATES; Bérczi (1940: 79, pl. 2, fig. 1), HUNGARY.

The shape of the sporangium, as in other endobiotic chytrids, undergoes considerable modification when more than one fungus is present within the limited confines of the substratum. Here, the sporangia often tend to be smaller and to lose their regular ellipsoidal or spherical shape and become irregular and saclike.

Zoospores of an undescribed parasite of rotifer eggs "near *O. gregarium,*" are described by Scherffel (1925a: 66, pl. 5, fig. 222). They differ from those of the present species in containing several globules rather than one. Both Butler and Sparrow noted that the resting spores sometimes lie loosely in a surrounding membrane. Butler suggested that this had come about because the fungus gained entrance after segmentation of the animal embryo had occurred. Since some of the sporangia in his material were similarly placed, this seems plausible. It is also possible that the spores arise by contraction and subsequent walling of their protoplasm, as in some species of *Pythium.*

The protoplasm of the eggs attacked by Nowakowski's fungus was pinkish and the thallus of the chytrid was similarly colored. The zoospores, however, appeared to be colorless. From the remarks of Fischer (1892: 31), it is probable that he observed the fungus, but the host is not given.

OLPIDIUM GRANULATUM Karling

Lloydia, 9: 3, pl. 1, figs. 1-18. 1946

"Sporangia, hyaline, smooth, oval, ellipsoid, 7–26 × 12–44 μ, usually numerous, up to 16 in a cell, subspherical, 8–50 μ diam., with one, 3.5–5 μ wide by 6–10 μ long, exit tube which usually does not extend far beyond the surface of the host cell. Emerged zoospores forming a globular mass at the exit orifice before dispersing; spherical, 3.5–4.5 μ, with numerous minute granules and a 38–45 μ long flagellum. Resting spores hyaline, smooth, spherical or oval, 14–22 μ; germination unknown" (Karling, *loc. cit.*).

Parasitic in rotifer eggs, BRAZIL.

OLPIDIUM ROTIFERUM Karling
Lloydia, 9: 6, pl. 1, figs. 19-34. 1946

"Sporangia gregarious, up to 15 in a cell, hyaline, smooth, predominantly pyriform, 12–40 × 20–70 μ, oval, 10–20 × 15–35 μ, subspherical 15–30 μ, with one short broad, 4–6 × 5–12 μ exit tube. Zoospores swarming in sporangium before emerging; later forming a globular mass at exit orifice; oblong, 3–3.5 × 6.5–7 μ, with one or two small lateral, elongate refractive bodies; flagellum 12–14 μ long. Resting spores hyaline, smooth, oval, 12–14 × 15–17 μ, spherical, 10–15 μ; germination unknown" (Karling, *loc. cit.*).

Parasitic in eggs and adults of rotifers, most commonly in the adult bodies, BRAZIL.

OLPIDIUM VAMPYRELLAE Scherffel
Arch. Protistenk. 54: 168, pl. 9, figs. 2-5. 1926

Sporangium spherical or broadly ovoid, colorless, 10-12 μ in diameter or 12–13 by 14–15 μ, with a short papilla-like refractive discharge tube 3–4 μ long by 2 μ wide which bores through the host wall; contents of the sporangium during maturation bearing small contractile vacuoles and exhibiting a slight amoeboid movement; zoospores moving in the sporangium before escape, discharged with the watery content of the tube upon the dissolution of its tip, each spore resting a moment at the tip of the sporangium before swimming away, body somewhat ovoid, 3 by 2 μ, with dense shining contents nearly free of granules and without an oil drop, with a single posterior flagellum; resting spore not observed.

In zoocysts of *Vampyrella*, HUNGARY.

Although forming contractile vacuoles and lacking an oil globule in the zoospore the organism is believed by Scherffel to be a species of *Olpidium* rather than a monad.

OLPIDIUM PSEUDOSPOREARUM Scherffel
Arch. Protistenk., 54: 170, pl. 9, figs. 6-7. 1926

Sporangia ovoid or somewhat irregular, becoming rather tubular if several occur in a cell, usually 12 μ long by 9 μ in diameter, varying in size according to the number occupying a single zoocyst, wall thin, colorless, smooth; plasma whitish, gleaming, with numerous minute oil droplets; discharge tube short, papilla-like, penetrating the host wall; zoospores very numerous, small, spherical, with an eccentric minute (1 μ) oil droplet and a very long posterior flagellum, movement hopping, gliding; resting spore not observed.

In zoocysts of *Pseudosporopsis bacillariacearum* (?) and *Pseudospora parasitica* (?), HUNGARY.

Zopf (1888: 351) also mentions an *Olpidium* in the zoocyst of *Pseudospora*. This fungus, however, formed a long discharge tube, thus differing from the present species. *O. pseudosporearum* differs from *O. vampyrellae* in that the zoospore possesses a globule. Furthermore, the sporangium has a less prominent discharge tube. Scherffe[1] has not distinguished this species from *O. difflugiae*.

OLPIDIUM NEMATODEAE Skvortzow

Arch. Protistenk., 57: 204, fig. 1. 1927

Sporangia occurring singly or in linear series, spherical, 15–35 μ in diameter, with a smooth thin wall, discharge tube narrowly cylindrical, 100–180 μ long by 7 μ in diameter, extending beyond the host wall; zoospores uniflagellate; resting spore 25–32 μ in diameter, wall smooth, 5 μ thick, of two layers.

In nematodes, Skvortzow (*loc. cit.*), MANCHURIA; cysts of *Heterodera schactii*, Rozsypal (1934: 413, pl. 2, figs. 72–79), GERMANY.

RECENTLY DESCRIBED TAXON [1]

OLPIDIUM LONGICOLLUM Uebelmesser

Arch. f. Mikrobiol., 25: 309, fig. 1. 1956. (= *Olpidium sp.* Harder and Uebelmesser, 1955)

Sporangium oval to round, often irregularly flattened, 50–60 μ broad by 60–80 μ long, smooth-walled, with an 80–200 μ long discharge tube; contents at first finely granular, later differentiated into round zoospores, 10 μ in diameter, with 80 μ long flagellum; resting spore spheri-

---

[1] Not included in the key.

cal, 60–70 μ in diameter with a smooth wall and numerous oil globules in the coarse contents.

Saprophytic in dead pine pollen, in sea-beach soil (never submerged),
ITALY (VENICE), ELBA, YUGOSLAVIA, SPAIN.

IMPERFECTLY KNOWN SPECIES OF OLPIDIUM

In Marine Algae

? OLPIDIUM AGGREGATUM Dangeard

Le Botaniste, 2: 237, pl. 16, figs. 25-26. 1890-91

Sporangium ovoid or ellipsoidal, its long axis parallel with that
of the host cell, with a long discharge tube arising at right angles
from the mid-region, its tip just penetrating the host wall or extending
slightly beyond it, wall stout, smooth, colorless; zoospores spherical,
with a colorless refractive globule, escape and flagellation not observed;
resting spore not observed.

Occurring in linear aggregates in a marine species of *Cladophora*,
FRANCE.

To judge from the shape of the sporangia of this species, as well
as from the fact that they occurred in linear aggregates in the alga, it is
very probable that Dangeard was dealing with *Sirolpidium*. Since the
flagellation of the zoospores was not observed, this cannot now be
said with certainty.

Tokunaga (1933b: 79, pl. 5, fig. 8) has reported this species from
Japan, where it was found in a marine *Cladophora*. The sporangia,
which were described as narrowly ellipsoidal to cylindrical, sometimes
irregular, and 26.4–90 by 12–27.6 μ, were said to discharge narrowly
ellipsoidal uniflagellate zoospores. The zoosporangia figured closely
resemble in shape, location within the host, and vacuolization those
formed by *Sirolpidium bryopsidis*.

? OLPIDIUM ENTOSPHAERICUM (Cohn) Fischer

Rabenhorst. Kryptogamen-Fl., 1 (4): 27. 1892

Chytridium (?) entosphaericum Cohn, Hedwigia, 4: 170, 1865; Schultze,
Archiv. micro. Anat., 3: 43, pl. 2, figs. 5, 5a. 1867.

Sporangium spherical, colorless, 16 μ in diameter, single in cells of the host, filling or partly filling the host cell.

In *Bangia fuscopurpurea* and *Hormidium penicilliformis*, GERMANY.

? OLPIDIUM LAGUNCULA H. E. Petersen

Oversigt. Kgl. Danske Vidensk. Selskabs. Forhandl., 1905 (5): 466, fig. I, 1-2

Sporangium variable in shape, more or less spherical or irregularly bottle-shaped, 12–45 μ long by 13–33 μ in diameter, with a thin smooth wall, discharge tube 10–55 μ in length; other characters unknown.

In *Dumontia filiformis*, Petersen (*loc. cit.*), DENMARK; *D. incrassata*, Aleem (1953: 5, figs. 1–4), SWEDEN; coll. Lodge, Aleem (*loc. cit.*), ISLE OF MAN.

? OLPIDIUM LAUDERIAE Gran

Nyt Mag. Naturvid., 38 (2): 123, pl. 9, figs. 8-9. 1900

Sporangium broadly ovoid, slightly irregular and bent, discharge tube broad and short, penetrating the wall of the host, the border of the orifice somewhat recurved and flangelike.

On *Lauderia borealis*, NORWAY (fixed material).

Said to be a species of *Eurychasma* by Petersen (1905: 469), who calls it *E. lauderiae* (Gran) H. E. Petersen, but considered a species of *Ectrogella* by Scherffel (1925a: 3), who applies to it the binomial *Ectrogella lauderiae* (Gran) Scherffel. Until the zoospores are observed it is impossible to say which of the three available combinations should be used.

Aleem (1953: 21) reports on finding, in *Lauderia* cells, "chytridiaceous zoospores similiar to those of *Ectrogella*," a rather anomalous statement.

? OLPIDIUM MARINUM Dangeard

Le Botaniste, 12: xvi, pl. 2, figs. 23-24. 1911 (1912)

Ectrogella marina (Dangeard) J. and G. Feldmann, Suppl. 6, Travaux de la Station Biologique de Roscoff, p. 133. 1954.

Sporangium spherical, with a more or less elongate discharge tube which projects slightly through the wall of the host; zoospores rounded, possibly with only a single flagellum; resting spore not observed. Parasitic in *Chlorodendron subsalsum*, FRANCE.

A subsequent (1955) paper by J. and G. Feldmann presents morphological data supporting their combination. See page 811.

In Fresh-Water Algae

? OLPIDIUM ALGARUM Sorokin

Arch. Bot. Nord France, 2: 30, fig. 32. 1883 (separate) [1]

Olpidium algarum var. *longirostrum* Sorokin, *loc. cit.*

Sporangium narrowly ellipsoidal, wall thin, smooth, colorless, resting with its long axis parallel with that of the algal cell, forming at one end a long, moderately broad, somewhat curving discharge tube with a funnel-like apex, which extends slightly beyond the outer wall of the alga; all other characters unknown.

On *"Confervacées"* (*Tribonema* ?), ASIATIC RUSSIA.

There is no *Olpidium algarum* of which two varieties, *longirostrum* and *brevirostrum*, have been described, and the former has therefore been taken as the type.

From the illustration given, the alga appears to be a *Tribonema*-like form. The cross wall shown between the parts of the two cells figured has apparently been stimulated to protective-plug formation, probably by another fungus. The sporangia have been calculated from the figures to be about 6 μ high by 12 μ wide, the tube about 12 μ long.

The species is not considered distinct from *Olpidium entophytum* by Fischer (1892: 25) and Minden (1915: 243).

De Wildeman (1893b: 49, pl. 7, fig. 4), using the name *Olpidium algarum* Sorokin, describes a form in *Desmidium swartzii* from Belgium which resembles Sorokin's var. *brevirostrum* in the shape of its sporangium, but which possesses a somewhat longer discharge tube. He suggests that the length of the tube depends on the size of the host cell, and, while he would conserve the name *O. algarum*, his form would be intermediate between the two varieties.

---

[1] See also Sorokin, *Revue Mycologique*, 11: 84, pl. 80, fig. 96. 1889.

? OLPIDIUM ALGARUM var. BREVIROSTRUM Sorokin

Arch. Bot. Nord France, 2: 30, fig. 32 bis. 1883 (separate) [1]

Sporangium spherical or broadly ellipsoidal, variously oriented in the algal cell, wall thin, smooth, colorless, discharge tube arising from one of the ends, short, narrow, isodiametric, protruding slightly beyond the outer wall of the alga; zoospores with a swollen, somewhat reniform apex and a colorless basal globule, flagellum fairly long; resting spore not observed.

In *Sphaerozosma vertebratum*, EUROPEAN RUSSIA, ASIATIC RUSSIA. As suggested by Fischer (1892: 25) and Minden (1915: 243) the species is only doubtfully distinct from *Olpidium entophytum*.

The sporangia have been calculated to be 4 by 6–9 μ; the zoospores, 1 μ in diameter, and the discharge tube, about 2 μ long.

? OLPIDIUM IMMERSUM Sorokin

Arch. Bot. Nord France, 2: 31, fig. 34. 1883 (separate) [2]

Sporangium broadly and somewhat irregularly saclike, slightly constricted in the region of the isthmus of the semicells of the host, wall thin, smooth, colorless, discharge tube narrow, markedly swollen where it meets the inner wall of the host, projecting for a variable distance extramatrically; other characters not observed.

In various desmids, *Staurastrum*, Sorokin (*loc. cit.*), ASIATIC RUSSIA; *Cosmarium*, *Staurastrum*, de Wildeman (1893b: 51, pl. 7, figs. 12–15, 17), BELGIUM; *Cosmarium sp.*, de Wildeman (1895a: 65, pl. 2, figs. 1–6), SWITZERLAND; desmid, coll. Massart, de Wildeman (1896b: 45, pl. 3, figs. 27–28), NORWAY.

Scherffel (1926a: 213) believes this to be the same organism figured by Reinsch (1878: pl. 17, figs. 11–12). The fungus in *Cosmarium* from Denmark, called by Petersen (1910: 538, fig. XVId) *Myzocytium irregulare*, also resembles *Olpidium immersum*. It is unfortunate that, in spite of the relatively numerous collections of this fungus, no observations on the zoospores have been made. Only after this has been done can its true relationships be decided.

---

[1] *Ibid.*, 85, pl. 80, fig. 101. 1889.
[2] *Ibid.*, 136, pl. 79, figs. 91-92. 1889.

? OLPIDIUM (?) MESOCARPI de Wildeman

Ann. Soc. Belge Micro. (Mém.), 20: 45, pl. 1, figs. 13-16. 1896

Sporangium smooth, ellipsoidal, more or less elongate, about 10 μ in diameter by 20–28 μ long, single, sometimes two sporangia in one cell of the host and then occupying all the width of the filament, discharge tube lacking, the papilla which perforates the algal wall forming upon its deliquescence a circular opening in the wall for the escape of the zoospores; zoospores and resting spore unknown.

In *Mougeotia* (*"Mesocarpus"*) *sp.*, BELGIUM.

Differing from most species of the genus in sometimes filling the host cell and in not forming a discharge tube. In these respects it resembles a *Rozella*.

? OLPIDIUM MOUGEOTIA Skvortzow

Arch. Protistenk., 51: 430, fig. 2. 1925

Sporangium spherical, 11–14.8 μ in diameter, with a short straight isodiametric discharge tube 5.7–6 μ long, the tip of which does not project beyond the outer surface of the algal wall; other characters unknown.

On *Mougeotia scalaris*, MANCHURIA.

? OLPIDIUM PUSILLUM (Sorokin) de Wildeman

Bull. Soc. Roy. Bot. Belg. (Mém.), 35: 16. 1896

Chytridium pusillum Sorokin, Arch. Bot. Nord. France, 2: 24, fig. 23. 1883 (separate) [1]. Non *C. pusillum* Scherffel, Arch. Protistenk., 73: 143. 1931.

Sporangium spherical, 4.5 μ in diameter, with a very short sessile discharge tube, wall thin, smooth, colorless; other characters unknown.

In cells of *Oedogonium sp.*, EUROPEAN RUSSIA, ASIATIC RUSSIA.

? OLPIDIUM ROSTRATUM de Wildeman

La Notarisia, 10 (3): 35. 1895; Ann. Soc. Belge Micro. (Mém.), 20: 40, fig. 1. 1896

Sporangium narrowly ellipsoidal or somewhat tubular, 28–40 μ long

[1] *Ibid.*, 82, pl. 80, figs. 112-113. 1889.

by 6 μ in diameter, the long axis parallel with that of the alga, with rounded ends, one of which bears a slightly bent spinelike prolongation 4.5 μ long, wall thin, smooth, colorless, discharge tube narrow, slightly prolonged beyond the algal wall, arising from the middle or end of the sporangium; other characters unknown.

In *Closterium sp.*, coll. Massart, NORWAY.

Observed only in fixed material of the desmid. The peculiar spine-like process may in reality be the axis of a rhizoidal system the remainder of which has been dissolved by the fixing solution. The organism strongly resembles *Mitochytridium.*

? OLPIDIUM SOROKINEI de Wildeman

Bull. Soc. Roy. Bot. Belg. (Mém), 35: 16. 1896

Olpidiopsis sorokinei de Wildeman, Ann. Soc. Belge Micro. (Mém.), 14: 22, fig. 7. 1890.

Sporangium narrowly tubular or somewhat saccate, its long axis parallel with that of the algal cell, with a short sessile lateral discharge tube, wall thin, smooth; zoospores very small, movement rapid, flagellation not observed; resting spore not observed.

In *Tribonema bombycina*, BELGIUM.

Empty sporangia exactly like those figured by de Wildeman have been found in *Tribonema bombycina* in Michigan. They were accompanied by a resting stage essentially like that in *Olpidiopsis oedogoniarum* and it is possible that de Wildeman's fungus is really a species of that genus. He separated it from *Olpidiopsis fusiforme* var. *oedogoniarum* (*O. oedogoniarum*) chiefly on the basis of difference in host plants.

? OLPIDIUM SPIROGYRAE Skvortzow

Arch. Protistenk., 51: 429, text fig. 1. 1925

Sporangium ellipsoidal, with a smooth somewhat stout colorless wall, 33.3–34 μ long by 14.8–15 μ broad, bearing a more or less projecting discharge tube, 7.4-9.2 μ long by 3.7-5 μ broad, which is swollen beneath the host wall, forming a bulblike expansion 3.7 μ wide, and is constricted where it arises from the sporangium; other characters not observed.

In *Spirogyra inflata*, MANCHURIA.

? Olpidium tuba Sorokin

Arch. Bot. Nord France, 2: 33, fig. 39. 1883 (separate) [1]

Sporangium broadly ellipsoidal, its long axis parallel with that of the alga, wall thin, smooth, colorless, discharge tube arising from one end, swollen beneath and on the outer surface of the algal wall, constricted where passing through the wall and terminating in a short narrow isodiametric part; other characters not observed.

In *"Confervacées,"* European Russia, Asiatic Russia.

In Microscopic Animals

? Olpidium arcellae Sorokin

Arch. Bot. Nord France, 2: 34, fig. 40. 1883 (separate) [2]

Sporangium spherical or subspherical, wall thin, smooth, colorless, with a long, isodiametric, slightly curved or undulate discharge tube which emerges through the pseudopodial opening of the animal shell; other characters not observed.

Saprophytic (?) on the protozoan *Arcella*, European Russia.

? Olpidium (?) difflugiae Scherffel

Arch. Protistenk., 54: 168, pl. 9, fig. 1. 1926

Sporangium broadly pyriform, 23 μ long by 15 μ in diameter, with a thin colorless smooth wall, discharge tube consisting of a broadly conical papilla which does not emerge from the host cell; other features not observed.

In *Difflugia sp.* (Rhizopoda), Hungary.

Said to differ from *Olpidium arcellae* Sorokin and *O. gregarium* in the lack of a well-defined discharge tube. Just how much significance is to be attached to this difference is doubtful, since from the figure given the sporangium appears immature. It seems probable that the tip of the discharge tube eventually becomes extramatrical.

? Olpidium leptophrydis Scherffel

Arch. Protistenk., 54: 171, pl. 9, fig. 8. 1926

Sporangium spheroidal, wall thin, smooth, colorless, forming a

[1] *Ibid.*, 136, pl. 80, fig. 97. 1889.
[2] *Ibid.*, 137, pl. 80, figs. 102-105. 1889.

broad conical, slightly tapering, mostly extramatrical discharge tube equal to the sporangium in length; other characters unknown.

On zoocyst of *Leptophrys vorax*, HUNGARY.

? OLPIDIUM MACROSPORUM (Nowak.) Schroeter

Kryptogamenfl. Schlesien, 3 (1): 182. 1885

Chytridium macrosporum Nowakowski, in Cohn, Beitr. Biol. Pflanzen, 2: 79, pl. 4, figs. 3-4. 1876.

Sporangia occurring singly in the eggs of the host, nearly filling these and hence ovoid, 55 μ long by 30 μ in diameter; zoospores ellipsoidal, 10 μ long by 6 μ broad, with finely granular contents and lighter central region, but without a pronounced refractive droplet, number and position of flagella not observed, escaping through a broad tube which exceeds 150 μ in length and which pierces the wall of the egg, the lower part of the tube persisting after discharge.

In rotifer (?) eggs, GERMANY.

Differing from *Olpidium gregarium* in occurring singly in the egg, in having a long discharge tube, and in forming large zoospores which lack a refractive droplet. Nowakowski states that the spores are formed in the same manner as in the Saprolegniaceae. From this fact, as well as from the large size of the spores and their want of a refractive globule, it is possible that the fungus is in reality a saprolegnian rather than a chytrid.

? OLPIDIUM ZOOTOCUM (Braun) Sorokin

Arch. Bot. Nord France, 2: 33, fig. 38. 1883 (separate) [1]

Chytridium zootocum Braun, Monatsber. Berlin Akad., 1856: 591.

Sporangium elongate, tubular, curved, discharge tube arising laterally and extending funnel-like beyond the wall of the animal.

In *Anguillula*, coll. Claparede, GERMANY.

Schroeter (1885: 182) placed in this species a parasite of *Anguillula* with a tubular sporangium which remains attached by an attenuated end to the cyst (5 μ in diameter) of the infecting zoospore. He questions, justifiably, the identity of his fungus with Braun's. Sorokin's

[1] *Ibid.*, 136, pl. 79, fig. 90. 1889.

fungus, found in the claw of a dead crustacean in European and Asiatic Russia, has a spherical sporangium and a narrow discharge tube. The original description is too lacking in essential information to make it possible to refer any fungus to the species.

EXCLUDED SPECIES OF OLPIDIUM

* OLPIDIUM ELLIPTICUM (Dang.) Saccardo and Traverso
Sylloge fungorum, 20: 217. 1911

Minutularia elliptica Dangeard, Le Botaniste, 2: 241, pl. 16, figs. 29-31. 1890-91.

Saccardo and Traverso have placed Dangeard's organism in the chytrids, although Dangeard states that it ingests solid particles of food and is a monad.

* OLPIDIUM INDICUM Wallich
Turner, Bih. Kgl. Svensk. Vetensk.-Ak. Handl., 25, Afd. 5, No. 10: 164, pl. 21, fig. 8. 1892

On *Oedogonium sp.* Unquestionably a choanoflagellate.

* OLPIDIUM LACERANS de Bruyne
Arch. de Biol., 10: 104, pl. 5, figs. 28-31. 1890

Not a fungus. The zoospores contain chlorophyll residue. The figures refer to the monad *Aphelidium lacerans.*

* OLPIDIUM PLUMULAE (Cohn) Fischer
Rabenhorst. Kryptogamen-Fl., 1 (4): 27. 1892

Chytridium plumulae Cohn, Hedwigia, 4: 169. 1865; Schultze, Archiv. micro. Anat., 3: 59, pl. 1, figs. 21-23. 1867.
Phlyctidium plumulae (Cohn) Rabenhorst, Flora Europaea algarum, 3: 279. 1868.

Sporangium inducing a rudimentary branchlike outgrowth of the host wall, ovoid or subglobose, lying between the wall and the host contents, without rhizoids, 15 μ in diameter, reddish or dark red; zoospores very numerous, discharged through an irregular lateral opening.

In *Antithamnion plumulae*, Cohn (*loc. cit.*), GERMANY; *Calithamnion plumulae*, Magnus (1875: 77), DENMARK.

Fischer (*loc. cit.*) gives *Chytridium antithamnii* Cohn and *Cyphidium plumulae* Magnus as synonyms.

According to J. and G. Feldmann (1955: 232) this species is based on normal structures of the alga, that is, the secretory cells.

* OLPIDIUM RAMOSUM Serbinow

Leningradskoe obshchestvo estestvoispytateleĭ Trudy (Trav. Société des Naturalistes de Leningrade), 30: 255. 1899

Evidently based on a mixture of an olpidioid chytrid and a form with a type of sexual reproduction like that of *Olpidiopsis* or *Lagenidium enecans*.

In pollen of *Pinus sylvestris*, RUSSIA.

PRINGSHEIMIELLA COUCH

J. Elisha Mitchell Sci. Soc., 55: 409. 1939

"Obligate endophytic parasites on Saprolegniaceae. Thalli from zoospores multiplying in host hyphae. Zoosporangial sori formed in the ends of host hyphae and resembling in superficial appearance and development the host zoosporangia. Sporangia globose or polygonal from pressure, each sporangium with an emergence papilla. Zoospores posteriorly uniflagellate, very minute. Resting bodies unicellular, spherical, brownish when mature, one to several formed within a larger polygonal or irregularly shaped cell. Zoosporangial and resting spore membranes bluish purple with chlor-iodide of zinc" (Couch, *loc. cit.*).

In hyphae of aquatic Phycomycetes.

Erected to accommodate a true chytrid, first seen by Pringsheim (1860), which has a superficial resemblance in the zoosporangial stage to *Woronina polycystis*.

PRINGSHEIMIELLA DIOICA Couch

J. Elisha Mitchell Sci. Soc., 55: 410, pl. 49. 1939

"Infection by zoospores which leave cyst on host wall. Thalli from zoospores multiplying in host hyphae and carried by plasma currents of host to the distal parts of hyphae. Sporangia formed in cylindrical compartments, the latter resembling in shape, size, and position the sporangia of the host. Compartments separated from healthy host hypha by cross wall. Each sporangium in a sorus developing from a separate thallus and forming an emergence papilla upon maturity. Sporangia spherical to oval or polygonal from pressure, 16–21 μ thick, with a cellulose membrane. Zoospores very minute, 1.8–3 × 3 μ, spherical or slightly elongated, with one minute glistening globule, and a single posterior flagellum, moving directly away after a brief pause at the sporangial mouth. Resting bodies (zygotes) formed only where two sexually opposite or sexually compatible strains are brought together, spherical, 15–17 μ thick, golden brown with an eccentric globule and a minutely rough or reticulate membrane, formed within a larger cell which is polygonal from pressure. Containing cell 25–30 μ thick; sometimes larger and containing as many as six zygotes. Germinating by uniflagellate zoospores after six weeks' rest" (Couch, *loc. cit.*).

Parasitic in *Achlya dioica*, Pringsheim (1860: 211, pl. 23, figs. 1–5), GERMANY; *Achlya sp.*, *A. flagellata*, coll. J. N. and A. B. Couch, Ward, Shanor, UNITED STATES.

The species is dioecious, resting spores being formed only in cultures containing compatible or sexually opposite strains.

PLEOTRACHELUS ZOPF

Nova Acta Acad. Leop.-Carol., 47: 173. 1884

(Fig. 12 E, p. 124)

Thallus endobiotic, holocarpic, without a specialized vegetative system, unwalled at first, with pseudopodia, forming the rudiment of the zoosporangium at maturity, causing hypertrophy of the host; zoosporangium inoperculate, lying free in the host cell, with many (rarely from one to two) discharge tubes; zoospores posteriorly uniflagellate, formed in the sporangium; resting spore not (?) observed.

In Phycomycetes, algae, and rhizoids of mosses.

Petersen (1905) included in this genus a number of *Pleotrachelus-*

like forms found by him in marine algae in Denmark. Some of these have upon later investigation (Sparrow, 1934c, 1936b) been found to possess biflagellate zoospores and have been referred either to *Petersenia* or to *Olpidiopsis*. Further work may establish the fact that the remainder of these marine fungi should be segregated from *Pleotrachelus*. A spherical thick-walled resting spore which produces zoospores upon germination has been figured by Morini (1913) in *Pleotrachelus zopfianus*, but further observations are needed to confirm the occurrence of such resting structures in the genus.

Future critical examination of all olpidioid fungi will no doubt result in the suppression of Zopf's genus, but it does not seem desirable to do this here. The peculiar lateral attachment of the flagellum of the zoospore in *P. wildemani* is also known in *Olpidiomorpha* (see p. 122). Its significance is not as yet clear. Recent work seems to indicate that in some chytrids flagellar attachment may often be subapical.

KEY TO THE SPECIES OF PLEOTRACHELUS

Sporangia predominantly spherical
   In *Pilobolus*
      Typical sporangia bearing numerous discharge tubes
                                   P. FULGENS, p. 159
      Typical sporangia bearing from one to two discharge tubes
                                   P. ZOPFIANUS, p. 160
   In rhizoids of mosses . . . . P. WILDEMANI, p. 160
Sporangia broadly oblong-cylindrical; in green algae
                                   P. PETERSENII, p. 161

PLEOTRACHELUS FULGENS Zopf

Nova Acta Acad. Leop.-Carol., 47: 173, pl. 16, figs. 25-36. 1884; Beitr. Physiol. Morph. niederer Organismen, 2: 7, pl. 1, figs. 11-14, pl. 2, figs. 1-5, 7-8. 1892

(Fig. 12 E, p. 124)

Sporangia from one to eighty in the host, causing a marked spherical, pyriform, or broadly fusiform swelling of the infected parts, exactly spherical, 6.5–250 µ in diameter, with a colorless or light-yellow or red to reddish-brown fairly stout cellulose wall and from one to thirty straight or somewhat crooked tapering radiating discharge tubes, all of which usually penetrate the host wall; zoospores 2.2–3 μ in diameter (up to 3.6 μ long when elongated), ovoid, the broader end anterior, with a small colorless refractive globule and several coarse granules, flagellum attached to the narrower end, escaping through the discharge tubes upon the dissolution of their apices and forming temporary groups, capable of amoeboid movement; resting spore not observed.

Parasitic in mycelium, gemmae, and suspensors of *Pilobolus crystallinus* var. *areolata*, *P. kleinii*, GERMANY.

In Zopf's second account of the species (1892: 7) the vegetative stage was described. His observations indicated that the fatty material of the host which was colored with carotene was absorbed by the amoeboid thallus. The contents of the maturing sporangium also appear from the figures to be orange red, but are evidently colorless at maturity, since the zoospores possess no pigmentation.

The chytrid was parasitized by a monad, *Endobiella destruens* Zopf.

Considerable variation in the size of the sporangia and the number of discharge tubes was noted. The largest sporangia usually occurred singly, formed about a thousand zoospores and had up to thirty discharge tubes; smaller ones contained fewer spores and discharge tubes, the smallest bearing only one or two tubes.

PLEOTRACHELUS ZOPFIANUS Morini

Mem. R. Accad. Sci. Istituto Bologna, Ser. VI, 10: 301, figs. 1-4. 1913

Sporangium spherical or subspherical, pale yellowish orange, 41–47 μ in diameter, with from one to two cylindrical discharge tubes; zoospores ovoid-pyriform, uniflagellate, 3–4 μ long; resting spore spherical, thick-walled, upon germination cracking open and liberating zoospores.

In the bicellular trophocysts of *Pilobolus pirottianus*, ITALY.

Doubtfully distinct from *Pleotrachelus fulgens*.

PLEOTRACHELUS WILDEMANI H. E. Petersen

Annales Mycologici, 8: 553, fig. XXVc. 1910. Emend. Ingold, Trans. Brit. Bryol. Soc., 2: 53, fig. 1. 1952

Sporangia one to four in the swollen host cells, spherical, 30–80 μ in diameter, with one or two discharge tubes 20–40 μ in length which just pierce the host wall but do not extend beyond it; zoospores initiating movement within the sporangium, escaping singly to the outside, ellipsoidal, 5 μ long by 3 μ broad with a lateral refractive globule and a single, laterally attached and posteriorly directed flagellum; resting spore not observed.

Parasitic in and causing hypertrophy of moss rhizoids, Petersen (*loc. cit.*), DENMARK; *Funaria hygrometrica*, coll. W. Tutin, Ingold (*loc. cit.*), GREAT BRITAIN.

The description is compiled from the papers of Petersen and Ingold.

Although the sporangia exhibited by Ingold's material possessed only one discharge tube, he is probably correct in assigning his fungus to Petersen's incompletely known species.

PLEOTRACHELUS PETERSENII Lund

Bot. Tidsskrift, 41: 241, fig. 1. 1930

Sporangium broadly oblong-cylindrical, straight or curved, 24–89 μ long by 9–28 μ in diameter, wall thin, smooth, colorless, with from one to six very narrow discharge tubes 5–11 μ (up to 25 μ) long; zoospores uniflagellate; resting spore not observed. (Modified from Lund.)

In *Oedogonium sp.*, DENMARK (S.).

A fungus with more tubular sporangia bearing inflated contorted branches has been tentatively identified with this species by Sparrow (1936a: 428, pl. 14, fig. 5). No zoospores were seen, and hence no positive identification could be made.

IMPERFECTLY KNOWN SPECIES OF PLEOTRACHELUS

? PLEOTRACHELUS INHABILIS H. E. Petersen

Oversigt. Kgl. Danske Vidensk. Selskabs. Forhandl., 1905 (5): 456, fig. IV, 1-6

A collective species containing *Pleotrachelus*-like forms found in *Polysiphonia violacea* and *Polysiphonia elongata*.

Two main types of sporangia occur: (1) those in tetrasporangia and tetraspores of *Polysiphonia violacea* and (2) those in parietal cells of the cystocarp of *P. elongata*.

1. Sporangia formed in tetraspores of *Polysiphonia violacea* and assuming their shape: Sporangia with smooth colorless walls which stain violet with chloriodide of zinc, with one or more (usually two or three) somewhat prolonged discharge tubes, 30–45 by 39–60 μ, of variable shape (if occurring in the tetrasporangium before formation of the tetraspores, somewhat regularly spherical and filling it or, in instances of multiple infection, spherical and grouped; if formed during division of the tetrasporangium into tetraspores, filling the two-celled or each of the four-celled [tetrasporic] structures); zoospores after formation moving within the sporangium and escaping individually, body ellipsoidal, 2–3 μ in diameter, flagellation unknown; other characters unknown.

2. Sporangia parasitic in parietal cells of the cystocarp of *Polysiphonia elongata*: Sporangia of irregular rounded form, with a smooth wall, oily refringent contents, and from one to three discharge tubes; large specimens 40 by 41 μ, discharge tube 22 μ; medium-sized ones 10 by 29 μ.

In *Polysiphonia*, DENMARK.

The lobations on sporangia formed in the dyads of the tetrasporangia (Petersen, *op. cit.*, fig. IV, 1) indicate a relationship of these forms to *Petersenia*, where, if the zoospores are found to be biflagellate, they should be placed.

Other imperfectly known types in marine algae are described by Petersen (*op. cit.*, p. 464).

? PLEOTRACHELUS MINUTUS H. E. Petersen

Oversigt. Kgl. Danske Vidensk. Selskabs. Forhandl., 1905 (5): 451, fig. II, 1-4

Sporangium of variable shape, spherical or elongate-cylindrical, with a smooth thin wall, largest 16–24 by 12–16 μ, with from one to three discharge tubes 4 μ long; host cell little hypertrophied.

In hairs of *Chorda filum*, Petersen (*loc. cit.*), DENMARK; *Chorda filum*, Aleem (1953: 7, figs. 7–8), SWEDEN; *Litosiphon pusillus*, J. Feldmann (1954: 132), FRANCE.

? P<small>LEOTRACHELUS OLPIDIUM</small> H. E. Petersen

Oversigt. Kgl. Danske Vidensk. Selskabs. Forhandl., 1905 (5): 455, fig. III, 7-9

Sporangia one or more in a host cell, not filling the lumen nor causing hypertrophy, regularly more or less spherical, with a smooth colorless wall which does not react to chloriodide of zinc, 9–30 μ in diameter, with from one to three discharge tubes 9–24 μ long; zoospores not seen; resting spore borne singly and loosely in a structure not differing in shape or size from the zoosporangium, with a smooth thickened wall.

In *Ectocarpus confervoides*, coll. Börgesen, Petersen (*loc. cit.*), F<small>ARÖE</small> I<small>SLANDS</small>; *Ectocarpus sp.*, *E. confervoides*, *Furcellaria* (coll. K. Rosenvinge), *Akinetospora*, Petersen (*loc. cit.*), *Polysiphonia sp.*, *Pylaiella littoralis*, Sparrow (1934c: 19, pl. 4, figs. L, N), D<small>ENMARK</small>; *Ectocarpus penicilliatus*, Aleem (1953: 6, figs. 5–6), S<small>WEDEN</small>; *Spermatochnus paradoxus*, J. Feldmann (1954: 132), F<small>RANCE</small>.

? P<small>LEOTRACHELUS PARADOXUS</small> H. E. Petersen

Oversigt. Kgl. Danske Vidensk. Selskabs. Forhandl., 1905 (5): 459, fig. IV, 7-8

Sporangium of variable shape, frequently irregular, sometimes more or less spherical, sometimes oblong, one or several in each host sporangium, when occurring singly filling the host structure, wall colorless, thin, smooth, turning violet with chloriodide of zinc, with one or several discharge tubes passing through the discharge pores of the host sporangium, causing thickening of the host wall; zoospores not observed.

In sporangia of *Rhizophydium discinctum*, coll. F. Börgesen, N<small>ORWAY</small>.

? P<small>LEOTRACHELUS RADICIS</small> de Wildeman

Ann. Soc. Belge Micro. (Mém.), 17: 23, pl. 3, figs. 20-25. 1893; *ibid.*, 19: 70, pl. 2, figs. 23-35. 1895

Sporangium spherical or ovoid, wall colorless or slightly yellow, with a large number of conical or tubular, sometimes irregular, discharge tubes; zoospores and resting spore not observed.

Three forms are distinguished:

1. Forma *major*, tubes numerous, wall colored, 65–85 μ in diameter. In roots of *Thlaspi arvense*, BELGIUM.

2. Forma *intermedia*, tubes rather numerous, wall very slightly colored and little thickened, 35–52 μ in diameter. In tissues of aquatic plants, SWITZERLAND.

3. Forma *minor*, tubes less numerous, rather slender, wall very slightly colored and little thickened, 17–26 μ in diameter. In tissues of aquatic plants ("vegetable debris"), SWITZERLAND.

Because of the shape and ornamentation of the sporangium and the central "spherule" with a more refractive portion in the contents, these structures strongly resemble the oöspores of an *artotrogus* type of *Pythium*.

? PLEOTRACHELUS (?) ROTATORIORUM Scherffel

Abstracts of Communications, V Inter. Bot. Congress, Cambridge, 1930: 222; Arch. Protistenk., 73: 139, pl. 9, fig. 1. 1931

Sporangium spherical to broad-oval, colorless, smooth- and thin-walled, 44–55 μ long by 51 μ wide, with three discharge tubes nearly as long (4.4 μ) as wide (6.6 μ) and not extending beyond the host wall; zoospores not observed.

In egg of *Anuraea cochlearis* (?), HUNGARY.

PLASMOPHAGUS DE WILDEMAN
Ann. Soc. Belge Micro. (Mém.), 19: 223. 1895
(Fig. 12 K, p. 124)

Thallus endobiotic, causing hypertrophy (swelling and elongation) of the host cell, plasmodial at first, later walled, holocarpic, without rhizoids; sporangium inoperculate, nearly filling the host cell, its wall distinct; zoospores posteriorly uniflagellate, with a single globule, discharged individually through a pore formed at the tip of a single short sessile (not projecting) papilla; resting spore not observed.

Whether or not the genus is distinct from *Olpidium* is a matter for further investigation. That the thallus nearly completely fills the host cell, that it lacks a definite discharge tube, and that it causes hypertrophy of the infected cell are all characteristics exhibited by one or another undoubted species of *Olpidium*. In these respects *Plasmophagus* also resembles species of *Rozella*. However, it differs from *Rozella* in that the walls of host and parasite are distinct, not fused.

PLASMOPHAGUS OEDOGONIORUM DE WILDEMAN

Ann. Soc. Belge Micro. (Mém.), 19: 223, pl. 8, figs. 1-9, pl. 9, figs. 1-9. 1895

Sporangium saclike and somewhat irregular, almost completely filling the swollen and elongated algal cell, 20–23 μ long by 8–11 μ broad (in *Tribonema*), wall thin, smooth, colorless, discharge papilla lateral, small, just penetrating the host wall; zoospores ovoid or obovoid, 3 μ long by 2 μ wide, with a colorless eccentric globule and a flagellum; resting spore not observed.

Parasitic in filaments of *Oedogonium sp.*, de Wildeman (*loc. cit.*), FRANCE; *Tribonema bombycina*, Sparrow (1933c: 513, fig. I, 1), UNITED STATES.

No measurements are given by de Wildeman and those contained in the description above refer to the organism in *Tribonema*. It is probable that the parasite of *Oedogonium* attained larger dimensions, but this is only conjecture.

ROZELLA CORNU

Ann. Sci. Nat. Bot., V, 15: 148. 1872

Figs. 12 F-I, p. 124; Fig. 14, p. 179)

Rozia Cornu, Bull. Soc. Bot. France, 19: 71. 1872. Non *Rozea* Bescherelle, Mém. Soc. Nationale Sci. Nat. Cherbourg, 16: 241. 1871-72.

Pleolpidium Fischer, Rabenhorst. Kryptogamen-Fl., 1 (4): 43. 1892.

Thallus endobiotic, holocarpic, at first naked and indistinguishable from the host contents, later walled, at maturity forming either the rudiment of the sporangium, the wall of which is fused with that of the hypertrophied host (except when intercalary), or the resting spore; sporangium inoperculate, thin-walled, smooth, with one or more discharge papillae; zoospores formed in the sporangium, posteriorly uniflagellate, often with a single globule; resting spore endobiotic, thick-walled, smooth or spiny, apparently asexually formed, lying loosely in the swollen, sometimes walled-off, portions of the host, upon germination functioning as a sporangium.

The taxonomic status of *Pleolpidium* and *Rozella* has been discussed in detail (Sparrow, 1938b; Karling, 1942b).

The observations of Foust (1937) on *Rozella allomycis* indicate that in some (but not all) specimens a single thallus may not only completely fill an infected part, but may also sometimes segment and, as in *R. septigena*, form several sporangia. If this segmentation is clearly shown not to be due to multiple infection then the diagnosis above should be modified to include this sorus formation, or a new genus should be erected for *R. septigena* Cornu, *R. allomycis*, and *R. achlyae*. Germination of the spiny resting spores has been secured by Foust and reinfection by means of the zoospores has been observed. The latter spores formed the typical sporangial stage, proving unquestionably that the two phases are related. Resting-spore germination by means of zoospores was observed by Karling (1942a), in *R. cladochytrii*. Butler (1907) concluded from observations on a number of species of *Rozella* that in some instances at least the plasma from several spores may unite in the host to form a true plasmodium, from which a single sporangium may arise. He does not, however, exclude the possibility that one thallus has gained the ascendency and developed at the expense of the rest.

The species are all parasitic in the hyphae and reproductive organs of other aquatic Phycomycetes. Although customary to consider that each species is restricted to a single host genus (or even species), in most instances the truth of this supposition awaits confirmation. Observations on a *Rozella* parasitic in *Dictyuchus anomalus* by Johnson (1955a) point to an even wider host range than suspected. Johnson was able to transfer his fungus not only to *D. monosporus* but to several species of *Achlya* as well. From this he concluded his fungus was *Rozella achlyae* and he suggests that past failures to induce artificial infection with species of *Rozella* (in other than the original host) may have been due to an inherent difference with respect to susceptibility and resistance. Even certain strains of *D. anomalus* appeared resistant to his material of *R. achlyae*. Furthermore, he believes that biological races of the parasite may exist which differ in their pathogenicity.

Environment and age of the host, no doubt, will also have some influence on whether or not infection takes place.

KEY TO THE SPECIES OF ROZELLA [1]

Thallus monosporangiate, that is, giving rise to one sporangium or
resting spore
Parasitic in fresh-water Phycomycetes
Parasitic in filamentous Phycomycetes and *Blastocladia*
Parasitic in the hyphae of *Monoblepharis*
R. MONOBLEPHARIDIS-POLYMORPHAE, p. 168
Parasitic in the sporangia of *Araiospora*
R. RHIPIDII-SPINOSI, p. 168
Parasitic in the sporangia and immature resting spores of
Blastocladia .... R. BLASTOCLADIAE, p. 169
Parasitic in the sporangia of *Apodachlya*
R. APODYAE-BRACHYNEMATIS, p. 169
Parasitic in *Pythium*
Resting spore smooth
Resting spore pale yellow .... R. CUCULUS, p. 170
Resting spore hyaline .... R. LAEVIS, p. 171
Resting spore spiny .... R. IRREGULARIS, p. 171
Parasitic in members of the Chytridiales or Lagenidiales
Parasitic in chytrids
Parasitic in monocentric chytrids
Parasitic in operculate chytrids
Parasitic in species of *Chytridium* .... R. CANTERAE, p. 172
Parasitic in species of *Chytriomyces*
R. CHYTRIOMYCETIS, p. 172
Parasitic in species of *Endochytrium*
R. ENDOCHYTRII, p. 173
Parasitic in inoperculate chytrids
Parasitic in species of *Polyphagus* .... R. POLYPHAGI, p. 173
Parasitic in species of *Rhizophlyctis*
R. RHIZOPHLYCTII, p. 174
Parasitic in species of *Rhizophydium*
R. RHIZOPHYDII, p. 174
Parasitic in species of the polycentric chytrids *Nowa-
kowskiella*, *Cladochytrium*, and *Septochytrium*
R. CLADOCHYTRII, p. 174
Parasitic in cells of *Lagenidium* (? and in *Myzocytium*)
R. PSEUDOMORPHA, p. 175

[1] Note that this key is not wholly dichotomous.

Parasitic in marine fungi; in sporangia of *Chytridium polysiphoniae*
R. MARINA, p. 176
Thallus polysporangiate, that is, giving rise to sporangia which form
linear conjoined segments ("sori") within the host hyphae;
resting spores solitary or numerous within the segments or hyper-
trophied parts of the host
Parasitic in members of the Saprolegniaceae
Parasitic in several species of *Achlya* and *Saprolegnia*
R. SEPTIGENA, p. 176
Parasitic in *Achlya flagellata* and *Dictyuchus*..... R. ACHLYAE, p. 177
Parasitic in *Allomyces* .... R. ALLOMYCIS, p. 178

ROZELLA MONOBLEPHARIDIS-POLYMORPHAE Cornu

Ann. Sci. Nat. Bot., V, 15: 150, pl. 4, figs. 13-18. 1872

Pleolpidium monoblepharidis (Cornu) Fischer, Rabenhorst. Kryptogamen-
Fl., 1 (4): 44. 1892.

Sporangium formed in intercalary swollen parts of the hyphae,
ovoid, the lateral walls fused with those of the host, with a single
small lateral discharge pore; zoospores not observed; resting spore
spherical, brown, the thickened wall densely covered with tenuous
spines, in intercalary or lateral swellings of the host hyphae, germination not observed.

Parasitic in *Monoblepharis polymorpha*, Cornu (*loc. cit.*), FRANCE;
Laibach (1927), Minden (1915: 254), GERMANY; *Monoblepharis macrandra*, Sparrow and Barr (1955: 554), UNITED STATES.

ROZELLA RHIPIDII-SPINOSI Cornu

Ann. Sci. Nat. Bot., V, 15: 153, pl. 5, figs. 1-9. 1872

Pleolpidium rhipidii (Cornu) Fischer, Rabenhorst. Kryptogamen-Fl., 1 (4):
44. 1892.

Pleolpidium araiosporae (Cornu) Minden, Kryptogamenfl. Mark Brandenburg, 5: 252. 1911 (1915).

Sporangium completely filling the abnormally swollen and obpyriform usually smooth sporangium of the host, with a prominent apical
papilla; zoospores variable in shape, reniform, spherical or ellipsoidal,
with a long posterior flagellum, discharged through a broad pore,
resting a few seconds at the orifice before swimming away; resting

spore spherical, yellowish brown or reddish, with dense contents, wall slightly thickened, covered with tenuous spines, germination not observed, predominantly formed in the spiny sporangia of the host.

Parasitic in smooth and spiny sporangia of *Araiospora spinosa,* Cornu (*loc. cit.*), FRANCE; Minden (1915: 252), GERMANY; R. K. Benjamin (comm.), UNITED STATES.

Cornu noted that the sporangial stage of the parasite was predominantly formed in the smooth sporangia of the host, the resting spores, in the spiny sporangia. The fungus developed extensively in his cultures and prevented the making of a complete study of the "*Rhipidium*" (*Araiospora*).

ROZELLA BLASTOCLADIAE (Minden) Sparrow

Mycologia, 30: 377. 1938

Pleolpidium blastocladiae Minden, Kryptogamenfl. Mark Brandenburg, 5: 253. 1911 (1915); Falck, Mykolog. Untersuch. Berichte, 2 (2): pl. 4, fig. 33. 1916.

Sporangium assuming the shape of the hypertrophied host sporangium, which becomes somewhat broader and more ovoid than normal, with an apical pore, collapsing after discharge of the zoospores; zoospores not observed; resting spore exactly spherical, brown, thick-walled, the exospore densely covered with tenuous spines, germination not observed.

Parasitic in sporangia and immature resting spores (?) of *Blastocladia pringsheimii,* Minden (*loc. cit.*), Laibach (1927: 624), GERMANY; Thaxter (1896a: 50), R. K. Benjamin (comm.), UNITED STATES; H. E. Petersen (1909: 424, fig. 26 c–d; 1910: 555, fig. 26 c–d), DENMARK; *B. pringsheimii, B. gracilis,* Waterhouse (1942: 317), GREAT BRITAIN.

ROZELLA APODYAE-BRACHYNEMATIS Cornu

Ann. Sci. Nat. Bot., V, 15: 161, pl. 5, figs. 10-14. 1872

Pleolpidium apodyae (Cornu) Fischer, Rabenhorst. Kryptogamen-Fl., 1 (4): 45. 1892.

Sporangium filling the sporangium of the host and assuming its shape, with a small apical papilla; zoospores somewhat elongate, with a posterior flagellum, escaping through a small pore resulting from the dissolution of the papilla; resting spore formed in the sporangium of the host, spherical, somewhat thick-walled, brownish(?), covered with very short tenuous spines.

Parasitic for the most part in the terminal segments (sporangia) of *Apodachlya brachynema*, FRANCE.

Plants of *Araiospora* occurring in the same tufts as the *Apodachlya* were not infected by the zoospores of *Rozella apodyae-brachynematis*. The spines on the resting spore are noticeably shorter than those of *R. rhipidii-spinosi*.

ROZELLA CUCULUS (Butler) Sparrow

Mycologia, 30: 377. 1938

Pleolpidium cuculus Butler, Mem. Dept. Agr. India, Bot. Ser., 1: 125, pl. 7, figs. 22-25. 1907.

Sporangium spherical, subspherical, or pyriform, formed in the sporangium of the host or in pronounced intercalary swellings of the hyphae, 19.2–24 µ in diameter, with a single papilla; zoospores obclavate, clavate, or ovoid, the flagellum emerging from the broader end; resting spore spherical, single, free in the sporangium or intercalary swelling of the host, 12–18 µ in diameter, with a smooth pale-yellow somewhat thickened wall, germination not observed.

Parasitic in sporangia of *Pythium intermedium*, Butler (*loc. cit.*), IRELAND, FRANCE; hyphae of *Pythium monospermum*, Tokunaga (1933b: 82, pl. 5, fig. 12), JAPAN.

Pleolpidium tuberculorum Vuillemin (1909) should perhaps be included under this species, since it differs from Butler's fungus only in having slightly larger and fewer zoospores and somewhat larger resting spores (17.5–23 by 15.4–20 µ). It was found in France parasitic in the sporangia of *Pythium*.

Chytridium simulans Dangeard (1896–97: 21, fig. 1) occurring in terminal or lateral swellings on *Pythium*, may be referable to *Rozella cuculus*. Resting spores, however, were not observed. The species is listed as a synonym of *R. cuculus* by Karling (1942b: 198).

ROZELLA LAEVIS Karling

Mycologia, 34: 201. 1942

"Sporangia solitary, partly or completely filling hypertrophied portions of the host hyphae, variable in size and shape, spherical, 20–52 μ, clavate, 10–20 μ × 30–112 μ, broadly and elongately pyriform with 1 to 3 exit papillae, 3–4 μ in diam. by 2–3 μ in height. Zoöspores hyaline, with a globular spot which is not markedly refractive, obclavate to pyriform, 1.5–1.8 μ × 2.9–3.3 μ; occasionally bi- and multiflagellate, flagellum 10–12 μ long. Resting spores spherical, 11–18 μ, oval, elongate or obpyriform with a large central vacuole and coarsely granular cytoplasm; wall smooth and hyaline, 1.5–2 μ thick; germination unknown" (Karling, *loc. cit.*).

Parasitic in *Pythium gracile*, causing marked hypertrophy, Karling (*loc. cit.*), UNITED STATES; *Pythium sp.*, Karling (1944f: 638, figs. 1–19), BRAZIL.

For further information on this species, see Karling's account and figures (1944f). As its author indicates, *Rozella laevis* differs from *Rozella cuculus* primarily in having hyaline rather than brown to pale-yellow resting spores. Just how significant this feature is awaits further study. It will be maintained as a distinct species here.

ROZELLA IRREGULARIS (Butler) Sparrow

Mycologia, 30: 377. 1938

Pleolpidium irregulare Butler, Mem. Dept. Agr. India, Bot. Ser., 1: 123, pl. 8, figs. 1-12. 1907.

"Sporangia formed in the hyphae of the host, irregular in shape, terminal and intercalary, averaging 23 μ in diameter, with a single papilla; zoospores obclavate, with a single cilium borne posteriorly; durable spores single, free in the cavity of the host-filament which is enlarged to contain them, numerous, 11–15 μ in diameter, spherical, of a pale yellow colour, with a moderately thick wall, provided with short regular spines; germination not observed" (Butler, *loc. cit.*).

Parasitic in *Pythium* (?) *vexans*, Butler (*loc. cit.*), GREAT BRITAIN; *Pythium sp.*, Gaertner (1954b: 21), EGYPT, NORTHWEST AFRICA, EQUATORIAL EAST AFRICA, SOUTH AFRICA; Gaertner (*op. cit.*, p. 40), SWEDEN.

The record of this fungus in *Pythium monospermum* attributed by Karling (1942b: 198) to Tokunaga (1933b) is apparently an error. Whether or not the parasite of *Pythium* with spherical zoospores 7–9 μ in diameter, which emerge from one to several pores, reported from China by Shen and Siang (1948: 181), should be placed here seems doubtful.

ROZELLA CANTERAE, sp. nov.[1]

Sporangium assuming the shape of the unhypertrophied host sporangium and completely filling it; zoospores ovoid, with a small refractive anterior globule and posterior flagellum, escaping after the operculum of the host is dehisced; resting spore somewhat ovoid, with a thick wall, the outer wall of which bears hexagonal ridges and spines.

Parasitic in sporangia of *Chytridium oedogonii* (Canter), GREAT BRITAIN.

The species is based on the observations of Canter (1950d: 357, fig. 3, g–n, pl. 29, figs. 4–5) of an unnamed *Rozella*.

ROZELLA CHYTRIOMYCETIS Karling

Mycologia, 38: 107, figs. 9-19. 1946

"Sporangia solitary, hyaline, filling host cell and conforming with the latter in size and shape, usually spherical, 10–40 μ, with one to three exit papillae; wall of sporangium usually indistinguishable from that of host cell. Zoospores hyaline, oblong or slightly clavate, 3 × 1.5 μ, with a minute, .5–.7 μ, refractive globule; swirling in sporangium before emerging; darting about rapidly in swimming, rarely becoming amoeboid. Resting spores partly or almost completely filling host cell, oval or spherical, 7–20 μ, with large central vacuole, and coarsely granular cytoplasm; wall dark brown, rarely smooth, usually spiny or echinulate; germination unknown" (Karling, *loc. cit.*).

Parasitic in *Chytriomyces hyalinus*, UNITED STATES.

---

[1] *Rozella canterae*, sp. nov. — Sporangium ad formam sporangii hospitis normalis exacte conformans. Zoosporis ovoideis, globulo anteriori parvo et flagello posteriori praeditis, delapsu hospitis operculi liberatis. Sporis perdurantibus subovoideis, crasse circumvallatis, extus hexagonaliter costatis, spinosis. Parasitica in sporangiis *Chytridii oedogonii*, GREAT BRITAIN.

ROZELLA ENDOCHYTRII Karling

Torreya, 41: 106. 1941

"Sporangia solitary in a host cell, spherical, 15–200 μ, oval, elongate, pyriform and irregular, depending on the size and shape of the host cell; wall of sporangium usually indistinguishable from that of the host, hyaline and smooth with one to several exit papillae, 2–6 μ high. Zoöspores obclavate, 3.4–4 μ × 1.5 μ, aguttulate but with optically denser apical and basal regions which give them a characteristic appearance; swirling in the sporangium before dehiscence; emerging in a stream and becoming actively motile in a few seconds. Resting spores unknown" (Karling, 1942b: 200).

Parasitic but not causing apparent hypertrophy in sporangia of *Endochytrium operculatum*, Karling (*loc. cit.*), UNITED STATES; Karling, (1944f: 644), BRAZIL.

The species has been described in developmental detail by Karling (1942a: 31, figs. 25–47).

ROZELLA POLYPHAGI Sparrow

Mycologia, 30: 377. 1938

(Fig. 12 F-G, p. 124)

Pleolpidium polyphagi Sparrow, Trans. Brit. Mycol. Soc., 18:215. 1933.

Sporangium colorless, spherical, completely filling the often markedly swollen prosporangium of the host, 20–48 μ in diameter, possessing at maturity from two to six prominent papillae 4–8 μ in diameter, through which the innumerable minute posteriorly uniflagellate narrowly ovoid zoospores 2–3 μ long by 1.5–2 μ in diameter, with a single globule, are discharged; resting spore not observed.

Parasitic in prosporangia of *Polyphagus laevis*, GREAT BRITAIN.

The species was described and figured in Sparrow (1936a: 426, pl. 14, figs. 19–20).

Scherffel (1925b: 6, pl. 1, fig. 10) observed in the prosporangia of *Polyphagus parasiticus* a brownish rough-walled resting structure. Though the structure may be the resting spore of *Rozella polyphagi*, the presence on it of a delicate rhizoid makes this improbable.

ROZELLA RHIZOPHLYCTII Karling

Amer. J. Bot., 29: 32, figs. 36-47. 1942

"Sporangia solitary, filling host cell and conforming with the latter's size and shape, spherical, 20–110 μ, oval, and irregular with 1 to 4 exit papillae which usually project out of the short necks of the host; wall of sporangium usually indistinguishable from that of the host cell. Zoospores hyaline, broadly pyriform, 2.5–3 μ × 1.5–2 μ, tapering slightly at the anterior end, with a minute globule near the posterior end; posteriorly uniflagellate, rarely bi- and multiflagellate; flagellum 16–18 μ long; swirling in the sporangium before emerging; darting about rapidly in swimming, occasionally becoming amoeboid. Resting spores slightly yellow, oval and spherical, 14–18 μ in diam., with a large central vacuole and coarsely granular cytoplasm; wall spiny, 1.8 μ thick, spines 1.5–2 μ long; apparently transformed directly into a zoosporangium in germination and forming zoospores" (Karling, *loc. cit.*).

Parasitic in *Rhizophlyctis petersenii*, Karling (*loc. cit.*), causing no apparent hypertrophy or septation of the host cells, UNITED STATES; *Rhizophlyctis rosea*, Karling (1944f: 644), BRAZIL.

ROZELLA RHIZOPHYDII Karling

Mycologia, 36: 645, figs. 20-28. 1944

"Sporangia solitary, filling host cell and conforming with the latter's size and shape, spherical, 15–30 μ, oval, 10–12 × 13–20 μ or pyriform, 12–15 × 16–25 μ with 1–3 low exit papillae; wall of sporangium indistinguishable from that of host. Zoöspores hyaline, oval or slightly pyriform, 2–2.5 × 3–4 μ; with a small globule near the posterior end; flagellum 12–14 μ long. Resting spores unknown" (Karling, *loc. cit.*). Parasitic in *Rhizophydium globosum*, BRAZIL.

ROZELLA CLADOCHYTRII Karling

Torreya, 41: 105. 1941

"Sporangia solitary in a host cell, spherical, 10–40 μ, ovoid, ellipsoid, 10–15 μ × 15–35 μ, pyriform, and obclavate, hyaline and smooth with one to three exit papillae; wall of sporangium usually indistinguishable from that of host cell. Zoöspores obclavate, 3.3–5 μ × 1.8–2 μ, aguttulate; rarely bi- and multiflagellate as the result of unequal cleavage; flagellum 14 μ long; emerging fully formed in a stream from the exit papillae and becoming actively motile in a few seconds. Resting spores faintly yellow, oval, spherical, 8–22 μ, with a large central vacuole and coarsely granular cytoplasm; wall 1–1.8 μ thick, smooth or spiny, spines 1.5–3 μ long; transformed directly into a zoösporangium in germination and forming zoöspores" (Karling, 1942b: 200).

Parasitic in *Nowakowskiella profusum, N. elegans, N. ramosum, Cladochytrium replicatum, C. crassum,* and *C. hyalinum,* Karling (*loc. cit.*; 1948c: 508), *Septochytrium macrosporum,* Karling (1942c: 621), UNITED STATES; *Cladochytrium replicatum,* Karling (1944f: 643), BRAZIL.

An extensive account of the structure and reproduction of this species has been given by Karling (1942a: 25, figs. 1–24). Originally discovered in *Nowakowskiella profusum,* it was induced to infect most of the other fungi noted above. It was found to cause slight to marked hypertrophy.

ROZELLA PSEUDOMORPHA (Scherffel) Sparrow

Aquatic Phycomycetes, p. 124. 1943

Olpidium (?) *pseudomorphum* Scherffel, Arch. Protistenk., 54: 510, pl. 28, figs. 1-5. 1926.

Sporangium filling the vegetative cell of the host, and hence assuming its shape and size, forming a fairly stout tapering discharge tube; zoospores narrowly ellipsoidal, ovoid, or plump and rodlike, somewhat arched, with from three to five refractive granules, flagellum fairly long, trailing, attached at the concave side of the body, zoospores emerging individually from the discharge tube and remaining for a time near the orifice undergoing amoeboid change of shape, movement hopping; resting spore unknown.

Parasitic in vegetative cells of *Lagenidium rabenhorstii,* HUNGARY.

A fungus also considered to be this species was found by Scherffel (*loc. cit.*) in vegetative cells of *Myzocytium proliferum.* It differed from the *Lagenidium* parasite only in the fact that the zoospores had a single basal refractive droplet and exhibited a swimming, not a hopping, type of movement.

Because of the fact that the fungus sporangium completely fills the host cell it is referred to *Rozella*, even though the formation of a pronounced discharge tube appears rare among members of the genus.

ROZELLA MARINA Sparrow

Mycologia, 30: 377. 1938

Pleolpidium marinum Sparrow, Biol. Bull., 70: 256, figs. 32-33. 1936.

Sporangium spherical, completely filling the enlarged host sporangium, 30–45 μ in diameter, at maturity forming from one to three pores, through which the zoospores are discharged; zoospores ellipsoidal, 3 μ long by 2 μ in diameter, posteriorly uniflagellate, without globules; resting spore not observed.

Parasitic in the sporangia of *Chytridium polysiphoniae*, UNITED STATES.

ROZELLA SEPTIGENA Cornu

Ann. Sci. Nat. Bot., V, 15: 163, pl. 6. 1872. Non Fischer, Jahrb. wiss. Bot., 13: 321, pl. 14, fig. 19, pl. 15, figs. 20-28. 1882

(Fig. 12 H-I, p. 124)

Sporangia possibly formed by successive fractionation of one thallus, in transversely or obliquely walled-off segments of the sometimes slightly swollen host hyphae which they completely fill, with from one to several discharge papillae; zoospores minute, numerous, arched, posteriorly uniflagellate, without globules; resting spore spherical, with a slightly thickened wall covered with short tenuous spines, brownish, with dense contents, formed in spherically swollen short lateral branches of the hyphae, which are continuous with the main axis or separated from it by a cross wall, germination not observed.

Parasitic in *Achlya racemosa*, *A. polyandra*, *Saprolegnia spiralis*, Cornu (*loc. cit.*), FRANCE; *Saprolegnia dioica*, Pringsheim (1860: 205, pl. 22, figs. 1–6), GERMANY; *Saprolegnia sp.*, Cejp (1934: 228, fig. 4), CZECHOSLOVAKIA.

The fungus of Sorokin (1883: 25, fig. 25) in *Achlya racemosa* in

European and Asiatic Russia was said to form small uniflagellate zoospores and larger biflagellate ones. Cornu observed a similar phenomenon, but attributed the occurrence of the large spores to poor environmental conditions. Sparrow (1932b: 273; 1936a: 425) has recorded this species from the United States and England, but no zoospores were observed and the identifications are therefore subject to doubt.

Cornu's name was applied, in error, by Fischer (1882: 365) to a similar-appearing parasite in *Saprolegnia* which forms biflagellate zoospores. The findings of Foust (1937) and Shanor (1942c) indicate that Cornu's observations on the uniflagellation of the zoospores of his parasite are correct. If fractionation of the thallus in this species and the following ones is definitely proved to occur after infection by a single zoospore, they should be removed from *Rozella* and placed in a new genus.

Pringsheim, who, incidentally, figures zoospores killed with iodine as uniflagellate, considered the fungus to be the antheridia of the *Saprolegnia*.

ROZELLA ACHLYAE Shanor

J. Elisha Mitchell Sci. Soc., 58: 100, pl. 17. 1942

"An endophytic parasite of *Achlya flagellata* causing very slight or no hypertrophy. Young plasmodium hardly distinguishable in the host protoplasm, hyaline and very nearly optically homogeneous. Sporangia formed in linear sori, cylindrical to somewhat barrel shaped, length and width depending largely upon that of host hyphae; exit papillae short, about 1.5 μ in length, rupturing following gelatinization of the tips. Zoospores swimming in a jerky and darting manner, ovoid, 2–3 × 3–4 μ with a single refractive globule, single flagellum posteriorly attached, usually 12–15 μ in length. Resting bodies produced in segments formed in host hyphae that resemble sporangial sori, each segment containing from one to many resting bodies. Resting bodies spherical to oval, 12.6–23.7 μ in diameter (not including spines), mostly 15.8–17.3 μ, usually covered with fine tenuous spines which commonly measure about 1.6–2.3 μ in length, wall of mature resting bodies thick, reddish-brown to amber brown in color. Resting spore germination follows a dormant period and is accomplished by the formation of posteriorly uniflagellate zoospores which escape through an exit papilla" (Shanor, *loc. cit.*).

Parasitic in *Achlya flagellata*, coll. Olive, Shanor (*loc. cit.*); Karling (1942b: 204; 1948c: 508); *Dictyuchus anomalus*, by inoculation in *Achlya flagellata*, *A. proliferoides*, *D. monosporus*, Johnson (1955a: 119, figs. 1–7), UNITED STATES; *Achlya flagellata*, Karling (1944f: 646), BRAZIL.

Shanor was unable to infect other species of *Achlya* or species of *Saprolegnia*, *Isoachlya*, *Protoachlya*, *Thraustotheca*, *Brevilegnia*, *Dictyuchus*, or *Aphanomyces* with *Rozella achlyae*. It should be noted, however, that none of the hosts in which the preceding species, *R. septigena*, has been reported weie used in his inoculation experiments. If these were proved capable of infection by *R. achlyae*, its validity could well be questioned.

ROZELLA ALLOMYCIS Foust

J. Elisha Mitchell Sci. Soc., 53: 198, pls. 22-23. 1937

(Fig. 14, p. 179)

Sporangia filling the more distal parts of the host hyphae, developing linearly, from one to five in basipetal succession, generally barrel-shaped, 20–40 μ long by 12–20 μ in diameter (usually 24.6 by 15.9 μ), occasionally divided by one or more partitions into several smaller sporangia, usually with one discharge papilla 1.3 μ long; zoospores ovoid, the broader end anterior, 3–4 μ wide, having a single globule, with a posterior flagellum 16 μ long; resting spores formed behind the sporangia in from one to thirty-five swollen spherical, subspherical, barrel-shaped, nearly cylindrical, or irregular segments 20–70 μ long by 20–40 μ in diameter, each segment containing from one to sixteen yellow to reddish-brown resting spores, the latter spherical, 12–20 μ in diameter (average 15.9 μ) including the spines, with a thick (1.5 μ) wall covered by slender long (1.3 μ) spines, contents with a central hyaline globose mass surrounded by granular protoplasm, upon germination functioning as a sporangium, the uniflagellate zoospores eventually forming new sporangia. (Modified from Foust.)

Parasitic in *Allomyces arbuscula*, Foust (*loc. cit.*), *A. javanicus*, Sparrow (1943: 123, fig. 7), Karling (1948c: 508), UNITED STATES; *A. arbuscula*, F. T. Wolf (1941a: 170), BRAZIL, ARGENTINA; *Allomyces sp.*, coll. C.

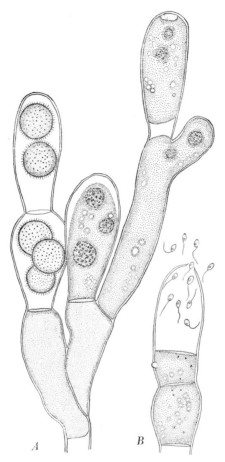

FIG. 14. *Rozella allomycis* Foust parasitic in *Allomyces*

A. Tip of parasitized plant, showing (left) mature resting spores in zoosporangia of host and (right) immature thalli in zoosporangia and hyphae of host. *B.* Discharging sporangium of parasite; at least two sporangia have been formed in a single sporangium of *Allomyces.*
(Drawn by V. M. Cutter, Jr.)

D. LaRue, NICARAGUA (Sparrow, 1943: 123); Shen and Siang (1948: 180, fig. 1), CHINA; *A. arbuscula*, Sparrow (1952a: 35), CUBA; *Allomyces sp.*, Gaertner (1954b: 40), SWEDEN.

Germination of the resting spores, which, either wet or dry, retain their vitality for several months, was secured after a rest period of only a week when new water and fresh young *Allomyces* plants were added to the culture.

Miss Foust was unable to find evidences of a separate wall produced by the parasite. She noted that some sporangial rudiments laid down one or more partitions within the primary segment which were horizontal, vertical, or at angles to the original septa. If these septations should be clearly shown to be the result of only a single infection they would be of great interest, as has been indicated elsewhere (see p. 177).

The "*Rozella allomycetes*" mentioned by Nabel (1939: 527), but not described, probably belongs here.

EXCLUDED SPECIES OF ROZELLA

*ROZELLA ALLOMYCETES Nabel, nom. nud.

Archiv f. Mikrobiol., 10 (4): 527. 1939

A name unaccompanied by a description. Probably referable to *Rozella allomycis* Foust.

*ROZELLA BARRETTII Karling

Mycologia, 34: 202. 1942

"Sporangia terminal and intercalary, of the same size as and indistinguishable from the host sporangia until zoöspores are formed; opening by one or more exit papillae which project through the host wall. Zoöspores numerous and minute. Resting spores unknown.

"Parasitic in *Phytophthora cactorum* in California, U.S.A., causing local spherical swellings in the host hyphae as well as completely filling the sporangia" (Karling, *loc. cit.*).

Based on an incompletely known form described by Barrett (1934: 1138). Since the flagellation of the zoospores is not known, the fungus cannot be placed generically.

*Rozella maximum

A species name used by Karling (1942a: 24) in error, presumably for *Rozella marina* Sparrow.

IMPERFECTLY KNOWN GENERA OF THE OLPIDIACEAE

? BLASTULIDIUM Pérez

C. R. Soc. Biol., 55: 715, figs. A-E. 1903

? Blastulidium paedophthorum Pérez

Loc. cit.

Thallus endobiotic, with a thin wall, ellipsoidal, 25 μ long by 20 μ in diameter, or consisting of a few cells with short rudimentary branches; sporangium inoperculate, formed from the whole thallus or its segments; zoospores ovoid, with one long axillary flagellum, formed in the sporangium, where motion is initiated, and escaping from it through a short neck; resting spore (?) citriform, with a thickened wall, germination not observed.

Parasitic in eggs and embryos of various Crustacea, *Daphnia obtusa*, *Simocephalus vetulus*, *Chydorus sphaericus*, *Lynceus*, larvae of *Corethra* (gnat), Pérez (*loc. cit.*), Chatton (1908: 34), FRANCE.

Pérez considered the organism a haplosporidian (Protozoa), but Chatton, after noting the flagellation of the spore, referred it to the chytrids, particularly to *Olpidium* and *Synchytrium*.

The genus is a puzzling one, and, since no clear picture of it is given by either Pérez or Chatton and the term "axillary" does not indicate to what pole of the spore the flagellum is attached, it will remain so until new observations of a purely morphological nature are made. It may be related to *Septolpidium*.

Blastulidium was considered distinct from *Olpidium* by Chatton because of the formation of a large central vacuole and the fact that the thallus was occasionally septate and yeastlike.

Pérez described external ellipsoidal bodies adherent to the Crustacea as possibly representing the resting stage, but Chatton believed these to be single or conjugated zoospores which had fixed themselves on the animal, infected it, and developed. The resting stage observed by

Chatton consisted of a thick-walled citriform structure, which he conjectured was probably formed after the parasite quit the dead host, moved amoeboidly away, and encysted.

? CHYTRIDHAEMA Moniez

C. R. Acad. Sci. Paris, 104: 183. 1887

? CHYTRIDHAEMA CLADOCERARUM Moniez

Loc. cit.

Sporangium inoperculate, a flattened sac without cross walls or a discharge tube, formed within the body cavity of the host; zoospores top-shaped, 3 μ long, with dense contents, bearing a refractive protuberance on the broad base, the opposite extremity prolonged into a flagellum, many formed in a sporangium.

Parasitic in Crustacea, *Sinocephalus retulus*, *Acroperus leucocephalus*, FRANCE.

Little of taxonomic significance can be obtained from the description. The sporangia are said to fill the body cavity of the animal, whereas the zoospores were found in abundance in the blood. It is not definitely stated whether the flagellum is anterior or posterior. Moniez thought the organism resembled olpidiaceous and lagenidiaceous fungi. He considered that the protuberance on the zoospore was a sort of antheridium and that the sporangia were formed by the whole mycelium of a chytrid.

ACHLYOGETONACEAE

Thallus endobiotic, holocarpic, becoming transversely septate at maturity and forming from two to several linearly arranged inoperculate sporangia; zoospores posteriorly uniflagellate; resting stage not known with certainty.

Occurring primarily in fresh-water algae.

The family differs from the Olpidiaceae in forming in linear series from the thallus two or more sporangia. Resting structures have not as yet been adequately demonstrated, although they have been reported as occurring in *Achlyogeton* (Martin, 1927) and *Bicricium*.

KEY TO THE GENERA OF THE ACHLYOGETONACEAE

Thallus forming typically a linear series of more than two sporangia
  Zoospores encysting at the orifice of the discharge tube
                                            Achlyogeton, p. 183
  Zoospores clustering at, but eventually swimming directly away
    from, the orifice of the discharge tube without encysting
                                    Septolpidium, p. 187
Thallus forming two sporangia, which are separated by a more or less
  well-defined isthmus .... Bicricium, p. 188

ACHLYOGETON Schenk

Bot. Zeitung, 17: 398. 1859

(Fig. 15 A-B, p. 186)

Thallus endobiotic, holocarpic, unbranched, without rhizoids, walled, at first tubular, later segmented and forming a chainlike series
of cells each of which develops a discharge tube and becomes an inoperculate sporangium; zoospores posteriorly uniflagellate, with a refractive globule, escaping as separate bodies and forming a motionless group at orifice of discharge tube, encysting, emerging from the
cellulose cysts after a period of rest and swimming away, the empty
cysts persistent for a time; resting spore not (?) observed.

Parasites of green algae and eelworms.

The similarity in body plan of *Achlyogeton* to *Myzocytium* has resulted in the former's usually being placed in the Lagenidiales rather
than in the Chytridiales. This, as Butler (1928: 820) pointed out, has
been a cause of difficulty to those attempting to discover the true
affinities of these fungi. The flagellation of the spore marks the genus
as unquestionably a member of the Chytridiales.

Karling (1942e: 94) doubted Schenk's observation that the zoospores
of *Achlyogeton* are posteriorly uniflagellate. This is a critical point,
for if they are proved to be biflagellate, the genus must once more
be returned to a biflagellate family, possibly the Lagenidiaceae, and
the family name replaced. In connection with work on a phycomycetous
parasite of insects considered to be *Myiophagus ucrainica* (Wize) Sparrow[1], Karling (1948a: 252) again questions the validity of *Achlyo-*

---

[1] The *Myiophagus* studied by Karling was in the sporangial stage only. Hence, its
identification with *M. ucrainica*, known only from the resting-spore stage, is open
to question. As Karling himself noted, his material might well be referred to a blastocladiaceous fungus.

geton and also the use of the name in denoting a family. He suggests Septolpidiaceae in its place. Since he had no new evidence on *Achlyogeton*, he concluded, however, that Achlyogetonaceae should be retained.

ACHLYOGETON ENTOPHYTUM Schenk

Bot. Zeitung, 17: 398, pl. 13, fig. A, 1-8. 1859

(Fig. 15 A-B, p. 186)

Sporangia from two to fifteen, strongly constricted at the stout cross walls, individuals ellipsoidal or subellipsoidal, 15–55 μ by 9.6–20.4 μ, wall smooth, slightly thickened, discharge tube arising at right angles to the long axis of the sporangium, fairly broad, generally expanded where it makes contact with the inner wall of the alga and prolonged outside for a varying distance (up to 60 μ); zoospores ovoid or broadly pyriform, with a colorless refractive basal globule, a vacuole, and a flagellum about three times as long as the body, emerging as elongate bodies upon the rupturing of the slightly expanded tip of the discharge tube and forming at the orifice a group of spherical cysts 4 μ in diameter, issuing from these after a period of rest and swimming away; resting spore possibly not as yet observed.

In *Cladophora sp.*, Schenk (*loc. cit.*), GERMANY; "*Confervacées*," Sorokin (1883: 38, fig. 48), ASIATIC RUSSIA; *Cladophora sp.*, Martin (1927: 188, fig. 1), UNITED STATES; *Cladophora sp.*, Tokunaga (1934a: 227, fig. 1), JAPAN.

Sorokin (1876: 63, pl. 3, figs. 2–5) reported the species as occurring in *Anguillula* in European Russia. A further morphological study of this form is necessary before it can be considered identical with the alga inhabitant. It is certain from Sorokin's account that the typical encystment of the spores occurred after discharge. From his Plate 3, figure 5, it is also evident that the sporangia which had thin cross walls were not simultaneously formed from the tubular thallus, but progressively, as in *Septolpidium*.

Both Martin and Tokunaga noted resting bodies associated with sporangia. As Tokunaga suggested, the round thick-walled resting cells observed by him, each of which was accompanied by a companion cell, were probably formed by a species of *Olpidiopsis* parasitizing the sporangia of the *Achlyogeton*. The resting cells found by Martin were possibly of similar origin, although in this instance either the companion cell had disintegrated or the spore was formed asexually.

IMPERFECTLY KNOWN SPECIES OF ACHLYOGETON

? ACHLYOGETON (?) ROSTRATUM Sorokin

Ann. Sci. Nat. Bot., VI, 4: 64, pl. 3, figs. 40-45. 1876 [1]

Sporangia ten or more, slightly constricted at the thin cross walls, individuals ellipsoidal or somewhat irregular, 7–9 μ long by 5–6 μ wide, wall smooth, slightly thickened, discharge tube arising from the mid-region of the sporangium, long, often somewhat tortuous, expanded where it makes contact with the inner wall of the substratum and penetrating the latter with a short narrow tube; zoospores and resting spore not observed.

In *Anguillula*, Sorokin (*loc. cit.*), EUROPEAN RUSSIA; filaments of "*Conferves*," Sorokin (1883: 38, fig. 49), EUROPEAN RUSSIA, ASIATIC RUSSIA.

Sorokin was uncertain of the generic disposition of his fungus. Fischer (1892) and Minden (1915) have supposed it to be a *Myzocytium*, probably because of the presence of a swelling on the basal part of the discharge tube. The figure given in Sorokin's (1883) paper shows the thallus to be nearly devoid of constrictions.

? ACHLYOGETON SALINUM Dangeard

Le Botaniste, 24: 240, pl. 24, figs. 1-3. 1932

Sporangia in chains of six or more, ellipsoidal, with a single discharge tube.

In *Cladophora sp.* (marine), FRANCE.

From the figures given, the fungus is very probably *Sirolpidium bryopsidis*, which is occasionally found in *Cladophora*. Dangeard thought it might prove to be a species of *Myzocytium*, but this is unlikely since the thallus is successively divided into sporangia and the zoospores are completely formed within the sporangium.

[1] See also Sorokin, *Revue Mycologique*, 11: 138, pl. 81, fig. 119. 1889.

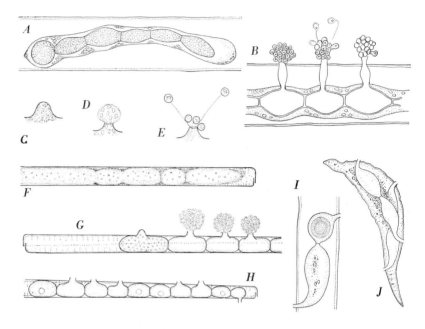

FIG. 15. Achlyogetonaceae

A–B. Achlyogeton entophytum Schenk in filaments of *Cladophora*: *A*, thallus, showing segmentation into a linear series of zoosporangia; *B*, discharged zoosporangia with clusters of encysted zoospores at orifices of discharge tubes; in left-hand cluster zoospores are all encysted, in middle one they are emerging from cysts, and in right-hand group all but one have emerged, leaving the empty cysts behind. *C–H. Septolpidium lineare* Sparrow in diatoms: *C*, discharge papilla just before moment of discharge; *D*, first zoospores emerging en masse; *E*, zoospores swimming directly away from sporangium; this behavior is not usual, but is occasionally observed; *F*, immature thallus in diatom, showing progressive segmentation of tubular body into sporangia; *G*, group of sporangia produced from single thallus; sporangium on left has formed a papilla; remainder have discharged their zoospores, which form motionless clusters at orifices of discharge tubes; *H*, chain of empty sporangia. *I–J. Bicricium* in algae and eelworms: *I*, *Bicricium transversum* Sorokin, two-linked thallus in *Cladophora*; a resting structure is present in one segment; *J*, *Bicricium lethale* Sorokin, two pairs of empty sporangia in body of eelworm.

(*A–B*, Schenk, 1859a; *C–H*, Sparrow, 1936a; *I–J*, Sorokin, 1883)

? Achlyogeton solatium Cornu
Bull. Soc. Bot. France, 17: 297. 1870

Thallus filamentous, branched, growing through several host cells; sporangia of irregular size, each with a long exit tube; zoospores three to twelve, encysting at the orifice of the tube, emerging from the cysts.

Parasitic in *Oedogonium obsidionale*, France.

SEPTOLPIDIUM Sparrow

Trans. Brit. Mycol. Soc., 18: 215. 1933; J. Linn. Soc. London (Bot.), 50: 428. 1936

(Fig. 15 C-H, p. 186)

Thallus endobiotic, cylindrical, unbranched, holocarpic, without specialized vegetative system, at maturity successively divided by transverse walls into a series of conjoined segments, each of which becomes an inoperculate sporangium with a single evacuation tube through which the posteriorly uniflagellate zoospores are discharged; resting spore not observed.

A monotypic genus known thus far only in diatoms.

Septolpidium closely resembles *Achlyogeton* except that the zoospores lack an encysted stage (Fig. 15 C–E, G).

Septolpidium lineare Sparrow [1]

Trans. Brit. Mycol. Soc., 18: 215. 1933; J. Linn. Soc. London (Bot.), 50: 428, fig. 1. 1936

Thallus narrowly cylindrical, smooth-walled, with slightly tapering ends, 75–130 μ long by 5–12 μ in diameter; divided at maturity into a linear series of truncated conjoined sporangia; sporangia 8-37 μ long by 5–12 μ in diameter, each forming a single broad abruptly tapering evacuation tube 3–5 μ in diameter which protrudes from the host cell and through which the numerous zoospores are discharged; zoospores spherical, 3–4 μ in diameter, with from one to four spherical or irregularly shaped refractive granules, often forming upon emergence a spherical motionless temporary cluster at the mouth of the

[1] See also Paterson (*Mycologia*, 50: 93. 1958).

discharge tube, ultimately swimming away, sometimes assuming motility directly after emergence.

Parasitic in *Synedra sp.*, GREAT BRITAIN.

BICRICIUM SOROKIN
Arch. Bot. Nord France, 2: 37. 1883 (separate) [1]
(Fig. 15 I-J, p. 186)

Thallus endobiotic, holocarpic, at maturity divided into two segments separated from each other by a narrow septate isthmus; sporangia inoperculate, one sporangium formed from each of the segments, each bearing a single discharge tube; zoospores posteriorly uniflagellate; resting spore thick-walled, formed in a segment of the thallus.

In fresh-water green algae and eelworms.

The genus has been rejected by Fischer (1892), Minden (1915), Karling (1942e), and others, being considered by them to be based on two-celled forms of *Myzocytium*. Scherffel (1926a: 213), however, points out that, in contrast to *Myzocytium*, uniflagellate zoospores are formed in *Bicricium*. He further implies that in the formation of the resting spore no sexuality is involved, since one of the two thalli opens to the outside and probably is a sporangium. If the fungus were a species of *Myzocytium* this thallus would ordinarily function as an antheridium. The argument is weakened here, however, by the fact (not mentioned by Scherffel) that the "oögonium" also possesses an open tube (Sorokin, *op. cit.*, fig. 46).

The proper disposition of the genus is still a matter of doubt. Enough is known about it, however, to place it in the Achlyogetonaceae near *Achlyogeton* and *Septolpidium*.

BICRICIUM LETHALE Sorokin
Arch. Bot. Nord France, 2: 37, fig. 45. 1883 (separate) [2]
(Fig. 15 J, p. 186)

Sporangia irregularly narrowly ellipsoidal, strongly constricted at the thin cross wall which separates them, each of the free ends pro-

---

[1] See also Sorokin, *Revue Mycologique*, 11: 138. pl. 81, fig. 119. 1889.
[2] *Ibid.*, pl. 83, figs. 72-74. 1889.

vided with a single fairly long gradually tapering tube, the tip of which penetrates the wall of the substratum; zoospores narrowly ovoid, with a strongly acuminate apex and a small basal colorless globule, uniflagellate, emerging through the open end of the discharge tube; resting spore not observed.

In dead eelworms, EUROPEAN RUSSIA, ASIATIC RUSSIA.

IMPERFECTLY KNOWN SPECIES OF BICRICIUM

? BICRICIUM NASO Sorokin

Arch. Bot. Nord France, 2: 37, fig. 47. 1883 (separate) [1]

Sporangia narrowly ovoid, one in each semicell of the alga, the narrower end terminating in a distinct swelling which gives rise to a long discharge tube penetrating the wall of the substratum and elongating for a considerable distance outside, the isthmus joining the two sporangia consisting of a long narrow tube; all other characters unknown.

In *Arthrodesmus sp.*, ASIATIC RUSSIA.

Sorokin suggests that the parasites of desmids figured by Reinsch (1878: pl. 17, figs. 6, 11–12) might better be placed in *Bicricium*, rather than in *Myzocytium*, where Cornu (1877b: 228) said they belonged. A comparison of Reinsch's figures with those of *Myzocytium* by Zopf (1884: pl. 14), leaves little doubt as to the correctness of Cornu's contention. It is probable that the present species of *Bicricium*, with its discharge tube bearing a bulbous endobiotic base, also belongs in *Myzocytium*, since it has a very different aspect from the other species.

? BICRICIUM TRANSVERSUM Sorokin

Arch. Bot. Nord France, 2: 37, fig. 46. 1883 (separate) [2]

(Fig. 15 I, p. 186)

Sporangium narrowly ellipsoidal, with a narrow discharge tube; zoospores not observed; adjacent cell subspherical, bearing a spherical thick-walled resting spore, method of formation and germination unknown.

In filaments of *Cladophora sp.*, ASIATIC RUSSIA.

[1] *Ibid.*, pl. 81, fig. 117. 1889.
[2] *Ibid.*, pl. 78, fig. 76. 1889.

SYNCHYTRIACEAE

Thallus endobiotic, holocarpic, without a specialized vegetative system, at maturity converted either into a sorus of inoperculate sporangia, a prosorus, or a resting spore; sporangia formed within or outside, always at first surrounded by a common soral membrane; zoospores posteriorly uniflagellate, with a single globule; sexual reproduction, where known, by conjugation of isogamous planogametes, the zygote forming the thick-walled endobiotic resting spore, which upon germination functions either as a sporangium or a prosorus.

Synchytrium, the largest genus of the family, is composed of species all of which are obligate parasites of flowering plants (see Tobler, 1913; Minden, 1915)[1]. Many of them, as *S. endobioticum*, the cause of the black-wart disease of Irish potatoes, attack hosts of economic importance. This genus is included in the key but is not treated here. Species of the genera *Endodesmidium* and *Micromyces* (including those formerly in *Micromycopsis*) are parasitic on green algae and have thus far been observed primarily on members of the Conjugatae.

Well-authenticated occurrences of sexuality have been observed only in *Synchytrium* (Curtis, 1921; Kusano, 1930a), although Couch (1931: 231) presents evidence that the resting spore of *Micromyces* may possibly be formed from a zygote.

KEY TO THE GENERA OF THE SYNCHYTRIACEAE

[Parasitic on flowering plants; thallus large, never amoeboid, forming a simple sorus surrounded by a common soral membrane, prosorus, or resting spore; prosorus never forming a discharge tube; zoospores freed outside the host cell .... SYNCHYTRIUM [2]]

Parasitic on algae; thallus small, always forming a prosorus or a resting spore; sori simple or compound[3], sessile or at the tip of a discharge tube; zoospores freed inside or outside the host cell

Sorus sessile on prosorus, wall not divided into segments; sporangia small, spherical, amoeboid, occasionally uniflagellate

ENDODESMIDIUM, p. 191

[1] Recently Karling (1953 *et seq.*) has initiated a comprehensive series of researches on *Synchytrium*.

[2] Not treated; see Tobler (1913), Minden (1915), and Karling (1953 and many subsequent papers).

[3] See p. 193.

Sorus sessile on the prosorus or formed at the tip of a discharge tube, wall always divided into a varying number of segments, not surrounded by a common soral membrane at maturity, simple or compound .... MICROMYCES, p. 192

ENDODESMIDIUM CANTER

Trans. Brit. Mycol. Soc., 32: 72. 1949

(Fig. 16 F-G, p. 196)

"Thallus endobiotic, holocarpic, at first naked, later transformed into a smooth-walled prosorus; sorus endobiotic, thin walled, smooth, the content dividing into numerous bodies which emerge through papillae in the external medium or into the cavity of the host; sporangia spherical producing minute zoospores; zoospores posteriorly uniflagellate with a conspicuous oil globule" (Canter, *loc. cit.*).

Parasites of desmids.

In this genus the sporangia are usually liberated from the sorus as sluggishly moving amoeboid or, occasionally, uniflagellate structures which soon come to rest, encyst, and give rise to from two to five minute zoospores. The fate of these zoospores is unknown; probably they reinfect desmids. It is, however, possible that they function as gametes. See discussion under *Micromyces*, p. 193.

ENDODESMIDIUM FORMOSUM Canter

Trans. Brit. Mycol. Soc., 32: 73, figs. 1-2, pl. 7, 8. 1949

"Prosorus oval, 28.5×16.5 to $15.6 \times 10.6\,\mu$, with a smooth, usually purple wall; sorus subspherical, $16-25\,\mu$ high $\times 21-12\,\mu$ broad, having at maturity two oppositely directed dehiscence papillae, the content dividing into about fifty bodies ($4\,\mu$ in diameter) with a conspicuous mass of oil and rarely a single, short posterior flagellum ($6-8\,\mu$ long), emerging through the papillae; sporangia spherical, $4\,\mu$ in diameter, discharging two to five minute spherical zoospores $1\,\mu$ in diameter, with a conspicuous oil globule and long posterior flagellum; movement active swimming; resting spore similar to prosorus, wall slightly thicker" (Canter, *loc. cit.*).

Parasitic in *Netrium oblongum, Cylindrocystis crassa*, and *C. brebissonii*, GREAT BRITAIN.

MICROMYCES Dangeard, emend.[1]

Le Botaniste, 1: 55. 1889

(Fig. 16 A-E, H, p. 196)

Micromycopsis Scherffel, Arch. Protistenk., 54: 202. 1926.

Synchytrium subgenus *Microsynchytrium* Karling, Mycologia, 45: 279. 1953.

Thallus at first naked, somewhat amoeboid, later walled, endobiotic, holocarpic, without a specialized vegetative system, forming the rudiment of the prosorus or resting spore; prosorus thick-walled, spiny or smooth-walled; sorus simple or compound, formed as a direct outgrowth of the prosorus or at the tip of a discharge tube, if simple, dividing into a variable number of inoperculate, uni- or multiporous, smooth or spiny, thin- or somewhat thick-walled angular sporangia not enclosed in a common soral wall which give rise directly to zoospores, if compound, dividing into sporangia which give rise to spherical, amoeboid, occasionally uniflagellated primary zoospores, each of which after encystment produces a few minute secondary zoospores; zoospores minute, posteriorly uniflagellate; resting spore thick-walled, upon germination functioning as a prosorus.,

For some time it has been increasingly evident from the investigations of Canter (1949c), Rieth (1950a), and others that the distinctions between *Micromyces* and *Micromycopsis* were breaking down (Sparrow, 1932b). Future work is expected to reveal new forms which will further obliterate any remaining differences between them and will sustain this merger.

Canter's (1949c) excellent series of observations on these curious endophytic algal parasites confirmed beyond question the formation of two kinds of sori: one, the usual chytridiaceous simple type whose sporangia give rise directly to zoospores, and another, a more complex type whose soral segments produce feebly moving, often posteriorly uniflagellate structures. These soon encyst and give rise to active zoospores which presumably infect new host plants. Canter calls the amoeboid bodies produced by the second type of sorus "primary zoospores," and the motile bodies derived from it "secondary zoospores." Since the soral segments give rise to what are functionally sporangia

[1] See Rieth (1956a) for a synopsis of this genus.

rather than zoospores, the sori in these cases are here termed "compound" to distinguish them from the similar "simple" ones that form zoospores directly.

As regards sexuality, the striking similarity of the swarmers from compound sori to those in the "Cystogenes" species of *Allomyces* (p. 625) was remarked by Canter and is re-emphasized here. It is entirely conceivable that the secondary zoospores are, indeed, isogamous gametes, such as are unquestionably formed in certain species of *Synchytrium*.

In commenting upon the phylogenetic implications of the flagellate sporangial stage ("primary zoospores") Canter (*l. c.* p. 92) states: "Such a phase is normally present in *M[icromycopsis] fischeri* and *Endodesmidium formosum*. The latter may be regarded as the most primitive type, the primary non-swarming swarmers being formed separately. *Micromycopsis fischeri*, however, differs from *Endodesmidium* in the sorus being divided into sporangia each of which liberates five or more of these primary zoospores, which after liberation behave in a similar manner. Passing to *Micromycopsis cristata* this flagellate sporangial stage is rarely recorded and more typically the behavior is as in *M. zygnaemicola* and *Micromyces* spp., where there is apparently only one sporangial stage liberating the normal chytridiaceous zoospores, which correspond to the secondary zoospores of the former types.

"It thus appears that during the course of development of these organisms the primary non-swarming zoospore stage and the subsequent formation of secondary sporangia is suppressed and we get, as in most species of *Synchytrium*, a sorus of sporangia immediately giving rise to chytridiaceous zoospores. *S. fulgens* Schröter may be considered as representing the culmination of suppression in which the sorus of sporangia is formed within the prosorus."

Karling (1953) presents reasons for uniting *Synchytrium* and *Micromyces*, citing the similarities of the two as outlined by Couch (1931), and merges them, erecting a subgenus *Microsynchytrium* for the disposition of *Micromyces*. He does not, however, include either of the obviously closely related genera *Endodesmidium* or *Micromycopsis* (here treated under *Micromyces*). From personal observations on both the algal parasites and *Synchytrium* and from the observations of others, it is the opinion of this writer that the differences indicated in the generic key are of sufficient import to warrant the maintenance of *Micromyces.*

KEY TO THE SPECIES OF MICROMYCES

Prosorus spiny-walled
 Spines of prosorus scattered
  Sori typically sessile, smooth-walled
   Spines slender, up to 7.5 μ long
    Zoospore spherical, 1 μ in diameter ..... *M. zygogonii*, p. 195
    Zoospore fusiform, 6 by 2 μ .... *M. petersenii*, p. 198
   Spines up to 22 μ in length .... *M. longispinosus*, p. 198
  Sori typically formed at the orifice of a discharge tube
   Sporangia ten to one hundred; sorus covered with low,
    coarse blunt spines, divided into polygonal areas
              M. mirabilis, p. 199
   Sporangia four to six in number; sorus covered with minute
    blunt spines, divided radially ...... *M. intermedia*, p. 200
 Spines of prosorus seriate or helically seriate
  Spines of prosorus typically seriate in rings; sorus simple,
   smooth-walled; sporangia tetrahedral, sessile
               M. ovalis, p. 200
  Spines of prosorus typically helically seriate; sorus compound,
   spiny, usually formed at the orifice of a discharge tube;
   sporangia spherical
    Prosorus 13-16 μ by 18-20 μ; sorus covered by blunt spines
           M. cristata var. *cristata*, p. 201
    Prosorus 8.5-10.4 μ; sorus covered by sharp spines
            M. cristata var. *minor*, p. 201
Prosorus smooth-walled
 Sorus smooth-walled, simple or compound
  Sorus simple, sessile or rarely at orifice of a tube; sporangia
   tetrahedral, zoospores numerous .... *M. laevis*, p. 202
  Sorus compound, typically formed at the orifice of a tube; spo-
   rangia spherical, zoospores few (two to six) *M. fischeri*, p. 202
 Sorus spiny-walled, simple
  Sorus composed of three tetrahedral sporangia
             M. zygnaemicola, p. 203
  Sorus composed of seven to fifteen pyramidal segments
             M. oedogonii, p. 203

MICROMYCES ZYGOGONII Dangeard
Le Botaniste, 1: 52, pl. 2, figs. 1-10. 1889
(Fig. 16 C, p. 196)
Synchytrium zygogonii (Dang.) Karling, Mycologia, 45: 278. 1953.

Prosorus spherical, 11–18 μ in diameter, with a thickened colorless wall the outer surface of which is covered with numerous slender sharp tapering spines 4–7.5 μ long; sorus emerging through a small pore formed in the wall of the prosorus, at first spherical, 13–25 μ in diameter, with a thin wall, at maturity becoming somewhat angular owing to the formation of from four to eight pyramidal truncate sporangia with rounded bases, sporangia 6–11 μ broad by 12 μ high, with from one to three small discharge papillae; zoospores spherical, ovoid or fusiform, 1–2 μ long, with a minute colorless refractive globule and a fairly long flagellum, movement hopping or amoeboid; resting spore spherical, about 12.5 μ in diameter, covered with somewhat shorter spines than those on the sporangium, inner wall thick, brownish or brownish red, germination not observed.

Parasitic in various Conjugatae and often causing pronounced swelling and elongation of the host cell. In *Zygogonium sp.*, Dangeard (*loc. cit.*; 1890–91c: 245, pl. 17, figs. 2–8), *Spirogyra quadrata*, Denis (1926: 14, fig. I, 2), FRANCE; *Zygogonium sp.*, de Wildeman (1891: 172), BELGIUM; *Mougeotia sp.*, Petersen (1910: 556, fig. 27c), DENMARK; Conjugatae, Pringsheim (1895), Minden (1915: 281), *Netrium sp.*, *Mougeotia sp.*, Schulz (1922: fig. 91; 1923: figs. 10–11), *M. scalaris*, Heidt (1937: 204, figs. 1–8), *Spirogyra mirabilis*, Rieth (1950a: 510; 1950b: 264, figs. 1–10), *Mougeotia sp.*, Rieth (1956a: 35, fig. 16), GERMANY; *Mougeotia sp.*, Huber-Pestalozzi (1931: 88, pl. 3, figs. 1–23), SWITZERLAND; *Mougeotia sp.*, *Zygogonium sp.*, Couch (1937: 595, figs. 1–8), *Mougeotia sp.*, Sparrow (1943: 137), *Spirogyra sp.*, Sparrow (1952d: 760), UNITED STATES; *Spirogyra sp.*, Canter (1949c: 82, figs. 8 a–i, 9, 11 a–b, 12 a–g; pl. 10, figs. 1–3), GREAT BRITAIN.

Huber-Pestalozzi (*loc. cit.*) and Heidt (*loc. cit.*) give references to the older algological literature containing descriptions of "asterospheres." (See also Thwaites, 1846–47; Shadbolt, 1852; Smith, 1853; de Bary, 1858; Reinsch, 1879; Pringsheim, 1895.)

De Wildeman (1900a: 1) has given the name *Micromyces mesocarpi*

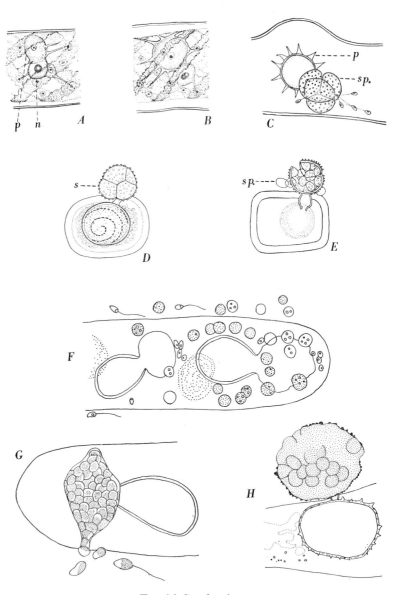

FIG. 16. Synchytriaceae

to a species which differs from the present one in not causing hypertrophy of the algal cell and in forming the sorus at the tip of a narrow canal on the outside of the host.

The presence of distinct hypertrophy in infected cells has been noted by all observers of *Micromyces zygogonii*, as has also the attraction of the young thallus for the host nucleus rather than for the chloroplast. The infected cell may become from two to three times longer and wider than healthy cells. Lateral expansion is often accompanied in its later stages by a strong bulging out of the side wall. This wall may fracture at its apex and allow for the passage of the undigested contents of the alga. If disintegration of the algal wall does not take place elsewhere the same orifice undoubtedly also allows the zoospores access to the outside medium. Heidt, who maintained infected algae for months in 1 per cent agar, observed that the parasite could cause elongation not only of the whole cell but also of a part of the cell and that the same parasite might in one culture bring about complete disintegration of the cell and in another only slightly affect

---

Explanation of Figure 16

A–B. Micromyces longispinosus Couch in *Spirogyra*: *A*, portion of cell of *Spirogyra* with two young thalli (*p*) attached to host nucleus (*n*); *B*, nearly mature spiny thallus attached to host nucleus. *C. Micromyces zygogonii* Dangeard, part of empty *Mougeotia* cell with discharged spiny prosorus (*p*) and four sporangia (*sp*); uppermost sporangium is discharging zoospores. *D–E. Micromyces cristata* var. *cristata* (Scherffel) Sparrow in *Hyalotheca*: *D*, empty endobiotic resting spore (seen from top), with the tube and epibiotic rough-walled sorus (*s*) of sporangia to which it has given rise; spiral arrangement of spines on resting spore is clearly seen; *E*, smooth-walled endobiotic resting spore and, connected to it by a tube, the ruptured sorus, within which are undischarged sporangia; several empty sporangia (*sp*) have fallen away from the group. *F–G. Endodesmidium formosum* Canter in *Netrium*: *F*, two germinated prosori with discharged sori; the cystlike sporangia have produced zoospores both inside and outside the host cell; *G*, mature sorus discharging nonswarming amoeboid structures (one bearing a flagellum) which will encyst and function as sporangia. *H. Micromyces mirabilis* (Canter), comb. nov., in *Closterium*; large prosorus with immature external sorus showing beginning of differentiation into sporangia.

(*A–B*, Couch, 1931; *D–E*, Scherffel, 1926a; *F–H*, Canter, 1949c)

its vitality. Attempts to infect Conjugatae with the fungus appear to have been uniformly unsuccessful.

Cytological observations by Dangeard (1890–91c) showed that the prosorus was uninucleate and that after formation of the sorus active nuclear division occurred, accompanied by a distinct decrease in nuclear size.

MICROMYCES PETERSENII Scherffel

Arch. Protistenk., 54: 209, pl. 10, figs. 78-79. 1926

Synchytrium petersenii (Scherffel) Karling, Mycologia, 45: 278. 1953.

Prosorus spherical, with sparingly dispersed short conical spines covering the outer surface; sorus as in *Micromyces zygogonii*; zoospores narrowly spindle-shaped, 6 μ long by 2 μ thick, with a large laterally placed strongly refractive colorless oil globule and a long extremely delicate posterior flagellum, movement somewhat amoeboid.

In *Mougeotia sp.*, HUNGARY.

Scherffel considers that the species is distinct from *Micromyces zygogonii* on the basis of differences in host plant and character of the spines and especially in the large (6 by 2 μ) fusiform rather than spherical (1 μ in diameter) zoospores. Primarily because of these large zoospores it is maintained here as a separate species.

A fungus in *Mougeotia* referred to this species by Canter (1949c: 86, figs. 8 j–m, 10a, 12h, pl. 10, figs. 4–5), differs from it, as she indicates, by its much longer spines (up to 6–12 μ), resembling in this respect *M. zygogonii* and *M. longispinosus*. The ovoid zoospores, 5.5 by 1.5 μ, however, are much longer than those of either of them and for this reason she has referred her fungus to *M. petersenii*. Whether it is to be regarded as a variety or distinct from Scherffel's fungus is uncertain.

MICROMYCES LONGISPINOSUS Couch

Mycologia, 29: 592, figs. 9-14. 1937

(Fig. 16 A-B, p. 196)

Synchytrium longispinosus (Couch) Karling, Mycologia, 45: 278. 1953.

Prosorus more or less spherical, 10–33.6 μ in diameter (mostly

21 μ), outer wall irregularly reticulate, bearing from twelve to twenty-four straight or somewhat curved hyaline tapering spines up to 22 μ long (mostly about 12 μ), sorus smooth-walled, spherical or ovoid; sporangia from eight to twenty-four or more, usually polygonal, sometimes pyramidal with rounded base and truncate apex, 8.4 μ high by 9.6 μ broad; zoospores numerous, subspherical or ovoid, 1 μ thick, with one or two globules and a slender flagellum, escaping through a pore formed in the narrow apex; resting spore subspherical, 16–21 μ in diameter, somewhat angular, thick-walled, with long tapering spines, pale yellow brown, upon germination functioning as a prosorus. (Modified from Couch.)

Parasitic in *Spirogyra sp.* (Couch, *loc. cit.*), UNITED STATES; *Mougeotia sp.*, Kobayashi and Ookubo (as *Olpidiopsis sp.*) (1954b: 571, fig. 12), JAPAN.

As in *Micromyces zygogonii* the thallus and prosorus are uninucleate (Fig. 16 A–B, p. 196), nuclear division taking place only in the sorus. Couch (*op. cit.*) also presents evidence that the resting spore upon germination is uninucleate. There is some reason to believe that, as in *Synchytrium*, the so-called "zoospores" may behave as planogametes and fuse in pairs, giving rise to a planozygote which presumably penetrates the alga and forms the resting spore. What is known of the cytology of *Micromyces* indicates that it closely resembles *Synchytrium*.

Further observations are needed on the method of infection. Earlier, Couch (1931) had stated that in *Micromyces zygogonii* the zoospore softens the wall and forms a perforation through which it flows. Whether or not a cyst is left on the surface has not been determined. In view of the small size of the zoospore such a cyst, if formed, would probably be a difficult structure to observe.

MICROMYCES MIRABILIS (Canter), comb. nov.

(Fig. 16 H, p. 196)

Micromycopsis mirabilis Canter, Trans. Brit. Mycol. Soc., 32: 82, figs. 6-7, pl. 11, figs. 1-3. 1949.

"Prosorus (resting spore?) very elongate, 75 × 20 to 112 × 57 μ; less elongate, 21 × 12.8 to 67 × 55 μ or spherical, 12 × 10 to 37 ×

35 μ; wall thick, hyaline, outer layer with broad-based spines. Sorus epibiotic, spherical, 28–80 μ in diameter, wall yellowish brown covered with small spines, formed at the end of an exit tube and at maturity containing ten to one hundred triangular zoosporangia 13 – 21 μ high × 7–14 μ broad at the base. Zoospores not observed" (Canter, *loc. cit.*).

Parasitic in *Closterium lunula, C. dianae, C. costatum, C. kutzingii,* and *Closterium sp.,* GREAT BRITAIN.

MICROMYCES INTERMEDIA (Canter), comb. nov.

Micromycopsis intermedia Canter, Trans. Brit. Mycol. Soc., 32: 79, fig. 5, pl. 10, figs. 9-10. 1949.

"Prosorus spherical, 10.7–17.8 μ in diameter, wall brown, spiny, granular or smooth; sorus epibiotic, sessile on the host wall or at some distance from it; spherical, wall yellowish brown, covered with minute blunt spines, splitting into four to six parts to expose the same number of broadly triangular sporangia; zoospores twenty to thirty, oval (3.5 × 1.5 μ) with a conspicuous oil globule, and smaller refractive globule at the side. Resting spores unknown" (Canter, *loc. cit.*).

In *Zygnema spp.,* GREAT BRITAIN.

MICROMYCES OVALIS Rieth[1]

Österr. Bot. Zeitschr., 97: 516, figs. 1-12. 1950

Synchytrium ovalis (Rieth) Karling, Mycologia, 45: 278. 1953.

Prosorus ellipsoidal, up to 12–18 μ long by 8 μ in diameter, the outer wall bearing four to six rings of coarse, shark's-tooth-like spines which in exceptional cases may be spirally arranged; sorus spherical or subspherical, smooth-walled, forming four tetrahedral sporangia which for the most part do not become free from one another, the inner wall remaining connected, the sorus wall tearing apart at the line of contact of the sporangia; zoospores numerous, somewhat spherical, about 1 μ in diameter with a posterior flagellum, escaping through one or two pores on the sporangium wall into the host cell; resting spore probably like the prosorus.

[1] See var. *giganteus*, p. 204.

Parasitic in *Mougeotia sp.*, AUSTRIA.

In one instance a prosorus developed a discharge tube at the tip of which the sorus was formed. Because of this Rieth considered it likely that transitional forms between *Micromyces* and *Micromycopsis* exist. In contrast to *M. zygogonii*, which may cause an increase in both length and breadth of infected host cells, this species induces only abnormal elongation.

MICROMYCES CRISTATA var. CRISTATA (Scherffel), comb. nov.

(Fig. 16 D-E, p. 196)

Micromycopsis cristata Scherffel, Arch. Protistenk., 54: 202, pl. 9, figs. 65-68, pl. 10, figs. 69-76. 1926

Prosorus spherical and 11–16 μ (mostly 14 μ) in diameter or spheroidal and 13–16 by 18–20 μ, with a thickened dark-brown wall, the outer surface bearing a helical series of spines making from five to six equidistant turns, occasionally smooth-walled or with irregularly arranged spines, discharge tube cylindrical, clavate, or irregularly curved, never extending beyond the host wall; sorus compound, sessile, spherical, equal in size to the prosorus, wall thickened, deep blackish brown, the outer surface covered uniformly with short blunt spines; soral wall at maturity splitting along three or four planes; soral segments very thin-walled, spherical or by mutual contact somewhat polygonal; sporangia spherical, 4 μ in diameter, amoeboid, with a large colorless globule and a 6–8 μ long flagellum, escaping through a pore; zoospores three to five in a sporangium, minute, actively swimming; resting stage not observed.

Parasitic or, perhaps, only saprophytic in *Hyalotheca dubia*, Scherffel, (*loc. cit.*), HUNGARY; *Hyalotheca dissiliens*, Cejp (1933a: 2, pl. 1, fig. 4), CZECHOSLOVAKIA.

MICROMYCES CRISTATA var. MINOR (Sparrow), comb. nov.

Micromycopsis cristata var. *minor* Sparrow, Mycologia, 24: 273, fig. 1 d-e. 1932.

Prosorus bearing a helical series of spines, occasionally smooth-walled, 8.5–10.4 μ (usually 8 μ) in diameter; discharge tube narrowly cylindrical, isodiametric; sorus sessile, 7.8 μ in diameter, brown, covered with short sharp spines, splitting into three parts; other phases not observed.

In *Spirogyra sp.*, UNITED STATES.

Differing from *Micromyces cristata* in being of smaller size and bearing sharp spines on the sorus wall.

MICROMYCES LAEVIS Canter

Trans. Brit. Mycol. Soc., 32: 87, fig. 10b-g, pl. 10, figs. 6-8. 1949

Synchytrium laevis (Canter) Karling, Mycologia, 45: 278. 1953.

"Prosorus spherical, 7.6–18 μ in diameter, with a smooth colourless wall; sorus endobiotic, smooth walled, spherical, with four to eight sporangia; soral wall splitting into as many parts as sporangia, zoospores [oval] numerous, 1 μ in diameter, with a single oil globule, and posterior flagellum. Resting spores, 12.7 μ in diameter, brown walled, rarely covered with numerous short fine hairs; on germination functioning as a prosorus" (Canter, *loc. cit.*).

In *Mougeotia sp.*, Canter (*loc. cit.*), GREAT BRITAIN; Rieth (1956a: 27, figs. 1–10, pl. 1), GERMANY.

MICROMYCES FISCHERI (Scherffel), comb. nov.

Micromycopsis fischeri Scherffel, Arch. Protistenk., 54: 208, pl. 10, fig. 77. 1926.

Prosorus ovoid, 12 by 17 to 25 by 40 μ, to spherical, 8–12 μ in diameter, densely granular, brownish, with a large eccentric oil globule, a thick smooth wall, discharge tube cylindrical, usually not extending beyond the surface of the outer wall of the host; sorus spherical, compound, 8–20 μ in diameter, with a thin smooth colorless wall, sessile on host cell, brownish at maturity, rarely sessile on the endobiotic prosorus, divided into two to sixteen segments by somewhat radially arranged sutures, the whole cut off by a wall from the discharge tube; each soral segment forming five sporangia ("primary zoospores"), 4.3 by 2.4 μ, with an anterior mass of oil and a posterior flagellum, movement jerky and amoeboid, forming after encystment two to six posteriorly uniflagellate ("secondary") zoospores, 2 μ in diameter which swim actively; other characters unknown.

In *Zygogonium, sp.*, Scherffel (*loc. cit.*), HUNGARY; *Tetmemorus bre-bissonii*, Canter (1949c: 73, figs. 3–4, pl. 9, figs. 1–3), GREAT BRITAIN. The species differs from *Micromyces cristata* in having a smooth-walled prosorus and in forming more segments in the sorus. Scherffel's figure of *M. fischeri* bears a close resemblance to his figure (fig. 76) of *M. cristata*.

MICROMYCES ZYGNAEMICOLA (Cejp), comb. nov.

Micromycopsis zygnaemicola Cejp, Bull. Internat. Acad. Sci. Bohême, 42 (3): 2, pl. 1, figs. 5-10; pl. 2, figs. 3-4. 1933 (separate).

Prosorus spherical and 10–13 μ in diameter or ellipsoidal and 9–10 by 12–13 μ, with a thickened smooth wall, discharge tube 3–4 μ in diameter, long; sorus nonsessile, borne at the tip of the discharge tube, spherical, 13–15 μ in diameter, with a somewhat thickened brownish wall covered by short blunt spines; soral wall at maturity splitting along three sutures into three tetrahedral portions; sporangia spherical or nearly so, thin-walled; zoospores and resting spore not observed. Parasitic in *Zygnema stellina*, GERMANY.

MICROMYCES OEDOGONII (Roberts), comb. nov.

Micromycopsis oedogonii Roberts, Trans. Brit. Mycol. Soc., 36: 320, figs. 1-12, pl. 17. 1953.

Prosorus mostly spherical, 14–30 μ in diameter, smooth-walled with greyish brown contents, causing swelling of newly formed host cells, discharge tube cylindrical, 2–13 μ long, not extending beyond the host wall; sorus epibiotic, sessile, spherical, the wall brownish and covered with short blunt spines, soral wall at maturity splitting into a series of polygonal plates, the bases of seven to fifteen pyramidal otherwise thin-walled sporangia; zoospores of one type only, about fifty in a sporangium, subspherical, 2 μ in diameter, with a colorless droplet and single flagellum. Resting spores not observed.

Parasitic in vegetative cells of *Oedogonium sp.*, GREAT BRITAIN. This species occurs in great abundance on *Oedogonium* but has not been found on associated Oedogoniaceae or Conjugatae. It differs from other members of *Micromyces* in its host and from its closest relative, *M. intermedia*, in having more sporangia in a sorus and in having a smooth, colorless prosorus wall.

RECENTLY DESCRIBED TAXA [1]

MICROMYCES GRANDIS Miller

J. Elisha Mitchell Sci. Soc., 71: 247, figs. 1-29. 1955

"Prosorus 30.4–51.2 μ (most about 40.0–48.0 μ) in diam., with a thickened hyaline wall, covered with many (17–25) long, sharp spines, 38.4–67.2 μ (most about 51.2–60.6 μ) in length; spines usually curved at their ends; contents of the prosorus with many highly refractive globules grouped towards the center; as the host cell becomes moribund, germinating to form a globose sorus at first slightly smaller than the prosorus; swelling to about 1/5 again the size of the prosorus as its contents divide into many (33–54) zoosporangia; zoosporangium pyramidal in shape, with a rounded to polygonal base and a truncated apex, 9.6–11.2 μ × 16.0–23.1 μ; contents of zoosporangium dividing into many zoospores; soral membrane splitting along the lines of cleavage of the bases of the zoosporangia, releasing them; occasionally the soral membrane not splitting, the zoosporangia remaining in the intact sorus; zoospores ovoid, with a single globule of oil and a single posteriorly directed flagellum, 2.1–2.8 (average about 2.3) μ in diam., escaping from the sporangia and swimming through the ruptured host cell wall; resting bodies, yellow-green to golden-brown, 16.0–32.0 μ in diam., the walls thickened, outer layer averaging 1.4, the inner 1.1 μ in thickness; outer wall invested with 20–24 short spines; resting body functioning as a prosorus" (Miller, *loc. cit.*).

In cells of *Spirogyra sp.* (NORTH CAROLINA), UNITED STATES.

MICROMYCES OVALIS var. GIGANTEUS Sparrow and Barr

Mycologia, 47: 546, fig. 21. 1955

"Prosorus hyaline to light yellow, ellipsoid, 36–40 μ long by 16–21 μ in diameter, bearing six circular rows of spines, 4–6 μ long; sorus, sporangia and zoospores not observed" (Sparrow and Barr, *loc. cit.*).

---

[1] Not included in the key.

Parasitic in and causing elongation of the cells of *Zygnema sp.*, UNITED STATES.

Rieth (1956a) suggests the prosorus may be a resting spore.

IMPERFECTLY KNOWN SPECIES OF MICROMYCES

? MICROMYCES ECHINOCYSTIS Linder

Nat. Mus. Canada Bull., No. 97, Biol. Ser. No. 26, p. 240, pl. 12, figs. A-C, pl. 15, fig. B. 1947

"Prosori ellipsoid, broadly ellipsoid, or more rarely globose, 24–27– (40.5) × 19.5–21–(27) µ, subhyaline to yellowish, ornamented with numerous, curved, pointed spines 1.9–3.3 µ long and 1–1.5 µ in diameter at the base.

"Mostly solitary in the cells of *Zygnema sp.* and *Mougeotia sp.*, not causing any pronounced enlargement of the host cell, although there may be a slight enlargement and some elongation" (Linder, *loc. cit.*).

Parasitic in *Zygnema sp.* and *Mougeotia sp.* (F. slide No. 2709, Type), CANADIAN EASTERN ARCTIC.

? MICROMYCES MINIMUS Linder

Nat. Mus. Canada Bull., No. 97, Biol. Ser. No. 26, p. 239, pl. 12, fig. E, pl. 15, fig. A. 1947

"Prosori globose, light coloured to deep yellow-brown, of two types: (1) large 10.5–16.5 µ in diameter, ornamented with short, straight, and relatively thick spines 0.5–0.75 µ long; and (2) small prosori 7.5 µ in diameter and smooth.

"Solitary or several in a cell of *Zygnema sp.*, the infected host cells not inflated, but almost twice as long as the normal host cell" (Linder, *loc. cit.*).

Parasitic in *Zygnema sp.* (F. slide No. 2708, Type), CANADIAN EASTERN ARCTIC.

This species, *Micromyces wheldenii* and *M. echinocystis* were described by Linder on the basis of spiny cysts discovered in preserved material of algae collected by Polunin. In no instance were sori or sporangia seen. *Micromyces minimus* bears a strong resemblance to the species of *Micromyces* described by Canter (1949c: 84) in connection with *M. zygogonii* (see p. 195). Both fungi have two types of prosori, the one covered by low straight spines and the other having smooth walls. In Linder's material the smooth-walled prosori were distinctly smaller than the spiny and both types were found together. In Canter's, they were approximately equal in size except for a single case (*op. cit.*, fig. 9 j) in which the two occurred in the same cell. The smooth-walled one was noticeably smaller. Her fungus did not attack *Zygnema*, the host of Linder's species. Whether in both instances one is dealing with variation in wall ornamentation within a single species or with a mixed infection is uncertain.

? MICROMYCES SPIROGYRAE Skvortzow

Arch. Protistenk., 51: 433, fig. 6. 1925

Synchytrium spirogyrae (Skvortzow) Karling, Mycologia, 45: 278. 1953.

Prosorus spherical or ellipsoidal, with a thick wall, the outer surface densely covered with slender rodlike isodiametric spines 3.5–3.8 μ long; sorus, sporangia, and zoospores not observed; resting spore 22.5–26 μ long by 18–22.5 μ wide, with a thick brown wall, densely covered with spines, germination not observed.

In *Spirogyra inflata*, Skvortzow (*loc. cit.*), MANCHURIA; *Spirogyra sp.*, Litvinow (1953: 77), LATVIA.

The true affinities here cannot be determined until the zoospores have been observed.

? MICROMYCES WHELDENII Linder

Nat. Mus. Canada, Bull., No. 97, Biol. Ser. No. 26, p. 240, pl. 12, fig. D, pl. 15, fig. C. 1947

"Prosori light coloured to yellow-brown, globose, 22.5–30 μ in diameter, covered by a spiny membrane, the spines hyaline, up to 2 μ long, straight, bluntly or sharply pointed, and arising from the coloured subhemispherical bases.

"Solitary in *Zygnema* sp., causing a globose or elongate-ellipsoid enlargement of the host cell" (Linder, *loc. cit.*).

Parasitic in *Zygnema sp.* (F. slide No. 2716, Type), CANADIAN EASTERN ARCTIC.

? MICROMYCES SP. Canter

Trans. Brit. Mycol. Soc., 32: 84, fig. 9. 1949

Prosorus brownish, spherical to subspherical, 6–22 μ in diameter, with a thick hyaline, smooth or spiny wall; sorus approximately equal in diameter to the prosorus, smooth-walled, divided at maturity to form 4–8 broadly pyramidal sporangia 12–15 μ high by 8–3(?) μ broad containing numerous posteriorly uniflagellate uniguttulate zoospores 2 μ in diameter; resting spore not observed.

Parasitic in *Mougeotia sp.*, GREAT BRITAIN.

This fungus was discussed by Canter in connection with *Micromyces zygogonii*. It differs in having two types of prosori: some with lower spines than in that species and others that are smooth-walled. Unlike *M. zygogonii*, it is confined to a single species of host, does not produce hypertrophy, and causes a blackish residue of host material to collect at the cross walls of the infected cells. (See also remarks under ? *Micromyces minimus*, p. 205).

PHLYCTIDIACEAE

Thallus epi- and endobiotic, monocentric, eucarpic, the epibiotic cyst either expanding and becoming an inoperculate sporangium, a prosporangium, or a thick-walled resting spore and the endobiotic part functioning as the vegetative system, or the cyst not enlarging and either evanescent or persistent, in which case the endobiotic part forms the reproductive organ as well as the vegetative system; zoospores posteriorly uniflagellate, generally with a single globule; sexual reproduction, where known, by fusion of aplanogametes borne in thalli; resting spore upon germination functioning as a sporangium or prosporangium.

Primarily parasites and saprophytes of fresh-water algae, microscopic animals, and submerged pollen grains.

The family includes the greater part of the fungi commonly referred to as "chytrids" and corresponds roughly to the "Rhizidiaceae" (excluding *Rhizidium* and its close allies) of most monographers.

KEY TO THE SUBFAMILIES AND GENERA OF THE PHLYCTIDIACEAE

Sporangium epibiotic or extracellular [1], resting spore epi or endobiotic; vegetative system varied in nature; zoospore cyst usually persistent and functional ..... Subfamily Phlyctidioideae, p. 210

Body of the encysted zoospore wholly or in part enlarging to form a sporangium, the latter usually sessile, with or without a sterile base

Epibiotic or extracellular part completely fertile; endobiotic part varied

Endobiotic part a distinctly double-contoured tube, irregular sac, sphere, digitation, or papilla, never branched or tapering

Endobiotic part not digitate

Resting spore completely filling its container
PHLYCTIDIUM, p. 210

Resting spore formed in the distal part only of its container .... SEPTOSPERMA, p. 225

Endobiotic part a complex of blunt digitations arising from a central knob .... LOBORHIZA, p. 227

Endobiotic part a single tapering rhizoid or a branching system of rhizoids arising from an apophysis or directly from the tip of the germ tube or a prolongation of it

Endobiotic part a tapering rhizoid or a branching system of rhizoids arising from the tip of the germ tube

Sporangium and resting spore epibiotic; rhizoids developed to a varying degree; parasitic or saprophytic on a variety of substrata .... RHIZOPHYDIUM, p. 230

Sporangium and resting spore extracellular; rhizoids forming a bushy tuft or of small extent; parasitic on plankton algae .... DANGEARDIA, p. 319

Endobiotic part with the rhizoids arising from an apophysis

Sporangium without an apiculus, the discharge pore usually apical; resting spore epibiotic
PHLYCTOCHYTRIUM, p. 323

Sporangium with an apiculus, and lateral discharge pore; resting spore endobiotic .... BLYTTIOMYCES, p. 354

---

[1] That is, imbedded in material of the host, as, for example, in a gelatinous sheath, but resting on the cytoplasm (*Dangeardia*, etc.).

Epibiotic part typically with a sterile septate base or a small knoblike structure on which the sporangium rests; endobiotic part knoblike or rhizoidal
    Sterile part an inconspicuous knob on which the sporangium rests; endobiotic part knoblike
                                 PHYSORHIZOPHIDIUM, p. 358
    Sterile part conspicuous and an integral component or continuation of the base of the fertile portion, rarely lacking; endobiotic part rhizoidal or straplike
                                       PODOCHYTRIUM, p. 359
Body of the encysted zoospore either sessile and enlarging to form a prosporangium or lying free in the water, not enlarging, and producing at the tip of the germ tube an appressorium which expands to form the sporangium; sterile base never formed
    Body of the encysted zoospore sessile, enlarging to form a prosporangium, the endobiotic part consisting of a series of intercommunicating broad lobes . . . . SACCOMYCES, p. 364
    Body of the encysted zoospore producing at the tip of a germ tube an appressorium which expands to form the sporangium, endobiotic part completely rhizoidal, or apophysate and bearing a distal complex of stubby digitations
        Endobiotic part not apophysate . . . . . SCHERFFELIOMYCES, p. 365
        Endobiotic part apophysate . . . . CORALLIOCHYTRIUM [1], p. 368
Sporangium endobiotic, resting spore endobiotic; vegetative system rhizoidal; zoospore cyst usually evanescent
                      Subfamily ENTOPHLYCTOIDEAE, p. 369
Vegetative part rhizoidal, generally monophagous
    Sporangium spherical, pyriform or irregular, never strongly tubular; typically forming a single discharge tube or pore
        Sporangium formed from a localized primary swelling at the tip of the germ tube or from a secondary expansion of the more proximal part of the rhizoidal rudiments
            Rhizoids or rhizoidal axes arising directly from the sporangium . . . . ENTOPHLYCTIS, p. 369
            Rhizoids arising from an apophysis . . . DIPLOPHLYCTIS, p. 383
        Sporangium formed by vesiculation of the dorsal side of the rhizoids, strongly dorsi-ventrally differentiated
                            PHLYCTORHIZA, p. 391
    Sporangium strongly tubular; forming one or more discharge tubes . . . . MITOCHYTRIDIUM, p. 395

[1] Johns (1956) has merged this genus with the preceding.

Vegetative part an isodiametric coenocytic or septate tube; generally extending through several host cells
Vegetative part broadly tubular, nonseptate .... Rʜɪᴢᴏsɪᴘʜᴏɴ, p. 397
Vegetative part a narrow septate tube .... Aᴘʜᴀɴɪsᴛɪs, p. 401

SUBFAM. PHLYCTIDIOIDEAE

Sporangium epibiotic or extracellular; resting spore epi- or endo-biotic; vegetative system varied in nature; zoospore cyst usually persistent and functional.

PHLYCTIDIUM (Bʀᴀᴜɴ) Rᴀʙᴇɴʜᴏʀsᴛ

Flora Europaea algarum, 3: 278. 1868 (sensu recent. Serbinow, Scripta Bot. Horti Univ. Imper. Petro., 24: 158. 1907)

(Fig. 19 A-B, p. 318)

Chytridium, subgen. Phlyctidium Braun, Abhandl. Berlin Akad., 1855: 74. 1856. Non Phlyctidium Wallroth, Flora cryptogamica Germaniae, 2: 416. 1833.

Tylochytrium Karling, Mycologia, 31: 287. 1939.

Hapalopera Fott, Studia Bot. Čechica, 5 (3-4): 170. 1942.

Thallus epi- and endobiotic, monocentric, eucarpic, the epibiotic part forming the rudiment of the sporangium or resting spore, the endobiotic part producing the unbranched, tubular, peglike, clavate, knoblike, or discoid haustorium; sporangium inoperculate, uni- or multiporous; zoospores formed within the sporangium, posteriorly uniflagellate, generally with a single globule; resting spore thick-walled, borne like the sporangium, asexually formed or sexually after terminal or lateral fusion of two isogamous gametes, one of which has previously come to rest and germinated and the other encysted upon it.

Primarily parasites and saprophytes of fresh-water algae.

It is sometimes difficult to determine whether a fungus is a species of Phlyctidium or Rhizophydium. The distinctions given here are no doubt artificial and the genus Phlyctidium has not been recognized by all investigators (Scherffel, 1926a: 186). In practice, however, its separation from Rhizophydium is highly useful. If the haustorium gives definite evidence of being almost isodiametric or is distally expanded, unbranched throughout, and must be depicted as a double rather than a single line, the fungus is placed in Phlyctidium.

Karling (1939a) suggested the suppression of the name *Phlyctidium*, because of its earlier use by Wallroth (1833) for a genus of Ascomycetes, and the substitution of a new name, *Tylochytrium*. All species of Wallroth's genus have long since been transferred to other genera and *Phlyctidium* possesses no status among the Ascomycetes. In view of this, as well as of the long- and well-established use of the name for certain chytridiaceous fungi, *Phlyctidium* should be treated as a *nomen conservandum*, a course now evidently concurred in by Karling (1946d).

KEY TO THE SPECIES OF PHLYCTIDIUM [1]

Wall of sporangium persistent at least for a short time at discharge
of the zoospores, of uniform thickness
Endobiotic part (haustorium) uniformly tubular, clavate apophysate or expanded distally
Sporangium smooth-walled
Haustorium apophysate, sporangium spherical or ovoid
P. apophysatum, p. 212
Haustorium lacking an apophysis, sporangium spherical,
citriform, ellipsoidal, ovoid or urceolate
Sporangium spherical, ovoid, or when a prominent lateral
papilla is formed, somewhat anatropous, with 1-3
blunt conical discharge papillae ...... *P. laterale*, p. 213
Sporangium citriform or ovoid, broader than high, with
two opposite discharge papillae .... *P. irregulare*, p. 214
Sporangium spherical or ellipsoidal, somewhat urceolate
after discharge, 16-70 µ in diameter, haustorium a
distally expanded peg .... *P. megastomum*, p. 214
Sporangium urceolate, 15-17 µ in diameter, haustorium
tubular throughout .... *P. olla*, p. 215
Sporangium wall ornamented
Sporangium broadly urceolate or broadly ovoid, with an
apical collarette of from four to eight plain prominent teeth
P. brebissonii, p. 216
Sporangium spherical or slightly ovoid, wall covered with
short sharp spines .... *P. spinulosum*, p. 216
Endobiotic part spherical, knoblike, discoid, or very short and
peglike or needle-like
Sporangium attached laterally, appearing more or less procumbent, sessile, irregularly shaped, in general broadly pyri-

---

[1] Note that this key is not consistently dichotomous. See also new taxa, p. 223.

form or ovoid and asymmetrical, strongly arched or reflexed (anatropous), attached laterally near the narrower
end .... *P. anatropum,* p. 217
Sporangium basally attached, upright, pyriform, obpyriform,
ellipsoidal, ovoid or spherical
Sporangium obpyriform, haustorium needle-like or peglike,
mycetophagous .... *P. mycetophagum,* p. 217
Sporangium pyriform, ovoid, oblong-ovoid, ellipsoidal
Haustorium small and knoblike, formed just beneath the
sporangium; the latter symmetrically pyriform, with
a small papilla .... *P. chlorogonii,* p. 218
Haustorium spherical, formed at the tip of a slender fila-
ment arising from the base of the sporangium; the
latter pyriform or ellipsoidal with a broad blunt apex
P. eudorinae, p. 219
Sporangium ovoid or spherical
Haustorium knoblike or discoid; sporangium spherical,
parasitic on *Bumillaria* .... *P. bumilleriae,* p. 220
Haustorium a short blunt peglike tube which projects only
slightly beyond the inner face of the algal wall
Sporangia 10-24 μ in diameter; zoospores 3 μ; in fresh-
water algae ...... *P. brevipes* var. *brevipes,* p. 221
Sporangia 20-30 μ in diameter; zoospores 4-5 μ; in
marine algae ...... *P. brevipes* var. *marinum,* p. 221
Wall of sporangium wholly or in part deliquescing at zoospore discharge and of uniform thickness, or basally thickened and collapsing and sometimes fragmenting at zoospore discharge
Wall uniformly delicate, completely deliquescing and liberating
the spores .... *P. piriformis,* p. 222
Wall with a thickened basal portion, collapsing and fracturing at
zoospore discharge .... *P. tenue,* p. 222

PHLYCTIDIUM APOPHYSATUM Canter

Trans. Brit. Mycol. Soc., 31: 95, fig. 1. 1947

"Thallus monocentric, consisting of an extramatrical sporangium
[spherical to oval] 9–17 μ in diameter, an intramatrical apophysis,
either spherical, 5 μ in diameter, or subspherical, 6.7 × 10 μ, never
exceeding diameter of the sporangium, continuous with a tubular rhizoid (24 × 7 μ) to (12 × 3.3 μ). Zoospores oval 1.4 × 2.4 μ with a
minute colourless globule, and posterior flagellum 13 μ long, discharged

on deliquescence of the apex of the sporangium. Resting spores not observed" (Canter, *loc. cit.*).

Parasitic on *Mougeotia sp.*, Canter (*loc. cit.*; 1953: 282), GREAT BRITAIN.

Canter (1953) states that the species exhibits endo-exogenous development.

PHLYCTIDIUM LATERALE (Braun) Sorokin

Arch. Bot. Nord France, 2: 20, fig. 15. 1883 (separate).

Chytridium laterale Braun, Monatsber. Berlin Akad., 1855: 382; Abhandl. Berlin Akad., 1855: 41, pl. 2, figs. 20-21, 23-26. 1856.

Rhizophydium laterale (Braun) Rabenhorst, Flora Europaea algarum, 3: 281. 1868.

Sporangium sessile, spherical, ovoid or because of the formation of a prominent lateral papilla, somewhat anatropous, 10–16 μ in diameter, with one to three blunt, conical discharge papillae, wall smooth, colorless; endobiotic part consisting of an unbranched, peglike (occasionally bulbous) structure two to three times as long as thick, which barely penetrates the host wall; zoospores somewhat oblong, 2 μ in diameter, and 10–12 μ long, with an eccentric globule, assuming motility before discharge, escaping through one to three pores formed upon the deliquescence of the papillae; resting spore 12 μ in diameter, colorless, germination not observed.

On living and dead cells of *Ulothrix zonata*, Braun (*loc. cit.*), Schenk (1858a: 237), GERMANY; *Stigeoclonium*, Sorokin (*loc. cit.*), ASIATIC RUSSIA, EUROPEAN RUSSIA; *Ulothrix zonata*, Serbinow (1907: 157, pl. 6, figs. 18–21), EUROPEAN RUSSIA; *Ulothrix sp.*, Ingold (1940, comm.), GREAT BRITAIN; *Ulothrix sp.*, Litvinow (1953: 78), LATVIA.

The description is based on that given by Braun and on three other undoubted records for the species. Information and figures supplied by C. T. Ingold (1940, comm.) from abundant living material confirms the existence of a lateral-pored chytrid with an endobiotic system completely devoid of rhizoids. The similar-appearing fungus identified by Karling as *Rhizophydium laterale* (Braun) Rabenhorst (1938e), which has a tuft of rhizoids terminating the haustorial axis and a part of the zoospore cyst persisting as a hemispherical protrusion, is considered a new species of *Rhizophydium*, *R. karlingii* (p. 243).

There is strong likelihood that *Phlyctidium laterale* is confined to *Ulothrix* or at least to members of the Ulotrichales. Sparrow's (1932b: 274) doubtful report of it on zygospores of *Spirogyra* is probably referable to another fungus.

PHLYCTIDIUM IRREGULARE de Wildeman

Ann. Soc. Belge Micro. (Mém.), 14: 21. 1890

Rhizophydium irregulare (de Wild.) Fischer, Rabenhorst. Kryptogamen-Fl., 1 (4): 105. 1892.

Sporangium citriform or ovoid, 11–14.5 μ broad by 8–12 μ high, the longer axis parallel with that of the host cell, with two opposite lateral papillae (sometimes only one), 3.2–3.8 μ broad by 1.2–1.5 μ high, wall thin or somewhat thickened, smooth, colorless, resting on a short 1.2–1.5 μ thick stalk, or sessile; haustorium a continuation of the sporangial stalk, tubular, unbranched, 2.7–4.0 μ in diameter; zoospores spherical, 3.5 μ in diameter, with an eccentric, colorless globule and an 8 μ long flagellum, escaping upon the dissolution of the tip of one (always?) of the discharge papillae; resting spore not known with certainty.

Parasitic on small diatoms, de Wildeman (*loc. cit.*), BELGIUM; *Hantzschia amphioxys*, Scherffel (1925b: 24, pl. 2, fig. 51), HUNGARY; *Gomphonema constrictum*, Friedmann (1952: 192, fig. 2 o–r), AUSTRIA.

Friedmann (*loc. cit.*) has made the most complete study of this species and has seen the hitherto unobserved endobiotic part and zoospore discharge. He points out that the smooth-walled, subspherical resting spore (14–15 μ in diameter by 12 μ high) with branched rhizoidal system, that was associated by Scherffel with the fungus, probably belongs to a species of *Rhizophydium* or of *Chytriomyces*. On the basis of his determination of the nature of the haustorium, he replaces the species in *Phlyctidium*.

PHLYCTIDIUM MEGASTOMUM Sparrow

Aquatic Phycomycetes, p. 148. 1943

Sporangium sessile, spherical or ellipsoidal, becoming somewhat urceolate after discharge, 16.3–70 μ in diameter, with a broad apical papilla, wall smooth, colorless, double-contoured, endobiotic part a short distally expanded peg; zoospores at first spherical, later pyriform, with a colorless globule and a long flagellum, 6.5 μ in diameter, enlarging during swarming to 16.3 μ, moving within the sporangium and escaping through a broad apical pore, surrounded by an evanescent layer of slime; resting spore subspherical, 16.3–26 μ in diameter, with a thick brownish outer wall and a thin wavy inner one, endobiotic part like that of the sporangium, germination not observed.

On vegetative cells and heterocysts of *Anabaena flos-aquae*, RUSSIA.

This species is based on the fungus misidentified by Raitschenko (1902) as *Rhizophydium sphaerocarpum*.

The broad orifice of the discharge sporangium characteristically bore remnants of the inner wall around its margin. Examples of internally proliferated sporangia were frequent. New sporangia were formed in this "false proliferation," from a zoospore which had failed to emerge or from a zoospore which had swum into an empty sporangium. The remarkable increase in size and shape of the zoospore during motility appears to be borne out by the figures, but confirmation of this unique phenomenon is needed.

PHLYCTIDIUM OLLA Sparrow

Mycologia, 25: 517, fig. I, 14. 1933

Sporangium sessile, urn-shaped, smooth-walled, 13–15 μ high by 15–17 μ in diameter, with a broad apical papilla; haustorium unbranched, inflated, tubular, about 2 μ in diameter by about 12 μ long; zoospores emerging through a broad pore after the deliquescence of the papilla, ovoid, 5 μ long by 3 μ in diameter, posteriorly uniflagellate, with a single globule; resting spore not observed.

Parasitic on *Spirogyra sp.*, UNITED STATES.

In its symmetrical urceolate sporangium this species resembles *Rhizophydium sphaerocarpum* (Zopf) Fischer. The inflated character of the haustorium, however, distinguishes it as a species of *Phlyctidium*. *P. olla* differs from *P. megastomum* primarily in the smaller size of its sporangium (15–17 μ in diameter compared with 16–70 μ) and in the long tubular rather than short clavate haustorium. If Raitschenko's

observations on the extraordinary change in size of the zoospores of
P. megastomum during motility are correct (6.5 μ to 16.3 μ) a further
difference is found, for in *P. olla* they remained 5 by 3 μ. Finally, no
"false proliferation" of the sporangium was noted in the present species.

PHLYCTIDIUM BREBISSONII (Dang.) Sparrow

Aquatic Phycomycetes, p. 149. 1943

Chytridium brebissonii Dangeard, Le Botaniste, 1: 59, pl. 3, fig. 17. 1889.
Rhizophydium brebissonii (Dang.) Fischer, Rabenhorst. Kryptogamen-Fl.,
   1 (4): 97. 1892.

Sporangium sessile, broadly urceolate or broadly ovoid, with an
apical collarette of from four to eight prominent plain teeth, wall
fairly stout, smooth, colorless; rhizoid a broad, nearly isodiametric,
apparently unbranched filament; zoospores numerous (one hundred
or more), ovoid, 2.7 μ in diameter, with a colorless eccentric globule
and a long flagellum, emerging in a compact mass through a large
apical pore; resting spore not observed.

Parasitic on *Coleochaete scutata* in culture dishes, FRANCE.

It seems probable that if the conspicuous rhizoid were branched
in the host cell evidences of this would have been observed by Dangeard. The zoospores are cited as "2 μ 7" (2.7 μ?) in diameter. Possibly a species of *Rhizophydium*.

PHLYCTIDIUM SPINULOSUM Sparrow

Mycologia, 25: 516, fig. I, 2. 1933

Sporangium sessile, spherical or slightly ovoid, colorless, generally
about 10 μ in diameter, wall covered with short sharp spines 2 μ
high; haustorium a single unbranched slightly inflated tube, 10 μ
long by 3 μ in diameter; zoospores (usually about eight) 3 μ in diameter, with a single globule and flagellum, escaping through a subapical
pore; resting spore not observed.

Parasitic in *Cladophora sp.*, UNITED STATES (rare, occurring with
Phlyctochytrium quadricorne).

An incompletely known form found by Sparrow (1933c: 518, pl.
49, fig. 12) in *Cladophora sp.* has a spherical sporangium about 15 μ

in diameter which bears a series of tenuous radiating hairs on the outer surface. The haustorium consists of a stout somewhat irregular unbranched filament 40 μ long by 8 μ in diameter and slightly expanded at the point of contact of the inner wall of the alga. No zoospore discharge was seen. Except for the haustorium the organism resembles an immature specimen of *Phlyctochytrium chaetiferum*.

PHLYCTIDIUM ANATROPUM (Braun) Rabenhorst
Flora Europaea algarum, 3: 279. 1868
(Fig. 19 A-B, p. 318)

Chytridium anatropum Braun, Flora (N.S.), 14: 599. 1856; Monatsber. Berlin Akad., 1856: 588.

Sporangium sessile, procumbent or upright, irregular, broadly pyriform, ovoid, asymmetrical, strongly arched or reflexed (anatropous), rarely symmetrical, attached laterally near the narrower end to the algal cell, 5–14 μ wide by 15–33 μ (rarely 50 μ) long, wall thin, smooth, colorless; haustorium very small, rounded or short-peglike; zoospores elongate, 5 μ long by 2 μ wide, with a minute, inconspicuous globule and flagellum, discharged through a single pore (rarely two) formed at either of the apices and remaining in a loose cluster at the orifice before creeping away, movement strongly amoeboid, the body forming pronounced pseudopodia, swimming motion not observed; resting spore spherical or ovoid, with a smooth thick faintly brownish wall, 10 μ in diameter, contents with globules, haustorium like that of the sporangium, germination not observed.

Parasitic on *Chaetophora elegans*, Braun (*loc. cit.*), *Oscillatoria sp.*, Schenk (1858b: 8), GERMANY; *Stigeoclonium sp.*, Sparrow (1933c: 516, pl. 49, figs. 4–8), Couch (1935a: 170, figs. 56–63), UNITED STATES; *Tribonema sp.*, Bérczi (1940: 80, pl. 2, figs. 5, 6), HUNGARY.

PHLYCTIDIUM MYCETOPHAGUM Karling
Amer. J. Bot., 33: 756, figs. 44-55. 1946

"Sporangia hyaline, smooth predominantly obpyriform (8–30 μ high by 10–25 μ in greatest diameter) with a tapering or slightly inflated base, occasionally almost spherical or oval, with 1–4 low, in conspicuous, apical or subapical exit papillae. Zoospores spherical (2–2.9 μ) with a minute (0.5–0.8 μ) refringent, hyaline globule; flagellum 8–10 μ long. Rhizoid unbranched, usually thread-like or filamentous, up to 8 μ long and 0.8–1.2 μ in diameter, rarely knobbed at the end, or peg-like. Resting spores doubtful" (Karling, *loc. cit.*).

Parasitic on the sporangia, resting spores, rhizoids, and mycelium of *Rhizophydium keratinophilum*, *R. coronum*, *Rhizophlyctis rosea*, *Chytriomyces hyalinus*, *C. aureus*, *C. appendiculatus*, *Siphonaria variabilis*, *Asterophlyctis sarcoptoides*, *Septochytrium variabile*, *Polychytrium aggregatum*, *Rhizidiomyces hirsutus*, *Thraustotheca clavata*, *Aphanomyces sp.*, *Achlya flagellata*, *Zoophagus insidians*, and a species of Fungi Imperfecti, UNITED STATES.

The species is remarkable for the wide range of hosts it will attack.

PHLYCTIDIUM CHLOROGONII Serbinow

Scripta Bot. Horti Univ. Imper. Petro., 24: 156, pl. 5,
figs. 11-17. 1907

Phlyctidium acre Serbinow, nom. nud., Dnevnik IX Sezda Rusk. Est.
i vz., 1901 (10): 474.

Rhizophydium chlorogonii Jaczewski, Opredelitel gribov.... I. Fikomitsety, p. 38. 1931.

Sporangium sessile, broadly and symmetrically pyriform, with a rather small protruding apical papilla, 6–8 μ in diameter, wall thin, smooth, colorless; haustorium an inconspicuous knoblike structure; zoospores spherical, 1.5 μ in diameter, with a small colorless refractive globule and flagellum, emerging individually by means of their own motility through a small apical pore; resting spore not observed.

On moribund and dead *Chlorogonium euchlorum*, Serbinow (*loc. cit.*), RUSSIA(?); (?) *Chlorogonium elongatum*, Scourfield (1936: 120, pl. 1), GREAT BRITAIN.

Scourfield's record is open to question, since the endobiotic part (seen in one instance) was rhizoidal.

The species was first mentioned in the minutes of the Ninth Congress of Russian Naturalists and Physicians as *Phlyctidium acre*, but for some reason the name *P. chlorogonii* was applied to it in the complete description made later (1907) in Russian and German. The size of the zoospore of *P. chlorogonii* is given as 1–5 μ in the German text, which is obviously a misprint for the 1.5 μ found in the Russian description.

An incompletely observed chytrid with spherical or ellipsoidal sporangia was also shown by Serbinow (1907: 158, pl. 4, fig. 37) to possess a small knoblike haustorium like that of *Phlyctidium chlorogonii.*

PHLYCTIDIUM EUDORINAE Gimesi

Hydrobiologiai Tanulmányok (Hydrobiologische Studien) II. *Phlyctidium eudorinae* Gim., n. sp...., pp. 1-5, Németül 6-8, 1 pl., figs. A, 1-8, B, 1-6. Budapest, 1924

Phlyctidium eudorinae Skvortzow, Arch. Protistenk., 57: 205, fig. 3. 1927.
Rhizophydium beauchampi Hovasse, Ann. Protistol., 5: 73, figs. 1-4. 1936.

Sporangium imbedded, except for its apex, in the gelatinous sheath of the host colony, generally sessile on the cell of the alga, broadly pyriform or ellipsoidal, with a blunt apex, 10–18 μ high by 4–10 μ wide, wall smooth, colorless, delicate, evanescent after spore discharge; part within the algal contents consisting of a spherical haustorium 1–5 μ in diameter, attached to the base of the sporangium by a slender filament; zoospores 3.5 μ long by 2.6 μ in diameter, escaping upon the rupturing of the apex of the sporangium; resting spore pyriform, thick-walled, 10 μ in diameter, with a large globule in the contents, borne like the sporangium, germination not observed.

Parasitic on *Eudorina sp.*, Gimesi (*loc. cit.*), HUNGARY; *Eudorina elegans*, Skvortzow (*loc. cit.*), MANCHURIA; *Eudorina illinoiensis*, Hovasse (*loc. cit.*), FRANCE.

A comparison of the figures and descriptions of the Hungarian and French fungi shows them to be nearly, if not absolutely, identical. One difference is in the number of zoospores formed, Gimesi stating that from nine to twelve were produced, Hovasse, from twenty to nearly one hundred. Since both accounts were lacking in certain minor but essential points the diagnosis above represents a combination of the two descriptions. Gimesi observed the resting spores, which were formed after terminal or lateral copulation of isogamous gametes in gametangia (see "Sexual Reproduction," p. 70). Hovasse gives more complete details on the morphology, development, cytology, and biology of the species. He noted that over 90 per cent of the colonies collected from the pond over a period of ten days were infected by the fungus. The least infected had from one to two chytrids on them, the most, from seventeen to eighteen. Sterility of the colony resulted from heavy infections of the germinocysts. Coenobia bearing numerous chytrid invaders soon dropped to the bottom of the pond and disintegrated.

Concerning the development of the thallus Hovasse observed that the zoospore appears to attack the moving colony, attaching itself on the surface at the point where the flagella emerge. A slender tube is produced from the spore body and passes through the flagellar canal and into the cell contents, expanding distally to form the spherical haustorium. The more proximal portion of the tube and eventually the body of the zoospore itself expand and form the sporangium. The young sporangium is at first terminated by a beaklike process, the body of the zoospore, which disappears later; at maturity the tip of the sporangium is broad. Both Gimesi and Hovasse noted that the young thallus is binucleate.

Hovasse's preparations showed that the single nucleus of the spore migrated from the spore body into the expanding rudiment of the sporangium. There it enlarged and divided, although actual mitotic figures were not observed. The subsequent divisions of the daughter nuclei were not exactly synchronous, one nucleus, for example, being in late anaphase while the other was only in the metaphase. Division was intranuclear, and a centrosome was present at either pole of the spindle. In later stages enlargement of the nuclei occurred, followed by a simultaneous division which reduced their size and changed their configuration. Division of the cytoplasm was preceded by the appearance of large osmophilic vacuoles at one pole of each of the nuclei. Actual cytoplasmic division then progressed rapidly to all parts of the sporangium and separated the polygonal elements, each of which surrounded a nucleus. These segments became the zoospores.

PHLYCTIDIUM BUMILLERIAE Couch

J. Elisha Mitchell Sci. Soc.. 47: 256, pl. 17, figs. 66-68. 1932

"Sporangia sessile, globose, 5.4–7.6 μ thick, with a small bulbous or discoid base which extends into the host cell. Spores emerging through an apical pore. Spores not seen. Resting spores not seen" (Couch, *loc. cit.*).

Parasitic on *Bumilleria sp.*, UNITED STATES; ? *Zygnema sp.*, Bérczi (1940: 80, pl. 2, fig. 7–10), HUNGARY.

The fungus attacked the healthy cells of the alga and destroyed them. Couch considered the species close to *Phlyctidium chlorogonii*.

PHLYCTIDIUM BREVIPES var. BREVIPES (Atkinson) Minden

Kryptogamenfl. Mark Brandenburg, 5: 313. 1911 (1915)

Rhizophydium brevipes Atkinson, Bot. Gaz., 48: 322, fig. 2. 1909.

Sporangium sessile, ovoid or spherical, 10.2–24 μ in diameter, with a protruding apical papilla, wall smooth, colorless, double-contoured; haustorium consisting of a short blunt peglike tube which projects only slightly beyond the inner face of the algal wall; zoospores ovoid, about 3 μ in diameter, with a colorless globule and flagellum, escaping through an apical pore about 4 μ in diameter formed upon the deliquescence of the papilla; resting spore not observed.

On gametangia of *Spirogyra varians*, Atkinson (*loc. cit.*), UNITED STATES; vegetative cells of *Oedogonium sp.*, *Spirogyra sp.*, Tokunaga (1934b: 388, pl. 11, figs. 1–2), JAPAN.

Atkinson observed that several zoospores which at maturity were unable to escape formed long germ tubes that penetrated the wall of the sporangium. Not having reached a suitable substratum by this means, they quitted their cysts, swarmed again, came to rest, and once more penetrated the sporangium wall with their germ tubes. Atkinson saw in the production of this long germ tube a method whereby the zoospore might without swimming be able eventually to reach a favorable substratum.

PHLYCTIDIUM BREVIPES var. MARINUM Kobayasi and Ookubo

Bull. Nat. Sci. Mus. (Tokyo), (N.S.) 1 (2) (35): 62, fig. 1. 1954

"Zoosporangium solitary, epibiotic, sessile, globose, subglobose or ovoid, 25–34 μ high, 20–30 μ in diameter (commonly 34 × 30 μ), hyaline, smooth, somewhat thick-walled (2–3 μ thick), with a broad apical or subapical papilla. Rhizoid (haustorium) simple, short, thick and peglike, projecting only slightly beyond the inner face of the hostwall. Zoospores emerging one by one through a pore after the deliquescence of the papilla, globose, about 4–5 μ in diameter, with a globule and a 15 μ long posterior flagellum. Resting spore not observed" (Kobayasi and Ookubo, *loc. cit.*).

On *Bryopsis sp.*, JAPAN.

Differing slightly from *Phlyctidium brevipes* in its somewhat larger sporangia and zoospores and in its marine habitat.

PHLYCTIDIUM PIRIFORMIS (Fott), comb. nov.

Hapalopera piriformis Fott, Studia Bot. Čechica, 5 (3-4): 170, pl. 19, figs. 1-5. 1942.

Sporangium obpyriform or lacrimoid, on a very short or a long slender stalk, wall delicate, 24 μ long; rhizoid a fine thread; zoospores spherical, 2–3 μ in diameter, with a single oil droplet and 13–15 μ long flagellum, liberated upon the deliquescence of the entire sporangium wall; resting spore not observed.

Parasitic on *Characium ancora*, CZECHOSLOVAKIA.

Since partial or nearly complete deliquescence of the sporangium wall occurs in other chytrids, this character alone is not of generic significance. Because it is soon lost in the host contents, whether or not the rhizoid is unbranched is not certain.

PHLYCTIDIUM TENUE Sparrow

Mycologia, 44: 760, fig. 1 a-g. 1952

Sporangium sessile, somewhat hemispherical, 15–16 μ in diameter by 12–14 μ high; wall smooth, colorless, distinctly thickened on the lower part of the sporangium so as to form a cuplike base; haustorium slender, double-contoured, usually straight, unbranched, isodiametric, of variable length; zoospores numerous, oblong, 5 μ long by 2.5 μ wide, with a centric, colorless refractive globule and a single posterior flagellum 15 μ long, escaping through a single apical pore after which the sporangium wall collapses; resting spores epibiotic, sessile, spherical, and 13–15 μ in diameter, or ellipsoidal and 10 by 12 μ, with a slightly thickened wall, large central colorless oil globule, and an un-branched endobiotic haustorium, possibly sexually formed, the adnate contributing thallus 3 μ in diameter, germination not observed.

On moribund vegetative cells of *Zygnema sp.*, UNITED STATES.

This species differs from all the rest in the genus in the basal thickening of the otherwise delicate sporangium wall.

RECENTLY DESCRIBED TAXA[1]

PHLYCTIDIUM GLOBOSUM Skuja

Nova Acta Reg. Soc. Sci. Upsaliensis, Ser. IV, 16 (3): 367, pl. 63, figs. 1-5. 1956

Sporangium sessile, erect, globose to broadly ovate, with an acuminate papillate apex, 10–13 μ in diameter or 10–14 μ wide by 12–15 μ long, wall moderately thin, smooth, colorless; endobiotic part an irregularly lobate, transversely elongate saclike haustorium; zoospores thirty-two or more, globose or broadly ovate, 1.5–2 μ in diameter, with a basal colorless globule and long flagellum, escaping upon the deliquescence of the apical papilla; resting spores not observed.

In resting spores of the phytoplankter *Aphanizomenon flos-aquae* (1 per cent of filaments infected), SWEDEN.

Whether or not this can be considered a species of *Phlyctidium* is questionable. A new species name will have to be given it, if kept in this genus, since the same binomial, *P. globosum* (Braun) Sorokin, has been applied to *Rhizophydium globosum*.

PHLYCTIDIUM KERATINOPHILUM Ookubo and Kobayasi

Nagaoa, 5: 1, fig. 1. 1955

"Sporangia at first imbedded in the cortex of hairs, at maturity emerging their upper half from the bursting place, globose, ellipsoid or pyriform, papillately or conically elongated at the base, smooth, thin-walled, colorless, apically or laterally with one papilla (5-10 μ high), containing 20–30 zoospores; haustorium not observed. Zoospores ellipsoid or pyriform, 3–4 × 3.5–5 μ, containing several oil drops at their anterior part and with one refracting body at posterior

[1] Not included in the key.

part, swimming away one by one through the pore of papilla. Resting spores imbedded in hair, then emerging, globose or subglobose with thick and rough wall, 17–25 μ in diameter, containing one large oil globule; germination not observed" (Ookubo and Kobayasi, *loc. cit.*). Human hair (as bait), JAPAN.

IMPERFECTLY KNOWN SPECIES OF PHLYCTIDIUM

? PHLYCTIDIUM DANGEARDII Serbinow

Scripta Bot. Horti Univ. Imper. Petro., 24: 163, pl. 6, figs. 22 A-C. 1907

Rhizophydium dangeardii Jaczewski, Opredelitel gribov . . . . I. Fikomitsety, p. 38. 1931.

Tylochytrium dangeardii (Serbinow) Karling, Amer. J. Bot., 29:24. 1942.

Sporangium sessile on the prosporangium of the host, spherical or ovoid, wall smooth, colorless, two-layered, with a single small protruding apical papilla; haustorium not observed; zoospores ovoid, with a small globule and flagellum, about 1.5 μ long, escaping through a small sessile apical pore; resting spore borne like the sporangium, spherical, thick-walled, the inner wall smooth, the outer irregularly undulate, germination not observed.

Parasitic on prosporangia of the chytrid *Saccomyces*, RUSSIA.

No rhizoid is figured by Serbinow. It is possible that the fungus, although placed in *Phlyctidium*, is in reality a *Rozella* parasitic in the sporangium, rather than the prosporangium, of the host.

? PHLYCTIDIUM MINIMUM Schroeter

Kryptogamenfl. Schlesien, 3 (1): 191. 1885

Rhizophydium minimum (Schroeter) Fischer, Rabenhorst. Kryptogamen-Fl., 1 (4): 105. 1892.

Sporangia sessile, spherical, mostly of the same size, about 6 μ in diameter, with a short spherical haustorium.

On *Mougeotia pleurocarpa*, GERMANY.

Fischer believes this may possibly be only the immature stage of "*Chytridium mesocarpi* Fisch." It was not mentioned by Schroeter

(1893) when *Phlyctochytrium* was segregated from *Rhizophydium*, although from its haustorium it may belong in that genus.

Couch (1932: 252) has identified a fungus on *Bumilleria* with this species (see *Rhizophydium sp.*, p. 311).

? PHLYCTIDIUM SP. Serbinow

Scripta. Bot. Horti Univ. Imper. Petro., 24: 158, pl. 4, fig. 37. 1907

Rhizophydium serbinovii Jaczewski, Opredelitel gribov.... I. Fikomitsety, p. 38. 1931.

Sporangium at first spherical, then ovoid, with a simple unbranched expanded rounded haustorium, which penetrates only to the second membrane of the "*Gloeocystis*" stage.

In "*Gloeocystis*" stage of *Euglena*, RUSSIA.

? PHLYCTIDIUM SP. Sparrow

Mycologia, 25: 518, pl. 49, fig. 12. 1933

Sporangium spherical, about 15 μ in diameter, the wall covered by a series of tenuous, radiating hairs; haustorium a stout (40 μ long by 8 μ in diameter) somewhat irregular unbranched filament slightly swollen at the point of contact with the inner wall of the substratum; other characters unknown.

On *Cladophora*, UNITED STATES.

SEPTOSPERMA WHIFFEN

Mycologia, 34: 552. 1942

(Fig. 19, L-M, p. 318)

"Thallus extramatrical, eucarpic. Zoosporangia, arising by enlargement of zoospore, spherical, ovoid, or ellipsoid, each sporangium with a single exit pore. Zoospores uniguttulate and posteriorly uniciliate. Resting bodies elongated, ellipsoid to clavate, divided by cross wall into an empty proximal portion and a distal portion containing protoplasm and one or more oil globules. Zoosporangia and resting bodies attached to host by bulbous, discoid, or slightly branched haustorium" (Whiffen, *loc. cit.*).

The genus differs from *Phlyctidium* only in the septate nature of the resting spore. This peculiarity is shown by several other chytrids, notably *Nowakowskiella hemisphaerospora*.

KEY TO THE SPECIES OF SEPTOSPERMA

Sporangium ovoid or ellipsoid; resting spore same shape as sporangium .... *S. anomalum*, p. 226
Sporangium spherical to pyriform; resting spore clavate
S. rhizophidii, p. 226

SEPTOSPERMA ANOMALUM (Couch) Whiffen
Mycologia, 34: 552. 1942
Phlyctidium anomalum Couch, J. Elisha Mitchell Sci. Soc., 47: 256, pl. 17, figs. 69-83. 1932.

Sporangium sessile, ovoid, or ellipsoid, smooth-walled, 3.8–6.1 μ broad by 12 μ high; haustorium bulbous or discoid; zoospores 8–30, spherical, 2.3 μ in diameter, with a single glistening droplet, discharged through an apical pore, the sporangium collapsing, more or less, after spore discharge; resting spores formed from a cell of about the same size and shape as mature sporangium, the protoplasm collecting in the distal half of the cell, which becomes thick-walled, leaving the proximal half empty, with one to three oil globules, rarely occupying the entire (parent) cell.

Parasitic on sporangia of *Phlyctidium bumilleriae*, Couch (*loc. cit.*), UNITED STATES; *P. bumilleriae*, Bérczi (1940: 80, pl. 2, figs. 7–10), HUNGARY; *Chytriomyces tabellariae*, Canter (1949a: 19, fig. 3), *Zygorhizidium willei*, *Micromyces sp.*, *Rhizophydium planktonicum* (Canter, 1953: 288), GREAT BRITAIN.

In this curious example of hyperparasitism of one chytrid by another, both Couch and Canter noted that none of the infected sporangia of the host ever reached maturity. Canter further observed that the resting spores of the host were never attacked.

SEPTOSPERMA RHIZOPHIDII Whiffen
Mycologia, 34: 552, figs. 28-52. 1942
(Fig. 19 L-M, p. 318)
"Zoösporangia varying in shape from spherical to pyriform, 8.2 μ

to 24.4 μ in diameter, wall smooth with a single inconspicuous exit pore at maturity; zoöspores spherical, 1.6 μ to 2.0 μ in diameter. Resting sporangia clavate, stalked, 4.1 μ × 16.4 μ to 6.1 μ × 25.1 μ, at maturity stalk empty of protoplasm, apical portion filled with numerous small oil globules. Germination of resting sporangia not observed" (Whiffen, *loc. cit.*).

Parasitic on *Rhizophydium macrosporum*, Whiffen (*loc. cit.*), cyst of microscopic animal, Sparrow (1952d: 762), UNITED STATES; *Rhizophydium spp.*, *Rhizidium richmondense*, *Rhizophlyctis sp.*, Willoughby (1956: 135, figs. 8–9), GREAT BRITAIN.

LOBORHIZA HANSON
Amer. J. Bot., 31: 169. 1944
(Fig. 19 J-K, p. 318)

"Thallus epi- and endobiotic, monocentric, eucarpic; epibiotic part forming the rudiment of the sporangium or resting spore, endobiotic part forming a polylobate haustorium; sporangium inoperculate, sessile; zoospores posteriorly uniflagellate, fully formed within the sporangium and emerging singly; resting spore thick walled, stipitate, usually formed by the fusion of isomorphic motile gametes [gametangia] one of which has previously come to rest and germinated on the host; germination unknown" (Hanson, *loc. cit.*).

The genus is distinct from the closely related *Phlyctidium* and *Rhizophydium* by reason of formation of a polydigitate absorbing organ and true internal proliferation of the sporangium.

The type of sexual reproduction here is like that found in *Phlyctidium eudorinae* (see "Sexual Reproduction," p. 70).

LOBORHIZA METZNERI Hanson
Amer. J. Bot., 31: 169, figs. 1-31. 1944

"Zoosporangia pyriform 17 × 31 μ to 46 × 67 μ in diameter, imbedded except for their apices in the gelatinous sheath of coenobia, sessile on cellular elements of all phases of *Volvox carteri* with the exception of the purely vegetative cells of each phase and the thick walled zygote of female colonies, secondary and tertiary sporangia

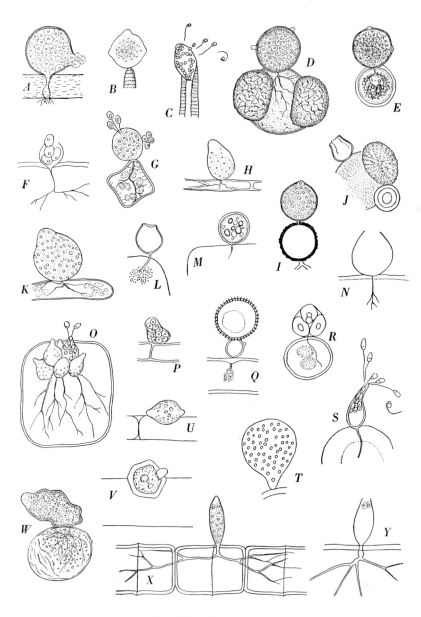

Fig. 17. *Rhizophydium*

arising in empty sporangia by internal proliferation. Intramatrical haustorium polydigitate or polylobate. Zoospores amoeboid upon liberation, spherical when actively swimming, 3.7 to 3.9 μ in diameter, with a single posterior flagellum 26 μ long, one posterior highly re-

---

Explanation of Figure 17

A. Rhizophydium karlingii, sp. nov., on *Ulothrix*, sporangium discharging zoospores. *B. Rhizophydium subangulosum* (Braun) Rabenhorst, sporangium with discharge papillae, resting on tip of filament of *Oscillatoria*. *C. Rhizophydium megarrhizum* Sparrow, on *Lyngbya*, discharging sporangium with its broad undulating rhizoid. *D–E. Rhizophydium sphaerotheca* Zopf: *D*, mature sporangium with protruding discharge papillae, on pine pollen; *E*, sporangium with two discharge papillae, on microspore of *Isoetes*. *F. Rhizophydium constantineani* Saccardo on *Vaucheria*, sporangium discharging its few zoospores. *G. Rhizophydium cyclotellae* Zopf on *Cyclotella*, sporangium discharging its zoospores through two pores. *H. Rhizophydium asymmetricum* (Dang.) Minden on *Tribonema*, mature sporangium. *I. Rhizophydium sp.*, germination of resting spore by formation of sporangium. *J. Rhizophydium pollinis-pini* (Braun) Zopf on pine pollen, empty pyriform sporangium above at left, resting spore below; rhizoidal system not shown. *K. Rhizophydium sciadii* (Zopf) Fischer on *Ophiocytium*, mature sporangium. *L–M. Rhizophydium sphaerocarpum* (Zopf) Fischer on *Spirogyra* and *Mougeotia*: *L*, empty sporangium; *M*, resting spore. *N. Rhizophydium vermicola* Sparrow, on nematode, empty sporangium. *O. Rhizophydium zoophthorum* (Dang.) Fischer on rotifer, group of sporangia on carapace. *P–Q. Rhizophydium granulosporum* Scherffel on *Tribonema*: *P*, mature sporangium; *Q*, spiny resting spore on smooth-walled basal male cell. *R. Rhizophydium mischococci* Scherffel on *Mischococcus*, mature sporangium. *S. Rhizophydium simplex* (Dang.) Fischer on cyst of *Cryptomonas*, discharging sporangium. *T. Rhizophydium clinopus* Scherffel on diatoms, sporangium. *U–V. Rhizophydium goniosporum* Scherffel on *Tribonema*: *U*, sporangium with opposed discharge papillae; *V*, angular resting spore with adherent male cell. *W. Rhizophydium gibbosum* (Zopf) Fischer on rotifer egg, maturing sporangium. *X. Rhizophydium fusus* (Zopf) Fischer on *Melosira*, mature sporangium. *Y. Rhizophydium messanense* Morini on *Cladophora*, sporangium.

(*A*, Karling, 1938e; *B*, Braun, 1856a; *C*, after Dangeard, 1886a; *D–E*, *G*, *K*, Zopf, 1887; *F*, after Constantineanu, 1901; *H*, after Dangeard, 1890-91c; *I*, Karling, 1939c; *J*, after Braun, 1856a; *L–M*, after Zopf, 1884; *N*, *U–V*, Sparrow, 1936a; *O*, *S*, Dangeard, 1889b; *P–Q*, Scherffel, 1925b; *R*, Scherffel, 1926a; *T*, Scherffel, 1931; *W*, after Zopf, 1888; *Y*, Morini, 1896)

fractive globule, and one or two oscillating granules in small vacuoles. Resting spore extramatrical, stipitate, with a golden wall, .746 to 1 μ thick, ornamented with irregular lobes, spherical at maturity, 16.4 to 33.6 μ, rarely elliptical, 11.9 × 16.4 to 15.4 × 19.4 μ, containing one very large globule of refringent material 10.4 to 12.6 μ in diameter; formed as a result of lateral fusion of isomorphic motile gametes [gametangia], one of which has previously come to rest and germinated; germination not observed" (Hanson, *loc. cit.*).

Parasitic on all parts but the purely vegetative cells and thick-walled oöspores of *Volvox carteri*, UNITED STATES.

RHIZOPHYDIUM SCHENK[1]

Verhandl. Phys.-Med. Gesell. Würzburg, A.F., 8: 245. 1858
(Fig. 17, p. 228; also, Figs. 4 B-O, p. 72; 8 F-H, p. 97; 10 A-L, p. 108; 18 A-E, F, H-J, p. 286; 20 F, p. 330)

Chytridium subgen. *Sphaerostylidium* Braun, Abhandl. Berlin Akad., 1855: 75. 1856.
Rhizophyton Zopf, Nova Acta Acad. Leop.-Carol., 52 (7): 343. 1888.

Thallus epi- and endobiotic, monocentric, eucarpic, generally monophagous; the epibiotic part forming the rudiment of the sporangium or resting spore, the endobiotic, the branched (rarely unbranched) rhizoidal system; sporangium inoperculate, sessile, or rarely on an extramatrical stalk, uni- or multiporous, the wall occasionally deliquescing wholly or in part; zoospores formed within the sporangium, posteriorly uniflagellate, generally with a single globule; resting spore thick-walled, contents with one or more globules, borne like the sporangium, asexually formed or sexually after receiving the contents of a small adnate contributing thallus which persists as a cyst, upon germination functioning as a sporangium or prosporangium.

Parasites and saprophytes on a wide variety of plant and animal substrata.

This is the largest and most complex genus of the chytrids, one in which extensive morphological studies and cross-inoculation work will be necessary before the limits of the species can be established. One, *Rhizophydium graminis* Ledingham (1936), is parasitic on the roots of

[1] See also Sparrow (1957a) for the new species *R. elyensis* and *R. stipitatum*.

wheat; another, *R. fungicola* Zimmerman (1902), on the hyphae of *Gloeosporium. Mastigochytrium saccardiae* Lagerheim (1892), which is parasitic on perithecia of *Saccardia durantae*, may possibly be referable to *Rhizophydium*.

It is well realized that the present treatment of this most difficult genus is far from adequate. Characters which appear from the original description of a species to be fixed, well marked, and distinctive are usually found, upon careful investigation of a great many individuals, to be subject to wide variation. Thus, the number of discharge pores, the size and shape of the sporangium, the extent of the rhizoidal system, the nature of the substratum, and so forth, do not always prove constant or decisive. Before much reliance can be placed on an analytical key, such as the one immediately following, for the identification of a member of the genus, the whole complex of the "species" should be studied, the original papers consulted, and the figures compared.

In this treatise those species with a tapering unbranched rhizoid have been placed in *Rhizophydium* rather than in *Phlyctidium*, where at first sight they might seem to belong.

The treatment of such collective species as *Rhizophydium globosum*, *R. sphaerocarpum*, and so on, has been a subject for much deliberation. There has been no attempt to solve with finality the many problems associated with them. An effort has been made, however, to adhere to the original conception of these species as much as possible. This has left some well-described forms without names. It is hoped that further study will show either that they are worthy of specific rank or that they should be placed under an already described species.

KEY TO THE SPECIES OF RHIZOPHYDIUM [1]

Sporangium predominantly spherical, subspherical, or ovoid, occasionally broadly obpyriform[2] or angular and upright
SECTION I [3], p. 237
   In fresh-water or inland salt pools
     Sporangium wall smooth

---

[1] Note that this key is not strictly dichotomous.
[2] That is, having the distal part broadest (reverse of British usage).
[3] See also recently described taxa at end of each section.

Discharge pores variable in number and position, sessile or only
slightly elevated, rarely lacking
Sporangium predominantly spherical, subspherical, or angu-
lar
Globule of zoospore small (less than half the diameter of
the spore body)
Sporangium wall persistent after discharge of zoospores;
on various types of substrata
Typical sporangium large; zoospores numerous
On green algae
Rhizoidal axis not inflated and haustorial; rhi-
zoids extensive
Resting-spore wall covered with minute spines;
primarily on desmids ...... *R. globosum*, p. 237
Resting spore wall smooth or somewhat undulate, bearing a small male cell; on
Spirogyra .... *R. couchii*, p. 241
Rhizoidal axis somewhat inflated; rhizoids not
extensive
Sporangium spherical, with a single prominent
lateral discharge papilla; zoospores without a prominent oil globule; on sporelings
of *Oedogonium*............ *R. canterae*, p. 242
Sporangium spherical or slightly flattened,
with one to three sublateral, lateral, or
subapical discharge papillae; zoospores
with a prominent oil globule; on *Ulothrix*
R. karlingii, p. 243
On blue-green algae
Rhizoids delicate; inconspicuous
Sporangium with a single broad apical discharge papilla, not angular; causing ringlike contortion and excessive slime se-
cretion of the host trichomes *R. deformans*, p. 243
Sporangium with two to four discharge papil-
lae which impart an angular shape; not
causing hypertrophy of the host
R. subangulosum, p. 244
Rhizoids coarse, conspicuous.. *R. megarrhizum*, p. 246
On other Phycomycetes
On reproductive organs of *Pythium R. pythii*, p. 247
On *Choanephora* .... *R. mycetophagum*, p. 247

On chytrids
Rhizoidal system tubular with short, lateral,
stubby extensions; on *Phlyctochytrium*
aureliae .... *R. chytriophagum*, p. 248
Rhizoidal system slender, with delicate taper-
ing branches
On *Chytriomyces*...... *R. chytriomycetis*, p. 248
On *Rhizophlyctis* (*Karlingia*) and *Septochy-*
trium .... *R. hyperparasiticum*, p. 248
On spores of higher plants (pollen, etc.)
Sporangium spherical; pores sessile
Resting spores not observed *R. sphaerotheca*, p. 249
Resting spores quickly and abundantly formed,
wall beset with bullations *R. bullatum*, p. 250
Sporangium angular, the apices terminating in
pores .... *R. racemosum*, p. 251
On plant debris; sporangium surrounded by one to
several hyaline zones or "halos" *R. coronum*, p. 251
On animals or material of animal origin
On cysts of *Vampyrella*; sporangium with several
subapical discharge papillae *R. vampyrellae*, p. 252
On *Amoeba* and insect exuviae; sporangium with
one apical discharge papilla ... *R. amoebae*, p. 253
On chitinous substrata ..... *R. chitinophilum*, p. 253
Typical sporangium small (6-12 μ in diameter);
zoospores few
On filaments of *Vaucheria*.......*R. constantineani*, p. 254
On *Asterionella*; resting spore smooth
R. planktonicum, p. 254
On *Rhizophlyctis*; resting spore bullate
R. marshallense, p. 255
Sporangium wall deliquescing upon or after discharge
of zoospores; on algae
On the green alga *Sphaerocystis* *R. sphaerocystidis*, p. 255
On the desmids *Staurastrum* and *Arthrodesmus*
R. difficile, p. 256
On diatoms
Wall completely deliquescing and releasing
zoospores
On *Cyclotella*................*R. cyclotellae*, p. 257
On *Melosira*................. *R. melosirae*, p. 258
On *Achnanthes*...............*R. achnanthis*, p. 258
Wall deliquescing only after zoospores have es-
caped through one to three discharge pores;
on *Fragilaria* ....*R. fragilariae*, p. 259

Globule of zoospore more than half the diameter of body
of zoospore .... *R. macrosporum*, p. 259
Sporangium predominantly ovoid or somewhat citriform
Papilla obliquely placed; primarily on *Tribonema*
R. asymmetricum, p. 260
Papilla terminal; primarily on green algae
Papilla small; resting spore unknown   *R. mammillatum*, p. 260
Papilla broad; resting spore sexually formed
R. uniguttulum, p. 262
Discharge pores one or two, terminating very distinct dis-
charge tubes
Discharge tube single, apical .... *R. ampullaceum*, p. 262
Discharge tubes two, opposed (occasionally one)
Tubes narrow, hornlike; rhizoids branched
R. rostellatum, p. 263
Tubes broad, giving the sporangium a triangular ap-
pearance; rhizoids unbranched........ *R. haynaldii*, p. 264
Sporangium wall ornamented
Sporangium wall bearing long, slender, branched or un-
branched hairs on its upper part; on green algae
R. chaetiferum, p. 264
Sporangium wall bearing short, simple, bifurcate, or dichot-
omously branched spines; on keratinized tissues
R. keratinophilum, p. 265
In marine waters; on *Codium* .... *R. codicola*, p. 266
Sporangium predominantly spherical at first and urceolate after dis-
charge, or pyriform, conical, or flask-shaped....... SECTION II, p. 268
Sporangium spherical at first but urceolate (occasionally pyriform)
after discharge
Rhizoids branched
On pollen .... *R. pollinis-pini*, p. 268
On *Ophiocytium* .... *R. sciadii*, p. 271
Rhizoids little if at all branched
On algae
Sporangium very small (up to 7 μ in diameter); on diatoms
(*Asterionella*) .... *R. schroeteri*, p. 272
Sporangium larger; on blue-green or green algae
On blue-green algae (*Oscillatoria*)
R. oscillatoriae-rubescentis, p. 272
On green algae
Sporangium 6-18 μ in diameter by 20 μ high; on various
green algae, primarily Conjugatae
R. sphaerocarpum, p. 273

Sporangium flask-shaped, except for apex of neck immersed in the
host sheath, usually stalked; on *Apiocystis*..... *R. anomalum*, p. 287
Sporangium predominantly obovoid, obovate, or obpyriform[1]
                                                 Section III, p. 288
Zoospores liberated upon deliquescence of the upper half of the
sporangium wall; on diatoms .... *R. clinopus*, p. 288
Zoospores liberated upon formation of one or more apical, sub-
apical, or lateral discharge pores
Sporangium sessile on gelatinous colonial sheath of the host,
borne on the tip of a long threadlike stalk which penetrates
the host cell, with two subapical, opposite discharge papillae;
on *Gemellicystis* .... *R. fulgens*, p. 289
Sporangium sessile on the host cell proper
Sporangium with a single lateral pore; on *Oedogonium*
                                       R. parasiticum, p. 290
Sporangium with an apical pore
Discharge pore very broad, its edge reflexed; resting spore
spiny, without an adherent male cell; on *Glenodinium*
                                       R. echinatum, p. 290
Discharge pore smaller, its edge not reflexed; resting spore
smooth-walled, resting on a small male cell; on *Stigeo-
clonium* .... *R. ovatum*, p. 291
Sporangium predominantly citriform or saddle-shaped, ovoid or
oblong, or spherical at first but becoming broadly ellipsoidal or
fusiform; the long axis of the sporangium *parallel* with the surface of the substratum .... Section IV, p. 292
Resting spore spherical or subspherical, without an adherent male
cell; on *Chlamydomonas* and *Gonium* .... *R. transversum*, p. 292
Resting spore spherical, oval, or polygonal, with a male cell adherent
or connected to it by a conjugation tube of variable length
Resting spore spherical, with radiating columnar bands of refrac-
tive material in its wall; male cell connected by a conjugation
tube of variable length; on *Spirotaenia* .... *R. columnaris*, p. 293
Resting spore oval to subspherical, wall homogeneous; male cell
directly adnate or connected by a short tube to resting spore
Sporangium saddle-shaped, on *Stylosphaeridium* or epiphytic on
Coelosphaerium .... *R. ephippium*, p. 294
Sporangium oblong to oval, on *Dinobryon*..... *R. oblongum*, p. 295
Resting spore polygonal, with one or two small adherent male
cells; on *Tribonema* .... *R. goniosporum*, p. 295
Sporangium predominantly cylindrical, fusiform, broadly or narrowly
ellipsoidal or angular: the long axis frequently at right angles or
slightly inclined to that of the substratum .... Section V, p. 296

[1] See note 2, p. 231.

SECTION I[1]

RHIZOPHYDIUM GLOBOSUM (Braun) Rabenhorst

Flora Europaea algarum, 3:280. 1868 (sensu strictu Cohn, Nova Acta
    Acad. Leop.-Carol., 24:142. 1853)

Chytridium globosum Braun, Monatsber. Berlin Akad., 1855:381; Abhandl. Berlin Akad., 1855:34, pl. 2, figs. 14-18. 1856.

Phlyctidium globosum (Braun) Sorokin, Arch. Bot. Nord. France, 2: 19,
fig. 12. 1883 (separate).

Sporangium sessile, completely spherical, 12–50 μ in diameter or
over, wall double-contoured, smooth, colorless, with from two to
four protruding discharge papillae on the upper half; rhizoidal system
branched, fairly extensive, arising from a short stalk or directly from
the tip of the penetration tube; zoospores very numerous, somewhat
ellipsoidal, 2–3 μ in diameter, with a flagellum about 20 μ long, escaping individually through one apical pore or through from two to
four sessile or slightly elevated pores on the upper half of the spo-

---

[1] See also the following imperfectly known species of *Rhizophydium*:

rangium and swimming immediately away; resting spore sessile, spherical, 25–30 μ in diameter, with a thick brownish wall, outer surface covered with small spines, germination not observed.

Parasitic on *Closterium sp.*, causing an epidemic in culture dishes, *Navicula sp.*, (?) *Sphaeroplea annulina*, Cohn (*loc. cit.*, pl. 16, figs. 10–20), (?) vegetative cells of *Oedogonium rivulare*, (?) *Melosira varians*, (?) *Eunotia amphioxys*, Braun (*loc. cit.*), germlings of *O. tumidulum*, Kloss (in Braun, 1856b: 587), *Closterium lunula*, *Penium digitus*, *Pinnularia viridis*, Schroeter(?)(1885: 191), GERMANY; *Pleurotaenium trabecula*, *Closterium sp.*, *Staurastrum sp.*, Cejp (1933a: 3, pl. 1, figs. 5–8, pl. 2, fig. 1), CZECHOSLOVAKIA; *Closterium spp.*, diatoms, Dangeard (1886a: 295), FRANCE; *Penium digitus*, *Pleurotaenium trabecula*, *Genicularia sp.*, *Spirotaenia sp.*, Serbinow (1907: 160, pl. 5, figs. 1–3), FINLAND; *Oedogonium sp.*, Litvinow (1953: 79), LATVIA; *Spirogyra sp.*, Atkinson (1894: 503; 1909a: 321, figs. 1 a–d), *Cladophora glomerata*, Karling (1941a: 387), *Oedogonium sp.*, Karling (1941b: 108), *Spirogyra sp.*, Karling (1948c: 508), UNITED STATES; *Ulothrix sp.*, W. R. I. Cook (1932a: 136, figs. 13–19), GREAT BRITAIN; *Spirogyra sp.*, Tokunaga (1934b: 390, pl. 11, fig. 5), JAPAN; *Spirogyra sp.*, Bérczi (1940: 81), HUNGARY; pine pollen, Gaertner (1954b: 21), EGYPT, NORTHWEST AFRICA, WEST AFRICA, EQUATORIAL EAST AFRICA, SOUTH AFRICA.

Though spherical sporangia of this species were observed by Braun on several hosts, it was Cohn who reported the nonsexual reproduction and the branched rhizoids. Braun identified the sporangial part of Cohn's fungus with his own, but declared that the rhizoids probably belonged to another organism! Cohn also observed the penetration of the germ tube of the zoospore and the formation of the rhizoids within the alga. Later, however, he declared the same species on *Sphaeroplea* to be without rhizoids.

The species is a difficult one to delimit and, as Fischer (1892: 91) aptly pointed out, is either a widespread omnivorous organism or is a collective species in need of further investigation. No sound limitations can be established for it until the morphological variations which occur on different substrata in strains derived from single spores are studied and such studies have not as yet been forthcoming. In the preceding diagnosis an attempt was made to stay within the confines of Cohn's concept of the species. The resting-spore stage is that described by Serbinow. No forms were included which did not fall within these limits. Mere records, as well as globose types which were imperfectly observed, were excluded. The following were considered inadmissible:

1. Schenk (1858a: 237), on *Oedogonium sp.* (1858b: 8), on *Oscillatoria sp.* and *Anabaena sp.*, GERMANY. No zoospore discharge observed.

2. Sorokin (1883: 19, fig. 12), as *Phlyctidium globosum* on diatoms, "*Cladophorae*," EUROPEAN RUSSIA. No zoospore discharge observed.

3. Dangeard (1888c: 142, pl. 5, figs. 16–18), on *Glenodinium*, FRANCE. Probably a new species.

4. Dangeard (1889b: 62, pl. 3, fig. 16), on *Vampyrella sp.*, FRANCE See *Rhizophydium vampyrellae* (Dang.) Minden, page 252.

5. Dangeard (1887a: xxiii; 1889b: pl. 3, figs. 12–13), on *Chlamydomonas, Phacotus,* etc., FRANCE. The fungus on *Chlamydomonas* is probably a new species.

6. De Wildeman (1890: 20), on *Melosira varians*, BELGIUM. Sporangium spherical, about 16 μ in diameter; escape of the zoospores not observed; appeared to be seven zoospores within the sporangium, each about 5 μ in diameter.

7. De Wildeman (1891: 170), on *Hyalotheca sp., Penium sp., Staurastrum sp.*, BELGIUM. Only the sizes of the sporangia are given (12.5–23.5 μ in diameter).

8. De Wildeman (1894: 157), on *Melosira sp.*, FRANCE. Record only.

9. H. E. Petersen (1910: 552, fig. 24c). Petersen records it on *Penium*, possibly also on other desmids, DENMARK. The substratum of the fungi shown in the figure is not given. From the needle-like unbranched rhizoid, the fungus appears closer to *Phlyctidium*.

10. Schulz (1923: 181, fig. 13), on *Pleurotaenium trabecula*, DANZIG. Sporangium spherical; rhizoids branched; no zoospore discharge observed.

11. Graff (1928: 160), on diatoms, UNITED STATES. Sporangium spherical, 25–40 μ in diameter; zoospores escaping through a large terminal opening; rhizoids "similar in development to those of *R. sphaerocarpum* (Zopf) A. Fisch." Probably referable to *Rhizophydium sphaerocarpum*.

12. Couch (1932: 246). See *Rhizophydium couchii* Sparrow, page 241. This species also includes the form described by Domján (1936: 42), "Type III," and Sparrow (1933c: 520).

13. Sparrow (1933c: 519), on *Oscillatoria spp.*, *Spirogyra spp.*, *Navicula sp.*, UNITED STATES. Records only. The fungus called *Rhizophydium pollinis*, described by Sparrow (1932b: 275, fig. 2d) on pine pollen in the United States, fits closely the description of *R. globosum*. The resting spores, however, are smooth-walled, a fact inadvertently omitted in the description. See *R. sphaerotheca*, p. 249.

14. Sparrow (1936a: 441). Three fungi on different substrata, ENGLAND: (1) on rotifer (pl. 19, fig. 19); spherical sporangia 15–20 μ in diameter, ellipsoidal sporangia 43 by 37 μ; zoospores in both types 3 μ in diameter, escaping by from two to three pores; rhizoids stout, well developed; (2) on pollen of *Typha*; sporangium spherical, 12–17 μ in diameter; zoospores 3 μ in diameter, escaping through several pores; rhizoidal system delicate, branched (see *Rhizophydium sphaerotheca*, p. 249); (3) on *Oscillatoria* (see *R. subangulosum*, p. 244).

15. Sparrow (1936b: 258), UNITED STATES: (1) parasitic on *Bryopsis plumosa* (marine); sporangium spherical, 13–18 μ in diameter; rhizoids delicate, branched; zoospores not described; (2) saprophytic on *Rhizosolenia spp.* (marine); sporangium spherical or subspherical, 9–12 μ in diameter; rhizoidal system, so far as observed, consisting of a single delicate unbranched peg; zoospores not observed. The form on *Bryopsis* may possibly be identical with the incompletely known *Rhizophydium marinum* de Wild. Observations on the zoospore discharge of both these organisms are necessary to place them generically.

16. Aleem (1953: 15, fig. 29), on the marine alga *Acrochaetium* (?), SWEDEN. Aleem doubtfully ascribes a fungus with nearly spherical smooth-walled sporangia, 13 μ in diameter, to this species. It was attached to the host cell by a "faint" rhizoidal system. Zoospores, 2 μ in diameter, were seen within the sporangium but their escape was not observed.

Domján (1936) attempted to divide the fungi she found into types I, II, and III, but the descriptions and figures of these types are too meager to be interpreted.

The descriptions of the two following forms designated as *Rhizo-*

phydium globosum have not been examined: Schaarschmidt (1883: 62) and Entz, Jr. (1931: 12), both based on material from Hungary. See also *Rhizophydium pollinis-pini*, p. 268.

RHIZOPHYDIUM COUCHII Sparrow

Aquatic Phycomycetes, p. 167, Fig. 2 G-I. 1943

(Fig. 4 G-I, p. 72)

Sporangium sessile, spherical, slightly subspherical, or somewhat ellipsoidal, with from one to three protruding discharge papillae, 11–30 μ in diameter, wall of variable thickness (up to 2 μ), smooth, colorless; rhizoidal system extensive, much branched, arising from a more or less prolonged, sometimes slightly inflated main axis; zoo-spores spherical or slightly ovoid, 2–5 μ in diameter, with a small eccentric colorless globule and a long flagellum, escaping slowly, often amoeboidly, through one apical pore or through from two to three apical, subapical, and lateral pores formed upon the deliquescence of the papillae, movement hopping; resting spore spherical or somewhat ellipsoidal, 10–14 μ in diameter, with a thick smooth colorless wall which is occasionally surrounded by an irregular brownish incrustation, contents with a large oil globule, rhizoidal system branched, germi-nation not (?) observed; contributing thallus spherical, thin-walled, 5 μ in diameter, adnate to the receptive plant, sessile, rhizoidal system rudimentary if present.

On *Spirogyra areolata*, *Spirogyra sp.*, *Mougeotia sp.*, Couch (1932: 246, pl. 14), *Spirogyra sp.*, Sparrow (1933c: 520, pl. 49, figs. 15–22), UNITED STATES; *Spirogyra*, water of salinity 9.6–10.1 per cent, Aleem (1952a: 2650), FRANCE.

The species was described by Couch (*loc. cit.*) under the name *Rhizophydium globosum* and by Sparrow (1933c) as *Rhizophydium sp.* It differs from *R. globosum* in several features, as Couch has pointed out. Most important of these is that the resting spore is smaller (10–14 μ), smooth-walled, and sexually formed (see under "Sexual Repro-duction," p. 70). *R. globosum* "Type III" of Domján (1936) is, from the figures, very similar to *R. couchii*. Since her form is described only in Hungarian a further comparison has not been attempted.

Only one (apical) pore was observed in the sporangia of Sparrow's material, whereas Couch reports one or several in his fungus. This difference is not considered of great significance in view o f the striking similarities which are otherwise apparent in the two fungi. Germination of the resting spores of material which is probably this species has been described by Karling (1939c) (Fig. 17 I, p. 228).

RHIZOPHYDIUM CANTERAE, sp. nov.[1]

Sporangium sessile, spherical, with a smooth, thin, colorless wall, 7.5–34.3 μ in diameter, the larger ones occurring singly on the abnormally curved host cell, the smaller ones gregarious, up to fourteen on a single cell; endobiotic part consisting of a sparingly branched rhizoidal system arising from a short, rarely slightly inflated main axis; zoospores somewhat elongate, 4 μ long by 2 μ in diameter, lacking a conspicuous globule but bearing one or two minute, highly refractive granules laterally placed near the point of attachment of the single posterior flagellum, escaping upon the deliquescence of a single, conspicuous lateral papilla; resting spores spherical, asexually formed, 21.4–35 μ in diameter, with a 2 μ thick, smooth wall, contents oily, rhizoids and germination not observed.

Parasitic on sporelings of *Oedogonium sp.*, Scherffel (1926a: 230, pl. 10, figs. 116–117), HUNGARY; same host, Canter (1947b: 96, fig. 2, pl. 9), GREAT BRITAIN.

The species is based on Scherffel's observations and, in particular, on those of Canter. It bears some resemblance to *Rhizophydium karlingii*, except that it differs in having zoospores without a conspicuous globule and in certain other features.

[1] *Rhizophydium canterae* sp. nov. — Sporangia sessilia, sphaerica, membrana tenui, incolorata, 7.5-34.3 μ diam., majora singula in abnormaliter curvatis hospitis cellulis posita, cetera minora gregaria (usque ad 14) in cellula hospitis una. Pars endobiotica ex axi primario brevi rare inflato et ramis rhisoideis paucis constans. Zoosporae breviter elongatae, 4 μ longa, 2 μ diam., sine globulo conspicuo, sed 1 vel 2 granula refractiva lateralia prope flagellum singulum posticum includentes, liberatae per papillam singulam conspicuam lateralem deliquescentem. Sporae perdurantes globosae, asexualiter originatae, 21.4-35 μ diam., membrana crassa, laevi, intus oleaginosae; rhizoideis germinationeque nondum observatis.

Ab auctore non visum, sed fundatum ex observationibus cll. Scherffelii et (praecipue et typice) Canterae. *Rhizophidio laterali* similis sed differi zoosporis sine globulo conspicuo notisque ceteris.

Parasitica in *Oedogonium sp.*, HUNGARY and GREAT BRITAIN.

RHIZOPHYDIUM KARLINGII, sp. nov.[1]

(Fig. 17 A, p. 228)

Sporangium sessile, spherical, 9–18 μ (13.5 μ av.), slightly flattened and oval, occasionally bearing a portion of the unexpanded zoospore cyst, with one to three discharge papillae, the single ones for most part being sublateral or near the base, others subapical, lateral or rarely apical, wall smooth, very thin, 0.8–1.7 μ in thickness; endobiotic part usually consisting of a knob- or peglike structure 4–12 μ long by 4 μ in diameter, sometimes distally inflated, rarely tapering, which may pierce the wall and from the tip of which a delicate branched rhizoidal system of variable extent emerges; zoospores nearly spherical, 2.5–3.2 μ in diameter, with a small refractive basal globule and flagellum 12–15 μ long, emerging upon the deliquescence of one or more discharge papillae through an orifice 3–5 μ in diameter; resting spore oval, slightly oblong or spherical, 8–15 μ in diameter, yellowish to amber in color, sometimes bearing a portion of the unexpanded zoospore cyst, smooth-walled, contents without a conspicuous oil globule, germination not observed.

Parasitic on *Ulothrix zonata*, UNITED STATES.

The species is based on the fungus described by Karling (1938e) as *Rhizophydium laterale* (Braun) Rabenh. (see *Phlyctidium laterale*, p. 213).

RHIZOPHYDIUM DEFORMANS Jaag and Nipkow

Berichte Schweiz. Bot. Gesell., 61: 483, pls. 11-12. 1951

Sporangium sessile, spherical or elongate, surrounded by the ellip-

---

[1] *Rhizophydium karlingii* sp. nov. (*R. laterale* Karling [1938e], non *R. laterale* [Braun] Rabenhorst. Vide, p. 213.) — Sporangium sessile, subglobosum, 9-15 μ (med. 13.5 μ), minime applanatum vel ovoideum, interdum partem cistae zoosporae inexpansae ferens, papillis efferentibus 1-3, singulis prope basem vel lateralibus, ceteris subapicalibus, lateralibus vel raro apicalibus; membrana laevi, tenui (crassitie 0.8-1.7 μ). Pars endobiotica bulbiformis vel raro radiciformis, interdum membranam transcurrens, apice ramosis, ramis tenuissimis rhizoidalibus plus minusve extensis. Zoosporae subglobosae, diametro 2.5-5.2 μ, globulo basali parvo refractivo et flagello praeditae, deliquescentia unae vel plurium papillarum efferentium per orificia 3-5 μ diametientia. Spora perdurans ovalis, suboblonga vel rotunda, 8-15 μ diam., flavescens vel luteola, interdum partem cistae zoosporae inexpansa ferens, tenuiter circumvallata, laevis, sine globulo conspicuo oleaginoso; germinatione nondum observata.
Parasitica in cellulis *Ulothricis zonatae*, UNITED STATES.

soid or broadly discoid gelatinous vesicular host mass, 32–58 μ in diameter, with broad apical papilla, thin smooth hyaline wall; rhizoid delicate, simple or sparingly branched, undulate; zoospores spherical, 2.5–3.5 μ in diameter, with a hyaline globule and long flagellum, emerging through a tube 6 μ long by 4.5 μ wide in the gelatinous material formed by the deliquescence of a papilla, at once motile.

Parasitic on the planktonic alga *Oscillatoria rubescens*, SWITZERLAND.

Although not well marked morphologically this species is remarkable in the reaction it produces on the host. Infected trichomes secrete large amounts of slime and eventually curl up to form a tight slimy capsule completely hiding the fungus. The authors suggest the term "ring disease" ("Ringelkrankheit") for the epidemic.

RHIZOPHYDIUM SUBANGULOSUM (Braun) Rabenhorst

Flora Europaea algarum, 3: 281. 1868. Non *R. subangulosum* sensu Dangeard, Bull. Soc. Linn. Normandie, III, 9: 88. 1884-85, et auct. recent.

(Fig. 17 B, p. 228)

Chytridium subangulosum A. Braun, Monatsber. Berlin Akad., 1855: 382; Abhandl. Berlin Akad., 1855: 44, pl. 3, figs. 27-31. 1856.

Sporangium sessile on the apical or other cells of the trichome of the alga, spherical at first but at maturity, upon the formation of from two to three papillae, becoming somewhat angular, 10–25 μ in diameter, wall slightly thickened, smooth, colorless; endobiotic system consisting of a delicate sparingly branched or occasionally unbranched rhizoid; zoospores spherical, 2–2.5 μ in diameter, with a colorless basal globule and a long flagellum, escaping through several pores formed upon the deliquescence of the papillae; resting spore not observed.

On *Oscillatoria tenuis* var. *subfusca*, Braun (*loc. cit.*), (?) germinating spores of *Aspidium*, Schenk (1858b: 8), isolated from soil, Reinboldt (1951: 178), GERMANY; *Oscillatoria sp.*, Sparrow (1936a: 442, pl. 17, fig. 3), *Lyngbya sp.*, Ingold (1949: 442), GREAT BRITAIN; *Oscillatoria tenuis*, Bérczi (1940: 83), HUNGARY; *Aphanizomenon gracile*, possibly *Oscillatoria agardhii*, Fott (1950: 7, fig. 19), CZECHOSLOVAKIA; *Oscillatoria rubescens*, Jaag and Nipkow (1951: 485, figs. 26–28), SWITZER-

LAND; pine pollen, Gaertner (1954b: 21), EGYPT, NORTHWEST AFRICA, WEST AFRICA, EQUATORIAL EAST AFRICA, SOUTH AFRICA; Gaertner (*op. cit.*, p. 40), SWEDEN.

As previously pointed out (Sparrow, 1936a), this species has apparently been misinterpreted. Braun did not observe the rhizoids (although Rabenhorst [*loc. cit.*] states that they are present), but he gave careful figures of the sporangia and zoospores.

The sporangia differ little from those of *Rhizophydium globosum*. Their angularity becomes evident only when the prominent discharge papillae are formed.

No figures or description are given of Schenk's fungus. Dangeard (1884–85a: 88; 1886a: 294, pl. 13, figs. 1–5) described and illustrated a form which differs from Braun's in several important features. The sporangium is obpyriform or casklike rather than globose, and at maturity it is somewhat angular because of the formation of several papillae. The rhizoid is broad and tubular, unbranched, and extends through a number of cells of the host, becoming somewhat constricted in passing through the transverse cell walls. Subsequent investigators of the chytrids have interpreted Braun's species as modified by Dangeard (de Wildeman, 1890: 17, fig. 5; Minden, 1915: 323, fig. 14 a–b; Sparrow, 1936a: 439, pl. 17, figs. 1–2). It is surprising, as Minden has pointed out, that Braun did not observe the very broad and extensive rhizoid if it was actually present in his material. In view of the fact that it has been shown (Sparrow, *loc. cit.*) that there exists a parasite of *Oscillatoria* with spherical sporangia (angular at maturity) and a very delicate rhizoidal system, it seems more logical to suppose that this was the type observed by Braun, not the form with broad tubular "mycelium." The latter has been termed *Rhizophydium megarrhizum* (see below).

Fischer (1892: 90) thinks that the fungus found by Schenk on *Aspidium* spores may be referable to *Rhizophydium sphaerotheca* rather than to the present species. Although this is probable, there seems to be no reason, other than similarity of substratum, for this conjecture.

RHIZOPHYDIUM MEGARRHIZUM Sparrow

Aquatic Phycomycetes, p. 171, fig. 11c. 1943

Chytridium subangulosum, sensu Dangeard, Bull. Soc. Linn. Normandie, III, 9: 88. 1884-85.

(Figs. 10 F, p. 108; 17 C, p. 228)

Sporangium sessile, spherical, broadly ellipsoidal, or obpyriform, with a broad rounded apex, 9–25 μ in diameter, becoming somewhat angular upon the formation of from one to four projecting discharge papillae, wall smooth, colorless; rhizoids broad, sparingly branched, often undulate, invading as many as 70 host cells, up to 150 μ in length; zoospores from ten to sixty or more, spherical, 2.5–3.5 μ in diameter, with a colorless basal globule and a long flagellum, discharged through pores formed upon the deliquescence of the papillae; resting spore asexually formed, spherical, 5.4–9 μ in diameter, with a thick, smooth wall and oleaginous refractive contents, germination not observed.

Parasitic on *Oscillatoria sp.*, *Lyngbya sp.*, Dangeard (1884–85a: 88; 1886a: 294, pl. 13, figs. 1–5), FRANCE; *Oscillatoria spp.*, de Wildeman (1890: 17, fig. 5), BELGIUM; *Oscillatoria sp.*, Minden (1915: 323, fig. 14a–b), GERMANY; *Oscillatoria sp.*, Sparrow (1936a: 439, pl. 17, figs. 1–2), *Lyngbya sp.*, Ingold (1949: 442), *Oscillatoria agardhii* var. *isothrix*, Canter and Lund (1951: 368, fig. 4, pl. 17, fig. C), Ingold (in Canter and Lund, *loc. cit.*), GREAT BRITAIN; *Oscillatoria rubescens*, *Oscillatoria sp.*, Canter (1953: 285), Canter and Lund (*loc. cit.*), SWITZERLAND; *Oscillatoria sp.*, (MICHIGAN) UNITED STATES.

See the discussion under *Rhizophydium subangulosum*, page 245.

Ordinarily the sporangia are attached to the apical cells of the trichomes, but they may be located elsewhere, the rhizoid then penetrating only one cell of the alga. The form illustrated by de Wildeman has a subsporangial cylindrical prolongation into the host cell; the rhizoid arises from this prolongation. A similar structure is found on an unnamed chytrid inhabitant of *Oscillatoria* figured by Sparrow (1933c: 528, fig. I, 21).

Canter and Lund (1951) give an illuminating account of the relationship of this parasite of the planktonic *Oscillatoria agardhii* var. *isothrix* to the increase in abundance of planktonic diatoms.

RHIZOPHYDIUM PYTHII de Wildeman

Ann. Soc. Belge Micro. (Mém.), 21: 12, pl. 1, figs. 10-17. 1897

Sporangium sessile, spherical, with one short papilla (occasionally two), of varying size, wall smooth, colorless; rhizoids very delicate, branched, arising from a short main axis; zoospores spherical, with a small centric globule and a long flagellum, escaping through pores formed upon the dissolution of the papillae; resting spore not observed. Parasitic on the oöspores (and sporangia?) of *Pythium monospermum* (*complens*), FRANCE.

Although the sporangia are said to be spherical, the figures show such wide variations that it is difficult to decide just what shape is to be considered typical. *Rhizophydium pythii* was thought by de Wildeman to perhaps be only a form of *R. globosum*.

The fungus is said in the text of the original description to parasitize the oöspores, whereas in the formal diagnosis it is said to be "sur les zoosporanges."

RHIZOPHYDIUM MYCETOPHAGUM Karling

Amer. J. Bot., 33: 329, figs. 17-18. 1946

"Thalli numerous, up to 25 on a host cell. Sporangia sessile, hyaline, smooth, spherical (7–20 μ), broadly pyriform (8–12 × 11–19 μ), with one to three exit papillae. Zoospores spherical (3.5–5 μ), with a conspicuous (1–1.5 μ) refractive globule. Rhizoidal system relatively delicate but richly branched. Resting spores spherical (6–14 μ) with a thick, dark brown rough wall, and one to several large refractive globules; germination unknown" (Karling, *loc. cit.*).

Parasitic on the conidiophores and hyphae of the mucor *Choanephora sp.*, BRAZIL.

The species appeared limited in its host range and did not attack other chytrids, Oömycetes, pollen grains, or algae. No other mucors were available at the time for cross-inoculation experiments. This and the species *Pleotrachelus fulgens* and *P. zopfianus* are the only known chytrid parasites of mucors.

RHIZOPHYDIUM CHYTRIOPHAGUM Ajello

Mycologia, 37: 113, figs. 14-28. 1945

"Zoosporangia epibiotic, eucarpic, spherical, 10–30 μ in diameter, hyaline, smooth-walled, attached to the host by a tubular haustorium 4.2–7.3 μ long, 2.2 μ wide, with short lateral extensions 1.5 μ long. Zoospores spherical, 2.2–2.9 μ in diameter with a single posterior flagellum 15 μ long, and a centrally located refractive globule. Resting spores extramatrical, spherical, 6–15 μ in diameter, wall 1.4 μ thick, golden-brown in color, at germination functioning as a prosporangium" (Ajello, *loc. cit.*).

Parasitic upon *Phlyctochytrium aureliae*, UNITED STATES.

The zoospores are liberated after the sporangium wall ruptures; no discrete pore is evidently formed.

Ajello noted that the parasite had little or no adverse effect upon the host unless more than one was present or unless infection occurred early in the host's development.

RHIZOPHYDIUM CHYTRIOMYCETIS Karling

Mycologia, 38: 105, figs. 1-8. 1946

"Thalli usually numerous, up to 20 on one host sporangium. Sporangia hyaline, smooth, sessile or stalked, spherical, 8–30 μ, with one to three exit papillae. Rhizoidal system finely branched, main axis up to 3 μ in diameter. Zoospores hyaline, spherical, 2–2.8 μ, with a minute, .5–.8 μ, hyaline refractive globule. Resting spores dark brown, spherical, 7–18 μ, with one or more large refractive globules; functioning as a pro-sporangium in germination" (Karling, *loc. cit.*).

Parasitic on *Chytriomyces hyalinus* and *C. aureus*, UNITED STATES.

This and the following species (*Rhizophydium hyperparasiticum*) are scarcely separable from one another save on the basis of differences in host plants, which, incidently, are all chytrids.

RHIZOPHYDIUM HYPERPARASITICUM Karling

Amer. J. Bot., 33: 329, figs. 1-4, 9-13. 1946

(Fig. 18, A-E, p. 286)

"Thalli, numerous, up to 80 on a host sporangium. Sporangia sessile, hyaline, smooth, spherical (7–42 μ), oval or slightly flattened (7–15 × 10–24 μ), with one to several low exit papillae. Zoospores spherical (2.5–3.5 μ), with a minute refractive globule; emerging from one or more of the exit papillae. Rhizoidal system richly branched; coarseness, degree of branching, and length dependent to some degree on size of host sporangia. Resting spores smooth, hyaline, spherical (5–10 μ), oval or slightly angular, with one or more large refractive globules; germination unknown" (Karling, *loc. cit.*).

Parasitic on the sporangia and resting spores of *Rhizophlyctis rosea* and *Karlingiomyces granulata* and on the sporangia of *Septochytrium macrosporum* and *S. plurilobulum* (Karling, *loc. cit.*), BRAZIL; pine pollen, Gaertner (1954b: 21), SOUTH AFRICA.

With respect to this species, Karling says that the parasites found on *Septochytrium* differ somewhat from those on *Rhizophlyctis* and *Karlingiomyces*. Hence, it is not absolutely certain that they all belong to the same species.

RHIZOPHYDIUM SPHAEROTHECA Zopf

Abhandl. Naturforsch. Gesell. Halle, 17: 92, pl. 2, figs. 33-41. 1887

(Fig. 17 D-E, p. 228)

Sporangia sessile, single or in groups, spherical or subspherical, with from two to five protruding papillae (one in smallest sporangia), small plants, 4–5 μ in diameter, largest seldom exceeding 22 μ, wall smooth, colorless, distinctly double-contoured; rhizoidal system arising from a main axis, much branched; zoospores few in small sporangia, up to three hundred in large ones, spherical or ellipsoidal, 2.5–3 μ in diameter (see below), with a relatively large eccentric colorless globule 0.9-1.2 μ in diameter, a minute shining granule, and a delicate flagellum, emerging from the sporangia through comparatively large, circular, occasionally slightly protruding pores formed upon the deliquescence of the papillae, movement amoeboid as well as swimming; resting spore not observed.

On microspores of *Isoetes lacustris*, *I. echinospora*, pollen of *Pinus spp.* (*P. sylvestris*, etc.), Zopf (*op. cit.*, p. 82, pl. 1, figs. 1–6, 16 a–c), isolated from soil, Reinboldt (1951: 178), GERMANY; gymnospermous pollen, *Pseudotsuga mucronata* pollen, Graff (1928: 161), pine pollen,

Sparrow (1932b: 275, fig. 2d; 1952d: 762), UNITED STATES; *Typha* pollen, Sparrow (1936a: 441, pl. 17, fig. 16), GREAT BRITAIN; fern spores and pollen grains, Karling (1946c: 334, figs. 31–32), BRAZIL; pine-pollen bait, soil, Sparrow (1952a: 36), CUBA; pine pollen, Gaertner (1954b: 21), EGYPT, NORTHWEST AFRICA, WEST AFRICA, EQUATORIAL EAST AFRICA, SOUTH AFRICA; Gaertner (*op. cit.*, p. 40), SWEDEN.

Rhizophydium sphaerotheca differs from *R. pollinis-pini* primarily in the number and position of the pores (there is only a single terminal one in the latter). As understood here, *R. sphaerotheca* includes all "*Rhizophydium globosum*" forms with multiporous, spherical, or subspherical sporangia and a branched rhizoidal system which inhabit the submerged microspores or microgametophytes of pteridophytes and spermatophytes. Certain of the plants considered *R. pollinis-pini* by Zopf (*loc. cit.*) and some later investigators fall within these limits.

The zoospores in the multiporous forms called *R. pollinis-pini* by Zopf varied from 4 μ to 6 μ in diameter, and the sporangia in some instances attained a diameter of 36 μ.

RHIZOPHYDIUM BULLATUM Sparrow

Mycologia, 44: 762, fig. 1 h-i. 1952

(Fig. 20 F, p. 330)

Sporangia sessile, in groups, spherical, with a smooth, double-contoured wall, varying from 6.6–15.4 μ in diameter; rhizoidal system very delicate, much branched; zoospores numerous, spherical, 3 μ in diameter, with a single basal colorless globule and long posterior flagellum; escaping through two to five sessile pores; resting spores spherical, 6.6–11 μ in diameter, sessile, occurring in groups or occasionally singly, with a thickened brownish wall beset with coarse bullations; contents bearing a single large globule; germination not observed.

Parasitic on pine-pollen bait, UNITED STATES.

In the shape and size of its sporangia *Rhizophydium bullatum* resembles *R. sphaerotheca* Zopf. No resting spores have ever been definitely associated with Zopf's species, but in Sparrow's they were abundantly and quickly formed. The resting spores of *R. bullatum* are very like those of *R. closterii* Karling; sporangia of the two, however, are quite different. It is entirely possible that there are a number of spherical multiporous sporangial types which differ only in the character of their resting spore.

RHIZOPHYDIUM RACEMOSUM Gaertner

Archiv f. Mikrobiologie, 21: 125, fig. 7. 1954

Sporangium at first spherical, later irregular in form and size, 10 by 10 μ, 18 by 14 μ, 20 by 19 μ, 22 by 25 μ, with a conspicuous vacuole and irregularly sized large oil drops, at maturity with rounded corners at which the wall tears liberating the zoospores; rhizoidal system delicate, barely visible, at first unbranched, then with short bushy branches; zoospores, 2–2.5 μ in diameter, with a single droplet and 25 μ long flagellum, movement hopping; resting spores in clusters of up to forty, adhering to one another, 7–8 μ at maturity.

Pine pollen, Gaertner (*loc. cit.*; 1954b); EGYPT, EQUATORIAL AFRICA, SOUTH AFRICA.

The species resembles *Rhizophydium subangulosum* but lacks papillae. The resting stage is difficult to interpret.

RHIZOPHYDIUM CORONUM Hanson

Torreya, 44: 31. 1944

(Fig. 8, F-H, p. 97)

"Zoosporangia hyaline, spherical, 11–49 μ in diameter, ovoid 10–48 × 14–54 μ, with laminated walls, outer lamina often disintegrating around the upper half of the sporangium; one to five exit papillae, 3–3.7 × 9–11 μ. One to several concentric halos surrounding the developing sporangia, reduced to one at maturity, which generally deliquesces before spore discharge begins. Zoospores hyaline, spherical, 3.7–4.5 μ, with one large refractive globule, 1.5 μ in diameter, the first zoospores emerging as a coherent mass, separating after 6–14 minutes, the remainder swimming in the sporangium and emerging singly. Rhizoids fairly rigid, with 1.5–4.5 μ, thick walls, straight, coiled, sparingly or richly branched, one rhizoid often predominant and very prolonged, up to 500 μ in length. Resting spore spherical or sub-spherical, 22–35 μ in diameter, with a lamellated wall like that of the sporangium, 0.7–1.3 µ, thick, with a faint golden tint; contents of resting spore consisting of one or more large central globules surrounded by a peripheral layer of smaller globules; enveloped like the zoosporangium by one or several halos, acting like a prosporangium upon germination, giving rise to a hyaline zoosporangium 29–37 µ in diameter, which in turn is enveloped by a halo" (Hanson, *loc. cit.*).

Saprophytic on grasses, bleached corn leaves, and cellophane, UNITED STATES.

The curious "halo" developed by this species is indeed remarkable and bears some resemblance to the gelatinous hull formed by the incompletely known ? *Rhizophydium gelatinosum* Lind (p. 307) and the planktonic parasite *R. difficile* Canter (p. 256).

The developmental morphology and the cytology are discussed and the species is figured in Hanson (1945b).

RHIZOPHYDIUM VAMPYRELLAE (Dang.) Minden

Kryptogamenfl. Mark Brandenburg, 5: 320. 1911 (1915)

Chytridium vampyrellae Dangeard, Le Botaniste, 1: 63, pl. 3, figs.14-16. 1889.

Sporangium sessile, spherical, with a thickened smooth wall and several subapical discharge papillae; rhizoids branched, arising from a central somewhat thickened main axis; zoospores very narrowly ellipsoidal or ovoidal when escaping through the pores formed upon the deliquescence of the papillae, the conspicuous colorless globule anterior or basal, the flagellum of moderate length; resting spore (?) spherical, with a thick smooth wall and an apparently unbranched rhizoid, germination not observed.

On cysts of *Vampyrella* parasitizing colonies of *Gloeocystis vesiculosa*, FRANCE.

Considered doubtfully distinct from *Rhizophydium globosum* by Dangeard. The zoospores were observed to become very constricted and elongated when passing through the gelatinous layer of the colonies of *Gloeocystis*. Their shape during swimming evidently was not observed. In Dangeard's explanation of Plate 3, "Figure 16c" is referred to as a resting spore of the fungus. There is no such figure number, and it is assumed here that Dangeard meant Figure 16a. The species is kept distinct for reasons mentioned in the discussion of *Rhizophydium globosum* (see p. 239).

(see p. 239).

RHIZOPHYDIUM AMOEBAE Karling

Amer. J. Bot., 33: 331, figs. 5-8. 1946

"Thalli numerous up to 14 on a host cell. Sporangia sessile, smooth, spherical (8–20 μ) with a low apical exit papilla and a fairly thick, brown, smooth wall. Zoospores oval (2 × 3 μ) with a minute (0.5–1 μ), somewhat laterally located refractive globule. Rhizoidal system relatively sparse but frequently branched. Resting spores spherical (8–14 μ) with a thick, dark brown wall and one to several large refractive globules; functioning as prosporangia in germination" (Karling, *loc. cit.*).

Parasitic on *Amoeba terricola* and saprophytic on insect exuviae, BRAZIL.

Characterized by spherical brown-walled sporangia, oval zoospores with a minute laterally located refringent globule, thick-walled and dark-brown resting spores.

Indications were that the fungus was only weakly, if at all, parasitic on amoebae.

RHIZOPHYDIUM CHITINOPHILUM Antikajian

Mycologia, 39: 613, figs. 1-20. 1947

"Sporangia sessile, hyaline, smooth, spherical (7–69 μ), subspherical (15–66 × 17–74 μ), oval (7–66 × 11–87 μ), or pyriform (8–58 × 11–96 μ); neck of sporangium (4–17 × 11–28 μ); exit papillae one or two, low and broad, usually apical, filled with hyaline matrix (4–13 μ) high and (7–21 μ) wide. Zoospores spherical, approximately 3.6 μ with a minute refractive globule less than 0.7 μ and a large somewhat refractive, granular body about 2.2 μ; flagellum (21–26 μ). Rhizoids (2–16 μ) in diameter, richly branched, usually arising from a single point at the base of the sporangium, rarely from several points. Resting spores smooth, brown with coarsely granular contents; wall of resting spore 0.7 μ; on germination functioning as a prosporangium" (Antikajian, *loc. cit.*).

Saprophytic on chitin, Antikajian (*loc. cit.*)., chitin bait, from moist soil, Karling (1948c: 508), UNITED STATES.

The fungus is said to be limited to chitinous substrata.

RHIZOPHYDIUM CONSTANTINEANI Saccardo

Sylloge fungorum, 17: 512. 1905

(Fig. 17 F, p. 228)

Rhizophydium vaucheriae Constantineanu, Revue Gén. Bot., 13: 380, fig. 81. 1901. Non *Rhizophydium vaucheriae* de Wildeman, Mém. Herb. Boissier, 1900 (15): 6.

Sporangium sessile, spherical or subspherical, 6–8 µ in diameter, wall smooth, colorless; rhizoidal system very delicate, consisting of a few short branches which arise from a main axis; zoospores from four to six, spherical, 3.5 µ in diameter, with a colorless, eccentric globule, escaping through a small apical pore and forming a temporary group attached to the pore by the tips of the flagella; resting spore not observed.

On filaments of *Vaucheria sp.*, Saccardo (*loc. cit.*), RUMANIA; *Oedogonium sp.*, *Cosmarium sp.*, Richards (1956: 261, pl. 6, figs. 1–2), GREAT BRITAIN.

The species has been discussed by Minden (1915: 326) under *Rhizophydium sphaerocarpum* (Zopf) Fischer. From the smaller size of its sporangia, however, and the branched nature of the rhizoids, it cannot without further study be referred to Zopf's fungus.

RHIZOPHYDIUM PLANKTONICUM Canter [1]

Canter and Lund, New Phytologist, 47: 259, figs. 10-11. 1948

(Fig. 10 H-I, p. 108)

"Thallus epibiotic sessile or stalked, sporangium spherical, 4.5–9.3 µ in diameter, with 4–15 zoospores. Zoospores spherical 3–3.7 µ in diameter, uniguttulate, posteriorly uniflagellate, emerging in a mass on gelatinization of the apex of the sporangium wall. Intramatrical rhizoid unbranched or once branched, not tapering. Resting spores spherical 4–7 µ in diameter, wall smooth, the content with numerous small oil globules; arising from fusion of the contents of a small male with a larger female cell, the former remaining as an appendage to

[1] See also Paterson (*Mycologia*, 50: 93. 1958).

the mature resting spores. Germination unknown "(Canter, *loc. cit.*). Parasitic on the planktonic diatom *Asterionella formosa*, GREAT BRITAIN.

Canter notes that this species is almost always present if the host is. She says, however, that the greater part of the year its frequency is too low to appreciably affect the number of *Asterionella* cells. At certain times, particularly in autumn and winter, the *Rhizophydium* multiplies rapidly to epidemic proportions (see p. 107).

Canter and Lund (1951) suggest that *Rhizophydium planktonicum* may be an aggregate species. They believe the fungus described and figured by Huber-Pestalozzi (1946: 94, fig. 5 a–c) on *Asterionella formosa* from Swiss plankton is not identical with *R. planktonicum*, because of the presence of a swelling on the terminus of the rhizoid in the Swiss form.

RHIZOPHYDIUM MARSHALLENSE Sparrow

Mycologia, 40: 450, figs. 13, 15-17. 1948

Sporangium sessile, spherical, 10–12 μ in diameter, colorless, smooth-walled; endobiotic part consisting of a slender, at least once-branched, rhizoid; zoospores somewhat ovoid, 2 μ or less in diameter, each with a single hyaline, minute refractive globule and a posterior flagellum, escaping through a minute variously placed pore; resting spore spherical, 10–15 μ in diameter, faintly golden and densely covered with prominent knoblike bullations, endobiotic part like that of the sporangium; germination not observed.

Parasitic on thalli and sporangia of *Rhizophlyctis spp.*, ELEUGELAB ISLAND, EINWETOK ATOLL, and RONGELAP ISLAND, RONGELAP ATOLL, MARSHALL ISLANDS.

How this, as well as several other species found on these remote atolls, got there and survived in the nearly pure coral sands is an interesting problem in distribution.

RHIZOPHYDIUM SPHAEROCYSTIDIS Canter

Ann. Bot. London (N.S.), 14: 280, fig. 10. 1950

"Thallus consisting of a sporangium sessile on the outside of the mucilage sheath surrounding the host, an unswollen stalk-like region within the mucilage, and a branched rhizoidal system inside the host cell.

"Sporangium spherical (5–11 μ) containing 8 to 50 zoospores. At maturity the entire sporangium wall deliquescing and the zoospores when fully delimited swim away. Zoospores spherical (3 μ), uniguttulate, posteriorly uniflagellate.

"Resting spores spherical (5–7 μ), wall smooth, containing one or two large oil globules; formed after fusion of a small male cell with a larger female, the former remaining as an appendage to the mature spore. Germination unknown" (Canter, *loc. cit.*).

Parasitic on the planktonic alga *Sphaerocystis schroeteri*, Canter (*loc. cit.*), *Dictyosphaerium pulchellum*, Canter (1953: 285), GREAT BRITAIN.

Said by Canter (1951: 144) to resemble *Rhizophydium fulgens* in habit.

This curious species resembles *Nowakowskia hormothece* (p. 448) and *Solutoparies pythii* (p. 427) in the complete dissolution of the sporangium wall. Unlike them, however, the protoplasmic mass undergoes the greater part, if not all, of its cleavage into zoospores free in the water. Further studies may indicate that this is a generically distinct form.

RHIZOPHYDIUM DIFFICILE Canter

Trans. Brit. Mycol. Soc., 37 :119, figs. 4-5, pl. 3, fig. 4. 1954

(Fig. 10 D-E, p. 108)

"Thallus monocentric, eucarpic, consisting of an epibiotic spherical sporangium formed by enlargement of the zoospore and a complicated branched endobiotic rhizoidal system of limited extent. Sporangium (12–20 μ in diameter) containing up to ninety zoospores. Entire wall of sporangium dissolves on dehiscence. Zoospore spherical 2.5 μ in diameter, with a large posterior globule (1–1.35 μ), and a flagellum 12 μ long; movement smooth gliding. Resting spore spherical (8–13.6 μ in diameter) formed after fusion of a small male with a larger female cell. Male directly adherent to wall of female. Wall thick, smooth, brownish, surrounded by a halo or beset with strands of mucilaginous (?) material; content [with] numerous small globules. Rhizoidal system as for sporangium; germination unknown" (Canter, *loc. cit.*).

Parasitic on the planktonic desmids *Staurastrum jaculiferum* and *Arthrodesmus sp.*, GREAT BRITAIN.

As in *Rhizophydium sphaerocystidis* the entire sporangium wall disappears. In this species, however, the zoospores are mature when liberated. Although no evidence of the sporangium remains after discharge, infected host cells are readily recognized by their reddish content, the remains of the chytrid rhizoidal system, and a slight thickening of the desmid wall at the point of infection. The curious gelatinous halo around the sexually formed resting spore recalls *R. coronum* Hanson (p. 251).

RHIZOPHYDIUM CYCLOTELLAE Zopf

Abhandl. Naturforsch. Gesell. Halle, 17: 94, pl. 2, figs. 13-22a. 1887

(Fig. 17 G, p. 228)

Sporangia sessile, single or in groups, subspherical or broadly obpyriform, up to 12 μ in diameter, with a smooth delicate wall which collapses and disappears after spore discharge; rhizoidal system well developed, extremely delicate, with branches arising from a main axis; zoospores spherical, 1.8–2.5 μ in diameter, with a relatively large eccentric colorless globule and a delicate flagellum, escaping through from one to three very small sessile pores, capable of amoeboid movement; resting spore not observed.

Parasitic on *Cyclotella sp.* in culture dishes; not capable of infecting *Melosira* or naviculoid or synedroid diatoms, pine pollen, or *Lycopodium* spores. Zopf (*loc. cit.*), in a *Stinkhaale* (= 'sulphurous' or 'salt pool'?), GERMANY; *Cyclotella chaetoceras*, Domján (1936: 42, pl. 1, fig. 171), HUNGARY.

Infection always took place along the silica-free region between the girdle band and valve, obviating the necessity for penetration of the siliceous wall of the diatom. The contents of the latter, with the exception of the brown remains of the chromatophores, were all consumed.

RHIZOPHYDIUM MELOSIRAE Friedmann

Österreich. Bot. Zeitschr., 99: 179, fig. 1 a-k. 1952

Sporangia usually borne at the tip of a more or less elongate extra-matrical, delicate stalk, spherical, 11–18.3 μ in diameter, wall thin, smooth, colorless, deliquescing completely upon discharge of the zoospores; endobiotic part a continuation of the extramatrical sporangial stalk which penetrates between the valves of the host and forms within a tuft of delicate sparingly branched rhizoids; zoospores nearly spherical, 2.4–3.0 μ in diameter, with an eccentric, colorless globule, the single flagellum 8 μ long, liberated upon the deliquescence of the sporangium wall; resting spore (?) irregularly spherical, 12.5–15.0 μ in diameter, with a thick smooth wall, rhizoids and germination not observed.

Parasitic on *Melosira varians*, AUSTRIA.

The species is found continuously during the cooler months of the year, but only reaches epidemic proportions as the temperature increases.

Friedmann (*loc. cit.*) determined that some component of light (very likely the yellow) inhibited dissolution of the sporangium wall and, hence, zoospore discharge. From this he conjectures that under natural conditions zoospore discharge occurs only at night.

RHIZOPHYDIUM ACHNANTHIS Friedmann

Österreich. Bot. Zeitschr., 99: 181, fig. 1 l-v. 1952

Sporangium sessile or borne at the tip of a more or less elongate extramatrical, delicate stalk, spherical, 3.5–4.5 μ in diameter, or obovoid to transversely ovoid, 3.3–4.0 × 4.7–6.7 μ, wall smooth, colorless, deliquescing completely upon discharge of the zoospores; endobiotic part arising directly from the base of the sporangium or as a continuation of the extramatrical sporangial stalk, composed of delicate, sparingly branched rhizoids or a single unbranched one; zoospores spherical, 2.5 μ in diameter, with an eccentric colorless globule and long flagellum; resting spore not observed.

Parasitic on *Achnanthes affinis*, AUSTRIA.

Another instance, as in *Rhizophydium fragilariae*, of the assumption of the deliquescing sporangium wall habit by a plankton parasite.

RHIZOPHYDIUM FRAGILARIAE Canter

Ann. Bot. London (N.S.), 14: 275, fig. 9. 1950

(Fig. 10 A, p. 108)

Sporangia epibiotic, spherical to subspherical, 3–10 μ in diameter, containing three to twenty zoospores; sporangium wall deliquescing at maturity, forming one to three openings through which the zoospores emerge; zoospore spherical, 2–2.4 μ, with a conspicuous anterior globule and single posterior flagellum; endobiotic rhizoid a short unbranched or once-branched thread; resting spore not observed.

Parasitic on the planktonic diatom *Fragilaria crotonensis*, GREAT BRITAIN.

Although Canter's form is said to be confined to this species of *Fragilaria*, the fungus figured by Huber-Pestalozzi (1946: 95, fig. 5e) on *Fragilaria capucina* from Swiss plankton may possibly belong here. See remarks under *Rhizophydium achnanthis*, above.

RHIZOPHYDIUM MACROSPORUM Karling

Bull. Torrey Bot. Club, 65: 439, pl. 20, figs. 1-17. 1938

"Thalli eucarpic, numerous, gregarious. Zoosporangia hyaline, smooth, predominately spherical 22–110 μ, oval, broadly pyriform, and urceolate with 1 to 5, usually 2 or 3, low inconspicuous exit papillae. Zoospores spherical 4.5–6 μ, hyaline, with an unusually large, 3–4 μ clear refractive globule and a 25–35 μ long cilium; occasionally becoming amoeboid; initial swarmspores emerging in a small globular mass surrounded by a hyaline matrix and lying quiescent for a few moments before separating; the remainder becoming active within the sporangium and emerging usually one by one. Rhizoidal system usually extensively developed, coarse, and branched, main axis occasionally 6 μ in diameter; delimited from the sporangia by a cross wall at maturity; arising from a single point or rarely from several places at the base of the sporangium. Resting spores hyaline, smooth, spherical, 15–30 μ, oval, 18 × 20–33 × 36 μ, or slightly irregular with a wall 1.5–2 μ thick, and one or more large refractive globules; germination unknown" (Karling, *loc. cit.*).

On cooked ground beef, dead cells of *Cladophora glomerata*, *Pithoph-*

ora sp., *Nitella flexilis*, *Chara coronata*, root tips of *Allium cepa* and *Narcissus*, UNITED STATES.

RHIZOPHYDIUM ASYMMETRICUM (Dang.) Minden

Kryptogamenfl. Mark Brandenburg, 5: 328. 1911 (1915)

(Fig. 17 H, p. 228)

Chytridium asymmetricum Dangeard, Le Botaniste, 2: 243, pl. 17, fig. 1. 1890-91.

Sporangium sessile, ovoid, 16 μ high by 10 μ in diameter, with a prominent slightly oblique apical papilla, wall stout, smooth, colorless; rhizoids delicate, branched, arising from a short slender main axis; zoospores very small, spherical, with an eccentric colorless globule and a fairly long flagellum, emerging through a pore formed upon the deliquescence of the papilla; resting spore not observed.

Parasitic on *Tribonema bombycina* var. *minor*, FRANCE.

Considered by Fischer (1892: 94) to be merely an irregular form of *Rhizophydium mammillatum* (Braun) Fischer. Minden (*loc. cit.*) though placing it in *Rhizophydium*, where, from its inoperculate type of discharge, it unquestionably belongs, briefly discusses it under *R. mammillatum*.

Because of the characteristically tilted papilla the species should be retained, at least for the present.

RHIZOPHYDIUM MAMMILLATUM (Braun) Fischer

Rabenhorst. Kryptogamen-Fl., 1 (4): 93. 1892 (sensu Dangeard, Le Botaniste, 2: 242, pl. 16, fig. 32. 1890-91)

Chytridium mammillatum Braun, Monatsber. Berlin Akad., 1855: 381; Abhandl. Berlin Akad., 1855: 32, pl. 2, figs. 9-12. 1856.

Sporangium sessile, long-ovoid or narrowly to somewhat broadly citriform, with a more or less prominent apical papilla, 10–33 μ high by 10–22 μ in diameter, wall smooth, colorless, slightly thickened; rhizoids delicate, branched, short, arising from a slender main axis; zoospores spherical or somewhat ovoid, 2–4 μ in diameter, with a minute eccentric globule and a long flagellum, emerging through a small apical pore; resting spore not observed.

On *Coleochaete pulvinata*, Braun (*loc. cit.*), Schroeter (1885: 190), swarm spores of *Stigeoclonium sp.*, Pringsheim (in Braun, 1856a), *Draparnaldia nudiuscula*, Rabenhorst (1868: 280), GERMANY; *Conferva abbreviata*, Lagerheim (1884 [1]: 100), SWEDEN; *Draparnaldia sp.*, Dangeard (1890–91c: 242, pl. 16, fig. 32), FRANCE; *Tribonema bombycina*, de Wildeman (1890: 18), BELGIUM; *Draparnaldia glomerata*, Serbinow (1907: 158, pl. 4, figs. 29–34), RUSSIA; "*Conferva*," Valkanov (1931a: 362), BULGARIA; oögonia of *Oedogonium sp.*, vegetative cells of *Draparnaldia sp.*, Couch (1932: 251, pl. 15, figs. 36–39), UNITED STATES; *Spirogyra maxima*, Bérczi (1940: 82, pl. 1, figs. 6, 7, 9, pl. 2, fig. 12), HUNGARY; *Ulothrix sp.*, Litvinow (1953: 80), LATVIA; *Cladophora sp.*, Richards (1956: 261, pl. 6, figs. 3–5), GREAT BRITAIN.

Neither Braun nor Pringsheim observed the endobiotic system or the zoospores of this species. Braun does state definitely, however, that the sporangium is inoperculate. Since these essential features are lacking in the original description the fungus described by Dangeard (*loc. cit.*) (and later by Serbinow) is taken as typifying the species. Schenk's fungus (1858a: 236, pl. 5, figs. 1–5), termed *Chytridium mammillatum*, though like Braun's in the shape of its sporangium, possesses a peglike unbranched endobiotic part such as characterizes species of *Phlyctidium*. Actual discharge of the sporangium was not observed, and Schenk's fungus might well have been a *Chytridium*. Schenk remarks, however, that no opercula were found on the discharged sporangia, which, incidentally, were only one half the size of those described by Braun.

The specimen figured by de Wildeman (1891: 170, fig. 1) and tentatively assigned to this species differs from it in having pyriform sporangia and a small knoblike endobiotic part (see *Chytridium pedicellatum*, p. 534).

The fungus of Constantineanu (1901: 379, fig. 80), found on *Spirogyra* in Rumania and called *Chytridium mammillatum*, possesses broadly ovoid, subspherical, or somewhat irregular bicornate sporangia and cannot be included in the present species. Further investigations may show it to be new.

Couch's fungus differs from Braun's and Dangeard's in having a broader, more prominent papilla or beak, and in the rhizoidal system, which arises from a short peglike axis rather than from a more elongate slender thread.

RHIZOPHYDIUM UNIGUTTULUM Canter

Trans. Brit. Mycol. Soc., 37: 113, figs. 1-2, pl. 3, figs. 1-2. 1954

(Fig. 10 G, p. 108)

"Thallus monocentric epibiotic consisting of a sporangium and a meagre, branched rhizoidal system just within host cell-wall. Sporangium broadly ovoid, oval or globose, 3–13 μ broad and 4.5–15.5 μ high, developed by direct enlargement of the zoospore; dehiscing by deliquescence of the apex. Zoospore spherical, 2–2.5 μ in diameter, with a single basal refractive globule and posterior flagellum 12 μ long. Resting spore formed after sexual fusion of a small male cell (an encysted zoospore) which settles on and makes contact directly or via a short tube with a slightly larger female cell; spherical (5.5–9.5 μ) wall smooth, thick, surrounded by mucilaginous envelope; content one large and a few smaller globules. Germination not observed" (Canter, *loc. cit.*).

Parasitic on *Gemellicystis neglecta* in the plankton, GREAT BRITAIN.

Here, as in a number of other parasites of phytoplankters, discharge of the zoospores is accomplished by dissolution of a considerable part of the sporangium wall.

RHIZOPHYDIUM AMPULLACEUM (Braun) Fischer

Rabenhorst. Kryptogamen-Fl., 1 (4): 101. 1892

Chytridium ampullaceum Braun Monatsber. Berlin Akad., 1855: 384; Abhandl. Berlin Akad., 1855: 66, pl. 5, figs. 24-27. 1856.

Olpidium ampullaceum (Braun) Rabenhorst, Flora Europaea algarum, 3: 282. 1868.

Sphaerostylidium ampullaceum (Braun) Sorokin, Arch. Bot. Nord France, 2: 20, fig. 17. 1883 (separate).

Sporangium sessile or, rarely, on a short stalk, spherical, 6–8 μ in diameter, with an apical discharge tube 4–5 μ long by 2 μ in diameter, wall thin, smooth, colorless; rhizoids feebly developed, branched; zoospores with a single globule and a posterior flagellum, discharged through the somewhat flaring funnel-like apex of the opened discharge tube; resting spore not observed.

Clustered on filaments of *Mougeotia sp., Oedogonium vesicatum, O. undulatum,* Braun (*loc. cit.*), GERMANY; on various algae, *Spirogyra, Cladophora,* Sorokin (1874b: 6, pl. 1, figs. 6–11, and *loc. cit.*), EUROPEAN RUSSIA; *Oedogonium crassusculum* var. *idiosporum,* W. R. I. Cook (1932a: 135, figs. 7–12), GREAT BRITAIN; *Oedogonium sp.,* Atkinson (1909a: 338), *O. crenulato-costatum, O. plagiostomum, Mougeotia sp.,* Graff (1928: 159), UNITED STATES; *Oedogonium sp.,* Litvinow (1953: 80), LATVIA; pine pollen, Gaertner (1954b: 21), EQUATORIAL EAST AFRICA, SOUTH AFRICA.

Braun considered the species a very doubtful member of the chytrids. This view has been shared by Petersen (1910: 551, footnote), who believes the form should be entirely excluded from the chytrids and placed in the Infusoria. As has been pointed out by Graff (*loc. cit.*), Petersen gives no reasons for this change. It is possible that Petersen is correct insofar as the form observed by Braun himself is concerned. The curious production of a delicate, scarcely visible, tilted conical prolongation of the discharge tube is not found on any other chytrid, and the general resemblance of Braun's figures to the immature stages of certain sessile choanoflagellates is very marked. Since the name has been applied by later investigators to what is unquestionably a chytrid, however, and since figures of spore discharge have been shown (see especially Sorokin, 1874b), it is probably best to retain Braun's species name.

RHIZOPHYDIUM ROSTELLATUM (de Wild.) Fischer

Rabenhorst. Kryptogamen-Fl., 1 (4): 105. 1892

Chytridium rostellatum de Wildeman, Ann. Soc. Belge Micro. (Mém.), 14: 19, fig. 6, 1890.

Sporangium sessile, ovoid, with a single subapical beaklike prolongation or, more often, with two opposite diverging ones, wall thin, smooth, colorless; rhizoidal system delicate, branched, arising from a short thin main axis; zoospores spherical, with a large globule, escaping through a pore formed at the tip of each beak of the sporangium; resting spore not observed.

On *Spirogyra crassa,* BELGIUM.

Resembling somewhat *Phlyctochytrium biporosum* Couch, but differing in the more pronounced beaks and in the nature of the rhizoidal system.

RHIZOPHYDIUM HAYNALDII (Schaarschmidt) Fischer

Rabenhorst. Kryptogamen-Fl., 1 (4): 92. 1892

Phlyctidium haynaldii Schaarschmidt, Magyar Növénytani Lapok. Kolozs-vár, 1883 (7): 58, pl. 2; Hedwigia, 22: 125. 1883.

Sporangium sessile, oblong-ovoid or pyriform, with rounded base, the apex bearing two broad diverging opposite tubular processes, generally of equal magnitude, which when strongly opposed give a triangular aspect to the sporangium; rhizoid delicate, unbranched; zoospores from eight to ten, ellipsoidal, 2 μ long, with a long flagellum and a colorless eccentric oil droplet, escaping individually through pores formed at the tips of the two apical processes, movement hopping; resting spore not observed.

On *Ulothrix zonata*, Schaarschmidt (*loc. cit.*), Scherffel (in Moesz, 1938: 72), (?) *Spirogyra maxima*, Bérczi (1940: 81, pl. 1, figs. 10–11; pl. 2, fig. 11), HUNGARY; (?) *Hormiscia uniflexa* (coll. Andrée), Lager-heim (1899: 436), KING CHARLES LAND, ARCTIC REGION.

In the shape of its sporangium and the possession of two apical discharge pores the species resembles *Rhizophydium rostellatum*, *Phlyctochytrium biporosum*, and *Phlyctidium irregulare*. Certain British specimens doubtfully placed in *Phlyctochytrium biporosum* by Sparrow (1936a: 443, fig. 3 m–n,p) may belong here. Serbinow (1907: 157) considers the species synonymous with *Phlyctidium laterale*, but the configurations of the sporangia of the two species are totally unlike.

The record of Lagerheim (*loc. cit.*) is of doubtful validity. It is based on preserved material and is unsupported by figures or by an adequate description.

RHIZOPHYDIUM CHAETIFERUM Sparrow

Occ. Papers Boston Soc. Nat. Hist., 8: 295. 1937; Papers Mich. Acad. Sci., Arts, Letters, 24, Pt. I: 122, pl. 2, figs. 1-13. 1939

Sporangium spherical, rarely subspherical, colorless, predominantly

12 μ in diameter, the upper two thirds of the wall covered with long slender branched or unbranched hairs up to 30–50 μ in length; rhizoidal system delicate, profusely branched, arising from the tip of the slender penetration tube; zoospores spherical, 3 μ in diameter, with a single globule and a single posterior flagellum, discharged upon the deliquescence of an apical or subapical papilla, the aperture thus formed widening considerably after emergence of the spores; resting spore epibiotic, spherical or slightly subspherical, 12 μ in diameter, with a thickened wall covered by short processes, long hairs, or both, contents with a single large oil globule, rhizoidal system branched, germination not observed.

Saprophytic on *Cladophora sp.*, *Oedogonium sp.*, Sparrow (*loc. cit.*); saprophytic on vegetative filaments of *Spirogyra sp.*, *Oedogonium sp.*, Sparrow (1952d: 762), dead internodes of *Chara coronata*, Karling (1941b: 108), UNITED STATES; *Bulbochaete sp.*, Fott (1950: 7, fig. 20), CZECHOSLOVAKIA.

In the ornamentation of its sporangium the species resembles *Chytridium chaetophilum* Scherffel and *Phlyctochytrium chaetiferum* Karling. The resting spores resemble those of an imperfectly known species, *Rhizophydium* (?) *setigerum* Scherffel (1925b: 48, pl. 2, fig. 95).

RHIZOPHYDIUM KERATINOPHILUM Karling
Amer. J. Bot., 33: 753, figs. 1-43. 1946
(Fig. 18 I-J, p. 286)

"Sporangia sessile, hyaline, predominantly spherical (7–50 μ) with 2–5 fairly prominent exit papillae, 3–4 μ by 4–6 μ broad; wall ornamented with short, simple bifurcate or dichotomously branched spines (2–6 μ high) or long (15–45 μ), simple or branched threads. Rhizoids fairly extensive (up to 120 μ) and richly branched; main axis up to 5 μ in diam. Zoospores spherical (2.5–3 μ) with a minute, spherical (0.3–0.5 μ), hyaline, refringent globule; flagellum 10–13 μ long. Resting spores spherical (7–15 μ) or oval (5–6 × 7–14 μ) with a thick (2–3.5 μ) brown, prominently-warted wall; content coarsely but evenly granular, growing out to form a superficial zoosporangium during germination" (Karling, *loc. cit.*).

Saprophytic on keratinized tissues, BRAZIL, IRELAND, HOLLAND Karling (*loc. cit.*); saprophytic on human hair, Sparrow (1952d: 763) hair, skin, and feathers as bait from moist soil, Karling (1948c: 508). Sparrow (MICHIGAN) UNITED STATES; pine pollen, Gaertner (1954b: 21), EGYPT, NORTHWEST AFRICA, WEST AFRICA, EQUATORIAL EAST AFRICA, SOUTH AFRICA; Gaertner (*op. cit.*, p. 41), SWEDEN; Sparrow, 1957a: 524, GREAT BRITAIN.

The species is apparently widespread and has been collected from a number of localities in Great Britain and the United States, primarily on human hair.

RHIZOPHYDIUM CODICOLA Zeller

Publ. Puget Sound Biol. Station, 2: 122, pl. 20, figs. 1-4. 1918

Sporangium sessile, spherical to almost obpyriform, 16–24 μ in diameter, with a smooth colorless relatively thick wall; rhizoidal system extensive, coarse, much branched, the ultimate branches delicate, arising from a stout irregularly expanded somewhat lobed main axis; zoospores spherical, 2.5–3 μ in diameter, with a colorless basal globule and a long flagellum, emerging through a large lateral irregular aperture in the sporangium wall; resting spore not observed. (Modified from Zeller.)

On *Codium mucronatum* (marine), UNITED STATES.

RECENTLY DESCRIBED TAXA [1]

RHIZOPHYDIUM CLADOPHORAE (Kobayasi and Ookubo), comb. nov.

Phlyctidium cladophorae Kobayasi and Ookubo, Bull. Nat. Sci. Mus. (Tokyo), (N.S.), 1 (2) No. 35: 63, fig. 2. 1954.

"Zoosporangium epibiotic, sessile, globose or subglobose, 10–15 μ in diameter, hyaline, smooth, thin-walled, with a broad apical or rarely sublateral pore. Rhizoid (haustorium) simple, filamentous, short. Zoospores produced 10–20 in one zoosporangium, globose, 2–3 μ in diameter, with one globule and posterior 10 μ long flagellum, moving in zoosporangium and then darting away through pore. Resting spore not observed" (Kobayasi and Ookubo, *loc. cit.*).

On *Cladophora sp.*, JAPAN.

[1] Not included in the key. See also Scholz, *Archiv. f. Mikrobiol,*, 29: 354. 1958.

Because of the tapering, unbranched rhizoid this species is considered to belong in *Rhizophydium*. It is probably closely related to *R. sphaerocarpum* or to *R. vaucheriae.*

RHIZOPHYDIUM HALOPHILUM Uebelmesser

Arch. f. Mikrobiol., 25: 312, fig. 2. 1956

Sporangium spherical, 60–80 μ in diameter, with twenty-five to thirty regularly arranged hyaline papillae 5–6 μ high by 4 μ in diameter; rhizoidal system with a well-developed single main axis and lateral branches; zoospores escaping singly through pores formed upon the deliquescence of the papillae, spherical, 5.5–6 μ diameter, contents finely granular with a half-moon-shaped refractive posterior area, lacking a globule, flagellum 30 μ long; resting spore not observed.

Pine-pollen bait, seaside soil, cultivated in sea water (VENICE) ITALY, NORTH SEA, BALTIC, MEDITERRANEAN; saline soil (UTAH) UNITED STATES.

RHIZOPHYDIUM PEDICELLATUM Paterson

Mycologia, 48: 274, fig. 2, a-e. 1956

"Sporangium clavate to ovate, smooth walled, 9–14.5 μ high by 7–12 μ in diameter, borne on an extramatrical stalk, 3–9 μ long, usually procumbent, with the main axis and stalk parallel with the host, or erect, with the stalk more or less perpendicular to the host filament; rhizoids coarse, branched and tapering; zoospores numerous, spherical, 2–4 μ in diameter with a single eccentric refractive globule, 1–2 μ in diameter, a small dark granule, and a posterior flagellum 15 μ long, escaping through a single apical pore; resting spore not observed" (Paterson, *loc. cit.*).

Parasitic on *Melosira italica*, UNITED STATES.

RHIZOPHYDIUM PILIGENUM Ookubo and Kobayasi

Nagaoa, 5: 3, fig. 2. 1955

"Sporangia sessile, globose or subglobose, 45–50 μ in diameter, thin-walled, colourless, with 5–10 papillae, one or two of them becoming somewhat cylindrical, 10–13 μ in diameter, ca. 10 μ high, perforated; rhizoid arising from the base of sporangium, forked, very obscure. Zoospores formed in large numbers, ellipsoid or subglobose, 5–7 μ in length, posteriorly containing one globule and with a posterior flagellum, 16–17 μ in length. Resting spores not observed" (Ookubo and Kobayasi, *loc. cit.*).

Human hair and nails used as bait, JAPAN.

RHIZOPHYDIUM SUBGLOBOSUM Kobayasi and Ookubo

Bull. Nat. Sci. Mus. (Tokyo), (N.S.), 1 (2) No. 35: 63, fig. 3. 1954

"Zoosporangium scattered, epibiotic, globose, subglobose or ovoid, sessile, sending a short (9–10 μ) stalk-like penetration tube through host-wall, 30–50 μ long, 30–60 μ in diameter, smooth, hyaline, somewhat thick-walled, with one apical broad pit or laterally with several pits. Apophysis none. Rhizoid 3–5 branched just beneath the penetration tube, each branchlet moreover dichotomously branched. Zoospores numerous, swimming away one by one through pores, spherical, about 6 μ in diameter, with one posterior flagellum and one small globule. Resting spores not observed" (Kobayasi and Ookubo, *loc. cit.*).

On *Bryopsis sp.* (marine), JAPAN.

The species is said to be allied to *Rhizophydium globosum*, but distinct from it, in its greater number of zoospores and more extensive rhizoidal system, and from *R. marinum*, in the larger size of its sporangia.

SECTION II[1]

RHIZOPHYDIUM POLLINIS-PINI (Braun) Zopf, pro parte

Abhandl. Naturforsch. Gesell. Halle, 17: 82, pl. 1, figs. 16-20. 1887

(Fig. 17 J, p. 228)

Chytridium pollinis-pini Braun, Monatsber. Berlin Akad., 1855: 381; Abhandl. Berlin Akad., 1855: 40, pl. 3, figs. 1-15. 1856.

Chytridium vagans Braun, Monatsber. Berlin Akad., 1856: 588.

Phlyctidium vagans (Braun) Rabenhorst, Flora Europaea algarum, 3: 278. 1868.

---

[1] See also the following imperfectly known species of *Rhizophydium*:

R. leptophrydis, p. 312   R. pyriformis, p. 310
R. persimilis, p. 310   Rhizophydium spp., pp. 310-312

Phlyctidium pollinis (Braun) Sorokin, Arch. Bot. Nord France, 2: 19, fig. 13. 1883 (separate).
Phlyctidium pollinis-pini (Braun) Schroeter, Kryptogamenfl. Schlesien, 3 (1): 190. 1885. (See p. 270).

Sporangium sessile, spherical or nearly so, somewhat urceolate after discharge, with a more or less prominent fairly broad apical papilla, 10–25 μ in diameter, wall smooth, colorless, of variable thickness up to 1.4 μ; rhizoids branched, arising from a more or less prolonged axis; zoospores spherical or ellipsoidal, 2–4 μ in diameter, with a colorless eccentric globule and a long flagellum, emerging singly and slowly through a broad apical pore formed upon the deliquescence of the papilla, movement hopping; resting spore sessile, spherical, 10–15 μ in diameter, with a smooth thick wall and a large globule; rhizoidal system branched, germination not observed.

Parasitic or saprophytic on floating pollen of *Pinus sylvestris*, Braun (*loc. cit.*), *Pinus spp.*, pollen of various angiosperms used as bait in water cultures (*Phlox, Tropaeolum, Helianthus, Populus*, etc.), Zopf (*loc. cit.*), pine pollen, Schroeter (1885: 190), Sydow (Exsiccati: Sydow, Phyco. et Prot. 47; Mycoth. March. 4714), isolated from soil, Remy (1948: 214), GERMANY; pollen of fir, Sorokin (1883: 19, fig. 13), SOUTH RUSSIA; pollen grains of "barrträd," Lagerheim (1884 [1]: 100), SWEDEN; Maurizio (1895: 14), SWITZERLAND; pollen of *Pinus sylvestris*, Valkanov (1931a: 362), BULGARIA; pine pollen, Couch (1932: 250, pl. 15, figs. 20–25), *Pinus sylvestris* pollen, Karling (1941b: 108), pine pollen, Sparrow (1952d: 763), UNITED STATES; fern spores and pollen grains, Karling (1946c: 334), BRAZIL; *Keteleeria* pollen, Shen and Siang (1948: 181), CHINA; pine-pollen bait, soil, Sparrow (1952a: 36), CUBA.

The species with multiporous sporangia described by Zopf and widely reproduced as illustrative of *Rhizophydium pollinis-pini* (see Fischer, 1892: fig. 16b; Migula, 1903: pl. 2 K, fig. 5; Fitzpatrick, 1930: fig. 20a) is *R. sphaerotheca* (see p. 249). Since no description or figures were published of the form on *Tribonema bombycina*, collected by Itzigsohn (see Braun, 1856b: 588), it cannot be compared with the present species. Presumably, there was a close resemblance, for Braun considered his fungus on pine pollen to be identical with it and suggested that the species might more suitably be called "*Chytridium vagans*" rather than "*C. pollinis-pini.*" The fungus on pine pollen in France which Cornu (1872a: 121) referred to *R. pollinis-pini* had endobiotic resting spores. These spores have been thought by Fischer (1892: 89) to belong to one of several endobiotic Phycomycetes which also inhabit pollen grains. Schenk's fungus (1858b: 8) on *Chlamydomonas sp.* is probably *R. globosum.* The chytrid briefly described by Serbinow (1907: 156) as a facultative parasite of coniferous pollen grains was shown, when the rhizoids were stained, to be a species of *Phlyctidium* rather than of *Rhizophydium* (see, however, Couch's [1932] observations on the rhizoids and see *Phlyctidium pollinis-pini* below).

Species of *Rhizophydium* which attack the germinating oöspores of various members of the Peronosporaceae have been assigned to *R. pollinis-pini* by Schroeter (1879: 84) and by Melhus (1914: 55, pl. 4). De Bary (1863: 21) also mentioned a "*Chytridium*" parasitic on germinating oöspores of *Albugo.* It is evident from the description and figures of the fungus studied by Melhus that his material was not *R. pollinis-pini.* If the flagellation of the zoospores has been correctly interpreted, it may be a species of *Rhizidiomyces.* Whether the other forms inhabiting peronosporaceous oöspores are identical with Melhus' fungus cannot be ascertained. The latter may be described as follows:

Sporangium obpyriform or ovoid, up to 40 μ in diameter, often narrowing at the base to form a short stalk, wall fairly thick, colorless, with a single apical or lateral papilla (occasionally two) 3–5 μ in diameter; rhizoids fairly coarse, branched, arising from a central axis which is cylindrical or, sometimes, irregularly inflated; zoospores spherical or pyriform, 3 μ in diameter, with a slightly eccentric colorless globule and an anterior flagellum 12 μ in length, escaping individually and fully formed through an apical or lateral pore (occasionally two); resting spore (?) with a thick smooth yellow-brown wall, formed "inside the old sporangium," germination not observed.

? *Phlyctidium pollinis-pini* (Braun) Schroeter

Kryptogamenfl. Schlesien, 3 (1): 190. 1885. Non Sorokin, Arch. Bot. Nord France, 2: 19. 1883 (separate)

Sporangium sessile, spherical, 20–25 μ in diameter, with a slightly protruding apical papilla, wall fairly thick, with a faint reddish shimmer, contents colorless, with from one to two globules; zoospores about 2.5 μ in diameter, with a colorless oil droplet, discharged through an apical pore.

On pine pollen, Schroeter (?), GERMANY.

Serbinow (1907: 156) asserted that a facultative parasite of pollen observed by him in Russia has sporangia which agree with Zopf's *Rhizophydium pollinis-pini*, but which, in contrast to it, have an unbranched rhizoid. Since Zopf had both true *R. pollinis-pini* and what is called here *R. sphaerotheca* and since Serbinow did not further describe the sporangia of his organism, it is impossible to say what the latter observer had. It is evident, however, from Serbinow's emphatic statement, that a *Phlyctidium* species does occur on pollen. Schroeter's specific description is included here since it appears to be based, for the most part, on Braun's *Rhizophydium pollinis-pini*. Because of Sorokin's previous application of *Phlyctidium* to Braun's fungus, Schroeter's combination cannot be used. A new name will be needed if Serbinow's observations are confirmed.

RHIZOPHYDIUM SCIADII (Zopf) Fischer

Rabenhorst. Kryptogamenfl., 1 (4): 94. 1892

(Fig. 17 K, p. 228)

Rhizophyton sciadii Zopf, Abhandl. Naturforsch. Gesell. Halle, 17: 91 pl. 2, figs. 23-32. 1887.

Sporangium sessile, at first spherical or somewhat flattened at the base, at maturity pyriform, with a broad blunt apex (the papilla), up to 20 μ high by 17 μ in diameter, walls smooth, colorless, slightly thickened; rhizoidal system extensive, arising from one or two main axes, richly branched; zoospores as many as eighty to one hundred in the larger sporangia, spherical or ellipsoidal, 2.3–4 μ in greatest diameter, with a relatively large (1–1.3 μ in diameter) refractive, slightly eccentric, colorless globule and a very delicate flagellum, emerging upon the deliquescence of the thin-walled blunt apex of the sporangium; resting spore not observed.

Parasitic on *Ophiocytium* (*Sciadium*) *arbusculum* in fresh and salt water (in culture dishes), GERMANY.

In attacked plants the plasma, nucleus, and chromatophore were destroyed, the residue of the latter forming yellow-brown or dirty red-brown clumps or granules in the cell. Staining was necessary to demonstrate the full extent of the rhizoidal system.

RHIZOPHYDIUM SCHROETERI de Wildeman

Mém. Herb. Boissier, 1900 (15): 5, fig. 3; Bull. Acad. Roy. Belg. (Sci.), V, 17: 289, fig. 3. 1931

Sporangium sessile, spherical, ellipsoidal, or ovoid, up to 7 μ in diameter, with a prominent apical or subapical papilla, wall smooth, colorless; endobiotic system very delicate, consisting of an unbranched or once-branched rhizoid; zoospores rarely more than twelve, spherical, about 1 μ in diameter, with an eccentric globule, escaping upon the dissolution of the papilla, the wall of the empty urceolate sporangium disintegrating after discharge; resting spore not observed.

On the planktonic diatom *Asterionella gracillima*, coll. Schroeter, SWITZERLAND.

Considered by Minden (1915: 326) to probably be a small form of *Rhizophydium sphaerocarpum*, which it resembles in its general aspect. One of the sporangia that de Wildeman (1931: fig. 3) illustrated is borne on a short needle-like stalk.

RHIZOPHYDIUM OSCILLATORIAE-RUBESCENTIS Jaag and Nipkow

Berichte Schweiz. Bot. Gesell., 61: 485, pl. 13, figs. 20-25. 1951

Sporangium sessile usually lateral on the trichome, globose or broadly ellipsoidal or pyriform, about 16–20 μ in diameter, with broad rounded apex, finally subangular, with a papilla, wall smooth, hyaline; rhizoid very delicate, unbranched, short or up to 180 μ long; zoospores 6–30, spherical, about 2.5–3.5 μ in diameter with a basal hyaline globule and long flagellum; resting spore (not known with certainty to belong to the species) spherical, thick-walled, 8–12 μ in diameter with a spherical male cell 4 μ in diameter adherent to it.

Parasitic on the planktonic alga *Oscillatoria rubescens*, SWITZERLAND.

In contrast to *Rhizophydium deformans* (p. 243), no contortion of the host trichome is produced by this species. The resting spore described was not associated with certainty with the sporangial stage. Jaag and Nipkow believe their fungus to be closely related to *Rhizophydium sciadii* Zopf but to differ from it in having an unbranched rather than branched rhizoid.

RHIZOPHYDIUM SPHAEROCARPUM (Zopf) Fischer

Rabenhorst. Kryptogamen-Fl., 1 (4): 95. 1892

(Fig. 17 L-M, p. 228)

Rhizidium sphaerocarpum Zopf, Nova Acta Acad. Leop.-Carol., 47: 202, pl. 19, figs. 16-27. 1884.

Sporangium sessile, subspherical, ovoid, or urceolate, with a broad (4–7 µ in diameter) protruding apical papilla, 6–18 µ in diameter and up to 20 µ high, wall colorless, smooth, of two layers, the outer thicker than the inner; endobiotic part consisting of a slender, generally unbranched rhizoid; zoospores spherical or ovoid, 1.5–2 µ in diameter, from a few to forty in a sporangium, with a colorless centric or slightly eccentric globule and a long flagellum, emerging in an evanescent vesicle, movement amoeboid or hopping; resting spore sessile, spherical, about 11–18 µ in diameter, with a thick smooth colorless wall, contents with a large eccentric globule, rhizoid like that of the sporangium, germination not observed.

On *Spirogyra*, *Mougeotia*, *Oedogonium*, and other algae, Zopf (*loc. cit.*), isolated from soil, Reinboldt (1951: 178), GERMANY; *Mougeotia genuflexa*, coll. Marchal, de Wildeman (1890: 13, fig. 3), BELGIUM; *Mougeotia parvula*, Atkinson (1909a: 326, fig. 3a-g), *M. sphaerocarpa*, *Mougeotia sp.*, Graff (1928: 161), UNITED STATES; *Oedogonium sp.*, Skvortzow (1925: 430), MANCHURIA; *Spirogyra sp.*, *Mougeotia (Gonatonema) sp.*, Tokunaga (1934b: 390, pl. 11, figs. 6, 8–9), JAPAN; *Spirogyra maxima*, Bérczi (1940: 82), HUNGARY; (as "*Phlyctidium sphaerocarpum*"), *Oedogonium*, *Spirogyra*, Litvinow (1953: 79), LATVIA; pine pollen, Gaertner (1954b: 21), EQUATORIAL EAST AFRICA, SOUTH AFRICA, Gaertner (*op. cit.*, p. 41), SWEDEN.

This species, like *Rhizophydium globosum*, has become a collective one, and a number of fungi with ovoid, spherical, or urceolate sporangia which possess a broad discharge papilla have been referred to it. The above diagnosis does not include types with a well-developed much-branched rhizoidal system or those growing on organisms other than algae. These limitations may subsequently be shown to be too restrictive and the extent of rhizoidal development a poor specific character (see, for example, *Chytridium lagenaria*, p. 522).

The following have been excluded:

1. De Wildeman (1893b: 61, pl. 6, figs. 13–16, pl. 7, fig. 18), on *Mougeotia* and *Spirogyra*, BELGIUM. The sporangia resemble those of the present species, but no rhizoidal system was observed. De Wildeman noted that on *Mougeotia* the fungus caused marked bending of the host cells.

2. Raitschenko (1902: 124, figs. 1–8), on the heterocysts of *Anabaena flos-aquae*, RUSSIA. The endobiotic part is a stout unbranched peg (see *Phlyctidium megastomum*, p. 214).

3. Valkanov (1931a: 362, fig. 1), on *Mougeotia sp.*, BULGARIA. From the figures, the sporangia are nearly or completely spherical and the rhizoids much branched. No discharge of the zoospores was observed. The fungus stimulated the host to form a protective plug of wall material.

4. Skvortzow (1927: 206), on *Spirogyra*, MANCHURIA. No mention is made of the character of the rhizoids.

5. Sparrow (1933c: 519, pl. 49, fig. 1; 1936a: 442, pl. 19, figs. 15–18), on nematodes, UNITED STATES, GREAT BRITAIN (see *R. vermicola*, p. 277) Though resembling *Rhizophydium sphaerocarpum* in the shape of its sporangium, in its rhizoid, and in the method of spore discharge, Sparrow's fungus differs in several particulars. The zoospores in both the American and the British collections were about 4–5 μ in diameter and formed in a thin-walled sporangium, whereas, to judge from Zopf's figures, the sporangium in his species is thick-walled and the zoospores are estimated to be about 2.5 μ in diameter. Another difference is the type of substratum. How far we are justified in supposing that a single species of chytrid is capable of penetrating all types of walls—cellulose, chitinous, or siliceous—cannot at present be said with certainty. *R. gibbosum*, the peculiar sporangia of which cannot be confused with those of any other species, was observed by Zopf

on both diatoms and rotifer eggs. Arbitrarily, however, and with some justification on morphological and physiological grounds, this inhabitant of nematodes is segregated for the present from *R. sphaerocarpum*.

6. Domján (1936: 42, pl. 1, figs. 3–4, 13, 26), on *Spirogyra, Zygnema,* and *Closterium,* HUNGARY. The sporangia and resting spores resemble somewhat those of *Rhizophydium sphaerocarpum,* but the rhizoidal system is richly branched and extensive.

7. Tokunaga (*loc. cit.,* pl. 11, fig. 7), on *Cladophora sp.,* JAPAN. The rhizoids are too richly branched for this species. The fungus resembles closely Domján's organism.

8. *Rhizophydium sphaerocarpum* var. *cryophilum* Laszló Bérczi (in Kol, 1942: 29, figs. 4–5), on the snow alga *Ancyclonema nordenskioldii,* ALASKA. This form is too little known to be recognized. Although its sporangium resembles that of *R. sphaerocarpum,* its rhizoid is branched.

The chytrid supposed by Dangeard (1890–91c: 244, pl. 16, fig. 9) to be Zopf's species and called *Chytridium sphaerocarpum* by Dangeard is operculate and has been retained in *Chytridium.*

RHIZOPHYDIUM VAUCHERIAE de Wildeman

Mém. Herb. Boissier, 1900 (15) : 6, Bull. Acad. Roy. Belg. (Sci.), V, 17 : 285, fig. 1, *1-10.* 1931

Sporangium sessile, spherical, 26–50 µ in diameter, with a broad prominent apical papilla, wall somewhat thickened, colorless, smooth; endobiotic part consisting of an unbranched rhizoid; zoospores spherical, 1.5 µ in diameter, with a conspicuous colorless globule, escaping successively through a large apical pore formed upon the dissolution of, or rarely the dehiscence of, the apical papilla, the empty sporangium strongly urceolate, the irregular discharge pore with a slightly recurved margin; resting spore not observed.

Parasitic, often in large numbers, on the oögonia of *Vaucheria sessilis,* coll. Massart, BELGIUM.

Further observations on the process of zoospore discharge are necessary. Typically, the conspicuous papilla is dissolved, but on rare occasions it is said to persist and to be thrown back as a sort of operculum. De Wildeman believes dissolution of this cap occurs at a varying rate, depending upon conditions in the medium. The fungus is of particular interest because of the significance of the type of sporangial discharge in relation to our present concept of genera. The situation is evidently similar to that in *Blastocladia pringsheimii* (Sparrow, 1932b: 291), where a cap is often observed for a short time at the apex of the mass of emerging zoospores but more often dissolves completely before the swarmers are discharged.

De Wildeman believes the species to be near *Rhizophydium sphaerocarpum.*

The wall of the egg was often stimulated to thicken around the rhizoid of the parasite. The vegetative cells were not attacked, nor was pollen of *Alnus* and *Salix* occurring in the water with the alga.

RHIZOPHYDIUM CARPOPHILUM (Zopf) Fischer

Rabenhorst. Kryptogamen-Fl., 1 (4): 95. 1892

Rhizidium carpophilum Zopf, Nova Acta Acad. Leop.-Carol., 47: 200, pl. 20, figs. 8-16. 1884.

Sporangia sessile, often clustered, at first spherical or ovoid, becoming somewhat pyriform after discharge, 9.6–25.2 μ in diameter, wall thin, smooth, colorless; endobiotic part consisting of a tenuous unbranched or sparingly branched rhizoid; zoospores two to forty or more, spherical or slightly ellipsoidal, 3–6 μ in diameter, with a colorless eccentric globule and a very long flagellum, emerging through an apical fairly broad slightly elevated pore, movement swimming or amoeboid; resting spore sessile, spherical, 5–9 μ in diameter, with a slightly thickened smooth wall and a large colorless oil globule, germination not observed.

On oögonia and oöspores of *Saprolegnia sp., Achlya sp.,* etc., occurring in clusters of one hundred or more on a single oögonium, Zopf (*loc. cit.*), isolated from soil, Remy (1948: 214), Reinboldt (1951: 178), GERMANY; (?) on sporangium of *Olpidiopsis saprolegniae,* Sparrow (1932b: 276, fig. 1b), oögonia and oöspores of *Saprolegnia sp., Achlya sp.,* oöspores of *Monoblepharis macrandra,* Sparrow (1933c: 519), *Saprolegnia sp.,* Karling (1941a: 386), UNITED STATES; oögonia of *Achlya racemosa,* Tokunaga (1934b: 389, pl. 11, fig. 3), JAPAN; eggs of *Achlya sp.*, *Dictyuchus monosporus*, oöspores of *Monoblepharis macrandra*, Sparrow (1936a: 442, pl. 17, figs. 4–5), GREAT BRITAIN; *Saprolegnia ferax*, Karling (1946c: 329, figs. 14–16), BRAZIL; *Achlya sp.*, soil, Sparrow (1952a: 35), CUBA; pine pollen?, Gaertner (1954b: 21), EGYPT, NORTHWEST AFRICA, WEST AFRICA, EQUATORIAL EAST AFRICA, SOUTH AFRICA; Gaertner (*op. cit.*, p. 41), SWEDEN.

This fungus is a very virulent parasite and soon destroys the eggs of the host. Zopf noted that, if oöspores were not already differentiated in the oögonia when the attack occurred, the contents of the infected oögonium contracted into a ball of fatty material. The species, while common in gross water cultures of higher Phycomycetes, is for the most part found after vigorous growth of the host plant has ceased. It has been cultivated on agar, pollen grains, and boiled maize stems by Couch (1939a).

The organism termed *Rhizophydium carpophilum* by Coker (1923: 186, pl. 62, figs. 11–13) differs in certain essential features, particularly in the possession of an inflated rhizoid. It may be a species of *Phlyctochytrium*. No zoospore discharge occurred in the form observed by Sparrow on *Olpidiopsis* which was, in turn, parasitizing a species of *Achlya*; hence, its generic disposition is doubtful.

RHIZOPHYDIUM VERMICOLA Sparrow

Aquatic Phycomycetes, p. 188, fig. 11 N. 1943

(Fig. 17 N, p. 228)

Sporangium sessile, spherical, urceolate after discharge, 15–20 μ in diameter, with a broad apical papilla, wall thin, smooth, colorless; endobiotic part consisting of a slender unbranched rhizoid; zoospores spherical, about 4–5 μ in diameter, with a colorless eccentric globule and a long flagellum, emerging apparently imbedded in a gelatinous matrix or surrounded by a vesicle through a wide apical pore formed upon the deliquescence of the papilla, soon assuming individual motility and swimming away; resting spore not observed.

On *Anguillula* infected by other fungi, Sparrow (1933c: 519, pl. 49, fig. 1), UNITED STATES; Sparrow (1936a: 442, pl. 19, figs. 16–18), GREAT BRITAIN.

In both cases the chytrid was found on worms harboring other fungi. In the American material it occurred with *Harposporium anguillulae*, and in the British with undetermined species of *Lagenidium* and *Aphanomyces*.

The fungus has previously been discussed as *Rhizophydium sphaerocarpum* (Zopf) Fischer, but it differs from that species in certain minor features (see p. 274). Buckley and Clapham (1929: 6, text figs. 19–21, pl. 1, figs. 1–3) have described as *R. carpophilum* a fungus on eggs of *Dibothriocephalus latus* (a helminth), in England, which may possibly be referable to the present species. The sporangia were larger (up to 35 μ in diameter), and the main rhizoid formed delicate branches at its tip. The zoospores, however, were the same size (4.5–5 μ) as those of *R. vermicola*.

RHIZOPHYDIUM MISCHOCOCCI Scherffel

Arch. Protistenk., 54: 195, pl. 9, fig. 56. 1926

(Fig. 17 R, p. 228)

Sporangium sessile, broadly pyriform, with a thin smooth colorless wall, 5 μ high by 5 μ in diameter (at the base); endobiotic system consisting of a long, fairly thick, unbranched rhizoid; zoospores four, each with a fairly large colorless globule, escaping through an apical pore, the wall of the sporangium collapsing after discharge, motile zoospores not seen; resting spore not observed.

On *Mischococcus confervicola*, HUNGARY.

Scherffel asserted that if *Phlyctidium* is segregated from *Rhizophydium*—which he does not favor—his fungus more properly belongs in the former genus. It is retained here because its slender rhizoid is uninflated and not *haustorial*, as in typical *Phlyctidium*.

RHIZOPHYDIUM AGILE (Zopf) Fischer

Rabenhorst. Kryptogamen-Fl., 1 (4): 96. 1892

Rhizophyton agile Zopf, Nova Acta Acad. Leop.-Carol., 52: 343, pl. 20, figs. 1-7. 1888.

Sporangia occurring singly or in groups on the surface of the gelatinous sheath of the host, sessile, variable in shape, broadly pyriform, sometimes somewhat angular and blunt-cornered, usually not over 10–15 μ in diameter, often having a narrow conical base, with a small nearly sessile or slightly protruding apical papilla, wall colorless, smooth, delicate, collapsing and disintegrating after spore discharge; rhizoids richly branched, arising from the tip of a single stalk which passes through the gelatinous sheath of the host; zoospores not over fifty, spherical, with a single slightly eccentric colorless globule and occasionally from one to two smaller ones, flagellum delicate, movement quick, in zigzag lines, or amoeboid; resting spore not observed.

Parasitic on *Chroococcus turgidus*, causing an epidemic both in the field and in gross culture that destroys up to 75 per cent of the individuals, Zopf (*loc. cit.*), GERMANY; Serbinow (1907: 159, pl. 4, figs. 35–36), RUSSIA.

The parasite caused a swelling of the gelatinous sheath and a quick discoloration of the cell contents. The latter became olive green, then dirty yellow brown.

Serbinow noted that the fungus was a facultative parasite or even a true saprophyte. The sporangia figured by him are more regularly pyriform than those in Zopf's organism, and the rhizoid is an apparently unbranched slender thread. In these characters it approaches *Rhizophydium simplex* (Dang.) Fischer.

RHIZOPHYDIUM ACUFORME (Zopf) Fischer

Rabenhorst. Kryptogamen-Fl., 1 (4): 93. 1892

Rhizidium acuforme Zopf, Nova Acta Acad. Leop.-Carol., 47: 209, pl. 21, figs. 33-44. 1884.

Sporangium sessile, broadly pyriform, 6–16 μ in diameter, with a single apical papilla, wall thin, smooth, colorless; rhizoids delicate, sparingly branched, arising from a main axis; zoospores about 2–2.5 μ in diameter, with a single colorless globule, escaping through an apical pore formed upon the deliquescence of the papilla; resting spore sessile, spherical, generally smaller than the sporangium, with a smooth thickened wall, the contents bearing a large globule, rhizoids delicate, sparingly branched, arising from a main axis, germination not observed.

Parasitic on moving cells of a *Chlamydomonas*-like alga, Fischer (*loc. cit.*), GERMANY; *Chlamydomonas sp.*, de Wildeman (1890: 9), BELGIUM;(?) *Palmodictyon sp.*, Couch (1932: 251, pl. 15, figs. 26–35; see below), UNITED STATES.

Zopf's material was found in March, while the ice was still on the pond and the temperature of the water was 11°–13° Réaumer (13.8°–16.3° C.). Up to ten chytrids were found on a single zoospore of the host. De Wildeman (*loc. cit.*) noted that the host cell continued to move even when infected by as many as six zoospores of the chytrid. In such instances, however, the sporangia of the parasite did not mature. In the early stages of development the fungus had no visible effect on the alga, but as the parasite matured the host lost its motility and finally succumbed to the invader.

The form described by Couch (*loc. cit.*) on *Palmodictyon sp.* differs in certain essential features from that of Zopf. Its sporangia are smaller (6.2–9 μ in diameter) and the discharge papilla, which may be subapical or even lateral, is much broader and longer (up to one half as long as the diameter of the sporangium). Furthermore, certain sporangia formed zoospores about one half the size of those formed by other sporangia. Couch (*loc. cit.*) considers the organism to be intermediate between *Rhizophydium acuforme* and *R. minutum* Atkinson.

Grove (1917) recorded this species from Great Britain on *Chlamydomonas intermedia*, but Canter (1953) questioned the identification, because the rhizoidal system of the fungus differs slightly from that of Zopf's form.

RHIZOPHYDIUM MINUTUM Atkinson

Bot. Gaz., 48: 328, fig. 4. 1909

"Zoosporangia obpyriform or flask-shaped, broadly papillate, 5–6 μ in diameter, sessile with a few slender rhizoidal filaments at the base in the host cell. Apex opening by a single pore. Zoospores two to four in a zoosporangium, oval, uniciliate, with a single oil drop, 2.5 μ in diameter" (Atkinson, *loc. cit.*).

On *Spirogyra varians*, Atkinson (*loc. cit.*), UNITED STATES; *Spirogyra sp.*, Bérczi (1940: 82, pl. 2, fig. 13), HUNGARY; pine pollen, Gaertner (1954b: 21), SOUTH AFRICA; *Spirogyra sp.*, Lacy (1955: 209), INDIA.

RHIZOPHYDIUM EUDORINAE Hood

Proc. Birmingham Nat. Hist. and Phil. Soc., 12: 45, figs. 1-5. 1910; Trans. Brit. Mycol. Soc., 5: 236, figs. 1-4. 1916

Sporangium imbedded in the gelatinous sheath of the host colony, sessile on the cell, broadly pyriform with a prolonged neck, the broad apex extending slightly beyond the outer surface of the gelatinous sheath, 20–35 μ high by 10–17 μ in diameter, wall thin, smooth, colorless; rhizoid delicate and unbranched; zoospores numerous, ovoid, 2 μ in diameter, with a minute colorless eccentric globule and a single flagellum, emerging from the apex of the sporangium in a compact irregular mass imbedded in mucilaginous material from which, after a period of rest, they escape; resting spore within the gelatinous sheath, supported by a short stalk on the host cell, asexually formed, spherical, 10–16 μ in diameter, with a thick dark rough wall, germination not observed.

Parasitic on the planktonic alga *Eudorina elegans*, GREAT BRITAIN. The development of this species is similar to that of *Phlyctidium eudorinae*. The zoospore comes to rest on the surface of the gelatinous sheath of the host colony and produces a slender threadlike penetration tube which pierces the sheath and becomes attached to the nearest algal cell. Hood states that branches of the thread may penetrate two adjacent cells and that two zoospores may have one thread in common. The latter statement seems very improbable. After attachment to the algal cell the body of the zoospore enlarges and is drawn gradually within the gelatinous sheath, so that often the mature sporangium is sessile on the host cell, with its apex slightly protruding from the sheath. The character of the rhizoid within the host cell is not mentioned. From the description and the figures given, presumably that part of the infection tube within the sheath expands and forms the lateral walls of the sporangium. A somewhat similar type of development is found in *Dangeardia*.

Canter (1946: 134) believes this species is not valid, but represents a mixture of *Dangeardia mammillata* and an epibiotic chytrid possibly belonging to *Rhizophydium* or to *Chytridium*.

RHIZOPHYDIUM BRAUNI (Dang.) Fischer

Rabenhorst. Kryptogamen-Fl., 1 (4): 94. 1892

Chytridium brauni Dangeard, Bull. Soc. Bot. France, 34: xxii. 1887; Le Botaniste, 1: 57, pl. 3, fig. 11. 1889.

Sporangium sessile on the gelatinous envelope of the algal colony, narrowly pyriform or ovoid, the attenuated apex often slightly curved, wall stout, smooth, colorless; rhizoid a long slender unbranched (?) filament which penetrates the algal cells; zoospores from fifteen to twenty-five, spherical, 2 μ in diameter, with an eccentric colorless globule and a long flagellum, escaping through an apical pore formed upon the deliquescence of a papilla; resting spore not observed.

Parasitic on *Apiocystis brauniana*, FRANCE.

If subsequent investigations show that the rhizoid is unbranched within the algal cells and does not taper, then the species might better be placed in *Phlyctidium*. The sporangia are described by Dangeard as ovoid, but from the figures they distinctly appear narrowly pyriform. *Rhizophydium simplex* seems doubtfully distinct from this species.

RHIZOPHYDIUM SIMPLEX (Dang.) Fischer

Rabenhorst. Kryptogamen-Fl., 1 (4): 101. 1892

(Fig. 17 S, p. 228)

Chytridium simplex Dangeard, Le Botaniste, 1: 60, pl. 3, figs. 18-20. 1889.

Sporangium resting directly on the host cell or on the surface of the gelatinous sheath, narrowly pyriform, 8–15 μ long by 6–7 μ in diameter, prolonged apically into a slightly bent tube, wall thickened a little, smooth, colorless; endobiotic part consisting of an unbranched rhizoid which penetrates the protoplasm of the host; zoospores few to from thirty to forty, ellipsoidal or spherical, 1.5–3 μ in diameter, with a colorless basal globule and a long flagellum, emerging through a small pore formed at the tip of the sporangium; resting spore spherical, 6–7 μ in diameter, with a thick smooth colorless wall, rhizoidal system like that of the sporangium; germination not observed.

Parasitic on cysts of *Cryptomonas sp.* in culture jar, Dangeard (*loc. cit.*), FRANCE; dead colonies of *Pandorina*, Sparrow (1933c: 519), UNITED STATES; *Spirogyra, Chlorococcum* (?), Sparrow (1936a: 439, fig. 3 h–k), GREAT BRITAIN.

Dangeard observed that changes in the host contents quickly occurred after infection by the fungus. The olive-colored plasma was reduced to reddish granules and the cellulose wall lost its structure and expanded. The swarmers of the alga were not attacked.

The British material differed from Dangeard's species in having fewer and larger (3 μ in diameter rather than 1.5 μ) zoospores formed in the sporangium. Certain of the sporangia appeared to show internal proliferation, but owing to their small size this could not be determined with absolute certainty.

Perhaps only doubtfully distinct from *Rhizophydium brauni.*

RHIZOPHYDIUM PSEUDODISTOMUM Scherffel

Abstracts of Communications, V Inter. Bot. Congress, Cambridge, 1930: 222; Arch. Protistenk., 73: 140, pl. 9, fig. 2 a-b. 1931

Sporangium sessile, distinctly pyriform, with a broad convex base and a prominent apiculus, 16–20 μ high by 13–18 μ in diameter, wall thin, smooth, colorless; rhizoids well developed, branched; zoospores not observed, apparently emerging through a discharge tube 2 μ long by 5 μ in diameter which forms subapically on the sporangium, the apiculus becoming slightly lateral as a consequence; resting spore not observed.

Parasitic on *Oocystis solitaria* var. *wittrockiana*, HUNGARY.

The parasite soon destroyed the contents of the host cell and reduced them to a reddish-brown mass.

The unnamed fungus found on *Protoderma* from North Africa by Sparrow (1938a: 147, fig. 2a) with a pyriform sporangium bearing two prominent apical papillae may possibly be referable to this species. The endobiotic system consisted, so far as could be observed, of a short peglike structure, but whether this gave rise distally to branches was not determined.

RHIZOPHYDIUM GRANULOSPORUM Scherffel

Arch. Protistenk., 53: 44, pl. 2, figs. 81-86. 1925
(Fig. 17 P-Q, p. 228)

Sporangium sessile, broadly pyriform, with a broad apex, 7–14 μ high by 5–9 μ in diameter, usually appearing tilted on the surface of the host, wall thin, smooth, colorless; rhizoids extremely delicate, feebly developed, arising from a short main axis; zoospores ovoid, 3 μ long by 2 μ in diameter, with a large colorless slightly eccentric globule and a long flagellum, escaping through a broad pore formed upon the dissolution of an apical, subapical, or occasionally lateral papilla; resting spore spherical, 5–7 μ in diameter, wall thick, colorless, moderately covered with short rodlike protuberances, resting on the apex or side of the companion cell, germination not observed; companion cell single (rarely two), spherical or turbinate, smoothwalled, 2.5–3 μ in diameter, sessile or with a short extramatrical stalk, rhizoid unbranched.

Parasitic on *Tribonema bombycina*, Scherffel (*loc. cit.*), HUNGARY; Sparrow (1939a: 124, pl. 2, figs. 14–25), UNITED STATES.

In the American material both conjugating thalli appeared to develop on the host wall, although in two instances the receptive thallus seemed to make contact only with the "male" plant. Once the "female" alone was attached to the algal cell. It was observed that the characteristic spines appeared on the receptive thallus soon after fertilization and before thickening of the wall had been initiated.

RHIZOPHYDIUM VERRUCOSUM Cejp
Bull. Internat. Acad. Sci. Bohême, 42 (3): 4, pl. 1, figs. 9-10, pl. 2, fig. 2. 1933 (separate)

Sporangium sessile, narrowly pyriform or ovoid, almost citriform, 14–22 by 32–41 μ (high?), wall stout, its outer surface densely covered by warts, with a prolonged slightly curved smooth apiculus (papilla?) 12 μ long by 7 μ in diameter; rhizoidal system delicate, composed of short branches; zoospores spherical, 2–3 μ in diameter, with a single globule, uniflagellate, undergoing a period of rest (outside?) before swarming; resting spore subspherical, rarely irregular, 25–30 μ in diameter, with a thick wall covered with coarse warts, contents with numerous oil globules, rhizoids not observed, germination not observed.

On *Closterium sp.*, GERMANY.

RHIZOPHYDIUM ZOOPHTHORUM (Dang.) Fischer

Rabenhorst. Kryptogamen-Fl., 1 (4): 94. 1892
(Fig. 17 O, p. 228)

Chytridium zoophthorum Dangeard, Bull. Soc. Bot. France, 34 : xxii. 1887; Le Botaniste, 1 : 58, pl. 3, figs. 10, 21. 1889.

Sporangia sessile, often in clusters, ovoid or somewhat pyriform, with a prominent apiculus, 20–25 μ long by 15–17 μ in diameter, wall thin, smooth, colorless; rhizoids extensive, richly branched, arising as secondary branches from a main axis; zoospores ovoid, 3 μ (long?), with dense granular plasma, a slightly refractive colorless basal globule, and a flagellum 30 μ in length, escaping through a narrow pore formed at the tip of the apiculus; resting spore not observed.

Parasitic on adults and eggs of rotifers, Dangeard (*loc. cit.*), FRANCE; liver-fluke eggs, coll. J. Bayley Butler, Sparrow (1943: 196), IRELAND; rotifer eggs, Karling (1946b: 10, pl. 2, figs. 43–45), BRAZIL.

The habitat, ovoid sporangium with prominent apiculus, and richly branched rhizoidal system are distinctive features of this species. The living material from Ireland, on liver-fluke eggs, was kindly sent for examination by Professor Bayley Butler, of University College, Dublin, in 1933. Other of the eggs were infected by *Catenaria* and a fungus similar to *Rhizophydium globosum*. The thalli of the present species frequently formed dense clusters at the operculate apex of the fluke eggs. A similar gregarious habit was noted by Dangeard on rotifer eggs.

RHIZOPHYDIUM APICULATUM Karling

Amer. J. Bot., 33: 331, figs. 33-37. 1946
(Fig. 18 H, p. 286)

"Thalli numerous, up to 26 on a host. Sporangia hyaline, smooth, fairly thick-walled, pyriform (6–10 × 14–18 μ), slightly obclavate, flattened, or anatropous with one to three prominent exit papillae which may often become extended to short tubes, 4 × 6 μ long. Zoospores spherical, 3–3.5 μ, with a small refractive globule. Rhizoidal system richly branched. Resting spores hyaline, smooth, spherical (8–12 μ), pyriform (10 × 14 μ), often apiculate; containing a large

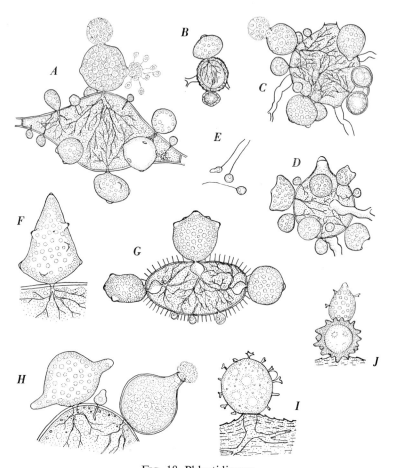

FIG. 18. Phlyctidiaceae

A–E. Rhizophydium hyperparasiticum Karling, parasitic on various phycomycetes: *A*, thalli and sporangia on *Septochytrium*; *B*, parasitized sporangium of a chytrid; *C*, chytrid sporangium heavily parasitized; *D, Septochytrium* sporangium heavily parasitized; *E*, zoospores of parasite. *F. Rhizophydium conicum* Karling, sporangium on *Netrium sp.* *G. Phlyctochytrium nematodeae* Karling, thalli and sporangia on nematode egg. *H. Rhizophydium apiculatum* Karling on protozoan. *I–J. Rhizophydium keratinophilum* Karling on hair: *I*, nearly mature sporangium; *J*, germinated resting spore.

(*A–F, H*, Karling, 1946c; *G*, Karling, 1946b; *I–J*, Karling, 1946d)

central refractive globule surrounded by several smaller ones; functioning as prosporangia in germination" (Karling, *loc. cit.*).

Parasitic on a protozoan, Karling (*loc. cit.*), BRAZIL; UNITED STATES; snake-skin bait, soil, Sparrow (1952a: 36), CUBA.

Characterized by predominantly pyriform sporangia with one to three prominent exit papillae often terminating short tubes.

RHIZOPHYDIUM CONICUM Karling

Amer. J. Bot., 33: 333, figs. 23-24. 1946

(Fig. 18 F, p. 286)

"Thalli numerous, up to 30 on a host. Sporangia hyaline, smooth, conical or pyramidal (14–16 × 20–28 μ) with two to six narrow exit papillae, 2 μ in diam. Zoospores spherical (2–2.5 μ), with a minute refractive globule; emerging from one or more of the lateral papillae. Rhizoidal system well developed and richly branched. Resting spores conical (6–8 × 10–14 μ), or slightly irregular, hyaline and smooth with one or more large refractive globules; germination unknown" (Karling, *loc. cit.*).

Parasitic on *Netrium sp.*, BRAZIL.

Distinguished by cone-shaped or slightly pyramidal sporangia, with two to six narrow exit papillae, and conical, hyaline, smooth resting spores.

RHIZOPHIDIUM ANOMALUM Canter

New Phytologist, 49: 102, figs. 1-2. 1950

"Thallus monocentric, eucarpic consisting of a sporangium, unswollen stalk-like portion and a meagre branched rhizoidal system. Sporangium flask-shaped, 3.8 μ broad × 7.7 μ high to 12.4 μ broad × 28 μ high, embedded except for the apex of the neck in the gelatinous host sheath. Zoospores 5–50 in a sporangium, emerging singly on deliquescence of the apex of the neck. Zoospore spherical, 2.6 μ in diameter, uniguttulate, posteriorly uniflagellate. Resting spore spherical, 6–11 μ in diameter with a smooth wall and a large oil globule, sexually formed.

"A zoospore, which later becomes the female gametangium whose contents constitute the female gamete encysts near the apex of the male thallus (the latter resembling an early stage in sporangial development), both (male?) increasing in size, especially the female which eventually receives the content of the male, expands and becomes transformed into a zygote. Germination unknown." (Canter, *loc. cit.*). Parasitic on *Apiocystis brauniana*, GREAT BRITAIN.

The sexual-reproductive process, preceding resting-spore formation, appears to be similar to that of *Rhizophydium ovatum* (p. 291).

RECENTLY DESCRIBED TAXON [1]

RHIZOPHYDIUM UTRICULARE Uebelmesser

Arch. f. Mikrobiol., 25: 314, fig. 3, 1956

Sporangium sac- or pear-shaped, rarely spherical, 120 μ long by 80–100 μ in diameter; rhizoid very delicate, little-branched; zoospores globose, 8 μ in diameter, lacking a globule, the contents granular in the anterior portion, and the remainder hyaline, with a 60–70 μ long flagellum, escaping through three to seven pores formed upon the deliquescence of large prominent papillae; resting spore spherical, 25–30 μ in diameter, with a stout smooth wall, contents with small globules.

Pine-pollen bait, normal soil, AUSTRALIA; saline soil, UNITED STATES.

SECTION III[2]

RHIZOPHYDIUM CLINOPUS Scherffel

Abstracts of Communications, V Inter. Bot. Congress, Cambridge, 1930: 222; Arch. Protistenk., 73: 141, pl. 9, fig. 3 a-g. 1931

(Fig. 17 T, p. 228)

Sporangium sessile on the raphe of the host, obovoid or obpyriform, with a broad more or less sharply defined stalklike basal part which is usually inclined somewhat to the long axis of the main body of the sporangium, with which it is continuous, wall smooth, delicate, 11–24 μ in diameter by 6–19 μ high, usually 16–18 μ in diameter by

---

[1] Not included in the key.
[2] See also the following imperfectly known species of *Rhizophydium*:
  R. septocarpoides, p. 313   Rhizophydium sp., p. 313.

8–10 μ high; rhizoid unbranched, 1 μ in diameter; zoospores formed in large numbers, spherical, 3 μ in diameter, with a colorless globule 1 μ in diameter and a long flagellum, released upon the deliquescence of the entire upper half of the sporangium wall, movement hopping or amoeboid; resting spore (?) sessile, subspherical, with a flattened base, 8 μ in diameter, wall thick, smooth, colorless, contents with a colorless refractive oil globule, 5 μ in diameter, endobiotic part enclosed in a plug of host wall material, germination not observed.

On moribund diatoms, *Cymatopleura elliptica, C. solea, Nitzschia sigmoidea, Cymbella, Navicula sp.*, Scherffel (*loc. cit.*), HUNGARY; *Cymbella aspera*, Friedmann (1952: 182, figs. 2m, n), AUSTRIA.

The resting spores, found only on *Nitzschia sigmoidea*, have not been related with certainty to the sporangial stage.

The species resembles *Podochytrium* in the possession of a poorly defined fertile basal region on the sporangium, and may ultimately be referred to this genus. It differs from *P. emmanuelensis* in its method of spore discharge, that is, discharge by the deliquescence of the upper part of the sporangium, and in having a smooth-walled resting spore.

RHIZOPHIDIUM FULGENS Canter

Ann. Bot. London (N.S.), 15: 144, figs. 9-11, pl. 11. 1951

(Fig. 10 L, p. 108)

"Thallus monocentric eucarpic, consisting of a sporangium developed from the encysted zoospore, an unswollen stalk-like region within the mucilage envelope of the alga, and a branched rhizoidal system inside the host cell. The sporangium varies in shape from obovate to oval (6 μ high × 4.5 μ broad to 10 μ high × 8 μ broad) and contains from 4 to 18 zoospores. The zoospores (2.5 μ in diameter) are anteriorly uniguttulate and posteriorly uniflagellate; they escape from the sporangium via two pores formed in the apical corners of the wall. Resting spore asexually formed, oval in shape (6 μ high × 4.5 μ broad to 8 μ high × 6 μ broad) with a smooth, thick, colourless wall. The content contains numerous small peripheral refractive globules and one or two larger globules. On germination functioning as a prosporangium" (Canter, *loc. cit.*).

Parasitic on the planktonic green alga *Gemellicystis neglecta*, GREAT BRITAIN. "In its habit this fungus resembles *Rhizophidium sphaerocystidis* Canter which likewise infects a planktonic alga surrounded by a wide mucilage envelope. In both fungi the sporangium develops from the encysted zoospore while the germ-tube remains as a stalklike portion. However, in the method of dehiscence and in resting-spore formation these fungi differ greatly" (Canter, *op. cit.*, p. 144).

RHIZOPHYDIUM PARASITICUM Shen and Siang

Science Reports of National Tsing Hua University, Ser. B: Biol. and Psych. Sciences, 3: 181, fig. 2. 1948

"Zoosporangia, epibiotic, obpyriform, 20–22 μ long, 18–20 μ wide, wall 1–1.5 μ thick, opening by a lateral pore, 5.4 μ in diameter, allowing the fully formed zoospores to ooze out in the form of a sporal globe; rhizoids beneath the sporangium very delicate, hardly visible; zoospores spherical, posteriorly uniflagellate, 5.4 μ in diameter, containing a well defined refractive body, about 3.3 μ in diameter; emptied zoosporangia persistent; resting spores unknown" (Shen and Siang, *loc. cit.*).

Parasitic in the zygote of *Oedogonium sp.*, CHINA.

From the figures, the sporangium appears to have a short, solid pedicel.

RHIZOPHYDIUM ECHINATUM (Dang.) Fischer

Rabenhorst. Kryptogamen-Fl., 1 (4): 96. 1892

Chytridium echinatum Dangeard, Journ. de Botanique, 2: 143, pl. 5, figs. 11-15. 1888.

Sporangium sessile, very broadly obpyriform with a strongly obtuse somewhat lobed apex, urceolate at maturity, 13.5 μ high by 10.8 μ in diameter (at apex?), wall thin, smooth, colorless; rhizoidal system consisting of an unbranched short tapering stalk; zoospores spherical, 2.5 μ in diameter, with a basal colorless globule and a long flagellum, emerging through a very broad apical opening with a reflexed rim and forming a compact temporary mass surrounded by mucus; resting spore sessile, spherical or subspherical, 10 μ in diameter, with a thick wall covered with somewhat long colorless stout spines, contents coarsely granular, yellowish, with a large oil globule, germination not observed.

Parasitic on *Glenodinium cinctum*, FRANCE.

There is some question as to the method of zoospore discharge in this species. Fischer and Minden have considered it to occur inoperculately and have placed the organism in *Rhizophydium*. Dangeard says of the discharge that the "... partie terminale du sporange s'enlevanten forme de calotte pour la sortie des zoospores." Though the word "opercule" is not used here, he clearly states that the top of the sporangium is lifted up by the emerging spores, and the sharply defined reflexed rim of the open sporangium gives additional evidence that such has been the case. In contrast to those of most species of *Chytridium*, however, the resting spores—if indeed they belong to the fungus—are epibiotic, as in *Zygorhizidium*, but, unlike those of *Zygorhizidium*, they are apparently asexually formed.

Possibly belonging in *Phlyctidium* or *Chytriomyces*.

RHIZOPHYDIUM OVATUM Couch
Mycologia, 27: 168, figs. 28-55. 1935
(Fig. 4 B-F, p. 72)

Sporangium sessile, obpyriform or obovoid, broadest in the distal half, with a broad apical papilla, 8.4–16.8 by 16–30 μ (mostly 13 by 20–25 μ), wall fairly thin, smooth, colorless; rhizoid (possibly two) very short and delicate, arising from a minute bulbous main axis; zoospores (gametes?) somewhat ovoid, 3 by 4 μ, with a large colorless eccentric oil globule and a long flagellum, emerging with great rapidity through an apical pore formed upon the deliquescence of the papilla and swimming away; resting spore spherical, 5.4–9.6 μ (mostly 8.4 μ) in diameter, with a slightly thickened smooth colorless wall and a large slightly eccentric colorless globule, sexually formed, the motile female gamete coming to rest and encysting on the upper surface of an undeveloped spherical (3.6–5 μ in diameter), subspherical, or ovoid (5.4–9.6 μ in diameter) male thallus, which is provided endobiotically with a small bulbous swelling and a short rhizoid, both then increasing somewhat in size, especially the more distal female structure, which eventually receives the contents of the male, expands, and becomes transformed into the resting spore, the latter germinating after a short resting period (from two to three days) to form zoospores. (Modified from Couch.)

On *Stigeoclonium sp.*, UNITED STATES; *Oedogonium sp.*, Bérczi (1940: 82, pl. 2, figs. 14–16), HUNGARY.

Couch was unable to determine whether the gametes were borne in sporangia with the zoospores or formed in separate gametangia (see under "Sexual Reproduction," p. 71). The species is an exceedingly interesting one, and further investigations on the nature and fate of the motile bodies produced by the germinating resting spore and on the cytological details of germination would be of greatest value.

SECTION IV[1]

RHIZOPHYDIUM TRANSVERSUM (Braun) Rabenhorst

Flora Europaea algarum, 3: 281. 1868

Chytridium transversum Braun, Monatsber. Berlin Akad., 1855: 382; Abhandl. Berlin Akad., 1855: 44, pl. 4, figs. 1-6. 1856.

Sporangium sessile, at first spherical, becoming broadly ellipsoidal or fusiform, the apices strongly papillate, slightly curved at maturity, up to 16.6 μ in diameter, with its long axis perpendicular to its point of insertion on the algal cell; endobiotic part so far as observed consisting of a slender unbranched rhizoid; zoospores ellipsoidal, with a colorless basal globule, apparently emerging through pores formed upon the deliquescence of the two opposite papillae (rarely, also, a third, apical, papilla); resting spore sessile, subspherical or spherical, outer wall smooth, yellowish, inner wall colorless, contents with from one to two large globules, upon germination forming zoospores which escape through an apical pore.

On actively motile cells of *Chlamydomonas pulvisculus*, also pos-

[1] See also the following imperfectly known species of *Rhizophydium*:
R. asterosporum, p. 313   R. spirotaeniae, p. 315
R. barkerianum, p. 314

sibly on *C. obtusa, Gonium terras,* Braun (*loc. cit.*), GERMANY; *Chlamydomonas pulvisculus, Hormiscia sp.,* de Wildeman (1890: 15; 1894: 156), BELGIUM; *Chlamydomonas dillii,* Dangeard (1900–1901e: 282, figs. A–L), FRANCE; pine pollen, Gaertner (1954b: 21), EGYPT, SOUTH AFRICA.

Braun noted that the swarmers were attacked by the chytrid zoospores, up to twelve parasites being formed on a single host cell. Eventually infected swarmers came to rest and were killed by the fungus. Dangeard observed the penetration of the alga by the slender germ tube of the fungus, but was unable to determine whether or not this tube remained unbranched during the subsequent development of the parasite. Eventually the contents of the alga were reduced to an amorphous reddish mass. Although the resting spores noted by Dangeard were said to be spherical, in the figures they appear rather subspherical.

Rhizophydium goniosporum, which has similar sporangia to this species, differs in having polygonal resting spores, sexually formed. The sporangia of the fungus identified with this species by Cook (1932a: 136, figs. 20–25) are too spherical for it to be *R. transversum.* It may possibly be *R. acuforme.*

RHIZOPHYDIUM COLUMNARIS Canter
Trans. Brit. Mycol. Soc., 31: 135, figs. 3-4, pl. 11, figs. 3-5. 1947

"Thallus monocentric, epibiotic. Sporangium broadly ovoid, with its longer axis parallel to the host wall; wall smooth, colourless with a conical protuberance on its upper surface; large sporangia 25–63 μ broad × 16–27 μ high; dwarf sporangia 8–15 μ broad × 9–13 μ high; dehiscing by two broad, lateral, oppositely placed pores, very rarely one apical pore. Zoospores spherical, 2.6 μ in diameter, uniflagellate, with a conspicuous anterior oil globule and a darker area laterally; emerging singly, movement even gliding. Rhizoidal system branched arising from an indistinct main axis. Resting spore sexually formed, epibiotic, spherical, 10–20 μ, wall up to 3 μ thick, colourless, smooth, with columnar bands of refractive material; central contents granular, germination not observed. Male thallus epibiotic, spherical, connected to the female by a narrow cylindrical conjugation tube 2 μ diameter and up to 38 μ long" (Canter, *loc. cit.*).

Parasitic on *Spirotaenia condensata*, GREAT BRITAIN.

Canter noted that the fungus seemed specific to *Spirotaenia* since other associated members of the Conjugatae were not attacked. Her observations on sexuality in this species give further support to the idea, first proposed by her in the case of *Zygorhizidium*, that the nature of the thallus produced by the zoospores (whether asexual or sexual) is determined by the environmental conditions and not by any inherent difference in the swarmers that develop upon germination of the resting spores.

RHIZOPHYDIUM EPHIPPIUM Canter

Ann. Bot. London (N.S.), 14: 273, figs. 5-6. 1950

(Fig. 10 B, p. 108)

"Thallus eucarpic, epibiotic, sporangium saddle shaped, 8 μ broad by 4 μ high to 15 μ broad by 5 μ high, containing 8 to 30 zoospores. Zoospores spherical, 2 μ in diameter, uniguttulate, posteriorly uniflagellate, emerging singly after dissolution of two oppositely directed lateral papillae. Intramatrical rhizoidal system composed of one or a few short threads. Resting spores oval to subspherical, 5 μ broad by 3.7 μ high to 7 μ broad by 5 μ high, arising from fusion of the content of a small male with a larger female thallus, the former remaining as an appendage to the mature resting spore. Wall smooth, colourless, beset with a narrow central projecting band of wall material, content consisting of two large refractive globules, germination unknown" (Canter, *loc. cit.*).

Parasitic on *Stylosphaeridium stipitatum*, GREAT BRITAIN.

While the sporangial stage undoubtedly resembles that of *Rhizophydium transversum*, this species differs in having the resting spore sexually formed.

The saddle-shaped sporangium perched on the apex of the host cell is a striking object.

RHIZOPHYDIUM OBLONGUM Canter
Trans. Brit. Mycol. Soc., 37: 116, text-fig. 3, pl. 5, fig. 4. 1954
(Fig. 10 J-K, p. 108)

"Thallus monocentric, eucarpic and epibiotic within the envelope of the host cell. Sporangium oblong to oval, 3–7 μ wide and 7–24 μ long, or subspherical 4.5–9 μ wide and 5.5–9.5 μ long, developed by enlargement of the zoospore. Rhizoid consisting of a minute main axis bearing a tuft of short rod-like branches. On dehiscence, sporangium wall dissolves at one or both ends and owing to its delicate nature becomes invisible. Zoospores 2.5 μ (20–60 in a sporangium), oval when swimming, with flagellum and oil globule anterior but former directed backwards. Resting spore oval to subspherical, 5–9 μ long and 4–6 μ broad, with a thick, smooth wall and containing several small globules. Resting spore formation preceded by fusion of unequal gametes; male attached directly or by means of a conjugation tube (up to 5 μ long) to the female. Germination unknown" (Canter, *loc. cit.*).

Parasitic on *Dinobryon spp.* in plankton; *D. divergens*, *D. stipitatum*, Canter (*loc. cit.*), GREAT BRITAIN; *Dinobryon sp.*, coll. V. Tonolli, Canter (*loc. cit.*), ITALY; coll. A. Lundh, Canter (*loc. cit.*), SWEDEN.

The parasite rests between the lorica and protoplast of the host, and a feebly developed rhizoidal system penetrates the latter. The algal cell is at first only slightly affected, since its flagella continue to move even when a large sporangium of the parasite is maturing on it.

Further observations on the structure of the zoospore are needed. If, as Canter states, confirmation is obtained of the anteriorly attached, posteriorly directed flagellum, transfer to another genus may be necessary. It is possible that many other "posteriorly uniflagellate" chytrids have a similar attachment of their flagellum.

RHIZOPHYDIUM GONIOSPORUM Scherffel
Arch. Protistenk., 53: 20, pl. 1, figs. 40-42, pl. 2, figs. 43-50. 1925
(Fig. 17 U-V, p. 228)

Sporangium sessile, broadly citriform or broadly ovoid, occasionally irregular, with a slightly flattened upper surface, its long axis parallel with that of the host filament, 5–11 μ high by 7–16 μ broad, with two lateral opposite papillae (rarely one), wall thin, smooth, colorless; rhizoidal system delicate, branched; zoospores ovoid or somewhat rodlike, 3–6 μ long by 2–3 μ in diameter, with an eccentric colorless globule and a short flagellum, escaping amoeboidly through one or two pores formed upon the deliquescence of the papillae, movement a brisk gliding; resting spore sessile, polyhedral, six- to eight-cornered in optical section, the corners often somewhat protruding, 6–7 μ in breadth, wall thick, colorless, contents with few to many refractive globules, endobiotic part consisting of a central, possibly branched, axis, germination not observed; companion cells one or two, spherical or ovoid, 3 μ in diameter, wall thin, smooth, colorless, attached directly to the receptive thallus (resting spore), into which its contents are discharged and from which after fertilization it is separated by a cross wall.

Parasitic on *Tribonema bombycina*, Scherffel (*loc. cit.*), *Zygnema sp.*, Bérczi (1940: 81), HUNGARY; Sparrow (1936a: 439, fig. 2 a–j), GREAT BRITAIN; Sparrow (1943: 201, fig. 11 U–V), UNITED STATES.

As pointed out by Scherffel, the sporangia of this species are like those of *Rhizophydium transversum*, which occurs on members of the Volvocales, and of *Phlyctidium irregulare*, found on *Hantzschia* and other diatoms. But the angular resting spore, formed after a sexual process, and the host distinguish *R. goniosporum* from both these species.

Scherffel noted that the parasite formed rose-red products of decomposition in the host cell. These were not observed by Sparrow. The American material differed from Scherffel's in having smaller zoospores (3 by 2 μ as compared with 6 by 3 μ), which bore an anterior rather than a basal globule.

SECTION V[1, 2]

RHIZOPHYDIUM MESSANENSE Morini

Malpighia, 10: 79, pl. 3, figs. 1-4. 1896

(Fig. 17 Y, p. 228)

Phlyctochytrium messanense (Morini) Minden, Kryptogamenfl. Mark Brandenburg, 5: 339. 1911 (1915).

---

[1] See also the following imperfectly known species of *Rhizophydium*:
R. coleochaetes, p. 315   R. hormidii, p. 316
[2] See *R. palagicum* and *R. horizontale* Paterson (*Mycologia*, 50: 85. 1958).

Sporangium narrowly ellipsoidal to cylindrical, 48–54 μ high by 17–22 μ in diameter, wall thin, smooth, colorless; rhizoids branched, arising from a stout main axis which is slightly expanded just beneath the host wall; zoospores spherical, pale rose-colored, 3.25–4 μ in diameter, with an oil globule, escaping through a wide apical pore; resting spore spherical, 21–31 μ in diameter, with a thick smooth brownish-red exospore, forming zoospores upon germination.

In *Cladophora*, ITALY.

The slight inflation of the subsporangial part of the main rhizoidal axis is not of sufficient import to warrant transference of the species to *Phlyctochytrium*. From the figure, the resting spore upon germination appears to have cracked open and emitted the spores through a wide aperture.

RHIZOPHYDIUM HYALOBRYONIS Canter

Ann. Bot. London (N.S.) 15: 148, figs. 12, 13. 1951

(Fig. 10 C, p. 108)

"Thallus monocentric consisting of a sporangium and branched rhizoidal system. Sporangium cylindrical, 4.5 μ high × 2.5 μ broad to 15.5 μ high × 5.0 μ broad, usually with its long axis set at right angles to that of the host envelope. On dehiscence the apex of the sporangium dissolves and from 6 to 18 zoospores emerge. Zoospore spherical, 2.5–3 μ in diameter with a refractive globule and single posterior flagellum. Resting spore cylindrical, oval, or bean-shaped, 4.5 μ high × 3 μ broad to 9.5 μ high × 4.5 μ broad; wall, smooth, colourless, content composed of several small refractive globules. The resting spore is formed after fusion of the content of a small male 2.3 μ diameter, with a larger female cell. The empty male cell remains adherent to the mature resting spore. Germination not observed" (Canter, *loc. cit.*).

Parasitic on the planktonic alga *Hyalobryon polymorphum*, GREAT BRITAIN.

In early stages of development of the parasite the flagella of the alga are still motile.

RHIZOPHYDIUM FUSUS (Zopf) Fischer

Rabenhorst. Kryptogamen-Fl., 1 (4): 99. 1892

(Fig. 17 X, p. 228)

Rhizidium fusus Zopf, Nova Acta Acad. Leop.-Carol., 47: 199, pl. 18, figs. 9-12. 1884.

Sporangium sessile or borne on a short stalk, narrowly to broadly fusiform, usually slightly tilted, 10.4–20 μ high by 3–8 μ in diameter in mid-region, wall thin, smooth, colorless; rhizoids extensive, much branched, monophagous or polyphagous, arising from a relatively stout central axis; zoospores spherical, 2–2.5 μ in diameter with a colorless globule and a flagellum, emerging through a small apical often slightly protruding pore; resting spore not observed.

Parasitic on *Synedra sp.*, Zopf (*loc. cit.*), GERMANY; various diatoms, de Wildeman (1890: 12), BELGIUM; *Melosira*, de Wildeman (1894: 156), FRANCE; *Cymbella, Gomphonema constrictum*, Scherffel (1902a: [106]), HUNGARY; *Melosira varians*, Sparrow (1932b: 276, fig. 2 a–b; 1933c: 519), UNITED STATES; *Surirella sp., Pinnularia sp.*, Tokunaga (1934b: 389, pl. 11, fig. 4), JAPAN; *Melosira varians*, Sparrow (as *Rhizophydium lagenula*, 1936a: 439, fig. 4 k–m), GREAT BRITAIN; *Synedra sp.*, coll. P. W. Richards, Sparrow (1938a: 148, fig. 2d), SARAWAK; *Melosira ambigua*, Rohde and Skuja (in Skuja, 1948: 381, pl. 39, figs. 22–25), SWEDEN; *Melosira sp.*, Litvinow (1953: 81), LATVIA.

Doubt exists as to whether or not Zopf's species is identical with Braun's *Chytridium lagenula* on *Melosira* (Braun, 1856a: 31, pl. 2, figs. 2–3). Scherffel (1926a, see *C. lagenula*, p. 504) believes that two distinct fungi were grouped under this name by Braun, one occurring on *Melosira* and the other on *Tribonema*. Since the rhizoids were not observed by Braun in either form, it is difficult to attempt an analysis of his species. Zopf's specific name is preferred for the parasite of diatoms, because it applies to a more completely known organism.

Rhizophydium fusus is parasitic and, as Zopf noted, consumes the nucleus and plasma of the host cells, leaving only an olive-green or brownish residue of chloroplast material. On *Melosira* the rhizoids may ramify through several (five to six) cells of the host. The sporangia described by Rohde and Skuja are the largest yet reported for the species; they are 15–25 μ long by 5–9 μ broad.

Cejp (1933a: 4, pl. 1, fig. 11) has described as *Rhizophydium lagenula* (Braun) Fischer an organism on *Mougeotia* that agrees with *R. fusus* in the fusiform shape of the sporangium, but which is larger (30 μ or more long by 8–10 μ in diameter) and which forms epibiotic spherical thick-walled resting spores, 25 μ in diameter. He considers *R. lagenula* to be identical with *R. fusus*.

RHIZOPHYDIUM NODULOSUM Karling

Mycologia, 40: 328, figs. 1-10. 1948

"Sporangia hyaline, smooth, predominantly angular or nodular, up to 65 μ in diam., oval, 10–25 $\times$ 15–50 μ, spherical, 10–35 μ, oblong, pyriform or irregular with 1–15 prominent exit papillae, 4–8 μ high by 8–15 μ broad at the base. Zoospores spherical, 2.8–3.2 μ, with a minute refractive globule, 0.4–0.8 μ diam.; flagellum 15–18 μ long. Rhizoids usually well developed but sparingly branched, arising from one to several points on the base of the sporangium, main axes up to 7 μ in diam., branches extending for distances of 30–270 μ. Resting spores unknown" (Karling, *loc. cit.*).

Saprophytic on dead human hair and other keratinized substrata in muck soil and fresh water, UNITED STATES.

The species is characterized by the strikingly gibbose sporangia, which have an angular or nodular appearance, due to the prominent discharge papillae.

RHIZOPHYDIUM GIBBOSUM (Zopf) Fischer

Rabenhorst. Kryptogamen-Fl., 1 (4): 102. 1892

(Fig. 17 W, p. 228)

Rhizophyton gibbosum Zopf, Nova Acta Acad. Leop.-Carol., 52: 344, pl. 20, figs. 8-20. 1888.

Sporangium sessile, occasionally stalked, ovoid, pyriform, or fusiform, with several or many humplike lobes which give an irregular gibbose appearance to the whole structure, sporangia, when few on a cell, up to 25–45 μ long by 10–20 μ in diameter, when many, 11 μ long by 8 μ in diameter, upright or somewhat tilted, with a single terminal broad papilla, wall colorless, fairly stout; rhizoids profusely branched, arising from a main axis, which is occasionally slightly swollen; zoospores spherical, small, 2.5–3.9 μ in diameter, with a delicate flagellum and a few small colorless globules, escaping upon the deliquescence of the papilla; resting spore extramatrical, irregular in shape, 6–12 μ in diameter, hyaline, smooth, with one to several large refractive globules in the cytoplasm germination not observed.

Parasitic on *Penium*, *Cylindrocystis*, *Phycastrum*, palmellaceans, pinnularians, rotifer eggs, Zopf (*loc. cit.*), *Spirogyra sp.*, Rieth (1954: 171), GERMANY; rotifer eggs, Scherffel (1904: 116), HUNGARY; *Navicula sp.*, Sparrow (1933c: 519, pl. 49, fig. 13), UNITED STATES; rotifers and nematodes, Karling (1946b: 2), BRAZIL.

On desmids the sporangia were generally grouped at the isthmus of the cell. Rotifer eggs soon died after being attacked and their contents, eventually, were nearly completely absorbed by the fungus.

The species is of interest because of its ab'lity to live on a variety of substrata. Since the sporangium has so distinctive a configuration there is little question but that the same organism is involved in all the instances reported.

IMPERFECTLY KNOWN SPECIES OF RHIZOPHYDIUM

SECTION I

On Fresh-Water Algae

? RHIZOPHYDIUM CAUDATUM (Reinsch) de Wildeman
Bull. Soc. Roy. Bot. Belg. (Mém.), 35: 38. 1896

Olpidium caudatum Reinsch, J. Linn. Soc. London (Bot.), 15: 215. 1877.
Sphaerostylidium caudatum (Reinsch) Berlese and de Toni, in Saccardo, Sylloge fungorum, 7: 309. 1888.

Like *Rhizophydium ampullaceum*, but larger (12–13 μ in diameter) and with thicker walls.

On *Schizosiphon kerguelenensis*, coll. Eaton, KERGUELEN ISLANDS.

? Rhizophydium decipiens (Braun) Fischer

Rabenhorst. Kryptogamen-Fl., 1 (4): 100. 1892

Chytridium decipiens Braun, Monatsber. Berlin Akad., 1855: 383; Abhandl. Berlin Akad., 1855: 54, pl. 5, figs. 1-4. 1856.
Phlyctidium decipiens (Braun) Cornu, Ann. Sci. Nat. Bot., V, 15: 121. 1872.
Olpidiella decipiens (Braun) Lagerheim, Journ. de Botanique, 2: 439. 1888.
Olpidium (?) decipiens (Braun) H. E. Petersen, Bot. Tidsskrift., 29: 423. fig. 25 f. 1909; Ann. Mycologici, 8: 555, fig. 25f. 1910.

Sporangium within the oögonium of the alga but resting on the surface of the oöplasm, spherical, subspherical, ovoid, or, if several sporangia in a cell, occasionally somewhat irregularly tubular, variable in size, up to 41 μ in diameter, wall smooth, colorless, thin or slightly thickened, discharge tube broad, short-cylindrical or only slightly elevated, its apex protruding through the oögonial pore; rhizoids not observed; zoospores numerous, spherical or slightly elongate, 2.5–4 μ in diameter, with a colorless, eccentric globule and a long flagellum, movement hopping or amoeboid; resting spore lying in the oögonium, apparently without rhizoids, ovoid or somewhat angular, rarely spheroidal, 18–36 by 20–39 μ, wall very thick (2–6 μ), colorless, often showing radial striations, contents evenly granular, without a large globule, germination not observed.

In oögonia of *Oedogonium echinospermum*, *O. tumidulum*, Braun (*loc. cit.*), *O. vaucherii*, coll. Pringsheim, Braun (*loc. cit.*), Germany; *Oedogonium sp.*, Cornu (1872a: 121), France; *Oedogonium sp.*, Sorokin (1883: 26, fig. 26), European Russia, Asiatic Russia; *Oedogonium sp.*, de Wildeman (1893b: 59, pl. 7, figs. 5–11), Belgium; coll. Pittier, de Wildeman (*loc. cit.*), Costa Rica; *Oedogonium sp.*, Petersen (1909: 423; 1910: 555, fig. 25f), Denmark; *Oedogonium vaucherii*, *O. cardiacum*, *O. sexangulare*, *O. rufescens*, Scherffel (1926a: 219, pl. 10, figs. 98–102), Hungary.

It is debatable whether or not this is a species of *Rhizophydium* (see remarks under *Latrostium*, p. 758). As Petersen (*loc. cit.*) points out, no rhizoids have ever been found. Scherffel, however, who has made the most critical study of it, emphasizes the fact, pointed out by Braun, that the sporangium is "extramatrical" and rests on the egg cell, which in turn is surrounded by the oögonial wall. He further states that even if a rhizoidal system were definitely shown not to be present in the dense host plasma he could not consider it a species of *Olpidium* since the discharge tube does not penetrate the host wall. Further observations, particularly on stained material, will be necessary before this fungus can without doubt be referred to *Olpidium*, *Rhizophydium*, or, possibly, to *Entophlyctis*.

Braun (1856a) records the remarkable fact that the zoospores of the species which remained in the sporangium swarmed for as much as 108 hours. Sorokin (*loc. cit.*) describes them as being actively motile after 48 hours.

? RHIZOPHYDIUM DIGITATUM Scherffel
Arch. Protistenk., 54: 223, pl. 10, figs. 103-104. 1926

Sporangium single, somewhat broadly ovoid, with truncate apex, 8 μ in diameter, wall thin, smooth, colorless, bearing on the rim of the flattened top five coarse, hollow, thin-walled sharp, somewhat incurved teeth 4 μ long by 2 μ thick; rhizoid broad, somewhat swollen at place of attachment to the rounded base of the sporangium, thin-walled, prolonged into a coarse filament which penetrates the host cytoplasm, where it probably branches; zoospores and resting spores unknown.

On *Gloeocystis*, *Mougeotia sp.*, Scherffel (*loc. cit.*), HUNGARY. *Zygnema sp.*, Linder (1947: 243, pl. 13, fig. G) (F. slide No. 2704), CANADIAN EASTERN ARCTIC.

A form with four teeth, incompletely observed by Sparrow (1933c: 529, fig. I, 17), may be referable to this species.

? RHIZOPHYDIUM DUBIUM de Wildeman
Ann. Soc. Belge Micro. (Mém.), 19: 113, pl. 3, figs. 26-28. 1895

Sporangium sessile, spherical, with a protruding apical papilla, wall thin, smooth, colorless; rhizoids branched, delicate, arising from a short central axis; zoospores not observed, apparently emerging through a wide pore formed upon the deliquescence of the papilla; resting spore not observed.

On filaments of *Spirogyra*, FRANCE.

? RHIZOPHYDIUM EPITHEMIAE Valkanov

Arch. Protistenk., 73: 362, fig. 2. 1931

Sporangium sessile, spherical, up to 21 μ in diameter, colorless, with a prominent thick-walled subapical wartlike protrusion, wall otherwise thin, smooth; rhizoids fairly stout, short, branched, arising from a short main axis; zoospores not observed, apparently emerging through a fairly large lateral pore; resting spore not observed.

Parasitic on *Epithemia zebra*, BULGARIA.

The curious wartlike protrusion may possibly be the case of the infecting zoospore which, as in *Chytridium schenkii*, has persisted.

? RHIZOPHYDIUM FALLAX Scherffel

Arch. Protistenk., 53: 30, pl. 2, figs. 60-62. 1925

Sporangium sessile, spherical, variable in size, wall smooth, color-less, fairly thick; endobiotic part not distinctly observed, being surrounded by a large pale reddish-brown peglike thickening of the host wall; zoospores narrowly ovoid, with a colorless lateral oil globule and a short slowly moving posterior flagellum attached to the narrower end of the body, emerging individually through one (or more ?) minute needle-like scarcely perceptible lateral pore, movement gliding or amoeboid, never hopping; resting spore epibiotic, sessile, spherical, 8–10 μ in diameter, with a smooth double wall 1 μ thick, contents with a large (8 μ in diameter) colorless eccentric globule or with from two to three globules, endobiotic part like that of the sporangium, germination not observed; companion cells one or two, smooth-walled, 3 μ in diameter, directly attached to the receptive thallus (resting spore), wall at first thin, later thickening.

On *Mougeotia sp.*, HUNGARY.

Differing from *Rhizophydium globosum* in lacking a prominent exit pore and in having ovoid gliding spores and smooth colorless resting spores.

Further observations on the endobiotic system will be necessary to determine whether this is a species of *Rhizophydium* or of *Phlyctidium*.

? Rhizophydium hyalothecae Scherffel
Arch. Protistenk., 54: 201, pl. 9, fig. 64. 1926

Sporangium borne at the tip of a narrowly clavate extramatrical stalk, imbedded, with the exception of its apex, in the gelatinous sheath of the host, ovoid, 23 μ high by 22 μ in diameter, apex somewhat flattened, bearing a crown of prominent, solid, somewhat incurved, plain, long (2 μ) teeth (undetermined number), wall smooth, somewhat thick, colorless; endobiotic system not observed; zoospores spherical, with an eccentric colorless globule and a single flagellum, discharge not seen; resting spore not observed.

On *Hyalotheca dissiliens*, HUNGARY.

Further observations on the number of teeth and the nature of the endobiotic system are needed before the species can be adequately defined.

? Rhizophydium v. mindeni Valkanov
Arch. Protistenk., 73: 363, figs. 6-8. 1931

Sporangium spherical, with from twenty to thirty long delicate hairs radiating from the upper part, discharging its spores by means of a terminal splitting; otherwise unknown.

On oögonia of *Oedogonium sp.*, BULGARIA.

Probably referable to *Chytridium chaetophilum* or *Rhizophydium chaetiferum*.

? Rhizophydium multiporum de Wildeman
Mém. Herb. Boissier, 1900 (15): 7; Bull. Acad. Roy. Belg. (Sci.), V, 17: 287, fig. 2. 1931

Sporangium sessile, spherical, subspherical, or somewhat ovoid, 32–52 μ in diameter, with three or more prominent somewhat tubular papillae about 4 μ in diameter, wall smooth; rhizoids, zoospores, and resting spore not observed.

Parasitic on oögonia of *Vaucheria sessilis*, coll. Massart, BELGIUM. The fungus was never found on the vegetative filaments of the alga. It could not be induced to live on the pollen of *Salix* or *Alnus*. It is distinguishable from other multiporous species of the genus by the prominent discharge tubes.

? RHIZOPHYDIUM OEDOGONII Richter
Bibliotheca Botan., 42: 12, fig. 6. 1897

Sporangia in groups, sessile, somewhat irregularly ellipsoidal with outgrowths which result in a spherical-tetrahedral shape, at maturity bearing two lateral opposite spines, breadth from spine to spine 28 μ, thickness 14–17 μ; other features not observed.

On filaments of *Oedogonium sp.* (preserved material), GREENLAND.

? RHIZOPHYDIUM SPOROCTONUM (Braun) Berlese and de Toni
Saccardo, Sylloge fungorum, 7: 299. 1888; emend. Scherffel, Arch. Protistenk., 54: 222, pl. 10, figs. 96-97. 1926

Chytridium sporoctonum Braun, Monatsber. Berlin Akad., 1855: 381; Abhandl. Berlin Akad., 1855: 39, pl. 2, fig. 13. 1856.

Sporangium sessile, spherical, 7 μ in diameter, wall smooth, thin; rhizoids not seen; zoospores not observed, liberated through a broad apical pore; resting spore (?) epibiotic, spherical, 15–19 μ in diameter, with a very thick (4 μ), pale ocher-yellow wall of two layers, outer wall 2.5 μ thick in surface view, covered with raised punctations, appearing prismatic in optical section, inner wall 1.5 μ thick, strongly refractive, homogeneous; germination not seen.

On oögonia of *Oedogonium vaucherii*, Braun (*loc. cit.*), GERMANY; *Oedogonium vaucherii* in company with *Chytridium olla*, Scherffel (*loc. cit.*), HUNGARY.

Fischer and others have regarded this species as based only on the immature sporangia of a *Rhizophydium*, possibly *R. globosum*. The small size of the empty sporangia found by Scherffel and the fact that his fungus occurred on the same host as Braun's led him to suggest the reëstablishment of the species. Unfortunately, the lack of information on the exact nature of spore discharge and on the rhizoids, and want of positive proof other than association that the resting spores (observed by him) and sporangial stage belong to the same fungus make this suggestion of questionable value.

? RHIZOPHYDIUM SP. Viégas and Teixeira
Bragantia, 3: 225, pl. 3. 1943

Sporangium globose, hyaline, 7–9 μ in diameter, with a smooth delicate wall, without discharge papillae, rhizoids hyaline, very delicate, tapering, irregularly branched, arising from a small, subsporangial apophysis; zoospores $\frac{1}{2}$–1 μ in diameter, uniflagellate; resting spore asexually formed, 5–6 μ in diameter with a smooth wall.

On filaments of *Spirogyra*, BRAZIL.

Although the zoospores were observed, their method of escape (whether through one or more pores) was evidently not noted. It may, possibly, be a species of *Phlyctochytrium*.

? RHIZOPHYDIUM SP. Kobayashi and Ookubo

Rept. Osegahara Gen. Sci. Survey Comm., 1954: 575, fig. 18. 1954

Sporangium spherical or broadly obpyriform, covered by low bullations and bearing a single (?) subapical, slightly elevated discharge pore; endobiotic system a slender, short unbranched or once-branched rhizoid.

On *Chlamydomonas nivalis*, "red snow," JAPAN.

Observations on zoospore discharge are needed to validate this fungus. From the nature of the wall of the sporangium it appears to be a distinct species.

On Marine Algae

? RHIZOPHYDIUM DISCINCTUM H. E. Petersen

Oversigt. Kgl. Danske Vidensk. Selskabs. Forhandl., 1905 (5): 484, fig. XI, 1-3

Sporangium sessile, at first spherical or subspherical, becoming somewhat angular with the formation at maturity of one or two subapical or lateral papillae, 8–30 μ in diameter, resting on a broad base, wall smooth, colorless, thick (1–2 μ or more); endobiotic part consisting of a stout unbranched (?) tube; zoospores 1–5 μ in length, method of discharge and flagella not observed; resting spore not observed.

On *Spongomorpha vernalis*, H. E. Petersen (*loc. cit.*), DENMARK; *Acrosiphonia incurva*, coll. F. Börgesen, H. E. Petersen (*loc. cit.*), NORWAY; *Ceramium diaphanum*, Sparrow (1936b: 257, figs. 29–30), UNITED STATES; *Polysiphonia sp.*, Aleem (1953: 13, figs. 27–28), SWEDEN.

Petersen distinguished sporangia of two sizes: some 8–15 μ in diameter on *Spongomorpha*, and others up to 30 μ in diameter on *Acro-*

siphonia. Observations on the escape and flagellation of the zoospores and on the nature of the endobiotic part are needed to confirm the present generic disposition of the species.

The fungus termed *Rhizophydium polysiphoniae* (Cohn) Petersen by Martin (1922: 236, figs. 1–10) may, because of its thick wall and somewhat angular sporangia, possibly be referred to *R. discinctum.* Martin's fungus, however, possessed a relatively extensive branched rhizoidal system. If this had been present in *R. discinctum* it seems probable that the two observers would have seen it.

Sparrow considered that his fungus, which appeared on *Ceramium* maintained in a laboratory aquarium for a week, was only weakly if at all parasitic.

? RHIZOPHYDIUM GELATINOSUM Lind

Ann. Mycologici, 3: 427, 3 figs. (p. 427). 1905

Sporangium sessile, spherical, 20–30 μ in diameter, with a short stalklike base, wall thin, smooth, colorless, surrounded by a gelatinous hull about 3 μ thick; rhizoids not observed; zoospores not observed, apparently escaping through eight sessile pores 4–6 μ in diameter formed on the upper surface of the sporangium; resting spore not observed.

On *Acrosiphonia* (*Cladophora*) *pallida*, coll. Svedelius, SWEDEN.

The organism is remarkable for the number of pores formed and for the thick gelatinous sheath which surrounds the sporangia. That the structure is fungoid at all is doubtful.

? RHIZOPHYDIUM MARINUM de Wildeman

Ann. Soc. Belge Micro. (Mém.), 17: 11. 1893

Sporangium sessile, spherical, 7–15 μ in diameter, wall smooth, colorless; rhizoids few; zoospores and resting spore not observed.

On *Melosira sp.*, in marine aquarium, BELGIUM.

Possibly a marine form of the "*Rhizophydium globosum*" type, as are those mentioned by Sparrow (1936b: 258).

? RHIZOPHYDIUM SP. Aleem

Arkiv. f. Botanik, 3: 15, fig. 30. 1953

Sporangium spherical, 17 μ in diameter, with a thin, smooth wall, rhizoidal system not observed; zoospores about 1 μ in diameter, probably escaping through a minute pore.

On heterocyst of *Calothrix sp.* (marine), SWEDEN.

On Aquatic Phycomycetes

? RHIZOPHYDIUM PARASITANS Scherffel

Arch. Protistenk., 53: 26, pl. 2, figs. 52-56. 1925

Sporangium sessile, spherical, 8–10 μ in diameter, with a thin smooth colorless wall; endobiotic part not observed; zoospores spherical, mostly 4 μ in diameter, with a colorless eccentric globule and a posterior flagellum about 24 μ in length, emerging through a wide pore at the apex of the sporangium and either forming a compact motionless group at the orifice before dispersing or escaping individually and amoeboidly, in either case assuming suddenly a lively hopping movement; resting spore sessile, spherical, 6 μ in diameter, with a thick smooth colorless wall, the outer margin dark and sharply defined, contents coarsely granular, with an eccentric colorless fat globule, 2 μ in diameter, germination not observed.

Parasitic on sporangia of *Rhizophydium goniosporum* parasitizing *Tribonema bombycina*, HUNGARY.

A curious condition of hyperparasitism is shown by this species. Scherffel noted that certain sporangia of *Rhizophydium goniosporum* had within them a spherical thick-walled resting structure or "cyst" of uncertain origin. The sporangia of *R. parasitans* were found only on sporangia of *R. goniosporum* which contained the remains of these cysts. Against the hypothesis proposed by Scherffel, namely, that the epibiotic sporangia of *R. parasitans* were in reality sporangia formed by germination of the endogenous cysts, was the fact that epibiotic resting spores also occurred on *R. goniosporum*. These were never found, however, on sporangia bearing the endogenous parasite. If these facts present the correct interpretation of the structures observed by Scherffel, then the sporangial stage of the species is parasitic on the encysted stage of an unidentified organism, possibly a monad, which in turn has parasitized the sporangium of *R. goniosporum*, which in turn has parasitized the alga *Tribonema!* The resting stage of *R. para-*

sitans, on the other hand, is directly parasitic on the sporangium of *R. goniosporum,* or—a possibility not mentioned by Scherffel—on the feeding or "vegetative" stage of the extraneous, cyst-forming organism. Further observations, particularly on the nature of the endobiotic system and on just what structure is penetrated by the zoospore of *Rhizophydium parasitans,* will be necessary before this puzzle can be solved.

? RHIZOPHYDIUM SP. Karling

Amer. J. Bot., 33: 334, figs. 29-30. 1946

Sporangium nearly spherical, with two subapical discharge papillae; rhizoidal system much branched, arising from the tip of a central axis; zoospores globose, with coarsely granular, nonrefringent contents, oil globule lacking.

On elm-pollen bait, BRAZIL.

Said to differ from all other species of the genus in that its zoospores lack a globule.

On Microscopic Animals

? RHIZOPHYDIUM CHRYSOPYXIDIS Scherffel

Arch. Protistenk., 54: 174, pl. 9, fig. 12. 1926

Sporangium sessile, ovoid, 8 μ long by 6 μ in diameter, with a prolonged apical beak and a narrow base, wall thin, smooth, colorless; endobiotic part consisting of a short fairly thick unbranched tube which terminates in a knob-shaped swelling; zoospores and resting spore not observed.

Attached to the mid-region or under part of the lorica of *Chrysopyxis sp.,* HUNGARY.

Possibly a species of *Phlyctidium.*

On Unknown Substratum

? RHIZOPHYDIUM TRANZSCHELII Jaczewski

Opredelitel gribov.... I. Fikomitsety, p. 39. 1931

Sporangium spherical, 39 μ in diameter, with a single opening; zoospores 4–5 μ long; resting spore spherical, 15 μ in diameter.

RUSSIA.

SECTION II

On Fresh-Water Algae

? RHIZOPHYDIUM (?) PERSIMILIS Scherffel
Arch. Protistenk., 54: 199, pl. 9, figs. 60-61. 1926

Sporangium sessile, broadly pyriform, with a broad flat-arched somewhat conical apex, 20–24 μ high by 15–16.6 μ in diameter, wall rather thick, smooth, colorless; endobiotic part not observed; zoospores and method of sporangial discharge not observed; resting spore (?) sessile, spherical, 8–12 μ in diameter, with a somewhat thickened wall covered on its outer surface with small wartlike granulations, contents with a large eccentric oil globule, germination not observed; male cell spherical, 4–6 μ in diameter, wall smooth, thick, attached laterally to the receptive thallus (resting spore).

On *Tribonema bombycina*, HUNGARY.

As Scherffel suggests, the resting spore is very much like that formed by *Rhizophydium granulosporum*. The sporangia of the latter are, however, distinctly smaller than those associated with the present species. Endogenous cysts belonging to an unknown parasitic organism were found in the sporangia.

? RHIZOPHYDIUM PYRIFORMIS Valkanov
Arch. Protistenk., 73: 362, figs. 3-5. 1931

Sporangium sessile, narrowly pyriform with a broad rounded apex, broadly obpyriform or oblong with one constriction (rarely with two); rhizoids branched, arising from the base of a broad penetration tube; zoospores not observed, apparently escaping through a terminal opening; resting spore not observed.

Parasitic on ripe oöspores of *Vaucheria sp.*, BULGARIA.

? RHIZOPHYDIUM SP. Karling
Bull. Torrey Bot. Club, 65: 451, pl. 21, figs. 18-33. 1938

"*Rhizophidium sp.* occurs saprophytically on a wide variety of dead filamentous and unicellular algae, flagellates, rhizopods, rotifers, liver fluke ova and ovarian tissue, eggs, larvae and exuviae of insects, cooked striated muscle cells and root tips of various plants. The sporangia may be almost spherical (10–52 μ), slightly depressed, wedge-shaped and somewhat triangular (14 × 29 μ – 25 × 30 μ), oval and occasionally slightly irregular with 1 to 11 exit papillae. The smaller sporangia may often resemble those of *R. agile, R. gibbosum, R. rostellatum* and *Phlyctochytrium bisporum [biporosum].* Resting spores have so far not been found" (Karling, *loc. cit.*).

? RHIZOPHYDIUM SP. Scherffel

Arch. Protistenk., 53:28, pl. 2, figs. 57-59. 1925.

Sporangium sessile, upright, pyriform, 8 μ high by 5 μ in diameter at the base, wall smooth, colorless; endobiotic system not observed; zoospores not observed; immature resting spore ovoid, with a flattened base, wall thin, smooth, colorless, contents homogeneous, with one or two large oil droplets, becoming spherical at maturity; contributing thalli from one to three, small, somewhat spherical or ovoid, attached directly or by a short copulation tube to the base of the receptive thallus; other characters unknown.

On *Tribonema bombycina,* HUNGARY.

Scherffel is not certain that the sporangial stage he observed belonged to the fungus which was forming resting spores.

? RHIZOPHYDIUM SP.

Sporangium sessile, spherical, subspherical, or broadly urceolate, with an apical or subapical papilla, 5.5–10 μ in diameter, wall smooth, thin, colorless; zoospores not observed, apparently emerging through a single somewhat broad apical or subapical pore; rhizoidal part consisting of a tuft of poorly developed digitations which arise from a short stout main axis; resting spore epibiotic, spherical, 10 μ in diameter, with a thick smooth colorless wall, rhizoids consisting of a tuft of short digitations, germination not observed.

On *Bumilleria sp.,* Couch (1932: 252, pl. 17, figs. 84–87), UNITED STATES; *Spirogyra sp.,* Sparrow (1936a: 443, fig. 3s), GREAT BRITAIN.

Since the discharge of the zoospores has not been observed, the fungi of Couch and Sparrow may belong in an operculate genus. Though the sporangia of the American and British forms differ slightly in shape, the former being spherical or subspherical, the latter more urceolate, they agree in being attached to the host cell by short digitate rhizoids. Couch states that the resting spore is surrounded by a gelatinous sheath. This has been interpreted in the British fungus as wall material.

Couch discussed his fungus under the name *Rhizophydium minimum* (Schroeter) Fischer, but it differs markedly from that species and from other members of the genus in the character of its endobiotic system. Further study may possibly show the fungi on *Bumilleria* and *Spirogyra* to be distinct.

? RHIZOPHYDIUM SP. Karling

Amer. J. Bot., 33: 331, figs. 19-22. 1946

Sporangia broadly or narrowly pyriform, rarely sessile, typically borne at the tip of a slender, tapering stalk 10–50 μ in length, whose distal end forms a sparse rhizoidal system within the substratum, with a single terminal discharge pore; zoospores spherical with a single oil globule; other characters unknown.

Parasitic on the soma and cysts of a stalked protozoan, angiosperm-pollen bait, BRAZIL.

On Microscopic Animals

? RHIZOPHYDIUM LEPTOPHRYDIS Scherffel

Arch. Protistenk., 54: 172, pl. 9, fig. 9. 1926

Sporangium sessile, very broadly pyriform, with a prominent broad conical subapical protrusion (papilla?), 24 μ high by 21 μ in diameter, the protrusion 10 μ in diameter at the base by 5 μ high, wall thin, smooth, colorless; rhizoidal system, zoospores, and resting spore not observed.

On the zoocyst of the vampyrellan *Leptophrys vorax*, HUNGARY.

Differing from *Rhizophydium vampyrellae* (Dang.) Minden in having a pyriform rather than a spherical sporangium.

SECTION III

On Fresh-Water Algae

? RHIZOPHYDIUM SEPTOCARPOIDES H. E. Petersen

Bot. Tidsskrift, 29: 420, fig. 24d. 1909; Ann. Mycologici, 8: 552, fig. 24d. 1910

Sporangium resting on a short needle-like extramatrical stalk, obpyriform, 8–16 μ high, the basal part distinctly cylindrical, wall thin, smooth, colorless; rhizoids poorly developed, once-branched, arising from a main axis which is continuous with the short extramatrical stalk; zoospores and resting spore not observed.

On *Closterium spp.*, DENMARK.

This incompletely known species resembles a small form of *Chytridium versatile*. Until spore discharge is described it cannot be placed generically with any certainty. Sparrow (1936a: 437, fig. 3t) has described a fungus on diatoms in England which resembles Petersen's species very closely in size and shape. Here again, however, no spore discharge was witnessed.

? RHIZOPHYDIUM SP. Karling

Bull. Torrey Bot. Club, 76: 360, figs. 53-59. 1949

Sporangia broadly obpyriform or clavate, 15–22 × 24–30 μ, with a tapering, curved base and broad, almost flat apex; rhizoids short, broad in diameter, branched, occasionally reduced to digitate structures; other characters unknown.

Parasitic on *Chytriomyces fructicosus*, UNITED STATES.

Probably *Rhizophydium utriculare* Uebelmesser (1956).

SECTION IV

On Fresh-Water Algae

? RHIZOPHYDIUM ASTEROSPORUM Scherffel

Arch. Protistenk., 53: 17, pl. 1, figs. 30-39. 1925

Sporangium sessile, short cylindrical, pouchlike, or somewhat tubular, slightly curved and attenuated at one end, its long axis parallel or nearly so with that of the host filament, wall smooth, thin, colorless; endobiotic part not observed; zoospores (quiescent) spherical, with a small colorless globule, escaping through a broad pore formed at the narrower end of the sporangium; resting spore somewhat elongate and irregularly starlike, 12 μ long by 6–9 μ high, the outer surface of the thickened wall bearing prominent blunt conical solid refractive outgrowths 3 μ high by 3 μ broad at the base, contents with a few large or numerous smaller colorless oil globules, rhizoids (seen once) numerous, delicate; companion cell spherical, smooth-walled, 2 μ in diameter, directly attached at various points to the resting spore.

Parasitic on *Tribonema bombycina*, HUNGARY.

The resting spore, as Scherffel points out, is shaped very much like the sporangium of the incompletely known *Chytridium cornutum* Braun. Only quiescent zoospores within the sporangium were observed by Scherffel.

? RHIZOPHYDIUM BARKERIANUM (Archer) Rabenhorst

Flora Europaea algarum, 3: 281. 1868

Chytridium barkerianum Archer, Quart. J. Micro. Sci. (N.S.), 7: 89. 1867.

Sporangium sessile, strongly flattened, with a concave upper surface from the center of which arises a slender stalk terminating in a small swelling, deeply three- to four-lobed, the lobes of equal size, with rounded apices and radiating in one plane; rhizoids, where observed, rootlike; zoospores escaping from the open ends of the lobes; resting spore not observed.

On *Zygnema sp.*, IRELAND.

This curious species, said by its author to be related to *Rhizophydium cornutum* (Braun) Rabenhorst and *R. transversum*, is of doubtful validity. The peculiar central stalk terminating in a knob is difficult to interpret unless it be the cyst of the zoospore. If so, the fungus would have a type of development like that of the *Scherffeliomyces*.

? RHIZOPHYDIUM SPIROTAENIAE (Scherffel) Sparrow

Aquatic Phycomycetes, p. 216. 1943

Chytridium (?) spirotaeniae Scherffel, Arch. Protistenk., 53: 14, pl. 1, figs. 26-29. 1925.

Sporangium epibiotic, broadly ovoid, its longer axis parallel with that of the host cell, with a conical protuberance (papilla) eccentrically placed on the somewhat flattened upper surface, 12–14 μ in diameter by 8–9 μ high, wall smooth, colorless, thin, opening with an apical or lateral pore; rhizoids not observed; resting spore epibiotic, sessile (?), colorless, spherical, 11–20 μ (generally 16 μ) in diameter, wall of two layers, the outer densely covered with broad, blunt or pointed, straight or slightly curved, solid, refractive, raylike protuberances 3 μ wide at the base by 2–3 μ high, inner wall smooth, 2 μ thick, contents colorless, with numerous coarse globules (fat?), germination not observed; male cell epibiotic, sessile (always?), rounded, smooth, thinwalled, apparently without rhizoids, connected to the resting spore by a cylindrical tube 2 μ in diameter which is expanded distally to form a spherical or pyriform swelling, the tubular part sometimes lacking.

Parasitic on *Spirotaenia condensata*, HUNGARY.

Because of lack of data on the rhizoids and type of discharge, the fungus cannot yet be accurately placed generically. Scherffel suggested that it is a species of either *Zygorhizidium* or *Rhizophydium*, depending on whether it is operculate or inoperculate. It is here considered to belong to *Rhizophydium* because of the epibiotic resting spore and the shape of the sporangium. It could, of course, be a species of *Chytriomyces*.

SECTION V

On Fresh-Water Algae

? RHIZOPHYDIUM COLEOCHAETES (Nowak.) Fischer

Rabenhorst. Kryptogamen-Fl., 1 (4): 99. 1892

Chytridium coleochaetes Nowakowski, in Cohn, Beitr. Biol. Pflanzen, 2: 80, pl. 4, figs. 5-10. 1876.
Olpidium coleochaetes (Nowak.) Schroeter, Kryptogamenfl. Schlesien, 3 (1): 182. 1885.

Sporangium resting on the surface of the egg of the host but elongating within, filling the trichogyne and extending and expanding beyond it, terminating distally in a short tubular portion with a blunt rounded apex, the whole body thus being unequally spindle-shaped, up to 125 μ in length (average 80 μ) by 12 μ in greatest diameter, wall thin, smooth, colorless; rhizoids not observed; zoospores small, spherical, 2 μ in diameter, with a minute colorless refractive globule and a flagellum, emerging through a pore formed at the apex of the sporangium; resting spore not observed.

Parasitic on oögonia of *Coleochaete pulvinata*, GERMANY.

The zoospore gains access to the oögonium by swimming down the open trichogyne. The developing fungi, of which as many as four attack a single egg, then consume the entire contents of the oösphere, leaving only a small amount of reddish-brown residue.

Whether or not this is a species of *Olpidium*, as Schroeter has supposed, depends upon the interpretation of the position of the sporangium and the possible absence of rhizoids. Fischer and Minden consider the body of the fungus to be extramatrical in the already opened oögonium. The apparent lack of a rhizoidal system even in nearly empty oögonia, however, appears to strengthen Schroeter's interpretation. New observations will be necessary before a final generic disposition can be made.

? RHIZOPHYDIUM HORMIDII Skvortzow
Arch. Protistenk., 51: 430, text fig. 5. 1925

Sporangium narrowly clavate or curved and fusiform, 5.7–7 μ long by 1.5–2 μ in diameter, wall thin, smooth, colorless; rhizoids delicate; zoospores one or two, 1 μ in diameter, with an oil droplet and a single flagellum; resting spore not observed.

On *Hormidium flaccidum*, *Mougeotia viridis*, MANCHURIA.

Neither the description nor the figures are adequate enough to characterize this species properly.

REJECTED SPECIES OF RHIZOPHYDIUM

* RHIZOPHYDIUM MICROSPORUM (Nowak.) Fischer
Rabenhorst. Kryptogamen-Fl., 1 (4): 97. 1892

Chytridium microsporum Nowakowski, in Cohn, Beitr. Biol. Pflanzen, 2: 81, pl. 4, fig. 11. 1876.
Phlyctidium microsporum (Nowak.) Schroeter, Kryptogamenfl. Schlesien, 3 (1): 190. 1885.

Sporangium sessile, more or less spherical or ovoid, 30–50 μ in diameter, wall thin, colorless; rhizoids not observed; zoospores minute, somewhat elongate with a narrower anterior end, 2 μ long by $\frac{2}{3}$ μ wide, with a strongly refractive anterior granule and a single fairly strong anterior flagellum, emerging in great numbers from an imperceptible orifice and quickly swimming away; resting spores not observed.

On filaments of *Mastigothrix aeruginea*, imbedded in the gelatinous sphere of *Chaetophora*, GERMANY.

From the anterior flagellation of the zoospore, the fungus belongs to none of the three genera to which it has been assigned. If further study confirms the observations of Nowakowski on this point it should be placed in the Hyphochytriales.

* RHIZOPHYDIUM MONOPORUM Maire
Bull. Soc. Linn. Normandie, VI, 2: 68. 1910

Sporangium opening by a single pore; rhizoids absent.
On pollen grains of *Pinus*, FRANCE.
Insufficiently described.

* RHIZOPHYDIUM (?) SETIGERUM Scherffel
Arch. Protistenk., 53: 48, pl. 2, fig. 95. 1925

Resting spore sessile, spherical, thick-walled, the upper part of the outer wall with a tuft of long radiating hairs; other features unknown.
On oöspore of *Oedogonium sp.*, HUNGARY

Although it is impossible to assign this resting spore to any genus of chytrids, it closely resembles that of *Rhizophydium chaetiferum*.

* RHIZOPHYDIUM UTRICULUS Scherffel
Arch. Protistenk., 54: 173, pl. 9, fig. 11. 1926

Sporangium sessile, consisting of an irregular more or less cylindrical short tube resting with its smaller, somewhat curved base on

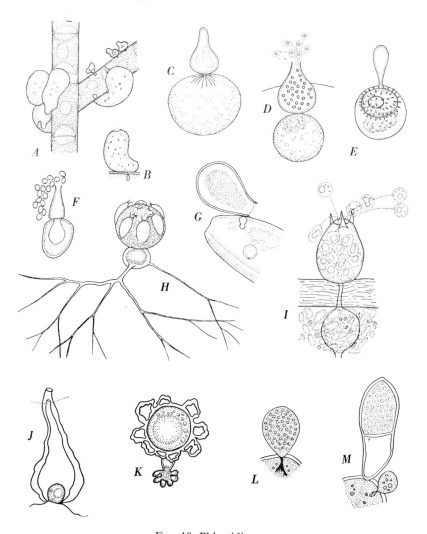

FIG. 19. Phlyctidiaceae

A–B. Phlyctidium anatropum (Braun) Rabenhorst: *A*, groups of sporangia on *Stigeoclonium*; *B*, single upright sporangium on surface of host. *C–E. Dangeardia mammillata* B. Schröder on *Pandorina*: *C*, strongly apiculate sporangium with its bushy rhizoids resting on surface of a cell of a colony; *D*, discharging sporangium with upper part protruding from surface of gelatinous sheath of algal colony; *E*, spiny resting spore within (?) host cell; cyst and the substratum, 13–14 μ long by 6–8 μ in diameter, wall thin, smooth, colorless; endobiotic part not observed; zoospores not observed, apparently emerging through the broad open apex; resting spore not observed.

On cyst (?) of an unidentified chrysomonad, HUNGARY.

The description is lacking in too many essential features for the fungus to be placed anywhere generically.

DANGEARDIA B. SCHRÖDER

Berichte Deutsch. Bot. Gesell., 16: 321. 1898

(Figs. 19 C-E, p. 318; 20, D, E, p. 330)

Thallus intramatrical, epi- and endobiotic, monocentric, eucarpic, consisting of the rudiment of the sporangium, which is sessile on the host contents but imbedded, except for its apex, in the gelatinous sheath of the host, and a complex of short unbranched or branched rhizoids; sporangium inoperculate, zoospores posteriorly uniflagellate, with a single globule, some having, in addition, a minute rod-shaped oscillating anterior granule, formed in the sporangium, liberated through an apical pore; resting spore epibiotic, with a thick smooth, spiny or

infection tube (appendix) are still persistent. *F. Achlyella flahaultii* Lagerheim, sporangium on surface of *Typha* pollen; zoospores have encysted after discharge from sporangium. *G. Physorhizophidium pachydermum* Scherffel, sporangium on surface of diatom (*Amphora?*); upper half of knoblike subsporangial structure rests on surface of host; lower half is within it. *H. Phlyctochytrium bullatum* Sparrow on *Oedogonium*, epibiotic sporangium ornamented with outer whorl of six bosses and inner whorl of four bifurcated teeth; subsporangial apophysis from which rhizoidal system arises is endobiotic. *I. Phlyctochytrium planicorne* Atkinson on *Cladophora*, discharging sporangium ornamented with four plain apical teeth surrounding discharge pore through which zoospores are emerging. *J–K. Loborhiza metzneri* Hanson on reproductive cells of *Volvox carteri*: *J*, empty sporangia showing internal proliferation and beginning of a new sporangium; *K*, resting spores showing strongly lobed haustorial apparatus. *L–M. Septosperma rhizophydii* Whiffen on *Rhizophydium macrosporum*: *L*, sporangium; *M*, immature thallus and two-celled resting spore.

(*A–B*, Sparrow, 1933c; *C–E*, Schröder, 1898b; *F*, Lagerheim, 1890; *G*, Scherffel, 1926a; *H–I*, Sparrow, 1938c; *J–K*, Hanson, 1944a; *L–M*, Whiffen, 1942a) warty wall, formed sexually after conjugation with a small male thallus by means of a tube or asexually at the tip of a fusiform persistent germ tube, at germination functioning as a prosporangium.

Parasites of fresh-water algae.

According to Canter's (1946) account of *Dangeardia mammillata*, the zoospore encysts on the surface of a coenobium, produces a fine germ tube which grows through the mucilage sheath of the host to the nearest cell. After it reaches this it broadens, proximally to distally, until the thallus is almost cylindrical. The base continues to swell, and the whole becomes a flask-shaped sporangium, which is imbedded, except for the apex of the neck, in the sheath. The rhizoids are numerous, short, usually unbranched, 3 μ long, and arise in a tuft from the sporangial base to penetrate the host cell. Zoospores range from twenty to one hundred and emerge separately, squeezing out of an opening formed by the deliquescence of the apex. As soon as the first spores are freed, the remainder become active and swarm over each other within the sporangium. A sporangium empties within 5 to 10 minutes after opening, but does not at once collapse. It shrivels up fairly soon however.

Zoospores in *Dangeardia mammillata* are of two kinds. Some are spherical, 2–5 μ in diameter, with a conspicuous oil globule surrounded by less dense protoplasm; others are often somewhat oval, 3.5 μ by 1.8 μ, and appear slightly flattened. The latter contain, in addition to the globule, a "minute, rod-shaped, oscillating granule." All of them have a single posterior flagellum. Only one kind of spore is formed in any one sporangium. In her November collections Canter found only zoosporangia, but by mid-December resting spores had appeared. These are sexually formed, by the union of a larger, flask-shaped thallus (female) almost identical with the zoosporangium and a smaller one (male) resembling a young asexual sporangium. Evidence indicates that the male derives only from the zoospore with the moving granule, but further work with single-spore cultures is needed to substantiate this.

The young resting spore cannot only be recognized by an associated male thallus but by its clavate germ tube and oily contents. The male germ tube, which is rarely branched, contacts directly the swollen base of the female plant and its contents flow into the latter. In a few instances no males were attached to the resting spore. These may have been parthenogenetically developed. After fusion, the wall of the neck in the female thickens, from the outside inward, normally to produce a solid, highly refractive core. The neck varies in length, but often is narrowed where it joins the base (the actual resting spore). A mature spore is oval to spherical, 7.5–13 μ in diameter, with a thick wall that may be smooth, granular, or distinctly spiny. The contents are oily, usually with many scattered droplets but sometimes with a single large globule.

The zygote germinates readily in the laboratory. A thin-walled sporangium forms on the surface of the resting spore. The latter functions, therefore, as a prosporangium. The zoospores are posteriorly flagellate. Like the zoosporangia, the germ sporangia yield zoospores of one type, either with a single oil globule or with a globule and an oscillating granule.

Although the chytrid Canter found agrees in the main with *Dangeardia mammillata*, it differs from that of Schröder's original description in having the resting spores *epibiotic* and sexually formed. She believes Schröder misinterpreted the spore as endobiotic, since a resting spore viewed from above a host cell often may appear so. The epibiotic position of the resting spore has been confirmed for *Dangeardia laevis* by Sparrow and Barr (1955).

KEY TO THE SPECIES OF DANGEARDIA

Resting-spore wall spiny, warty or sometimes smooth, sexually formed
D. mammillata, p. 321
Resting-spore wall always smooth, asexually formed .... *D. laevis*, p. 322

DANGEARDIA MAMMILLATA B. Schröder

Berichte Deutsch. Bot. Gesell., 16: 321, pl. 20, figs. 1-14. 1898

(Fig. 19 C-E, p. 318)

Sporangium flask-shaped or pyriform, with a somewhat prolonged apex, 10–30 μ long by 7–20 μ in diameter, wall smooth, colorless, slightly thickened; rhizoids short, bushy, generally unbranched; zoospores of two types, spherical, 2.5 μ in diameter with a single colorless oil globule and flagellum 15 μ long, or somewhat oval, 3.5 by 1.8 μ, with an oil globule and an anterior minute rod-shaped oscillating granule, moving away directly from the sporangium or resting a short time at the orifice before assuming motility, movement hopping; resting spore sexually formed with its thick-walled clavate germ tube persistent, lying on the surface of the host cell, oval, spherical, 7.5–13 μ in diameter, or ellipsoidal and 13.6 μ long by 10.2 μ broad, wall thick, smooth, granular, papillate, or spiny, contents with a large eccentric globule or numerous scattered ones, at germination functioning as a prosporangium and forming a thin-walled zoosporangium; male thallus clavate, connected by a tube to the base of the receptive thallus, which becomes the resting spore.

Parasitic in nonsexual colonies of *Pandorina morum*,[1] Schröder (*loc. cit.*), GERMANY; Bartsch (comm.), UNITED STATES; *Eudorina elegans*, Ingold (1940: 102), Griffiths (1925: 75), Canter (1946: 128, figs. 1–5, pl. 7; 1951: 153), GREAT BRITAIN.

Skvortzow (1927: 206, figs. 5–8) reported this fungus from Manchuria. No bushy rhizoids nor resting spore were observed; hence, his organism may be referable to *Rhizophydium eudorinae* (see p. 281).

DANGEARDIA LAEVIS Sparrow and Barr

Mycologia, 47: 549, figs. 1-20. 1955

(Fig. 20 D-E, p. 330)

"Zoosporangium flask-shaped or pyriform, embedded in the gelatinous sheath, zoospore cyst forming the apex of the somewhat elongated neck, 22–38 μ in total length by 8–16 μ in diameter, neck 4.8 μ in diameter, wall smooth, colorless, slightly thickened; rhizoids several, short, unbranched; zoospores globose or ovoid, 3.2–4.8 μ in diameter, with a posterior flagellum 8–16 μ long and an eccentric colorless refractive globule 1–1.6 μ in diameter, the first ones to emerge resting in a cluster at the orifice before assuming motility, the later ones emerging singly and swimming away at once, movement hopping; resting spore immersed in the gelatinous host sheath, globose, with a long, broad, persistent germ tube, terminated by the somewhat wider and

---

[1] According to Hood (1910), the host figured is *Eudorina elegans*.

thicker walled zoospore cyst, with a thick, smooth, hyaline, 2.5–3 μ wall, 13–21 μ in diameter, contents finely granular, 8–15 μ in diameter, with a large eccentric globule, apparently asexually formed, germination not observed" (Sparrow and Barr, 1955: 550).

Parasitic in ?*Gloeodinium sp.* (det. G. M. Smith), UNITED STATES.

PHLYCTOCHYTRIUM SCHROETER

Engler and Prantl, Natürlichen Pflanzenfam., 1 (1): 78. 1892 (1893)

(Fig. 19 H-I, p. 318)

Phlyctidium (Braun) Rabenhorst, Flora Europaea algarum, 3: 278.
1868; Schroeter, pro parte, Kryptogamenfl. Schlesien, 3 (1): 190. 1885.
Rhizidium sensu Fischer, Rabenhorst. Kryptogamen-Fl., 1 (4): 106. 1892.
Non Braun, Monatsber. Berlin Akad., 1856: 591.

Thallus epi- and endobiotic, monocentric, eucarpic, consisting of the epibiotic rudiment of the sporangium, the endobiotic apophysis, and the branched rhizoidal system; sporangium inoperculate, epibiotic, uni- or multiporous, separated by a cross wall from the endobiotic system, zoospores posteriorly uniflagellate, generally with a single globule, formed within the sporangium; resting spore borne like the sporangium, thick-walled, apparently asexually produced, upon germination forming a zoosporangium or prosporangium.

Primarily parasites and saprophytes in fresh-water algae. Less often found on fungi and in rotting parts of higher plants.

The method of infection, establishment of the rhizoids, and formation of the apophysis are essentially like that in *Entophlyctis* except that the epibiotic part persists, receives the contents of the endobiotic system, and becomes the sporangium. Apophysate species of *Chytridium*, as *C. lagenaria* for example, exhibit the same sequence of development as does *Phlyctochytrium*, but have never been segregated from *Chytridium* as have the inoperculate forms from *Rhizophydium*. This separation of apophysate from nonapophysate species has in most instances been readily accomplished. In several, however, the subsporangial swelling is not always definite, and in at least one (*P. biporosum*) it appears to be inconstant in its occurrence.

KEY TO THE SPECIES OF PHLYCTOCHYTRIUM [1]

Sporangium wall smooth, not ornamented
  Sporangium with a single apical or lateral discharge papilla
    Sporangium spherical, subspherical, ovoid, ellipsoidal, pyriform
    or domelike, sessile, apophysis with or without rhizoids
      Sporangium predominantly short-ovoid or pyriform, with an
      apical discharge pore; not proliferating; apophysis spheri-
      cal, apparently without rhizoids .... *P. hydrodictyi*,[2] p. 326
      Sporangium predominantly ovoid, with its long axis parallel to
      that of host cell; with a single large lateral discharge pore;
      internally proliferating; apophysis spherical bearing deli-
      cate rhizoids .... *P. proliferum*, p. 327
      Sporangium predominantly narrowly ellipsoidal; on marine
      algae .... *P. japonicum*, p. 327
    Sporangium predominantly spherical, subspherical, domelike,
    somewhat pyriform or ovoid, with a blunt rounded apex,
    apophysis always bearing rhizoids
      Sporangium spherical or pyriform
        Sporangium spherical; resting spore, where known, with
        bluntly spiny wall
          Sporangium 5-7 μ in diameter, with an apophysis of the
          same size; rhizoids limited, delicate.... *P. equale*, p. 328
          Sporangium 10-40 μ in diameter; apophysis much small-
          er than the sporangium; rhizoids extensive
            Sporangium with a cylindrical discharge tube 18-20 μ
            long .... *P. longicollum*, p. 328
            Sporangium with a sessile discharge pore ...*P. hallii*, p. 329
        Sporangium spherical or broadly pyriform; resting-spore
        wall warty .... *P. closterii*, p. 331
      Sporangium subspherical, ovoid, or domelike, apophysis ex-
      panded laterally, or subspherical
        Rhizoids arising from a single main axis laterally placed on
        apophysis .... *P. laterale*, p. 332
        Rhizoids arising from a basal main axis on apophysis, or
        from several axes
          Apophysis minute; on *Chlamydomonas* ... *P. vernale*, p. 332
          Apophysis conspicuous; on other algae .. *P. lagenaria*, p. 332
  Sporangium narrowly obpyriform, rarely ellipsoidal, sessile or on
  a slender stalk .... *P. chaetophorae*, p. 333

[1] See also *P. punctatum* and *P. irregulare* Koch (1957), and recently described
taxa, p. 346. Note that key is not strictly dichotomous.
[2] Further observations will probably show that rhizoids are formed.

Sporangium with more than one discharge papilla
  Sporangium truncate, with two broad, oppositely placed apical
    discharge papillae; apophysis slightly developed, rhizoid
    somewhat broad, unbranched or branched .. *P. biporosum*, p. 334
  Sporangium somewhat spherical ellipsoidal or urceolate with one
    to thirty-five discharge papillae
    Endobiotic apophysis unbranched, somewhat spherical or sac-
      cate; parasitic
      Zoospores 3-4 μ in diameter, with one or two oil drops; para-
        sitic on ascospores .... *P. lippsii*, p. 335
      Zoospores 3-7 μ in diameter, with a single globule; parasitic
        on pollen grains, *Synchytrium* resting sporangia, marine
        algae or nematodes
        Parasitic on pine pollen
          Resting spore with numerous stout, blunt papillae
                                  P. papillatum, p. 336
          Resting spore smooth-walled .... *P. palustre*, p. 336
        Parasitic on eggs, cysts, and adults of nematodes; resting
          spore smooth-walled .... *P. nematodeae*, p. 337
        Parasitic on resting sporangia of *Synchytrium endobioticum*;
          resting spore wall roughened .... *P. synchytrii*, p. 337
        Parasitic on the marine alga *Cladophora japonica*
                                  P. marinum, p. 337
    Endobiotic apophysis branched or unbranched and taproot-
      like; saprophytic or parasitic
      Apophysis branched; saprophytic on animal substrata
                              P. kniepii, p. 338
      Apophysis taproot-like, sometimes branched; on pollen
                              P. africanum, p. 338
Sporangium wall ornamented
  Sporangium wall covered with long delicate flexible branching hairs
                              P. chaetiferum, p. 339
  Sporangium wall dentigerate
    Teeth bipartite, scattered over entire surface of sporangium
                              P. aureliae, p. 339
    Teeth plain or bipartite
      A single apical spine always present, with up to four whorls
      of teeth on body of sporangium.......... *P. mucronatum*, p. 340
      No apical spine present, teeth confined to apex of sporangium
      Teeth plain (not bipartite), four in number .. *P. planicorne*, p. 341
      Teeth bipartite, variable in number or ten in a six-four
        arrangement
        Teeth forming a single whorl around the discharge papilla

PHLYCTOCHYTRIUM HYDRODICTYI (Braun) Schroeter

Engler and Prantl, Natürlichen Pflanzenfam., 1 (1): 78. 1892 (1893)

Chytridium hydrodictyi Braun, Monatsber. Berlin Akad., 1855: 383; Abhandl. Berlin Akad., 1855: 52, pl. 4, figs. 20-25. 1856.

Phlyctidium hydrodictyi (Braun) Rabenhorst, Flora Europaea algarum, 3: 279. 1868.

Rhizidium hydrodictyi (Braun) Fischer, Rabenhorst. Kryptogamen-Fl., 1 (4): 108. 1892.

Sporangium sessile, short-ovoid or pyriform, with a rounded apex, 5–25 μ in diameter by 15–33 μ high, wall thin, smooth, colorless; endobiotic part consisting of a spherical subsporangial swelling about 5 μ in diameter, apparently without rhizoids; zoospores spherical, 3 μ in diameter, with a single globule, uniflagellate, escaping fully formed through an apical pore; resting spore not observed.

On diseased cells of *Hydrodictyon utriculatum*, Braun, Frantzius (in Braun, 1856a: 53), Bail (1855: 682), Rabenhorst (*loc. cit.*), GERMANY; *Hydrodictyon reticulatum*, de Wildeman (1891: 171), BELGIUM; *Hydrodictyon reticulatum*, Valkanov (1931a: 363), BULGARIA; *Rhizoclonium hieroglyphicum*, Sparrow (1932b: 277, fig. 2c), UNITED STATES.

Presumably this is one of the first chytrids seen by Braun, in 1846 (Braun, 1856a: 22). He describes the globules of the zoospores in the sporangium as yellowish or greenish yellow, a feature not mentioned by subsequent observers. Escape of the mature zoospores was observed by both Frantzius and Bail. The formation by the host of a protective plug of wall material at the point of entrance of the parasite was noted by Braun.

It is probable that further observations on this species will reveal the presence of rhizoids.

PHLYCTOCHYTRIUM PROLIFERUM Ingold

Trans. Brit. Mycol. Soc., 25: 45, fig. 1, pl. 4, fig. 1. 1941

"Sporangium ovoid, 10–15 × 6–10 μ, with the longitudinal axis parallel to the surface of the host cell. Sporangium dehiscing by large lateral pore. Zoospores spherical, 3 μ in diameter, uniguttulate. New sporangia formed by a process of internal proliferation. Intramatrical part spherical or sub-spherical, 3–5 μ in diameter. Resting spores spherical or ovoid, 8 μ in diameter, smooth-walled, extramatrical, with a single conspicuous oil drop" (Ingold, *loc. cit.*).

Parasitic on living *Chlamydomonas*, GREAT BRITAIN.

Ingold is of the opinion that the secondary sporangia of this species develop as do those of *Thraustochytrium* (p. 830), that is, from a portion of the protoplasm which does not take part in the original cleavage of the zoospores.

PHLYCTOCHYTRIUM JAPONICUM (Kobayasi and Ookubo), comb. nov.

Rhizophydium japonicum Kobayasi and Ookubo, Bull. Nat. Sci. Mus. (Tokyo), 33: 54, fig. 1. 1953.

Zoosporangia scattered, elongated ellipsoidal, 12–25 μ high, 5–10 μ in diameter, thin-walled, smooth, colorless, at maturity forming a broad apical discharge pore; rhizoidal system composed of a main axis and rhizoids, the main axis expanded as a prolongation of the base of the zoosporangium, clavate or tuberous, 3–10 by 2–5 μ, sometimes lacking, rhizoids short, one to five arising from the base of the main axis, simple or branched; zoospores globose or ellipsoid, 2.5–5 μ (commonly 4 μ) in diameter, hyaline, containing a refractive globule, with a posterior flagellum; resting spores not observed. (Modified from Kobayasi and Ookubo.)

On *Gracillaria confervoides* (marine), JAPAN.

Somewhat resembling the fresh-water *Rhizophydium messanense* (p. 296), but, since a pronounced apophysis is typically formed, the species is placed in *Phlyctochytrium*.

PHLYCTOCHYTRIUM EQUALE Atkinson

Bot. Gaz., 48: 338, fig. 8. 1909

Sporangium sessile, spherical, 5–7 μ in diameter, with a short apical discharge tube 1.5 μ high by 2 μ in diameter, wall thin, colorless; rhizoids delicate, branched, of limited extent, arising from the base of the spherical subsporangial apophysis, which is equal to the sporangium in diameter (5–7 μ); zoospores not described; resting spore not observed.

Parasitic on *Spirogyra insignis*, Atkinson (*loc. cit.*), *S. spreeiana*, Graff (1928: 162), UNITED STATES.

Graff pointed out that the toothlike projections described by Atkinson as being on either side of the exit pore are in reality the side walls of the short discharge tube viewed in optical section. He also states that there is no cross wall separating the endo- and epibiotic parts of the fungus and that the sporangium is not spherical but dumbbell-shaped, and neither wholly outside nor wholly inside the host. Further observations on this feature, which, incidentally, has also been noted by Schenk in *Phlyctochytrium lagenaria*, are needed. Atkinson did not see zoospore discharge, and Graff describes it as occurring "in a manner typical for the genus."

PHLYCTOCHYTRIUM LONGICOLLUM Sparrow

Mycologia, 44: 763, fig. 1 j. 1952

(Fig. 20 A, p. 330)

Sporangium sessile, spherical, smooth-walled, 17–20 μ in diameter, bearing at maturity a cylindrical, straight or somewhat undulating discharge tube 18–20 μ in length by 5 μ in diameter; rhizoids delicate, much branched, arising from a single main axis at the base of a spherical, 8 μ in diameter, subsporangial, endobiotic apophysis; zoospores ellipsoidal to nearly oblong, 3.3 by 2.2 μ, with several minute, basal, colorless, refractive granules and a long posterior flagellum; resting spores not observed.

Parasitic on encysted *Euglena* sp., UNITED STATES.

Superficially resembling *Rhizidiomyces apophysatus* (p. 754), in the possession of a long discharge tube, but differing from it in the nature of its zoospores.

PHLYCTOCHYTRIUM HALLII Couch

J. Elisha Mitchell Sci. Soc., 47: 253, pl. 16, figs. 40-51. 1932

"Sporangia sessile, one to many on the host cell, often growing on the end of the cell; spherical, with a smooth rather thick wall; variable in size, when mature 10–40 μ thick, usually 20–25 μ thick. Sporangia with a bulbous base which may be as large as 5 × 10 μ; bulbous base sometimes apparently absent. From the base a very conspicuous rhizoidal system arises. Spores formed as in *Rhizophidium*. Spores emerging through a large conspicuous pore, after which the spores slowly free themselves from the mass. The process of spore discharge strikingly resembles that of *R. sphaerocarpum* as figured by Zopf (1884). Spores 2.1–4.2 μ thick, with a glistening droplet and one posteriorly directed cilium. Spores darting here and there with great rapidity. Resting cells thick-walled, bluntly spiny, with vesicle from which rhizoids arise, no small accompanying cell seen" (Couch, *loc. cit.*).

On *Spirogyra sp.*, Couch (*loc. cit.*), UNITED STATES; *Chara fragilis*, Ookubo (1954: 60, fig. 47), JAPAN.

During the process of infection the inner wall of the alga is depressed by the penetration tube. As development of the chytrid proceeds the chromatophores of the host lose their spiral arrangement and collapse toward the parasite. Eventually, the pyrenoids are broken up, the starch disappears, and the chloroplasts become bluish green and finally brown. Discharge of the zoospores regularly occurs in the late afternoon or early evening.

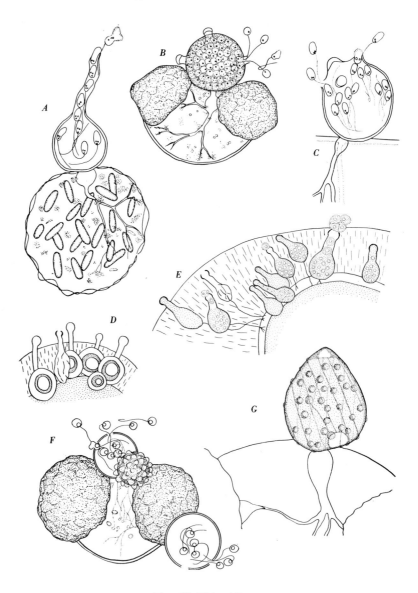

Fig. 20. Phlyctidiaceae

PHLYCTOCHYTRIUM CLOSTERII (Karling), comb. nov.

Rhizophydium closterii Karling, Amer. J. Bot., 33: 333, figs. 25-28. 1946.

"Thalli numerous, up to 18 on a host. Sporangia hyaline, smooth, spherical (10–18 μ), or broadly pyriform (12–18 × 14–24 μ), with a low broad exit papilla, up to 8 μ in diam. Zoospores spherical (2–2.5 μ), with a minute refractive globule. Rhizoidal system fairly coarse, richly branched and sometimes extending to the full length of the host cell, usually inflated slightly at the base of the sporangium. Resting spores spherical (10–16 μ), with a thick (2–2.5 μ), warty, light-brown wall and coarsely granular content; functioning as prosporangia in germination" (Karling, *loc. cit.*).

Parasitic on *Closterium sp.*, Karling (*loc. cit.*), BRAZIL; *Closterium sp.*, Sparrow (1952d: 763), UNITED STATES.

Sparrow observed only the zoosporangia. They conformed exactly to those of Karling's species. The constancy of occurrence of the subsporangial swelling in Sparrow's material and (from the figures) in Karling's as well indicates that the species is better placed here in *Phlyctochytrium* rather than in *Rhizophidium*.

PHLYCTOCHYTRIUM LATERALE Sparrow

J. Linn. Soc. London (Bot.), 50: 445, pl. 17, figs. 6-10. 1936

Sporangium sessile, subspherical or domelike, 10–13 μ in height by 12–15 μ in diameter, wall smooth, thin, colorless; rhizoids branched or occasionally unbranched, arising from a main axis which emerges somewhat laterally from a subspherical subsporangial apophysis 6–7 μ

Explanation of Figure 20

A. *Phlyctochytrium longicollum* Sparrow, discharging sporangium on cysts of *Euglena sp.* B. *Phlyctochytrium papillatum* Sparrow, discharging sporangium on pine pollen. C. *Blyttiomyces laevis* Sparrow, discharging sporangium on *Zygnema sp.* D–E. *Dangeardia laevis* Sparrow and Barr: D, resting spores and a discharged sporangium seated on host cell, and immersed in gelatinous sheath; E, sporangia, some of which are discharging zoospores. F. *Rhizophydium bullatum* Sparrow, on pine pollen, two discharging sporangia and a single resting spore. G. *Blyttiomyces helicus* Sparrow and Barr, on pine pollen, sporangium with helically banded wall and large basal discharge pore. (A–C, F, Sparrow, 1952d; D–E, G, Sparrow and Barr, 1955)

high by 9–10 μ in diameter; zoospores spherical, 4–5 μ in diameter, with a prominent eccentric colorless globule and a single flagellum, liberated successively through a fairly large apical pore; resting spore sessile, spherical, 12 μ in diameter, with a smooth thick wall, contents with a large colorless centric globule, rhizoidal system stout, branching, arising from a subsporangial apophysis, germination not observed. Parasitic on *Spirogyra sp.*, GREAT BRITAIN.

The formation of a single, relatively stout, rhizoidal axis, which arises laterally from the apophysis segregates the species from *Phlyctochytrium lagenaria*.

PHLYCTOCHYTRIUM VERNALE (Zopf) de Wildeman

Bull. Soc. Roy. Bot. Belg. (Mém.), 35: 48. 1896

Rhizidium vernale Zopf, Nova Acta Acad. Leop.-Carol., 47: 234, pl. 21, figs. 12-20. 1884.

Rhizophydium vernale (Zopf) Sparrow, Mycologia, 24: 277, text fig. 2f. 1932.

Sporangium sessile, subspherical, with a slightly flattened apex, wall somewhat thickened, smooth, colorless; rhizoids coarse, sparingly branched, not extensive, arising from a main axis which is slightly expanded beneath the inner face of the host wall, forming a small apophysis; zoospores rather quickly formed, spherical, with a single prominent colorless globule and a flagellum, emerging through a fairly wide subapical slightly protruding pore; resting spore not observed. Parasitic on *Chlamydomonas sp.*, GERMANY.

No text and no sizes or magnification of the figures are given by Zopf. The first formal description of the species is in Fischer (1892: 108) and is derived, as is the present one, from Zopf's figures.

The fungus reported as "*Rhizophydium vernale*" on the zygospore of *Spirogyra* (Sparrow, 1932b: 277, fig. 2f) possessed an apical or nearly apical papilla on the sporangium, which was 20–25 μ in diameter. Further observations are desirable before deciding finally whether or not it should be included in the present species of *Phlyctochytrium*.

PHLYCTOCHYTRIUM LAGENARIA (Schenk) Domján

Folia cryptogam., 2 (1): 18, pl. 1, figs. 45-46, 48, 52-55, 62-63, 67, 69. 1936

Chytridium lagenaria Schenk, pro parte, Verhandl. Phys.-Med. Gesell. Würzburg, A. F., 8: 241, pl. 5, figs. 12, 14-15. 1858. Non *C. lagenaria* Schenk, Ueber das Vorkommen contractiler Zellen im Pflanzenreiche, p. 5. Würzburg, 1858.

Sporangium sessile, subspherical, or ovoid, with a blunt rounded apex, 7.8–20 μ in diameter (see discussion below), wall somewhat thickened, smooth, colorless, not giving a cellulose reaction; rhizoids unbranched or branched, arising from a single basal stalk or from several places on a subsporangial broadly expanded and flattened (5.2–15.6 μ wide by 5.2–11.2 μ high) or spherical apophysis; zoospores ovoid, 2–5.2 μ in diameter, with a colorless eccentric globule and a long flagellum, emerging through a broad apical pore; resting spore not observed.

On *Zygnema sp.*, *Spirogyra crassa*, *Oedogonium sp.*, Schenk (1858a), GERMANY; *Spirogyra sp.*, Domján (*loc. cit.*), HUNGARY.

The sizes given in the Hungarian portion of Domján's paper are as follows: sporangia, 7.8–15.6 μ wide by 7.8–15.6 μ high; apophysis, 5.2–15.6 μ wide by 5.2–11.25 μ high; zoospores, 5.2 μ in diameter. The last measurement is more than twice that given by Schenk (2 μ). Since only the diameter of the sporangium is given by Schenk, Domján's figures on its height have not been included in the diagnosis.

From both Schenk's and Domján's accounts, the apophysis often equals and even exceeds the diameter of the sporangium. Schenk observed that zoospores were formed in the apophysis as well as in the sporangium.

The separation of the inoperculate form first observed by Schenk from the operculate *Chytridium lagenaria* (p. 522), which he found soon after, has been suggested before (Sparrow, 1936a: 437), and Domján's placing of the fungus in *Phlyctochytrium* appears wholly justifiable.

PHLYCTOCHYTRIUM CHAETOPHORAE de Wildeman
Bull. Soc. Roy. Bot. Belg. (Mém.), 35: 46. 1896
Rhizidium chaetophorae de Wildeman, La Notarisia, 10 (3): 35. 1895; Ann. Soc. Belge Micro. (Mém.), 19: 217, pl. 7, figs. 15-21. 1895.

Sporangium sessile or on a slender stalk, narrowly obpyriform, rarely ellipsoidal, 20–38 μ long by 15–20 μ in diameter, wall smooth, thin, colorless; endobiotic part consisting of an ovoid subsporangial swelling with a few scarcely visible rhizoids; zoospores about 3 μ in diameter, emerging through a broad apical pore with an irregular margin; resting spore unknown.

On *Chaetophora elegans*, coll. Goffart, BELGIUM.

No information is given on the number of flagella on the zoospores.

PHLYCTOCHYTRIUM BIPOROSUM Couch

J. Elisha Mitchell Sci. Soc., 47: 254, pl. 17, figs. 52-65. 1932

Sporangium sessile, spherical or ovoid at first, becoming truncated and angular in outline upon the formation of two broad oppositely placed apical sessile or slightly elevated discharge papillae, 10–12 μ high by 8–13 μ in diameter, wall delicate, disappearing soon after zoospore discharge, smooth, colorless; rhizoid somewhat broad, unbranched or branched, slightly expanded immediately beneath the host wall; zoospores spherical or somewhat ovoid, 2–2.6 μ in diameter, with a minute refractive basal granule and a long flagellum, emerging through two pores formed upon the deliquescence or bursting of the two discharge papillae, movement amoeboid or swimming; resting spore not observed.

On *Vaucheria sp.*, *Bumilleria sp.*, *Oedogonium sp.*, Couch (*loc. cit.*), *Spirogyra sp.*, Sparrow (1933c: 522, fig. I, 19–20), UNITED STATES; (?) *Spirogyra sp.*, Sparrow (1936a: 443, fig. 3 m–p), GREAT BRITAIN (see *Rhizophydium haynaldii*, p. 264); pine pollen, Gaertner (1954b: 21), EGYPT, NORTHWEST AFRICA, EQUATORIAL EAST AFRICA, SOUTH AFRICA; Gaertner (*op. cit.*, p. 41), SWEDEN.

The very slight development of the subsporangial apophysis, which in some cases is completely lacking, makes the generic disposition of the species difficult. Couch could not be certain that the rhizoid branched, but such branches have been observed by Sparrow (1933c). The zoospores of Sparrow's fungus differed from Couch's in having a centric globule. Sparrow has tentatively referred to this species a fungus found on *Spirogyra* in Great Britain which has sporangia essentially like those of Couch's fungus save that the papillae are more definitely elevated, the zoospores slightly larger (3 μ), and the unbranched (rarely branched) rhizoid never expanded to form a subsporangial apophysis. In these respects it approaches *Rhizophydium haynaldii* and the incompletely known *R. rostellatum* (de Wild.) Fischer.

Further study will be necessary to determine the degree of variability of the rhizoidal system in this fungus before it can be said with certainty that all these biporous forms belong to a single species.

PHLYCTOCHYTRIUM LIPPSII Lohman

Mycologia, 34: 105, figs. 1-15. 1942

"Zoösporangia external to nutritive host cell, single or aggregated, occasionally short-stalked but typically sessile, obovate when densely clustered, to globose or globose-flattened when free, 7 to 36 μ in diameter, with smooth, hyaline to pale yellowish wall which at maturity in the larger individuals is approximately 1 μ in thickness, appearing double, with 1 to 3, occasionally as many as 10, smooth, obtusely rounded exit papillae; zoöspores as few as 6 or 8 in small sporangia, as many as 60 or more in the largest; at first narrow elliptic, 3.5 μ long but after swimming a few minutes elliptic-ovoid, 3 to 4 μ in diameter, with one or two oil drops and posterior flagellum about 25 μ long—at 15 to 20° C. swimming before emission, then escaping freely without vesicle formation and swimming away in a zigzag course; subsporangial vesicle thin-walled, variable in size and shape, 2 to 4 μ in diameter and bead-like, or occasionally 8 to 10 μ in diameter and broadly fusoid—sometimes not evident; rhizoids dendroid and delicate but sometimes from the bead-like apophysis stoutish bifurcate, with delicate terminal branching; resting spores not observed; sporangia viable after normal desiccation for 6 weeks at room temperature" (Lohman, *loc. cit.*).

Parasitic on *Ascobolus immersus, A. leveillei, A. stercorarius, Ascophanus holmskjoldii, Lasiobolus equinus,* and *Sordaria coronifera*; typically upon free or undischarged ascospores of *Ascobolus,* UNITED STATES.

PHLYCTOCHYTRIUM PAPILLATUM Sparrow

Mycologia, 44: 764, fig. 1 p-q. 1952

(Fig. 20 B, p. 330)

Sporangium sessile, spherical, 23–25 μ in diameter, with three to five distinctly elevated, discharge papillae, 4 μ in diameter; rhizoidal system moderately coarse, branched, arising from the base of a subsporangial endobiotic, somewhat ovoid apophysis; zoospores spherical, 4 μ in diameter, with a single minute, colorless eccentric globule and a long flagellum, emerging through three to five pores formed upon the deliquescence of the discharge papillae; resting spores sessile, subspherical, 27 μ in diameter, with a moderately thick wall beset with numerous stout, blunt, colorless papillae, rhizoidal system like that of the sporangium, germination not observed.

Parasitic on pine pollen in association with *Rhizophidium bullatum* (p. 250).

The species appears to be nearly identical with that described from pollen grains as "*Phlyctochytium* n.sp." by Reinbolt (1951: 197, fig. 9).

PHLYCTOCHYTRIUM PALUSTRE Gaertner

Archiv f. Mikrobiologie, 21: 123, figs. 5-6. 1954

Sporangium round, somewhat flattened at the base, 10–40 μ in diameter, wall smooth, with three to five small, conical papillae, 3 μ long by 2.5 μ at base; rhizoids usually very delicate, one to three axes arising from a 5 μ in diameter apophysis; zoospores 3–4 μ, with one large oil droplet, several small granules and a 25 μ long flagellum, escaping upon the dissolution of the papillae; resting spore spherical, 20–28 μ in diameter with a smooth, 1–1.5 μ thick wall, large oil globule and finely granular contents.

Isolated from soil on pollen, Gaertner (*loc. cit.*), GERMANY.

On nutrient agar the sporangia attained a size of 55 μ, but there was no increase (beyond five) in number of discharge papillae. In cultures with diminished bacterial populations there was a tendency for the thalli to be interbiotic on the pollen grains.

PHLYCTOCHYTRIUM NEMATODEAE Karling

Lloydia, 9: 7, pl. 2, figs. 35-39. 1946

(Fig. 18 G, p. 286)

"Sporangia usually numerous, extramatrical, hyaline, smooth, spherical, 16–24 μ, oval, 15–18 × 19–22 μ, rarely slightly urceolate, 10–16 × 18–26 μ, with one to five low exit papillae. Apophysis oval, subspherical, 4–7 μ in diameter. Rhizoidal system richly branched. Zoospores oval, 2.5–3 μ, with a .5 to 1 μ in diameter refractive globule, and a 12 μ long flagellum. Resting spores extramatrical, hyaline, smooth, oval to spherical, 7–10 μ, with one large and several small refractive globules; germination unknown" (Karling, *loc. cit.*).

Parasitic in eggs, cysts, and adults of nematodes, from soil, BRAZIL.

Although the species behaved as a virulent parasite in the eggs, Karling was not certain that it was capable of killing active adults.

PHLYCTOCHYTRIUM SYNCHYTRII Köhler

Arb. biol. Abt. (Anst.-Reichsanst.) Berlin, 13: 382, pls. 1-2. 1924

Sporangium sessile, usually spherical, up to 50 μ or more in diameter, with from one to nine strongly protruding finger-like papillae, wall smooth, slightly thickened, colorless; endobiotic part very thin-walled, irregularly expanded or subspherical, flattened against the host wall; zoospores spherical, 4 μ in diameter (occasionally 4.5 μ or more), with one or several minute eccentric oil droplets and a flagellum 20–25 μ long, discharged through the nearly sessile circular pores 4 μ in diameter formed upon the deliquescence of the papillae; resting spore epibiotic, spherical (?), 14 μ in diameter, colorless, with a roughened outer wall, upon germination forming a spherical sporangium 9 μ in diameter.

Parasitic on resting sporangia of *Synchytrium endobioticum*, GERMANY.

Profuse development of sporangia of the parasite occurred when the host sporangia were spread out on moist gypsum blocks.

PHLYCTOCHYTRIUM MARINUM Kobayasi and Ookubo

Bull. Nat. Sci. Mus. (Tokyo), 33: 55, fig. 2. 1953

Zoosporangia scattered, epibiotic, sessile, ellipsoidal, pyriform or globose, 28–40 μ high, 18–30 μ in diameter, somewhat thick-walled, smooth, hyaline, with several (three to seven) sessile discharge pores 3–5 μ in diameter; apophysis endobiotic, connected with the sporangium by a narrow short neck, large, subspherical or turbinate, 30–60 μ in length, 15–20 μ in diameter, somewhat longitudinally furrowed; rhizoid unbranched, arising from the base of the apophysis, attenuated distally; zoospores numerous, ovoid, about 4 μ in diameter, with a refractive globule and a long posterior flagellum, swimming away individually through the discharge pores; resting spores not observed. (Modified from Kobayasi and Ookubo.)

Parasitic on *Cladophora japonica* (marine), JAPAN.

The fungus attacked the alga, while it was growing in artificial sea water.

PHLYCTOCHYTRIUM KNIEPII Gaertner

Archiv f. Mikrobiologie, 21: 117, figs. 1-2. 1954

Sporangium spherical, 10–250 μ in diameter, wall smooth, colorless, with three to thirty-five cylindrical, 3 by 3 μ papillae; rhizoidal system strongly developed, somewhat coarse, usually with one, frequently with several, subsporangial swellings arising from a single point at the base of the sporangium (that is, a branched apophysis); zoospores 3 by 4 μ, with a 20–25 μ long flagellum and usually one, rarely two, strongly refractive oil droplets and several dark-appearing granules; resting spore resembling the sporangium but with 6–16 μ long, frequently sickle-shaped papillae and thicker wall with an inner hyaline layer, when spherical, 10–60 μ in diameter, when irregular, 40 by 63 μ to 40 by 20 μ, upon germinating the papillae deliquescing and typical zoospores produced.

From soil, isolated on fly leg, Gaertner (*loc. cit.*), SOUTH AFRICA; pine pollen, Gaertner (1954b: 21), EGYPT.

This species is distinguished from others of the multiporous group by the frequently strongly developed branched apophysis and the peculiar resting spores with their very long papillae.

PHLYCTOCHYTRIUM AFRICANUM Gaertner

Archiv f. Mikrobiologie, 21: 120, figs. 3-4. 1954

Sporangium spherical, somewhat flattened at the base, 25–35 μ diameter, wall smooth, with three to five small hyaline discharge papillae; rhizoidal system richly branched, arising from all parts of a coarse, trunklike or taproot-like unbranched or branched apophysis; zoospores rounded or oblong and tapering basally, with one to three strongly refractive oil droplets and 22–25 μ long flagellum, escaping upon the dissolution of the papillae; resting spore not observed.

Pine pollen, soil, Gaertner (*loc. cit.*), NORTH AFRICA; soil, Gaertner (1954b: 21), EGYPT, WEST AFRICA, SOUTH AFRICA.

On nutrient agar the plants attained a size of 250 μ and the sporangia bore up to ten discharge papillae.

PHLYCTOCHYTRIUM CHAETIFERUM Karling
Mycologia, 29: 179, figs. 1-3. 1937

Sporangia sessile, broadly pyriform, ovoid, or subspherical, with a broad protruding apical papilla, 12–30 μ high by 18–45 μ in diameter, the subspherical ones 15–47 μ in diameter, wall somewhat thickened, colorless, with from three to thirty or more delicate flexible branching hairs up to or exceeding 200 μ in length; rhizoids one or several, branched, extensive, arising from one to several main axes which branch off from a spherical (8–11 μ in diameter), irregular, elongated, or fusiform subsporangial apophysis; zoospores spherical, 2.5–4 μ in diameter, with a highly refractive colorless centric globule and a long flagellum, emerging in a group surrounded by an evanescent vesicle or individually; resting spore ovoid or subspherical, from 9 μ (high?) by 10 μ (in diameter?) to 14 by 17 μ, or spherical and 10–17 μ in diameter, wall smooth, moderately thick, colorless, contents with one or more large oil globules, endobiotic system like that of the sporangium, germination not observed. (Modified from Karling.)

Saprophytic on cells of *Hydrodictyon reticulatum*, *Oedogonium sp.*, Karling (*loc. cit.*), *Cladophora sp.*, Sparrow (1943: 229), UNITED STATES.

PHLYCTOCHYTRIUM AURELIAE Ajello
Mycologia, 37: 111, figs. 1-13. 1945

"Sporangia extramatrical, variable in form but predominantly spherical, 12–35 μ in diameter, colorless, covered with numerous hyaline, solid, bicornuate teeth, 3.5–4.5 μ long and 3.5–6.5 μ wide, single pronged teeth occasionally formed, tips of teeth at times becoming filiform and elongate, attaining lengths of 20 to 50 μ; endobiotic system approximately 150 μ long consisting of a spherical apophysis, 3–7 μ in diameter, sometimes irregular or elongate with well developed rhizoids that branch profusely. Zoospores spherical, 4–4.5 μ in diameter, with a single centrally situated refractive globule, 2 μ in diameter and a single posterior flagellum, 15–20 μ long. Resting spores unknown" (Ajello, *loc. cit.*).

Saprophytic on decaying vegetation, Ajello (*loc. cit.*), shrimp skeleton, Sparrow and Barr (1955: 554), UNITED STATES; insect exuviae, Ajello (*loc. cit.*), Sparrow (1937a: 28, fig. 1 k, pl. 1, fig. 19), DENMARK.

The Danish material is probably referable to this species; possibly, to the next one, *Phlyctochytrium mucronatum*.

PHLYCTOCHYTRIUM MUCRONATUM Canter

Trans. Brit. Mycol. Soc., 32: 240, figs. 1, 2. 1949

"Thallus epibiotic, monocentric, consisting of a sporangium, apophysis and extensive rhizoidal system. Sporangia more or less spherical 5.7–31 μ in diameter (including spines), with a single pyramidal apical spine 1.4–5.2 μ long × 0.9–4.3 μ broad at the base and with one to four whorls of lateral simple, or Y-shaped spines (absent in very small sporangia). Sporangium dehiscing by a lateral pore; contents emerging in an undifferentiated mass continuous with the sporangium. Zoospores spherical, 4–5 μ in diameter, with a posterior oil globule, above which is a clearer area with a black granule; remainder of the protoplasm is coarsely granular. Apophysis spherical 1.3–3.5 μ in diameter. Rhizoidal system one to three main axes leaving the apophysis, often branching dichotomously and tapering towards their extremities, up to 85 μ long. Resting spores not observed" (Canter, *loc. cit.*).

Saprophytic on *Closterium pritchardianum*, *C. costatum*, GREAT BRITAIN.

In contrast to *Phlyctochytrium aureliae*, the spines occur in one to four whorls, not haphazardly, on the sporangium.

The sporangia were attacked by a chytridiaceous hyperparasite.

PHLYCTOCHYTRIUM PLANICORNE Atkinson

Bot. Gaz., 48: 337, fig. 7. 1909

(Fig. 19 I, p. 318)

Sporangium sessile, occasionally stalked, broadly ellipsoidal, narrowly to broadly ovoid, or narrowly pyriform, variable in size, 6–24 μ high by 6–17 μ in diameter, wall thin, colorless, smooth, bearing at the apex and around the discharge papilla a collarette of four (rarely six) solid highly refractive slightly converging plain teeth rarely more than 4 μ high; rhizoidal system extremely variable in its development, consisting of a few short branches or an extensive much-branched complex, in either type arising from a fusiform to spherical subsporangial apophysis 3–13 μ in diameter when spherical, when subspherical up to 12 μ in diameter by 10 μ high; zoospores spherical, 3–6 μ in diameter, with a prominent eccentric colorless globule about 3 μ in diameter and a few minute droplets in the plasma, flagellum about 30 μ long, emerging individually through an apical pore and eventually swimming away, or discharged in a compact group possibly surrounded by an evanescent vesicle, movement swimming or amoeboid; resting spore not observed.

Parasitic on *Spirogyra varians*, Atkinson (*loc. cit.*), *Rhizoclonium hieroglyphicum*, *Spirogyra sp.*, Sparrow (1932b: 279, fig. 3 e–k), saprophytic on *Cladophora sp.*, *Oedogonium sp.*, Sparrow (1938c: 486, figs. 1–6), saprophytic in decaying stems of *Acorus calamus*, Sparrow (1943: 230), oögonia of *Oedogonium sp.*, Sparrow (1952d: 765), UNITED STATES; *Vaucheria sp.*, Bérczi (1940: 83, pl. 2, figs. 21-22), HUNGARY.

PHLYCTOCHYTRIUM ZYGNEMATIS (Rosen) Schroeter

Engler and Prantl, Natürlichen Pflanzenfam., 1 (1): 79. 1892

Chytridium zygnematis Rosen, in Cohn, Beitr. Biol. Pflanzen, 4: 266, pl. 13, figs. 1-14, pl. 14, figs. 15-27. 1887.

Rhizidium zygnematis (Rosen) Dangeard, Le Botaniste, 1: 64. 1889.

Sporangium sessile or occasionally stalked, spherical or broadly ovoid, about 15–17 μ in diameter, with an apical collarette of four somewhat elevated, upright, solid, shallowly bipartite teeth which surround the discharge papilla; rhizoids well developed, branched, arising from the base or the sides of a spherical (about 7 μ in diameter), broadly ellipsoidal, or somewhat irregularly saclike subsporangial apophysis, sometimes apparently absent; zoospores spherical or somewhat ovoid, 3–4 μ in diameter, with a conspicuous eccentric colorless globule and a long flagellum, emerging in a compact mass, probably surrounded by the inner layer of sporangium wall, through an apical pore, movement hopping; resting spore not observed.

On *Zygnema cruciatum*, *Z. stellinum*, Rosen (*loc. cit.*), FRANCE (STRASBOURG); Minden (1915: 343), GERMANY; *Zygnema sp.*, Bérczi (1940: 84), HUNGARY; zygospores of *Spirogyra sp.*, Sparrow (1952a: 36), CUBA.

The sporangium in this species tends to be more spherical and the teeth are more shallowly cleft than in *Phlyctochytrium quadricorne* or *P. dentatum*.

Rosen's rather complete investigation of his species established the fact that the apophysis is a secondarily formed structure which appears on the endobiotic system after the establishment of the rhizoids. Remarkable variations in the character and the position of the apophysis and rhizoids were also noted. Abnormal forms with more than one apophysis, others with the apophysis outside the substratum rather than inside it, and so on, were described and figured. Smaller "Frostsporangien" frozen in the ice but still viable were found. Rosen's fungus only attacked filaments of *Zygnema* which were in a moribund or enfeebled condition, and it could not be transferred to other, associated, algae.

PHLYCTOCHYTRIUM MAGNUM Linder
Nat. Museum Canada, Bull. No. 97, Biol. Ser. No. 26, p. 243, pl. 12, fig. H
1947

"Sporangia extramatrical, obovoid [basally expanded], 23.8 × 18.5 μ, ornamented below the apex by four pairs of short, relatively stout, bluntly pointed, divergent spines, which are up to 4 μ long, and which are joined at the base; within the host is formed an irregular, broadly pyriform vesicle that measures up to 12.5 μ in diameter" (Linder, *loc. cit.*).

Parasitic on *Zygnema sp.* (F. slide No. 2718, Type), CANADIAN EASTERN ARCTIC.

Known only from preserved material.

PHLYCTOCHYTRIUM DENTATUM (Rosen) de Wildeman
Bull. Soc. Roy. Bot. Belg. (Mém.), 35: 46. 1896

Chytridium dentatum Rosen, in Cohn, Beitr. Biol. Pflanzen, 4: 266, pl. 14, fig. 29. 1887.
Rhizidium dentatum (Rosen) Dangeard, Le Botaniste, 1: 64. 1889.

Sporangium sessile or occasionally stalked, somewhat cylindrical or ovoid, with four apical bipartite prominent converging teeth, wall thin, smooth, colorless; rhizoids delicate, branched, arising from several places on a spherical or subspherical subsporangial apophysis; zoospores and resting spores not observed.

On *Spirogyra orthospira*, Rosen (*loc. cit.*), FRANCE (STRASBOURG); *Spirogyra sp.*, coll. Scherffel, Domján (1936: 43, pl. 1, figs. 96–97), Bérczi (1940: 83), HUNGARY.

Rosen was unsuccessful in his attempts to inoculate *Zygnema* and *Oedogonium* with this fungus.

The species resembles *Phlyctochytrium urceolare* in the shape of its sporangium, but differs in having four teeth rather than six.

Minden (1915: 344) uses the binomial *Phlyctochytrium dentatum* (Rosen) Schroeter, but the combination was not actually used by Schroeter when he established the genus. Fischer (1892: 110) calls it *Rhizidium dentatum* (Rosen) Fischer. In a list of Hungarian fungi Moesz (1938: 72) uses the binomial *Phlyctidium dentatum* (Rosen) Schroeter. Since no such combination was apparently ever made by Schroeter, it is presumed that *Phlyctidium* was used in error for *Phlyctochytrium*.

PHLYCTOCHYTRIUM QUADRICORNE (de Bary) Schroeter
Engler and Prantl, Natürlichen Pflanzenfam., 1 (1): 79. 1892

Chytridium quadricorne de Bary. See Rosen, in Cohn, Beitr. Biol. Pflanzen, 4: 266, pl. 14, fig. 28. 1887.
Rhizidium quadricorne (de Bary) Dangeard, Le Botaniste, 1: 64. 1889.

Sporangium sessile, broadly cylindrical or broadly ovate, 10–11 μ high by 13 μ in diameter, with a rounded or flattened base, bearing an apical collarette of four solid upright deeply incised bipartite prominent teeth, wall fairly stout, colorless; rhizoids present or absent, when present branched, arising from the base of a spherical (about 7 μ in diameter) or occasionally fusiform subsporangial apophysis; zoospores spherical, 6 μ in diameter, with an eccentric colorless globule and a long flagellum, emerging in a compact mass probably surrounded by a slime sheath through an apical pore formed within the collarette of teeth and resting motionless for a time before assuming individual motility, movement hopping or amoeboid; resting spore not observed.

On *Oedogonium rivulare*, de Bary (in Rosen, 1887), FRANCE (STRASBOURG); *Vaucheria polysperma*, Scherffel (1926a: 224, pl. 10, figs. 105–106), HUNGARY; substratum (?), Karling (1932: 49, fig. 19), *Cladophora sp.*, Sparrow (1933c: 523, text fig. I, 4, resting spore?), UNITED STATES; *Cladophora sp.*, Sparrow (1936a: 445, fig. 4 o), GREAT BRITAIN.

A glycerin mount of the type material is in the British Museum (N. H.), in the de Bary collection, but it was not available for examination.

Scherffel (*loc. cit.*) used the binomial *Rhizidium quadricorne* de Bary; there appears to be no evidence, however, that de Bary ever cited his fungus in this manner.

A thick-walled subspherical resting body 15 μ in diameter has been found in certain sporangia of this species (Sparrow, 1933c). It may belong to an extraneous parasitic organism.

The teeth of the fungus figured by Karling (*loc. cit.*) are more like those of *Phlyctochytrium zygnematis* (Rosen, *op. cit.*, pl. 13, fig. 12, lower), being shallowly rather than deeply incised. Too little is known at present of these species to judge how much weight is to be given variations of this nature.

A form with nearly spherical sporangia and four strongly diverging bipartite teeth found by Sparrow (1938c: fig. 33) on *Cladophora* in Michigan is perhaps referable to this species.

PHLYCTOCHYTRIUM BULLATUM SPARROW

Occ. Papers Boston Soc. Nat. Hist., 8: 296. 1937; Amer. J. Bot., 25: 487, figs. 7-14. 1938

(Fig. 19 H, p. 318)

Sporangium subspherical or broadly urn-shaped, 10.5–23 μ high by 12–26 μ in diameter, colorless, with two concentric whorls of solid apical converging teeth, the inner circle being composed of four minute divergingly bipartite sessile ones which immediately surround the discharge papilla, the outer circle, of six bipartite strongly diverging longer ones each of which terminates the inwardly arching tip of a broad flangelike solid boss 5–7 μ long by 3 μ wide by 3–5 μ high; endobiotic system composed of a broadly fusiform sometimes spherical or irregular subsporangial swelling, 10–20 μ wide by 6–10 μ high, from one side or, occasionally, from opposite sides of which emerges a wide rhizoid which usually branches at some distance from the swelling and ramifies through one or more cells of the alga; zoospores spherical, 8 μ in diameter, the clear plasma containing a single large slightly eccentric spherical or hemispherical oil globule, 4–5 μ in diameter, and a few minute peripheral granules, with a single posterior flagellum about 40 μ in length; resting spores not observed.

Saprophytic and weakly parasitic on *Cladophora sp.*, Sparrow (1933c: fig. I, 16), oögonia of *Vaucheria*, Sparrow (1943: 233), UNITED STATES.

PHLYCTOCHYTRIUM URCEOLARE Sparrow

Occ. Papers Boston Soc. Nat. Hist., 8: 296. 1937; Amer. J. Bot., 25: 491, figs. 31-41. 1938

Sporangium colorless, somewhat variable in shape but predominantly cylindrical and expanding slightly distally until reaching the first whorl, which is composed of six sessile bipartite solid upright or slightly diverging teeth, where it tapers sharply toward the apical discharge papilla, which is surrounded by a whorl of four minute bipartite upright solid teeth, 10–14 μ high by 7–11 μ in diameter tapering to 5–6 μ at the apex; endobiotic system composed of a narrowly to broadly fusiform or occasionally spherical subsporangial swelling 3–5 μ in diameter by 7–10 μ in height (3–7 μ in spherical examples), the swelling if narrowly fusiform generally bearing at its base a single rhizoid which ultimately branches, if broadly fusiform or spherical, bearing two oppositely placed rhizoids which eventually branch; zoospores spherical, 4 μ in diameter, with a single slightly eccentric spherical colorless oil globule 2 μ in diameter and a single posterior flagellum about 20 μ in length; resting spores not observed.

Saprophytic and weakly parasitic on *Cladophora sp.*, UNITED STATES. Probably identical with the fungus incompletely observed on *Cladophora* from Ithaca, New York (Sparrow, 1933c: 523, text fig. I, 3). It differs from *Phlyctochytrium dentiferum* in having a more cylindrical sporangium, which is slightly expanded distally up to the place of emergence of the outer whorl of teeth, where it tapers sharply toward the blunt rounded papillate apex. The papilla is surrounded by the inner whorl of teeth.

PHLYCTOCHYTRIUM DENTIFERUM Sparrow

Occ. Papers Boston Soc. Nat. Hist., 8: 295. 1937; Amer. J. Bot., 25: 489, figs. 15-32. 1938

Sporangium slightly subspherical, 10–15 μ high by 10–14 μ in diameter, colorless, with two apical concentric whorls of solid converging apical teeth, the inner circle being composed of four minute (about 2 μ high by 2 μ wide) divergingly bipartite sessile ones which immediately surround the discharge papilla, the outer, of six larger (about 4 μ high by 2.5 μ wide) bipartite sessile or slightly elevated ones; endobiotic system composed of a broadly fusiform spherical or irregular subsporangial swelling, 5–15 μ in diameter by 5–12 μ in height, from opposite sides of which emerges a moderately broad distally branching rhizoid; zoospores spherical, 7 μ in diameter, with a single large slightly eccentric colorless oil globule 4 μ in diameter and a single posterior flagellum about 30 μ in length; resting spore not observed.

Saprophytic and weakly parasitic on *Cladophora sp.*, UNITED STATES; zygospores of *Spirogyra sp.*, Sparrow (1952a: 36), CUBA.

RECENTLY DESCRIBED TAXA [1]

PHLYCTOCHYTRIUM BRYOPSIDIS Kobayasi and Ookubo

Bull. Nat. Sci. Mus. (Tokyo), (N.S.), 1 (2), No. 35: 66, fig. 5. 1954

"Zoosporangia gregarious, epibiotic, sphaerical or subsphaerical, with rounded apex, 11–15 μ long, 8–20 μ in diameter, thin–walled, smooth,

---

[1] Not included in the key.

hyaline, with one large apical pore, containing few (30–40) zoospores. Apophyses endobiotic, connected with sporangium directly or by narrow and very short penetration tube, smaller than zoosporangium, globose, conic, turbinate, or bilaterally elongated, thin-walled, hyaline. Rhizoid extensive, arising from two or three places on the apophysis, laterally or dichotomously branched, containing oil globules at intervals. Zoospores, when mature, rotate for a while in zoosporangium, and then liberate one by one from apical pore, globose, 3.5–4 μ in diameter, with one posterior flagellum and a refractive globule. Resting spores sphaerical or subsphaerical, sessile, about 10 μ in diameter, borne like the zoosporangia, hyaline, smooth, thick-walled, 3-4 times thicker than those of zoosporangia, with a large colorless eccentric globule, germination not observed" (Kobayasi and Ookubo, *loc. cit.*).

Parasitic on *Bryopsis sp.* (marine), JAPAN.

PHLYCTOCHYTRIUM CLADOPHORAE Kobayasi and Ookubo

Bull. Nat. Sci. Mus. (Tokyo), (N.S.), 1 (2), No. 35: 64, fig. 4. 1954

"Zoosporangia scattered, epibiotic, sessile, ovoid or subsphaerical, 22–40 μ high, 30–40 μ in diameter, somewhat thick-walled, smooth, hyaline, without distinct papilla, when matured with one broad pit, or rarely with 2–3 lateral pits, containing numerous zoospores, without discharge tube. Apophyses endobiotic, connected with sporangium by short neck, smaller than zoosporangium, variously sac-shaped, frequently flattened against the host-wall and bilaterally elongated, sending rhizoids from one or several spots. Rhizoids arising from the main axis or two or three places on the apophysis, simple or dichotomously branched, not so long. Zoospores medially sized, spherical or ellipsoidal, 3–5 μ in diameter, with one posterior flagellum and a refractive globule. Resting spores not observed" (Kobayasi and Ookubo, *loc. cit.*).

Parasitic on *Cladophora sp.* (marine), JAPAN.

PHLYCTOCHYTRIUM SEMIGLOBIFERUM Uebelmesser

Arch. f. Mikrobiol., 25: 319, fig. 5. 1956

Sporangium spherical, 40–80 μ (up to 500 μ on agar), wall thin and smooth, with two to five prominent, 10 μ broad, hemispherical papillae;

zoospores emerging singly, 6 μ in diameter, with two small anterior globules and a 25 μ long flagellum; apophysis broadly turnip-shaped when growing in pollen, narrow and more elongate on agar, the rhizoids strongly developed, branched, arising from the base of the apophysis; resting spore spherical, 20–30 μ in diameter, with a smooth, thick wall bearing discharge papillae, upon germination functioning directly as a sporangium.

Pine-pollen bait, cultivated on agar, seashore, GERMANY (BALTIC, NORTH SEA), various places along MEDITERRANEAN.

PHLYCTOCHYTRIUM SPECTABILE Uebelmesser
Arch. f. Mikrobiol., 25: 315, fig. 4. 1956

Sporangium spherical, 60–100 μ in diameter, with fifteen to twenty-five small hourglass-shaped papillae; rhizoidal system consisting of a subsporangial apophysis and extensive, branched, delicate rhizoids; zoospores spherical, 6 μ in diameter, with a lateral globule and flagellum 60 μ long; resting spore spherical, 60–100 μ in diameter, contents bearing a large eccentric oil globule, smooth-walled, with a strongly developed rhizoidal system arising from an apophysis, germination not observed.

Pine-pollen bait, soil (UTAH) UNITED STATES.

PHLYCTOCHYTRIUM STIPITATUM Kobayasi and Ookubo
Nagaoa, 4: 60, fig. 48. 1954

Sporangia exobiotic, stipitate, globose or depressed-globose, 45–55 μ in diameter, with a thin, smooth wall and apical or subapical papilla; exobiotic stipitate portion of apophysis columnar, 25–40 μ long by 10 μ wide, thick-walled, hyaline; zoospores about 20, subglobose or ovoid, 20 × 23 μ, hyaline, with a single refractive globule and posterior flagellum; rhizoids oriented from the base, di- or trichotomously branched, elongate, with abruptly attenuated apices; resting spores not observed.

On submerged grass stems, JAPAN.

This chytrid, as its authors suggest, should doubtless be placed in a new genus.

PHLYCTOCHYTRIUM UNISPINUM Paterson
Mycologia, 48: 270, fig. 1 a-i. 1956

"Sporangium sessile, the wall in part formed by the separation of the zoospore cyst, each half of which remains an unmodified hemispherical projection, giving the whole a somewhat irregular ellipsoid appearance, 12.5–17.5 μ from one portion of the zoospore cyst wall to the opposite wall, bearing at maturity a single apical spine, 3.5–6.5 μ long; endobiotic system a spherical apophysis 7–21 μ in diameter with a single isodiametric rhizoid, 0.5–1 μ wide; zoospores spherical, 6–7.5 μ in diameter, with a single eccentric oil globule surrounded by granular protoplasm, discharged into the basal portion of the spine which swells into a vesicle, liberated upon the dissolution of the vesicle, leaving the terminal part of the spine undissolved and free in the medium; resting spore not observed" (Paterson, *loc. cit.*).

Saprophytic on *Oedogonium sp.*, *Zygnema sp.*, and *Stigonema sp.*, UNITED STATES.

The type of sporangial development, involving separation and retention of the rigid wall of the encysted zoospore, is unique.

PHLYCTOCHYTRIUM VARIABILE Rieth
Die Kulturpflanze, 2: 180, fig. 9. 1954

Sporangium subspherical, bowl-like, bearing on the broadly arched apex variable numbers of four-parted teeth and on the rim a crown of solid two-pronged teeth, (6)–10–(12) μ high (including teeth) by (5)–9–13–(17) μ in diameter; endobiotic part with one, rarely two subsporangial apophyses and branched rhizoids; zoospores nearly spherical, 2.6–3.6 μ in diameter with a refractive droplet; resting spore not observed.

Saprophytic on *Spirogyra sp.*, GERMANY.

Close to *Phlyctochytrium mucronatum* Canter and *P. aureliae* Ajello.

PHLYCTOCHYTRIUM VAUCHERIAE Rieth
Die Kulturpflanze, 4: 185, fig. 1, pl. 6. 1956

Sporangium epibiotic, sessile, highly variable in size and shape, typically somewhat saccate, with one or two broad uptilted discharge papillae and a third humplike thick-walled persistent one which is the wall of the original spore cyst, sometimes reduced to a simple upright saccate structure with one discharge papilla, intermediate forms common; endobiotic system composed of one (rarely two) spherical, sub-spherical, or somewhat saccate, pronounced apophysis (typically smaller than the sporangium but in reduced sporangia equaling or exceeding it in breadth) and main axis of the branched rhizoidal system arising from the base of apophysis; zoospores spherical or oval, about $5\,\mu$ in diameter,[1] with a single, usually eccentric oil droplet and posteriorly directed flagellum, escaping individually through pores formed upon deliquescence of the two (sometimes only one) functional papillae; resting spore not observed with certainty.

On *Vaucheria intermedia, V. compacta, V. thuretii,* saline water, GERMANY.

IMPERFECTLY KNOWN SPECIES OF PHLYCTOCHYTRIUM

? PHLYCTOCHYTRIUM AUTRANI de Wildeman
Bull. Soc. Roy. Bot. Belg. (Mém.), 35: 46. 1896

Rhizidium (?) autrani de Wildeman, Ann. Soc. Belge Micro. (Mém.), 19: 72, pl. 2, figs. 17-21. 1895.

Epibiotic body consisting of a terminal globular structure with a slightly elevated apical pore and a basal ovoid-elongate generally clavate part, the two united by a short or somewhat elongate constricted isthmus; rhizoid consisting of an endobiotic needle-like stalk; zoospores and resting spore not observed.

On *Cosmarium,* SWITZERLAND.

The species may ultimately be referred to *Scherffeliomyces.*

? PHLYCTOCHYTRIUM CATENATUM (Dang.) Schroeter
Engler and Prantl, Natürlichen Pflanzenfam., 1 (1): 79. 1892

Rhizidium catenatum Dangeard, Le Botaniste, 1: 65, pl. 3, fig. 24 a-b. 1889.

Sporangium obpyriform, with three or four lateral or basal swellings on its outer surface, wall colorless, relatively thick; rhizoids branched,

---

[1] No dimensions are given in the text. They must be calculated from the drawings and scales given.

arising from a subsporangial apophysis; zoospores spherical, 3 μ in diameter, with a colorless globule, escaping through a sessile or slightly elevated apical pore; resting spore not observed.

In cells of *Nitella tenuissima*, FRANCE.

Fischer and Minden think that this species forms epibiotic sessile sporangia. Dangeard does not describe their position in relation to the host cell. From the fact that comparison is made in the description with *Diplophlyctis intestina* it is very probable that the fungus is entirely endobiotic and hence not a species of *Phlyctochytrium*, but rather of *Diplophlyctis*.

Fischer and Minden also believe the swellings on the surface of the sporangium to be quiescent zoospores. Scherffel (1925b: 48), however, suggests that they may be male cells similar to those found in some species of *Rhizophydium*.

? PHLYCTOCHYTRIUM DESMIDIACEARUM Dangeard
Le Botaniste, 28: 196, pl. 19, figs. 1, 3-9, 11-20. 1937

Sporangium sessile, narrowly to broadly ovoid or somewhat narrowly urceolate, with an apical collarette of not more than four bipartite shallowly cleft prominent teeth, wall thin, smooth, colorless; rhizoids branched, arising from a main axis at the base of a broadly fusiform or spherical subsporangial apophysis; zoospores spherical, 2–3 μ in diameter, with a colorless eccentric globule and a long flagellum, escaping through a large apical pore; resting spore asexually formed, extramatrical, generally sessile, spherical, 20–25 μ in diameter, with a thickened smooth colorless wall, contents with a large central vacuole surrounded by numerous small globules, endobiotic system like that of the sporangium but usually with a much smaller apophysis, germination not observed.

On *Closterium ehrenbergii* and related species and on *Netrium digitus*, FRANCE.

Since observations on the precise number and arrangement of the teeth were incomplete the species cannot be adequately defined. It is of interest, however, because of the resting spores, this being probably the first undoubted instance of their occurrence in the *Dentigera* group (see *Phlyctochytrium quadricorne*, p. 343).

Observations of great biological interest were made by Dangeard on the reaction of the host to this parasite (see "Parasitism," p. 118).

A sequence of development similar to that in *Chytridium lagenaria* was observed in this species. After infection the endobiotic system reached nearly its full size and complexity before growth of the epibiotic part—the case of the infecting zoospore—was initiated.

? PHLYCTOCHYTRIUM PANDORINAE (Wille) de Wildeman
Bull. Soc. Roy. Bot. Belg. (Mém.), 35: 47. 1896

Chytridium (Phlyctidium) pandorinae Wille, Bih. Kgl. Svensk. Vetensk.-Ak. Handl., 8, Afd. 1, No. 18: 46, pl. 2, fig. 86. 1884.
Rhizidium pandorinae (Wille) Fischer, Rabenhorst. Kryptogamen-Fl., 1 (4): 109. 1892.

Sporangium partly imbedded in the gelatinous sheath of the host colony, subspherical, with an apical wartlike protuberance and an apical or subapical elevated discharge pore; subsporangial part tubular, inflated in the mid-region, terminating on the surface of the host cell wall; zoospores and resting spore not observed.

On *Pandorina morum*, URUGUAY.

? PHLYCTOCHYTRIUM SPIROGYRAE de Wildeman
Ann. Soc. Belge Micro. (Mém.), 20: 48. 1896

Rhizidiomyces spirogyrae de Wildeman, Ann. Soc. Belge Micro. (Mém.), 19: 111, pl. 4, figs. 14-22. 1895.

Sporangium sessile, spherical or slightly ovoid, wall thin, smooth, colorless; rhizoids of limited extent, branching within the zygospore of the host, arising from a fairly large spherical or ovoidal endobiotic subsporangial apophysis which rests either on the wall of the zygospore or in the contents; zoospores not observed, presumably escaping through a broad apical slightly protruding pore, the sporangium proliferating; resting spore endobiotic, lodged either in the zygospore or the gametangium, spherical or ovoid, with a thickened (rough?) wall, germination not observed.

On zygospores of *Spirogyra*, FRANCE.

From the position of the resting spores, it is possible that this is a species of *Chytridium* with proliferating sporangia. Observations on the discharge of the zoospores are necessary before it can be placed generically and the apparent proliferation confirmed.

? PHLYCTOCHYTRIUM SP. Sparrow

Rev. Soc. Cubana Bot., 9: 36, pl. 1, fig. J. 1952

Sporangium subspherical, 35 μ in diameter by 20 μ high, with a broad apical discharge pore 10–12 μ in diameter around which are four very inconspicuous plain teeth 3 μ high; rhizoidal system branched, arising from a single stout main axis which emerges from a subsporangial apophysis 10 μ in diameter; zoospores spherical, 3 μ in diameter, with a basal globule and a central refractive arc-shaped structure (nuclear cap?), emerging *en masse* from the sporangium in a quiescent group, later assuming motility; resting spore not observed.

Parasitic on an oögonium of *Achlya sp.*, CUBA.

EXCLUDED SPECIES OF PHLYCTOCHYTRIUM

* PHLYCTOCHYTRIUM EUGLENAE (Dang.) Schroeter

Engler and Prantl, Natürlichen Pflanzenfam., 1 (1): 79. 1892

Rhizidium euglenae Dangeard, Ann. Sci. Nat. Bot., VII, 4: 301, pl. 13, figs. 11-19. 1886; Le Botaniste, 1: 64, pl. 3, fig. 22. 1889.

Sporangium narrowly elongate-pyriform, ovoid, subspherical, or somewhat angular and irregular, 30 μ long by 10–18 μ in diameter, wall thin, smooth, borne on a spherical apophysis about 5–6 μ in diameter, which either rests directly on the wall of the host cell or is attached to it by a slender unbranched stalk; endobiotic rhizoid an unbranched tube; zoospores spherical, 2 μ in diameter, with a basal colorless globule and a flagellum, discharged through a single apical pore (rarely two); resting spore spherical, thick-walled, brownish, the outer surface either smooth, slightly verrucose, or covered with short slender spines, borne on an extramatrical or endobiotic spherical apophysis from the base of which a slender unbranched filament arises, germination not observed.

Parasitic on resting cells of *Euglena*, Dangeard (*loc. cit.*), FRANCE; coll. Marchal, de Wildeman (1890:11, fig. 2), BELGIUM.

Since the apophysis of the sporangium is epibiotic the species cannot be placed in *Phlyctochytrium* as here defined. The resting spores Dangeard first described for this species (1886a) differ from those he described in the 1889 paper in being rough-walled and not apophysate, rather than spiny-walled and apophysate. There is a strong possibility that two different organisms are involved.

Dangeard pointed out that the position of the apophysis (whether sessile or borne on a stalk) depended upon the proximity of the germinating zoospore to the host cell. Thus, if the zoospore was at some distance from the *Euglena* a stalk was formed, otherwise the apophysis was sessile. He distinguished two forms of his fungus: (1) "*Chytridium*-Form" in which the apophysis was endobiotic, and (2) "*Rhizidium*-Form" in which it was epibiotic. It is possible the "*Chytridium*-Form" is in reality another fungus. As understood here, the species forms typically an epibiotic apophysis.

Minden identifies with Dangeard's organism a fungus discussed by Schenk (1858a: 246) as *Chytridium euglenae* Braun, and uses the binomial *Phlyctochytrium euglenae* (Schenk) Schroeter. Schenk, however, was unquestionably dealing with *Polyphagus euglenae*. Furthermore, Schenk's fungus, though described in the course of a discussion of Braun's genus *Rhizidium*, was always referred to by him as *Chytridium euglenae* and not *Rhizidium euglenae*, as Minden implies. It is interesting to note that Minden (1915: 383) in describing *Polyphagus euglenae* asserts that Schenk's fungus belongs in *Polyphagus*. See also *Chytridium euglenae* Braun, page 532.

Dangeard's fungus is considered by Minden to be synonymous with *Saccomyces dangeardii* (*S. endogenus*).

Braun's *Chytridium euglenae*, collected by von Siebold and Meissner, is probably identical with the present species but is too little known to be considered here.

BLYTTIOMYCES Bartsch, emend.

Mycologia, 31: 559. 1939

Thallus epi- and endobiotic, monocentric, eucarpic, consisting of the epibiotic rudiment of the sporangium, provided with an apiculus, which develops from the distal portion of the zoospore cyst, and one or more endobiotic apophyses, the distal one of which bears a branched rhizoidal system; sporangium inoperculate, epibiotic, uni- or multiporous, the pores subapical, delimited from the endobiotic system by a septum; zoospores uniflagellate with a single globule, formed within the sporangium; resting spore endobiotic, variable in shape, formed by growth and encystment of an apophysis, upon germination forming an epibiotic zoosporangium.

Parasitic on algae (Conjugatae), saprophytic on pollen.

The generic concept has been expanded to include forms with more than one discharge pore.

KEY TO THE SPECIES OF BLYTTIOMYCES

Sporangium wall ornamented
    Sporangium wall covered with short spines; with a single subapical
      or lateral discharge pore .... *B. spinulosus*, p. 355
    Sporangium wall bearing a series of low helical bands; with one or
      two basal discharge pores .... *B. helicus*, p. 356
Sporangium wall smooth............................. *B. laevis*, p. 357

BLYTTIOMYCES SPINULOSUS (Blytt) Bartsch
Mycologia, 31: 559, figs. 1-24. 1939
(Fig. 21 A, p. 360)

Chytridium spinulosum Blytt, Vidensk. Selsk. Skr. Christiana (Mat.-Nat. Kl.), 1882 (5): 27.

"Zoosporangia multispored, aggregated, globose, inoperculate, hyaline, aculeated, 14.2–28 × 16.8–32.3, averaging 23.4 μ in diameter × 28.2 μ high exclusive of apiculus; with a single lateral exit pore about 40° from apex; aculei narrow, hyaline, about 0.5–2.0 μ long, with rounded apices; apiculus cuculate, hyaline, smooth-walled, 5.6 μ in diameter × 3.5–4.9, averaging 3.8 μ high. Zoospores spherical to ovoid, hyaline, 4.2–7.0 μ in diameter, with a large, clear, refractive globule; flagellum approximately 25 μ long; zoospore case becoming thickened distally, persisting as sporangial apiculus after germination. Intramatrical portion of thallus coarse, extensive; consisting of 2 tandem apophyses separated by zygospore wall of host, rarely with 3 apophyses, and with an extensive, branched rhizoid, up to 3.6 μ in diameter, extending from distal apophysis, tapering to delicate points. Apophyses spherical, ovoid or spindle-shaped, with smooth, hyaline membrane; proximal apophysis 5.6–7.0, averaging 5.9 μ in diameter, distal one 4.2–21.1, averaging 11.2 μ in diameter. Resting spores smooth, spherical, ovoid or irregular, 14.0–32.2, averaging 22.2 μ in diameter, with 2-layered, hyaline wall 3.0–5.0 μ thick; endospore 2.0–3.8 μ, exospore about 1.0–1.2 μ thick; with finely granular cytoplasm, containing 1 to several oleaginous-like globules; germinating by the formation of an extramatrical, aculeated sporangium lacking an apiculus; liberating zoospores" (Bartsch, *loc. cit.*).

Parasitic and saprophytic in zygospores of *Spirogyra majuscula*, *S. weberi*, Bartsch (*loc. cit.*), *Spirogyra sp.*, Sparrow (1952d: 765, fig. 1 k) UNITED STATES; *Spirogyra sp.*, Blytt (*loc. cit.*), NORWAY; *Spirogyra sp*, H. E. Petersen (1909: 409, fig. XIX; 1910: 543, fig. XIX), DENMARK; *Spirogyra sp.*, Scherffel (1926a: 216, pl. 10, figs. 90–95), HUNGARY; *Spirogyra majuscula*, Denis (1926: 19, fig. 3), FRANCE; *Spirogyra sp.*, Cejp (1932a: 1, pl. 1, figs. 1–4, pl. 2, figs. 1–2), CZECHOSLOVAKIA; *Spirogyra sp.*, Shen and Siang (1948: 182, fig. 3), CHINA; *Spirogyra sp.*, *Mougeotia sp.*, Sparrow (1952a: 36), CUBA.

BLYTTIOMYCES HELICUS Sparrow and Barr

Mycologia, 47: 551, figs. 22-23. 1955

(Fig. 20 G, p. 330)

Zoosporangium broadly ovate to globose, 16–33.5 μ high (including the apiculus) by 14–26.5 μ in diameter, wall light brown and bearing narrow low 0.8–1 μ thick helical bands which extend from the base to the thick, light-brown apiculus 2–2.5 μ high by 4–6 μ in diameter; endobiotic part coarse and extensive, consisting of an apophysis, 4–7 μ in diameter, from which emerges basally a rhizoidal axis 2.1–3 μ in diameter, which branches distally; zoospores spherical, 4–4.8 μ in diameter, with an eccentric, colorless refractive globule 1.6–2 μ in diameter, and a long posterior flagellum, moving in the sporangium before escaping through one, occasionally two, basal discharge pores, movement a rapid darting; resting spores endobiotic, smooth-walled. (Modified from Sparrow and Barr.)

On pine-pollen bait in sphagnum-bog debris, UNITED STATES; pine pollen, Rieth (1956b: 185, fig. 2), GERMANY.

More material of this bizarre species was found in Cheboygan County, in 1956, by W. J. Koch. In it anastomosis of the helical bands sometimes occurred.

Smooth-walled endobiotic resting spores thought possibly to belong to this species were seen and so regarded by Rieth (1956b).

BLYTTIOMYCES LAEVIS Sparrow

Mycologia, 44: 765, fig. 1, 1-o. 1952

(Fig. 20 C, p. 330)

Sporangium sessile, ovate, smooth-walled, 14–17 μ high by 12–16 μ in diameter, with a subapical prominent thick-walled, strongly convex apiculus, 2.5–3.5 μ high by 3–4 μ in diameter; rhizoids coarse, sparsely branched, arising from a small subsporangial apophysis.; zoospores numerous, slightly ovoid, 3 μ in diameter, with one or two minute, colorless, refractive granules and a long posterior flagellum, escaping through one to three subapical pores; resting spore not observed.

Parasitic on filaments of *Zygnema sp.*, UNITED STATES.

The only smooth-walled member of the genus that is now known.

IMPERFECTLY KNOWN SPECIES OF BLYTTIOMYCES

? BLYTTIOMYCES SP. Sparrow

Mycologia, 44: 767. 1952

Sporangium spherical, 12–13 μ in diameter, wall minutely spiny, with an apiculus 3 μ in diameter and one to three discharge pores; endobiotic system consisting of a spherical apophysis 3 μ in diameter from which a sparingly branched rhizoidal system emerges; zoospores and resting spores not observed.

On *Netrium sp.*, UNITED STATES.

PHYSORHIZOPHIDIUM Scherffel

Arch. Protistenk., 54: 181. 1926

(Fig. 19 G, p. 318)

Thallus epi- and endobiotic, monocentric; sporangium inoperculate, formed near the surface of the substratum from the enlarged body of the encysted zoospore and producing by the deliquescence of a papilla one or more pores for the escape of the zoospores; thallus with an endobiotic swelling with or without rhizoids and a secondarily formed epibiotic subsporangial swelling; zoospores posteriorly uniflagellate, produced within the sporangium, with a single oil droplet; resting spore not observed.

On diatoms.

Distinct from *Phlyctidium* and *Rhizophydium* primarily in the secondary formation of a subsporangial epibiotic knoblike swelling.

Physorhizophidium pachydermum Scherffel

Arch. Protistenk., 54: 181, pl. 9, figs. 21-40. 1926

Sporangium at first spherical, by the formation of a broad conical truncate outgrowth from one side becoming at maturity ovate, humped, or irregular, 8–21.6 μ high by 10–27 μ long, generally with the long axis at right angles to that of the penetration tube, with a thick smooth wall on which is formed at or near the tip of the conical lateral outgrowth a single prominent conical basally, laterally, or apically directed thin-walled discharge papilla; haustorium typically spherical, provided with delicate branched rhizoids (?) and, between the outer surface of host wall and the base of sporangium, with an epibiotic, subsporangial swelling of the same size as, or slightly larger than, the haustorium; zoospores spherical, 2.7 μ in diameter, with a single minute (less than 1 μ) eccentric basal oil droplet and a posterior flagellum from four to five times as long as the body, emerging actively through a pore 3–7 μ in diameter formed upon the deliquescence of the papilla; resting spore not observed.

Parasitic on *Amphora ovalis*, Scherffel (*loc. cit.*), Hungary; *Navicula sp.*, Sparrow (1943: 242), United States.

Scherffel noted that the parasites avoided the girdle-band face and bored through the siliceous cell wall.

PODOCHYTRIUM Pfitzer

Sitzungsber. Niederrhein. Gesell. Natur- und Heilkunde, 1869: 62. 1870

(Fig. 21 B-E; K-L, p. 360)

Septocarpus Zopf, Nova Acta Acad. Leop.-Carol., 52: 348. 1888.
Rhizidiopsis Sparrow, Trans. Brit. Mycol. Soc., 18: 216. 1933; J. Linn. Soc. London (Bot.), 50: 450. 1936.

Thallus epi- and endobiotic, monocentric, eucarpic, the epibiotic part consisting of the unexpanded body of the encysted zoospore and an apical prolongation, the endobiotic part rhizoidal or straplike, arising from the tip of a needle-like penetration tube; sporangium inoperculate, epibiotic, formed from the apical prolongation of the sterile epibiotic cyst of the zoospore, from which it is usually separated by a cross wall; zoospores posteriorly uniflagellate, with a single globule; resting spore sessile, flattened, thick-walled, upon germination producing a sporangium.

Members of the genus are confined to diatoms, so far as now known.

Sparrow and Paterson recently (1955) discussed the status of *Rhizidiopsis*. Since the basal septum on the sporangium is so variable in its occurrence, the chief point of distinction of *Rhizidiopsis* from *Podochytrium* breaks down.

KEY TO THE SPECIES OF PODOCHYTRIUM

Endobiotic system composed of delicate, branched rhizoids
  Sporangium clavate .... *P. clavatum*, p. 361
  Sporangium lanceolate...................... *P. lanceolatum*, p. 362
Endobiotic system composed of coarse, straplike rhizoids
  Sporangium narrowly clavate, hornlike, 33-58 μ long; on *Stephano-*
    discus .... *P. cornutum*, p. 362
  Sporangium more broadly clavate, 6-26 μ long; on *Melosira*
                      P. emmanuelense, p. 363

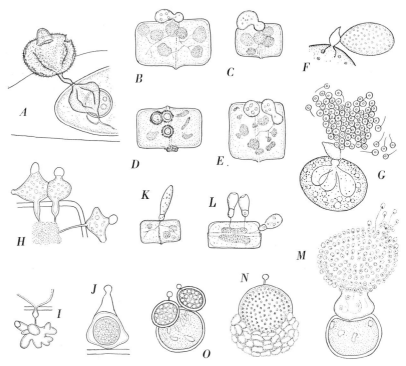

FIG. 21. Phlyctidiaceae

A. *Blyttiomyces spinulosus* (Blytt) Bartsch, empty sporangium on zygospore of *Spirogyra*; spiny sporangium is epibiotic on surface of host gametangium; apiculus is terminal, discharge pore lateral; apophysis is within zygospore of host and gives rise at its base to rhizoidal system; resting spore is endobiotic. *B–E. Podochytrium emmanuelense* (Sparr.) Sparrow and Paterson on *Melosira*: B–C, E, maturing sporangia on surface of host; main body is produced as outgrowth from cyst of infecting zoospore; D, epibiotic resting spores. *F–G. Saccomyces endogenus* (Nowak.) Sparrow on *Euglena*: F, prosporangium on outer surface of encysted host; sporangium appears as broad lateral outgrowth; G, release of zoospores upon bursting of sporangium wall; endobiotic apophysis and broad finger-like lobes of haustorial system are apparent within the *Euglena*. *H–J. Coralliochytrium scherffelii* Domján on *Zygnema*: H, group of sporangia with adherent cysts on surface of host cell; I, base of sporangium with endobiotic apophysis and stalk at tip of which is gnarled digitate absorbing organ; J, epibiotic resting spore on surface of host. *K. Podochytrium lanceolatum* Sparrow on cell of *Melosira. L. Podo-*

PODOCHYTRIUM CLAVATUM Pfitzer

Sitzungsber. Niederrhein. Gesell. Natur- und Heilkunde, 1869: 62. 1870
(Fig. 21 L,¶p. 360)

Septocarpus corynephorus Zopf, Nova Acta Acad. Leop.-Carol., 52: 348, pl. 20, figs. 21-28. 1888.

Sporangium sessile, occasionally borne on a short needle-like portion of the penetration tube, clavate or obpyriform, wall smooth, often stout, colorless, not giving a cellulose reaction, 8–19.2 μ high by 5–8.4 μ in diameter, resting directly on a knoblike sterile basal cell, 2.5–3 μ in diameter; rhizoids extremely delicate, branched, arising from the tip of a sometimes prolonged penetration tube; zoospores spherical, 3 μ in diameter, with a single colorless slightly eccentric globule, sometimes moving within the sporangium, emerging upon the dissolution of a broad scarcely visible apical papilla and either forming a temporary motionless mass at the orifice or swimming directly away; resting spore not observed (?).

Parasitic on *Pinnularia*, Pfitzer (*loc. cit.*), Zopf (*loc. cit.*), GERMANY; various diatoms, de Wildeman (1890: 26), BELGIUM; *Melosira*, de Wildeman (1894: 157), FRANCE; *Pinnularia*, *Melosira varians*, *Amphora*, *Gomphonema micropus* (possibly resting spore of fungus), Scherffel (1926a: 174, pl. 9, figs. 13–16), HUNGARY; *Navicula spp.*, Sparrow (1933c: 524, fig. I, 13), *Pinnularia sp.*, Sparrow and Barr (1955: 554), UNITED STATES; *Fragilaria sp.*, Sparrow (1936a: 449, fig. 4 b, g-h), GREAT BRITAIN; *Tabellaria flocculosa*, Tokunaga (1934b: 391, pl. 11, figs. 11–12), JAPAN.

Scherffel has described an epibiotic "stopper-like" resting spore, 6–8 μ long by 4–5 μ thick, with rounded apex, smooth thickened wall, and fatty contents as possibly belonging to this species. The resting

---

chytrium clavatum Pfitzer on cell of *Fragelaria*. M–O. *Scherffeliomyces parasitans* Sparrow on *Euglena*: M, discharging sporangium resting on host cell; N, mature sporangium with attached zoospore cyst; O, two epibiotic resting spores with attached zoospore cysts.

(*A*, Bartsch, 1939; *B–E*, *K–O*, Sparrow, 1936a; *F–G*, Serbinow, 1907; *H–J*, Domján, 1936)

structure was borne in the larger, upper, part of a septate toplike body, the lower part of which was empty.

Whereas Zopf observed the fungus to gain entrance into the host only at the unsilicified line of fusion of the valves, Scherffel has noted that germinating zoospores may in some cases bore through the valve at any point.

PODOCHYTRIUM LANCEOLATUM Sparrow

Trans. Brit. Mycol. Soc., 18: 216. 1933; J. Linn. Soc. London (Bot.), 50: 450, fig. 4 c-f. 1936

(Fig. 21 K, p. 360)

Sporangium sessile, lanceolate or somewhat fusiform, often slightly tilted, with a small apical papilla, wall smooth, colorless, 20–25 μ high by 8–10 μ in diameter, tapering at each end to 3–4 μ, resting upon a sterile cuplike or occasionally knoblike base 4–5 μ in diameter; rhizoidal system consisting of a few sparsely branched rhizoids arising from the tip of a prolonged needle-like penetration tube; zoospores spherical, 3–4 μ in diameter, with a single refractive eccentric globule and a long flagellum, emerging through a small apical pore formed upon the deliquescence of a papilla; resting spore not observed.

On *Melosira varians*, GREAT BRITAIN.

Differing from *Podochytrium clavatum* in the shape and greater length of its sporangium, smaller apical pore, and complete lack of a stalk on the sterile part. The species resembles to a certain degree the immature plant of *P. clavatum* figured by Zopf (1888: pl. 20, fig. 25e).

PODOCHYTRIUM CORNUTUM Sparrow

Trans. Brit. Mycol. Soc., 34: 172, fig. 1. 1951

(Fig. 11 H, p. 110)

Sporangium smooth-walled, narrowly clavate, 33–58 μ (av. 45 μ) long by 10–13 μ in broadest distal portion, tapering to 3–4 μ in diameter at the base of the narrow, 10 μ long concomitant sterile part; the whole resting upon the rounded body, 3–4 μ in diameter, of the encysted zoospore; rhizoidal system coarse, much branched, usually conspicuously expanded at the point of origin of the primary branches; zoospores spherical (?), 3–4 μ in diameter, with a globule, escaping through a broad apical pore 9–10 μ in diameter; resting spore not observed.

Parasitic in, and causing an epidemic of, the planktonic diatom *Stephanodiscus niagarae*, UNITED STATES.

An exceedingly high percentage of the diatom population was infected by the chytrid. Although as many as fifty to sixty or more thalli were sometimes present on one diatom, a single infection could result in total destruction of the host.

PODOCHYTRIUM EMMANUELENSE (Sparrow) Sparrow and Paterson

Mycologia, 47: 274. 1955

(Fig. 21 B-E, p. 360)

Rhizidiopsis emmanuelensis Sparrow, Trans. Brit. Mycol. Soc., 18: 216. 1933; J. Linnean Soc. London (Bot.), 50: 451, pl. 18, figs. 1-13. 1936.

Sporangium smooth-walled, obpyriform or clavate, 6–26 μ long by 5–13.5 μ in diameter, the long axis often parallel with that of the host filament, sessile, or on a short pedicel, attached by its narrower end to the rounded cyst, 3–4 μ in diameter, of the zoospore with which it is either continuous or more often cut off by a cross wall, forming from four to twelve or more zoospores, 3–4 μ in diameter, which at maturity are discharged through a single apical pore; endobiotic system composed of branched broad coarse straplike elements, 1–2 μ in diameter, with relatively blunt apices; resting spore spherical or somewhat flattened, thick-walled, 4–4.5 μ in diameter, surrounded by a dark-brown rough incrustation, upon germination producing a sporangium.

Parasitic on *Melosira varians* and *Nitzschia* (?) *sp.*, Sparrow (1936a: 451), *Melosira sp.*, Ingold (1941, comm.), GREAT BRITAIN; *Pinnularia viridis*, *Pinnularia sp.*, *Melosira varians*, *Melosira sp.*, *Amphora ovalis*, *Gomphonema macropus*, *Tabellaria flocculosa*, Friedmann (1952: 192, fig. 3), AUSTRIA; *Melosira sp.*, Sparrow and Paterson (1955), UNITED STATES.

The fungus that Friedmann described as *Podochytrium clavatum* is placed in *P. emmanuelense* by reason of its coarse, straplike rhizoidal system.

SACCOMYCES Serbinow

Scripta Bot. Horti Univ. Imper. Petro., 24: 162. 1907

(Fig. 21 F-G, p. 360)

Thallus epi- and endobiotic, monocentric, eucarpic, consisting of the epibiotic rudiment of the prosporangium formed from the body of the encysted zoospore and the endobiotic vegetative system, which is often apophysate and broadly lobed, digitate, or saccate; prosporangium epibiotic, sessile; sporangium inoperculate, subapical or lateral, very thin-walled, ellipsoidal or long-tubular, bursting apart at maturity; zoospores posteriorly uniflagellate, with a single globule; resting spore asexually formed, borne like the sporangium, germination not observed.

On Euglenophyceae.

In its method of zoospore formation *Saccomyces* bears a resemblance to *Polyphagus*. The character and development of the endobiotic vegetative system, which occupies only one host cell, distinguish it, however, from that genus.

Saccomyces endogenus (Nowak.) Sparrow

Aquatic Phycomycetes, p. 246. 1943

Polyphagus endogenus Nowakowski, Akad. umiejetnošci Krakowie. Wyd-ziat mat.-przyród., Pamietník, 4: 191, pl. 10, figs. 108-114. 1878.

Saccomyces dangeardii Serbinow, Scripta Bot. Horti Univ. Imper. Petro., 24: 162, pl. 6, figs. 22-33. 1907.

Prosporangium pyriform, about 5 μ high by 3 μ in diameter (cal-culated), with a pronounced apiculus, wall thin, smooth, colorless; sporangium broadly ellipsoidal or elongate-tubular, occasionally branched, 15–30 μ long by 8–10 μ in diameter, wall delicate, evanescent; endobiotic part consisting of a subsporangial apophysis (occasionally absent), from the base of which protrude from two to four very broad distally swollen digitations; zoospores nearly spherical, 2 μ in diameter, with a colorless centric or eccentric globule and a long flagellum, escaping upon the bursting of the sporangium wall; resting spore spherical, about 10 μ in diameter, with a thick wall, the outer surface covered by coarse conical spines, germination not observed.

On encysted *Euglena sp.*, Nowakowski (*loc. cit.*), GERMANY (?); *Euglena viridis* Serbinow (*loc. cit.*), RUSSIA.

There is little question but that this organism was first described and figured by Nowakowski. He did not appear to recognize that the sporangium always arose as a lateral outgrowth of a prosporangium, nor did he observe the often apophysate and strongly digitate character of the endobiotic part. His Figures 110–112 of the sporangial stage and Figure 114 of the resting stage are, however, strikingly similar to those of Serbinow and leave little doubt as to the identity of the organisms.

SCHERFFELIOMYCES SPARROW

Mycologia, 26: 377. 1934; J. Linn. Soc. London (Bot.), 50: 446. 1936

(Fig. 21 M-O, p. 360)

Scherffelia Sparrow, Trans. Brit. Mycol. Soc., 18: 216. 1933. Non *Scherffelia* Pascher, Hedwigia, 52: 281. 1912.

Thallus extramatrical, epibiotic, and endobiotic, monocentric, eucarpic, consisting of the extramatrical persistent cyst of the zoospore, the proximal part of the germ tube, the epibiotic expanded rudiment of the sporangium, and the endobiotic vegetative system; sporangium inoperculate, zoospores uniflagellate, with a single globule; resting spore thick-walled, borne like the sporangium, contents with globules, germination not observed.

Parasites of fresh-water green algae.

The genus appears closely allied to *Phlyctidium* and *Rhizophydium*, but differs in its peculiar method of development, first noted by Zopf (1884). *Coralliochytrium*[1] has the same type of development, but, unlike *Scherffeliomyces*, forms angular multiporous sporangia, a thick-walled apophysis, and a stubby branched haustorial system.

KEY TO THE SPECIES OF SCHERFFELIOMYCES [2]

Sporangium spherical or subspherical; globule of zoospore orange
S. parasitans, p. 366
Sporangium pyriform; globule of zoospore colorless
S. appendiculatus, p. 366

[1] See remarks under *Coralliochytrium*, p. 368.
[2] See also *Scherffeliomyces leptorrhizus* Johns, p. 367.

SCHERFFELIOMYCES PARASITANS Sparrow

Mycologia, 26: 377. 1934; J. Linn. Soc. London (Bot.), 50: 446, pl. 18, figs. 14-28. 1936

(Fig. 21 M-O, p. 360)

Scherffelia parasitans Sparrow, Trans. Brit. Mycol. Soc., 18: 216. 1933.

Sporangium sessile, at first lachrymose, becoming spherical or subspherical at maturity, resting in the concavity formed by the collapsed host cell, 17–22 μ in diameter, joined by a narrow tube of varying length to the spherical (2.5–3 μ in diameter) cyst of the zoospore, contents at first colorless, at maturity charged with orange oil droplets, with a barely perceptible single short unbranched endobiotic tube; zoospores minute, innumerable, spherical or ovoid, 2–3 μ in diameter, with a single orange globule, emerging in a compact mass from the broad mouth of the sporangium and remaining for a few seconds at the orifice, the mass then becoming disorganized as the spores assume motility, movement swimming or strongly amoeboid; resting spore spherical or ovoid, thick-walled, brownish, 8–10 μ high by 10–14 μ in diameter, attached by a narrow, often somewhat curved tube to the spherical (3 μ in diameter) cystospore, germination not observed.

Parasitic on resting cells of *Euglena sp.*, GREAT BRITAIN.

SCHERFFELIOMYCES APPENDICULATUS (Zopf) Sparrow

J. Linn. Soc. London (Bot.), 50: 449. 1936

Rhizidium appendiculatum Zopf, Nova Acta Acad. Leop.-Carol., 47: 203, pl. 20, figs. 17-27. 1884.

Rhizophydium appendiculatum (Zopf) Fischer, Rabenhorst. Kryptogamen-Fl., 1 (4): 101. 1892.

Sporangium within the gelatinous sheath of the host, sessile on the contents of the alga, pyriform, up to 14 μ long by 11 μ in diameter, with a prominent sometimes elongate apiculus, wall thin, smooth, colorless, cystospore ellipsoidal or ovoid, laterally attached by a short tube to the apiculus, contents colorless; rhizoidal system sparingly branched, arising from the tip of a short axis; zoospores from a few to twenty or thirty, spherical, with a basal colorless globule and a long flagellum, escaping through an apical pore; resting spore borne like the sporangium and similar to it in shape, wall thick, smooth, colorless, contents with one to many globules.

Parasitic in the *Palmella* stage of *Chlamydomonas sp.* and in immature swarmers within the mother cell, never on moving individuals, Zopf (*loc. cit.*), GERMANY; Scherffel (1914), HUNGARY.

The organism occurred in epidemic proportions in Zopf's material. De Wildeman (1895a: 71) has referred to this species a fungus on an undetermined alga from Switzerland. No appendicular structure was observed, however, and he rightly suggests the possibility that it may be *Rhizophydium simplex*. Similarly, Cook (1932a: 139, figs.26–31) has called a fungus found by him on *Chlamydomonas* in England *Rhizidium appendiculatum*, but, if the sequence of development described is correctly interpreted, it cannot be referred either to *Scherffeliomyces* or to *Rhizidium*.

RECENTLY DESCRIBED TAXON [1]

SCHERFFELIOMYCES LEPTORRHIZUS Johns

Mycologia, 48: 433, figs. 1-12. 1956

"Sporangium ovoid or subspherical, 15–26 × 18–27 μ in diameter, wall colorless, attached by a short apical process to a spherical cysto-spore 4–5.5 μ in diameter; intramatrical portion consisting of a single slender stalk terminated by a tuft of branched isodiametric rhizoids, infrequently with an intramatrical subsporangial vesicle. Zoospores posteriorly uniflagellate, 4–5 μ in diameter, equipped with a single eccentric oil globule, fully formed in the sporangium, discharged at maturity through the deliquescence of a single subapical papilla; emerging in a mass and remaining briefly motionless at the orifice, the mass soon dispersing as the zoospores assume motility; resting spores ovoid, with a terminally attached cystospore, 10–15 × 22–27 μ, with a thick wall, similar to the sporangia in morphology and development, germination not observed" (Johns, *loc. cit.*).

Parasitic on *Zygnema sp.*, UNITED STATES.

[1] Not included in the key.

CORALLIOCHYTRIUM Domján

Folia cryptogam., 2 (1): 22. 1936
(Fig. 21 H-J, p. 360)

Thallus extramatrical, epi- and endobiotic, monocentric, eucarpic, the epibiotic part forming the rudiment of the sporangium from the enlarged extramatrical part of the germ tube of the encysted zoospore, the endobiotic part forming a subsporangial apophysis from the base of which emerges a single short rhizoid bearing at its tip a complex of stubby, thick, branched digitations; sporangium inoperculate, epibiotic, sessile, the cyst of the zoospore attached to it directly or by a short tube, forming more than one discharge papilla; resting spore epibiotic, apparently asexually produced, borne within a structure formed like and resembling a sporangium, germination not observed.

On *Zygnema*.

The genus bears a marked similarity in its method of development to *Scherffeliomyces*. It differs, however, in the character of the haustorial system and the method of zoospore discharge (through several openings).

Johns (1956) gives evidence to show that *Coralliochytrium* should, in fact, be merged with *Scherffeliomyces* and he has placed Domján's *C. scherffelii* in Sparrow's genus under the binomial *Scherffeliomyces scherffelii* (Domján) Johns.

CORALLIOCHYTRIUM SCHERFFELII Domján

Folia cryptogam., 2 (1): 22, pl. 1, figs. 5-12, 14-23, 27-35, 38-41, 47, 49. 1936

Sporangium sessile, somewhat irregularly angular-pyriform (polygonal in cross section at the base), the shape depending in part upon the number (from two to five) of broad very prominent elongate discharge papillae formed, 15.4–23.8 µ broad by 17.6–23.8 µ high (majority 22 µ in breadth), wall smooth, thick, colorless, bearing at the apex the cyst of the zoospore and its connective; subsporangial endobiotic apophysis bulbous, 3.3–4.4 µ in diameter, lateral walls thick, base generally thin-walled, the delicate basal rhizoid bearing distally the broad stubby digitations; zoospores spherical, 2.2 µ in diameter, with a colorless eccentric globule and a long flagellum, emerging singly through from two to five pores formed upon the deliquescence of the papillae; resting spore spherical, with a moderately thick colorless wall, 13.2 μ in diameter, contents with numerous small oil droplets, germination not observed.

On *Zygnema sp.*, HUNGARY.

SUBFAM. ENTOPHLYCTOIDEAE

Sporangium endobiotic, resting spore endobiotic; vegetative system rhizoidal; zoospore cyst usually evanescent.

ENTOPHLYCTIS FISCHER

Rabenhorst. Kryptogamen-Fl., 1 (4): 114. 1892

(Fig. 22, p. 371)

Thallus endobiotic, monocentric, eucarpic, consisting of the evanescent epibiotic cyst of the zoospore and the endobiotic rudiment of the sporangium or resting spore and a rhizoidal system arising from it; sporangium inoperculate, with a discharge tube the tip of which at least is extramatrical; zoospores posteriorly uniflagellate, usually with a single globule, formed within the sporangium, escaping upon the deliquescence of the tip of the discharge tube; resting spore thick-walled, endobiotic, borne like the sporangium, apparently asexually developed, upon germination forming zoospores in an externally produced sporangium.

Primarily inhabitants of fresh-water green algae. Several species have been described by Němec (1912) as parasites of phanerogams.

There is some question as to the precise method of development of the thallus in *Entophlyctis*. All the earlier investigators stated that the rhizoids are outgrowths of the rudiment of the sporangium—the endobiotic part of the thallus being first established. Indeed, Karling (1928a), in an hour-by-hour account of the formation of the sporangial rudiment in *E. helioformis*, has described and figured such a sequence. Later, however, (1931a) he observed that in "*E. cienkowskiana*" (now *E. confervae-glomeratae*) the rudiments of the rhizoidal system are laid down first by the penetrating zoospore. Thereafter, by a subsequent enlargement of the more proximal part of the germ tube, the incipient sporangium arises behind the point of origin of the primary branches of the rhizoids. Such a sequence needs further confirmation in other species of *Entophlyctis*.

Germination of the resting spores has been observed by Fisch (1884a), Karling (1941b), and Haskins (1946). In all instances the resting spore functioned as a prosporangium and an external, thin-walled zoosporangium was produced.

Specific concepts in *Entophlyctis* are by no means clear, and considerable work must be done before they can be adequately defined. The characters most used at present to distinguish species are the shape and size of the sporangium, the number and, particularly, the place of origin of the rhizoids on the sporangium, and the host. As Karling (1931a) aptly points out, since very little is known concerning the range of variation of a single species under different conditions in diverse substrata (and, one may add, since little is known of the resting stage), no critical analysis can yet be attempted.

KEY TO THE SPECIES OF ENTOPHLYCTIS [1]

Protoplasm colorless at maturity; coloration, if present, only in the
  oil globule of the zoospore
  Epibiotic cyst persistent, functioning in the discharge of zoospores
    Rhizoidal system limited, delicate; on *Chlamydomonas* and *Gloeo-
      cystis* .... *E. apiculata*, p. 372
    Rhizoidal system extensive, coarse; on *Spirogyra* . *E. bulligera*, p. 373
  Epibiotic cyst not functional, evanescent
    Zoospores with an orange-colored globule
      Sporangium spherical or ovoid; rhizoids arising from one or
        more places on the sporangium .... *E. rhizina*, p. 374
      Sporangium variable in shape; rhizoids arising for most part
        from one basal axis .... *E. texana*, p. 375
    Zoospores with a colorless globule
      Rhizoids coarse, strongly dichotomously branched, main axes
        lateral; sporangium subspherical or oblong . *E. pygmaea*, p. 376
      Rhizoids delicate, regularly or irregularly branched
        Rhizoids arising in most cases from a single basal axis; spo-
          rangium spherical, broadly ellipsoidal, or pyriform; in
          green algae

[1] See also the recently described taxon on p. 381.

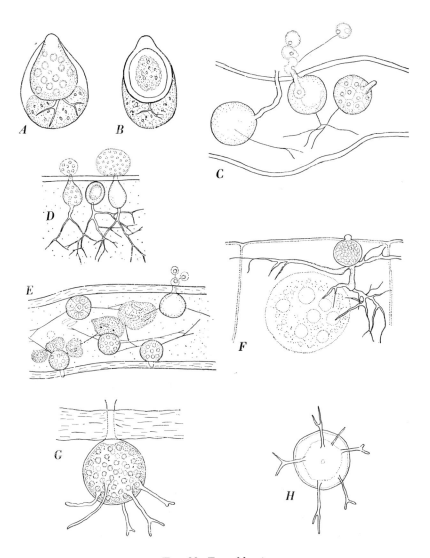

FIG. 22. *Entophlyctis*

A–B. Entophlyctis apiculata (Braun) Fischer in *Gloeococcus* (*Chlamydo‾ monas?*): *A*, habit of sporangial plant; *B*, resting spore. *C. Entophlyctis* (?) *vaucheriae* (Fisch) Fischer in *Cladophora*. *D*. Discharging sporangia and a resting spore of *Entophlyctis confervae-glomeratae* (Cienkowski) Sparrow in

Sporangium predominantly spherical, basal axis delicate
E. vaucheriae, p. 377
Sporangium predominantly spherical, broadly ellipsoidal,
or somewhat pyriform, main axis relatively stout
E. confervae-glomeratae, p. 377
Rhizoids arising from three to twelve main axes; in Chara-
ceae .... *E. helioformis*, p. 379
Protoplasm bright orange at maturity; zoospore lacking a single prom-
inent oil globule .... *E. aurea*, p. 380

ENTOPHLYCTIS APICULATA (Braun) Fischer

Rabenhorst. Kryptogamen-Fl., 1 (4): 117. 1892

(Fig. 22 A-B, p. 371)

Chytridium apiculatum Braun, Monatsber. Berlin Akad., 1855: 383; Abhandl. Berlin Akad., 1855: 57, pl. 5, figs. 5-20. 1856.
Olpidium apiculatum (Braun) Rabenhorst, Flora Europaea algarum, 3:
283. 1868.
Rhizidium apiculatum (Braun) Zopf, Nova Acta Acad. Leop.-Carol., 47:
207, pl. 21, figs. 21-31. 1884.

Sporangium broadly pyriform or nearly spherical, its papillate
apiculus 3 μ long, piercing the host wall, main body resting between
the retracted host contents and the wall, up to six sporangia in a cell,
11–13 μ in diameter, wall smooth, colorless; rhizoids imbedded in the
host plasma, short, delicate, sparsely branched, arising from a short
main axis; zoospores from three to twenty, small, spherical or ellipsoidal, with an eccentric colorless globule and a long flagellum, escaping
upon the dissolution of the apex of the apiculus; resting spore spherical,
subspherical, or ellipsoidal, with a thick colorless smooth wall, contents
densely granular, rhizoidal system like that of the sporangium, germination not observed.

Parasitic in immobile and moving cells of *Gloeococcus* (*Chlamy-*

Spirogyra. E. Entophlyctis (?) *rhizina* (Schenk) Minden in *Vaucheria. F.
Entophlyctis bulligera* (Zopf) Fischer in *Spirogyra*; epibiotic knob is persistent case of zoospore. *G–H. Entophlyctis helioformis* (Dang.) Ramsbottom
in *Nitella*: *G*, mature sporangium bearing stubby rhizoids; *H*, underside
of empty sporangium showing attachment of stubby rhizoids.

(*A–B, F*, Zopf, 1884; *D–E*, Sparrow, 1936a; *C, G–H*, Sparrow, 1943)

domonas?) *mucosus,* Braun (*loc. cit.*), *Chlamydomonas pulvisculus* (coll. Pringsheim), Braun (1856a: 57), *Gloeocystis* or *Gloeococcus mucosus,* Kloss (in Braun, 1856b: 588), *Gloeococcus* (*?*), Zopf (*loc. cit.*), GERMANY; *Gloeococcus mucosus,* Sorokin (1874b:10 , pl. 1, figs. 11–43; 1883: 32, fig. 36), RUSSIA; *Gloeococcus,* de Wildeman (1890: 10), BELGIUM; *Chlamydomonas sp.,* Constantineanu (1901: 382), RUMANIA; *Euglena sp.,* Bérczi (1940:86, pl. 2, fig. 38), HUNGARY.

Sparrow (1936a: 451, pl. 14, figs. 7–9) tentatively referred a fungus on resting cells of *Euglena sp.* in England to this species. However, since no rhizoids were observed in the dense contents the fungus might have been a species of *Olpidium.* Indeed, the same might be said of Braun's specimens. It was only after Zopf extracted the chlorophyll of his host plants that he was able to detect the rhizoids.

Zopf, to whom we owe most of our knowledge of the species, found it during February and March in several localities. It caused an epidemic of nearly three weeks' duration in one pond, where very few of the millions of algal cells escaped infection. He confirmed the observation of all investigators of the species, namely, that actively moving swarm cells of the alga were attacked by the fungus zoospores.

Braun states that the epibiotic cyst of the infecting zoospore and the germ tube are persistent in this species, the former producing the apiculus, the latter, the body of the sporangium. Zopf's figures bear out these observations.

ENTOPHLYCTIS BULLIGERA (Zopf) Fischer

Rabenhorst. Kryptogamen-Fl., 1 (4): 116. 1892

(Fig. 22 F, p. 371)

Rhizidium bulligerum Zopf, Nova Acta Acad. Leop.-Carol., 47: 195, pl. 18, figs. 5-8. 1884.

Sporangium spherical, variable in size, with an epibiotic knoblike or ovoid part—the body of the infecting zoospore—which functions as a discharge tube at maturity, wall slightly thickened, smooth, colorless; rhizoidal system extensive, branched, often passing through several cells of the alga, arising from a single point on the underside of the sporangium or from numerous places on the lower half, rhizoids often becoming strongly expanded main axes where they join the sporangium; zoospores from thirty to forty in large sporangia, discharged through a pore formed in the epibiotic apiculus; resting spore not observed. In moribund vegetative cells and gametangia of *Spirogyra crassa*, Zopf (*loc. cit.*), GERMANY; *Spirogyra crassa, Oedogonium sp.*, de Wildeman (1890: 7; 1891: 172), BELGIUM; *Spirogyra crassa*, Atkinson (1909a: 338), UNITED STATES; *Oedogonium sp.*, Valkanov (1931a: 363), BULGARIA; vegetative cells of *Zygnema* and *Mougeotia*, Domján (1936: 46, pl. 1, figs. 71, 82–83), *Oedogonium sp.*, Bérczi (1940: 86), HUNGARY; *Oedogonium sp.*, Litvinow (1953: 82), LATVIA; *Spirogyra sp.*, Richards (1956: 263), GREAT BRITAIN.

As in *Entophlyctis apiculata*, the cyst of the infecting zoospore in this species is persistent and functions in spore discharge. Neither empty sporangia showing this pore nor zoospores were described by Zopf. Empty sporangia figured by Domján, however, bear out Zopf's contention that the apiculus functions as a discharge tube.

Valkanov gives the diameter of the sporangium as 17–18 μ; Domján records the size as 10–15 by 7.5–10 μ, with the knob 3.7–7.5 μ in diameter.

ENTOPHLYCTIS RHIZINA (Schenk) Minden

Kryptogamenfl. Mark Brandenburg, 5: 354. 1911 (1915)

Chytridium rhizinum Schenk, Verhandl. Phys.-Med. Gesell. Würzburg, A. F., 8: 238, pl. 5, figs. 6-13. 1858.

Sporangium spherical or somewhat ovoid, 8–27 μ in diameter, wall smooth, usually double-contoured, forming a single extramatrical discharge tube (rarely two) 4–14 μ long by 1 μ in diameter; rhizoids arising from one or more places on the lower side of the sporangium, branched, somewhat stout, with a visible lumen as they approach the sporangium; zoospores spherical, 2 μ in diameter, with a reddish yellow globule and a flagellum; resting spore not observed.

In *Vaucheria geminata, V. sessilis*, Schenk (*loc. cit.*), GERMANY; Voronichin (1920: 10), RUSSIA; *Spirogyra maxima*, Bérczi (1940: 86, pl. 1, figs. 1–5, 8, pl. 2, fig. 39), HUNGARY; *Vaucheria sp.*, Litvinow (1953: 82), LATVIA.

Minden (*loc. cit.*) considers *Entophlyctis vaucheriae* (Fisch) Fischer synonymous with Schenk's species. The presence of a colored globule in the zoospore of Schenk's fungus (not mentioned by Minden) is in itself sufficient to distinguish the two. Schenk's species bears a close resemblance to *Cladochytrium nowakowskii* (see *C. replicatum*, p. 464), and it is not impossible that when the sporangia and rhizoids were crowded in the algal cell the turbinate cells were overlooked.

Though the rhizoids are said by Schenk to emerge from more than one place on the sporangium, all his figures except the immature stage in Figure 10 show a definite basal main axis. His statement that the flagellum of the zoospore is anterior during motility is probably erroneous, since even with the best modern optical equipment this structure can rarely be detected while rapidly vibrating.

Schenk believed his fungus was identical with "*Rhizidium*" *confervae glomeratae* Cienkowski, differing only in the lack of amoeboid motion by the spores, their failure to form a motionless group at the orifice of the sporangium, and their not entering as a whole into the algal cell (probably an erroneous observation by Cienkowski). Cienkowski's fungus appears to form predominantly spherical rather than ovoid sporangia, the discharge tubes never extend an appreciable distance outside the algal wall, and the globule of the zoospore is colorless.

The species is reported as occurring in Bulgaria, in *Vaucheria sp.*, by Valkanov (1931a: 363), and in Hungary by Domján (1936: 46, pl. 1, fig. 137) (see also Moesz, 1938: 71). Neither Valkanov nor Domján mentions a colored globule in the zoospore. A fungus closely resembling Schenk's but with colorless globules has been found in Great Britain (Sparrow, 1936a) in *Vaucheria*, see Figure 22 E, p. 371.

ENTOPHLYCTIS TEXANA Karling

Torreya, 41: 106. 1941

Sporangium variable, subspherical, 18–45 μ in diameter, pyriform, 10–22 by 20–40 μ, elongate, truncate, 15–25 by 35–60 μ, lobulate or irregular, with one to several discharge tubes of variable length and diameter, with golden-red globules; zoospores spherical, 4–4.5 μ in diameter, with a conspicuous golden-red highly refractive globule and a flagellum 20–24 μ long, upon emergence forming a globose mass before assuming individual motility; rhizoidal system arising for the most part from one place on the base of the sporangium, coarse, much branched, 100–600 μ in length, sometimes penetrating more than one cell of substratum, main axes 3–7 μ in diameter; resting spores mostly spherical and 18–24 μ in diameter, oblong, 10–13 by 15–18 μ, elongate and truncate, 10–22 μ, with one to three large centric globules 8–15 μ in diameter, golden-red or rust-colored, wall rust-colored, smooth, 1.5–2 μ thick, germinating by a pore to form a zoosporangium.

Saprophytic in dead leaves of *Elodea canadensis, Eriocaulon septangulare*, and *Vallisneria sp.*, UNITED STATES.

Only the Latin description of this species, unaccompanied by figures, has been published. No comparison was made by its author with *Entophlyctis rhizina* with which, from Schenk's figures, it may be identical.

ENTOPHLYCTIS PYGMAEA (Serbinow) Sparrow

Aquatic Phycomycetes, p. 256. 1943

Catenaria pygmaea Serbinow, Scripta Bot. Horti Univ. Imper. Petro., 24: 161, pl. 3, figs. 1-15. 1907.

Sporangium endobiotic, single, subspherical or long-cylindrical with rounded ends, 17–26 μ long by 6-12 μ in diameter, terminal or intercalary, separated by cross walls from the rhizoidal system, with a single short papilla which penetrates the wall of the substratum; rhizoidal system strongly dichotomously branched, polyphagous, the main axis arising from one or opposite ends of the sporangium, broad and tubular, up to 3 μ in diameter, the branches rhizoidal; zoospores spherical, 1.5 μ in diameter, with a single globule, posteriorly uniflagellate, emerging upon the deliquescence of the papilla and forming a temporary compact motionless mass at the orifice before assuming motility; resting spore borne like the sporangium, spherical, with a thickened colorless wall and a central oil globule, germination not observed.

Parasitic in *Mougeotia sp.*, Serbinow (*loc. cit.*), FINLAND; saprophytic in *Mougeotia*, Sparrow (1943: 257), UNITED STATES; *Mougeotia sp.*, Litvinow (as *Catenaria pygmaea*) (1953: 84), LATVIA.

The thallus of this organism is definitely monocentric and, so far as could be determined, the sporangium is inoperculate.

ENTOPHLYCTIS VAUCHERIAE (Fisch) Fischer
Rabenhorst. Kryptogamen-Fl., 1 (4): 117. 1892
(Fig. 22 C, p. 371)
Rhizidium vaucheriae Fisch, Sitzungsber. Phys.-Med. Soc. Erlangen, 16:
55, pl. 1, figs. 10-23. 1884.

Sporangium spherical, with a beaklike or narrowly cylindrical apical discharge tube more or less prolonged extramatrically, wall smooth, colorless, thin or slightly thickened; rhizoids arising basally from a delicate central axis or occasionally from two places on the lower part of the body, delicate, fairly extensive, and much branched; zoospores relatively few, a large amount of contents usually remaining in the sporangium after their formation, spherical, with a centric or eccentric colorless globule and a short flagellum, discharge not described; resting spore endobiotic, thick-walled, the outer wall brown, the inner lustrous, contents finely granular, vacuolate, with a more or less large oil globule, germinating in the spring by the swelling of the endospore, which bursts the exospore, the former emerging as a subspherical structure within which are produced zoospores.

In *Vaucheria sessilis, Spirogyra sp.*, Fisch (*loc. cit.*), GERMANY; alga (?), Petersen (1910: 545), DENMARK; Sparrow (1943: 257), UNITED STATES.

Doubtfully distinct from *Entophlyctis confervae-glomeratae*. In certain of Fisch's figures the fungus appears polycentric, as in *Cladochytrium*. This is probably an error in observation due to several plants being superimposed. *Rhizidium spirogyrae* was the name given by Fisch to what was probably the same fungus growing in *Spirogyra*. No description accompanied his name.

ENTOPHLYCTIS CONFERVAE-GLOMERATAE (Cienkowski) Sparrow
Aquatic Phycomycetes, p. 258. 1943
(Fig. 22 D, p. 371)
Rhizidium confervae-glomeratae Cienkowski, Bot. Zeitung, 13: 233, pl.
5 A, figs. 1-6 (not fig. 6c). 1857.
Rhizidium cienkowskianum Zopf, Nova Acta Acad. Leop.-Carol., 47: 196,
pl. 17, figs. 14-24; pl. 18, figs. 1-4. 1884.
Entophlyctis cienkowskiana (Zopf) Fischer, Rabenhorst. Kryptogamen-Fl.,
1 (4): 118. 1892.

Sporangium spherical, broadly ellipsoidal, or somewhat pyriform, 5–25 μ in diameter, wall thin, smooth, colorless, discharge tube single (rarely two), narrowly cylindrical, straight or contorted, varying in length from a wartlike nearly sessile protuberance 3 μ long to several times the diameter of the sporangium; rhizoids branched, fairly extensive, predominantly arising from a somewhat prolonged basal axis (occasionally two axes), sometimes arising from several places on the lower part of the sporangium; zoospores spherical, 2.5–5 μ in diameter, with a strongly refractive colorless globule and a long flagellum, emerging singly and somewhat amoeboidly from the orifice of the discharge tube and resting for a time (or clustering temporarily) before swimming away; resting spore formed and borne like the sporangium, spherical, with a thick, faint-golden-brown wall, contents with a large oil globule filling the lumen of the spore, germination not observed.

In *Cladophora glomerata*, Cienkowski (*loc. cit.*), ITALY (?); dead or moribund *Cladophora*, Zopf (*loc. cit.*), Minden (1915: 357), GERMANY; *Cladophora glomerata*, Sorokin (1883: 34, fig. 41), EUROPEAN RUSSIA, ASIATIC RUSSIA; *Cladophora sp.*, Dangeard (1886a: 293), de Wildeman (1894: 158), FRANCE; *Spirogyra crassa*, de Wildeman (1890: 7), BELGIUM; *Cladophora*, Karling (1931a: 443, pl. 35–38), Sparrow (1933c: 524), UNITED STATES; *Spirogyra sp.*, Sparrow (1936a: 452, pl. 14, figs. 13–17), parasitic in *Oedogonium sp.*, *Spirogyra sp.*, Richards (1956: 262, pl. 6, fig. 6), GREAT BRITAIN.

As understood here, this collective species includes all forms with smooth-walled resting spores and spherical, broadly ellipsoidal, or somewhat pyriform sporangia bearing rhizoids which emerge typically from a main basal axis or less typically from several axes formed on the lower half of the sporangium. Dangeard (*loc. cit.*) attempted to distinguish it from *Entophlyctis helioformis* by the smaller number of rhizoids localized at the base of the sporangium. Such a localization is apparent in most specimens but not in all. This interpretation of the species is at variance with Zopf's statement that the rhizoids arise mostly from all sides of the sporangium. It is possible that it will be better eventually to segregate his species from the present one. Typical of the species as here understood are the figures of Cienkowski (*loc. cit*), Karling (*loc. cit.*), and Sparrow (1936a: pl. 14, figs. 13–17). With this interpretation of the species, *E. vaucheriae* is scarcely distinct from *E. confervae-glomeratae* save for the difference in host plant. It is probable that when more is known about the resting stages of these fungi sharper lines of specific differentiation will be revealed than are now apparent.

The fungus in *Vaucheria* from England tentatively described as *Entophlyctis confervae* by Sparrow (1936a: pl. 14, fig. 18), with spherical sporangia and delicate isodiametric rhizoids arising laterally or nearly basally on the sporangium, is distinct from this species. Since the resting stage was not found, however, it is thought best to leave it unnamed. It resembles the fungus called *E. rhizina* by Domján (1936: 46, pl. 1, fig. 137), see Figure 22 E, p. 371.

ENTOPHLYCTIS HELIOFORMIS (Dang.) Ramsbottom

Trans. Brit. Mycol. Soc., 5: 318. 1915

(Fig. 22 G-H, p. 371)

Chytridium helioformis Dangeard, Bull. Soc. Bot. France, 33: 356. 1886; Ann. Sci. Nat. Bot., VII, 4: 293. 1886.

Chytridium heliomorphum Dangeard, Journ. de Botanique, 2: 143, pl. 5, figs. 19-23. 1888.

Entophlyctis heliomorpha (Dang.) Fischer, Rabenhorst. Kryptogamen- Fl., 1 (4): 118. 1892.

Sporangium spherical or ovoid, 6–20 μ in diameter, wall smooth, colorless, somewhat thickened, discharge tube cylindrical, of variable length; rhizoids unbranched or sparingly branched, arising from three to twelve main axes formed at any place on the sporangium; zoospores spherical, 3–4 μ in diameter, with a conspicuous centric or eccentric colorless globule and a long flagellum, escaping individually upon the rupturing of the tip of the discharge tube, movement swimming with axial rotation, or amoeboid; resting spore borne like the sporangium, spherical, subspherical, or broadly ovoid, 8–24 μ in diameter, with a double wall, the outer thicker than the inner, contents yellowish, with numerous oil globules, germination not observed.

Saprophytic in *Nitella tenuissima*, *Vaucheria sp.*, *Chara sp.*, Dangeard (*loc. cit.*), FRANCE;? *Chara spp.*, *Nitella spp.*, Karling (1928a: 32, pl. 1, figs. 1–35), *Chara sp.*, *Nitella tenuissima* (?), Sparrow (1943: 260), UNITED STATES.

This is the most ubiquitous member of the genus. It is abundant in dead plants of *Chara* and *Nitella*. Karling, who studied the development of what is probably not this species (*loc. cit.*), later reported (1931a: 443) negative results in his attempts to grow the fungus on moribund and dead sterile internodes of *Chara* and *Nitella*, or on filaments of *Spirogyra*, *Vaucheria*, *Oedogonium*, *Mougeotia*, and *Hydrodictyon*.

Although the rhizoids are said by some investigators to be extensive and profusely branched, in the present writer's material they were for the most part as Dangeard figured them, that is, relatively short and once-branched. The diagnosis, therefore, is in conformity with Dangeard's original description.

The change in specific name from the Greek-Latin hybrid *helioformis* to *heliomorphum* was made by Dangeard without explanation.

ENTOPHLYCTIS AUREA Haskins

Trans. Brit. Mycol. Soc., 29: 138, figs. 9-15; pl. 8. 1946

"Zoosporangia usually intramatrical, spherical or variously shaped, 15–470 µ in diameter; contents yellow to pale orange in colour when young, bright orange at maturity; wall hyaline and layered, innermost layer giving marked cellulose reaction with chloriodide of zinc, outer layer not staining. Exit tubes one to ten, short with reflexed rims, 4.2–21 µ in diameter at orifice, 5.3–35.7 µ at base, 6.3–50.3 µ in height, with gelatinous plugs. Rhizoids arising from one to twenty places on the sporangium, stout, up to 63 µ in diameter at point of origin, cut off from mature sporangium by cellulose cross-walls; much branched, extending up to 750 µ in length. Zoospores spherical to subspherical, 4.5–5.2 µ in diameter, with several small refractive granules or globules; uniflagellate, flagellum five times diameter of zoospore in length; number of zoospores great, emerging initially through one exit tube to form a spherical or irregular mass, lying quiescent for a few moments before swimming away, remaining zoospores escaping through all exit tubes; movement gliding and darting, intermittently amoeboid. Resting spores borne and shaped similarly to zoosporangia, 22–106 µ in diameter, contents with one to several large orange-brown globules (11.4–60.8 µ in diameter), with or without smaller parietal colourless globules;

wall thick (3–10 μ), hyaline, layered, inner layer at germination giving marked cellulose reaction; functioning as prosporangium in germination to give rise through a narrow pore to an extramatrical evanescent zoosporangium, or through a wide opening to a sac-like zoosporangium" (Haskins, *loc. cit.*).

Saprophytic in various grasses, in wheat, oat, and maize leaves, in regenerated cellulose film, filter paper, and lens paper submerged in water, Haskins (1939), CANADA; Haskins (1946), GREAT BRITAIN.

We are inclined to agree with Karling (1947b: 66) that Haskins' fungus is in reality a species of *Rhizophlyctis* ("*Karlingia*").

RECENTLY DESCRIBED TAXON [1]

ENTOPHLYCTIS CONFERVAE-GLOMERATAE (Cienkowski) Sparrow
f. MARINA Kobayashi and Ookubo

Bull. Nat. Sci. Mus. (Tokyo), (N.S.), 1 (2), No. 35: 67, fig. 6. 1954

"Thallus endobiotic, monocentric, composed of a zoosporangium and well-developed rhizoids. Zoosporangium subglobose, ovoid, pyriform, or frequently deformed, 5–20 μ in diameter, with an apical discharge tube which is narrow, cylindric, varying in length, attenuated, scarcely protruding on the wall of host cell. Rhizoids with 1–3 main axes, arising from one or two opposite places on the lower side of zoosporangium, containing few oil-like globules. Zoosporangial protoplasm discharging through tube as a mass leaving one or several oil-like globules, and forming a sphaerical vesicle just outside the host cell, and after a resting period, producing many zoospores which swim away separately, leaving evanescent membrane of vesicle. Zoospores globose, 3–5 μ in diameter, hyaline. Resting spore endobiotic, globose, about 20 μ in diameter, pale brown, somewhat thick-walled, slightly echinulate with 2–5 spines, with a small globose apophysis and extending rhizoid" (Kobayashi and Ookubo, *loc. cit.*).

On *Cladophora japonica*, JAPAN.

If we have interpreted correctly the development and zoospore,

[1] Not included in the key.

production (outside in a vesicle), this fungus probably belongs elsewhere, possibly in a new genus. It is certainly not a form of *Entophlyctis confervae-glomeratae.*

IMPERFECTLY KNOWN SPECIES OF ENTOPHLYCTIS

? ENTOPHLYCTIS CHARACEARUM de Wildeman

Ann. Soc. Belge Micro. (Mém.), 20: 131, pl. 12, figs. 1-10. 1896

Sporangium unknown; resting spore spherical, ellipsoidal, or irregularly polygonal, 17–25 μ in diameter, with a thick smooth brownish wall; rhizoids much branched, generally arising from two stout main axes (occasionally one); germination not observed.

In oögonia of Characeae, SWITZERLAND.

The resting spores are certainly those of some chytrid, but until the sporangial stage is observed, it is difficult to say to which of several genera the fungus belongs.

? ENTOPHLYCTIS MAXIMA Dangeard

Le Botaniste, 24: 242, pl. 24, figs. 4-5. 1932

Sporangium very broadly pyriform, 40 μ in diameter, with a broad apical papilla, 5–15 μ in diameter, which just pierces the algal wall; rhizoids branched, arising from as many as three main axes on the lower half of the sporangium; zoospores and resting spore not observed.

In *Cladophora glomerata,* FRANCE.

Karling (1937a) considers this incompletely known form to be synonymous with *Endochytrium operculatum* (see p. 569).

? ENTOPHLYCTIS TETRASPORA (Sorokin) de Wildeman

Bull. Soc. Roy. Bot. Belg. (Mém.), 35: 51. 1896

Rhizidium tetrasporum Sorokin, Arch. Bot. Nord France, 2: 35, fig. 42. 1883 (separate).[1]

Sporangium pyriform, wall smooth, thin, colorless, with a short discharge tube which just pierces the wall of the alga; rhizoids short, apparently unbranched, forming a cluster at the base of the sporangium;

[1] See also *Revue Mycologique,* 11: 137, pl. 80, fig. 98. 1889.

zoospores four, spherical, with a short flagellum and a colorless eccentric globule; resting spore not observed.

In *Rhynchonema* (*Spirogyra?*) *sp.*, RUSSIA.

The validity of the species has been questioned by Fischer and Minden. Sorokin's figure shows two empty sporangia (one with three zoospores near the orifice) and another in which four zoospores occupy only a small part of the available space. It is possible that the sporangium on which the four-spored character was based was already partly emptied.

? ENTOPHLYCTIS WORONICHINII Jaczewski

Opredelitel gribov.... I. Fikomitsety, p. 44. 1931

Sporangium of irregular shape and 19.8–13.7 μ in diameter or rounded and 10–11 μ in diameter, wall of two layers, colorless, 2–4 μ thick.

In zoospores of *Vaucheria sessilis*, *V. geminata*, RUSSIA.

DIPLOPHLYCTIS SCHROETER

Engler and Prantl, Natürlichen Pflanzenfam., 1 (1): 78. 1892 (1893)

(Fig. 23, p. 385)

Thallus endobiotic, monocentric, eucarpic, consisting of the rudiment of the sporangium, an apophysis, and an extensive branched rhizoidal system, the cyst of the infecting zoospore evanescent; sporangium inoperculate, with a discharge tube and an apophysis, zoospores posteriorly uniflagellate, with a single globule, fully formed within the sporangium, emerging through a pore produced at the tip of the discharge tube; resting spore thick-walled, borne like the sporangium, sexually or asexually formed, upon germination functioning either as a sporangium or a prosporangium.

Species of *Diplophlyctis* are primarily inhabitants of moribund and dead members of the Characeae and, less often, the Chlorophyceae. Indeed, it is difficult to find old plants of *Nitella* and *Chara* in which one species, *D. intestina*, is not present in abundance.

As indicated in the diagnosis, two methods of resting-spore germination have been described in the literature. Zopf (1884: 195) states that in *Diplophlyctis intestina* the resting structure becomes transformed into a sporangium and produces a discharge tube through which the zoospores emerge. Karling (1936b: 469), on the other hand, who has observed many instances of germination in this same species, states that the contents emerge through a pore and form a thin-walled zoosporangium sessile to the thick-walled structure. Germination in the latter manner has been witnessed in *Diplophlyctis laevis* (Richards, 1951).

Evidence for sexual reproduction preceding resting-spore formation in *Diplophlyctis intestina* has been presented by Sparrow (1936d). More recently, Haskins (1950) furnished confirmation for it in the case of another species. He observed that in *D. sexualis* bodies resembling zoospores, which had germinated within small sporangia ("male gametangia"), produced rhizoidal systems which penetrate the wall of the structure bearing them and anastomose with the rhizoidal system of the receptive thallus. The female, after receiving the contents of the male, formed a resting spore. Since asexual resting spores were recorded also it is, of course, a question whether here the "sexuality" is not, in fact, a process of "rejuvenescence" similar to that noted in *Chytridium lagenaria* (Sparrow, 1936a). Cytological evidence is needed to settle this point, but support for the occurrence of sexuality is given by the failure of the unfused male and female plants to develop.

As in *Entophlyctis*, the order in which rudiments of the thallus in members of *Diplophlyctis* develop varies. Schenk (1858b), Zopf (1884), and Karling (1928b) all show clearly that in *D. intestina* in a characean substratum, the rudiment of the sporangium is immediately laid down at the tip of the penetration tube by the zoospore and that the apophysis, from which the rhizoidal system emerges, is formed next. The sequence is illustrated in a series of continuous observations by Zopf. A further study by Karling (1930) on this species indicates that the rudiments of the rhizoidal system were first to originate from the germ tube, then those of the sporangia were formed at the tip of one of the diverticulae. Lastly, the apophysis appeared as a swelling between a sporangium and its concomitant rhizoidal element. This second type of development has also been reported in *D. laevis* by Sparrow (1939a) and Richards (1951). In his study of *D. sexualis* Haskins (1950), however, states that "at the end of a branch (usually a short lateral one) of a germ tube from the encysted zoospores, a tiny more or less dumb-bell-shaped

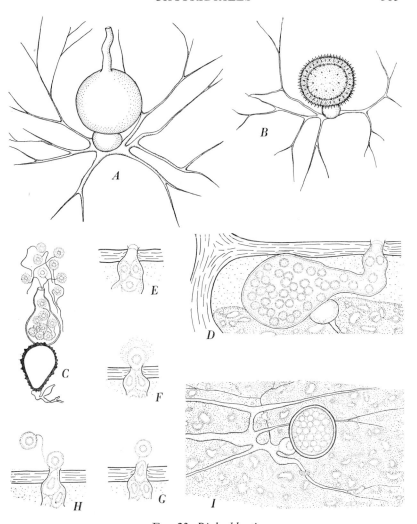

FIG. 23. *Diplophlyctis*

A–C. Diplophlyctis intestina (Schenk) Schroeter in *Nitella*: *A*, empty apophysate sporangium with discharge tube; *B*, spiny resting spore; *C*, discharging sporangium formed at germination of resting spore. *D–I. Diplophlyctis laevis* Sparrow in *Cladophora*: *D*, mature sporangium with discharge tube opening on outside surface of algal wall; *E–H*, successive stages in discharge of zoospores; *I*, resting spore.

(*A–B*, Sparrow, 1932b; *C*, Karling, 1936b; *D–I*, Sparrow, 1939a)

swelling appears. The distal part of the swelling enlarges more rapidly than the proximal part and becomes the rudiment of the zoosporangium, while the proximal swelling enlarges to become the apophysis. The apophysis, then, appears at the same time as the sporangium." We are inclined to believe that all observations reported are correct and that in this genus, as elsewhere, nothing is static about the precise sequence of development of parts of the thallus.

KEY TO THE SPECIES OF DIPLOPHLYCTIS

Resting spore spiny or verrucose
  Resting spore spiny
    Sporangium typically with one discharge tube
      Resting spore typically spherical, subspherical, or broadly ellip-
      soidal; primarily in moribund or dead members of the
      Characeae .... *D. intestina*, p. 386
      Resting spore typically oval and somewhat bean-shaped; sapro-
      phytic on vegetable debris .... *D. amazonense*, p. 388
    Sporangium typically with more than one discharge tube
      D. sexualis, p. 389
  Resting spore verrucose .... *D. verrucosa*, p. 390
Resting spore smooth .... *D. laevis*, p. 390

DIPLOPHLYCTIS INTESTINA (Schenk) Schroeter

Engler and Prantl, Natürlichen Pflanzenfam., 1 (1): 78. 1892

(Fig. 23 A-C, p. 385)

Rhizidium intestinum Schenk, pro parte, Ueber das Vorkommen contractiler Zellen im Pflanzenreiche, p. 5, figs. 1-9. Würzburg, 1858.
Entophlyctis intestina (Schenk) Fischer, Rabenhorst. Kryptogamen-Fl.,
  1 (4): 116. 1892.

Sporangium predominantly spherical, subspherical, pyriform, or obliquely ellipsoidal, occasionally somewhat cylindrical, clavate, or irregular, variable in size, up to 80 μ or more in diameter, wall thin, smooth, colorless, discharge tube generally single, cylindrical, slightly tapering distally, of variable length, apophysis appearing basal, variable in shape and size, usually spherical, subspherical, or pyriform and 3–6 μ in diameter; rhizoids richly branched, extensive, up to 400 μ in length, ordinarily arising from a single short basal axis, the main branches stout, tips delicate; zoospores variable in number, spherical or somewhat ovoid, 4–6 μ in diameter, with a large, colorless, eccentric globule and a long flagellum, emerging individually through a pore at the tip of the discharge tube and swimming directly away or forming a temporary motionless mass at the orifice before escape, movement swimming or amoeboid; resting spore spherical, subspherical, or broadly ellipsoidal, variable in size, up to 22 by 28 μ, wall thick, yellowish or brown, the outer surface covered by minute short sharp spines, apophysis and rhizoidal system like those of the sporangium, upon germination either forming a tube and functioning as a zoosporangium or becoming a prosporangium and producing a sessile thin-walled zoosporangium.

Saprophytic or weakly parasitic in dead or moribund internodal cells of *Nitella flexilis*, Schenk (*loc. cit.*), *N. mucronata*, *N. flexilis*, Zopf (1884: 191, pl. 19, figs. 1–15), GERMANY; *Nitella tenuissima*, *Chara poly-canthum*, Dangeard (1886a: 296, pl. 13, figs. 20–23; 1890–91b: 91, pl. 4, figs. 13–18), FRANCE; "Characeae," Petersen (1909: 413; 1910: 548), DENMARK; *Chara coronata*, *C. fragilis*, *C. delicatula*, *Nitella flexilis*, *N. glomerulifera*, *Lamprothamnus alopecuroides*, *Lychnothamnus bar-batus*, Karling (1928b: 204, text figs. 1–2, pl. 14; 1930: 770, text figs. 1–2, pls. 46–49; 1936b: 469, text figs. 1–8; 1941b: 108; 1942c: 621; 1948c: 509), *Nitella flexilis*, Sparrow (1932b: 283, figs. 2 e, j; 1936d: 321, figs. 1–2; 1952d: 767), UNITED STATES; *Nitella sp.*, Shen and Siang (1948: 183), CHINA; *Nitella sp.*, Sparrow (1952a: 37), CUBA; *Nitella sp.*, Canter (1953: 289), GREAT BRITAIN.

In spite of the fact that this species has been the object of a considerable amount of study there remain certain features in need of further clarification. Sparrow (1936d), as mentioned earlier, presented evidence for a sexual process essentially like that found in *Siphonaria*, *Rhizo-closmatium*, and *Asterophlyctis*. Small undeveloped thalli 10 μ high by 5 μ in diameter, with a small rhizoidal system, were almost constantly associated with the resting spores. In particularly good specimens there was a definite connection between the rhizoidal systems of the two types of structures. Anastomosis was usually achieved by the rhizoid of the larger body, into which the contents of the smaller presumably passed. Sparrow's observations seemed to indicate that connection of the two and transference of material took place at a very early stage in thallus development.

Dangeard (1886a) noted that the sporangium alone, or the sporangium and the apophysis, may occasionally be epibiotic.

DIPLOPHLYCTIS AMAZONENSE (Karling), comb. nov.

Nephrochytrium amazonensis Karling, Mycologia, 36: 352, figs. 1-28. 1944.

"Thallus monocentric, usually intramatrical; consisting of a sporangium or resting spore subtended by an apophysis from which arises an extensive, richly branched rhizoidal system. Sporangia hyaline, smooth, pyriform, 12–30 × 50–140 μ, almost spherical, 10–60 μ in diam., obclavate, flattened and often somewhat kidney-shaped with a short, 5 × 10 μ, or an elongate, 5–7 × 20-130 μ, tapering exit tube. Tip of tube swelling and softening to form a plug of hyaline material; operculum subsequently developed down in exit tube; operculum shallow saucer-shaped, deeper bowl- or cup- and occasionally somewhat cone-shaped, 4–7 μ in diam. Zoospores emerging fully developed and forming a globular mass at the exit orifice before dispersing; spherical, 5–6.5 μ, with a large refractive globule and a 35–38 μ long flagellum. Apophysis oval, 5–12 × 8–22 μ, flattened, obpyriform, or almost spherical. Rhizoidal system arising from base of apophysis, extending over a radius of 80–400 μ, main axis up to 8 μ in diam., richly branched. Resting spores usually oval and somewhat bean-shaped, 20–28 × 30–40 μ, almost spherical, 15–35 μ, and sometimes irregular; content coarsely granular and brown; wall dark brown, 2–3 μ thick, usually spiny, sometimes verrucose or covered with numerous short setae, rarely smooth; functioning as prosporangia in germination" (Karling, *loc. cit.*).

Saprophytic in decaying vegetable debris, Karling (*loc. cit.*), BRAZIL; on onion skin and cellophane from soil, Karling (1948c: 509), UNITED STATES.

In view of the variation in sequence of thallus development in *Diplophlyctis* and Haskins' (1950) subsequent observations on the inconstancy of formation of endoopercula in *D. sexualis*, placement of the Brazilian species in this genus seems justified. Indeed, prior doubts as to its affinities with *Nephrochytrium* were expressed by its author.

DIPLOPHLYCTIS SEXUALIS Haskins

Mycologia, 42: 775, figs. 1-10. 1950

"Asexual thallus monocentric, usually intramatrical, consisting of a sporangium or resting spore subtended by an apophysis from which arises a somewhat coarse, branched rhizoidal system. Sporangia hyaline, smooth, spherical, 50–170 μ in diameter, or variously shaped, walls not staining with zinc chloroiodide. Exit tubes one to several, short and broad, or occasionally very long up to 150 μ. Dehiscence by deliquescence of tips of exit-tubes or by tip of tube softening to form an evanescent gelatinous plug beneath which an "endo-operculum" may or may not develop. Endo-opercula, when formed, shallow saucer-shaped, to cone-shaped with long spine. Zoöspores spherical to sub-spherical, 5–6 μ in diameter each with single, large, prominent, highly refractive globule and a 30–40 μ flagellum, remaining temporarily motionless immediately after discharge, intermittently amoeboid. A-pophysis spherical or variously shaped, joined to sporangium by a wide isthmus. Sporangium and apophysis originating at the same time at the end of an usually short branch of the germination tube from the encysted zoöspore. Rhizoidal system usually arising from basal half of apophysis, stout, extensive, and much branched. Resting spores spherical, 16–23 μ in diameter; contents coarsely globular; wall thick, layered, dark brown, densely spiny, spines short and stout to long and hair-like; formed asexually or only after sexual fusion. Female thalli as for resting spores and remaining abortive unless fertilized. Male thalli consisting of a gametangium, apophysis and rudimentary sparsely-branched rhizoidal system. Gametangium hyaline, thin-walled containing 4 to many gametes. Gametes encysting *in situ* producing fine sparsely-branched rhizoid-like germination tubes which penetrate gametangium wall to anastomose with rhizoidal system of female thallus, through which anastomosis the content of the male cell passes to enter the female cell, which immediately develops into normal, brown, spiny-walled resting spore. Resting spores functioning as pro-sporangia in germination, each producing one sessile, thin-walled zoosporangium" (Haskins, *loc. cit.*).

Saprophytic in decaying vegetable debris, boiled leaves of maize, cellophane, and lens paper (Haskins, *loc. cit.*), CANADA, UNITED STATES. See the discussion on endooperculation, page 63.

DIPLOPHLYCTIS VERRUCOSA Kobayasi and Ookubo

Nagaoa, 4: 58, fig. 45. 1954

Zoosporangia few, endobiotic, globose, depressed globose or ellipsoidal, thin-walled, hyaline, smooth, 20–50 μ in diameter, with a single apical, basal or lateral, cylindrical, erect or somewhat curved discharge tube about 35–55 μ long; zoospores numerous, hyaline, about 6 μ in diameter with a single refractive globule and long posterior flagellum; apophysis small, subglobose, thin-walled, hyaline, the rhizoids basally or bilaterally attached, tapering and dichotomously branched; resting spores globose, 40–50 μ in diameter, with a thick, verrucose wall, pale yellow-brown, with a large oil globule, the apophysis and rhizoidal system like that of the sporangium, germination not observed.

Parasitic in *Chara fragilis*, JAPAN (Ookubo).

Very distinct from the other species in the constantly verrucose character of the resting-spore wall; less obviously so in the sporangial stage.

DIPLOPHLYCTIS LAEVIS Sparrow

Occ. Papers Boston Soc. Nat. Hist., 8: 296. 1937; Papers Mich. Acad. Sci., Arts, Letters, 24 (1938), Pt. I: 121, pl. 1, figs. 1-14. 1939

(Fig. 23 D-I, p. 385)

Sporangium broadly or irregularly pyriform, 20–35 μ long by 13–35 μ in diameter at the base, with a subspherical, subsporangial, or lateral apophysis 4–5 μ in diameter, from which one or several stout branching rhizoids emerge, discharge tube broad, tapering, of variable length (up to 50 μ), its tip penetrating the host wall and generally protruding only slightly beyond it; zoospores spherical, 7 μ in diameter, with a single colorless oil globule 3 μ in diameter and a posterior flagellum 30 μ long; resting spore spherical or ellipsoidal, 11–18 by 12–18 μ, with a smooth wall about 2 μ thick surrounding the contents, in which are many oil globules of approximately the same size, and a spherical apophysis 5–7 μ in diameter, at germination functioning as a prosporangium.

Saprophytic in cells of *Cladophora sp.* (*loc. cit.*), *Nitella sp.*, Sparrow (1952d: 767), UNITED STATES; *Chara sp.*, vegetable debris, Richards (1951: 487, figs. 1–19, pl. 24), GREAT BRITAIN; substratum? plant tissue, Ookubo (1954: 58, fig. 46), JAPAN.

PHLYCTORHIZA HANSON

Amer. J. Bot., 33: 732. 1946

(Fig. 24 E–G, p. 396)

"Thallus monocentric, eucarpic, intramatrical. Zoosporangia developing as an outgrowth of the germ tube while the zoospore usually persists as a cyst. Rhizoidal system oriented on the base and periphery of the sporangium, frequently anastomosing. Zoosporangia variously shaped, with one basal, lateral, or apical exit papilla. Zoospores posteriorly uniflagellate. Resting spores variously shaped, thick walled, and apparently developing in the same manner as the sporangia; upon germination functioning as prosporangia" (Hanson, *loc. cit.*).

On insect integuments.

The account of development in *Phlyctorhiza endogena* is adapted from Hanson (1946). Upon germination the zoospore forms a stout germ tube, which penetrates the basement membrane of the integument and develops short irregular branches. Thalli are dorsiventrally differentiated, with the dorsal surface *Rhizophlyctis*-like, but not the ventral, which is traversed by rhizoids. The sporangial rudiment is believed to begin as a unilateral vesiculation of an incipient rhizoid. It becomes a thin flattened extension between the branches. The thalli strikingly resemble a bat's wing or duck's foot, with the sporangia corresponding to the web, the ventral parts of the rhizoids to the digits.

As the rhizoids grow out radially (more or less in one plane) the layers of the integument are spread apart. Vesiculation continues along the paths opened up in the substratum and the incipient sporangia are irregular or sometimes stellate in surface view. After vesiculation ceases the sporangia expand and become more regular, often circular, in shape. Sometimes with approaching maturity, additional vesiculations may occur on the dorsal side of the rhizoids. A few of them contain nuclei obtained apparently from the incipient sporangia. If the nuclei remain and multiply, septa form. Secondary sporangia then develop and the thallus becomes polycentric. Such instances, however, are the exception; only three were observed. Early stages of resting spores cannot be distinguished from sporangia. No sexuality was evident.

It should be noted that the remarkable method of formation of the sporangium by vesiculation along the rhizoids, a striking feature well borne out by the figures and description of development, is not referred to in the generic diagnosis.

PHLYCTORHIZA ENDOGENA Hanson

Amer. J. Bot., 33: 732, figs. 1-49. 1946

(Fig. 24 E-G, p. 396)

"Zoosporangia hyaline, smooth, flattened, depressed, usually somewhat kidney-shaped, 6×10–33.6×58.2 μ, frequently oval, 7×12–26.2×42 μ, irregular, 11×20–29×36 μ; with one basal, rarely lateral or apical exit pore, 2.9–4×5.2–7.5 μ in diameter. Sporangia developing as an outgrowth of the germ tube while the zoospore usually persists as a cyst. Rhizoidal system oriented on the base and periphery of the sporangium, often vesiculate at point of origin, frequently anastomosing, extending from 15–300 μ beyond the sporangium; vesiculate portions of rhizoids 3–8 μ in diameter. Zoospores elliptical, 2.2–2.9×2.9–3.7 μ, with one centric or excentric refractive globule; flagellum 20–26 μ long, emerging and swarming in a vesicle outside of the sporangium. Resting spores oval, 8.6–12×15–20 μ, reniform, 8.2–16.4×10.4–21.6 μ, irregular, 12–21.2×24–29 μ, with light golden to deep amber, smooth undulate, or tuberculate walls, 0.746–1.5 μ thick; contents densely and coarsely granular; upon germination functioning as prosporangium" (Hanson, *loc. cit.*).

Mosquito integuments, remains of mayflies, dragonflies, and gnats, UNITED STATES.

Two other species, *Phlyctorhiza variabilis* Karling (1947a: 27, figs. 1–48) and *P. peltata* Sparrow (1950: 52, figs. 1–7) have been referred to this genus.

The first fungus, a keratinophilic form, differs markedly from the type in that the sporangium does not arise by vesiculation of the dorsal side of the rhizoid but, typically (as in *Entophlyctis*), from the germ tube. Karling (1946e) had originally applied the binomial *Perirhiza endogena* n.g., n.sp., to this fungus, without descriptions. Later (1947a), he considered it tentatively a species of *Phlyctorhiza*. Further study (1951a) of material, from Israeli soil, which he considered to be *P. variabilis*, indicated that it had, in contrast to his original isolate, a strong tendency for polycentricity. He presents convincing evidence that the predominantly monocentric strains and the strongly polycentric one are actually the same organism and concludes, from this and other morphological evidence, that they are more closely related to *Catenaria* (of the Blastocladiales). Since, however, data on their sexuality, resting-spore formation, germination, and so forth, are as yet unavailable, he retains the fungus in the Chytridiales.

The second one, Sparrow's Cuban fungus, in which polycentricity is very rare and a discharge tube is lacking, appears more nearly to agree with the concept of *Phlyctorhiza*. There is some evidence that the sporangia arise by vesiculation of the rhizoids, but this is not certain. It is, therefore, kept as a questionable member of the genus until further observations are made.

Probably both Karling's and Sparrow's fungi should be removed from *Phlyctorhiza*.

***

? *Phlyctorhiza variabilis* Karling

Amer. J. Bot., 34: 27, figs. 1-43. 1947

Perirhiza endogena Karling, *nom. nud.*, Amer. J. Bot., 33, suppl. no. 3, p. 219. 1946.

"Thallus eucarpic, monocentric [or polycentric],[1] usually wholly intramatrical. Sporangia variable in size and shape; spherical (8–70 μ), oval (6–30 × 8–50 μ), oblong, narrowly or broadly fusiform (10–15 × 14–45 μ), pyriform, obpyriform, irregular, angular, or somewhat stellate, with one, rarely two or three exit tubes, 4–10 μ wide by 10–90 μ

[1] In the light of Karling's (1951a) study, "or polycentric" has been substituted for the "rarely polycentric" of the original description.

long. Zoospores oval or oblong (2–2.5 × 3.8–4.5 μ) with non-guttulate, finely granular content and a slightly tapering posterior end; flagellum 12–14 μ long. Rhizoids richly branched, usually arising from several points on surface of sporangium, main axes up to 8 μ in diam. and extending for a distance of 250 μ. Resting spores (?) or thick-walled, dormant sporangia of same size and shape as zoosporangia, hyaline, smooth; functioning directly as zoosporangia in germination" (Karling, *loc. cit.*).

Saprophytic in dead keratinized tissues of animals, Karling (*loc. cit.*, 1948c), BRAZIL, UNITED STATES; Karling (1951b), ALASKA; Karling (1951b), ISRAEL; from soil, substrate?, Gaertner (1954b: 22), EGYPT, NORTHWEST AFRICA, WEST AFRICA, EQUATORIAL EAST AFRICA, SOUTH AFRICA.

See also remarks under the following species.

? Phlyctorhiza peltata Sparrow
J. Wash. Acad. Sci., 40: 50, figs. 1-7. 1950

Thallus monocentric, rarely polycentric, resting on the surface of the substratum; rhizoids arising from several places on the thallus, 3 μ or less in diameter at point of origin, tapering and moderately branched distally; zoosporangia irregularly and elongately peltate, 15–28 μ along the long axis, 5–12 μ along the shortest; at maturity forming a single papilla, which at maturity deliquesces to form a sessile exit pore 5 μ in diameter; zoospores ovoid, 4 by 2 μ, with a minute refractive droplet and a long posterior flagellum attached to the narrower end of the body; resting spores not observed.

Saprophytic on snakeskin in stream, CUBA.

If this proves to be a species of *Phlyctorhiza*, it certainly differs strikingly from *P. endogena* in the shape of its sporangia.

This species and the preceding one seem to be better accommodated in *Entophlyctis* rather than *Phlyctorhiza*, reserving the latter genus for types which, as emphasized by Hanson (1946b) in her comparison with *Rhizophlyctis*, develop their sporangia by vesication or expansion of elements of the rhizoidal system.

MITOCHYTRIDIUM Dangeard

Bull. Soc. Mycol. France, 27: 202. 1911

(Fig. 24 C, p. 396)

Thallus endobiotic, eucarpic, monocentric, consisting of a broad, cylindrical, and unbranched, branched, or irregularly lobate tube, the rudiment of the zoosporangium, from which arise one or more delicate axes which become divided distally into rhizoids, wall giving a cellulose reaction with chloriodide of zinc; sporangium inoperculate, formed from the tubular part of the thallus which is cut off by cross walls from the rhizoids; zoospores posteriorly uniflagellate, with a single globule, completely formed within the sporangium and escaping successively to the outside by one or more short tubes which penetrate the wall of the substratum; resting spore (?) endobiotic, with rhizoids, apparently asexually formed, germination not observed.

A monotypic genus, members of which are parasitic in desmids.

The precise method of development is not known with absolute certainty. The observations of Couch (1935c: 293) indicate that the tubular part of the thallus—the rudiment of the future sporangium—is laid down before the purely vegetative part, that is, the rhizoids, and soon becomes separated from the more or less elongated penetration tube.

Both Dangeard and Couch state that thick-walled endobiotic resting bodies are formed. These appear, in contrast to the monocentric sporangial stage, to be polycentric in origin, several being produced on a common rhizoidal system. If both investigators did not, in fact, have a mixture of *Mitochytridium* and *Catenaria* (see Couch, *op. cit.*, pl. 62, fig. 9), this is an extraordinary condition, not found in any other of the chytrids except *Physoderma*.

The genus appears more nearly related to *Entophlyctis* than to any of the Cladochytriaceae, where it is usually placed.

Mitochytridium ramosum Dangeard

Bull. Soc. Mycol. France, 27: 202, fig. 1. 1911

Sporangium nearly isodiametric throughout, straight and unbranched or branched, twisted, and bearing short lobulations, up to 660 μ in

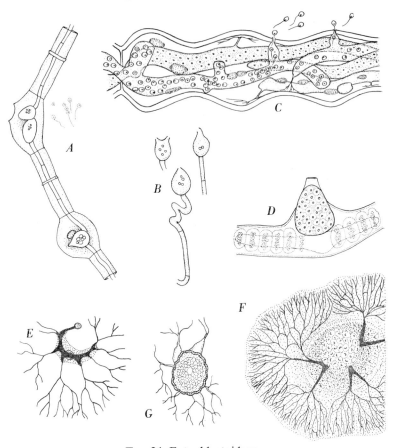

Fɪɢ. 24. Entophlyctoideae

A–B. Aphanistis oedogoniorum Sorokin in *Oedogonium sp.*: *A*, plants bearing sporangia in oögonia of host; a group of zoospores is shown to right of filament; *B*, different shapes assumed by zoosporangia. *C. Mitochytridium ramosum* Dangeard in *Docidium sp.*, portion of desmid cell with parts of several sporangia. *D. Rhizosiphon crassum* Scherffel in filament of *Filarszkya sp.*, mature sporangium with already opened discharge tube, resting laterally on broad prosporangium. *E–G. Phlyctorhiza endogena* Hanson in insect integument: *E*, early stage in vesication of rhizoidal system to produce sporangial rudiment, showing relationship between zoospore cyst, rhizoids and rudiment; *F*, discharge of zoospores of a mature sporangium; *G*, tuberculate resting spore with vesiculate rhizoids.

(*A–B*, Sorokin, 1883; *C*, after Couch, 1935c; *D*, Scherffel, 1926a; *E–G*, Hanson, 1946b)

length, 10–30 μ in diameter, wall somewhat thick, smooth, colorless; rhizoids extensive, branched, arising from main axes generally formed at the extremities of the sporangial rudiment; zoospores somewhat ovoid or spherical, 4–5 μ in diameter, with a colorless eccentric globule and a long flagellum, escaping successively through one or more short discharge tubes which penetrate the wall of the alga but do not extend beyond it; resting spores (?) spherical or elongated, thick-walled, 12–25 μ in diameter, several formed on the same thallus and connected to it by one or more rhizoids, the bases of which persist as spiny or blunt protuberances after the spore is free from the thallus, germination not observed.

Parasitic on *Docidium ehrenbergii*, Dangeard (*loc. cit.*), FRANCE; *Docidium sp.*, Couch (1935c: 293, pl. 62, figs. 1–12), UNITED STATES.

Couch noted that the thallus varies from a short unbranched structure to a long branched twisted body that may extend throughout the entire length of the desmid cell (660 μ). More than one thallus may be formed in a single host cell. Couch believed that the fungus was closely allied to the polycentric *Catenaria*. It appears, however, to be an *Entophlyctis*-like organism with a tubular reproductive rudiment.

RHIZOSIPHON SCHERFFEL

Arch. Protistenk., 54: 189. 1926

(Figs. 24 D, p. 396; 11 K-M, p. 110)

Thallus endobiotic, monocentric, eucarpic, polyphagous, consisting of a central structure at the tip of the penetration tube of the zoospore—the rudiment of the prosporangium—from which may emerge two broad isodiametric unbranched hypha-like vegetative structures on opposite sides (occasionally one or sometimes lacking); sporangium inoperculate, partly or wholly extramatrical, formed as an outgrowth of the prosporangium; zoospores posteriorly uniflagellate, with one or more globules, fully formed in the sporangium, escaping through a short discharge tube; resting spore thick-walled, with one or many globules, endobiotic, with or without a vegetative system, asexually or (?) sexually formed, upon germination functioning as a prosporangium.

Parasites of blue-green algae.

RHIZOSIPHON CRASSUM Scherffel

Arch. Protistenk., 54: 189, pl. 9, figs. 41-55. 1926

(Figs. 11 K,ᵣp. 110; 24 D, p. 396)

Prosporangium spherical or broadly fusiform when intercalary, somewhat clavate when terminal, on a broad tubular vegetative system; sporangium broadly and somewhat irregularly pyriform and 14–18 µ in diameter or flasklike and 9–26 µ high by 6.5–12 µ in diameter, arising laterally from an intercalary prosporangium or apically from a terminal one, with a broad conical prominent discharge tube, wall thin, smooth, colorless; zoospores spherical, 3 µ in diameter, with an inconspicuous faintly refractive basal globule 1 µ in diameter or with several highly refractive granules, with a posterior flagellum 18 µ long, escaping singly and amoeboidly through the open apex of the discharge tube and remaining for a time near the orifice before darting away; resting spore round-oblong, broadly fusiform and 10–12 by 15–25 µ, or nearly spherical (ellipsoidal) and 6–12 by 8–15 µ, wall double-contoured, smooth, colorless, contents with many colorless coarse highly refractive globules, upon germination forming a narrowly pyriform sessile sporangium with a smooth colorless thin wall.

Parasitic on *Filarszkya sp.*, Scherffel (*loc. cit.*), HUNGARY; *Anabaena spiroides* var. *crassa*, *Anabaena sp.*, *A. affinis* var. *intermedia*, coll. Griffiths (1925), Canter (1951: 129, figs. 1–3, pl. 8, pl. 9a), GREAT BRITAIN; *Anabaena spp.*, coll. Rohde, Canter (*loc. cit.*), SWEDEN.

Rhizosiphon crassum has a remarkable effect on the coloration of the filaments of *Filarszkya*. The infected cell and adjacent cells turn deep wine-red (see under "Parasitism," p. 116). Such a color change has not been noted in *Anabaena* (Canter, 1951: 135). An unusual feature of this species' development is the production of a strongly vacuolate foamy stage in the sporangium just prior to zoospore formation, a condition reminiscent of the Saprolegniales.

Scherffel considered that, in spite of the hypha-like nature of the vegetative system, this fungus was a chytrid allied to *Polyphagus* and *Saccomyces*. In all three genera the sporangium is an outgrowth of a prosporangium, but *Rhizosiphon crassum* differs from the other two in having a discharge tube and an endobiotic, apparently asexually formed, resting spore. Its method of development is unlike that in *Polyphagus*.

Canter (1951) gives a clear account of the development of *Rhizosiphon crassum* on *Anabaena*. According to her, the zoospore penetrates the mucilage sheath of the host, encysts, and produces a fine thread, the tip of which enters the host cell. The contents of the encysted spore flow through the tube and form a walled globose structure. The latter enlarges and from opposite sides two broad undulate blunt extensions protrude which pass through several host cells. The central spherical part of the thallus is the rudiment of the prosporangium. At maturity of the thallus, a small bud from the prosporangium emerges from the host cell just beside the point of penetration of the germ tube. This bud, the incipient sporangium, enlarges as the contents of the prosporangium and its outgrowths pass into it. The sporangium, which is external, as it matures becomes somewhat flask-shaped due to the development of a broad apical discharge tube. Its contents, at first granular, at maturity bear many irregularly placed, minute, refractive globules. The apex of the discharge tube becomes filled with a clear gelatinous material and, upon maturity, bulges out, expands, and deliquesces. The zoospores then emerge rapidly and individually.

How the resting spores develop is not yet clear. Not until a late stage are they distinguishable from the prosporangia. Pairs of encysted zoospores that are attached, in some instances, by long slender penetration tubes to the resting spore strongly suggest some sort of sexual process, but there is no definite evidence for it in *Rhizosiphon crassum*. The mature resting spore has a smooth, thickened wall and many globules. According to Scherffel (1926a) at germination it functions as a prosporangium.

Canter regards Whiffen's (1944) assignment of *Rhizosiphon* to the Polyphagoideae as hardly tenable, because the thallus arises at the tip of a germ tube. Rather, she says, in Whiffen's scheme it clearly belongs in the Diplophlyctoideae.

RHIZOSIPHON ANABAENAE (Rodhe et Skuja) Canter [1]

Ann. Bot. London (N.S.), 15: 141, figs. 4, 6-8, pl. 9, B-D, pl. 10. 1951

(Fig. 11 L, p. 110)

Phlyctidium anabaenae Rodhe and Skuja, Symbolae Botanicae Upsaliensis, 9 (3): 379, pl. 39, figs. 9-12. 1948.

Phlyctidium anabaenae Fott, Věstník Královské České Společnosti Nauk. Třída Mat.-Přirodovedĕcká Ročnik, 1950 (4): 4, figs. 7-14. 1951.

"Endobiotic prosporangium spherical, 5–11 μ in diameter, arising as a swelling from the tip of the germ-tube of the zoospore. Sporangium pear- (8–13 μ high by 4.6–8.5 μ in diameter), sack-, or retort-shaped (8–14 μ high by 18–27 μ long) with a mucilaginous dehiscence papilla. Resting-spore formation preceded by fusion of isogamous gametes, one of which has previously come to rest and ? germinated. Resting spore endobiotic, spherical to subspherical, 10–17 μ in diameter, with a thick, smooth, yellowish undulate wall; content consisting of several large globules" (Canter, *loc. cit.*).

Parasitic and causing hypertrophy of *Anabaena* in plankton, Rodhe and Skuja (*loc. cit.*), Sweden; *Anabaena affinis* var. *intermedia*, *A. spiroides*, Canter (1953: 287), GREAT BRITAIN.

In this species infection is confined to a single cell and no tubular outgrowths of the prosporangium are formed. Although this is not clear from Canter's description, the sporangium is transversely placed on the host cell, and is somewhat campylotropous or saddle-shaped, with a well-developed, lateral tubular part terminated by a discharge papilla.

Canter (1951), who studied this species from material furnished by Rodhe, noted that "Whereas the zoospore in *R. crassum* encysts on, or just within, the mucilage of the algal filament and produces a fine thread to the vegetative cell, the zoospore of *Phlyctidium* (*Rhizosiphon*) *anabaenae* always settles on a heterocyst. It then produces a short, lateral thread to an adjacent host cell." She concluded, therefore, that it was fairly certain that resting-spore formation was preceded by sexual reproduction. In this process two isogamous gametes adhere and encyst and the contents of both pass through a tube, formed by the receptive thallus, into the host cell where the resting spore is formed.

[1] See Paterson (*Mycologia*, 50:94. 1958).

IMPERFECTLY KNOWN SPECIES OF RHIZOSIPHON

? RHIZOSIPHON AKINETUM Canter

Trans. Brit. Mycol. Soc., 37: 123, text figs. 6-7, pls. 4, 5, figs. 1-3. 1954

(Fig. 11 M, p. 110)

"Thallus endobiotic, prosporangium oval to elongate-oval, 8.6–23 µ long and 5–11 µ high, arising as a swelling from the tip of the germ tube of the zoospore. Sporangium inoperculate (?) variable in shape, spherical or limoniform, 8–20 µ high and 6–8 µ broad, with a conspicuous papilla up to 2 µ high. Distal half of sporangium wall thick and covered with short rod-like markings. Empty zoospore case remaining on akinete or carried up on wall of sporangium. Zoospore 2.5–3 µ in diameter, content granular with several minute refractive globules. Resting spore formation preceded by fusion of isogamous gametes, one of which had previously come to rest and (?) germinated. Resting spore endobiotic, oval to elongate oval, 8–26 µ long and 7–16 µ high, with a thick smooth two-layered wall; content one or a few large globules. A triangle of highly refractive material occurs at the point of contact of the thickened thread from the gametes and the resting spore itself. Resting spore directly transformed into sporangium on germination" (Canter, *loc. cit.*).

Parasitic on akinetes of *Anabaena affinis* var. *intermedia* in the plankton, Canter (*loc. cit.*); *Anabaena affinis* var. *intermedia*, coll. Griffiths (1925), GREAT BRITAIN; *Anabaena macrospora*, coll. Fott, Canter (*loc. cit.*), CZECHOSLOVAKIA.

Because knowledge concerning sporangial discharge is lacking, Canter only tentatively places this fungus in *Rhizosiphon*. It is believed here that further observation of living material will validate assignment of the species to this genus.

APHANISTIS SOROKIN

Arch. Bot. Nord France, 2: 35. 1883 (separate)

(Fig. 24 A-B, p. 396)

Thallus endobiotic, monocentric, polyphagous, eucarpic, sterile part consisting of a branched or unbranched isodiametric septate filament;

sporangium inoperculate, terminal, separated by a cross wall from the vegetative part of the thallus, with or without one or more discharge tubes; zoospores posteriorly uniflagellate, with a single globule, escaping after the deliquescence of one or more papillae; resting spore not observed.

On *Oedogonium*.

Fischer, who put the genus in the Hyphochytriaceae, considered it too poorly known to place taxonomically, and in this Minden concurred. It seems likely that the presence of a septate "mycelium" bearing a zoosporangium which formed posteriorly uniflagellate zoospores was too bizarre to be acceptable to these monographers. The genus, though unusual, is adequately described and leaves no doubt as to just what type of organism Sorokin saw. A somewhat similar thallus is found in *Coenomyces* (p. 479).

APHANISTIS OEDOGONIORUM Sorokin

Arch. Bot. Nord France, 2: 35, fig. 43 a-d. 1883 (separate)[1]

(Fig. 24 A-B, p. 396)

Sporangium formed only in the oögonium of the alga, at first ovoid, later nearly spherical, with one or two (opposite) apical papillae which may be formed on more or less prolonged discharge tubes that are pointed toward the oögonial opening; vegetative system isodiametric, simple or branched, the septations occurring at relatively long intervals; resting stage not observed.

In filaments and oögonia of *Oedogonium sp.*, ASIATIC RUSSIA, EUROPEAN RUSSIA.

As in *Rhizophydium decipiens*, the fertilization pore of the oögonium was utilized for the setting free of the zoospores of the fungus into the outside medium.

IMPERFECTLY KNOWN SPECIES OF APHANISTIS

? APHANISTIS (?) PELLUCIDA Sorokin

Arch. Bot. Nord France, 2: 36, fig. 44. 1883 (separate)[2]

[1] See also *Revue Mycologique*, 11: 137, pl. 79, figs. 79-83, 85. 1889.
[2] *Ibid.*, fig. 84. 1889.

Sporangium terminal, ellipsoidal, with a sharp lateral beaklike discharge tube; vegetative system rudimentary, the few cells bearing lateral protrusions of variable extent; zoospores not observed; resting spore not observed.

In young plants of *Oedogonium sp.*, ASIATIC RUSSIA.

IMPERFECTLY KNOWN GENUS OF THE PHLYCTIDIACEAE

? ACHLYELLA LAGERHEIM

Hedwigia, 29: 144. 1890

(Fig. 19 F, p. 318)

Thallus epi- and endobiotic, monocentric, the epibiotic part consisting of the rudiment of the sporangium, the endobiotic part a broad rounded haustorium without rhizoids; sporangium inoperculate; zoospores emerging as nonflagellate individuals, encysting in a group at the orifice of the sporangium, emerging from the cyst through a minute pore, flagellation of the motile spores unknown; resting spore not observed.

On pollen of *Typha*.

Because of the lack of information on the development of the thallus and on the flagellation of the spore the relation of the genus to the chytrids is problematic.

? ACHLYELLA FLAHAULTII Lagerheim

Hedwigia, 29: 144, pl. 2, figs. 5-7. 1890

Sporangium inoperculate, sessile, narrowly pyriform, with a somewhat prolonged erect or bent apex, wall slightly thickened, colorless, smooth; haustorium broad, knoblike, thin-walled; zoospores discharged through a pore formed at the apex of the sporangium, cysts spherical; otherwise unknown.

On pollen of *Typha*, FRANCE.

RHIZIDIACEAE

Thallus predominantly interbiotic, monocentric, eucarpic, consisting of a well-developed, frequently extensive, rhizoidal system, of which at least the tips are endobiotic, and a reproductive rudiment which may be converted into a sporangium, prosporangium, gametangium, or resting spore; sporangium inoperculate; zoospores posteriorly uniflagellate (except where aplanospores are formed), often with a single globule; resting spore asexually formed or sexually by fusion of iso- or anisogamous aplanogametes which are never liberated into the outside medium, upon germination functioning as a sporangium or a prosporangium.

The family is characterized by the formation of an extensive, richly branched often polyphagous rhizoidal system and a reproductive rudiment, which ordinarily is not intimately connected with the substratum. It includes many of the most interesting and bizarre parasites of fresh-water algae, the curious group of species inhabiting the exuviae of aquatic insects, and many ubiquitous soil fungi. In some forms the zoospore bears a brightly colored globule. Where sexuality occurs, it takes place by the fusion of aplanogametes. The sexual process in *Polyphagus* (see under "Sexual Reproduction," p. 75) has been studied both morphologically and cytologically and is perhaps the best known among the chytrids. A type involving anastomosis of the rhizoids is found in *Rhizidium* and *Siphonaria*.

In Whiffen's (1944) classification all monocentric chytrids, whether operculate or inoperculate, are included in this family.

KEY TO THE SUBFAMILIES AND GENERA OF THE RHIZIDIACEAE

Body of encysted zoospore or aplanospore forming the rudiment of
    the sporangium; sexuality, where known, by conjugation of thalli
        by means of rhizoidal anastomosis ... Subfamily RHIZIDIOIDEAE, p. 405
Vegetative system consisting of an unbranched double-contoured
        tube; aplanospores formed . . . . SPOROPHLYCTIDIUM, p. 406
Vegetative system of richly branched rhizoids; zoospores formed
    Rhizoidal system arising predominantly from a single axis on the
        sporangium
        Sporangium wall smooth, persisting after spore discharge
            Main rhizoidal axis predominantly prolonged; resting spores
                asexually formed or sexually by rhizoidal anastomosis
                                   RHIZIDIUM, p. 407

SUBFAM. RHIZIDIOIDEAE

Reproductive rudiment formed from the body of the encysted zoospore or aplanospore; rhizoids arising directly from the body of the sporangium or from a single main axis, or an apophysis; resting spore asexually or sexually formed.

SPOROPHLYCTIDIUM Sparrow

Trans. Brit. Mycol. Soc., 18: 217. 1933; 21: 147. 1938

(Fig. 25 H, p. 411)

Thallus monocentric, eucarpic, consisting of a sporangial rudiment (the body of the encysted aplanospore) and a single unbranched nearly isodiametric tube, the tip of which is endobiotic; sporangium inoperculate, formed from the sporangial rudiment, spores (aplanospores) produced in the sporangium, at maturity liberated upon the formation of one or more discharge papillae, devoid of a flagellum; resting spore not known with certainty.

So far as is known, this is a monotypic genus, members of which live on fresh-water green algae.

Sporophlyctidium closely resembles *Sporophlyctis rostrata* in its main features. The relationship of the parasite to the alga is similar, as is the shape of the sporangium, the position of the discharge pore, and the nonflagellate zoospore (aplanospore). In *Sporophlyctidium*, however, the structure which makes contact with the host cell is never branched or rhizoidal, but unbranched and "inflated" (broad). Further, the spores of *Sporophlyctidium* are not formed in a vesicle (sporangium) extruded from the sporangium, but rather are segmented within the latter body and discharged individually. New investigations will be necessary before it can be said with absolute certainty that the resting spores found in the same material as the sporangia belong to the species.

SPOROPHLYCTIDIUM AFRICANUM Sparrow

Trans. Brit. Mycol. Soc., 18: 217. 1933; 21: 147, fig. 1 a-f. 1938

Sporangium narrowly obpyriform, smooth-walled, colorless, the narrower end continuous with the unbranched germ tube, 5 μ long by 3.5–4 μ in diameter, forming a single subapical pore through which the spherical aplanospores, 2 μ in diameter, with a single globule, are extruded; resting spore (?) similar in shape to the sporangium, 7 μ long by 4 μ in diameter, with a spherical companion cell 3 μ in diameter; germination not observed.

Parasitic on *Protoderma sp.*, coll. E. F. Warburg, NORTH AFRICA (TANGIER).

RHIZIDIUM BRAUN

Monatsber. Berlin Akad., 1856: 591; Flora, 14: 599. 1856

(Figs. 11 J, p. 110; 25 E-G, I-J, p. 411; 28 E-G, p. 440)

Thallus monocentric, eucarpic, consisting of a sporangial rudiment (the body of the encysted zoospore) and a broad main rhizoidal axis which bears secondary branches; zoosporangium inoperculate, formed from the sporangial rudiment; zoospores posteriorly uniflagellate, with a single globule, usually emerging imbedded in slime or surrounded by a vesicle through one or more pores, forming a motionless mass at the orifice, eventually separating and either swimming directly away or undergoing a period of collective swarming in a vesicle before escaping; resting spore thick-walled, borne like the sporangium on the thallus, asexually or sexually formed, upon germination functioning as a prosporangium.

On the cells and gelatinous sheaths of algae, in insect exuviae and vegetable debris.

The lack of figures in Braun's original account of the genus and the vagueness of his description have resulted in a variety of interpretations of *Rhizidium*. The confusion has largely centered around what was meant by the "two-celledness" (of the plant) which, together with "a prolonged main rhizoidal axis," was emphasized by Braun as characteristic of *R. mycophilum*, the type species. The accepted understanding of the type is that elaborated by Nowakowski (1876a: 87; 1876b: 215); see, however, page 410. The genus was understood by Fischer (1892: 106) to include the *Rhizophydium*-like forms with subsporangial apophyses now placed in *Phlyctochytrium*. Dangeard (1889b) interpreted *Rhizidium* similarly but assigned to it operculate as well as inoperculate species. Zopf (1884) evidently included in it all monocentric inoperculate chytrids with tapering rhizoids. Schroeter (1885: 193; 1893: 79) correctly interpreted the genus and re-established *Rhizidium* in its original sense.

As understood here, *Rhizidium* includes all monocentric chytrids that develop free in the medium, form their sporangium from the enlarged body of the encysted zoospore, and have a definite taproot-like main rhizoidal axis of variable length from which arise most of the rhizoids. No stress is laid upon the question of how many cells compose the whole plant.

The only authentic account of sexuality in *Rhizidium* comes from Canter (1950c). In *R. windermerense*, according to her, resting spores are formed after conjugation by means of rhizoidal anastomosis. As Canter describes the process, two spherical bodies (resembling encysted zoospores and regarded as sexual thalli) give rise to fine threads (conjugation tubes) that meet at their tips. Contents of the bodies pass from the sexual thalli along the tubes and a swelling is formed at their juncture. This is the incipient resting spore or zygote and the contained protoplasm is homogeneous and encompassed by a thin, colorless wall. No constant difference in size between the fusing sexual thalli is evidenced; when empty, they vary from 2.6 to 5.9 μ in diameter. At an early stage, sometimes even before the thalli lose their contents, a few fine branches are formed on the conjugation tubes which may extend to a host cell or into the surrounding mucilage. After protoplasmic fusion, a large rhizoidal system, similar in nature and almost in extent to that of the sporangium, is formed on the rudiment of the resting spore. The mature zygote is more or less spherical (14–17 μ) and has a thick, smooth wall which may become yellowish; the contents consist of numerous small globules.

The sexual process in *Rhizidium windermerense* resembles that in *Polyphagus*, especially *P. euglenae* Nowak. *sensu recent*. Bartsch, in which the resting spore develops subterminally (see Bartsch, 1945, figs. 9, 12). In *Polyphagus*, however, the conjugating thalli have already grown to considerable size before they fuse.

Karling (1944c), who observed resting-spore formation in several species of *Rhizidium*, makes no mention of their being sexually formed.

KEY TO THE SPECIES OF RHIZIDIUM

Sporangium predominantly with a single rhizoidal axis
  Sporangium appearing as a lateral outgrowth of the apex of the rhizoidal axis

RHIZIDIUM MYCOPHILUM Braun

Monatsber. Berlin Akad., 1856: 591; Flora, 14: 599. 1856

Sporangium elongate, saclike, arising laterally from near the apex of the somewhat obovate, pyriform, or citriform expanded tip of the rhizoidal axis, which it nearly equals in size; main rhizoidal axis sometimes with lateral rhizoids, tapering distally and becoming divided into delicate and repeatedly branched rhizoids; zoospores 5 μ or more in diameter with a well-defined globule and long flagellum; resting spore spherical, brownish, 16.5–20 μ in diameter, outer wall either covered by thick protuberances or almost spiny; germination not observed.

In the gelatinous colonial envelope of *Chaetophora*, GERMANY.

Rhizidium mycophilum is the type species of the genus. Our concept of it was built upon the earlier observations and figures of Nowakowski (1876a). Nowakowski identified with Braun's fungus a form having a rounded or somewhat elongate sporangium with a conspicuous prolongation terminating in a papilla. Its sporangium (up to three times as long as broad) rested at somewhat of an angle on the expanded upper part of a main rhizoidal axis which branched distally. After zoospore discharge the delicate sporangium wall soon collapsed and disintegrated, and the upper expanded part of the rhizoidal axis became converted into a second sporangium, cut off by a cross wall, in basipetalous fashion. Resting spores found in autumn were considered by him to belong to the sporangial stage. Some of them were ellipsoidal and had their outer wall densely covered with long hairs; at germination these functioned as prosporangia. Others, however (also figured in the process of germination), were completely smooth.

Braun's descriptions of his species (1856b, 1856c), even though not clear and lacking illustration, indicate that his fungus had a main rhizoidal axis distally divided into rhizoids and proximally expanded, and that from the upper end of this axis, which was sometimes provided with rhizoids, a lateral saclike elongated sporangium protruded. The fertile part was nearly equal in size to the upper expanded part and produced typical chytridiaceous zoospores. Sometimes, instead of such a zoosporangium, a smaller, spherical, brownish resting spore, with its outer wall covered with thick protuberances or spines (but not hairs), was produced. Nowakowski's fungus, therefore, differs in several features from Braun's. It does not have the sporangium strongly lateral in position or form new sporangia in basipetalous succession, and it has ovate or spherical resting spores whose outer walls are either covered with hairs or are smooth.

Karling (1944c) identified the sporangial stage of a *Rhizidium* that he collected, with Nowakowski's fungus. Emphasizing the differences in resting-spore characters between Braun's and Nowakowski's fungi, he combined his sporangial stage with Nowakowski's hairy type of resting spore (only seen by Nowakowski), and segregated them under a new binomial, *Rhizidium nowakowskii*. While he is correct in this, because of the differences in resting-spore features, Karling leaves unanswered the question of the proper disposition of the smooth-

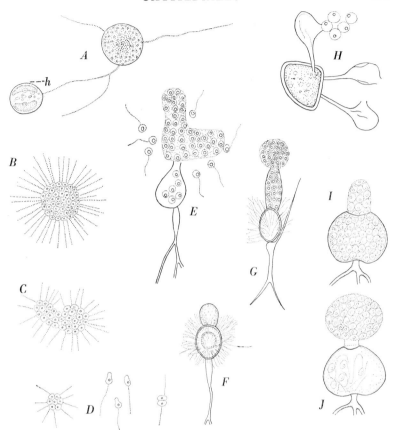

FIG. 25. Rhizidiaceae

A–D. Nowakowskia hormothecae Borzi parasitic on *Hormotheca*: *A*, nearly mature thallus; one branch of rhizoids is in contact with a host cell (*h*); *B*, mass of zoospores liberated upon dissolution of sporangium wall; *C–D*, stages in separation of zoospores from mass. *E–G. Rhizidium nowakowskii* Karling: *E*, discharging zoosporangium; the zoospores are escaping from slime mass in which they were imbedded at discharge; *F*, early stage in formation of zoosporangium at germination of resting spore; *G*, discharge of zoospores from zoosporangium formed at germination of resting spore. *H. Sporophlyctidium africanum* Sparrow on cell of *Protoderma*; one sporangium has just discharged spores which rest near orifice; two other empty sporangia are also shown. *I–J. Rhizidium ramosum* Sparrow in insect exuviae, two stages in discharge of short-stalked sporangia.

(*A–D*, Borzi, 1885; *E–G*, Nowakowski, 1876a; *H*, Sparrow, 1938a; *I–J*, Sparrow, 1937a)

walled resting spore which produced upon germination sporangia more like those of the nonsexual phase than did the hairy ones. Moreover, he failed to mention the basipetalous sporangial renewal, which is suggestive of a species of *Nowakowskiella*. Since Karling himself saw no resting spores and since Nowakowski figured two types, neither of which apparently occurred simultaneously with the sporangial stage, at best the concept of *R. nowakowskii* remains confused and synthetic. Whether the two types of resting spores actually represent two different species needs further proof. If the species is based on a mixture, it should be rejected.

RHIZIDIUM CHITINOPHILUM, sp. nov. [1]

Sporangium spherical or subspherical, 28–50 μ in diameter, with a smooth wall, colorless, appearing as a lateral outgrowth from the usually expanded proximal portion of the rhizoidal axis; rhizoidal system consisting of a stout main axis from which emerge branched rhizoids, its proximal portion somewhat expanded and forming an apophysis delimited by cross walls; zoospores spherical, 4 μ in diameter, or ellipsoidal and 5 μ long by 3 μ wide, with a single (rarely two) conspicuous, laterally placed, colorless globule and a flagellum, 30–33 μ long, emerging from a subapical or lateral pore in a compact subspherical mass, the individuals at first motionless but shortly undergoing a period of collective swarming, probably within a vesicle, during

---

[1] *Rhizidium chitinophilum*, sp. nov. — Sporangium globosum vel subglobosum, 28-50 μ diam., laeve, pellucidum, lateraliter ex parte axis rhizoidalis proxima oriens. Systema rhizoidale ex axe centrali et rhizoideis ramosis constans, parte proxima paulum expansa, apophyin inter septa transversalia formante. Zoosporae globosae, 4 μ diam., vel ellipsoidales, ca. 5 μ longae, 3 μ latae, emergentes ut massa compacta subglobosa, denique soluta; primum immobiles sed cito (probabiliter in vesicula) gregatim natantes et ad ultimum separatim dispersae, globulo singulo (raro 2) conspicuo excentrico pellucido; flagello 30-33 μ longo ex poro subapicali vel laterali protruso. Spora perdurans nondum visa.

Saprophytum in exuviis insectorum familiarum Ephemeridarum et Chironomidarum, United States, praecipue lectum prope locum dictum, "Clark's Pond, Canaan, New Hampshire," anno 1937, primo descriptum sub nomine *Rhizidio mycophilo* A. Braun, sed species distincta est. Figurae collectionis typicae in Proc. Amer. Phil. Soc., 78: tab. 2.

which the shape of the mass changes, eventually escaping singly; resting spore not observed.

Saprophytic in exuviae of midges and mayflies, Sparrow (1937a: 41, pl. 2, figs. 1–5), UNITED STATES.

This species is based on a fungus originally referred to *Rhizidium mycophilum* (Sparrow, *loc. cit.*). The identity of the British material originally discussed under the latter species (Sparrow, 1937a) is open to question and, hence, it is not included.

A remarkable swarming period is undergone by the zoospores after discharge. A few moments after the zoospores emerge they assume individual movement; the rounded mass then moves away from the immediate vicinity of the sporangium and becomes reniform. During the violent swarming that continues, the shape of the mass changes to broadly sagittate. Eventually, individuals escape by way of the two apices of the lobes of the "arrowhead." The method of escape and a boundary line of bacteria around the mass strongly indicates that a definite vesicle surrounds the zoospores.

RHIZIDIUM VORAX (Strasburger) Sparrow

Aquatic Phycomycetes, p. 279. 1943

Chytridium vorax Strasburger, Jenaische Zeitschr. f. Nat., 12: 564. 1878.
Rhizophlyctis vorax (Strasburger) Fischer, Rabenhorst. Kryptogamen-Fl., 1 (4): 120. 1892.

Sporangium spherical or nearly so, mostly about 40 µ in diameter, wall thin, smooth, colorless, with a short lateral discharge papilla; rhizoids extensive, branched, stout, strongly polyphagous, attacking as many as from thirty to forty host cells, arising from a broad main axis attached to the base of the sporangium; zoospores spherical, 6.6 µ in diameter, with a relatively large colorless basal globule, an anterior visible nucleus, and a flagellum, after discharge remaining for a time undergoing amoeboid changes of shape before rounding off and swimming away, movement swimming or amoeboid; resting spore not observed.

Parasitic on *Sphaerella* (*Haematococcus*) *lacustris*, occasionally attacking resting individuals of *Chilomonas* and other swarmers, GERMANY.

Strasburger noted that the colorless zoospores were phototactic, a curious physiological adaptation to their mode of life, that is, preying on motile algae.

Though the fungus was placed by Minden (following Fischer) in *Rhizophlyctis*, Strasburger clearly states that the zoospore upon coming to rest rounds off and "...entsendet nun von einer Stelle aus, der Cilieninsertionsstelle so schien es mir, die sich baumartig verzweigenden Keimfaden aus."

RHIZIDIUM WINDERMERENSE Canter

Ann. Bot. London (N.S.), 14:268, figs. 1-4, pl. 8, A and B. 1950

(Fig. 11 J, p. 110)

"Thallus monocentric, eucarpic, polyphagous, consisting of a sporangium (the body of the encysted zoospore) and a single main rhizoidal axis which by the development of secondary branches loses its original taproot-like appearance. Sporangium inoperculate, pear-shaped, 8 μ high by 6 μ broad to 26 μ high by 23 μ broad, containing from 5 to over 60 zoospores. Zoospores spherical, uniguttulate and uniflagellate, emerging in an undifferentiated mass. Zygospore spherical to subspherical, 14–17 μ in diameter, wall thick, smooth, sometimes yellowish, content consisting of numerous small globules; formed after conjugation of the tips of the rhizoids from two thalli, the contents of both passing out to form a swelling, the incipient resting spore at their point of fusion. Rhizoidal system as in the sporangium developing after fusion of the sexual thalli. The latter remain as empty appendages (2.6–5.9 μ diam.) on the rhizoidal system of the mature spore" (Canter, *loc. cit.*).

Parasitic on the planktonic alga *Gemellicystis neglecta* (Teiling) Skuja, Canter (*loc. cit.*), GREAT BRITAIN; host?, Canter (1951: 153), ITALY.

The sexual formation of the "zygospores" (resting spores) is discussed under the genus (p. 408).

RHIZIDIUM BRAUNII Zopf

Nova Acta Acad. Leop.-Carol., 52 (7): 349, pl. 23, figs. 1-7. 1888

Rhizophlyctis braunii (Zopf) Fischer, Rabenhorst. Kryptogamen-Fl., 1 (4): 120. 1892.

Sporangium spherical, ellipsoidal, ovoid, or pyriform, 12–24 μ in diameter, wall thin, smooth, colorless; rhizoids well developed, several millimeters in extent, much branched, strongly polyphagous, generally arising as branches of a clavate main axis; zoospores spherical or ellipsoidal, 2.7–4 μ in diameter, with a strongly refractive globule and a flagellum, discharge not described; resting spore spherical or broadly ellipsoidal, 9–16 μ in diameter, walls thick, the outer layer gelatinous, yellowish, the inner golden brown, refractive, apparently asexually formed on a rhizoidal system like that of the sporangium, contents coarsely granular with a lateral vacuole (globule?), germination not observed.

On diatoms from a salt pool, Zopf (*loc. cit.*), GERMANY; possibly also on desmids attacked by *Rhizophydium globosum*, Serbinow (1907: 161), FINLAND.

Minden (1915: 375) retained this fungus in *Rhizophlyctis*, but the presence of a pronounced central rhizoidal axis marks it as a species of *Rhizidium*. Serbinow's record is to be considered doubtful until further investigations indicate that the fungus, which inhabits salt pools, can also live in fresh water.

Rhizidium braunii was the first species described by Fischer as representative of his new genus, *Rhizophlyctis*. Since, however, *Rhizidium* in the sense of Braun (not Fischer) was also included in *Rhizophlyctis*, the present species should have been referred to it when, subsequently, Braun's genus was reëstablished in its original sense by Schroeter (1893: 79).

RHIZIDIUM RAMOSUM Sparrow

Proc. Amer. Phil. Soc., 78 (1): 44, pl. 2, figs. 8-13, pl. 4, fig. 1. 1937

(Fig. 25 I-J, p. 411)

Sporangium globose or rarely ellipsoidal, 20–45 μ in diameter, wall slightly thickened, colorless, often bearing several irregular refractive protuberances; with a short basal main axis from which arises a system of stout branching rhizoids; zoospores ellipsoidal, 6 μ long by 4 μ in diameter, with a lateral colorless globule and a single posterior flagellum, emerging from the sporangium in a compact column after the deliquescence of a single usually terminal discharge papilla; resting spore not observed.

Saprophytic in integuments of Phryganeidae, DENMARK; Chironomidae, Ephemerida, UNITED STATES.

Rhizidium ramosum differs from *R. mycophilum* in possessing a very short, rather than an elongated, subsporangial main axis. This terminates in a profusely branched rhizoidal system. A further variation is found in the peculiar refractive nodules which occur on some of its sporangia. Certain slight differences noted between the Danish and the American material do not, at least for the present, seem of sufficient import to separate the two as distinct species.

RHIZIDIUM NOWAKOWSKII Karling

Amer. J. Bot., 31: 255, figs. 31-33, 69-72. 1944

(Fig. 25 E-G, p. 411)

Rhizidium mycophilum Braun, sensu Nowakowski, in Cohn, Beitr. Biol. Pflanzen, 2: 87, 1876.

"Sporangia straight or slightly tilted on the rhizoidal axis, hyaline, smooth, spherical (15–10 μ) pyriform (8 × 10–25 × 35 μ), ellipsoidal or oval (15 × 20–70 × 100 μ), oblong (15 × 28–40 × 90 μ); apophysate or non-apophysate, apophysis oval, fusiform or almost spherical; opening by a prominent (3 × 4 μ) hyaline exit papilla. Rhizoidal axis broad, up to 6 μ in diam., and extending 100–300 μ, frequently branched and tapering abruptly. Zoospores spherical, 4–5 μ, with a large (2–2.8 μ), conspicuous, hyaline refringent globule and a 30–35 μ long flagellum; emerging in a globular mass which becomes enveloped by a vesicle in which the individuals swarm for several minutes before breaking out and swimming away. Resting spores hyaline, spherical or ellipsoidal, 15–30 μ in diam.; wall double-layered, inner layer smooth, outer layer bearing a felt-like covering of fine long hairs; content finely granular and hyaline with a large refractive globule; functioning as prosporangia in germination and giving rise to sporangia on their surface" (Karling, *loc. cit.*).

Saprophytic in the gelatinous envelope of *Chaetophora elegans*, Nowakowski (1876: 87), GERMANY; in the slime surrounding bits of

onion skin, Karling (*loc. cit.*), BRAZIL; cockroach wings, chitin, Karling (1948c: 509), UNITED STATES.
See the comments on this species under *Rhizidium mycophilum* (p. 410).

RHIZIDIUM BRAZILIENSIS Karling

Amer. J. Bot., 31: 254, figs. 1-19, 23-30. 1944

"Sporangia extramatrical, hyaline, smooth, spherical (10–40 μ), pyriform (8–40 × 12–50 μ), oval and slightly anatropous (15–20 × 18–30 μ), sometimes quite irregular and slightly stellate; usually apophysate, apophysis intra- or extramatrical, almost spherical (4–10 μ), oval or fusiform; sporangia opening by one to four conspicuous hyaline exit papillae arising from the surface of the sporangia or situated at the ends of one or more long (3–8 × 15–60 μ) tubes. Rhizoidal system usually intramatrical, main axis up to 6 μ in diam., extending from 50 to 220 μ, usually branching more or less dichotomously and tapering abruptly. Zoospores oval to slightly elongate, 3–3.5 × 5–5.5 μ, usually with one relatively small refractive globule lying at one side and slightly toward the base; emerging in a globular mass which becomes enveloped by a vesicle in which the individuals swarm for several minutes before breaking out and swimming away; flagellum 33–35 μ long. Resting spores extramatrical, hyaline, usually apophysate, spherical (10–25 μ), oval (10 × 14–20 × 23 μ), or oblong and slightly flattened with one to several large refractive globules; wall 1.5–2 μ thick, warty, horny or spiny; horns or spines varying from a few to more than fifty in number, short or up to 4 μ high and tapering abruptly. Resting spores functioning as prosporangia in germination, giving rise to thin-walled sporangia on their surface" (Karling, *loc. cit.*).
Saprophytic in fragments and exuviae of insects, in water, BRAZIL.

RHIZIDIUM LAEVIS Karling

Amer. J. Bot., 31: 254, figs. 20-22. 1944

"Sporangia extramatrical, hyaline, smooth, spherical (5–50 μ), or oval and slightly anatropous (6 × 8–20 × 30 μ), irregular and somewhat stellate with one to three exit papillae; apophysate, apophysis oval, fusiform and almost spherical, 4–10 μ in diam. Rhizoids intramatrical, usually arising at several points on the apophysis, relatively fine and richly branched, rarely extending more than 150 μ in extent. Zoospores oval, 3 × 4 μ, with a small (0.8–1.2 μ) refractive globule lying slightly toward one side, emerging as a globular mass which becomes enveloped by a vesicle in which the individuals swarm for several minutes before breaking out and swimming away; flagellum 28–30 μ long. Resting spores hyaline, oval (15 × 18 μ), elongate (9 × 25 μ), and slightly flattened, or spherical (12–18 μ), with several large refractive globules and a thick (1.5–2 μ) smooth wall; functioning as prosporangia in germination and giving rise to sporangia on their surface" (Karling, *loc. cit.*).

Saprophytic in fragments and exuviae of insects, from soil, BRAZIL.

RHIZIDIUM VERRUCOSUM Karling

Amer. J. Boi., 31: 255, figs. 34-63. 1944

(Fig. 28 E-G, p. 440)

"Thallus rarely wholly extramatrical. Sporangia extramatrical, non-apophysate with a verrucose light or reddish brown, crusty outer wall and a thinner hyaline inner wall; together up to 3.5 μ thick; spherical (6–60 μ), oval (15 × 20–30 × 40 μ), oblong (20 × 35 μ), pyriform, or egg-shaped; opening by a relatively large exit papilla which breaks through the verrucose wall, exit orifice circular, oval or oblong, 7–10 μ in diam. Rhizoidal system intramatrical, arising from one to three points at base of sporangium, delicate or coarse, main axis up to 10 μ in diam. and extending 300 μ in large thalli, becoming thick-walled and brownish with age. Zoospores oval, 3–3.5 × 5–5.5 μ, with a relatively small (1–1.5 μ) reddish-brown refractive globule lying slightly at one side; emerging in a globular mass which becomes enveloped by a vesicle in which the individuals swarm for several minutes before breaking out and swimming away. Resting spores doubtful; dormant sporangia spherical (8–22 μ) or oval (6 × 12–9 × 16 μ), with brown warty thick (4–6 μ) walls; functioning in germination directly as sporangia with an exit papilla" (Karling, *loc. cit.*).

Saprophytic on fragments and exuviae of insects, pieces of onion skin and grass leaves, in water, BRAZIL.

RHIZIDIUM ELONGATUM Karling

Amer. J. Bot., 36: 683, figs. 27-48. 1949

"Sporangia hyaline, smooth, rarely appendiculate, predominantly e-
longate (6–12 × 20–45 μ), irregular, pyriform (7–18 × 9–32 μ), oval,
rarely spherical (8–20 μ), with a single broad, 4–12 μ diam. inconspicuous exit papilla. Zoospores slightly oval (4.8–5.2 × 5–6.2 μ), with
a spherical (1.8–2.2 μ), hyaline refractive globule; flagellum 28–32 μ long;
usually swarming in a vesicle outside of the sporangium. Rhizoids
attached at base of sporangium, stiff or rigid-looking main axis up to
5 μ in diam., sparingly branched, and occasionally extending for a
distance of 200 μ. Resting spores unknown" (Karling, *loc. cit.*).

Saprophytic on chitinous substrata, UNITED STATES.

This and the following species would seem better accommodated in
Rhizophlyctis. The frequent possession of more than one rhizoidal
axis and, in *R. varians*, of more than one discharge pore argues for it.

RHIZIDIUM VARIANS Karling

Amer. J. Bot., 36: 681, figs. 1-26. 1949

"Thallus predominantly monocentric but often polycentric. Sporangia
hyaline, smooth, variable in shape, rarely apophysate, spherical (20–130
μ), broadly or narrowly pyriform (10–40 × 30–75 μ), oval (12–30 ×
18–60 μ), citriform, clavate, elongate, or slightly irregular with 1–4 low
or prominent exit papillae or tapering necks, 5–7 μ broad at base by
15–96 μ long, and filled with hyaline matrix. Zoospores spherical,
3.5–4 μ, with a spherical, 1.9–2.4 μ, hyaline refractive globule; swarming
in a vesicle outside of the sporangium. Rhizoids usually arising at base
of sporangium, but frequently from several points on its periphery,
coarse, main axes up to 17 μ in diam. at base, frequently branched and
extending for a distance of 500 μ. Resting spores predominantly spherical (8–22 μ), oval (10–15 × 12–18 μ), with a smooth, 1.8–2.4 μ, thick
wall, which becomes light brown with age, and filled with coarse, angular refractive bodies; functioning as prosporangia in germination" (Karling, *loc. cit.*).

Saprophytic in cellulosic substrates, UNITED STATES.

Both a *Rhizidium*-type and an *Entophlyctis*-type of development were undergone by this species and about 4 per cent of the thalli were even polycentric rather than monocentric!

RECENTLY DESCRIBED TAXON [1]

RHIZIDIUM RICHMONDENSE Willoughby

Trans. Brit. Mycol. Soc., 39: 128, figs. 1-3. 1956

Thallus monocentric, eucarpic, interbiotic, consisting of a globose or subglobose sporangium and branching rhizoids which arise from one point; sporangium 9.5–35 μ in diameter, bearing an obtuse apiculus, discharging upon the rupturing of the sporangium wall near the apiculus; zoospores globose, 3–3.3 μ in diameter, or ovate and 3–3.3 by 2.5–3 μ, with a large or small oil globule and posterior flagellum, 18–23 μ long; when discharged from the sporangium undergoing a period of collective swarming, possibly within a vesicle; resting spores not observed.

In onion-bulb epidermis and cellophane bait in a soil culture (Herb. I. M. I. 60445), GREAT BRITAIN.

Although the apiculus of the sporangium strongly resembled an operculum it was, rightly, not so regarded by Willoughby.

IMPERFECTLY KNOWN SPECIES OF RHIZIDIUM

? RHIZIDIUM LIGNICOLA Lindau

Verhandl. Bot. Vereins Prov. Brandenburg, 41: xxvii, figs. 1-12. 1900

Sporangium usually more or less flattened, ellipsoidal, pyriform, or saclike, rarely spherical, sometimes with a narrow stalklike base, rounded at the top, often irregular with hornlike outgrowths, 25–75 μ long by 20–25 μ broad, wall thickened, colorless or somewhat brownish, resting on a vesicular apophysis formed from the body of the encysted zoospore, discharging by the deliquescence of an apical pore after the expulsion of a plug (operculum?); zoospores spherical, 2–3 μ (up to 8 μ in culture) in diameter, with a posterior flagellum 40–50 μ long and an oil drop, discharge not observed.

Saprophytic on twigs of horse chestnut, GERMANY.

From the description given by Lindau, the fungus appears to have

[1] Not included in the key.

an endooperculum and apophysate sporangium. Its development when lying free in the water is like that of *Polyphagus*.

? RHIZIDIUM VARIABILE Canter

Trans. Brit. Mycol. Soc., 31: 100, figs. 4, 5, pl. 10, figs. 4, 5, 6. 1947

"Thallus monocentric, extramatrical part consisting of a sporangium 6–13 μ in diameter (developed from the encysted zoospore), and a single stout rhizoid, which may have one or more swellings. Intramatrical part sometimes swollen, tapering to a branched rhizoidal system. Sporangium containing 1–20 zoospores which emerge, surrounded by a vesicle, on deliquescence of the sporangial apex. Zoospores spherical 4.4–5 μ in diameter, with a single oil globule 1–2 μ in diameter, and a posterior flagellum 26 μ long. Sporangium wall collapsing after dehiscence. Resting spores not observed" (Canter, *loc. cit.*).

On dead *Spirogyra sp.*, GREAT BRITAIN.

Both the description and figures of this species are strongly indicative of abnormal development, probably due to lack of essential food materials. This supposition seems borne out by the fact that the fungus was found on *Spirogyra* which had so disintegrated as to be almost unrecognizable.

EXCLUDED SPECIES OF RHIZIDIUM

* RHIZIDIUM ALGAECOLUM Zopf, nom. nud.[1]

Nova Acta Acad. Leop.-Carol., 47: 204. 1884

In manuscript, not connected with any figure or description. On *Spirogyra*, GERMANY.

* RHIZIDIUM EQUITANS Zopf, nom. nud.

Pilzetiere oder Schleimpilze, p. 6. Breslau, 1885

Inadequately described. Zopf later (1890) called this fungus "*Rhizophydium equitans*," also a *nomen nudum*.

---

[1] Various names such as this one and combinations such as *Rhizidium olla*, *R. sphaerospermum*, and *Eurhizidium intestinum* occur in Zopf's papers. These should all be regarded as *nomina nuda*.

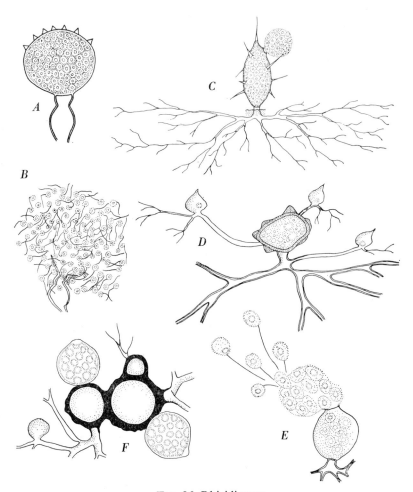

Fig. 26. Rhizidiaceae

A–B. Solutoparies pythii Whiffen on *Pythium sp.*: *A*, mature zoosporangium; *B*, zoospores emerging from gelatinous matrix left after dissolution of sporangium wall. *C–D. Siphonaria petersenii* Karling: *C*, discharging sporangium; *D*, sexually formed resting spore with three adherent male thalli. *E–F. Siphonaria sparrowii* Karling: *E*, emerged zoospores escaping from vesicle; *F*, two germinating resting spores with thin-walled sporangia on their surface, a male thallus on left.

(*A–B*, Whiffen, 1942a; *C–F*, Karling, 1945d)

* RHIZIDIUM LEPTORHIZUM Zopf, nom. nud.

Nova Acta Acad. Leop.-Carol., 47: 231, pl. 20, fig. 5 a-c. 1884

No description in the text. Figures referred to appear to be of young stages of *Rhizidiomyces apophysatus.*

* RHIZIDIUM SPIROGYRAE Fisch, nom. nud.

Sitzungsber. Phys.-Med. Soc. Erlangen, 16: 56. 1884

A binomial (unaccompanied by a description) used in mentioning a form of *Entophlyctis vaucheriae* inhabiting *Spirogyra.*

SIPHONARIA H. E. PETERSEN

Journ. de Botanique, 17: 220. 1903

(Figs. 4 V-W, p. 72; 26 C-F, p. 422; 27 F, p. 428)

Mature thallus monocentric, eucarpic, consisting of a sporangial rudiment (the body of the encysted zoospore), with or without an apophysis, and broad, thick-walled, wide-lumened rhizoids; sporangium inoperculate, formed from the sporangial rudiment; zoospores posteriorly uniflagellate, with a single globule, formed in the sporangium, discharged through a pore; resting spore borne like the sporangium on the rhizoidal system, thick-walled, sexually formed after conjugation of thalli by means of rhizoidal anastomosis, at germination functioning as a prosporangium; contributing thallus (or thalli) remaining small and rudimentary.

Known only in insect exuviae.

The sexual nature of the resting spore is characteristic of all species of the genus. Karling (1945d) found fairly commonly in *Siphonaria petersenii* that the rhizoid of the male thallus contacted the body of the female directly; sometimes the male body itself became attached to that of the female.

Karling has postulated two types of life cycles for *Siphonaria,* one on the supposition of genotypic sex segregation at meiosis in the germinating zygote (the most probable) and the other on the supposition of phenotypic sex segregation at the close of the sporangial and zoosporic period.

KEY TO THE SPECIES OF SIPHONARIA

Sporangium smooth-walled
  Discharge pore basal; zoospores with a small rust-colored globule
                                                    S. variabilis, p. 424
  Discharge pore apical; zoospores with a large hyaline globule
                                                    S. sparrowii, p. 425
Sporangium beset with solid spines .... *S. petersenii*, p. 425

SIPHONARIA VARIABILIS H. E. Petersen

Journ. de Botanique, 17: 220, figs. 11-17. 1903

(Figs. 4 V-W, p. 72; 27 F, p. 428)

Sporangium subglobose or broadly reniform, with a prominent basal papilla, widely variable in size, 12-39 μ in diameter by 11–36.4 μ in height (rarely 42 μ high by 38 μ in diameter), wall thin, smooth, colorless; rhizoids well-developed, stout, thick-walled, wide-lumened, branched, extending from the inconspicuous apophysis formed behind the downward-tilted discharge papilla; zoospores numerous, somewhat pyriform, or ovoid, the narrower end anterior, 5 μ long by 2.5 μ in diameter, the plasma bearing a laterally placed rust-colored globule and a larger hyaline spherical body, flagellum from four to five times the length of the body, movement darting, amoeboid usually only after partial or complete retraction of the flagellum; resting spore broadly ellipsoidal or reniform, contents coarsely granular, with globules, 13–15.6 μ high by 15.6–18.2 μ in diameter, with a brown, smooth, or slightly crenulated wall, 2–2.5 μ thick, borne like the sporangium, rhizoidal system less extensive, germination not observed; contributing thallus (sometimes two) somewhat obpyriform, 7–11 μ high by 5–8 μ in diameter, rhizoidal system limited in extent.

Saprophytic in empty submerged exuviae of Phryganeidae, Petersen (*loc. cit.*; 1909: 412, fig. 21b, d; 1910: 547, fig. 21 b, d), Sparrow (1937a: 32, fig. 2 a-j, pl. 1, figs. 1–12, pl. 4, figs. A-C), DENMARK; Odonata (Anisoptera) (dragonflies), Ephemerida (mayflies), Sparrow (1937a: 32), exuviae of various aquatic insects, Sparrow (1952d: 768), UNITED STATES; exuviae of insects, Karling (1945d: 586), BRAZIL; exuviae, Canter (1953: 290), GREAT BRITAIN.

The early stages in the development of this species need further study. The small size of the parts renders interpretation of details susceptible to error. Both Petersen and Sparrow noted sporangia of two size classes. This suggests the possibility that sexual differentiation of zoospores may be present (see discussion under the genus). None was noted by Karling (1945d) in *S. petersenii* and *S. sparrowii*.

SIPHONARIA SPARROWII Karling

Amer. J. Bot., 32: 581, figs. 27-53. 1945

(Fig. 26 E-F, p. 422)

"Thalli numerous, occurring inside insect exuviae. Sporangia extramatrical to substratum, nonapophysate, hyaline, smooth, spherical, 8–20 μ, or broadly pyriform with a low apical or subapical exit papilla. Zoospores spherical, 5.5–6 μ, with a large (3–3.5 μ) hyaline refractive globule; swarming in a vesicle outside the sporangium for several minutes before breaking out and swimming away. Rhizoidal system monoaxial, intramatrical, arising from base of sporangium, rhizoids thick-walled, coarse, tapering abruptly, and often branching at right or obtuse angles. Resting spores oval, spherical, 10–18 μ, with a thick (3–4 μ) amber to dark brown smooth wall; several spores frequently enveloped by a common thick wall; formed sexually by fusion of the content of one or more 'male' thalli with one 'female' thallus; functioning as prosporangia in germination" (Karling, *loc. cit.*).

Saprophytic in exuviae of mayflies, BRAZIL; UNITED STATES.

Differing from *Siphonaria variabilis* in having the zoospores larger with a colorless droplet, an apical discharge pore on the sporangium, and a distinct vesicle around them when emerged. The resting spores resemble somewhat those of *S. variabilis*. In some instances the conjugating thalli may be almost adnate.

SIPHONARIA PETERSENII Karling

Amer. J. Bot., 32: 580, figs. 1-26. 1945

(Fig. 26 C-D, p. 422)

"Thalli numerous, occurring inside of empty insect exuviae. Sporangia extramatrical to substratum, non-apophysate, orange-golden in color, predominantly elongately pyriform, 5–20 × 10–36 μ, occasionally elongated transversely to rhizoid axis, with a long sharp apical and

3–12 lateral, simple or bifurcate spines, 4–15 μ in length; exit papilla subapical, low and inconspicuous. Zoospores spherical, 3–3.5 μ, with a small (1.5 μ) golden-red globule; swarming in a vesicle for several minutes before breaking out and swimming away. Rhizoidal system intramatrical, monoaxial, arising from base of sporangium, richly branched and extending for a distance of 80 μ. Resting spores spherical, 10–15 μ, oval, or slightly angular and spiny, 6–8 × 10–14 μ, with a reddish brown (2 μ), slightly uneven, crusty and almost verrucose wall; containing numerous granules and globules; formed sexually by the fusion of the contents of one or more 'male' (?) thalli with a 'female' (?) thallus; germination unknown" (Karling, *loc. cit.*).

Saprophytic in the exuviae of mayflies and other insects, BRAZIL; UNITED STATES.

In its spinose sporangia this species is rather like *Asterophlyctis*. Here, however, the spines are solid and do not alter appreciably the shape of the sporangium, whereas in *Asterophlyctis* they are protuberances filled with cytoplasm and give shape to the sporangium. Furthermore, in *Siphonaria petersenii* no apophysis is formed.

SOLUTOPARIES Whiffen

Mycologia, 34: 543. 1942

(Fig. 26 A-B, p. 422)

"Thallus entirely extramatrical, monocentric. Sporangia developing by enlargement of zoöspore; rhizoidal system much-branched. Spore discharge by dissolution of sporangial wall, liberating the zoöspores which swim away singly. Zoöspore uniguttulate, posteriorly uniciliate. Resting spores unknown" (Whiffen, *loc. cit.*).

Parasitic on Phycomycetes.

This monotypic genus resembles *Nowakowskia* in the deliquescence of the sporangium wall but differs from it in that the zoospores swim away individually.

The method of development of the thallus is characteristically rhizidiaceous. It is not clear, however, either from the description or figures, whether one or more rhizoidal axes typify the mature thallus. Figures of the fully developed sporangium (which may not always bear spines) indicate a single axis which is swollen beneath the sporangium.

The latter is not sessile on this apophysis but separated from it by a short length of unexpanded rhizoidal axis. At spore discharge, the sporangium wall swells and thickens and its substance, including the spines, slowly dissolves. Coincidently, the spores become active and swim away. Only an irregular collar of sporangium wall persists at the base.

SOLUTOPARIES PYTHII Whiffen

Mycologia, 34: 543, figs. 1-27. 1942

"Thallus parasitic. Sporangia ovoid to spherical, 14.3 μ × 16.4 μ to 68.4 μ × 80.3 μ; wall spiny, spines conical, up to 5 μ in length. Rhizoidal system cut off by cross wall from mature sporangium, tips of rhizoidal branches adhering to but not penetrating host hyphae. Dissolution of sporangial wall complete except for basal portion, freeing the spore mass, enclosed in a gelatinous matrix; zoöspores separating as surrounding matrix dissolves, swimming away singly. Zoöspores spherical, 4.5 μ to 5.6 μ, hyaline with single colorless oil globule. Resting spores unknown" (Whiffen, *loc. cit.*).

Exoparasite of *Pythium sp.*, UNITED STATES.

Although the tips of the rhizoids were not observed to penetrate the host hypha but, rather, to wrap around it, wherever they made contact the host was stimulated to abnormal branching. These complexes of hyphae favored development of the parasite, since more hyphal elements of the host were made available in its immediate vicinity.

OBELIDIUM NOWAKOWSKI

Cohn, Beitr. Biol. Pflanzen, 2: 86. 1876

(Fig. 27 A-E, p. 428)

Mature thallus monocentric, eucarpic, consisting of a sporangial rudiment (the body of the encysted zoospore) which is differentiated into an apical solid mucro, a central thin-walled expanded sporogenous region, and a thick-walled cuplike or stalklike basal part resting on an apophysis from which radiate the main axes of the rhizoidal system; sporangium inoperculate, formed from the sporangial rudiment; zoospores posteriorly uniflagellate, with a single globule, formed in the sporangium, emerging through a lateral pore and undergoing a period

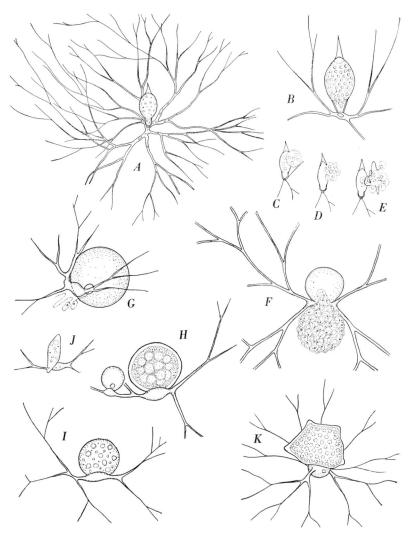

FIG. 27. Rhizidiaceae

A–E. Obelidium mucronatum Nowakowski: *A,* nearly complete thallus
with sporangium slightly tilted; *B,* mature sporangium; *C–E,* stages in discharge of zoospores. *F. Siphonaria variabilis* H. E. Petersen, discharging
sporangium. *G. Rhizoclosmatium aurantiacum* Sparrow, empty sporangium
and two zoospores. *H–I. Rhizoclosmatium globosum* H. E. Petersen: *H,*

of collective swarming before escaping; resting spore not observed. Saprophytes inhabiting insect exuviae.

Obelidium in its method of development, general structural features, possession of a subsporangial apophysis, type of zoospore discharge, and habitat is very similar to the other exuviae-inhabiting fungi, *Siphonaria, Rhizoclosmatium*, and *Asterophlyctis*. There is little doubt but that they are all closely related forms. It is probable that when resting spores of *Obelidium* are found and their method of development followed, further similarities will be discovered.

OBELIDIUM MUCRONATUM Nowakowski

Cohn, Beitr. Biol. Pflanzen, 2: 86, pl. 5, figs. 1-5. 1876

Sporangium ranging from 20–23 μ in height by 7–8 μ in diameter to 48–56 μ in height by 17–20 μ in diameter, consisting of a thick-walled cuplike or funnel-like base 4–12 μ in diameter by 4–10 μ in height, a narrowly to broadly ovoid, thin-walled mid-region, and a single solid refractive apical spine (rarely two, opposite) which is seldom more than one third of the total sporangial height; rhizoids profusely branched, extensive, radiating for 100 μ or more from their point of origin, in large specimens gradually increasing in diameter (up to 5 μ) as they approach the small subsporangial apophysis to which they are attached; zoospores spherical or slightly ellipsoidal, 2.5–3.5 μ in diameter, with a small eccentric highly refractive colorless globule and a flagellum 20 μ in length, movement hopping or amoeboid; resting spore not observed.

Saprophytic in empty submerged exuviae of Chironomidae, Nowakowski (*loc. cit.*), GERMANY; wing of submerged fly, Sorokin (1883: 22, fig. 20), ASIATIC RUSSIA; Phryganeidae, H. E. Petersen (1909: 412; 1910: 547), DENMARK; Chironomidae, Sparrow (1938d: 1, figs. 1–44), chitin bait, from moist soil, Karling (1948c: 509), UNITED STATES.

---

small male cell attached to resting spore; *I*, immature sporangium, showing fusiform apophysis. *J–K. Asterophlyctis sarcoptoides* H. E. Petersen: *J*, very young thallus showing irregular shape of reproductive rudiment, and apophysis from which rhizoids emerge; *K*, mature sporangium. All fungi figured occurred in insect exuviae.

(*A–E*, Sparrow, 1938d; *F–K*, Sparrow, 1937a)

For details of the morphology and development of this species see Sparrow (*loc. cit.*). The fungus may occasionally exhibit a *Chytridium* habit of growth, that is, the sporangium may rest on the wall of the integument (either inside or outside), the apophysis may be formed within the wall material as part of the penetration tube, and the rhizoids may extend out beyond.

Two organisms of uncertain relationships have been referred to this genus by Sparrow (1937a: 48, fig. 5); both of them inhabit insect exuviae.

The first, which was tentatively called *Obelidium* (?) *mucronatum*, was found in caddis-fly integuments in Massachusetts. The sporangium was broadly fusiform, 20–33 μ long by 7–8 μ in diameter, and rested on a thick-walled cuplike base which was 3–4 μ in diameter. The apical region was thin-walled and not prolonged into a mucro, the rhizoidal system delicate, much branched, and radiating in all directions from a single point on the base of the sporangium. Discharge of the zoospores was not observed, although empty somewhat collapsed sporangia occurred.

The second, called *Obelidium hamatum*, was found in midge exuviae in New Hampshire and described as follows:

"Main body of the sporangium extramatrical, broadly ovoid, thick-walled, 8–9 μ in diameter by 8–12 μ in length, possessing a basal, thin-walled stalk about 4 μ in diameter by 8–12 μ in length, continuous with it, and on which are two oppositely placed, intramatrical spines; rhizoidal system intramatrical, feebly developed, branched or unbranch-ed, emerging from the abruptly tapering tip of the intramatrical part of the stalk; zoospores ellipsoidal, 4 μ long by 2 μ in diameter, posteriorly uniciliate, uniguttulate, escaping by an opening at the base of the main body of the sporangium. Resting spores not observed."

Empty sporangia of this organism have been observed several times since, in exuviae collected in Michigan. In these instances they were entirely within the empty cavity of the exuviae. Once a single specimen was observed lying free among the tangled threads of *Mougeotia*. The new observations indicate that there is variation in the relation of the fungus to the substratum.

If further investigations seem to warrant the retention of these two fungi in *Obelidium* a modification of the genus will be necessary for their accommodation.

RHIZOCLOSMATIUM H. E. Petersen

Journ. de Botanique, 17: 216. 1903

(Fig. 27 G-I, p. 428)

Mature thallus monocentric, eucarpic, consisting of a sporangial rudiment (body of the encysted zoospore), apophysis, and delicate rhizoids; sporangium inoperculate, formed from the sporangial rudiment; zoospores posteriorly uniflagellate, with a single globule, formed in the sporangium, emerging in an evanescent vesicle to undergo a period of collective swarming before escaping, discharge pore basal, or rarely subapical or apical; resting spore borne like the sporangium on the rhizoidal system, thick-walled, sexually formed after conjugation of thalli by means of rhizoidal anastomosis, germination not observed; contributing thallus remaining small and rudimentary.

The species thus far described are known as saprophytes in insect exuviae and parasites of marine green algae.

KEY TO THE SPECIES OF RHIZOCLOSMATIUM

In insect exuviae in fresh water

Globule of zoospore colorless .... *R. globosum,* p. 431
Globule of zoospore rusty-orange .... *R. aurantiacum,* p. 432
In the marine alga *Codium fragile* .... *R. marinum,* p. 433

RHIZOCLOSMATIUM GLOBOSUM H. E. Petersen

Journ. de Botanique, 17: 216, figs. 1-2. 1903

(Fig. 27 H-I, p. 428)

Sporangium spherical or subspherical, 9–22 μ in diameter (or larger), wall slightly thickened, smooth, colorless; rhizoids extensive, delicate, much branched, arising from a transverse broadly fusiform (5 μ broad by 3 μ high), occasionally subspherical, pyramidal, or clavate apophysis; zoospores spherical, ovoid, or ellipsoidal, 3–4 μ long by 2–3 μ in diameter, with a colorless centric or eccentric globule and a flagellum about 20 μ long, movement darting; resting spore borne like the sporangium, subspherical, 8–14 μ high by 11–20 μ in diameter, with a smooth faintly brown wall about 2 μ thick, contents with globules, germination not observed; contributing thalli from one to two, spherical, 4–6 μ in diameter, with a poorly developed rhizoidal system.

Saprophytic in empty submerged exuviae of Phryganeidae, H. E. Petersen (*loc. cit.*; 1909: 415, fig. 21c; 1910: 548, fig. 21c), Sparrow (1937a: 38, text fig. 2 k–o, pl. 2, fig. 19), DENMARK; Chironomidae (midges), Odonata (Anisoptera) (dragonflies), Ephemerida (mayflies), Phryganeidae (caddis flies), Sparrow (1937a: 38, pl. 2, figs. 18, 20–24, pl. 4, figs. G-H), exuviae of various aquatic insects, Sparrow (1952d: 767), UNITED STATES; Chironomidae, Sparrow (1936a: 418; 1937a: 38), exuviae, Canter (1953: 290), GREAT BRITAIN; insect integument, Sparrow (1952a: 39), CUBA.

The most ubiquitous of the exuviae-inhabiting chytrids.

A form with larger sporangia and smaller zoospores, each with a rusty-red globule, has been segregated from *Rhizoclosmatium globosum* as *R. aurantiacum* Sparrow (1937a: 40). Although the colorless form is most frequent it is difficult to say which one should be considered the type of *R. globosum*. Petersen's attitude (comm. 1938) is that there is no difference between the colored and colorless individuals and that "...the coloration in most cases is due to age or to several external factors." The original description includes both forms. In view of the observed constancy of coloration in other chytrids, it is believed here that the colored globule in this species is due to a genotypic factor. Since colored and colorless types have been found in the same exuvia where they would receive equal illumination, light does not seem to be a factor in calling forth pigmentation. One other interpretation remains, namely, that these two types are gametangia and that the larger, colorless swarmers are female, and the smaller pigmented ones male gametes.

RHIZOCLOSMATIUM AURANTIACUM Sparrow

Proc. Amer. Phil. Soc., 78 (1): 40, pl. 2, figs. 14-17. 1937

(Fig. 27 G, p. 428)

Rhizoclosmatium globosum H. E. Petersen, pro parte, Journ. de Botanique, 17: 216. 1903.

Sporangium globose, 27–38 μ in diameter, with a smooth double-contoured colorless wall; rhizoids extensive, branched, delicate, arising as stout branches from the narrower ends of a broadly fusiform transverse subsporangial apophysis; zoospores somewhat ellipsoidal, 2.5 μ long by 2 μ in diameter, with a minute rusty-orange globule and a long flagellum, escaping by a basal pore formed near the apophysis; resting spore not observed.

Saprophytic in empty submerged exuviae of Phryganeidae, H. E. Petersen (*loc. cit.*), Sparrow (*loc. cit.*), DENMARK; Odonata (Anisoptera), Chironomidae, Ephemerida, Sparrow (*loc. cit.*), exuviae of aquatic insects, Sparrow (1952d: 767), UNITED STATES.

Distinct from *Rhizoclosmatium globosum* not only in the coloration of the globule of the zoospore but also in having larger sporangia and smaller zoospores.

RHIZOCLOSMATIUM MARINUM Kobayasi and Ookubo

Bull. Nat. Sci. Mus. (Tokyo), (N.S.), 1 (2), No. 35: 68, fig. 7. 1954

"Sporangium interbiotic, subglobose or somewhat flattened, ellipsoidal, sessile, 30–60 μ high, 30–40 μ in diameter, smooth, hyaline, thin-walled. Subsporangial apophysis smaller than sporangium, globose, or fusiform, transversely elongated, sending two or three rhizoids. Rhizoids extensive, commonly bilaterally elongated, sometimes very thick at the base, dichotomously or laterally branched, thin-walled. Zoospores emerging through a small discharge pore which opens at the base of zoosporangium as a white mass of cyst (vesicle) and then rapidly swimming away separately, ellipsoidal, 7 × 5 μ, hyaline, with a posterior 20 μ long flagellum and an eccentric globule. Resting spore unknown" (Kobayasi and Ookubo, *loc. cit.*).

Parasitic on *Codium fragile* (marine), JAPAN.

Distinct from the other species in possessing larger zoospores and in being parasitic on a marine alga. It is possibly a *Diplophlyctis sp.*

ASTEROPHLYCTIS H. E. PETERSEN

Journ. de Botanique, 17: 218. 1903

(Figs. 7, p. 94; 27 J-K, p. 428)

Mature thallus monocentric, eucarpic, consisting of a somewhat angular or stellate sporangial rudiment, apophysis, and rhizoids; sporangium inoperculate, formed from the sporangial rudiment; zoospores posteriorly uniflagellate, with a single globule; resting spore borne like the sporangium on the rhizoidal system, thick-walled, stellate, asexually formed or sexually after conjugation of thalli by means of rhizoidal anastomosis, upon germination functioning as a prosporangium; contributing thallus remaining small.

A monotypic genus; the single species known only in insect exuviae and on chitin bait.

Antikajian (1949) contends that her failure to find sexuality in her material of *Asterophlyctis sarcoptoides* is sufficient reason for removing the genus from its allies, *Siphonaria* and *Rhizoclosmatium*, and placing it in some sort of merger with *Rhizidium* and *Phlyctochytrium*. This separation from its obviously near relatives has little to recommend it. Karling's (1945d) earlier suggestion of combining both *Asterophlyctis* and *Rhizoclosmatium* with *Siphonaria* might prove feasible in the future when more is known about the species making up these genera.

ASTEROPHLYCTIS SARCOPTOIDES H. E. PETERSEN

Journ. de Botanique, 17: 218, figs. 3-8. 1903

Sporangium irregularly stellate, colorless, with a variable number of broadly conical or acute, often thick-walled, refractive protuberances, 17–28 μ broad by 18–25 μ high (rarely 52 by 33 μ); rhizoids originating from one or two (opposite) stout main axes extending from the spherical or subspherical (6–11 μ [rarely 13 μ] in diameter) apophysis, much branched, 100 μ or more in length; zoospores broadly ellipsoidal to subspherical, 5 μ long by 2–3 μ in diameter, with a centric or eccentric colorless globule and a long (35 μ) flagellum, emerging through a basal or lateral pore 4–5 μ in diameter, movement a swift darting or hopping; resting spore like the sporangium in shape but with a thicker wall, protuberances up to 9 μ long, acute, nearly solid, functioning as a prosporangium upon germination, the sporangium evenly contoured or forming a few spinelike protuberances; contributing thallus when formed somewhat ovoid, 5 μ high by 4 μ in diameter, thin-walled, apophysis and rhizoidal system poorly developed.

Saprophytic in empty submerged exuviae of Phryganeidae (caddis flies), Petersen (*loc. cit.*, 1909: 415, fig. 21e; 1910: 549, fig. 21e), Sparrow (1937a: 26, text fig. 1 a-k, pl. 1, figs. 13–16, 19), DENMARK; Chironomidae (midges), Ephemerida (mayflies), Phryganeidae, Sparrow (*loc. cit.*, pl. 1, figs. 17–18, pl. 4, figs. D-F), mayflies, Sparrow (1943: 295), chitin, from moist soil, Karling (1948c: 509), exuviae of various aquatic insects, Sparrow (1952d: 768), UNITED STATES; chitin, Karling (1945c: 362), BRAZIL; exuviae, Canter (1953: 290), GREAT BRITAIN.

Details of the morphology and development of the species are given by Sparrow (1937a); and by Antikajian (1949: 245), based on Karling's material (see also "Cytology," p. 92). The occurrence of sexuality has been observed in a number of instances by the present writer. The process differs in no essential features from that in *Siphonaria*, although the tenuity of the rhizoids and the smallness of the contributing thallus often make examination and interpretation extremely difficult. Antikajian (1949), however, was unable to confirm the presence of sexuality. Inasmuch as Haskins (1950) noted in *Diplophlyctis sexualis* and Karling (1945d) in *S. petersenii* that resting spores may be either sexually or asexually formed, it is apparent that a similar situation exists in *Asterophlyctis*.

Antikajian (1949) determined that, predominantly, the sporangium develops, as had previously been noted by other investigators, from the expanded body of the zoospore. In some instances, however, the nucleus of the encysted germinated zoospore passes out and the germ tube and the nucleated part enlarge to become the sporangium; the more distal portion then elongates and forms the rudiments of the rhizoids. The region of union of the primary rhizoidal branches then expands to form an apophysis. Rarely, the apophysis is absent. She at first cultivated the fungus on a 2 per cent chitin agar, but later found the chitin to be nonessential, the plants growing equally well on a peptone, yeast extract, dextrose, agar medium.

A form with a nearly spherical sporangium covered by small solid bipartite spines assigned to this species by Sparrow (1937a: pl. 1, fig. 19) has been identified with *Phlyctochytrium aureliae* by Ajello (1945).

RHIZOPHLYCTIS A. FISCHER

Rabenhorst. Kryptogamen-Fl., 1 (4): 119. 1892 (sensu recent. Minden, Kryptogamenfl. Mark Brandenburg, 5: 374. 1911 [1915])

(Fig. 28 A-D, p. 440)

Karlingia Johanson, Amer. J. Bot., 31: 397. 1944.

Thallus monocentric, eucarpic, ordinarily polyphagous, consisting of a reproductive rudiment (usually the body of the encysted zoospore) and several branched or unbranched rhizoidal axes only the ultimate tips of which are endobiotic; sporangium inoperculate, with one or more discharge papillae; zoospores formed within the sporangium, posteriorly uniflagellate, usually with a single globule, generally discharged in a compact group imbedded in a gelatinous matrix from which they eventually escape; resting spore thick-walled, borne like the sporangium on the thallus, upon germination functioning as a prosporangium.

On algae, insect integuments, and debris; abundant in soil.

As originally described in Fischer's monograph on the Phycomycetes the genus *Rhizophlyctis* also included *Rhizidium* Braun. Schroeter (1893: 79) reëstablished *Rhizidium* in its original sense and limited it to *Rhizidium mycophilum* Braun. *Rhizophlyctis* was retained as a genus but was not clearly separated from *Rhizidium* by him. This was later done by Minden, who emphasized the presence of a single main axis in the rhizoidal system of *Rhizidium* as contrasted with several axes, often of the same degree of development, in *Rhizophlyctis*. This morphological distinction is maintained here. Occasionally, as in *Rhizophlyctis borneensis*, the rhizoidal system may rise from a single central axis, but this is never broad and taproot-like, as in *Rhizidium*. The other extreme in rhizoidal development is to be found in *Rhizophlyctis petersenii*, where a number of broad rhizoids emerge from the rudiment of the sporangium (Fig. 28 A, p. 440). Further investigations may show these differences to be of no great significance, and the genus then should be merged with the older *Rhizidium*.

Johanson (1944) segregated the well-known *Rhizophlyctis rosea* de Bary and Woronin from *Rhizophlyctis* and placed it in a newly erected genus *Karlingia*. She based her decision on the presence of an endooperculum (see p. 437). There is little doubt from both the description and figures that de Bary and Woronin's fungus possessed such a structure. Both these competent investigators and Zopf, who observed a similar object in *Amoebochytrium*, noted that a pore developed in it through which the zoospores passed and that it was not dehisced.

Endoopercula (see p. 63) have recently been observed in species ascribed to *Rhizidium, Diplophlyctis, Nowakowskiella,* and *Nephro-chytrium* and are figured in older described chytrids such as *? Rhizidium lignicola* Lindau and the aforementioned *Amoebochytrium rhizidioides* Zopf. Several observers of undoubted *Rhizophlyctis rosea* have not, however, reported them; nor have they been seen in material of it by this author save once.

Since Karling (1947b: 65) has confirmed endooperculation in *Rhizophlyctis rosea* and verified it for other rhizophlyctoid fungi as well as for species of *Nowakowskiella* and *"Nephrochytrium,"* there is little doubt that the observations concerning this structure are correct. The present author, who has attempted to assemble all available published data as well as depend upon his own observations, concludes that endooperculation as opposed to true operculation is an unstable character. Under certain conditions one might then expect to find it in any chytrid, but perhaps especially in those sporangia in which the discharge papilla early in development liberates its gelatinous contents unaccompanied by immediate zoospore discharge. Haskins and Weston (1950) have expressed a similar opinion. Species of *Rhizophlyctis* are evidently particularly prone to form endoopercula. Few species of rhizophlyctoid fungi, since Johanson's study, have been described as without them. They have also been demonstrated in the true operculate as well as the inoperculate types.

Should subsequent observations on *Rhizophlyctis* species prove endooperculation to be a constant character, comparable with operculation in *Chytridium* and *Nowakowskiella,* recognition of *Karlingia* and generic segregation of such forms as *Diplophlyctis amazonense* and *Nowakowskiella granulata* would seem justified. In this publication the type of *Karlingia* is considered a true *Rhizophlyctis.* Hence, the species of *Karlingia* with exoopercula formed from wall material are better accommodated in a new genus, *Karlingiomyces* (see p. 559).

In *Rhizophlyctis,* as elsewhere, variations in thallus development occur. Not only does the sporangium occasionally form at the tip of a germ tube from the encysted spore body, but Karling (1947b) has noted the production, though rare, of polycentric thalli of limited extent.

KEY TO THE SPECIES OF RHIZOPHLYCTIS [1]

RHIZOPHLYCTIS BORNEENSIS Sparrow

Trans. Brit. Mycol. Soc., 21: 150, fig. 2 f-h. 1938

Sporangium free, pyriform or bursiform, 12–15 μ long by 7–10 μ in
diameter, smooth-walled, with a broad papilla; rhizoids from one to
three, arising from the middle or lower part of the sporangium, generally
branching in the vicinity of the host cell, polyphagous; zoospores
spherical, uniflagellate, from four to six formed in a sporangium, 4 μ
in diameter; resting spore not observed.

[1] See also *R. ingoldii* Sparrow (1957a) and recently described taxon, p. 446.

Parasitic on diatoms, coll. P. W. Richards, SARAWAK.
In the shape of its sporangium this fungus closely resembles *Rhizophlyctis mastigotrichis* (Nowak.) Fischer. It has, however, much smaller sporangia (12–15 by 7–10 µ as compared to ones 40 µ in diameter), the rhizoids are more delicate and attenuated, not swollen distally, and a smaller number of zoospores (from four to six rather than fifty or more) are produced in each sporangium.

RHIZOPHLYCTIS MASTIGOTRICHIS (Nowak.) Fischer

Rabenhorst. Kryptogamen-Fl., 1 (4): 121. 1892

Chytridium mastigotrichis Nowakowski, in Cohn, Beitr. Biol. Pflanzen, 2: 83, pl. 4, figs. 14-21. 1876.

Sporangium resting directly on or between the host filaments, spherical or somewhat ellipsoidal, about 40 µ in diameter, the apex prolonged into a short beak or a long tube, wall colorless, thin, smooth except in the apical region, where toothlike or small knoblike elevations may be present; rhizoids occasionally lacking, frequently from one to two, sometimes numerous, arising from the lower part of the rudiment of the sporangium, branched or unbranched, tapering or the tips expanding into a somewhat spherical haustorial structure where they make contact with the host cell; zoospores large, 8 µ long by 5 µ in diameter, ovoid with a blunt rounded anterior end, possessing a large narrowly ovoid strongly refractive globule, granular near the base and with a lateral extremely refractive elongate granule, flagellum attached at the narrower end, emerging from the tip of the discharge tube and forming a spherical motionless mass surrounded by an evanescent envelope of slime, movement somewhat slow in a straight or zigzag curving line, also amoeboid; resting spore not observed.

Parasitic on *Mastigothrix* (*Calothrix*) *aeruginea*, GERMANY; from soil, substrate ?, Gaertner (1954b: 22), SOUTH AFRICA.

RHIZOPHLYCTIS TOLYPOTRICHIS Zukal

Österr. botan. Zeitschr., 43: 310, pl. 11, fig. 13. 1893

Sporangium resting loosely on or occasionally within the swollen sheath of the alga, subspherical, sometimes slightly angular, with a

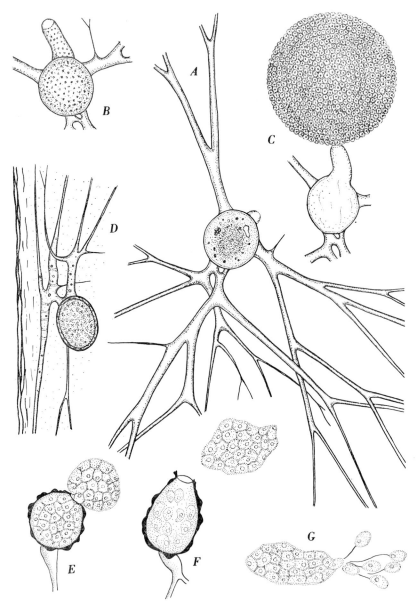

Fig. 28. *Rhizophlyctis petersenii* Sparrow and *Rhizidium verrucosum* Karling

colorless wall, the inner face somewhat irregularly thickened (wavy), the outer face smooth, 22–30 μ broad, with a short broad apical papilla; rhizoids dichotomously branched or unbranched, 1.5 μ in diameter, polyphagous, the endobiotic ones often running for some distance parallel with the axis of the alga; zoospores narrowly ovoid with a broad apex, 5–6 μ long by 3–3.5 μ broad, with one flagellum and one or more colorless globules in the contents, upon discharge resting temporarily in a mass in front of the orifice before swimming away, movement swimming or hopping; resting spore (?) formed by contraction of the contents of a sporangium-like structure, spherical or somewhat angular with rounded corners, 13–17 μ in diameter, with a thick colorless smooth wall and from one to two large globules, germination not observed.

On *Tolypothrix lanata*, GERMANY.

The somewhat angular resting spores, formed in the autumn, unlike those of other species in the genus rested loosely in a sporangium-like structure.

Zukal mentions another inhabitant of *Tolypothrix* which forms a broad curving filament in the alga. He suggests tentatively that it might be *Myzocytium*, but it may possibly be *Rhizosiphon* or *Lagenidium*.

RHIZOPHLYCTIS ROSEA (de Bary and Woronin) Fischer
Rabenhorst. Kryptogamen-Fl., 1 (4): 122. 1892

Chytridium roseum de Bary and Woronin, Berichte Verhandl. Naturforsch. Gesell. Freiburg, 3 (2): 52, pl. 2, figs. 17-20. 1865.
Rhizophydium roseum de Bary and Woronin, *loc. cit.*
Karlingia rosea (de Bary and Woronin) Johanson, Amer. J. Bot., 31: 399, figs. 1-37. 1944.

Explanation of Figure 28

A–D. Rhizophlyctis petersenii Sparrow: *A*, mature thallus, discharge tube beginning to form; *B*, mature sporangium with discharge tube; *C*, sporangium immediately after discharge, the zoospores, each with a small orange-colored oil globule, forming a motionless spherical cluster at tip of discharge tube; *D*, ellipsoidal resting spore formed just beneath wall of integument. *E–G. Rhizidium verrucosum* Karling, stages in the discharge of the zoospores from zoosporangia.

(*A–D*, Sparrow, 1937a; *E–G*, Karling, 1944c)

Sporangium variable in shape and size, spherical, ovoid, broadly clavate, or somewhat angular, 22–250 μ in diameter (occasionally only 3.3 μ), wall thick, smooth, colorless in small individuals, yellowish and minutely punctate in large ones, contents rose red, becoming light orange, golden, to brownish red at maturity, with one or several (up to twenty-four) broad discharge tubes filled with colorless gelatinous material; rhizoids one or more, laterally attached near the base of the sporangium or variously placed, up to 19 μ broad at point of origin, branched, extensive, up to 650 μ or more long, ramifying between the particles of the substrata; zoospores numerous, oval to spherical, rose-colored, 3.3–5.3 μ in diameter, with one or more dark globules or a single colorless globule, and a basal dense protoplasmic spot, escaping individually or in pairs, directly, or after the dehiscence of a basal membrane in the discharge tube ("endooperculum") or through a pore in this membrane, movement hopping or amoeboid; resting spore spherical, ovoid, or irregular, with a smooth somewhat thickened wall, contents granular, with globules, olive brown to orange brown, upon germination functioning as a prosporangium.

Forming rose-colored granulations on surface of moist soil in flower-pot, de Bary and Woronin (*loc. cit.*), moist blotting paper, Sorauer (in Schroeter, 1885: 191), soil, Remy (1948: 214), Harder (1948: 6), Reinboldt (1951: 178), GERMANY; parasitic on germinating spores of *Equisetum*, Cornu (1869b: 223), FRANCE; soil, blotting paper, Couch (1939a), M. W. Ward (1939), Whiffen (in M. W. Ward, 1939), Johanson (1944), Karling, (1948c: 509), soil, Sparrow (MICHIGAN) UNITED STATES; soil, coll. R. E. Coker, Cox (in Ward, 1939), GALAPAGOS ISLANDS; soil, Sörgel (1941), WEST INDIES; Shanor (1944), MEXICO; Shen and Siang (1948: 185), CHINA; Sparrow (1948: 447), MARSHALL ISLANDS; soil, Karling (1947b: 65), BRAZIL; soil, Sparrow (1952a: 37), CUBA; soil, Harder (1954: 4), SWEDISH LAPLAND; soil, substrate ?, Gaertner (1954b: 22), EGYPT, NORTHWEST AFRICA, WEST AFRICA, EQUATORIAL EAST AFRICA, SOUTH AFRICA; vegetable debris, Sparrow (1957a: 528), GREAT BRITAIN.

De Bary and Woronin did not consider the fungus a parasite. Cornu's observations indicated, however, that it occurred on the surface of the sand in his flats only where there were groups of *Equisetum* spores. The fact that the latter were always arrested in their development led him to suspect that *Rhizophlyctis rosea* was a parasite. Most of the above finds record the species from cellulose substrata. This species is the most widespread of all the Phycomycetes; it ranges from tropical land masses to remote Pacific coral atolls, from temperate regions to the Arctic. Its occurrence on such isolated atolls as Bikini, Rongerlap, and the like suggests that it is wind-borne.

Accounts of its development are given by Ward (1939) and Johanson (1944). Haskins and Weston (1950) made a study of the factors influencing its pigmentation and growth. They find that the coloration, which is probably due to carotenoid material, becomes more intense in well-aerated cultures grown in the light, especially on media of high pH value (6.8–7.0). Variations in type of development are given by Haskins (1948).

How many distinct species of chytrids have been ascribed to de Bary and Woronin's species awaits a comprehensive study, made from single-spore cultures, of all the pigmented forms of *Rhizophlyctis*.

RHIZOPHLYCTIS SPINOSA (Karling), comb. nov.

Karlingia spinosa Karling, Mycologia, 39: 60, figs. 23-33. 1947.

Sporangium smooth-walled, spherical and 5–400 μ in diameter, pyriform and 5–160 by 10–200 μ, oval and 4–70 by 7–100 μ, angular or irregular, with one to eighteen exit papillae or tubes, 4–10 μ long by 3–7 μ in diameter at base, the ends of which possess a hyaline glutinous plug which may protrude 5–12 μ above apex, contents golden red; rhizoids arising for the most part from several places on the sporangium, main axes mostly coarse, attaining a diameter of 10 μ, much branched and extensive; endooperculum hyaline, delicate, submerged in the papilla or exit tube, shallowly convex, 8 μ in diameter, sometimes sucked back into the sporangium; zoospores spherical or narrowly ovoid, 3.3–4.4 μ in diameter with one to five (six?) golden-brown refractive globules, and flagellum 28–32 μ long; resting spore spherical and 6–22 μ in diameter, oval and 8–12 by 10–15 μ, fusiform, elongate, clavate, or narrowly rectangular and 5–8 by 12–17 μ, spiny to verrucose with a golden-brown wall, contents coarsely granular bearing numerous golden globules, upon germination functioning as a prosporangium.[1] Saprophytic in vegetable debris in moist soil, Karling (*loc. cit.*), BRAZIL; UNITED STATES.

Karling separated this species from *Rhizophlyctis rosea*, with which it occurred in the same culture, on the basis of the character of the resting-spore walls. He cited other minor differences, such as number of zoospore globules and color. A few of the intramatrical resting spores had empty zoospore cases and germ tubes attached.

RHIZOPHLYCTIS CHITINOPHILA (Karling), comb. nov.

Karlingia chitinophila Karling, Mycologia, 41: 506, figs. 1-8. 1949.

Sporangia for the most part wholly extramatrical, hyaline, smooth-walled, spherical and 10–215 μ, oval and 15–30 by 20–45 μ, pyriform and 32–50 by 60–100 μ, citriform, elongate or angular or irregular, with one to twenty-six discharge papillae or tubes, 12–70 μ long by 5–8 μ in diameter, the ends of which possess a hyaline glutinous plug, which may protrude 5–15 μ above apex; rhizoids for the most part emerging from several places on the sporangium, main axes usually coarse, attaining a diameter of 20 μ, much branched and extensive; endo-operculum thin, hyaline, submerged in the exit papilla or tube, shallowly convex, up to 12 μ in diameter, expelled and carried away at zoospore discharge, accessory opercula drawn back into sporangium; zoospores hyaline, spherical, 3.18–3.71 μ in diameter, bearing numerous minute granules, flagellum 22–24 μ long; resting spore smooth-walled, spherical and 8–26 μ, oval and 8–18 by 11–23 μ, oblong, angular or irregular, greenish brown, with a wall 2–6.3 μ thick, sometimes with faint radial striations, contents coarsely granular, functioning as a prosporangium at germination.

Saprophytic on chitinous substrata in soil and water, Karling (*loc. cit.*), UNITED STATES; moist soil, coll. J. T. Baldwin, Karling (*op. cit.*, 508), LIBERIA.

Rhizophlyctis chitinophila is considered by Karling to be the hyaline

---

[1] This description and those of the following two species have been compiled from Karling's text, as well as from his technical Latin descriptions, in order to fill out essential morphological detail.

chitinophilic counterpart of *Rhizophlyctis rosea*. The species failed to grow on cellulose substrata and did not become colored under varying light conditions. As in others of the genus, a very few sporangia form from a local enlargement of the germ tube and, rarely, polycentric thalli develop.

RHIZOPHLYCTIS HYALINA (Karling), comb. nov.

Karlingia hyalina Karling, Mycologia, 39: 63, figs. 34-42. 1947.

Sporangium smooth-walled, hyaline, spherical and 8–85 μ, oval and 7–20 by 10–35 μ, pyriform and 10–30 by 20–55 μ, fusiform, angular or irregular, bearing one to seven exit papillae or tubes, 7–20 μ long by 3–6 μ in diameter, the tips of which are filled with a glutinous plug which may extend 4–10 μ beyond tip; rhizoids for the most part arising from several places on the sporangium, main axes mostly coarse, attaining a diameter of 12 μ, much branched and extensive, endooperculum hyaline, slender, delicate, shallowly convex, submerged in the exit papilla or tube, 6 μ in diameter, upon emergence of zoospores expelled and carried away; zoospores spherical, 4–5.5 μ in diameter, with a single large refractive, hyaline globule 2–2.5 μ in diameter, flagellum 30–36 μ long; resting spore not observed.[1]

Saprophytic in vegetable debris in moist soil, Karling (*loc. cit.*), BRAZIL.

As in certain other species of this genus, the sporangium forms typically from the body of the zoospore, which remains extramatrical and from which rhizoids are produced. In rare cases, however, the sporangia and rhizoids may develop intramatrically from a swelling near the tip of a branched germ tube. Infrequently, polycentric thalli with a large primary sporangium and a smaller one occur.

RHIZOPHLYCTIS PETERSENII Sparrow

Proc. Amer. Phil. Soc., 78 (1): 48, text figs. 3-4, pl. 3, figs. 1-7, pl. 4, fig. J. 1937

(Fig. 28 A-D, p. 440)

Sporangia spherical or irregularly shaped, smooth-walled, the spher-

---

[1] See p. 444, note.

ical specimens 50–75 μ in diameter, the irregular ones 60–170 by 40–140 μ, contents with numerous orange-brown droplets; rhizoids arising at from one to ten places on the sporangium, stout, up to 15.6 μ in diameter near the point of origin, extensive, much branched, 500 μ or more in length; zoospores up to several hundred in a sporangium, posteriorly uniflagellate, emerging through a discharge tube up to 50 μ long by 20 μ in diameter and forming a motionless globular cluster at the orifice before dispersing, nearly spherical, 5.2 μ in diameter, with a minute orange-brown globule and several refractive granules, movement swimming or amoeboid; resting spore intercalary or rarely terminal, relatively thick-walled, spherical, ellipsoidal, or irregular, with a densely granular orange-brown content.

In submerged empty larva cases of the Chironomidae, Odonata, Sparrow (*loc. cit.*); rotting oat leaves, Karling (1941b: 108), chitin bait, from moist soil, Karling (1948c: 509), Karling (1941a: 387; 1942c: 621), cellophane bait, Sparrow (1952d: 767), UNITED STATES; soil, Shanor (1944), MEXICO; boiled maize leaf, Sparrow (1952a: 39), CUBA; from soil, substrate?, Gaertner (1954b: 22), EGYPT, EQUATORIAL EAST AFRICA, SOUTH AFRICA; boiled grass leaves, Sparrow (1957a: 528), GREAT BRITAIN.

This is one of the largest and most striking species of the genus. The developing thallus consists of a sporangial rudiment which, though it is generally spherical, subspherical, or ellipsoidal, may occasionally be irregularly peltate and appressed to the inner surface of the substratum.

RECENTLY DESCRIBED TAXON [1], [2]

RHIZOPHLYCTIS HARDERI Uebelmesser

Arch. f. Mikrobiol., 25: 324, fig. 7. 1956

Sporangium spherical, smooth-walled, 40–60 μ in diameter; rhizoids arising from one or several places on the sporangium, delicate, branched, those within the substrate with a small apophysis; zoospores spherical, 4 μ in diameter, with a 20 μ long flagellum and small colorless basal

---

[1] Not included in the key.
[2] See also *R. ingoldii* in Sparrow (1957a).

globule, discharged through a 40 μ broad opening in a mass surrounded for a time by the gelatinized wall of the sporangium; resting spore with a smooth, thick wall and large refractive eccentric globule, bearing a somewhat apophysate rhizoidal system within the substratum and a bundle of rhizoids at the apex, at germination producing zoospores, 5.5 μ in diameter, endogenously as in the sporangium.

Pine pollen, in sea water and in fresh-water deposits, (VENICE) ITALY.

IMPERFECTLY KNOWN SPECIES OF RHIZOPHLYCTIS

? RHIZOPHLYCTIS PALMELLACEARUM B. Schröder

Biol. Centralbl., 18: 534. 1898

Sporangia ovoid, 5–7 μ long by 3–5 μ in diameter, with a yellowish smooth wall; rhizoids profusely dichotomously branched; all other characteristics unknown.

Parasitic in cells of a palmellaceous green alga, GERMANY.

Said by Schröder to be near *Rhizidium braunii* in its general features but much smaller.

? RHIZOPHLYCTIS SPP. Sparrow

Rev. Soc. Cubana Bot., 9: 37, pl. 1, figs. A-I. 1952

(1) Thallus consisting of a saccate plexus of lobulations, up to 320 μ in length by 96 μ in greatest diameter, from which at several places a very coarse, extensive branched rhizoidal system emerges; at maturity, up to six broad sessile discharge papillae formed; contents deep orange, cleaved into segments, approximately 5 μ in diameter; no zoospore discharge induced. (2) Thallus at maturity intricately lobed resembling a group of monocentric individuals, except that one segment has become walled off thus making the thallus polycentric; contents orange.

From soil, CUBA.

A fungus isolated from soil samples, collected by T. Schreuders near Batavia, Java, showed a similar somewhat lobulate reproductive rudiment. Whether all three are variations of the monocentric type, or represent a new group of organisms is at present problematical.

NOWAKOWSKIA Borzi

Bot. Centralbl., 22 (1): 23. 1885

(Fig. 25 A-D, p. 411)

Thallus monocentric, eucarpic, consisting of a sporangial rudiment (the body of the encysted zoospore) and from one to five rhizoids the tips of which are endobiotic; zoosporangium inoperculate, zoospores posteriorly uniflagellate, with a single globule, formed within the sporangium, liberated upon the dissolution and contraction of the sporangium wall as a flagellate compact motile group which disassociates into successively smaller groups and finally into individuals; resting spore not observed.

Parasitic on *Hormotheca.*

A monotypic genus. Differing from *Rhizophlyctis* in its method of zoospore liberation and the behavior of the freed spore mass. Some investigators consider this behavior abnormal and regard the fungus as a species of *Rhizophlyctis*. From the large numbers of plants developed in Borzi's cultures, it is hardly probable that he would have selected atypical ones in characterizing his genus.

Nowakowskia hormothecae Borzi

Bot. Centralbl., 22 (1): 23, pl. 1, figs. 1-10. 1885

Sporangium free in the medium, fully developed in from four to six hours, nearly spherical, 4–16 μ in diameter, with a smooth delicate colorless wall which gives a cellulose reaction, contents finely granular, multinucleate; rhizoids mostly three, rarely up to five, delicate, tapering, emerging from any point on the surface, unbranched or occasionally branched, varying in direction and length, polyphagous; zoospores minute, elongate with a median constriction, 1 μ long, flagellum posterior (?), 4–5 μ long, plasma thin, homogeneous, with a basal, anterior, or lateral refractive droplet, movement of the group rolling, duration of individual motility only a few minutes; resting spore not observed.

Parasitic on germinating spores of *Hormotheca sicula*, ITALY.

The cause of an epidemic in cultures of the host.

SUBFAM. POLYPHAGOIDEAE

Reproductive rudiment formed as an outgrowth from the body of the encysted zoospore; resting spore sexually produced by conjugation of directly adnate thalli or thalli joined by a conjugation tube; parasitic on fresh-water algae.

POLYPHAGUS Nowakowski

Cohn, Beitr. Biol. Pflanzen, 2: 203. 1876

(Figs. 4 Z-Z', p. 72; 5, p. 80; 29 F-J, p. 450)

Thallus generally lying free in the medium, monocentric, eucarpic, consisting of an expanded central part, the rudiment of the prosporangium, from which arise from two to three or more rhizoidal axes, the rhizoids profusely developed, much branched, strongly polyphagous, only the tips endobiotic; sporangium inoperculate, formed as an outgrowth from the prosporangium, from which it is cut off at maturity by a cross wall; zoospores posteriorly uniflagellate, with a single globule, completely formed in the sporangium, liberated through a pore produced in the wall of the sporangium; resting spore thick-walled, with a large globule, produced by the fusion of two anisogamous aplanogametes in the distal part of a conjugation tube formed generally by the smaller of two thallus-like gametangia, upon germination functioning as a prosporangium.

The species have thus far been found as parasites of *Euglena*, *Chlamydomonas*, *Tribonema*, and *Sphaerocystis*.

Through the early researches of Nowakowski (1876b; 1878), supplemented by later accounts of the morphology and cytology by Dangeard (1886a; 1900-1901c), Wager (1899a; 1913), Scherffel (1925b), and Bartsch (1945), *Polyphagus* has become one of the best known of the chytrids. The strongly polyphagous thallus of *P. euglenae* is ordinarily profusely developed, and both nonsexual and sexual reproductive organs are readily formed. Since the resting spore germinates after a relatively brief period of quiescence the whole life cycle can be easily followed in a short time, a situation of uncommon occurrence among the chytrids.

The most ubiquitous species of the genus is *Polyphagus euglenae*.

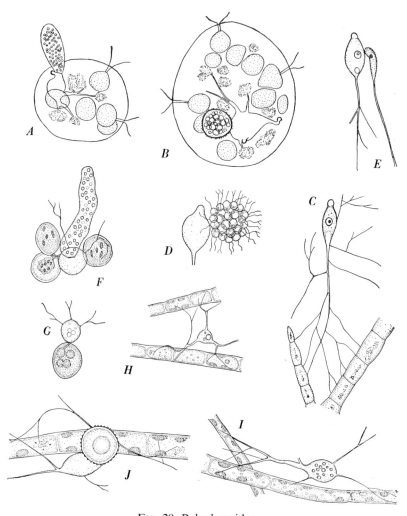

Fig. 29. Polyphagoideae

A–B. Endocoenobium eudorinae Ingold on colony of *Eudorina*: *A*, thallus with mature zoosporangium; thick-walled cyst of zoospore is at base of sporangium; *B*, mature spiny resting spore formed after fusion of two thalli. *C–E. Sporophlyctis rostrata* Serbinow on *Draparnaldia*: *C*, uninucleate thallus with rhizoids penetrating alga; *D*, group of aplanospores which have germinated after discharge from sporangium; *E*, male (smooth) and female (spiny)

P. parasiticus has also been reported in Europe in recent times by Scherffel (*op. cit.*), who gave an extensive account of its morphology and life history, and in the United States by Sparrow (1943); in both places it occurred as a parasite of *Tribonema bombycina*. *Polyphagus nowakowskii* Raciborski on *Chlamydomonas*, in Java, and *P. ramosus* Jaag and Nipkow on *Sphaerocystis*, in Switzerland, have been recorded only by their authors.

It is difficult to draw definitive lines between the species. Raciborski's fungus appears to differ from the others chiefly in forming smaller, colorless zoospores.

KEY TO THE SPECIES OF POLYPHAGUS

Parasitic on *Euglena* and *Chlamydomonas*; resting-spore wall spiny or
  smooth
 Zoospores cylindrical, ellipsoid or ovoid; globule colored
  Prosporangium typically fusiform oi clavate, occasionally globose;
   sporangia distinctly elongate, zoospores with a pale-golden
   globule; res'ing spore intercalary in the conjugation tube,
   wall spiny .... *P. euglenae*, p. 452
  Prosporangium typically globose; sporangia globose, ovoid or
   curved, zoospore with a bluish-green globule; resting spore
   terminal in the conjugation tube, wall smooth ...*P. laevis*, p. 453
 Zoospores spherical, globule colorless .... *P. nowakowskii*, p. 454
Parasitic on filaments of *Tribonema* and on *Sphaerocystis*; resting-spore
  wall spiny
 Parasitic on *Tribonema*; zoospores spherical, 6-8 μ in diameter; resting spore globose, 9-18 μ in diameter ...... *P. parasiticus*, p. 455
 Parasitic on the planktonic alga *Sphaerocystis*; zoospores spherical,
  4-5 μ in diameter; resting spore subglobose or ellipsoidal,
  12-24 μ long by 10-16 μ in diameter .... *P. ramosus*, p. 456

gametangia. *F–G. Polyphagus laevis* Bartsch: *F*, small mature sporangium produced from prosporangium resting between three parasitized cysts of *Euglena*; *G*, very young thallus resting directly on *Euglena*. *H–J. Polyphagus parasiticus* Nowakowski on *Tribonema*: *H–I*, young thalli lying between filaments of host; *J*, mature resting spore.

(*A–B*, Ingold, 1940; *C–E*, Serbinow, 1907; *F–J*, Sparrow, 1943)

POLYPHAGUS EUGLENAE Nowakowski

Cohn, Beitr. Biol. Pflanzen, 2: 203, pl. 8, figs. 1-7, 12; pl. 9, figs. 1-6, 14-15. 1876 (sensu recent. Bartsch, Mycologia, 37: 566, figs. 9-18. 1945)

(Fig. 5, p. 80)

Polyphagus euglenae Nowakowski pro parte (*loc. cit.*).

"Prosporangia extramatrical, lying free in the medium, rarely sessile, typically fusiform, clavate, commonly spherical, ellipsoid, elongated or irregular, 7.2–38.4, av. 18.1 μ in diameter $\times$ 12.2–200.0 or more, av. 36.2 μ long; with 2–8 rhizoidal axes about 6 μ in diameter at their point of origin, the latter branched and rebranched with their tips imbedded in a number of hosts. Zoosporangia typically lateral on a fusiform prosporangium, usually elongated, tubular and tapering toward the apex, occasionally short-cylindrical or curved, rarely ovoid or ellipsoid, 7.6–36.0, averaging 18.7 μ in diameter $\times$ 21.8–179.2 or more, av. 107.7 μ long, with thin smooth wall, opening by an apical deliquescence pore, containing one to many hundreds of zoospores. Zoospores cylindrical to ellipsoid, 3–5 μ in diameter $\times$ 6–13 μ long, containing a single posteriorly located pale yellow oil droplet and provided with a long posterior flagellum, escaping individually and generally swimming away immediately, positively phototactic, occasionally some zoospores germinating inside the sporangium. Antheridia fusiform, clavate, spheroid or irregular, 4.1–14.2, av. 9.4 μ in diameter $\times$ 6.6–35.4, av. 16.7 μ long; oogonia fusiform, saccular or irregular, 12.3–21.4, av. 16.3 μ in diameter $\times$ 14.8–61.7, av. 26.3 μ long. Zygospore spheroid, ovoid or wide-fusiform, 10.6–26.3, av. 17.9 μ in diameter $\times$ 18.0–27.0, av. 22.6 μ long, with a thick, 2-layered wall, the exospore bright yellow to amber or brown and beset with delicate conical spines or rarely with bullations, endospore smooth and hyaline; subterminal on an elongated conjugation tube 6.5–67.2, av. 18 μ long $\times$ 1.8 μ in diameter, separated from oogonium by a portion of that tube 4.9–13.2, av. 8.9 μ long $\times$ 3.3 μ in diameter; functioning in germination as a prosporangium" (Bartsch, *loc. cit.*).

On *Euglena sanguinia*, Gross (1851), *Euglena sp.*, Bail (1855: 678), *E. viridis*, Nowakowski (*loc. cit.*; 1878: 181), *Euglena sp.*, Fisch (1884a), Minden (1915: 382, fig. 28f [p. 364]), GERMANY; *Euglena*, Entz, Sr.

(1873: 1, pl. 1, figs. 12–17, pl. 2, figs. 6–8), HUNGARY; *Euglena viridis*, Blytt (1882: 29), NORWAY; *Euglena sp.*, Dangeard (1886a: 303, pl. 13, figs. 31–35; 1900–1901c: 213, figs. 2–3, pls. 6–7), FRANCE; *Euglena sp.*, de Wildeman (1890: 27), BELGIUM; encysted *Chlamydomonas reinhardi*, Serbinow (1907: 163), RUSSIA; *Euglena sp.*, H. E. Petersen (1909: 410; 1910: 544), Sparrow (1936a: 453), DENMARK; *Euglena viridis*, Wager (1913: 173, pls. 16–19), GREAT BRITAIN; cysts of *Euglena viridis* and *Chlamydomonas sp.*, Valkanov (1931a: 365), BULGARIA; *Euglena viridis*, Graff (1928: 165), *E. viridis* and *E. sanguinia*, cysts of *Chlamydomonas reinhardi*, *Chlamydomonas sp.*, Bartsch (*loc. cit.*), UNITED STATES.

Sparrow (1936a; 1943) suggested and Bartsch (1945) proved beyond question that Nowakowski was dealing with two different species of *Polyphagus*, one with spiny-walled and the other with smooth-walled resting spores. Bartsch (1945: 559) concluded from studies of unizygosporic cultures through many generations that "the nature of the zygospore wall is a persistent and inherited character whose fundamental features are influenced little if at all by environmental conditions." Because of this and differences between the two forms, he segregated Nowakowski's fungus with smooth walls as *P. laevis*.

Encysted prosporangia have been noted in *Polyphagus euglenae* by Dangeard and Wager. These are uninucleate and germinate to form a small sporangium. Sporangia of two size classes have been noted, as has also a relatively wide variation in the size of the zoospores. The possibility of the occurrence of sexual differentiation of the zoospores, as suggested by Kniep (1928), should not be overlooked in future investigations of this species.

The cytology of the species is well known from the researches of Dangeard and Wager (see "Cytology," p. 85).

POLYPHAGUS LAEVIS Bartsch

Mycologia, 37: 567, figs. 1-8, 19-23. 1945

(Figs. 4 Z-Ź, p. 72; 29 F-G, p. 450)

Polyphagus euglenae Nowakowski pro parte Cohn, Beitr. Biol. Pflanzen, 2: 203, pl. 8, figs. 8-11; pl. 9, figs. 7-13, 16. 1876.

P. euglenae var. *minor* Nowakowski, Akad. umiejetności Krakowie. Wydzíat mat.-przyród., Pamietník, 4: 174, pl. 10, figs. 97-100. 1878.

"Prosporangia extramatrical, lying free in the medium, rarely sessile, typically globose, 12.3–28.4, av. 22.4 μ in diameter, or ovoid, 11.2–26.2, av. 19.2 μ in diameter × 18.4–28.6, av. 24.0 μ long, occasionally irregular in shape, with 1–6 rhizoidal axes about 3 μ in diameter at their point of origin, the latter extensive, branched repeatedly and with their tips imbedded in a number of hosts. Zoosporangium located at any point on surface of prosporangium but typically diametrically opposite the insertion point of the most prominent rhizoidal axis, typically ovoid, 19.2–35.2, av. 27.5 μ in diameter × 25.6–41.6, av. 36.5 μ long, with thin smooth wall, opening by an apical or subapical deliquescence pore, containing several to many zoospores. Zoospores ovoid to elongated, 3.0–3.4, av. 3.3 μ in diameter × 5.0–6.5, av. 6.4 μ long, containing a single posteriorly located, pale bluish-green droplet and provided with a long posterior flagellum, escaping individually and generally swimming away immediately, positively phototactic, rarely germinating inside the sporangium. Antheridia spherical, ovoid or irregular, 4.2–15.4, av. 9.8 μ in diameter × 6.4–23.8, av. 16.5 μ long; oögonia spherical, ovoid or irregular, 14.0–28.2, av. 18.0 μ in diameter × 15.4–25.2, av. 20.8 μ in diameter. Zygospores ovoid, truncated, spheroid, elongated, reniform, lacrymoid, clavate, constricted, or irregular, 14.0–28.2, av. 19.7 μ in diameter × 19.6–35.0, av. 26.2 μ long, with thick, 2-layered wall, the exospore smooth, hyaline, rarely pale yellow, the endospore smooth and hyaline, terminal on a more or less elongated conjugation tube, 2.8–77.0, av. 28.2 μ long × 1.4–5.2, av. 3.0 μ in diameter and sessile on the larger gametic thallus, functioning in germination as a prosporangium" (Bartsch, *loc. cit.*).

On *Euglena*, Dangeard (1900–1901c), FRANCE; *Euglena*, Nowakowski (1876a; 1878), Minden (1915: 382), GERMANY; *Euglena*, Constantineanu (1901: 383), RUMANIA; *Euglena sp.*, Wager (1913: 180), Sparrow (1936a: 453, pl. 14, figs. 21–22; 1935a: fig. 2 h-i), GREAT BRITAIN; *Chlamydomonas*, Skvortzow (1927: 206), MANCHURIA; *Euglena viridis*, *Euglena sp.*, Bartsch (*loc. cit.*), UNITED STATES.

POLYPHAGUS NOWAKOWSKII Raciborski

Parasitische Algen und Pilze Java's, p. 6. Batavia, 1900

Prosporangium spherical, thin-walled, 9–16 μ in diameter, with several long branched delicate rhizoids the tips of which enter the host cells; sporangium variable in shape, unsymmetrical, mostly ovoid, with a broad base, larger than the prosporangium; zoospores spherical, 4 μ in diameter, with a colorless globule and a long flagellum; resting spore spherical, ovoid, elongate, or narrowly biscuit-shaped, 12–22 μ long by 8–12 μ broad, with a smooth yellowish thick wall, germination not observed.

Parasitic on *Chlamydomonas pluvialis*, JAVA, INDONESIA.

POLYPHAGUS PARASITICUS Nowakowski

Akad. umiejetności Krakowie. Wydzíat mat.-przyród., Pamietník, 4: 174, pl. 10, figs. 101-107. 1878

(Fig. 29 H-J, p. 450)

Prosporangium lying free between the filaments of the host, pyriform, clavate, or irregularly broadly fusiform, terminal or more often intercalary between two opposite main rhizoidal axes, from which, as well as from the body, arise more delicate branched rhizoids; sporangium generally formed as a lateral outgrowth from the prosporangium, ovoid, 16 μ long by 14 μ broad, wall thin, colorless; zoospores few, spherical, 6–8 μ in diameter, with a large (4 μ) colorless basal globule and a long flagellum, escaping upon the gelatinization of the upper half of the sporangium wall; resting spore formed in the tip of the laterally or apically applied conjugation tube, spherical, 9–18 μ (mostly 12–14 μ) in diameter, with a thick brownish wall covered with short conical spines, contents bearing a large (7–14 μ in diameter) colorless globule, upon germination functioning as a prosporangium.

Parasitic in *Tribonema bombycina*, Nowakowski (*loc.cit.*), GERMANY(?), Rieth (1954: 165, fig. 2), GERMANY; Scherffel (1902a; 1904; 1925b: 2, pl. 1, figs. 1–10), HUNGARY; Sparrow (1943: 301), UNITED STATES.

Scherffel (1925b) and more recently Rieth (*loc. cit.*) have given a complete account of this little-known species. In Michigan it is found in early spring among filaments of *Tribonema*.

The fungus with smooth-walled resting spore, figured by Rieth (1954: 167, fig. 2 H,I) on *Tolypothrix lanata*, appears to be a new species.

POLYPHAGUS RAMOSUS Jaag and Nipkow [1]

Berichte Schweiz. Bot. Gesell., 61: 493, pls. 14, 15. 1951

Prosporangium sessile on the gelatinous envelope of the host colony, ellipsoid, fusiform, or irregular, with a thin, smooth, hyaline wall, with one or more main rhizoidal axes which give rise to numerous branches the tips of which enter the host cells; sporangium an elongate, saccate, clavate, lateral outgrowth, 30–60 μ long by 14–18 μ in diameter, usually with the apex protruding beyond the colonial sheath; zoospores fifty to one hundred in a sporangium, spherical, 4–5 μ in diameter, with a large eccentric globule and posterior flagellum 40 μ long, escaping upon the gelatinization of the sporangium apex in a slimy mass and swimming away after a few minutes; resting spore formed in the tip of the conjugation tube, subglobose or ellipsoidal, 12–24 μ long by 10–16 μ in diameter, wall thick, dark-colored, beset with numerous spines, germinating after a few days to form a sporangium (as a lateral outgrowth) which produces about twenty zoospores differing in no respect from those in typical sporangia.

Parasitic on the plankton alga *Sphaerocystis schroeteri*, SWITZERLAND.

Similar to *Polyphagus parasiticus* on *Tribonema* but differing from it in having smaller zoospores and in being parasitic on *Sphaerocystis*.

The fungus is apparently host specific, since colonies of *Pandorina* and *Eudorina* occurring with it in the plankton were not infected.

SPOROPHLYCTIS SERBINOW

Scripta Bot. Horti. Univ. Imper. Petro., 24: 163. 1907

(Figs. 4 X-Y, p. 72; 29 C-E, p. 450)

Thallus monocentric, eucarpic, consisting of a reproductive rudiment (the body of the encysted spore) and a tapering main rhizoidal axis from which arise numerous secondary branches, tips of the ultimate branches endobiotic; prosporangium developed from the body of the encysted spore; aplanospores or zoospores formed in an inoperculate thin-walled sporangium produced laterally on the prosporangium, liberated upon rupturing of the sporangium wall; resting spore thick-walled, formed by the receptive thallus after conjugation of two unlike-sized thalli, the

[1] See Paterson (*Mycologia*, 50: 94. 1958).

smaller and receptive thallus, in the process, forming a tube which penetrates the contributing thallus and through which most of the contents of this thallus are discharged, germination not observed.

So far as is known parasitic only on the fresh-water green alga *Draparnaldia*, an inhabitant of cool, clear, running water.

Shen (1944) identified a fungus, which he found in China on *Draparnaldia*, with *Sporophlyctis rostrata* Serbinow and concluded that, because of the presence of motile zoospores rather than aplanospores, *Sporophlyctis* should be merged with *Polyphagus*. Undoubtedly, close similarities exist between the two genera but there is a fundamental difference in their type of sexual reproduction: in *Polyphagus* the zygote is always formed in or near the tip of a special conjugation tube, whereas in *Sporophlyctis* there is no such tube and the receptive structure, while smaller than the contributing thallus, is the thallus itself. This becomes walled off in its distal, expanded portion (from the body of the zoospore) and becomes converted into a resting spore. Other minor variations are also apparent, but the aforementioned feature is sufficient to separate the two genera. Shen's fungus is, therefore, here placed in *Sporophlyctis* (p. 458) and the generic description broadened to accommodate it.

KEY TO THE SPECIES OF SPOROPHLYCTIS

Prosporangium apiculate; sporangium spherical, producing aplanospores .... *S. rostrata*, p. 457
Prosporangium without an apiculus; sporangium narrowly ovate,
producing motile zoospores .... *S. chinensis*, p. 458

SPOROPHLYCTIS ROSTRATA Serbinow

Scripta Bot. Horti Univ. Imper. Petro., 24: 163, pl. 1, figs. 13-16, pl. 2, figs. 17-35. 1907

(Figs. 4 X-Y, p. 72; 29 C-E, p. 450)

Prosporangium ovoid, with a prominent apiculus, 30–39.5 μ long by 9–12.7 μ in diameter, wall thin, smooth, colorless, sporangium spherical or somewhat ellipsoidal, thin-walled, 23.7–31.6 μ in diameter ("20.5–26.8 $\mu \times$ 23.7–35.5 μ" [Serbinow, 1907]); rhizoids much branched, arising from the main axis or also occasionally from the body of the sporangium; aplanospores spherical, with a small eccentric colorless globule, germinating in the sporangium or upon the rupturing of its wall, free in the medium; resting spore ovoid, acuminate, 31.5 μ long by 23.5 μ wide, thick-walled, pale brown, the outer surface covered with minute spines, contents with a single globule, germination not observed; contributing thallus ovoid, smooth-walled.

Parasitic on *Draparnaldia glomerata*, Serbinow (*loc. cit.*), RUSSIA; *Draparnaldia plumosa*, Graff (1928: 166), UNITED STATES.

The immature thallus on *Draparnaldia* from Denmark figured by Petersen (1909: 410, fig. 20b; 1910: fig. 20b) and doubtfully assigned to *Sporophlyctis rostrata* is probably this species.

SPOROPHLYCTIS CHINENSIS, nom. nov.

Polyphagus rostratus (Serb.) Shen, Amer. J. Bot., 31: 233, figs. 1-21. 1944.

"Thallus holocarpic, hyaline, containing several refractive globules, polyphagous, attached to the algal filaments by means of the thread-like rhizoids which grow out from all parts of the plant, variable in shape and size, measuring 21–31 × 16–22 μ. Asexual reproduction by means of zoosporangia; mature thallus budding out an outgrowth which gradually enlarges and becomes a sporangium, spherical to elliptical, 17–21 × 25–29 μ. Sporangium quickly disintegrating after the emergence of the zoospores. Zoospores ovoid, 8–8.5 × 5.8–6.5 μ, posteriorly uniflagellate, with a central refractive body 2.5 μ in diameter, flagellum up to 28 μ long; swimming away directly from the sporangium without delay.

"Sexual reproduction by conjugation between two individuals; the smaller individual (18–21 × 4–6 μ) when conjugating with the larger one (16.4–18 × 31.2–36.6 μ), becoming spiny and finally being converted into the zygote. Mature zygotes spherical or subspherical (15.6–18 × 18–20.5 μ), yellowish brown, strongly spiny (spines 1 μ long), thick-walled, containing a central oily globule 11.4 μ in diameter. Germination unknown." (Shen, *loc. cit.*).

Parasitic on *Draparnaldia sp.*, CHINA.

Distinguished from *Sporophlyctis rostrata* by the lack of an apiculus on the prosporangium, the shape of the sporangium, and the motile spores.

ENDOCOENOBIUM INGOLD
New Phytologist, 39: 97. 1940
(Fig. 29 A-B, p. 450)

"The thallus is microscopic, living within the coenobium of members of the Volvocales. From the sac-like thallus rhizoidal outgrowths, branched or unbranched, make contact with the host cells. The thallus is not produced by the direct enlargement of the encysted zoospore, but by the enlargement of an outgrowth from it. The encysted zoospore persists on the surface of the host coenobium. The zoosporangium is elongated, and cut off from the thallus by a cross wall. Dehiscence is by an apical tear. The zoospores are uni-ciliate. The thick-walled resting spores are produced following a sexual process. In this process two thalli, which have developed in the same coenobium, fuse, and from the fusion-cell a warted zygospore is budded off" (Ingold, *loc. cit.*).

On *Eudorina elegans*, GREAT BRITAIN.

A monotypic genus.

ENDOCOENOBIUM EUDORINAE Ingold
New Phytologist, 39: 97, figs. 1-4, pl. 2. 1940

Sporangium 48–64 μ long by 18–36 μ in diameter; zoospores 50–200 in a sporangium, subspherical, 4–5 μ in diameter, with a refractive eccentric globule; resting spore 15–30 μ in diameter with its outer wall covered by low spines.

Parasitic on the plankton alga *Eudorina elegans*, Ingold (*loc. cit.*), GREAT BRITAIN; *Eudorina elegans*, Jaag and Nipkow (1951: 494, pl. 16), SWITZERLAND.

In the Swiss material up to 10 per cent of the colonies observed were infected.

Since the thallus develops as an outgrowth from the zoospore, Canter believes this fungus should be placed near *Entophlyctis*. Because of the formation of a prosporangium, however, it seems closer to *Polyphagus* and is maintained in the same subfamily for the present.

CLADOCHYTRIACEAE

Thallus intra- or extramatrical, or both, eucarpic, usually strongly polycentric, the vegetative system extensive, much branched, tubular, rhizoidal, septate or nonseptate, often with irregular swellings and septate turbinate cells; sporangia inoperculate, terminal or intercalary, zoospores posteriorly uniflagellate (the flagellum apparently lacking in one genus), with a single globule; resting spores thick-walled, apparently asexually formed, borne like the sporangia on the rhizoidal system, upon germination functioning as a prosporangium or zoosporangium.

Primarily saprophytic in decaying vegetable debris and parasitic in the eggs of microscopic animals and in fresh-water algae. One genus parasitic in marine algae.

"Endoopercula" have been found in some forms.

Because of the remarkable alternation of an epibiotic monocentric phase with an independent endobiotic strongly polycentric one, the genus *Physoderma*, formerly included here, is maintained distinct from the Cladochytriaceae, and is placed in a family of its own—the Physodermataceae (see p. 482).

KEY TO THE GENERA OF THE CLADOCHYTRIACEAE

Vegetative system predominantly rhizoidal and nonseptate except for the turbinate cells
  Zoospores flagellate, sporangia internally proliferous
    Sporangia and rhizoids predominantly endobiotic, the sporangia terminal or intercalary, often apophysate, with a discharge tube; zoospores at discharge forming a temporary motionless group .... CLADOCHYTRIUM, p. 461
    Sporangia and rhizoids predominantly extramatrical, sporangia without a discharge tube, borne at the tips of the rhizoids; zoospores at discharge swarming for a time in a vesicle at the orifice .... PHYSOCLADIA, p. 475
  Zoospores nonflagellate, strongly amoeboid, sporangia not proliferating .... AMOEBOCHYTRIUM, p. 476
Vegetative system predominantly tubular, septate or nonseptate
  Vegetative system intra- and extramatrical, mycelioid, with one or more axes, nonseptate or occasionally septate; sporangia of two types, smooth and tuberculate .... POLYCHYTRIUM, p. 477

CLADOCHYTRIUM NOWAKOWSKI, pro parte

Cohn, Beitr. Biol. Pflanzen, 2: 92. 1876 (sensu recent. Sparrow, Aquatic
Phycomycetes, p. 305. 1943)

(Fig. 30 I, p. 474)

Thallus predominantly endobiotic, polycentric, eucarpic, consisting
of an extensive much-branched rhizoidal system on which are formed
irregular swellings, septate turbinate cells, and the rudiments of the
sporangia and resting spores; sporangia inoperculate, intercalary or
terminal on short lateral branches, with a discharge tube, often proliferating; zoospores posteriorly uniflagellate, with a single globule,
formed in the sporangium, discharged through a pore at the tip of the
discharge tube; resting spores apparently asexually formed, borne like
the sporangia on the thallus, with a thickened smooth or spiny wall,
upon germination forming zoospores which escape through a discharge
tube or function as prosporangia.

Species of the genus are primarily inhabitants of decaying plant
tissues such as those of *Acorus*, grass stems, *Elodea*, and the like. They
have also been found in the gelatinous envelope of *Chaetophora* and in
plants of *Spirogyra*, *Coleochaete*, and so forth.

The genus as originally defined by Nowakowski included both
inoperculate and operculate forms. The latter were rightly segregated
from *Cladochytrium* by Schroeter (1893: 81) and placed in a new genus,
Nowakowskiella. From Nowakowski's description, *C. tenue* can be
considered typical of his genus. In that species the sporangia are
endobiotic, thin-walled, and discharge their zoospores through a tube
to the outside of the substratum. Resting spores in *Cladochytrium* are
borne on the thallus in the same fashion as are the sporangia (Sparrow,
1933c: 524, pl. 49, fig. 3; Karling, 1935: 449, figs. 21–29). At germination
they either form a discharge tube through which zoospores emerge or
function as prosporangia.

For a discussion of *Cladochytrium* versus *Physoderma* and *Urophlyctis*, see Sparrow (1943: 306) and Karling (1950).

CLADOCHYTRIUM TENUE Nowakowski

Cohn, Beitr. Biol. Pflanzen, 2: 92, pl. 6, figs. 6-13. 1876

(Fig. 30 I, p. 474)

Sporangia intra- or extramatrical, terminal or intercalary, formed from a swelling of the rhizoid or by enlargement of a segment of a septate turbinate cell, whereupon the sterile segment either remains at the base as an empty appendage or eventually becomes a sporangium, up to 66 μ in diameter, spherical, 8–30 μ, or somewhat pyriform, broadly oval or slightly citriform, 8–18 by 10–22 μ, with a low papilla or more or less prolonged regular or irregular rather stout discharge tube (rarely several) the tip of which is either extramatrical or penetrates a neighboring cell, wall smooth, colorless, proliferating, the secondary sporangia smaller; rhizoidal system extensive, main axes 1.5–3.5 μ in diameter, branching, with spindle-shaped, elongate, 5–8

---

[1] *Cladochytrium aneurae* Thirumalachar (*Trans. Brit. Mycol. Soc.*, 31: 8, figs, 1-3, 1947), which has been described from the liverwort *Aneura* from India, is not said to be aquatic.

[2] See also recently described taxon, p. 470.

by 10–17 μ, oval, 6–8 by 9–12 μ, spherical or oblong swellings which are often transversely septate and divided into two equal parts (occasionally three); zoospores spherical, 4.5–5.5 μ in diameter with a colorless eccentric, spherical or crescentic globule and a flagellum 25–28 μ long, emerging upon the deliquescence of the tip of the discharge tube and forming a temporary motionless group imbedded in "slime," movement amoeboid or swimming; resting spores spherical, 8–16 μ, oval, 10–12 by 14–16 μ, or broadly fusiform, with a colorless, smooth wall, upon germination functioning as a prosporangium.

In decaying tissues of *Acorus calamus, Iris pseudoacorus, Glyceria spectabilis*, Nowakowski (*loc. cit.*), soil, Remy (1948: 214), GERMANY; *Hippuris vulgaris*, de Wildeman (1895b: 91, pl. 3, figs. 14–23), FRANCE; leaves of "Massette," Constantineanu (1901: 385), RUMANIA; *Acorus calamus*, Sparrow (1943: 309, fig. 20 I), grass leaves (bait), soil, Karling (1948c: 510), UNITED STATES; vegetable debris, Karling (1945a: 33, figs. 31–51), BRAZIL; from soil, substrate?, Gaertner (1954b: 22), EGYPT.

The zoospore at germination produces one or two delicate filaments, which after a few days become elongate and irregularly branched. Spindle-shaped swellings soon appear and the sporangia are later formed from some of these.

De Wildeman's record is doubtful, since no zoospore discharge was observed. The same might be said for the occurrence in Rumania reported by Constantineanu. The fungus figured by Ookubo (1954, fig. 44) does not appear to relate to *Cladochytrium tenue*.

CLADOCHYTRIUM TAIANUM Shen and Siang

Sci. Repts. Nat. Tsing Hua Univ., Ser. B: Biol. and Psych. Sci., 3: 183, fig. 5. 1948

"Rhizomycelium intramatrical and extramatrical, extensively branched, and anastomosed, with numerous fusiform, usually biseptate, rarely multiseptate swellings; zoosporangia extramatrical, terminal or intercalary, non-apophysate, inoperculate, variable in shape and size, spherical, subspherical or ovoid, 22–42 μ in diameter; zoospores hyaline, spherical, 11 μ in diameter, containing a single refractive body measuring 7.2 μ in diameter, posteriorly uniflagellate, exit tube not formed;

resting spores terminal or intercalary mostly spherical, 13–14 μ in diameter, with a single central [colorless] oil globule, about 8.2 μ in diameter, wall smooth, about 1 μ thick" (Shen and Siang, *loc. cit.*).

Saprophytic on decaying grass leaves from swamp, CHINA.

Distinguished from *Cladochytrium tenue* by the large zoospores.

CLADOCHYTRIUM REPLICATUM Karling

Amer. J. Bot., 18: 538, pls. 42-44. 1931

(Fig. 6 A-J, p. 88)

Cladochytrium nowakowskii Sparrow, Amer. J. Bot., 18: 619, pl. 45, figs. H-N. 1931.

Entophlyctis aurantiaca Scherffel, in Domján, Folia cryptogam., 2: 26, pl. 1, figs. 50-51, 57-59, 72-73, 75. 1936.

Sporangia generally terminal on short lateral branches, predominantly spherical, ovoid, or pyriform and free in the cell of the substratum, or sometimes filling it and becoming irregular, symmetrical sporangia 8–18 μ in diameter, with a single narrowly cylindrical discharge tube of variable length (occasionally several), wall thin, smooth, colorless, proliferating; rhizoidal system delicate, much branched, extensive, bearing septate turbinate cells at frequent intervals; zoospores variable in number, spherical, 4–7.3 μ in diameter, with a cadmium-orange or golden-brown globule and a long flagellum, emerging through the tip of the discharge tube and forming a temporary motionless group at the orifice before swimming away, movement swimming or amoeboid; resting spores borne like the sporangia on the thallus, predominantly spherical, 9–21 μ in diameter, with a thickened spiny or smooth colorless wall and a large cadmium-orange or golden-brown globule in the contents, upon germination producing a discharge tube and functioning as a zoosporangium or as a prosporangium.

Saprophytic in a wide variety of vegetable materials and artificial media, Karling (1931b; 1935; 1937b), parasitic in *Spirogyra crassa*, *Oedogonium spp.*, *Coleochaete sp.*, cultivated on maize-meal agar, Sparrow (*loc. cit.*), saprophytic in *Elodea canadensis*, decaying grass culms, Sparrow (1933c: 524, pl. 49, fig.3), artificial media, Couch (1939a) Karling (1941a: 387), in rotting oat leaves, Karling (1941b: 108), Karling (1942c: 620), on onion skin and bleached grass leaves, Karling

(1948c: 509), from water and soil containing animal and vegetable debris, Karling (1949c: 299), saprophytic on vegetable debris, Sparrow (1952d: 768), UNITED STATES; saprophytic in *Elodea canadensis*, grass, Sparrow (1936a: 453), plant debris, Richards (1956: 263), GREAT BRITAIN, *Typha* leaves, Scherffel (in Domján, 1936), HUNGARY; decaying vegetable debris, Sparrow (1952a: 39), CUBA; Shanor (1944: 331), MEXICO; Karling (1945a: 35), BRAZIL.

This is a ubiquitous chytrid and rare are the submerged decayed bits of the softer parts of phanerogams which do not contain it. The species is readily distinguished from the less common *Cladochytrium tenue* by the brilliantly colored globule of the zoospore. This coloration makes its appearance early in the development of the sporangium.

Observations by Karling and later ones by Sparrow on what appears morphologically to be *Cladochytrium replicatum* indicate that it is primarily saprophytic. The fungus was grown on maize-meal agar by Sparrow (1931c), but it could not be freed from bacterial contamination. Material of it was later cultivated by Karling (1935), Couch (1939a) and others not only on maize-meal agar but also on prune, malt, potato-dextrose, and mannite-soil agars. Karling found that sporangia formed only in liquid media. Of the agars used, maize meal and mannite soil were most favorable.

In spite of the amount of study accorded *Cladochytrium replicatum* certain aspects of it still need clarification. Primarily, these center around the nature of the resting spore. Such structures were not observed in the original isolate. In a strain (supposedly of this species but termed *C. nowakowskii*) parasitic on algae, the single resting spore observed (Sparrow, 1931c) was essentially smooth-walled. In another, a saprophytic strain studied by Sparrow (1933a), the resting spores were unquestionably spiny. Karling (1935) described the wall as predominantly smooth, even though spiny ones were present "in a large number of sporangia." He was, incidently, unable to induce his strain to infect living algae. The fungus cytologically investigated by Karling (1937b), see "Cytology," page 87, produced both smooth and spiny-walled resting spores, and in another isolate he reported (1941b: 108) that only 10 per cent of the resting spores were smooth, the great majority being spiny. Since none of these studies was made from single-spore isolates, or their equivalent, it is entirely possible, as suggested by Sparrow (1936a) and later proved correct by Bartsch (1945) in the case of *Polyphagus euglenae*, that there are two distinct species involved. From the conflicting evidence concerning pathogenicity, it is also possible that different physiological strains exist.

? Cladochytrium aureum Karling
Bull. Torrey Bot. Club, 76: 298. 1949

Sporangia terminal or intercalary, oval or citriform, 8–19 by 10–23 μ, or subspherical and 8–36 μ, without discharge tubes; rhizoidal system delicate, extensive, the narrow part 1.2–3.5 μ in diameter, with septate oval and 6–8 by 9–12 μ, fusiform and 5–8 by 10–17 μ, or irregular swellings; zoospores spherical, 5.8–6.2 μ in diameter, with a conspicuous, 2–2.4 μ in diameter golden-orange to red globule and flagellum 27–29 μ long; resting spores spherical and 9–17 μ in diameter or oval and 8–12 by 11–16 μ or fusiform, germination not observed.

Saprophytic in vegetable debris, UNITED STATES.

The only significant difference between this species, as presented, and *Cladochytrium replicatum* is a lack of spines on the resting spore (see discussion under the latter species) and absence of a discharge tube on sporangium.

CLADOCHYTRIUM SETIGERUM Karling
Bull. Torrey Bot. Club, 78: 38, figs. 1-8. 1951

Sporangia commonly intercalary, oval, 11–27 by 19–44 μ, spherical, 13.2–28.5 μ, occasionally elongate and constricted, sometimes with a funnel-shaped elongate apophysis, bearing 10–50 simple or branched 5.5–30 μ long by 1.7–2.4 μ in diameter setae, with a single conical or hemispherical discharge papilla which is sessile or at the tip of a short tube 7–9 by 14–20 μ long; rhizoidal system extensive, delicate, branched, 1.7–2.8 μ in diameter, with a few nonseptate fusiform, elongate, or irregular enlargements 6–10 μ broad by 8–18 μ long; zoospores spherical, 3–3.4 μ in diameter, with a minute basal, colorless globule 0.8–1.2 μ in diameter and 16–19 μ long flagellum, upon discharge forming a temporary globular mass at the orifice before swimming away; resting spores not observed.

Saprophytic on cellulose substrata, soil, UNITED STATES.

As Karling (*loc. cit.*) implied, this inoperculate species is an almost exact counterpart of the operculate *Nowakowskiella atkinsii* Sparrow (p. 591). Although he did not regard the septate setigerate turbinate cells as such but as incipient sporangia (and so understood here), they are exactly like those in *N. atkinsii*. Mention of them is not included in the compiled species description, which is drawn both from Karling's Latin diagnosis and his English text.

CLADOCHYTRIUM CRASSUM Hillegas

Mycologia, 33: 618, figs. 1-40. 1941

"Rhizomycelium well developed, extensive, coarse, with numerous intercalary, non-septate, fusiform to globose swellings 3.85 × 15–18 × 25 μ, the tenuous portions as little as 1.5 μ in diameter, with trabeculae. Rhizoids 0.5 μ to 1.1 μ in diameter originating at various places along the rhizomycelium. Zoösporangia terminal or intercalary, seldom proliferating, non-apophysate, variously shaped, commonly spherical to slightly pyriform, 11 × 20–30 × 43 μ. Exit tube occasionally to 27 × 74 μ, papilla or pore, usually single, deliquescent. Zoöspores delimited within zoösporangium and emerging in a non-motile mass enveloped in slime, which remains at the mouth of the exit tube a few minutes before the zoöspores become active and swim away. Zoöspore hyaline, spherical to slightly pyriform, occasionally amoeboid, 4.9–6 μ in diameter with a clear highly refractive globule 2–2.75 μ in diameter, posterior flagellum 25–35 μ, swimming rapid and darting. Resting spore spherical (9.35–23 μ diameter) to fusiform (10 × 26 μ–14.8 × 23.1 μ), wall 1.5 μ thick, light brown in color, germination unknown" (Hillegas, *loc. cit.*).

Saprophytic on decaying vegetation, Hillegas (*loc. cit.*), in rotting oat leaves, onion skin and cellophane, moist soil, Karling (1941b: 108; 1942c: 620; 1948c: 509), UNITED STATES; vegetable debris, Karling (1945a: 34), BRAZIL.

Karling (1945a: 34) reported that the resting spores germinate after a dormant period of seven weeks. Some functioned directly as sporangia, whereas others produced a sporangium external to the spore.

CLADOCHYTRIUM HYALINUM Berdan

Amer. J. Bot., 28: 425, figs. 1-84. 1941

"Thallus intra- and extramatrical, polycentric, eucarpic. Zoosporangia imbedded in the substratum, or formed extramatrically, terminal or intercalary, apophysate, proliferating, spherical, 15–40 μ in diameter, subspherical, ovoid, pyriform, irregular, branched and lobed or greatly elongated, 4–40 μ × 12–100 μ. Exit tubes commonly single, 2–6 μ × 2–10 μ. Rhizomycelium sparse or copious and extensive, richly branched and anastomosed, 1.5–8 μ in diameter, with numerous round, oval, or fusiform swellings, 2–10 μ × 4–14 μ (generally 4–10 μ × 6–10 μ). Zoospores escaping in a globular mass, briefly quiescent previous to swimming away, hyaline, spherical, 8–10 μ in diameter, uninucleate and posteriorly uniflagellate with a single highly refractive and extremely mobile globule, 4–7 μ in diameter; flagellum 40–50 μ long; method of swimming rapid and darting. Resting spores usually spherical, 12–18 μ in diameter, sometimes oval, pyriform or elongated (10–12 μ × 25–28 μ) and subtended by several small, thin-walled cells; wall of resting spore smooth, hyaline, several-layered; content including numerous hyaline, rounded, refractive bodies, which later coalesce into a single, eccentric globule about 8–10 μ in diameter. Resting spore functioning as a prosporangium at germination, producing to the exterior, through a pore in its wall, a hyaline, thin-walled zoosporangium similar to the evanescent one" (Berdan, *loc. cit.*).

Saprophytic in grass leaves, Berdan (*loc. cit.*), in rotting oak leaves, Karling (1941b: 108), bleached grass leaves, Karling (1941a: 387; 1942c: 620; 1948c: 510), UNITED STATES; cellophane, corn leaves, Shanor (1944: 332), MEXICO; onion skin and corn leaves, Karling (1945a: 34), BRAZIL; grass, Haskins (1946: 135), GREAT BRITAIN.

The descriptions by Berdan and Karling[1] reveal no essential difference between their two species other than slight variations in the extreme values of size of parts and the presence of an endooperculum in Karling's fungus. A study by R. M. Johns (comm.) of a form similar to Karling's *Nowakowskiella macrospora*, save that no endooperculum is

---

[1] Of *Nowakowskiella macrospora*, Karling, p. 589, which was at first considered identical with *C. hyalinum*.

formed, further strengthens the view that the two are identical. See also remarks under the next species.

Striking features of the species are its large oil globule in the zoospore and strong tendency for extramatrical development. It resembles in the latter respect a *Nowakowskiella* rather than a *Cladochytrium*.

CLADOCHYTRIUM GRANULATUM (Karling), comb. nov.

Nowakowskiella granulata Karling, Bull. Torrey Bot. Club, 71: 374, figs. 1-29. 1944.

Rhizoidal system profusely developed, much branched, hyaline when young, brownish and thick-walled with age, slender parts 1.5–7 μ in diameter, expanded parts mostly nonseptate, oval (6–8 by 9–11 μ), broadly fusiform (5–9 by 8–13 μ), almost globose (6–10 μ in diameter), or irregular; sporangia terminal or intercalary, mostly nonapophysate, globose (12–35 μ in diameter), pyriform (12–22 by 15–30 μ), oval (10–18 by 12–25 μ), or occasionally irregular, with one to three discharge papillae, 3 by 5 μ, or one terminating a more or less elongate discharge tube which at its tip bears a plug of opaque gelatinous material and within it on the surface of the contents proper an oval, discoid, crateriform, saucer-, bowl-, cup-, or cone-shaped endooperculum, 3–7 μ in diameter; zoospores globose, 5–6.6 μ in diameter, with numerous golden-brown granules of uniform size in the contents and a flagellum about 35 μ in length; resting spores formed from the intercalary swellings, with a smooth, hyaline 1.5–2 μ thick wall, globose (15–24 μ in diameter), oval (15 by 20 μ), with a large (12 μ in diameter) refractive globule and numerous smaller ones, germination not seen.

In decaying vegetable debris, Karling (*loc. cit.*), BRAZIL.

As Karling recognized, the fungus strongly resembles a *Cladochytrium*. Since the type of operculation is not regarded here as comparable to that of a true species of *Nowakowskiella*, the species is placed in *Cladochytrium*. It has been suggested that the formation of the poorly defined endoopercula and the presence of *Cladochytrium*-like plugs of gelatinous material in the orifices of the discharge tubes points to the species as transitional between the inoperculate and operculate forms, or vice versa. Such a possibility is worthy of consideration. The presence of numerous granules rather than a single globule in the zoospore mark it as distinct.

RECENTLY DESCRIBED TAXON [1]

CLADOCHYTRIUM AURANTIACUM Richards

Trans. Brit. Mycol. Soc., 39: 264, figs. 1-3. 1956

Sporangia generally spherical to subspherical, 18–24 μ in diameter (usually about 22 μ), irregularly shaped when occurring within the narrow cells of substratum, with a narrow discharge tube 8–12 μ long, contents colorless when young, when maturing becoming shot through with reddish-golden or orange globules, proliferating; rhizoidal system profusely developed, about 2 μ broad with few irregular swellings and once or twice septate turbinate cells, 10–20 μ in diameter with hyaline globules in the contents; zoospores spherical, 6–7 μ in diameter with a large (3.7–4.2 μ in diameter) spherical eccentric orange globule and long posterior flagellum, escaping upon the deliquescence of the tip of the discharge tube and forming a motionless cluster before swimming away; resting spore not observed.

In fragments of leaves, stems, and roots of *Avena* and *Triticum*, GREAT BRITAIN.

Said to differ from *Cladochytrium replicatum* and *C. aureum* by the larger size of the parts, of the zoospores (especially their globule), and of the colorless turbinate cells.

IMPERFECTLY KNOWN SPECIES OF CLADOCHYTRIUM [2]

? CLADOCHYTRIUM CORNUTUM de Wildeman

Ann. Soc. Belge Micro. (Mém.), 20: 59, pl. 3, figs. 1-22. 1896

Sporangia formed extramatrically, subspherical or reniform, apophysate, not separated from the vegetative system by a cross wall, with a crown of from three to seven coarse plain teeth; rhizoidal system

---

[1] Not included in the key.

[2] For a discussion of certain shell-boring organisms supposedly belonging to this genus see pp. 472-473.

endobiotic, branched, extensive, with fusiform swellings; zoospores spherical, uniflagellate, with a small refractive eccentric globule, probably escaping through a pore formed within the apical collarette of teeth; resting spores not observed.

In rotting plant tissues, in company with *Cladochytrium tenue*, FRANCE.

Although the species is obviously distinct from other members of *Cladochytrium* by reason of the ornamentation of the sporangium, some features of it are puzzling. De Wildeman has shown in Figure 14 an empty sporangium within which are three empty saclike structures. These he thought belonged to a parasitic organism. Over half the figures of mature sporangia shown have "vacuoles" within them which in some cases approximate in size and shape the empty sporangia of the parasitic organism. Earlier monographers have doubted the validity of the species. This is not questioned here, yet the possibility that the concept is based on parasitized and hypertrophied specimens of *Phlyctochytrium planicorne*—found in the same habitat—cannot be entirely excluded.

? CLADOCHYTRIUM IRREGULARE de Wildeman

Ann. Soc. Belge Micro. (Mém.), 19: 91, pl. 3, figs. 1-13. 1895

A fungus parasitic in aquatic grasses with irregular tubular sporangia which resemble those of *Mitochytridium* and which are 200–235 (?) μ long by 15–40 μ wide and borne on a branched rhizoidal system has been called a species of this genus by de Wildeman (*loc. cit.*). No zoospores were observed, and its affinities are in doubt.

? CLADOCHYTRIUM POLYSTOMUM Zopf

Nova Acta Acad. Leop.-Carol., 47: 234, pl. 21, figs. 1-11. 1884

Sporangia spherical or fusiform, intercalary, originating as spindle-shaped enlargements on the vegetative system, forming from one to six long irregular discharge tubes; vegetative system extensive, branched, slender, rhizoidal; zoospores spherical with a brownish-orange oil globule; resting spores not observed.

In *Triaena*, GERMANY.

No description of the fungus occurs in Zopf's text, and a formal description was first given by Fischer (1892: 135).

An estimation of the sizes of the parts, arrived at by using as a measure the zoospore of *Rhizophydium carpophilum*, which is described as 4–5 μ in diameter and is drawn to the same magnification, indicates that the sporangia of *Cladochytrium polystomum* are 15–20 μ in diameter, the zoospores 3–4 μ, and the broadest part of the vegetative system 3 μ. This agrees well with the sizes of these parts in Karling's *C. replicatum*. Hence, save for the occurrence of several discharge tubes and the lack of proliferated sporangia, Zopf's fungus appears nearly identical with Karling's. The multiplicity of tubes is not unknown in *C. replicatum* and may have been due in Zopf's fungus to poor environmental conditions. Karling's name, however, is preferred, since the organism has been more completely described by him.

Shell-boring *"Cladochytria"*

Zebrowski (1936) and Porter and Zebrowski (1937) described from bits of calcareous Australian sand of uncertain geological age, presumably from Cambrian to Recent, a number of so-called "lime-loving" fungi which are believed to be members of the Cladochytriaceae. Through the kindness of Mr. Zebrowski a number of slides of these sands have been examined. As the photographs accompanying his paper clearly indicate, the bits of shell have been bored through by some organism that has a saclike enlargement from which radiate delicate rhizoidal canals. These sacs, presumed to be sporangia, empty to the outside of the shell by a tube. In certain instances, as for example in *Dodgella priscus*, which was found in shells and also in spicules of calcareous sponges, sporelike structures were observed in the sacs. Such "spores" were also found imbedded in cavities of varying depth on the outer surface of bits of shells. As Zebrowski supposes, it is possible that they secrete a substance which allows them to penetrate or burrow into the matrix. Indeed, it is necessary that they secrete some lime-dissolving fluid if they are to maintain themselves in such a substratum.[1]

It is obvious that the "fossil" nature and affinities of these forms must await the results of investigation on living material, which no doubt exists. Such investigation will be difficult because of the opaque nature of the substratum.

These shell-boring "fungi" have been known for a long time, and in 1860 Kölliker (1860a, 1860b) issued an extensive account of various "vegetable parasites" of shells, sponge spicules, scales of fishes, and the like. In Kölliker's paper are references to still earlier investigations. As a result of his studies he concluded that the extraneous structures were fungi and noted that they were very frequent in marine organisms and almost or wholly lacking in fresh-water forms. He also noted that not all marine animals were prey to the parasites, those with chitinous material are free of them. In the Mollusca, on the other hand, uninfected shells were the exception. Types with a thick periostracum and a prismatic layer were not attacked, the fungi evidently not being able to effect penetration. The shell-boring forms apparently accomplished their entrance by the secretion of an acid which dissolved the lime or, in the resistant sponge skeletons, possibly by mechanical action. Kölliker left open the question of whether they were algae or fungi, but was strongly inclined toward believing that they belonged to the latter group. Other fossil chytrids have been described by Daugherty (1941).

Opportunity was also afforded for examining sponge spicules with numerous canals in them. These were kindly sent by Dr. Arndt of the Berlin Zoological Museum. As in the shell-boring "Cladochytria," however, nothing could be definitely learned from prepared material concerning the affinities of these organisms. Until all of them have been studied in the living state and their spore structure determined little can be said of their relationships to the chytrids or, indeed, to the fungi.

---

[1] Other slides kindly sent by Mr. Zebrowski show cavities shaped exactly like certain monocentric chytrids such as *Asterophlyctis*.

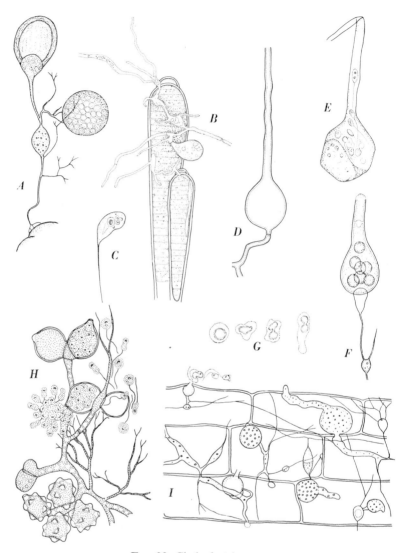

FIG. 30. Cladochytriaceae

A. *Physocladia obscura* Sparrow, habit of plant on pollen grain; an immature sporangium and a terminal empty internally proliferous one shown. B–E. *Coenomyces consuens* Deckenbach on a marine species of *Calothrix*:

PHYSOCLADIA Sparrow

Mycologia, 24: 285. 1932

(Fig. 30 A, p. 474)

Thallus predominantly extramatrical, rhizoidal, much branched, polycentric, with septate turbinate cells and nonseptate fusiform or irregular swellings, bearing the rudiments of the sporangia and resting spores; sporangia inoperculate, terminal, proliferating; zoospores posteriorly uniflagellate, with a single globule, produced within the sporangium, liberated through a pore formed upon the deliquescence of a papilla and undergoing a period of swarming in a vesicle at the orifice before escaping; resting spores thick-walled, borne on the thallus, germination not observed.

Known thus far only as a saprophyte of the staminate cones of *Pinus*.

This monotypic genus resembles *Nowakowskiella* very closely. It differs in having an inoperculate sporangium which forms a well-defined vesicle within which, upon discharge, the zoospores swarm before their escape.

Physocladia obscura Sparrow

Mycologia, 24: 285, fig. 4e. 1932

(?) *Nowakowskiella obscura* Sparrow, Amer. J. Bot., 18: 621, pl. 45, figs. A–G. 1931.

Sporangia terminal, spherical or subspherical, apophysate, 42 μ in

---

B, habit of plant bearing single sporangium; *C*, single zoospore with pale-yellow globule; *D*, empty sporangium with long discharge tube; *E*, partly discharged sporangium; remaining contents and globules are pale yellow. *F–G. Amoebochytrium rhizidioides* Zopf in slime sheath of *Chaetophora*: *F*, mature apophysate sporangium with globules of spores; septum in discharge tube is still present; *G*, some of shapes assumed by nonflagellated amoeboid spores. *H. Polychytrium aggregatum* Ajello, portion of thallus showing smooth- and rough-walled (tuberculate) zoosporangia and discharge of zoospores. *I. Cladochytrium tenue* Nowakowski in decaying tissue of *Acorus calamus*.

(*A*, Sparrow, 1931c; *B–E*, Deckenbach, 1902–3; *F–G*, Zopf, 1884; *H*, Ajello, 1942; *I*, Sparrow, 1943)

diameter, with a thin brownish wall which wrinkles after discharge, plasma colorless, rhizoidal system variable, delicate, bearing numerous fusiform spherical and irregular swellings and occasionally septate turbinate cells; zoospores spherical, 4.2 μ in diameter, with a centric colorless globule and a single flagellum, escaping upon the dissolution of an apical or subapical papilla into a broad flask-shaped vesicle in which they swarm; resting spores apparently terminal, on broad elements of the rhizoidal system, spherical, 21–50 μ in diameter, with a dark-brown thick rough wall, contents granular, germination not observed.

Saprophytic in staminate cones of *Pinus*, in water culture containing *Sphagnum*, UNITED STATES.

The rhizoidal system which ramified between the pollen sacs and inside between the pollen grains possessed numerous irregularities and swellings. The extramatrical rhizoids which bore the sporangia were tenuous, with large nonseptate fusiform swellings.

It is strange that this very characteristic form has not been seen again in the quarter century since its discovery. Fortunately, a slide of it is preserved to testify to its very existence!

AMOEBOCHYTRIUM ZOPF

Nova Acta Acad. Leop.-Carol., 47: 181. 1884

(Fig. 30 F-G, p. 474)

Thallus polycentric, eucarpic, consisting of a branched rhizoidal system bearing on it intercalary swellings; sporangia inoperculate, formed by enlargement of the body of the encysted zoospore or of the intercalary swellings of the rhizoids, cut off at maturity by cross walls from the vegetative system and often disarticulated; zoospores without flagella (always?), escaping by forcing one of the gelatinized cross walls, movement amoeboid; resting spores not observed.

A monotypic genus, with the species known only from the gelatinous sheath of *Chaetophora*.

No significant observations on this genus appear to have been published since Zopf's original description. Further study may give a clearer idea of the sequence of development than is to be found in Zopf's paper. From the figure he gives, an endooperculum is evidently formed in the sporangium. Zopf conjectured that flagellate zoospores may sometimes be formed. In addition to *Amoebochytrium*, nonflagellate spores have also been reported for *Sporophlyctis rostrata* and *Sporophlyctidium africanum* of the Rhizidiaceae.

AMOEBOCHYTRIUM RHIZIDIOIDES Zopf

Nova Acta Acad. Leop.-Carol., 47: 181, pl. 17, figs. 1-13. 1884

Sporangia relatively large, pyriform, basally apophysate with a more or less prolonged discharge tube which after disarticulation generally bears a short remnant of the concomitant rhizoid distally beyond the cross wall (endooperculum?), wall stout, smooth, cuticularized, brownish; rhizoidal system extensive, branched, with occasional intercalary fusiform swellings; zoospores large, ovoid, with a large refractive yellowish globule, discharged through a pore formed in the cross wall which terminates the tubelike prolongation of the sporangium, movement strongly amoeboid; resting spores not observed.

Saprophytic in the gelatinous matrix of colonies of *Chaetophora elegans*, growing between the radiating algal branches, Zopf (*loc. cit.*), from soil, substrata?, Harder (1948: 6), GERMANY.

POLYCHYTRIUM AJELLO

Mycologia, 34: 442. 1942

(Figs. 9, p. 102; 30 H, p. 474)

"Rhizomycelium intra- and extramatrical, extensive, coarse, branched, occasionally septate with rhizoids, conspicuous spindle organs or swellings lacking. Zoösporangia non-operculate, terminal and intercalary, variously shaped, spherical, clavate or pyriform. Zoöspores posteriorly uniflagellate, emerging fully formed in a globular mass and remaining quiescent for a few moments before swimming away" (Ajello, *loc. cit.*).

A monotypic genus; saprophytic on vegetable and chitinous debris in bogs.

The diagnosis, quoted directly from Ajello, does not contain the most important and distinctive feature of the fungus upon which the genus is based, namely, the simultaneous formation of two different types of sporangia on the same thallus. Although the specific diagnosis describes the sporangia as "smooth to tuberculate," the text, summary, and figures all indicate that they are either smooth *or* tuberculate and that both kinds occur together.

Ajello (1948a: 9) considered the possibility of the affinity of his fungus to the Blastocladiales and concluded that even though there are marked blastocladiaceous features, the lack of a side body and the monopolar method of germination offer stronger evidence for placing *Polychytrium* in the Chytridiales.

POLYCHYTRIUM AGGREGATUM Ajello

Mycologia, 34: 443, figs. 1-16. 1942

"Rhizomycelium extensive, coarse, tenuous portion, apart from rhizoids, 2–12 μ in diameter, profusely branched, occasionally septate, hyaline at first, becoming yellowish-brown at maturity. Zoösporangia in aggregates of two or more, terminal and intercalary, non-apophysate, hyaline at first, becoming yellowish-brown at maturity, wall .7 μ thick; smooth to tuberculate; spherical, 14 × 29 μ; ovoid, ellipsoid, 12–20 × 22–40 μ; clavate, obclavate, 12–24 × 29–102 μ; pyriform, obpyriform, elongate, cylindrical, 8–25 × 17–75 μ; tubercles on sporangia up to 7 μ wide at the base and 5.5 μ in height; exit pore or tube varying in length, diameter 3.5 μ; proliferating, exit tube of secondary or tertiary sporangia often penetrating the primary sporangial wall. Zoöspores delimited within the sporangium, emerging and forming a motionless, spherical mass at the mouth of the exit pore; spherical 4.4–5.5 μ with a conspicuous, large, lunate opaque region, 1.5–2 × 3–3.5 μ, surrounded by several opaque granules, no conspicuous single refractive globule present; flagellum 24–29 μ long. Resting spores unknown or doubtful" (Ajello, *loc. cit.*).

Saprophytic in decaying vegetation in bogs, chitinous substrata, coll. Karling, Ajello (*loc. cit.*), BRAZIL; chitin (MICHIGAN), UNITED STATES.

Ajello made a cytological study of the species (1948a, see p. 101) and a nutritional one (1948b). Both were based on an isolate from Brazilian mud that flourished on chitinous substrata. Growth on chitin appeared more normal than on the vegetable matter.

Karling (1949c) reported a strongly polycentric chytrid bearing only intercalary resting spores. He suggested that it might be *Polychytrium aggregatum*, but could not verify this because no sporangia were observed. Inasmuch as the thallus bears numerous intercalary swellings, which Ajello's fungus does not, Karling's form probably belongs elsewhere, perhaps in the Catenariaceae (p. 650).

It is abundant in bogs in Northern Michigan where it is obtained on shrimp chitin bait.

COENOMYCES Deckenbach

Scripta Bot. Horti Univ. Imper. Petro., 19: 115. 1902-3; Flora, 92: 265. 1903

(Fig. 30 B-E, p. 474)

Thallus epi- and endobiotic, eucarpic, consisting of a filamentous branched segmented loose hypha-like complex of tubes bearing occasional irregular intercalary swellings; sporangia inoperculate, borne extramatrically at the tips of hyphal branches or occasionally sessile on the host cell; zoospores posteriorly uniflagellate, emerging fully formed through a single (rarely more than one) long discharge tube; resting spores not observed.

A monotypic genus, known only in gelatinous material of blue-green algae.

Jaczewski (1931: 32) proposed a new generic name, *Deckenbachia*, nom. nov., for *Coenomyces*. The reasons for this change are not given in the Russian text, but presumably the name *Coenomyces* is preëmpted and is therefore a homonym.

Coenomyces consuens Deckenbach

Scripta Bot. Horti Univ. Imper. Petro., 19: 15, pls. 1-2. 1902-3; Flora, 92: 265, pls. 6-7. 1903

Mycelium divided by cross walls into long segments, much branched extramatrically and bearing frequent irregular swellings, the endobiotic part less branched, lying between the cells and the sheath of the alga, with occasional swollen appressoria; sporangia pyriform, ovoid, or bursiform, 15–22.5 μ in diameter by 21–24.7 μ long, with a cylindrical attenuated discharge tube (rarely two) 120–153 μ long by 6 μ in diameter, tapering to 2 μ at the tip, wall thin or somewhat thickened; zoospores ellipsoidal or pyriform, 1.5 μ in diameter, with a long flagellum and golden-yellow contents.

In the jelly and between the cells of *Calothrix sp.*, Deckenbach (*loc. cit.*), RUSSIA (marine); *Calothrix parasitica*, W. H. Weston, Jr., and D. M. Reynolds, *Rivularia atra* var. *confluens*, I. Lewis and Weston, in Sparrow (1943: 321), UNITED STATES.

Petersen (1906) reported finding this species in fresh-water blue-green algae in Denmark.

Little is known about the development of the species save that the zoospore upon germination produces two oppositely directed germ tubes. The cross walls do not occur at such frequent intervals as do those of the higher fungi, but rather separate the hyphae into a series of fairly long cylindrical segments. The fungus is remarkable in the possession of a definitely hypha-like vegetative system and chytridiaceous zoospores. There appears to exist an operculate counterpart of *Coenomyces* (see Sparrow, 1936a: 432, pl. 15, figs. 22–23) which inhabits decaying twigs in fresh water.

To afford a resting place for his extraordinary fungus Deckenbach erected a group, the "Coenomycetes," for filamentous fungi with a septate mycelium, reproducing by zoospores. From the type of zoospore germination and thallus, possibly belonging in the Blastocladiales.

IMPERFECTLY KNOW GENERA OF THE CLADOCHYTRIACEAE

? NEPHROMYCES GIARD

C. R. Acad. Sci. Paris, 106: 1180. 1888

Vegetative system in the kidney of ascidians, composed of coenocytic strongly entangled delicate filaments, the free ends terminated by spheroidal swellings, bearing irregularly cylindrical contorted intercalary swellings which become the inoperculate sporangia; zoospores minute, spherical, with a basal granule and a long delicate flagellum; zygospores formed by conjugation of from four to five filaments, granular or slightly echinulate, upon germination giving rise to two opposite germ tubes.

The affinities of this genus have not been ascertained. Harant (1931: 349) discussed a *Nephromyces* in the kidney of *Ctenicella appendiculata*. Although Giard allied it to *Catenaria* it still remains a puzzling organism. Three species are described from France: *Nephromyces molgularum* in *Molgula socialis*; *N. sorokini* in *Listhonephrya*, with regularly pyriform sporangia; and *N. roscovitanus* in *Anurella roscovitana*.

From what is known about these fungi it is evident that in this curious habitat — the ductless kidney of certain, perhaps all, marine ascidians — there may be a sort of commensalism which will repay careful investigation.

? SACCOPODIUM Sorokin

Hedwigia, 16 (6): 88, figs. 1-3 (lower plate). 1877[1]

Thallus tubular, without cross walls, branched, endobiotic with extramatrical unbranched sporangiophores; sporangia in clusters of from six to twelve at the tips of the extramatrical sporangiophores, spherical or pyriform, 4–5 μ in diameter, without a discharge tube; zoospores oblong, 1–1.5 μ (long?), emerging through an opening in the sporangium, flagella not observed; resting spore not observed.

A monotypic genus, represented only by *Saccopodium gracile* on *Cladophora*, ASIATIC RUSSIA.

Incomplete observations on a fungus on *Cladophora* collected in Michigan have convinced the present author that there exists a chytrid in which the sporangia occur in clusters at the tip of an extramatrical tubular sporangiophore. There were certain differences, however, particularly the apophysate character of the zoosporangia, which make it impossible to identify the Michigan fungus with Sorokin's.

GENUS OF DOUBTFUL AFFINITIES

? Myceliochytrium Johanson

Torreya, 45: 104. 1945

Thallus polycentric, intra- and extramatrical, consisting of fine, my-

---

[1] In *Arch. Bot. Nord France*, 2: 23, 1883, there appears another figure (Fig. 21), not found in the 1877 paper.

celioid, branched filaments of fairly uniform diameter; zoosporangia terminal, extramatrical, occurring singly or in clusters. Zoospores posteriorly uniflagellate; resting spores doubtful or unknown.

Other than Johanson's description, no figures or further account of this organism have been published. At a meeting of the Mycological Society of America in New York (1949), both Miss Johanson and Karling agreed that species of *Actinoplanes* (Actinomycetes) described at the same sessions by J. N. Couch were entirely similar to *Myceliochytrium*. It is mentioned by Karling (1954b) in connection with a description of an undoubted member of Couch's group.

? Myceliochytrium fulgens Johanson

Torreya, 45: 104. 1945

"Rhizomycelium delicate and narrow, 1.3–1.7 μ in diameter without intercalary enlargements. Zoosporangia hyaline and highly refractive with thin, .3–.6 μ walls, sub-spherical, 5.5–8.7 μ, somewhat rectangular and truncate, 6.6–17.5 μ × 10.3–26.2 μ, oval, ellipsoidal, 8.7–20.7 μ, urceolate, 9.6–21.0 μ, broadly pyriform, 6.2–38.5 μ, oblong, irregular, or frequently gibbose; dehiscing by rupture or deliquescence of the sporangial wall. Zoospores usually arranged in linear rows, giving sporangia characteristic appearance, spherical, 1.3–2 μ with a minute, .5 μ refractive globule; flagellum approximately 11 μ long; frequently swarming in sporangium, and emerging singly or in rows as sporangium swells and ruptures. Walls of sporangium and remainder of rhizomycelium reacting negatively to cellulose tests" (Johanson, *loc. cit.*).

Saprophytic on vegetable substrata, chitin, and keratinized substrata, Johanson, (*loc. cit.*), keratinized substrata, onion skin, cellophane, soil, Karling (1948c: 510), UNITED STATES; BRAZIL.

PHYSODERMATACEAE [1]

Chytridiaceous fungi forming thalli of two types, one monocentric and consisting of an endobiotic rhizoidal system and an epibiotic thin-walled sporangium, the other polycentric and wholly endobiotic and

[1] The family was first proposed by Sparrow (*Mycologia*, 34: 113) in 1942, but not diagnosed by him (*ibid.*, 44: 768) until 1952.

bearing turbinate cells and numerous thick-walled resting spores which germinate by zoospores to form the thin-walled epibiotic sporangia.

Obligate parasites, primarily of angiospermous marsh and aquatic plants.

The genus *Physoderma* as presently understood is coextensive with the family. Because certain members are parasitic on submerged aquatic flowering plants and many others (the majority, in fact) on marsh plants, mention here of the family and genus is logical.

Any classification of this group of fungi now attempted would, of necessity, be both makeshift and temporary. No arrangement based on host relationships alone (lacking knowledge of life cycles and proven host ranges) could be truly authoritative. The genus is being currently investigated and it is hoped that a sound taxonomic scheme will eventually result. Meanwhile, descriptions of the family and genus are given in this treatise. Concerning the species, interested students are referred to Karling's (1950) account of the genus, but references to a few aquatic forms described since his paper are included.

PHYSODERMA Wallroth

Flora Crypto. Germ., 2: 192. 1833

(?) *Urophlyctis* Schroeter, in Cohn, Kryptogamen-Fl. Schlesien, 3 (1): 196. 1885 (1889).

Monocentric thallus consisting of an epibiotic part, derived from the expanded body of the zoospore and an endobiotic part of bushy, stubby, or more or less prolonged rhizoids of limited extent, usually confined to one host cell, which either arise directly from the tip of the germ tube or from a small apophysis, epibiotic part becoming converted into a sporangium with a discharge papilla which after deliquescence liberates small zoospores; sporangia internally proliferous; polycentric thallus entirely endobiotic, exceedingly extensive, ramifying through many host cells, consisting of delicate freely branching rhizoids which bear intercalary, usually once- or twice-septate, turbinate cells; resting spores numerous, disproportionately large, thick-walled, dark-colored, somewhat spherical or ellipsoidal, or assuming the shape of the host cell, often flattened on one surface, formed either from one of the elements of a turbinate cell or as an outgrowth from it, often bearing pores through which protrude antler-like bushy projections, upon germination either cracking open or dehiscing circumscissily and forming a saclike, elongate endosporangium with a broad apical papilla that deliquesces to form a pore through which the relatively large zoospores emerge.

Obligate parasites of pteridophytes and angiosperms.

This is the oldest genus of chytrids. It was established by Wallroth (1833) on the basis of the resting-spore stage nearly twenty years before Braun founded *Chytridium*. Many years were to elapse, however, before *Physoderma* was unquestionably recognized (Schroeter, 1883) as a member of the Chytridiales.

The relationship of *Physoderma* to other polycentric chytrids and to *Urophlyctis* and a résumé of older authors' disposition of species of the genus are discussed in the previous edition of this book (1943) and need not be repeated here.

Whether or not Karling's (1950) implementation of Sparrow's (1943) suggestion that *Urophlyctis* be merged with *Physoderma* will prove a wise course, must await renewed investigations on species which have in the past been assigned to these taxa.

In *Physoderma* the extensive polycentric endobiotic thallus has never been observed to give rise to any type of reproductive organ save the thick-walled, flattened, elliptical, usually colored resting spores.[1] Each of these upon germination cracks open and produces a sporangium as a saclike extrusion. The zoospores from this sporangium come to rest on the surface of the host cell and form epibiotic sporangia, each of which has a bushy monophagous rhizoidal system. This phase is definitely epibiotic, monocentric, and on one host cell as contrasted with the strongly polycentric, and polyphagous phase within the host in which the resting spores are formed. What connection exists between these two thalli is not at present known. The "sporangia" may in reality be gametangia[2], the "zoospores," gametes, and the endobiotic

[1] According to Karling (1950), endobiotic, thin-walled sporangia have been found by Gopalkrishnan in *Physoderma graminis*, but no account of these has seemingly been published.

[2] This suggestion of the gametic nature of the zoospores from ephemeral sporangia has been unquestionably proven true in *Physoderma lycopi* and by Y. Lingappa in the case of *P. pulposa*.

phase diploid in nature (Sparrow, 1940a). Reduction division would then occur upon the germination of the resting spore. There is, as yet, no evidence to confirm this hypothesis.

The remarkable ephemeral epibiotic sporangia characteristic of this genus were apparently originally observed by Schroeter (1883) in *Physoderma* (*Urophlyctis*) *pulposa*. The zoospores from these sporangia at first formed on the young host plants new epibiotic sporangia with a short bushy endobiotic rhizoidal system. Later the zoospores formed germ tubes which penetrated the host and produced resting spore plants. The existence of the epibiotic stage was confirmed by Büsgen (1887) in *P. butomi* and then by Clinton (1902) in *P. maculare*, by Sparrow (1934a; 1940a; 1946; 1947a) in *P. menyanthis* and *P. maydis*, by Thirumalacher and Whitehead (1951) in *P. aeschynomenis*, by Couch (1953) in *P. maydis*, by R. M. Johns (1957) in *P. dulichii*, and by Sparrow (1957b) in *P. lycopi*.

PHYSODERMA MARSILIAE Brewster [1]

Mycologia, 44: 99, fig. 1. 1952

Parasitic on *Marsilea mucronata*, UNITED STATES.

PHYSODERMA AESCHYNOMENIS Thirumalachar and Whitehead

Mycologia, 43: 435, figs. 1-17. 1951

On the stems and rachis of *Aeschynomene indica*, INDIA

PHYSODERMA APONOGETONIS Sparrow

Trans. Brit. Mycol. Soc., 36: 348, fig. 1. 1953

Parasitic on leaves and petioles of *Aponogeton ʼundulatus*, GREAT BRITAIN (on material recently imported from Ceylon).

PHYSODERMA DULICHII Johns

Mycologia, 49: 298. 1957

On *Dulichium arundinaceum*.

[1] Species published since Karling (1950).

PHYSODERMA LYCOPI Sparrow

Amer. J. Bot., 44: 664, 26 figs. 1957

On *Lycopus americanus*.

OPERCULATAE

CHYTRIDIACEAE

Thallus epi- and endobiotic, monocentric, eucarpic, the epibiotic part either expanding and becoming an operculate sporangium and the endobiotic part forming the vegetative system, or not enlarging and forming an evanescent cyst, and the endobiotic part then forming the reproductive organs as well as the vegetative system, occasionally interbiotic; zoospores produced in the sporangium, posteriorly uniflagellate, generally with a single globule, released upon the dehiscence of the operculum; sexual reproduction, where known, by fusion of aplanogametes; resting spore inter-, epi-, or endobiotic, upon germination producing an epibiotic sporangium.

Parasites and saprophytes of fresh-water and marine algae, also of other Phycomycetes, pollen, and Protozoa. Members of the Chytridiaceae, with the inoperculate families Phlyctidiaceae and Rhizidiaceae, make up the majority of the "chytrids." They include the operculate counterparts of the other two groups, also monocentric, and exhibit a remarkable parallelism in body form. Species of *Chytridium* (the largest genus) with apophyses and those with unbranched rhizoidal systems have never been segregated into distinct genera as have like forms in the Phlyctidiaceae.

KEY TO THE SUBFAMILIES AND GENERA OF THE CHYTRIDIACEAE

Sporangium epi- or interbiotic, formed from the body of the encysted zoospore or as a lateral outgrowth of the main axis, external to substratum; resting spore endo-, epi-, or interbiotic

Subfamily CHYTRIDIOIDEAE, p. 488

Sporangium developing from all or part of the expanded body of the encysted zoospore, external to the substratum; parts variable in size

Rhizoidal system arising from one place on the base of the sporangium; the latter with a single discharge papilla

SUBFAM. CHYTRIDIOIDEAE

Sporangium epibiotic, sessile, or occasionally interbiotic; rhizoids entirely endobiotic or with the tips in the substratum, delicate, tapering; resting spore endo-, epi-, or interbiotic, sexually or asexually formed.

CHYTRIDIUM Braun

Betrachtungen über die Erscheinung der Verjüngung in der Natur..., p. 198.
Leipzig, 1851; Monatsber. Berlin Akad., 1855: 378

(Fig. 31 A-Q, p. 496)

Thallus epi- and endobiotic, monocentric, eucarpic, the epibiotic part forming the rudiment of the sporangium, the endobiotic part producing the vegetative system and resting spore; sporangium epibiotic, sessile, operculate, formed from all or part of the enlarged body of the encysted zoospore; zoospores posteriorly uniflagellate, usually with a single globule; rhizoidal system endobiotic, variable in character, arising either from the endobiotic tip of the germ tube or a prolongation of it or from an endobiotic subsporangial apophysis; resting spore endobiotic, thick-walled, often borne on a rhizoidal system, sexually or asexually formed, upon germination producing an epibiotic operculate zoosporangium.

Primarily parasites and saprophytes of fresh-water and marine algae.

Braun's subgeneric term *Euchytridium* has been used occasionally in a generic sense, notably by Sorokin (1883).

As understood here, *Chytridium* includes all monocentric, eucarpic chytrids, with or without a simple apophysis, which form an epibiotic sporangium, discharge their spores after the dehiscence of a single operculum, and have endobiotic resting spores. The nature of the rhizoidal system produced by different species of the genus is extremely variable and ranges from a delicate apparently unbranched needle-like tube in *C. lagenula* to the broad often apophysate tubular structure divided distally into tenuous branched rhizoids found in *C. olla*. An exception to the endobiotic nature of the rhizoid is found in *C. curvatum*, where the tip of the short subsporangial stalk evidently does not penetrate beyond the thin layer of gelatinous material surrounding the *Stigeoclonium* filament.

Segregation from *Chytridium* of the species with an unbranched rhizoid or with a subsporangial apophysis has never been made, as it has among the inoperculate species.

Scherffel (1925b: 7) suggested that *Zygorhizidium willei*, with *Chytridium*-like operculate sporangia and epibiotic resting spores, be included in a new subgenus of *Chytridium*, *Ectochytridium*. In view of the type of sexuality which occurs in *Zygorhizidium* Löwenthal (see p. 547) it would appear better to retain his genus as distinct. Furthermore, Karling (1945c) has erected a genus, *Chytriomyces*, whose characters are essentially those of Scherffel's subgenus *Ectochytridium*. Fisch (1884b) described copulation of motile bodies preceding the formation of endobiotic resting spores in "*Chytridium mesocarpi*" Fisch, p. 766. The correctness of his account has been questioned by both Fischer and Minden, neither of whom, however, noted that Fisch's fungus produced *anteriorly* uniflagellate zoospores and, hence, was no *Chytridium* (see Hyphochytriales, p. 743).

The only authentic detailed account of the sexual process in a member of this genus is that by Koch (1951). He reports that in *Chytridium sexuale* a zoospore comes to rest on the host cell and undergoes development similar to that of the sporangium. At an early stage in the formation of this female thallus a free-swimming spore attaches itself to the distal part, encysts, and penetrates by means of a tube. The contents of the male then pass through the tube and the combined protoplasts migrate into the endobiotic apophysis, which becomes converted into a thick-walled resting spore. As Koch mentions, such behavior also occurs in the zoospores of another apophysate species, *C. lagenaria* (Sparrow, 1936a), when it grows under conditions of poor nutrition. In the latter instance, however, revitalized growth of the receptive thallus rather than a resting spore resulted.

The curious expansion of only a portion of the cyst in the infecting zoospore of *Chytridium schenkii* and related species was first noted by Schenk (1858b).

In view of Karling's (1948b) statements indicating that he considers nonapophysate species of *Chytridium* belong elsewhere, it should be emphasized that Braun's material of *C. olla*, the type species, was without an apophysis and so, too, was American material collected by Sparrow (compare *C. brevipes* Braun).

KEY TO THE SPECIES OF CHYTRIDIUM [1, 2]

Occurring in fresh-water or inland salt pools

Rhizoids arising directly from the tip of the penetration tube, branched or unbranched

Rhizoids branched or, if unbranched, tapering and delicate

Sporangium ovoid or urceolate at maturity

Sporangium ovoid or narrowly urceolate, with a rounded base; operculum usually umbonate; on green algae

Sporangium 11.9-100 μ high by 10.6-55 μ in diameter; umbo, when present, not prolonged . . . . *C. olla*, p. 493

Sporangium smaller, about 16 μ in diameter; umbo distinct and prolonged . . . . *C. acuminatum*, p. 495

Sporangium broadly urceolate with a concave base; operculum smoothly convex, 20 μ in diameter; on cysts of *Vampyrella* . . . . *C. lateoperculatum*, p. 495

Sporangium distinctly pyriform, citriform, obpyriform, pestle-shaped, or cylindrical

Sporangium pyriform or citriform

Sporangium distinctly pyriform; rhizoidal axis elongate

Sporangium predominantly narrowly pyriform, asymmetrical (tilted); operculum inconspicuous; rhizoids tenuous; on green algae . . . . *C. sphaerocarpum*, p. 497

Sporangium broadly and symmetrically pyriform; operculum conspicuous, solid; rhizoids stout; on diatoms . . . . *C. perniciosum*, p. 498

Sporangium pyriform to citriform; rhizoidal axis short or wanting

Rhizoidal axis short; on *Stigeoclonium* . . *C. papillatum*, p. 499

Rhizoidal axis lacking, rhizoids arising from one or several places on the base of the sporangium; on sheath of *Microcystis* . . . . *C. microcystidis*, p. 500

Sporangium elongate-citriform to obpyriform, pestle-shaped, or cylindrical

Sporangium elongate-citriform to obpyriform; rhizoid needle-like or finely branched; on sporangia of *Rhizophydium* . . . . *C. rhizophydii*, p. 500

Sporangia obpyriform; not on chytrids

Sporangium with a knoblike or slightly prolonged base, borne usually on a short extramatrical stalk; on diatoms

---

[1] See also Fott (1957) for two new species on phytoplankton, *C. telmatoskenae* and *C. mallomonadis* and recently described taxa, p. 528.

[2] Note that this key is not strictly dichotomous.

Sporangium very broadly obpyriform, nearly as broad as long, extramatrical stalk rigid, prolonged into the base of the sporangium as a plug; rhizoids coarse .... *C. surirellae*, p. 501
Sporangium more narrowly obpyriform, nearly twice as long as broad, extramatrical stalk rigid; rhizoids delicate .... *C. versatile*, p. 501
Sporangium without a knoblike base, gradually tapering basally, sessile; on algae or microscopic animals
Operculum very broad; on living rhizopods
C. lecythii, p. 503
Operculum less than diameter of sporangium; on *Vaucheria* .... *C. pyriforme*, p. 503
Sporangium pestle-shaped, sessile or with a short, tenuous, extramatrical stalk; on *Tribonema* ..... *C. lagenula*, p. 504
Sporangium cylindrical .... *C. cocconeidis*, p. 505
Rhizoids, where known, unbranched, isodiametric
Sporangium wall smooth
Sporangium sessile, wall of uniform thickness; on diatoms
Sporangium narrowly to broadly obpyriform, procumbent
C. appressum, p. 505
Sporangium narrowly ovoid to pyriform ... *C. melosirae*, p. 506
Sporangium borne on a short epibiotic stalk, strongly arched, basal part thick-walled and sterile; on *Stigeoclonium*
C. curvatum, p. 506
Sporangium wall ornamented
Sporangium with an apiculus or nodular protuberance on upper part
Sporangium with an apiculus; operculum subapical; on *Epithemia*....................... *C. epithemiae*, p. 507
Sporangium with a small subapical nodular protuberance; operculum apical; on other diatoms .. *C. nodulosum*, p. 507
Sporangium bearing long setae or short conical spines; on green algae or pollen .... *C. chaetophilum*, p. 508
Rhizoids arising from a well-defined endobiotic subsporangial swelling (apophysis)
Sporangium with one or two apical teeth or spines
Sporangium with two opposed solid apical teeth; rhizoids broad, isodiametric, arising from opposite sides of a transversely fusiform apophysis; on *Tribonema*......... *C. confervae*, p. 509
Sporangium with a single apical spine surmounting the operculum; rhizoids delicate, tapering, arising from the basal region of the apophysis; on *Oedogonium* . *C. mucronatum*, p. 512

Sporangium without apical teeth
Sporangium wall with part of the case of the zoospore persisting
as a small protuberance
Sporangium arising as an apical outgrowth of the zoospore
case; rhizoids lacking; on *Vaucheria*
Sporangium typically perpendicular to host wall, sym-
metrical; resting spores unknown .... *C. cejpii*, p. 512
Sporangium typically inclined to host wall, strongly bent
and sometimes twisted; resting spores abundant,
sexually formed .... *C. sexuale*, p. 513
Sporangium arising as a more or less lateral outgrowth of the
zoospore cyst; with or without rhizoids; on green algae
Sporangium ovoid, ellipsoid, pyriform, or subspherical;
protuberance either colorless or amber or brown
Protuberance colorless
Resting spore smooth-walled; sporangium wall rigid
after discharge of zoospores
Sporangium ovoid, ellipsoid, or pyriform; protuberance basal or slightly elevated; operculum
small, rhizoids branched, tapering
C. schenkii, p. 514
Sporangium narrowly obovoid; protuberance basal;
operculum small; rhizoid tubular and unbranched .... *C. oedogonii*, p. 516
Sporangium spherical, subspherical, or ellipsoidal;
protuberance subapical or lateral; operculum
large .... *C. kolianum*, p. 516
Resting-spore wall covered by straight, bent, sharp or
blunt, or clavate outgrowths; sporangium wall
collapsing after spore discharge ... *C stellatum*, p. 517
Protuberance amber-colored or brown; sporangium
ovoid or subspherical .... *C. aggregatum*, p. 518
Sporangium utriculate or somewhat tubular, dorsally gib-
bose; protuberance colorless......... *C. gibbosum*, p. 519
Sporangium wall entirely smooth
Sporangium transversely placed on the substratum, ovate or
ellipsoidal; on *Chlorobotrys* .... *C. chlorobotrytis*, p. 519
Sporangium more or less upright
Sporangium broadly obovoid, often asymmetrical; apoph-
ysis spherical without rhizoids; on *Characiopsis*
C. scherffelii, p. 519
Sporangium spherical, subspherical, ovoid, urceolate, pyri-
form or citriform

CHYTRIDIUM OLLA Braun

Betrachtungen über die Erscheinung der Verjüngung in der Natur..., p. 198. Leipzig, 1851; Monatsber. Berlin Akad., 1855: 380; Abhandl. Berlin Akad., 1855: 23, pl. 1, figs. 1-10. 1856

(Fig. 31 A, p. 496)

Euchytridium olla (Braun) Sorokin, Arch. Bot. Nord France, 2: 21, fig. 19. 1883 (separate).

Sporangium sessile, rarely stalked, ovoid or somewhat urceolate, 11.9–100 μ high by 10.6–55 μ in diameter, the apex terminated by a broad convex umbonate or occasionally smooth operculum 7–14 μ in diameter, wall smooth, colorless, of varying thickness; rhizoids tenuous and much branched within the host contents, arising from a broad often irregularly expanded tubular endobiotic occasionally septate stalk of variable length, which originates at the base of the sporangium but is cut off from it by a cross wall at maturity; zoospores up to several hundred in large sporangia, spherical, 3.3–5 μ in diameter, with a colorless eccentric globule and a flagellum from four to six times the length of the diameter of the body, emerging individually or in a group imbedded in "slime" and remaining motionless for a time, movement hopping, amoeboid; resting spore formed on the endobiotic system, spherical, subspherical, or occasionally pyriform, 24–32.4 μ in diameter, wall smooth, thick, contents with a single large oil globule, upon germination producing an epibiotic operculate sporangium.

On oögonia and oöspores of various species of *Oedogonium*, Braun (*loc. cit.*), coll. Pringsheim, Braun (1856a: 23), Kny (1871a: 870), de Bary (1884: 177, fig. 76), GERMANY; Sorokin (1874b: 8, pl. 1, figs. 29–40; 1883: 21, fig. 19), Serbinov (1907: 77, pl. 5, figs. 9–10), Voronichin (1920: 11), EUROPEAN RUSSIA; coll. Haussknecht, Rabenhorst (1871: 17), ASIATIC RUSSIA; Tokunaga (1934b: 392), JAPAN; (?) oögonia of *Nitella tenuissima* (?), Sparrow (1936a: 430, pl. 15, figs. 1–11), GREAT BRITAIN; *Oedogonium sp.*, Lacy (1949: 136, fig. 2, C-C′), INDIA; oöspores of *Oedogonium sp.*, Sparrow (MASSACHUSETTS), Sparrow and Barr (1955: 554), UNITED STATES.

Since this species is the unquestioned type of the genus, although apparently not the first chytrid observed by Braun (see *Phlyctochytrium hydrodictyi*), it is of unusual importance. In it are embodied not only the characters of a *Chytridium*, but also those which to a degree must be exhibited by all "chytrids." As noted in the diagnosis of the order, these center around the structure of the zoospore.

The sporangia are extremely variable in size, a fact first pointed out by Kny, who found them ranging from 11.9–100 μ high by 10.6–55 μ in diameter. The more proximal portion of the rhizoidal system is apparently subject to considerable variation, sometimes being evenly tubular and sometimes in Kny's material expanded into an irregular or rounded apophysis. Occasional septations may also occur. Observations on the nature of the rhizoids are difficult within the host contents. Both Serbinov and Sparrow have confirmed the fact, first noted with uncertainty by Braun (1856a: 25), that distally the rhizoid becomes divided into a number of more delicate tapering branches.

The curious production of flamelike refractive outgrowths of the sporangium wall has been noted by Sparrow (1936a) on the fungus parasitizing oögonia of *Nitella*. It is possible that this is, in fact, another species and it is, therefore, questioned.

CHYTRIDIUM ACUMINATUM Braun

Monatsber. Berlin Akad., 1855: 380; Abhandl. Berlin Akad., 1855: 29, pl. 1, fig. 11. 1856

Sporangium sessile, ovate, ovate-pyriform, or urceolate, 16.6 μ high, with a distinctly umbonate operculum, wall smooth, colorless; rhizoids and zoospores not observed; resting spore endobiotic, spherical, smooth-walled, with a single globule.

On oögonia of *Oedogonium rothii*, possibly also on *O. echinospermum*, Braun (*loc. cit.*), GERMANY; diatoms, Sorokin (1883: 21, fig. 18), ASIATIC RUSSIA; zygospores of *Mougeotia sp.* Cornu (1872a: 121), FRANCE.

Differing from *Chytridium olla* in the smaller size of its sporangia and the more pronounced umbo on the operculum. Though considered by Fischer and Minden to be only a small variety of *C. olla*, with a prolonged umbo, further observations should be made on the fungus before it is reduced to synonymy. "*Chytridium acuminatum*" of Scherffel (1926a: 225), because of the formation of an endobiotic swelling, appears closer to *C. brevipes* Braun. Figures of the species are given in Cooke (1882–84: pl. 81, fig. 1).

CHYTRIDIUM LATEOPERCULATUM Scherffel

Arch. Protistenk., 54: 173, pl. 9, fig. 10. 1926

Sporangium sessile, broadly and symmetrically urn-shaped, 12 μ high by 20 μ wide, with a smooth colorless wall, its broad concave base resting on the rounded wall of the host, opening with a sharply circular split at the dehiscence of a slightly convex large disclike operculum 20 μ in diameter; zoospores and endobiotic system not seen; resting spore not observed.

On zoocyst of *Vampyrella pendula*, causing marked disorganization and clumping of the host contents, HUNGARY.

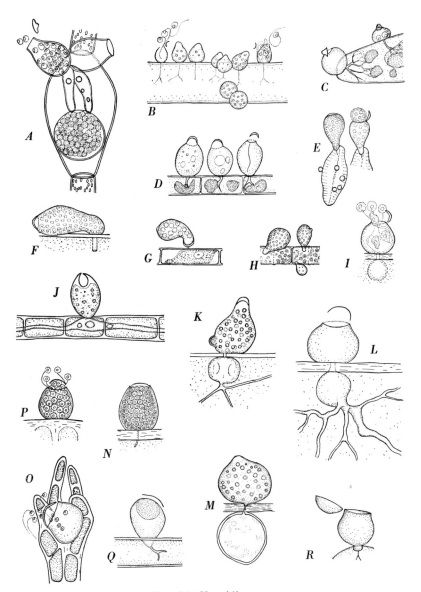

Fig. 31. Chytridiaceae

CHYTRIDIUM SPHAEROCARPUM Dangeard

Le Botaniste, 2: 244, pl. 17, fig. 9. 1890-91

(Fig. 31 B, p. 496)

Sporangium sessile, narrowly or occasionally broadly pyriform, usually asymmetrical, 8–18 μ long by 7–8 μ in diameter, with a prominent apical papilla surmounted by a very inconspicuous thin-walled convex operculum 3–5 μ in diameter, wall thin, smooth, colorless; rhizoidal system of varying length, consisting of an extremely tenuous long stalk which forms at its tip a few branches or remains unbranched;

Explanation of Figure 31

A. Chytridium olla Braun on oögonium of *Oedogonium*, two discharged sporangia. *B. Chytridium sphaerocarpum* Dangeard on hypha of *Achlya*. *C. Chytridium perniciosum* Sparrow on *Navicula*, two discharged sporangia on portion of diatom. *D. Chytridium papillatum* Sparrow on *Stigeoclonium*, immature and discharged sporangia on portion of algal filament. *E. Chytridium versatile* Scherffel on moving *Navicula*; to the left, five encysted zoospores and a mature sporangium on its flexible stalk; to the right, a discharging sporangium. *F. Chytridium appressum* Sparrow on *Melosira*, habit of a mature sporangium. *G. Chytridium curvatum* Sparrow on sheath of *Stigeoclonium*. *H. Chytridium nodulosum* Sparrow, on *Melosira*, three sporangia, the one in upper right showing characteristic protuberance (zoospore case?). *I. Chytridium inflatum* Sparrow on *Cladophora*, discharging apophysate sporangium. *J. Chytridium confervae* (Wille) Minden, immature sporangium on *Tribonema*. *K. Chytridium aggregatum* Karling on *Cladophora*, single apophysate sporangium from a group; persistent amber-colored case of zoospore appears as protuberance on left side of sporangium wall. *L–M. Chytridium lagenaria* Schenk on *Rhizoclonium* and *Oedogonium*: *L*, empty apophysate sporangium; *M*, germinating resting spore on *Oedogonium*; endobiotic resting spore has produced a germ tube, which has pierced wall of alga and formed at its tip, epibiotically, a zoosporangium. *N–P. Chytridium polysiphoniae* Cohn on the seaweeds *Polysiphonia* and *Ceramium*: *N*, mature sporangium on *Ceramium*; *O*, discharging sporangium on *Polysiphonia*; *P*, discharging sporangium on *Ceramium*. *Q. Chytridium megastomum* Sparrow, empty sporangium on hairs of the brown seaweed *Striaria*. *R. Zygorhizidium willei* Löwenthal on *Cylindrocystis*, empty sporangium, showing small endobiotic apophysis and once-branched rhizoid.

(*A*, Braun, 1856a; *B*, Sparrow, 1936a; *C–D*, Sparrow, 1933c; *E–I*, Sparrow, 1933a; *L*, Sparrow, 1936a; *M*, Karling, 1936a; *N*, Sparrow, 1934c; *O*, Sparrow, 1936b; *P–Q*, Sparrow, 1934c; *R*, Löwenthal, 1905)

zoospores spherical, 2.5–5 µ in diameter, with a colorless centric globule and a fairly long flagellum, escaping fully formed after the dehiscence of the operculum; resting spore not observed.

On *Zygnema sp.*, Dangeard (*loc. cit.*), FRANCE; *Spirogyra sp.*, *Stigeoclonium sp.*, Sparrow (1933a: 64, fig. 1 g-i), UNITED STATES; *Spirogyra sp.*, *Mougeotia sp.*, *Achlya* (?), Sparrow (1936a, fig. 3a-f), GREAT BRITAIN; ? *Cladophora sp*; Bérczi (1940: 84, fig. 27–29), HUNGARY.

Dangeard identified his fungus with *Rhizidium sphaerocarpum* Zopf (*Rhizophydium sphaerocarpum* [Zopf] Fischer), but placed it in *Chytridium* because of the lack of a basal cell (a feature of *Rhizidium* in the sense of Fischer) rather than because of the presence of an operculum.

The species is a difficult one to characterize, but its principal features are a narrowly pyriform sporangium, often appearing tilted (asymmetrical), an extremely delicate operculum, and a long rhizoid which sometimes forms a few branches at its tip. The chytrid on *Mougeotia* does not conform in this last detail, since the rhizoids branch near the host wall. Perhaps it should not be included here. Morphologically, the fungi found on *Spirogyra* and *Stigeoclonium* are indistinguishable from the fungus on *Achlya*.

Chytridium oocystidis Huber-Pestalozzi
Zeitschrift f. Hydrologie, 10 (1): 120, figs. 1-8. 1944

Sporangia sessile on the gelatinous sheath of the host colony, ovate to pyriform with a broad blunt apex, gregarious, rarely solitary, with a smooth, colorless wall, 13–14.5 µ long by 5.5–7.8 µ wide; rhizoidal system consisting of a single tenuous, unbranched rhizoid; zoospores spherical, with one oil droplet, discharged after the dehiscence of an operculum; resting spore not observed.

Parasitic on the planktonic alga, *Oocystis lacustris*, SWITZERLAND. Doubtfully distinct from *Chytridium sphaerocarpum*.

CHYTRIDIUM PERNICIOSUM Sparrow
Mycologia, 25: 526, pl. 49, figs. 9-11. 1933
(Fig. 31 C, p. 496)

Sporangium sessile, smooth-walled, spherical at first, becoming broadly pyriform, 10–16 μ high by 12–23 μ in diameter (up to 30 by 35 μ), with a prominent apical solid operculum which, upon discharge of the zoospores, remains attached to the sporangium and often falls back into place, covering the orifice; zoospores spherical, 3–4 μ in diameter, posteriorly uniflagellate, with a colorless globule; rhizoids stout, branching; resting spore spherical, 11–16 μ in diameter, endobiotic, with a smooth somewhat thickened wall and one or more large oil globules.

Parasitic on *Cymbella sp.*, Sparrow (*loc. cit.*), UNITED STATES; *Cymbella sp.*, Friedmann (1952: 187), AUSTRIA.

Large sporangia, about 30 μ high by 35 μ in diameter, were occasionally observed. Other, possibly abnormal, ones, ovoid, pyriform, or irregular in shape, with very thick walls and a hornlike broadly conical operculum, were also found. The fungus was an extremely virulent parasite and destroyed within a few days nearly all the diatoms present in the dish; after being attacked the chloroplasts of the alga rapidly became discolored and desiccated. In immature sporangia the operculum often appeared invaginated. Such a condition has also been observed in *Blastocladia* and *Nowakowskiella* and has been discussed by Scherffel (1926a: 226), who unquestionably correctly assigns to it a function in zoospore discharge.

CHYTRIDIUM PAPILLATUM Sparrow

Mycologia, 25: 525, text fig. I, 7. 1933

(Fig. 31 D, p. 496)

Sporangium sessile, pyriform to citriform, 10–11 μ high by 7–8 μ in diameter, smooth-walled, with a prominent broad apical papilla surmounted by a convex operculum; rhizoidal system short, delicate, sparsely branched, arising from a stouter endobiotic subsporangial stalk; zoospores spherical, about 3–4 μ in diameter, posteriorly uniflagellate, with a colorless globule; resting spore not observed.

On filaments of *Stigeoclonium sp.*, UNITED STATES.

In the shape of its sporangium and the nature of its rhizoidal system the organism is exactly like *Rhizophydium mammillatum* (Br.) Fischer. From the accounts of Braun, Sorokin, Dangeard (as *Chytridium asymmetricum*), and Couch, however, *R. mammillatum* is inoperculate (see

p. 260). Whether or not the fungus found by Pringsheim (reported in Braun, 1856a: 33, pl. 2, figs. 9–11) on *Stigeoclonium* was a *Chytridium* or a *Rhizophydium* cannot now be determined, since no discharge of the zoospores was observed.

CHYTRIDIUM MICROCYSTIDIS Rohde and Skuja

Symbolae Bot. Upsalienses, 9 (3): 382, pl. 39, figs. 26-27. 1948

Sporangium sessile on the colonial sheath of the host, erect or somewhat tilted, ovoid or obpyriform, becoming urceolate after discharge, with a prominent broad apical papilla surmounted by a strongly convex operculum, 13–23 µ long by 8–12 µ in diameter, with a delicate system of simple or branched rhizoids which emerge from one or several places on the base which is in contact with the colonial sheath of the host; zoospores spherical or ovate, about 3 µ in diameter, with an eccentric, hyaline colorless globule and long flagellum, escaping after dehiscence of the operculum; resting spore not observed.

Parasitic in *Microcystis aeruginosa*, *M. viridis*, *M. flos-aquae*, SWEDEN.

Said to be similar to *Chytridium papillatum* Sparrow but to differ in being larger and in having the rhizoids develop from several places on the base of the sporangium.

In general appearance and rhizoid origin, this fungus recalls a species of *Rhizophlyctis*. The species is placed next to *Chytridium papillatum* (even though the technical description states the sporangium is sometimes obpyriform), because of the remarks of the authors.

CHYTRIDIUM RHIZOPHYDII Karling

Mycologia, 40: 333, figs. 11-20. 1948

"Sporangia hyaline, smooth, elongately citriform or obpyriform, 10–18 µ × 22–32 µ, oval, 8–16 × 12–22 µ, or elongate; operculum persistent, shallow saucer-shaped, 8–15 µ diam. Zoospores spherical, 2–2.8 µ, with a minute hyaline refractive globule; flagellum 12–14 µ long. Rhizoids unbranched, tapering and needle-like or finely branched, 4–10 µ long. Resting spores unknown" (Karling, *loc. cit.*).

Parasitic on *Rhizophydium nodulosum*, UNITED STATES.

The fungus appeared to be restricted to *Rhizophydium* and did not attack seven other kinds of Phycomycetes in the same culture nor the filamentous and unicellular algae that were also present.

CHYTRIDIUM SURIRELLAE Friedmann

Österr. Bot. Zeitschr., 100: 7, fig. 1. 1953

Sporangium obpyriform, 10.5–18.5 μ long by 9–15.5 μ in diameter, with a thin, smooth, colorless wall, resting on a short rigid extramatrical stalk which in most cases projects slightly into the interior of the sporangium; rhizoidal system consisting of a few delicate bushy branches which terminate the unbranched intramatrical part of the sporangial stalk; zoospores spherical, 3 μ in diameter, with an eccentric colorless globule and long flagellum, emerging through a wide apical or slightly subapical pore formed upon the dehiscence of a circular, 6.5–10.5 μ in diameter operculum which usually remains adherent to the sporangium; resting spore not observed.

Parasitic on *Surirella ovata*, AUSTRIA.

From the figures given of empty sporangia the wall of the operculum is much thinner than that of the sporangium proper.

CHYTRIDIUM VERSATILE Scherffel

Arch. Protistenk., 54: 177, pl. 9, figs. 17-20. 1926

(Fig. 31 E, p. 496; also, Fig. 10 M, p. 108)

Chytridium versatile var. *acaulis* Canter, Trans. Brit. Mycol. Soc., 31: 102. figs. 6-7, pl. 10, figs. 7-8. 1947.

Sporangium narrowly to broadly obpyriform, tapering proximally to a knoblike or slightly prolonged base 3–5 μ in diameter, resting on a short (3.5 μ) slender flexible extramatrical stalk, wall smooth, colorless, thin or somewhat thickened, variable in size, large specimens up to 15–25 μ in diameter by 30–40 μ high, smaller ones 5 by 8 μ; rhizoids extremely delicate, branched, arising from the endobiotic tip of the stalk; zoospores spherical, 3–5 μ in diameter, with a relatively large colorless centric globule and a long flagellum, emerging upon the dehiscence of an apical convex smooth operculum 8–10 μ in diameter and forming a temporary motionless group surrounded by an evanescent vesicle or "slime"; resting spore not observed.

Parasitic on motile *Cymatopleura solea*, Scherffel (*loc. cit.*), *Melosira varians*, Domján (1936: pl. 1, fig. 110), HUNGARY; *Navicula sp.*, Sparrow (1933a: 63, fig. 1 a-c, m), UNITED STATES; *Synedra sp.* (*?*), *Tabellaria sp.*, Sparrow (1936a: 437, fig. 3 g,t; fig. 4a), *Nitzschia sigmoidea*, Canter (1947b: 101, figs. 6–7; pl. 10, figs.7–8), *Fragilaria crotonensis*, *Tabellaria flocculosa* var. *asterionelloides*, Canter (1950c: 273, figs. a-f), GREAT BRITAIN; *Melosira ambigua*, *Melosira sp.*, Rohde and Skuja (in Skuja, 1948: 381, pl. 39, figs. 14–21), SWEDEN.

A curious adaptation of this fungus to its mode of life on moving diatoms has been pointed out by Scherffel (see under "Structure of the Thallus," p. 53). He also noted that the method of development of the sporangium in this species is similar to that in *Podochytrium*. The body of the original zoospore persists, unexpanded, as the knoblike base, while the remainder of the sporangium is formed by elongation and expansion of the apical part. In contrast to most species of *Podochytrium*, however, the base remains continuous with the rest of the sporangium. In the Hungarian material no rhizoids were found within the host and this, together with the fact that several fungi were present in various stages of development on the moving diatoms, suggested to Scherffel that the adherent organism might be only a saprophyte on the gelatinous coating. Later observations (Sparrow, 1933a) disclosed that a true endobiotic system was developed and that the fungus might ultimately destroy its host.

Canter's (1947b: 102) variety *acaulis* is placed in synonymy. She erected it for a stalkless form on *Nitzschia sigmoidea*, but later (1953: 293) suggested its suppression, stating that the presence or absence of a stalk was evidently related to whether or not mucilage surrounded the diatom wall.

Chytridium lagenula Braun, *sensu recent.* Scherffel, appears to differ from *C. versatile* only in its host, in its smaller size, and in the somewhat broader base of the sporangium.

? Chytridium versatile var. *podochytrioides* Friedmann
Österrisch. Bot. Zeitschr., 99: 186, figs. 2 a-h. 1952.

Sporangium clavate or obpyriform, tapering proximally to a knob-like sterile base, 1.7–2.1 μ broad by 2.1–3.1 μ high, which is generally cut off by a cross wall, 30–41 μ high by 12–21 μ in diameter, resting on a very short flexible extramatrical stalk; rhizoids delicate, branched, bushy; zoospore discharge not observed; resting spore not observed. Parasitic on *Navicula oblonga*, AUSTRIA.

Friedmann considered it probable that the fungus entered the host through a pore of the "transapical stripe" on the frustule. The host seemed little affected by the presence of the parasite; diatoms with as many as five fungi on them continued to move.

Since no zoospore discharge was observed, it is impossible to place this fungus generically with certainty. If it is inoperculate, as seems likely from the figures, it is more closely allied to *Podochytrium*. If operculate, it cannot be either the fungus seen by Scherffel (1926a) or the one observed by Sparrow (1933a. 63, fig. 1 a-c, m; 1936a: 437, figs 3 g-t, 4a).

CHYTRIDIUM LECYTHII (Ingold) Goldie-Smith

Trans. Brit. Mycol. Soc., 29: 68, fig. 1. 1946

Rhizophidium lecythii Ingold, Trans. Brit. Mycol. Soc., 25: 47, fig. 3, pl. 4, figs. 2-5. 1941.

Sporangium obpyriform or top-shaped, 20–40 by 16–32 μ, by the dehiscence of a large operculum forming an apical pore, the empty sporangium vase-shaped; endobiotic system consisting of a stout straight stalk with fine rhizoids branching from its tip; zoospores posteriorly uniflagellate, with a small eccentric globule; resting spores not observed.

Parasitic on living individuals of the rhizopod *Lecythium hyalinum*, GREAT BRITAIN.

Goldie-Smith (*loc. cit.*) noted zoospore discharge (not seen by Ingold) occurred after the dehiscence of a very broad operculum, which consists of the whole upper one-quarter of the strongly obpyriform sporangium.

CHYTRIDIUM PYRIFORME Reinsch

J. Linn. Soc. London (Bot.), 15: 215. 1877

Zoosporangium obpyriform, gradually narrowing toward the base, 26–28 μ high by 13–17 μ in diameter, wall distinctly thickened; rhizoids tapering; zoospores subcylindrical or subcuneate, ejected upon the dehiscence of an apical convex smooth operculum.

In *Vaucheria sessilis* and *V. geminata*, coll. Eaton, KERGUELEN ISLAND. Shape said to approximate that of *Chytridium olla*, a statement hardly borne out by the description. The lack of figures makes the interpretation of this species difficult.

CHYTRIDIUM LAGENULA Braun, pro parte

Abhandl. Berlin Akad., 1855: 31, pl. 2, figs. 4-5 (sensu recent. Scherffel Arch. Protistenk., 54: 195, pl. 9, figs. 57-59. 1926)

Phlyctidium lagenula (Braun) Rabenhorst, pro parte, Flora Europaea algarum, 3:280. 1868.
Rhizophydium lagenula (Braun) Fischer, Rabenhorst. Kryptogamen-Fl., 1 (4): 99. 1892.

Sporangium sessile or with a short tenuous extramatrical stalk, narrowly obpyriform (pestle-shaped), with rounded apex, upright or slightly tilted, with a thin smooth wall, varying in size, large specimens 12–14 µ long by 5.5 µ in diameter, small ones 7 µ long by 4 µ in diameter; rhizoidal system not seen, the penetration tube stimulating the host to form a protective plug of wall material; sporangium opening upon the dehiscence of an arched apical operculum about 4 µ in diameter; zoospores few, spherical, 3 µ in diameter, with a single globule and probably a single flagellum, remaining motionless for a time at the mouth of the sporangium before swimming away; resting spore endobiotic, broadly ovoid or nearly spherical, 6–8 by 5 µ, with a thick smooth wall and a large eccentric colorless oil drop 4 µ in diameter, germination not observed.

On *Tribonema bombycina*, Braun (*loc. cit.*), GERMANY; Scherffel (*loc. cit.*), HUNGARY; Sparrow (1943: 336), UNITED STATES.

Scherffel believed his fungus to be a new species, but since he described a form almost identical with Braun's plant on *Tribonema* and applied Braun's name to it, it is here considered merely an amplification of a previously inadequately defined species. He divided Braun's *Chytridium lagenula* into two species, which differ in the size, shape, and method of opening of the sporangium, in the behavior of the zoospores, and in their hosts: (1) *Rhizophydium lagenula* (Braun) Fischer, on *Melosira*, which has a somewhat fusiform inoperculate sporangium, 30–33 μ long by 8 μ in diameter, and a zoospore with a very small globule, escaping at once from the sporangium; and (2) *Chytridium lagenula* Braun *sensu* Scherffel, on *Tribonema*, which has a more clavate operculate sporangium, 12–20 μ long by 5.5–8 μ in diameter, the zoospore having a larger globule and resting for a time before the mouth of the sporangium before assuming motility. He did not think *Rhizophidium fusus* Zopf is synonymous with *R. lagenula* (Braun) Fischer, but gave no reasons (see *R. fusus*, p. 298). Schenk (1858a: 236) reported it on *Stigeoclonium* in Germany, but the report seems doubtful.

See remarks under *Chytridium versatile*.

CHYTRIDIUM COCCONEIDIS Canter

Trans. Brit. Mycol. Soc., 31: 104, fig. 8, pl. 10, figs. 1-3. 1947

"Thallus monocentric, eucarpic, sporangium extramatrical cylindrical 15–29 μ in length, 5–6 μ in diameter, dehiscing by an apical lid, and containing 12–30 zoospores. Zoospores spherical 2–3 μ in diameter, with a colourless globule and single posterior flagellum. Extramatrical rhizoidal system simple or branched 2–9 μ in length, rarely absent. Intramatrical rhizoidal system not observed. Resting spores not observed" (Canter, *loc. cit.*).

On living cells of *Cocconeis pediculus*, GREAT BRITAIN.

CHYTRIDIUM APPRESSUM Sparrow

Amer. J. Bot., 20: 69, text fig. 1 p. 1933

(Fig. 31 F, p. 496)

Sporangium sessile, narrowly to broadly obpyriform, slightly constricted toward the base, 10–17 μ long by 6–10 μ in diameter, the long axis parallel with that of the algal filament, with a smooth colorless wall; endobiotic part consisting of a highly refractive narrowly cylindrical unbranched tube about 3 μ long; zoospores spherical or slightly subspherical, 3–5 μ in diameter, with a single colorless eccentric oil globule and a long flagellum, escaping upon the dehiscence of a convex terminal operculum, movement hopping; resting spore not observed.

Parasitic on *Melosira varians*, Sparrow (*loc. cit.*), UNITED STATES; Sparrow (1936a: 437, pl. 15, figs. 12–14), GREAT BRITAIN.

The development of the sporangium has not been studied; it is probably similar to that of *Chytridium schenkii.*

CHYTRIDIUM MELOSIRAE, sp. nov. [1]

Sporangium narrowly ovoid to pyriform, resting directly on the host cell and penetrating it with an unbranched, isodiametric rhizoid, when mature 11–17 μ long, 6–8 μ in diameter at base, and tapering to 4–5 μ in the neck region, wall smooth, hyaline, moderately thick; zoospores broadly ovoid to subglobose, 2–2.5 μ broad by 2–3 μ long, with a flagellum three to four times the body in length and a refractive anterior droplet, spores 16–48 in a sporangium, freed by the throwing off of a sporangial lid; resting spore not observed.

On *Melosira ambigua*, Rohde and Skuja (in Skuja, 1948: 381), SWEDEN.

A *Chytridium* much like that figured by Sparrow (1936a, fig. 4, j-n) on *Melosira*. The Swedish fungus is definitely not *Rhizophydium simplex*, to which species it was referred by Rohde and Skuja. The empty sporangia illustrated by them as on the same host filament possibly belong to another species.

CHYTRIDIUM CURVATUM Sparrow
Amer. J. Bot., 20: 69, text fig. 1 n. 1933
(Fig. 31 G, p. 496)

Sporangium strongly arched, broadly obpyriform or clavate, smooth-walled, 8 μ in diameter tapering to 5 μ in diameter by about 18 μ in length, with an apical operculum about 5 μ in diameter, having at the

---

[1] *Chytridium melosirae*, sp. nov. — Sporangium includens 16-48 zoosporas, liberatas per operculum dehiscens, anguste ovoideum vel pyriforme, sessile in cellulam hospitis et eamdem penetrans; axe penetranti simplici rhizoidali 11-17 μ longo, basi 6-8 μ diam., sursum angustato ad 4-5 μ prope cervicem, laevi, hyalino, modice crasso. Zoosporae late ovoideae vel subglobosae, 2-2.5 μ crassae, 2-3 μ longae; flagello triplo vel quadruplo longiori quam somate; globulo refractivo anteriori singulo.

In *Melosira ambigua*. Species Suecica sub nomine *Rhizophydii simplici*, a Rohde et Skuja descripta et delineata, sed valde differi.

base a thick-walled, goblet-like sterile portion from which a short peg-like hyaline stalk emerges, the latter not penetrating the host wall but merely attached to it; zoospores 5 μ in diameter, uniflagellate, with a single colorless oil globule, escaping upon the dehiscence of the operculum; resting spore not observed.

On *Stigeoclonium sp.* (gelatinous sheath ?), UNITED STATES.

Aside from its arched habit, the organism superficially resembles *Podochytrium clavatum* Pfitzer, especially in the possession of a thin sterile basal portion. The presence of an operculum, however, as well as the character and mode of attachment of the sporangium, sharply demarks it from *Podochytrium*, as well as from other species of *Chytridium*. It is probably saprophytic on the gelatinous sheath of the alga, since no disintegration of the contents of those cells bearing sporangia was noticed.

CHYTRIDIUM EPITHEMIAE Nowakowski

Cohn, Beitr. Biol. Pflanzen, 2: 82, pl. 4, figs. 12-13. 1876

Sporangium broadly subglobose, with a prominent rounded apiculus, 12 μ in greatest diameter, prolonged basally into a narrow stalk which rests with its knoblike tip on the surface of the host cell, wall somewhat thickened, colorless, smooth; rhizoids not observed; zoospores not observed, probably few, emerging upon the dehiscence of a subapical convex operculum; resting spore not observed.

On *Epithemia zebra*, GERMANY.

Nowakowski regarded the apical protuberance as a second, non-functional, operculum. It is more likely an apiculus similar to that formed in *Sporophlyctis*, *Blyttiomyces*, and several other chytrids.

The fungus on *Melosira* and *Tabellaria* doubtfully referred to this species (Sparrow, 1933a: 68, fig. 1 d-f) is now considered distinct from it. See *Chytridium nodulosum*, below.

CHYTRIDIUM NODULOSUM Sparrow

Aquatic Phycomycetes, p. 338. 1943

(Fig. 31 H, p. 496)

Sporangium ovoid to pyriform, 6–13 μ in diameter by 10–15 μ in length, with an apical operculum 5 μ in diameter and a subapical rounded protuberance, resting on a short basal cylindrical stalk which is slightly expanded at its terminus, wall smooth, colorless; rhizoids not observed; zoospores probably fully formed within the sporangium spherical, 3 μ in diameter, with a centric colorless globule and a fairly long flagellum, emerging upon the dehiscence of the operculum and forming a compact spherical mass at the orifice before dispersing; resting spore not observed.

Parasitic on *Melosira varians, Tabellaria sp.*, UNITED STATES.

This species was doubtfully assigned to *Chytridium epithemiae* Nowak. in a previous publication (Sparrow, 1933a: 68, fig. 1 d-f). Since little is known of Nowakowski's fungus save from his short description and his two figures, one of an empty sporangium, the other of an undischarged one, and since the operculum in his organism was subapical, it has been thought best to segregate from it the species on *Melosira* and *Tabellaria*.

A further study of the original drawings and a few sporangia still available in a glycerin mount seems to indicate that the sporangium stalk is extramatrical rather than within the alga as previously supposed. The subapical protuberance no doubt arises from a type of development similar to that found in *Chytridium schenkii*, where an unexpanded portion of the wall of the original zoospore persists.

CHYTRIDIUM CHAETOPHILUM Scherffel

Arch. Protistenk., 53: 45, pl. 2, figs. 87-94. 1925

Sporangium sessile, short and sausage-shaped, broad-ovoid from above, 9–11 μ long by 6 μ in diameter, resting crosswise on the seta of the alga, wall thin, colorless, the upper half bearing a tuft of long solid delicate unbranched hairs; rhizoid, so far as is known, consisting of a short peglike tube which just pierces the cell wall; zoospores spherical, 2–3 μ in diameter, with a prominent eccentric colorless oil globule and a long delicate flagellum, discharged after the gelatinization of a basal part of the sporangium or by a bursting apart of the sporangium, remaining motionless for a time after discharge, movement dancing or hopping; resting spore epibiotic, sessile, nearly spherical, 5–8 μ (mostly 8 μ) in diameter, with a thick double wall the outer surface of which bears a series of regularly arranged short rodlike blunt protuberances, contents granular, with a large (5 μ) oil globule, germination not observed; male cell laterally attached, spherical, smooth, thin-walled, 2–3 μ in diameter.

On setae of *Bulbochaete sp.*, Scherffel (*loc. cit.*), HUNGARY; *Oedogonium sp.*, Sparrow (1933c: 526, fig. I, 11–12), UNITED STATES; *Bulbochaete sp.*, *Typha* pollen, Sparrow (1936a: 438, pl. 15, fig. 18), *Bulbochaete sp.* coll. Odam, GREAT BRITAIN.

The proper disposition of this species is puzzling. If, as Scherffel asserts, the zoospores are discharged after the gelatinization of a basal part of the sporangium or by a bursting apart of the sporangium, and if the resting spores are epibiotic, the species can hardly belong in *Chytridium*. Mere bursting of the wall would not seem comparable with the formation of a definite operculum. Further observations on spore discharge and the nature of the rhizoidal system (it may, indeed, be *Phlyctidium*-like) are necessary to determine the precise affinities of the fungus. *Rhizophydium v. mindeni* Valkanov (1931a: 363) may be identical with Scherffel's organism, but since only empty sporangia without rhizoids were described, comparison of any significance is hardly possible.

No zoospore discharge was seen in any of the British or American material. The peglike endobiotic part resembles that formed by a species of *Phlyctidium*.

According to Dr. C. L. Odam (communication), the hairs are always bifurcated at their termini. The tips are extremely delicate and scarcely visible.

CHYTRIDIUM CONFERVAE (Wille) Minden

Kryptogamenfl. Mark Brandenburg, 5: 368. 1911 (1915)

(Fig. 31 J, p. 496)

Rhizidium confervae Wille, Vidensk. Selsk. Skr. Christiana (Mat.-Nat. Kl.). 1899 (3): 1, figs. 1-3.
Phlyctochytrium confervae (Wille) Lemmerman, Abhandl. Naturwiss. Vereins Bremen 17 (1): 194. 1901.

Sporangium sessile, rarely on a short isodiametric stalk, upright or slightly tilted, broadly or narrowly ovoid, occasionally obovoid, 18–40 μ high by 15–32 μ in diameter, with a flattened apex bearing two opposite solid slightly incurved sharp teeth up to 6 μ long by 2–4 μ at base (rarely one), wall smooth, colorless; rhizoids arising as single isodiametric filaments from either side (rarely one side) of a broadly fusiform, rarely spherical, subsporangial swelling 7–15 μ in diameter by 3–6 μ high, remaining isodiametric, rarely branched, and about 2–2.5 μ in diameter save when meeting a cross wall, where they expand to 4 μ or more, strongly polyphagous, penetrating as many as forty or more cells of the alga, which they stimulate to form protective thickenings of the transverse walls; zoospores spherical, 5 μ in diameter, with a slightly eccentric colorless strongly refractive protruding globule, flagellum 27 μ long, upon the dehiscence of a slightly convex round operculum 10–12 μ in diameter escaping fully formed in a compact temporarily vesiculate motionless group, suddenly assuming violent individual motion, eventually freeing their flagella and hopping away, movement intermittently amoeboid; resting spore not known with certainty.

Parasitic on *Tribonema bombycina*, Wille (*loc. cit.*), SWEDEN; Scherffel (1925b: 32, pl. 2, figs. 63–80), HUNGARY; Sparrow (1939a: 124), UNITED STATES; coll. Odam, communication and drawings, Sparrow (1957a: 532), GREAT BRITAIN; *Tribonema bombycina*, Rieth (1951: 259, figs. 1–14), GERMANY.

Scherffel found two types of resting structures associated with the sporangial stage of this species, but neither can be said with certainty to belong to it. The first was epibiotic, sessile, spherical or subspherical, and 9–16 μ (mostly 14 μ) in diameter exclusive of the ochre-yellow epispore, which was 2–3 μ thick, irregular, and covered with blunt knoblike protuberances; the endospore wall was smooth and 1.5–2 μ thick, and the fatty plasma of the contents bore a single colorless globule 8–11 μ in diameter. At the base was a smooth spherical or clavate empty structure which presumably functioned as a contributing cell in a sexual process. The second type of resting spore occurred singly within the horned sporangium; it was spherical and covered with a network of ridges.

Both forms have been observed in Michigan material, but neither has been convincingly connected with the sporangial stage of the species. Careful observations on the second type of spore, which, as Scherffel suggests, probably belongs to a parasitic organism, reveal minute spines in addition to the reticulations on the outer wall.

The reactions of the host to the incursions of the fungus are very marked and involve the formation of conspicuous protective plugs of cellulose on the walls wherever the vegetative system attempts entry. Scherffel has noted that, in this reaction, the nucleus of the alga is drawn away from its central position in the cell and, with a concentration of plasma, takes up a position close to the attacked cross wall. This, he asserts, lends support to the idea that the nucleus plays a role in wall formation. Under high magnifications it can be clearly seen that the protective plug when penetrated by the fungus is not pierced in a single place but in several. It is possible that the fungus is unwalled when passing through these plugs.

In the American material early stages in the development show that the rhizoid is well established before the apophysis makes its appearance. Although Scherffel states that no central vacuole is formed in the sporangium during the process of maturation, it has been observed in a number of instances in the Michigan material.

Rieth (1951), who made a careful study of this species, noted that the zoospores which germinate free in the medium will become transformed into small thalli and from the sporangium of each a single zoospore will be produced. He also observed extramatrical resting spores, associated with the sporangial stage, which were essentially like the unhorned ones previously reported by Scherffel (1925b). As in the latter's Hungarian material, each spore was resting on an epibiotic, small, empty cell, a phenomenon suggesting a type of sexuality like that in *Rhizophydium ovatum*. In that species the male is epibiotic and remains small, the female attaches to it distally, receives the contents of the male and expands into a resting structure. If this type of resting-spore formation is ever definitely connected with the sporangial stage, *Chytridium confervae* should be segregated from the genus *Chytridium*. Its strongly hypha-like vegetative system ramifying through many cells of the host and the extramatrical resting spores would be sufficient grounds for separation.

CHYTRIDIUM MUCRONATUM Sparrow and Barr
Mycologia, 47: 552, figs. 24-27. 1955

"Zoosporangium ovate or pyriform, sessile or with a very short stalk, 17.5–23.8 μ high by 11.2–15.4 μ in diameter, the apex terminated by a mucronate, solid operculum, 5–6 μ high by 5 μ in diameter, wall smooth, colorless, thin except at the base where the remnants of the zoospore cyst persist; endobiotic system consisting of a short stalk which broadens into a globose apophysis 5–9.8 μ in diameter from which emerge numerous, delicate, branched rhizoids which ramify throughout the host cell; zoospores emerging in an amoeboid mass after dehiscence of the operculum and remaining quiescent for a few minutes, then swimming away with a hopping movement, globose, 4.5–5.6 μ in diameter, containing an eccentric, colorless, refractive globule 1–1.5 μ in diameter, and numerous minute granules, flagellum 24–28 μ in length; resting spore not observed" (Sparrow and Barr, *op. cit.*:553).

Parasitic on *Oedogonium sp.*, UNITED STATES.

CHYTRIDIUM CEJPII Fott
Z. Věstník Král. čes. Spol. Nauk. Tř. Matem.-Přivo. Roč., 1950: 9, figs. 1-6, plate. (1951) (separate.)

"Sporangium upright, obovoid, affixed to the substratum with a basal spheric protuberance, the old zoospore. Length of the sporangium 35–45 μ, its breadth 15–21 μ; spheric protuberance 3–4 μ in diameter. Membrane firm, refractive, colourless. Operculum large, 10–15 μ in diameter, rejected after discharge of zoospores. Zoospores subspheric, 3–4 μ in diameter, with a typical eccentric oil drop, uniciliate, leaving successively the sporangium. Subsporangial vesicle (apophysis) small, spheric, 3–5 μ in diameter, connected by a fine thread with the protuberance. No rhizoids observed, resting spores unknown" (Fott, *loc. cit.*).

Collected on *Vaucheria sessilis* DC., CZECHOSLOVAKIA.

At this point, *Chytridium scherffelii* Bérczi (non Sparrow) (1940: 85, pl. 2, figs. 30–37) should be considered. Although resembling both this and *C. sexuale*, it is closer to *C. cejpii*. Bérczi's binomial is preëmpted by *C. scherffelii* Sparrow 1936. To effect a nomenclatorial change, until the status of these three species is clarified by further study, seems undesirable at this time.

Chytridium sexuale Koch

J. Elisha Mitchell Sci. Soc., 67: 267, pl. 19, figs. 1-9; pl. 20, figs. 10-27. 1951

"Sporangium, usually on an inconspicuous stalk up to 2.2 μ long, arising as an outgrowth of the distal end of the germinated zoospore, which is 2.5–4.0 μ wide and is the basal part of the sporangium; rarely perpendicular to the host wall and with radial symmetry, but usually somewhat inclined and bent slightly or through nearly a 180° angle and bilaterally symmetrical; rarely twisted or helicoidal; essentially obpyriform or spatulate and usually with a slight bulge in all directions between the zoospore and broadest part, and gibbous distally when bent over; 12–43 μ long × 6–21 μ wide (mostly 30–40 × 14–19 μ); wall colorless, smooth, remaining intact after discharge of zoospores; detached operculum 4.9–15.6 μ in diameter (mostly 11.0–12.5 μ). Motile cells spherical, 3.2–4.5 μ in diameter, with an eccentric, colorless, highly refractive globule 1.2–1.6 μ in diameter, and a flagellum about 17 μ long; emerging fully cleaved, separate and spherical, through a terminal, circular orifice when the operculum is completely detached, or through a slit when the operculum is only partly detached, lying quiescent for about one minute in a loose cluster while unwrapping their flagella, and then rapidly dispersing, some of them remaining within the sporangium and emerging one to a few at a time; swimming cell with a posteriorly attached and directed flagellum. Penetration tube of the encysted motile cell when passing through the host wall is 0.7–1.3 μ wide, reduced abruptly to 0.3–0.9 μ in width within the host protoplasm; distal end swelling to form the spherical apophysis, 3.2–9.2 μ in diameter (mostly 6.5–8.0 μ) with a smooth wall; no rhizoidal system. Resting body essentially spherical, 11.3–14.0 μ in diameter, protoplast 9.5–12.0 μ wide with a large, eccentric, colorless, highly refractive globule surrounded by many much smaller ones, and a wall 0.6–1.1 μ thick, including the covering of numerous, short, blunt warts; sexually formed; female thallus indistinguishable from young sporangial thallus, the epibiotic part 4.3–7.8 μ high, with the cyst portion inconspicuously to considerably expanded distally; contents of the encysted male cell, which is 3.2–3.9 μ in diameter, passing through a germ tube into the epibiotic, expanded part of the female thallus; the fusion protoplasm moving into the endobiotic, swollen tip of the germ tube, where the resting body or zygote matures; germination not observed" (Koch, *loc. cit.*).

Parasitic and weakly saprophytic on *Vaucheria geminata*, Koch (*loc. cit.*), UNITED STATES.

Chytridium sexuale Koch differs from *C. cejpii* Fott in the sporangia being almost constantly bent or even twisted and in the ready development of resting spores. Otherwise, the two are strikingly similar. See "Sexual Reproduction," p. 79.

CHYTRIDIUM SCHENKII (Schenk) Scherffel

Arch. Protistenk., 54: 237, pl. 10, figs. 125-129, pl. 11, figs. 130-132. 1926

> *Rhizidium intestinum* Schenk, pro parte, Ueber das Vorkommen contractiler Zellen im Pflanzenreiche, p. 5. Würzburg, 1858.
>
> *Rhizidium schenkii* Dangeard, Ann. Sci. Nat. Bot., VII, 4: 297, pl. 13, figs. 24-30. 1886.
>
> *Phlyctochytrium schenkii* (Dang.) de Wildeman, Ann. Soc. Belge Micro. (Mém.), 20: 48. 1896.

Sporangium variable in shape, ovoid, ellipsoid, or pyriform, 15 μ high by 10 μ in diameter, erect or procumbent, with a prominent apical papilla surmounted by a smooth convex operculum 3 μ in diameter, the colorless wall bearing a small lateral or basal colorless thick-walled hemispherical protuberance (the persistent zoospore case), otherwise thin and smooth; rhizoids branched, well developed in one or more cells of the substratum, occasionally becoming extramatrical, arising generally from the base of an endobiotic subsporangial spherical apophysis 8–10 μ in diameter; zoospores spherical, 2–3 μ in diameter, with a colorless eccentric or centric globule and a long flagellum, emerging upon the dehiscence of the operculum and forming a motionless mass possibly surrounded by a vesicle, after a period of rest assuming motility; resting spore endobiotic, spherical, 10 μ in diameter, colorless, with a thick smooth wall and highly refractive oily contents, apparently without rhizoids, at germination forming an epibiotic sessile narrowly ellipsoidal erect or somewhat procumbent sporangium 15 μ high by 10 μ in diameter, with a smooth colorless thin wall and an apical operculum 3 μ in diameter, zoospores spherical, 2 μ in diameter, with a single globule and a flagellum 10 μ in length.

On *Oedogonium sp.*, Schenk (*loc. cit.*), no specific substratum, Minden (1915: 340), GERMANY; *Closterium sp.*, Cejp (1933a: 5, pl. 1, fig. 12), CZECHOSLOVAKIA; *Bulbochaete sp.*, *Spirogyra sp.*, *Zygnema sp.*, *Closterium sp.*, *Cladophora sp.*, *Oedogonium sp.*, Dangeard (*loc. cit.*), *Spirogyra*, de Wildeman (1894: 155), FRANCE; *Oedogonium sp.*, de Wildeman (1895a: 72, pl. 2, figs. 13–16), SWITZERLAND; *Oedogonium sp.*, *Cladophora sp.*, de Wildeman (1890: 6, fig. 1), BELGIUM; oögonia, oöspores, vegetative cells of *Oedogonium sp.*, Scherffel (*loc. cit.*; 1914), *Oedogonium sp.*, *Spirogyra sp.*, Domján (1936: 49, pl. 1, figs. 42–43, 60–61), HUNGARY; *Oedogonium sp.*, *Bulbochaete sp.*, *Spirogyra sp.*, *Closterium sp.*, Petersen (1909: 416, fig. 22g; 1910: 550, fig. 22g), DENMARK; *Oedogonium sp.*, Sparrow (1932b: 280, fig. 3 a-d; 1933a: 67, fig. 1q), vegetative filaments of *Oedogonium sp.*, Sparrow (1952d: 768), UNITED STATES; *Cladophora*, *Closterium*, Litvinow (as *Phlyctochytrium schenkii*), (1953: 81), LATVIA.

In its present form *Chytridium schenkii* is probably a composite species made up of several varieties, some of which have been published as distinct entities. Thus *C. gibbosum* Scherffel and *C. aggregatum* Karling have been suggested by their authors to be only doubtfully distinct from it. They are, however, maintained separate in the present monograph. Some of the records of occurrence listed above are, from examination of the figures, to be accepted with reservations. It is remarkable that of the many reports of this fungus only one of the descriptions includes any measurements of the sporangium and apophysis; significant variations in the size of these structures, consequently, cannot be given.

The British fungus discussed as *Chytridium schenkii* (Sparrow, 1936a: 431) seems closer to *C. scherffelii* Sparrow.

Scherffel first emphasized the fact (noted by Schenk) that the sporangium developed by lateral and upward expansion of a portion of the body of the infecting zoospore and that the remainder persisted as a distinct protuberance on the sporangium wall. He also pointed out that similar protuberances are found on Schenk's and Dangeard's fungi.

It is not unlikely that an inoperculate form with this type of development and similarly shaped sporangia may be found, in which event doubt will be thrown on the advisability of considering Dangeard's form (in which no operculum was observed) identical with *Chytridium schenkii*.

CHYTRIDIUM OEDOGONII Couch

J. Elisha Mitchell Sci. Soc., 54: 256, pl. 24. 1938

Sporangium usually ovoid and broadest in its distal half, 14–45 μ high by 7.5–17.6 μ broad, attached by a narrow isthmus to the small unexpanded zoospore case from which it has arisen as a lateral outgrowth, with a low apical papilla surmounted by a shallowly convex operculum; rhizoidal system arising from a spherical, 6–16 μ in diameter, or oval, 7.5–12.5 by 16–22 μ, subsporangial apophysis, consisting of a system of rarely branched, isodiametric threads 1.5–5 μ broad; zoospores 4–5.5 μ in diameter, with a basal or lateral (rarely two) globule and long flagellum, escaping individually after dehiscence of the operculum or forming a temporarily motionless cluster at the orifice before swimming away; resting spore endobiotic, spherical, or slightly flattened, 10 μ by 15–31 μ or more, with a smooth thick (1.2 μ) hyaline to yellowish brown wall and one or more large refractive globules, germination not observed.

Saprophytic on *Oedogonium sp.*, Couch (*loc. cit.*), UNITED STATES; *Oedogonium sp.*, Canter (1950d: 354, figs. 1–3, pl. 28, 29), GREAT BRITAIN.

CHYTRIDIUM KOLIANUM Domján

Folia cryptogam., 2 (1): 27, pl. 1, figs. 88, 90-92, 101-106. 1936

Sporangium sessile, spherical, subspherical, or ellipsoidal, 17.5 μ in diameter by 12.5–20 μ high, wall smooth, thin, even, with the cyst of the infecting zoospore persisting as a subapical or lateral hemispherical refractive somewhat thick-walled appendage; rhizoids not well developed, branched, arising from the base of an endobiotic subsporangial somewhat ellipsoidal swelling, 10–22 μ in diameter by 12.5–25 μ high; zoospores typically chytridiaceous, 5 μ in diameter, emerging after the dehiscence of a persistent adherent operculum formed from the whole upper part of the sporangium; resting spore not observed.

Saprophytic on *Spirogyra*, *Zygnema*, HUNGARY.

The species differs from *Chytridium schenkii* in the shape of the sporangium and the larger operculum, from *C. gibbosum* in the shape of the sporangium and the evenness of its contour, and from *C. aggregatum* by the presumably colorless wall of the cyst.

CHYTRIDIUM STELLATUM (H. E. Petersen) Koch

J. Elisha Mitchell Sci. Soc., 67: 272, pl. 21, figs. 28-41. 1951

Phlyctochytrium stellatum H. E. Petersen, Bot. Tidsskrift, 29: 417. 1909; Ann. Mycologici, 8: 550, fig. xxiii. 1910.

"Sporangium extramatrical; sessile; procumbent, resting on the host wall; main body of sporangium thin-walled, arising as a lateral outgrowth from the basal part of the encysted and germinated zoospore, which becomes displaced laterally and is part of the sporangium; thin-walled part subspherical, elliptical, ovoid or somewhat irregular, 5.1-44.0 μ long × 4.4–26.4 μ wide; wall colorless, smooth, thin and delicate, collapsing after discharge of zoospores, except for persistent, thick-walled cyst; exit papilla, when discernible, broadly convex, variously located. Zoospores spherical, 4.2–5.5 μ in diameter with an eccentric, colorless, highly refractive globule, 2.2–3.3 μ in diameter, and a flagellum about five times as long as the diameter of the spore body; emerging through an orifice after the detachment of an operculum, about 5 μ in diameter, and forming a more or less globular mass, with individual zoospores distinct but adpressed, and lying quiescent for about one minute, while slightly parting and extending their flagella, and then rapidly dispersing, the swimming spore with a posteriorly attached and directed flagellum. Apophysis intramatrical, spherical, 6.0–15.4 μ in diameter, or slightly fusiform, wall holding shape after discharge of sporangium, connected to extramatrical, encysted zoospore by old germ tube, 0.5–1.5 μ in diameter; rhizoidal system coming out from base of apophysis, extensively branched, rhizoids 0.2–1.5 μ in diameter, with blunt tips, sometimes becoming extramatrical. Resting body apparently formed asexually, in intramatrical swelling; spherical, 11.0–26.4 μ in diameter with protoplast 8.8–14.3 μ wide, or subspherical; wall two-layered, hyaline, glistening, outer layer with numerous, prominent excrescences up to 6 μ long, straight or bent, pointed, blunt or regularly to irregularly clavate; with a large, eccentric, colorless, highly refractive globule surrounded by many much smaller ones; empty, extramatrical cyst remaining expanded or all but basal portion soon collapsing; germination not observed" (Koch, *loc. cit.*).

In *Spirogyra sp.*, Petersen (*loc. cit.*), DENMARK; *Zygnema sp.*, Scherffel

(1926a: 233, pl. 10, figs. 118–124), HUNGARY; *Zygnema sp.*, Koch (*loc. cit.*), UNITED STATES.

Koch's (*op. cit.*) careful study of the development of this species clearly shows that it had a very delicate operculum and that its resting spores were asexually formed.

CHYTRIDIUM AGGREGATUM Karling

Mycologia, 30: 302, text figs. 1-19. 1938

(Fig. 31 K, p. 496)

"Thalli numerous and gregarious, partly intra- and extramatrical, eucarpic. Zoosporangia extramatrical, formed as a lateral or slightly basal outgrowth from the encysted zoospore case and delimited from the apophysis by a cross wall at maturity; hyaline, smooth, oval, egg-shaped, subspherical, $4 \times 6\mu$—$10 \times 18\mu$, with a conspicuous amber or brown protuberance, the zoospore case, near the base, and an apical or slightly sub-apical exit papilla; operculum spherical, 4–8 μ, or slightly oval. Zoospores hyaline, conspicuously uniguttulate, spherical, 3–4.5 μ, posteriorly uniciliate; emerging in a globular mass and lying quiescent near the exit papilla for a few moments before moving apart; motility confined to a few jerky motions and amoeboid movements; settling down on the host cell and germinating in a mass in the vicinity of the zoosporangium. Apophysis intramatrical, spherical, 5–10 μ, oval, broadly spindle-shaped, elongated and occasionally constricted. Rhizoidal system well developed and branched, extending often to a distance of 110 μ; main axis 3–4 μ in diameter. Resting spores intramatrical, hyaline, spherical, 5–14 μ, oval, slightly citriform, $6 \times 9\mu$—$12 \times 14\mu$, somewhat depressed, and occasionally flattened or constricted, usually with a single large refractive globule and a 2.5–3 μ thick, smooth wall; germination unknown" (Karling, *loc. cit.*).

Saprophytic on *Spirogyra crassa, Oedogonium sp.,* and *Cladophora sp.,* Karling (*loc. cit.*), *Cladophora,* Sparrow (1943: 345), UNITED STATES.

Differing from *Chytridium schenkii* only in the brown or amber zoospore case. The gregarious habit is not constant, and the sporangia have been found many times in Michigan occurring singly on algal cells.

CHYTRIDIUM GIBBOSUM Scherffel

Hedwigia, 41: (105). 1902; Arch. Protistenk., 54: 239, pl. 11, figs. 133-134. 1926

Sporangium sessile, utriculate, somewhat tubular, gibbose dorsally, erect, oblique, or decumbent, thin-walled, bearing laterally at the base the thick-walled half-spherical unexpanded remnant of the zoospore case; rhizoids arising from two lateral opposite prolongations of a spherical or somewhat flattened endobiotic subsporangial apophysis; zoospores with a single globule and a flagellum, escaping upon the dehiscence of a slightly convex operculum 4 μ in diameter, movement hopping; resting spore not observed.

Saprophytic on filaments of *Cladophora fracta, Closterium sp.*, HUN-GARY.

Considered by Scherffel as being possibly only a subspecies of *Chytridium schenkii*, but differing from that species in having a more tubular and gibbose sporangium. On *Closterium* the sporangia were more ovoid than on *Cladophora*, approaching in this respect those of *C. schenkii*.

CHYTRIDIUM CHLOROBOTRYTIS Fott

Preslia, 24: 202, fig. 4. 1952

Sporangium ovate or ellipsoidal, transversely placed, 12–14 μ long by 9–10 μ high by 8 μ wide; endobiotic subsporangial part very delicate, spherical, 6–7 μ in diameter, without rhizoids, usually with a spherical, up to 4 μ in diameter, oil drop; zoospores not observed but presumably escaping upon the dehiscence at the narrower sporangial apex of an operculum 5 μ in diameter; resting spores endobiotic, spherical, 8–10 μ in diameter, with a slightly thickened wall and a large up to 8 μ in diameter refractive fat droplet, germination not observed.

Parasitic on *Chlorobotrys polychloris*, CZECHOSLOVAKIA.

CHYTRIDIUM SCHERFFELII (Scherffel) Sparrow

J. Linn. Soc. London (Bot.), 50: 431. 1936

Chytridium pusillum Scherffel, Abstracts of Communications, V Inter. Bot. Congress, Cambridge, 1930: 223; Arch. Protistenk., 73: 143, pl. 9, fig. 4 a-f. 1931. Non *C. pusillum* Sorokin, Arch. Bot. Nord France, 2: 24, fig. 23. 1883 (separate).

Zoosporangia broadly obovoid, with the half-spherical rounded top somewhat expanded laterally, tapering basally, mostly 6–10 µ high by 5–6 µ thick, larger specimens more oblong to obpyriform, up to 10 µ by 6 µ, with a delicate smooth colorless wall, often asymmetrical when several occur on the same host cell, the lower part being one-sidedly expanded and appearing inclined to the substratum, operculum strongly convex, usually persistent, 2–4 µ in diameter; endobiotic part a subsporangial spherical apophysis 4 µ in diameter, without rhizoids, often containing a large oil globule; zoospores emerging individually through a large apical opening, body spherical (2–3 µ in diameter), with a colorless eccentric globule and a single flagellum; resting spore not observed.

On *Characiopsis minuta (?)* (in plankton), Scherffel (*loc. cit.*), HUNGARY.

The fungus reported in *Oedogonium* from England by Sparrow as *Chytridium schenkii* (1936a: 431, pl. 15, figs. 15–16) may possibly belong here. It differs in having larger sporangia and a larger apophysis provided with rhizoids; endobiotic smooth-walled resting spores were found associated with the zoosporangia.

CHYTRIDIUM INFLATUM Sparrow

Amer. J. Bot., 20: 65, text fig. 1 j-l. 1933

(Fig. 31 I, p. 496)

Sporangium sessile, broadly pyriform or urn-shaped, with a prominent apical papilla surmounted by a strongly convex operculum, wall smooth, colorless; endobiotic part consisting of a spherical subsporangial apophysis apparently devoid of rhizoids; zoospores fully formed within the sporangium, uniflagellate, spherical, with a single centric colorless globule, upon the dehiscence of the operculum emerging and forming a temporary group with intertwined flagella before darting away, movement hopping; resting spore not observed.

Parasitic on *Cladophora sp.*, Sparrow (*loc. cit.*), UNITED STATES; *Oedogonium sp.*, Sparrow (1936a: 437, pl. 15, fig. 19), GREAT BRITAIN.

Two well-defined size classes were found:

1. Sporangium 15 µ in diameter by 17 µ high; apophysis 9 µ in diam-

eter; operculum 6 μ in diameter; zoospores 5 μ in diameter, with a small globule.

2. Sporangium 7 μ in diameter by 10 μ high; apophysis 5 μ in diameter; operculum 4 μ in diameter; zoospores 3 μ in diameter, with a relatively large globule.

The species is very doubtfully separate from *Chytridium lagenaria* Schenk, differing only in having more distinctly pyriform sporangia and a more strongly convex operculum.

CHYTRIDIUM CITRIFORME Sparrow

Rev. Soc. Cubana Bot., 9: 68, figs. H-J. 1952

Sporangium sessile, citriform, 23–26 μ by 13–20 μ, with a smooth, colorless wall and a 6–10 μ broad subapical papilla surmounted by a moderately convex operculum, 6–10 μ in diameter; endobiotic part consisting of a spherical, subsporangial apophysis, 10–12 μ (rarely 4 μ) in diameter, from the base of which emerges a branched rhizoidal system; zoospores formed within the sporangium, posteriorly uniflagellate, spherical or somewhat ovoid, 4 μ in diameter, with a single colorless centric globule, emerging upon the dehiscence of the operculum and forming a temporary motionless group before assuming motility; resting spore endobiotic, spherical, 14–16 μ in diameter, with a smooth, thickened, amber-colored wall; germination not observed.

Saprophytic on pollen of *Pinus caribaea* in aquatic debris, CUBA.

The subapical position of the discharge papilla imparts a highly characteristic tilted aspect to the sporangium.

CHYTRIDIUM BREVIPES Braun

Monatsber. Berlin Akad., 1856: 587

Sporangium sessile, obovoid, broadly ovoid, or urceolate, 27 μ high by 20 μ in diameter, the slightly convex operculum usually terminating in a conical umbo, wall smooth, colorless; endobiotic part consisting of a thin-walled spherical subsporangial swelling without rhizoids which at maturity is cut off from the sporangium by a knoblike or conical septum; zoospores spherical, 5 μ in diameter, with an eccentric colorless globule 2 μ in diameter in the finely granular plasma and a flagellum

45 μ in length, ejected at the dehiscence of the operculum through a broad apical pore and forming a temporarily motionless mass, movement hopping or amoeboid; resting spore endobiotic, smooth-walled, with a large oil globule, germination not observed.

On oögonia of *Oedogonium flavescens, O. apophysatum,* Braun (*loc. cit.*), GERMANY; *Oedogonium vaucherii, Oedogonium sp.,* Scherffel (1926a: 225, pl. 10, figs. 107–109, 111–114), HUNGARY; in oögonium of *Oedogonium sp.,* Shen and Siang (1948: 184, fig. 6; as *C. olla*), CHINA.

Considered by Fischer (1892: 126) and Minden (1915: 366) only a small form of *Chytridium olla.* The observations of Scherffel (*loc. cit.*) that the small size is maintained even when the fungus occurs alone on the host cell, as well as his confirmation of the fact noted by Braun (not mentioned by Fischer and Minden) that there was an endobiotic swelling, indicate that we are dealing with a distinct species. See remarks under *C. acuminatum* Braun, p. 495.

CHYTRIDIUM LAGENARIA Schenk, pro parte

Ueber das Vorkommen contractiler Zellen im Pflanzenreiche, p. 5, figs. 11-13.
Würzburg, 1858. Non *C. lagenaria* Schenk, Verhandl. Phys.-Med. Gesell.
Würzburg, A. F., 8: 241. 1858

(Fig. 31 L-M, p. 496)

Rhizidium lagenaria (Schenk) Dangeard, Le Botaniste, 1: 64, pl. 3, fig. 23.
1889.
Rhizidium westii Massee, British Fungi, p. 155, pl. 2, figs. 36-37. London,
1891.
Phlyctochytrium westii (Massee) de Wildeman, Bull. Soc. Roy. Bot. Belg.
(Mém.), 35: 48. 1896.

Sporangium sessile, spherical, subspherical, ovoid, urceolate, or broadly pyriform, somewhat dome-shaped when immature, variable in size, wall somewhat thickened, smooth, colorless; rhizoids generally stout, up to 9 μ in diameter at the point of origin, much branched, occasionally absent, when present usually arising from a single axis produced at the base of a spherical, subspherical, flattened, fusiform, or broad tubular apophysis of variable size; zoospores spherical or somewhat ovoid, 3–5.5 μ in diameter, with a colorless centric or eccentric globule and a flagellum about 20 μ in length, emerging through a large apical pore formed upon the dehiscence of a convex smooth operculum and collecting at the orifice in a temporarily motionless mass, movement swimming or amoeboid; resting spore spherical or ovoid, 18–30 μ in diameter, with a smooth colorless wall 2–3 μ thick, the contents with a single large colorless globule, rhizoidal system like that of the sporangium, upon germination forming an epibiotic sessile ovoid, subspherical, somewhat flattened, or pyriform operculate sporangium.

On *Nitella flexilis*, Schenk (*loc. cit.*), GERMANY; *Vaucheria sp.*, Dangeard (1889b: 64, pl. 3, fig. 23), FRANCE; *Spirogyra sp.*, *Cladophora sp.* (?), de Wildeman (1890: 14, fig. 4), BELGIUM (?); *Oedogonium sp.* (?), Constantineanu (1901: 383), RUMANIA; *Spirogyra sp.*, *Cladophora sp.*, Massee (1891: 155, pl. 2, figs. 36–37), *Rhizoclonium hieroglyphicum*, Sparrow (1936a: 432, pl. 16, figs. 1–24), zygospores of *Spirogyra sp.*, dead cells of *Cladophora sp.*, Canter (1953: 292), GREAT BRITAIN; *Oedogonium sp.*, Karling (1936a: 619, figs. 1–2; 1948c: 508), *Cladophora sp.*, Sparrow (1943: 348), UNITED STATES; *Cladophora sp.*, Bérczi (1940: 84, pl. 2, figs. 25, 26), HUNGARY; moribund cells of *Spirogyra sp.*, Sparrow (1952b: 69, figs. F–G), CUBA.

The records of de Wildeman and Constantineanu are open to question since no operculum was seen. Their fungi may in reality be *Phlyctochytrium lagenaria* (Schenk) Domján. *Rhizidium westii* Massee is considered doubtfully synonymous with *Chytridium lagenaria*. It resembles the latter in all observed essentials. No operculum was seen, but this may have been overlooked by Massee. Even if it had not been, his fungus still cannot, because of differences in the shape of the sporangium and the stoutness of the rhizoidal system, be referred to *Phlyctochytrium lagenaria*.

Chytridium lagenaria has been the object of rather intensive investigation (Sparrow, 1936a; Karling, 1936a) and a relatively large amount of data have been accumulated on its development and biology.

The fungus was transferred from *Rhizoclonium* to *Spirogyra sp.* and *Oedogonium sp.* to determine any morphological changes which might occur on these substrata (Sparrow, *loc. cit.*). It was found, under the conditions of the experiments (conducted in van Tieghem cells), that (1) the size and nature of the zoospore remained constant on the three algae; (2) an endobiotic apophysis was always formed and, though varying in size (average variation from 9–23 μ), was never larger than the operculate sporangium; (3) the sporangium maintained the same general shape (usually subspherical) at all times, but exhibited striking variations in size when growing on different algae. On *Rhizoclonium* the sporangia averaged 29 μ (limits of variation 20–35 μ); on *Spirogyra*, 8 μ (6–11 μ); and on *Oedogonium*, 13 μ (12–15 μ). These variations were not necessarily coördinated with differences in the diameter of the algal cell, for though the largest sporangia were formed on the alga having the largest cells (*Rhizoclonium*) the smallest were not formed on the most slender filaments (*Oedogonium*), but on *Spirogyra*. The rhizoidal system also underwent marked variation on the three algae, being extremely stout and well developed in *Rhizoclonium*, very sparse in *Spirogyra*, and either so tenuous as to be invisible or entirely lacking in *Oedogonium*.

Karling grew the fungus on a variety of Conjugatae and other green algae as well as on *Chara* and *Nitella*, all of which had been killed by boiling. No quantitative or qualitative data are given for the fungus on these different substrata. His successful efforts to cultivate it saprophytically makes Karling inclined to doubt that the species is at all parasitic and also makes him question the validity of the cross-inoculation experiments mentioned above so far as they indicate actual parasitism of the three hosts. The purpose of these experiments was not primarily to test the range of parasitism, but rather to observe morphological changes in the fungus when it was growing on different algae. It might be emphasized, however, that while the environment of a van Tieghem cell is not a natural one, it is not necessarily unfavorable, and that in both controls and infected cells the algae not only appeared healthy, save where attacked by the zoospores of the fungus, but showed evidences of cell division and growth. The demonstration of saprophytism is direct and certain; it is not, however, evidence which necessarily disproves a fact noted in many other fungi, namely, that they may at times also attack a viable organism.

From these researches it is certain, at any rate, that the species can exist on a fairly wide variety of substrata, and in view of this circumstance it is surprising that it has not been recorded more often. Such studies as have been made on *Chytridium lagenaria*, especially those dealing with qualitative and quantitative changes occurring in the fungus on different substrata, will eventually have to be made for all species of the order, before a really comprehensive taxonomic treatise can be prepared.

A curious conjugation of encysted zoospores with young thalli developing in pure water was observed (Sparrow, *loc. cit.*). After the contents of the quiescent spore had evacuated the cyst and had flowed into the receptive thallus, the latter underwent a remarkable vegetative development, which in some cases appeared to terminate in the production of a dwarf sporangium. The result of this fusion was not the formation of a resting structure, as might be expected, but the rejuvenation of vegetative growth and the prolongation of the life of the organism. These thalli continued their growth for nearly a week and became very extensive in contrast to ordinary germinating zoospores, which under the same conditions disintegrated within twelve hours.

Both Sparrow and Karling have observed the apparently asexually formed resting spores, which, as the latter investigator points out, are merely enlarged and encysted apophyses. Karling also observed their germination, in which process the resting spore functioned as a prosporangium.

CHYTRIDIUM LAGENARIA Schenk var. JAPONENSE Kobayasi and Ookubo
Bull. Nat. Sci. Mus. (Tokyo), 33: 56, figs. 3-A, 3-B. 1953

Sporangia gregarious on the surface of the host cell, sessile, ovoid, globose or pyriform, rather thin-walled, 7–18 μ high, 6–15 μ in diameter, hyaline, with an apical papilla, apical pore 5 μ in diameter, opening by the dehiscence of a convex smooth operculum; apophysis connected with the sporangium by a short and narrow neck, napiform or subspherical, about the same size as the sporangium or smaller, 7–15 μ in length, 6–9 μ in diameter, hyaline, homogeneous or somewhat granular; rhizoids rather stout, two or three originating from the base of the apophysis, branched, 2–4 μ in diameter at the point of origin; zoospores spherical or ovoid, hyaline, 2–3 μ in diameter, with 2–3 globules, a refractive body and a posterior 10–12 μ long flagellum, emerging through a pore one by one and swimming away; resting spore not observed. (Modified from Kobayasi and Ookubo.)

On *Cladophora japonica* (marine), JAPAN.

Considered possibly distinct from *Chytridium lagenaria* because its habitat is marine.

CHYTRIDIUM CODICOLA Zeller

Publ. Puget Sound Biol. Station, 2: 121, pl. 20, figs. 5-7. 1918

Sporangium erect, sessile, globose to ovoid, 20–34 μ in diameter, wall smooth, colorless; rhizoid broad, often swollen or vesiculate, or consisting of two lobelike saccate branches; zoospores spherical, 3–4 μ in diameter, with a single refractive colorless globule and a long flagellum, escaping through an apical or slightly subapical circular exit pore, 6–8 μ in diameter, formed upon the dehiscence of an operculum which does not interrupt the even contour of the sporangium; resting spore not observed. (Modified from Zeller.)

On *Codium mucronatum*, UNITED STATES (Pacific Coast).

CHYTRIDIUM POLYSIPHONIAE Cohn

Hedwigia, 4: 169. 1865; Schultze, Archiv mikro. Anat., 3: 40, pl. 2, fig. 2. 1867

(Fig. 31 N-P, p. 496)

Rhizophydium polysiphoniae (Cohn) H. E. Petersen, Oversigt Kgl. Danske Vidensk. Selskabs. Forhandl., 1905 (5): 486, fig. XI, 5-8.

Rhizophydium olla H. E. Petersen, *op. cit.*, p. 485, fig. XI, 4.

Sporangium sessile, subspherical, subangular, pyriform, or urceolate, 12–33 μ in diameter by 12–42 μ high, resting with its broad base on the substratum, wall fairly stout, colorless, yellowish, or dark, not of cellulose, smooth or densely punctate; rhizoids unbranched or branched; zoospores spherical, 2.5–4 μ in diameter, with a colorless centric or eccentric globule and a fairly long flagellum, escaping upon the dehiscence of an apical smooth convex operculum 7–13 μ in diameter; resting spore not observed.

On *Polysiphonia violacea*, Cohn (*loc. cit.*), GERMANY; *Polysiphonia violacea*, *P. urceolata*, coll. Rosenvinge, Petersen (*loc. cit.*), *Ceramium rubrum, Ceramium sp.*, coll. Rosenvinge, Petersen (*loc. cit.*), *C. strictum,* Petersen (*op. cit.*, p. 488, "no. 5"), *Delessaria sanguinea, Callithamnion sp.*, Petersen (*loc. cit.*), *Ceramium fruticulosum*, Sparrow (1934c: 23, pl. 4, figs. E-G), DENMARK; *Pylaiella litoralis*, coll. Rosenvinge, Petersen (*loc. cit.*), GREENLAND; *Polysiphonia fibrillosa, Ceramium rubrum*, Sparrow (1936b: 255, text fig. 31), UNITED STATES; *Callithamnion ? sp.*, apical cells of *Polysiphonia spp., Herposiphonia tenella*, Aleem (1950d: 435, fig. 26), *? Chondria tenuissima, Pylaiella litoralis*, Feldmann (1954: 132), *? Chondria tenuissima*, J. and G. Feldmann (1955: 248), FRANCE.

The species as described here is undoubtedly a composite one and much work will be needed to separate the varieties or even the species which it now embraces.

Cohn's fungus had irregularly pyriform sporangia, 25–33 μ in diameter, which rested with their broad bases on the alga. The wall was somewhat thickened, dark, and punctate, and no rhizoids were observed. At maturity an operculum 13 μ in diameter was dehisced from the protruding apex, allowing the zoospores, 2.5 μ in diameter, to escape. Petersen's specimens differed in having the operculum slightly subapical and the sporangium wall colorless and smooth; an unbranched rhizoid was observed. He (*op. cit.*, p. 487) suggests that the coloration and punctation of the sporangium wall described by Cohn were probably caused by age. Sparrow's Danish material differed from Cohn's chiefly in having a smaller operculum (7 μ in diameter), larger zoospores (4 μ in diameter), and a smooth colorless sporangium wall, and from Petersen's in having an apical operculum and rhizoids, which were probably branched, arising from a central stalk.

Rhizophydium olla Petersen on *Pylaiella* from Greenland cannot be distinguished morphologically from *R. polysiphoniae* on the basis of the description and figures given. Cohn has called attention to the fact that his fungus was confounded with the spermatia of *Nitophyllum* by Derbés and Solier. Other instances of early investigators confusing the fungus with an organ of the alga are given by Wright (1879b).

J. and G. Feldmann's recent record (1955) for the species, from the figures given, does not seem to relate to *C. polysiphoniae*. Furthermore, their fungus did not attack *Ceramium* but only *Chondria*.

CHYTRIDIUM MEGASTOMUM Sparrow

Dansk Bot. Ark., 8 (6): 21, pl. 4, A-D. 1934

(Fig. 31 Q, p. 496)

Sporangium sessile, obpyriform, 12–18 μ high, diameter at the base 5–7 μ, increasing distally to 10–15 μ at the apex, wall smooth, colorless; rhizoids rudimentary, sparingly branched, arising from a single stalk; zoospores spherical, 3 μ in diameter, with a small colorless slightly eccentric globule, discharged through a broad usually somewhat subapical pore 8–10 μ in diameter formed upon the dehiscence of a large convex operculum; resting spore not observed.

Parasitic on the setae of *Striaria attenuata*, Sparrow (*loc. cit.*), DEN-MARK; *Ceramium diaphanum*, Sparrow (1936b: 255), UNITED STATES.

Distinguished from its closest marine relative, *Chytridium polysiphoniae*, by the obpyriform shape of its sporangium and the subapical operculum.

RECENTLY DESCRIBED TAXA [1]

CHYTRIDIUM NEOCHLAMYDOCOCCI Kobayashi and Ookubo

Rept. Osegahara Gen. Sci. Surv. Comm., 1954: 571, fig. 13. 1954

Sporangia gregarious, epibiotic, ovoid or citriform, 8–10 μ high by 6.5–8 μ broad, with an obconical base and smooth, hyaline, thin wall and apical papilla surmounted by a discoid, 4–5 μ in diameter, operculum; endobiotic part with a poorly developed, or obscure elongate-obconical apophysis from which emerge distally a simple or two-to three-branched rhizoidal system of limited extent; zoospores about five, globose, 4–5 μ in diameter; resting spore not observed.

Parasitic on *Chlamydomonas nivalis* in "red snow," JAPAN.

Text in Japanese. Description in Latin.

CHYTRIDIUM PARASITICUM Willoughby [2]

Trans. Brit. Mycol. Soc., 39: 135, figs. 5-7. 1956

Sporangium pyriform, 8–27 μ long by 6–22 μ wide with a narrow

---

[1] Not included in the key.

[2] See also Willoughby, in *loc. cit.*, 41: 309-319, 1958, where a multioperculate chytrid on *Mucor* is described.

base, 2–3 μ in diameter which is an unexpanded portion of the cyst of the zoospore, sessile or on an extramatrical stalk up to 10 μ long, without an obvious papilla or operculum; rhizoidal system delicate, branched; zoospores spherical, 2.2–3.0 μ in diameter (av. 2.5 μ), with an anterior oil globule 1.0 μ in diameter and a posterior oscillating granule and flagellum 12–14.6 μ long, emerging in a mass upon the dehiscence of a terminal or lateral portion of the sporangium wall, after which the sporangium collapses; resting spore not observed.

Parasitic on *Rhizidium richmondense*, *Rhizophlyctis sp.*, *Entophlyctis sp.*, hyperparasitic on *Chytridium urceolatum*, and *Septosperma rhizophidii* (Herb. I.M.I., No. 60444), GREAT BRITAIN.

Chytridium parasiticum somewhat resembles *C. rhizophidii* Karling in its structural features and its hosts (other chytrids). As Willoughby points out, however, there are significant differences between them in the shape of the sporangium and operculum. *Chytridium parasiticum* does closely approximate the diatom parasite *C. surirellae*.

Note that in attacking *Septosperma* this species is parasitizing a chytrid which is parasitic on another chytrid which in its turn is a saprophyte!

CHYTRIDIUM SUBURCEOLATUM Willoughby

Trans. Brit. Mycol. Soc., 39: 132, fig. 4. 1956

Sporangium suburceolate, 4–16 μ high, with a colorless thin light-brown wall; rhizoidal system of variable extent, not clearly evident in host, of limited extent; zoospores spherical, 2–2.5 μ in diameter, with a lateral oil droplet, 0.6–0.8 μ in diameter, and a 14 μ long flagellum, escaping rapidly upon the dehiscence of a terminal (rarely two) operculum, movement hopping; resting spore not observed.

Parasitic on sporangia of *Rhizophlyctis richmondense* (Herb. I.M.I., No. 60443), GREAT BRITAIN.

The species was hyperparasitized by *Chytridium parasiticum* Willoughby (see p. 528).

CHYTRIDIUM TURBINATUM Kobayasi and Ookubo

Bull. Nat. Sci. Mus. (Tokyo), (N.S.), 1 (2) No. 35: 69, fig. 8. 1954

"Sporangium gregarious, ovoid or ellipsoid, apically with one conically protruding papilla, 7–15 μ high, 6–7.5 μ in diameter, thin-walled, hyaline, opened by the dehiscence of operculum, contained 20–30 zoo-spores, penetration tube none, or thick and short. Apophysis turbinate, smaller than zoosporangium, 3–5 × 4–5 μ, with one axial rhizoid. Rhizoid commonly simple, rather thick and short, longitudinally elon-gated, abruptly attenuated toward apex. Zoospores ellipsoid, 3 × 4 μ, containing [with] one refracting body and a posterior flagellum. Resting body not observed" (Kobayasi and Ookubo, *loc. cit.*).

Parasitic on *Bryopsis sp.* (marine), JAPAN.

Differing from other apophysate species of the genus in having a single, coarse, unbranched, tapering rhizoid.

IMPERFECTLY KNOWN SPECIES OF CHYTRIDIUM

? CHYTRIDIUM CHARACII Scherffel

Arch. Protistenk., 53: 13, pl. 1, fig. 25 a-c. 1925

Sporangium and zoospores not observed; resting spore epibiotic, narrowly ovoid, oblong, or somewhat clavate, with the long axis per-pendicular to the substratum, 5–6 μ in diameter by 10–14 μ high (smaller examples 4–7 by 7–9 μ), colorless, with an extremely thick wall of two layers, the inner thick, refractive, homogeneous, and smooth, the outer thicker at base or apex than in the mid-region, in optical section having a well-defined prismatic structure, in surface view covered by longi-tudinal rows of elongate warts, with a delicate branched rhizoid within the host, germination not observed; companion cell spherical or some-what clavate, thin-walled, 2–2.5 μ in diameter, sessile, without rhizoids, connected to the base of the resting spore by a more or less elongate narrow fertilization tube.

Parasitic on *Characium sp.*, HUNGARY.

Observations on the sporangial stage will be necessary before this fungus can be placed in the correct genus. Scherffel has suggested that it may belong possibly in either *Zygorhizidium* or *Rhizophydium*.

? CHYTRIDIUM CHLAMIDOCOCCI Braun

Abhandl. Berlin Akad., 1855: 45. 1856

Sporangia in groups, at first spherical, later somewhat oblong, not over 10 μ long, sometimes with an oblique apiculus.

On *Chlamydococcus pluvialis*, GERMANY.
Mentioned by Fischer and Minden under *Rhizophydium acuforme* (Zopf) Fischer.

? CHYTRIDIUM CORNUTUM Braun

Abhandl. Berlin Akad., 1855: 50, pl. 4, figs. 8-19. 1856

Rhizophydium cornutum (Braun) Rabenhorst, Flora Europaea algarum, 3: 281. 1868.
Phlyctidium cornutum (Braun) Sorokin, Arch. Bot. Nord France, 2: 19, fig. 14. 1883 (separate).

Sporangium sessile, at first spherical, later ellipsoidal with several hornlike outgrowths of different lengths, 10–12.5 μ in diameter (without protrusions); zoospores posteriorly uniflagellate; rhizoids and resting spore not observed.

On *Anabaena circinalis*, Braun (*loc. cit.*), GERMANY; *Hormidium varium*, Sorokin (1874b: 8, pl. 1, figs. 18–28; 1883: 19, fig. 14), EUROPEAN RUSSIA (southern part).

Sorokin (*loc. cit.*) states that the posteriorly uniflagellate ellipsoidal zoospores escape through a pore on the upper face of the sporangium. No endobiotic part has been observed, nor has the method of opening of the sporangium been described. The fungus may possibly belong in *Rhizophydium*.

? CHYTRIDIUM DEPRESSUM Braun

Monatsber. Berlin Akad., 1855: 383; Abhandl. Berlin Akad., 1855: 46, pl. 4, fig. 7. 1856

Sporangium very broadly pyriform, resting with its wide base on the host cell, somewhat flattened, with a prolonged erect or slightly bent apiculus, wall smooth, colorless, 37 μ broad by 25 μ high; rhizoids, method of discharge of zoospores, and resting spore not observed.

On *Coleochate prostrata*, coll. Pringsheim, GERMANY.

? CHYTRIDIUM ELODEAE Dangeard

Le Botaniste, 1: 61, pl. 3, fig. 25. 1889

Sporangium sessile (?), nearly spherical, variable in size, up to 30 μ in diameter, wall smooth, colorless; rhizoids not clearly seen; zoospores spherical, 3 μ in diameter, with a prominent colorless basal globule and a fairly long flagellum, emerging from a point on the sporangium and forming a large mass from which they slowly escape.

On the cortical cells of *Elodea canadensis*, FRANCE.

As suggested by Dangeard, this is probably an incompletely observed species of *Cladochytrium*. It should be noted, however, that the sporangia are said to be *"sur les cellules"* rather than inside.

? CHYTRIDIUM EUGLENAE Braun

Monatsber. Berlin Akad., 1855: 382; Abhandl. Berlin Akad., 1855: 47, pl. 4,
        figs. 26-27. 1856
    Phlyctidium euglenae (Braun) Sorokin, Arch. Bot. Nord France, 2: 20,
    fig. 16. 1883 (separate).

Sporangium inoperculate, extramatrical, somewhat irregularly tubular, with a small knoblike sterile continuous basal or lateral part resting on the host cell, 50–66 μ long by 16–33 μ in diameter; endobiotic part not observed; zoospores ovoid, longer than wide, 3.3 μ long, with a basal colorless globule and a smaller anterior vacuole, flagellum about three times the length of the body, escaping through a pore formed at the tip of the sporangium; resting spore not observed.

Parasitic on resting cells of *Euglena viridis*, coll. von Siebold and Meissner, Braun (*loc. cit.*), GERMANY; encysted *Euglena*, Sorokin (*loc. cit.*; 1874b: 7, pl. 1, figs. 12–17), RUSSIA.

Because of the lack of information on the vegetative system the species cannot be placed generically with certainty. Fischer and Minden have referred it to *Polyphagus euglenae*, but this course seems hardly justified because of the differences in shape of the sporangium, the formation of zoospores in the sporangium, the bulbous base, and colorless globule of the zoospore. On the other hand, the fungi collected by Bail and Gross and later mentioned by Braun (*loc. cit.*) in his discussion of this species probably are referable to Nowakowski's *Polyphagus*. Braun (1856b: 592) subsequently referred Bail's fungus to *Rhizidium*.

Rhizidium (= *Phlyctochytrium*) *euglenae* of Dangeard (1889b: 64) approaches closely the fungus found by von Siebold and Meissner.

? CHYTRIDIUM HAEMATOCOCCI Braun

Abhandl. Berlin Akad., 1855: 45. 1856

Known only from the figure of Vogt, in Desor (1844: 215–219, pl. 1, figs. 4 a-f) (see Braun, 1856a).

On *Haematococcus*, SWITZERLAND (?).

Mentioned by Fischer and Minden under *Rhizophydium acuforme* (Zopf) Fischer.

? CHYTRIDIUM MINUS Lacoste and Suringar

Nederl. Kruidk. Arch., 5 (2): 275, pl. A. 1861

Sporangium subglobose or short-oblong, 11–14 μ high by 9–12 μ in diameter, with a broad prominent apical papilla 1.3–2.5 μ high by 2.5–4 μ in diameter, wall smooth, golden, thin in the upper part but becoming thicker toward the base, where it is prolonged into a single slender extramatrical stalk (rarely two opposite stalks) which may encircle the substratum; zoospores, method of escape, and resting spore unknown.

On *Ulothrix albicans* (?), *"Conferva rhynophila,"* *Oedogonium sp.*, *Bulbochaete setigera* (on the setae), stipes of *Gomphonema navicella*, HOLLAND.

Tokunaga (1934b: 392, pl. 11, fig. 13) has referred to this species a fungus found by him in Japan on oögonia of *Oedogonium sp.* He characterized it as follows: "Zoosporangia epibiotic on sexual cells of the host, solitary or aggregated, spherical or ovoidal, 12–14.4 μ in diameter, with smooth membrane, an apical papilla and a broad, short rhizoid; zoospores globular, about 2–4 μ in diameter, with a single cilium; resting spores endobiotic, up to seven in a host cell, spherical, 13.2–15.6 μ in diameter, with smooth, thick membrane and a large oil drop." The very different nature of the rhizoid as well as the shape of the sporangium of the Japanese fungus makes it extremely doubtful that it is identical with Lacoste's and Suringar's species. Further, since an operculum has not been described as being present in either form, the placing of them in *Chytridium* seems hardly justified. The broad tubular rhizoid and the endobiotic resting spores of Tokunaga's fungus make it appear closer to *C. olla*. Sporangia exactly like those figured by Lacoste and Suringar have been found in Michigan on *Mougeotia*.

In none of the numerous specimens was the rhizoid ever observed to penetrate the algal cell. Indeed, the whole aspect of the organism was animal-like rather than fungoid in character.

? CHYTRIDIUM MURICATUM Scherffel

Arch. Protistenk., 54: 216, pl. 10, fig. 89. 1926

Sporangium sessile, between spines of the host, broadly ovoid, with a rounded base, somewhat higher than broad (15 by 12 µ), thick-walled, the outer surface fairly densely beset with scattered moderately thick conical spines 3 µ long; with a sharply defined smooth broad apical opening which probably resulted from the dehiscence of an operculum; other characters unknown.

On the zygote of *Staurastrum dejectum* var. *debaryanum*, HUNGARY.

This incompletely known form is interesting because of the sculpturing of the wall, in which character it resembles *Rhizophydium verrucosum*. It is not clear, however, whether the structure described is a sporangium or a germinated resting spore. Rhizoids and an operculum were probably formed but were not observed.

? CHYTRIDIUM PEDICELLATUM de Wildeman

C. R. Soc. Roy. Bot. Belg. (Bull.), 30: 170, fig. 1. 1891

Sporangium shaped like that of *Rhizophydium mammillatum*; endobiotic part consisting of a small knob; otherwise unknown.

Substratum (?), BELGIUM (?).

Possibly belonging in *Phlyctidium*.

? CHYTRIDIUM VOLVOCINUM Braun

Monatsber. Berlin Akad., 1856: 588

Rhizophydium volvocinum (Braun) Fischer, Rabenhorst. Kryptogamen-Fl., 1 (4): 104. 1892.

Sporangium pyriform or flasklike, resting on a short narrow base; apparently without rhizoids; zoospores and resting spore not observed.

On *Volvox globator*, coll. Cohn, GERMANY.

Described in Fischer as *Rhizophydium* (*Phlyctidium*) *volvocinum* and in Minden as *R. volvocinum* (Braun) Fischer.

? Chytridium xylophilum Cornu

Ann. Sci. Nat. Bot., V, 15: 116. 1872

Rhizidium xylophilum (Cornu) Dangeard, Le Botaniste, 1: 64. 1889.
Rhizophydium xylophilum (Cornu) Fischer, Rabenhorst. Kryptogamen-Fl.,
1 (4): 98. 1892.

Sporangia resting on the surface of the fibers, often in long rows, ovoid, acuminate, flattened, with or without a long tube which terminates in a papilla; rhizoids not observed; zoospores spherical, with an eccentric globule and a single flagellum, method of escape not described; resting spore free (?), spherical, with a moderately thick smooth wall and a large pale-brown oil globule.

Saprophytic on submerged decaying fibers of *Corylus avellana, Tilia*, hemp, France.

Both Dangeard (1886a: 300, pl. 13, figs. 6–9) and Scherffel (1926a: 247, pl. 11, figs. 144–146) have referred fungi to Cornu's incompletely known species. Dangeard's chytrid rested on "*fibres*" and had an ovoid sporangium with a prominent apical papilla. Sporangia were also found within the tissue, where they underwent deformation. Since the zoospores upon germination in water produced rhizoids they were probably present on the natural substratum, though unobserved. Discharge presumably was inoperculate, the zoospores clustering in a rounded motionless mass from which they soon escaped. Scherffel's fungus formed sporangia on the fibers of decayed *Typha* or in the cells. When free some assumed an irregular broadly pyriform shape, generally with a somewhat laterally placed prominent papilla bearing an operculum. Others were spheroidal with a slightly elevated papilla, or broadly ovoid with a somewhat lateral tapering discharge tube. They varied in size, being 20–36 μ in diameter by 16–34 μ high. The zoospores were spherical, 8 μ in diameter. No rhizoids were observed. Scherffel's fungus differed from both Cornu's and Dangeard's in having operculate sporangia. All these fungi have been incompletely observed, and since the rhizoidal system of Cornu's plant was not found it seems useless to attempt an interpretation of his species.

Sparrow (1936a: 432, pl. 15, figs. 21–26) described an operculate fungus with pyriform or irregular sporangia imbedded in the spongy woody tissue of submerged *Aesculus* and *Quercus* twigs in England and in *Betula* in New Hampshire. Here again, because of the difficulty of freeing the plants intact from their substratum, no complete picture of the vegetative system was obtained. From what was learned, however, this system was filamentous, hyphal, and at least occasionally septate. The sporangia were 17–45 µ in diameter by 20–45 µ high, were ordinarily provided with a broad somewhat attenuated discharge tube, and terminated in a smoothly convex or umbonate operculum. The zoospores were posteriorly uniflagellate, with a single globule, and 5–7 µ in diameter. Sparrow's form resembles a species of *Endochytrium* in being within the cells of the substratum and *Chytridium xylophilum* in the general shape of the sporangia and in the habitat, but if the septate hyphal characters of the mycelium are confirmed by subsequent investigation it probably represents the type of a new genus.

? CHYTRIDIUM SP., Schulz

Schriften f. Süsswasser und Meereskunde, 2 (11): 181, fig. 14. 1923

Sporangium sessile, spherical, 12–14 µ in diameter, wall thin, the outer surface with a minute spiral crisscross pattern, with two subapical convex opercula; rhizoid tubular, unbranched; zoospore discharge not observed; resting spore not observed.

On zygote of a desmid, GERMANY.

If the opercula described are not in reality protruding papillae, the form is apparently a new species. Observations on zoospore discharge, however, will have to be made before this can be said with certainty.

? CHYTRIDIUM SP., Fott

Preslia, 24: 208. 1952

Sporangium obovoid, twisted, upright, beneath gradually diminished, broad rounded above, 10–18 µ high by 9–12 µ in diameter, to all appearances opening by a fairly large apical operculum; endobiotic subsporangial part spherical, 6 µ in diameter.

Parasitic on *Chlorobotrys polychloris*, CZECHOSLOVAKIA.

EXCLUDED SPECIES OF CHYTRIDIUM
* CHYTRIDIUM ALARIUM Kibbe

Publ. Puget Sound Biol. Station, 1: 221. 1916

Cystidia of the alga *Alarium*. Not a fungus.

* CHYTRIDIUM DENTRITICUM Fuckel

Fuckel Herb. No. 1608. 1894

Specimen not examined – doubtless not identifiable if dried.

* CHYTRIDIUM DESTRUENS Nowakowski

Cohn, Beitr. Biol. Pflanzen, 2 (1): 75, pl. 4, figs. 1 a-c. 1876

This organism is *Minutularia destruens* Dangeard (1890–91c: 241), a monad.

Because of ingestion of solid particles, the species was considered by Dangeard to be a protozoan, in the zoosporic monads.

* CHYTRIDIUM MESOCARPI (Fisch) Fischer

Rabenhorst. Kryptogamen-Fl., 1 (4): 126. 1892

Euchytridium mesocarpi Fisch, Sitzungsber. Phys.-Med. Soc. Erlangen, 16: 101. 1884.

See page 766.

* CHYTRIDIUM MINIMUM Braun

Monatsber. Berlin Akad., 1855: 381

The antheridial cell of *Coleochaete pulvinata*, according to Pringsheim (in Braun, 1856a: 34).

* CHYTRIDIUM OBLONGUM Braun

Monatsber. Berlin Akad., 1855: 380

According to de Bary (in Braun, 1856b: 587), this is the dwarf male plant of *Oedogonium vesicatum*.

Recorded by Lagerheim (1884 (1): 100) from SWEDEN.

CHYTRIOMYCES KARLING, emend.

Amer. J. Bot., 32: 363. 1945

(Fig. 32 D-F, p. 554; also, Fig. 11, I, p. 110)

Thallus extramatrical or endobiotic, monocentric, eucarpic, the epibiotic part forming the rudiment of the sporangium oɪ resting spore, the endobiotic part producing the vegetative system; sporangium epibiotic, operculate, formed from all or part of the enlarged body of the encysted zoospore; zoospores posteriorly uniflagellate, usually with a single globule, often undergoing a period of swarming in a vesicle outside the sporangium before dispersing; rhizoidal system endobiotic, arising from the tip of the germ tube or from an apophysis; resting spore epibiotic or extramatrical, thick-walled, apparently asexually formed, upon germination functioning as a prosporangium.

Saprophytes on plant and animal substrata and parasitic on diatoms.

As originally diagnosed by Karling (1945c), the genus embraced only epibiotic forms which had apophysate operculate sporangia, zoospores that underwent a swarming period in a vesicle outside the sporangium, and extramatrical resting spores. Although no comparison was then made with the closely related *Chytridium*, the type species differed significantly from a member of this genus only in having an extramatrical rather than an endobiotic resting spore. As more monocentric epibiotic operculate fungi were discovered which had extramatrical resting spores but no apophysis or swarming period of zoospores, the concept of *Chytriomyces* evidently was expanded to include them (Karling, 1948b: 332). Further, since close comparison was made by Karling with *Amphicypellus* (p. 546), a fungus with a type of development like *Rhizidium*, it is possible but by no means clear he also intended that any operculate rhizidiaceous forms discovered in the future be included under *Chytriomyces*. If that is so, the operculate *Amphicypellus* would have nomenclatorial precedence. Karling's (1949d: 352) redefinition of *Chytriomyces* is incorporated in the description.

Whether or not a definite vesicle comparable, for instance, to that in *Pythium*, always surrounds the zoospores upon discharge is uncertain (see *Chytriomyces appendiculatus*). Doubt arises because other microscopic organisms are able to move freely in and out of the swarming group of zoospores. This swarming is found in other genera of chytrids and is not unique to *Chytriomyces*.

The commonest species is *Chytriomyces hyalinus*, which is readily obtainable on chitin bait in bogs.

KEY TO THE SPECIES OF CHYTRIOMYCES

Sporangium not appendiculate
With one discharge pore
Sporangium spherical, oval or ovoid, occasionally somewhat pyriform
Globule of zoospore golden red .... *C. aureus*, p. 539
Globule of zoospore hyaline
Zoospore spherical or oval, 2-3 μ in diameter; sporangia up to 30 μ in diameter
Sporangium spherical or slightly oval, apophysate; parasitic on *Aphanomyces* .... *C. parasiticus*, p. 540
Sporangium spherical or broadly pyriform, nonapophysate; on *Closterium*................... *C. closterii*, p. 540
Zoospore oval, 3-3.5 μ by 5-5.5 μ; sporangia up to 60 μ in diameter .... *C. hyalinus*, p. 541
Sporangium broadly pyriform or transversely flattened
Sporangia predominantly broadly pyriform, wall covered with abruptly tapering spines .... *C. spinosus*, p. 542
Sporangia transversely flattened, somewhat reniform; wall smooth .... *C. lucidus*, p. 542
With one to three discharge papillae or broad tubes; wall with one to six solid pegs or spines .... *C. stellatus*, p. 543
Sporangium appendiculate, that is, bearing part of the unexpanded body of the zoospore
Sporangium with one discharge papilla
Sporangium oval or obpyriform, with an extramatrical stalk, small (up to 13 μ high by 15 μ broad); on diatoms   *C. tabellariae*, p. 543
Sporangium extremely variable and irregular in shape, sessile, large (up to 250 μ in diameter), wall with brownish thickenings; on chitinous substrata .... *C. appendiculatus*, p. 544
Sporangium with one or two discharge papillae or one to three discharge tubes................................. *C. fructicosus*, p. 545

CHYTRIOMYCES AUREUS Karling

Amer. J. Bot., 32: 363, figs. 28-45. 1945

(Fig. 32 E-F, p. 554)

"Sporangia golden-red, smooth, spherical (8–40 μ), or slightly oval (10–20 × 12–23 μ); operculum apical or subapical shallow saucer-shaped, 4–6 μ in diam. Zoospores oval, 3–3.5 × 5 μ, with a golden-red refractive globule, 1.5–2 μ in diam.; flagellum 22–25 μ long; zoospores emerging and swarming in vesicle 2–32 minutes before breaking out and swimming away; vesicle continuous with interior of sporangium. Apophysis, when present, spherical to subspherical, 3–6 μ in diam. Resting spores spherical (6–20 μ), oval (6–10 μ × 12–16 μ), with a thick (2 μ), golden-brown smooth wall and numerous closely packed granules or globules; functioning as prosporangia in germination" (Karling, *loc. cit.*).

Saprophytic in exuviae of mayflies and on chitin, Karling (*loc. cit.*), BRAZIL; Karling (*loc. cit.*; 1948c: 509), UNITED STATES.

This species and *Chytriomyces hyalinus* were also grown on onion skin, which indicates that they are not strictly confined to chitinous substrata.

CHYTRIOMYCES PARASITICUS Karling

Bull. Torrey Bot. Club., 74: 334, figs. 1-15. 1947

"Sporangia smooth, hyaline, spherical, 8–30 μ, or slightly oval; operculum apical or subapical, 4–14 μ diam. Zoospores oval, 2.5–3 μ, with a minute, 0.4–0.6 μ diam., hyaline refractive globule; flagellum 14–18 μ long. Apophysis intra- or extramatrical, globular, 3–6 μ diam., or angular; rhizoids relatively short and finely branched. Resting spores unknown" (Karling, *loc. cit.*).

Parasitic on *Aphanomyces laevis*, causing local swelling and excessive branching of the mycelium, UNITED STATES.

Whether this turns out to be a species of *Chytriomyces* or *Chytridium* will depend upon the position of the resting spores when they are found.

The parasite eventually completely destroyed the host. The discharged zoospores were capable of undergoing several intermittent periods of swarming if escape was not at once effected from the confining vesicle.

CHYTRIOMYCES CLOSTERII Karling

Bull. Torrey Bot. Club, 76: 352, figs. 1-5. 1949

"Sporangia hyaline, smooth, non-apophysate, spherical, 5–25 μ, or broadly pyriform, 6–19 × 9–24 μ, with one apical exit papilla; operculum shallow saucer-shaped, 4–6 μ diam., non-persistent. Zoospores spherical, 2–2.5 μ, with a minute, 0.4–0.6 μ, hyaline refractive globule;

flagellum 9–12 µ long; swarming actively in a vesicle outside of the sporangium. Single rhizoidal axis attached at base of sporangium, sparsely branched and sometimes extending for a distance of 120 µ. Resting spores hyaline, smooth, [spherical], 7–12 µ, or oval with a large central globule surrounded by several smaller ones; content emerging through a pore in the wall during germination and forming a superficial sporangium" (Karling, *loc. cit.*).

Weakly parasitic on *Closterium rostratum*, UNITED STATES.

Apparently confined to one host species. It does not attack other species of *Closterium* or members of other genera of green algae.

CHYTRIOMYCES HYALINUS Karling

Amer. J. Bot., 32: 363, figs. 46-61. 1945

Chytriomyces nodulatus Haskins, Trans. British Mycol. Soc., 29: 137, figs. 1-8. 1946.

"Sporangia hyaline, smooth, usually spherical, 10–60 µ; operculum apical or subapical, shallow, saucer-shaped, 8–16 µ in diam. Zoospores oval, 3–3.5 × 5–5.5 µ, with a small (1–1.5 µ), hyaline refractive globule; flagellum 18–20 µ long; zoospores emerging and swarming in vesicle, 1–16 minutes before breaking out and swimming away; vesicle continuous with interior of sporangium. Apophysis when present spherical, subspherical, fusiform, or elongate, 3–7 µ in diam. Rhizoidal system well developed, main axis up to 7 µ in diam.; extending for a distance of 300 µ. Resting spores spherical (10–20 µ), oval (6–8 × 10–14 µ), elongate, clavate, pyriform, or slightly irregular, with a smooth, thick (2 µ), light-brown wall; containing a large central refractive globule surrounded by a few to several smaller ones; functioning as prosporangia in germination" (Karling, *loc. cit.*).

Saprophytic in exuviae and on chitin, BRAZIL; Karling (*loc. cit.*; 1948c: 509), chitin, Sparrow (MICHIGAN), UNITED STATES; from soil, substrate ?, Gaertner (1954b: 22), NORTHWEST AFRICA, SOUTH AFRICA.

Common in bogs in Michigan; nodulate as well as smooth-walled sporangia were observed.

The species frequently occurs in company with *Polychytrium aggregatum* on purified shrimp chitin bait.

CHYTRIOMYCES SPINOSUS Fay

Mycologia, 39: 152, figs. 1-39. 1947

(Fig. 32 D, p. 554)

"Zoosporangia hyaline, predominantly broadly pyriform, 11.3–45 × 11.3–40.5 μ, operculum apical, shallow saucer-shaped, 2.3–6 × 0.75–4.5 μ, and apiculate 1.5 × 6.9 μ, wall of sporangium 0.75–1.5 μ in thickness, covered with numerous, abruptly tapering spines, usually simple and solid, 2.5–4.9 × 1.4–5.9 μ, rarely bifurcate, occasionally abortive and peg-like. Rhizoids branched, arising usually from a single main axis, 1.6–3.6 μ diameter and extending to a distance of 387 μ. Zoospores emerge and swarm 1–7 minutes in a hyaline vesicle before escaping and swimming away; vesicle continuous with the sporangium.

"Resting spores predominantly ovoid and 15–33 × 10–33.5 μ or wedge-shaped and 15 × 15 μ, rarely spherical; usually covered irregularly with spines which may be simple or bifurcate; wall hyaline or slightly yellowish, 1.4–4.5 μ in thickness; containing a single large oil globule 6.8 to 21 μ in diameter. Resting spores function as prosporangia in germination, giving rise to hyaline subspherical thin-walled, smooth secondary sporangia 8.9 to 20.6 μ diameter" (Fay, *loc. cit.*).

Cellulose substratum, soil, Fay (*loc. cit.*), onion skin, from moist soil, Karling (1947d, figs. 41–42; 1948c: 509), UNITED STATES.

The illustrations of resting-spore germination given (Fay, *loc. cit.*, figs. 38–39) suggest parasitism by another chytrid. The germ sporangium is very disproportionate in size to the resting spore, residual oil material is left in the resting spore, and no operculum is mentioned or figured.

CHYTRIOMYCES LUCIDUS Karling

Bull. Torrey Bot. Club, 76: 353, figs. 6-17. 1949

"Sporangia hyaline, smooth, non-apophysate, usually flattened and elongated transversely to rhizoidal axis, 18–44 × 28–66 μ, often almost hemispherical, or reniform, with one low, 3–4 μ high by 6–15 μ broad, apical exit papilla; operculum very shallow saucer-shaped, 4–8 μ diam., usually non-persistent. Zoospores slightly oval, 5.8 × 6.2 μ, with a large hyaline, spherical, 3.6–3.9 μ, refractive globule. Rhizoids coarse, rigid and stiff-looking, main axes 4–12 μ in diam., often extending for a distance of 400 μ and becoming thick-walled with age. Resting spores hyaline, smooth, oval, slightly elongate, 15–18 × 20–25 μ, with numerous angular refractive bodies; germination unknown" (Karling, *loc. cit.*).

Saprophytic on cellulosic substrata, in soil and water, UNITED STATES. No swarming of the zoospores in a vesicle was noted here.

CHYTRIOMYCES STELLATUS Karling

Bull. Torrey Bot. Club, 74: 335. 1947

"Sporangia hyaline, smooth or with 1–6 short, solid, triangular pegs or spines, spherical, 9–50 μ, oval, broadly pyriform, 8–35 × 10–45 μ, narrowly pyriform, 6–20 × 14–38 μ, bean-shaped, anatropous or slightly angular with 1–3 exit papillae or long, 3–7 × 10–50 μ, necks; operculum saucer-shaped or slightly apiculate, 4–7 μ diam. Zoospores oval, 3.5–4 × 4.5–5 μ, with a small, 1.5–2.0 μ diam. hyaline refractive globule; flagellum 25–30 μ long. Apophysis conspicuous, spherical, 4–18 μ, oval, 4–8 × 6–14 μ, broadly fusiform or slightly angular. Rhizoids arising from the base or sides of apophysis, finely branched. Resting spores hyaline, [stellate], apophysate, spherical, 9–26 μ, oval, 10–14 × 15–22 μ, or slightly angular with few to numerous solid, short blunt or elongate, pointed, and rarely bifurcate pegs or spines, rarely smooth; content hyaline with one large, up to 10 μ in diam., or several smaller, refractive globules, emerging through a pore in the wall and forming a superficial zoosporangium during germination" (Karling, *loc. cit.*).

Saprophytic on chitinous substrata, in fresh water and muck soil, Karling (*loc. cit.*), BRAZIL; chitin, from fresh water and moist soil, Karling (1948c: 509), UNITED STATES.

The species has not as yet been figured.

CHYTRIOMYCES TABELLARIAE (C. Schröter) Canter

Trans. Brit. Mycol. Soc., 32: 16, figs. 1, 2. 1949
(Fig. 11 I, p. 110)

Phlyctidium tabellariae C. Schröter, Neujahrblatt Naturf. Gesell. Zurich, 99: Anmerk. 3, pl. 1, fig. 48. 1897.

Sporangium oval or obpyriform with a basal unexpanded portion of the cyst of the infecting zoospore persistent, its long axis oblique or nearly parallel with that of the host, 4.3–13 μ high by 6–15 μ broad, resting on a narrow, unbranched extramatrical stalk up to 13 μ in length, with a blunt lateral or basal discharge papilla surmounted by a convex operculum 4.3–8 μ in diameter; rhizoids branched, not tapering; zoospores 5–30, spherical, 3 μ in diameter with a conspicuous globule, emergence not observed; resting spore borne like the sporangium, oval, 9.9–12 μ broad by 5.7–6 μ high, with a thick, smooth wall, germination not observed.

Parasitic on *Tabellaria fenestrata*, Schröter (*loc. cit.*), SWITZERLAND; *T. flocculosa*, *T. fenestrata*, Canter (*loc. cit.*), GREAT BRITAIN.

Because of the operculate sporangium and extramatrical resting spore, Canter transferred Schröter's species to *Chytriomyces*.

CHYTRIOMYCES APPENDICULATUS Karling

Bull. Torrey Bot. Club, 74: 335, figs. 16-37, 43-48. 1947

"Sporangia appendiculate, smooth, hyaline when young, but usually becoming brown with age, highly variable in size and shape, rarely spherical, 10–80 μ, flattened or oval, 10–50 × 30–90 μ, oblong, 10–20 × 30–50 μ, irregularly pyriform, 20–180 × 35–250 μ, slightly bean-shaped, tilted, irregular and lobed with a 1–3 μ thick wall; operculum non-persistent, shallow saucer-shaped, 6–14 μ diam. Zoospores oval 4–5 × 6–6.5 μ, with a conspicuous, 1.8–2.8 μ diam., hyaline refractive globule; flagellum 28–32 μ long. Rhizoids coarse, main axes up to 18 μ in diam. in large thalli, branched, usually becoming thick-walled with age. Resting spores smooth and usually appendiculate, spherical, 10–25 μ, oval, 10–15 × 18–24 μ, predominantly irregular with a 2.5–5 μ thick, brown wall; content coarsely but evenly granular with a central vacuole, emerging through a pore in the wall during germination and forming a superficial zoosporangium" (Karling, *loc. cit.*).

Saprophytic on chitinous substrata in fresh water, muck, and moist soil, Karling (*loc. cit.*; 1948c: 508), UNITED STATES.

One of the peculiarities of this very distinct species is the tendency for some sporangia to form large amounts of "slime" beneath the area of discharge. In some material no vesicle was formed.

CHYTRIOMYCES FRUCTICOSUS Karling

Bull. Torrey Bot. Club, 76: 353, figs. 18-52. 1949

"Sporangia hyaline to light brown, often appendiculate and usually apophysate, variable in size and shape, almost spherical, 17–35 μ, oval, 31–42 × 37–50 μ, almost hemispherical, 15–55 μ diam., broadly and narrowly pyriform, obclavate, citriform, elongate, or slightly anatropous, with 1–2 low exit papillae or 1–3 tapering exit tubes, 8–12 μ broad at the base by 10–60 μ long. Operculum saucer- to bowl-shaped, 4–8 μ diam., non-persistent. Zoospores oval, 3.8–4.2 × 5.5–6 μ, with a hyaline, spherical, 1.2–1.8 μ, refractive globule; swarming actively and briefly in a vesicle outside of the sporangium. Apophysis variable in size and shape, rarely spherical, 8–20 μ, oval, 8–15 × 20–25 μ, fusiform, 12–15 × 27–30 μ, elongate, 18–20 × 30–32 μ, irregular or angular. Rhizoids bushy in appearance and frequently branched, angles of branching obtuse and frequently at right angles; main axes centered on the base of the apophysis or arising at several points on the periphery, 3–8 μ in diam., branches occasionally extending for a distance of 275 μ. Resting spores light amber to greenish brown, usually spiny, occasionally verrucose or echinulate; spines up to 15 μ long by 3 μ wide at base; spherical, 18–30 μ, including spines, oval or slightly angular, with finely granular content; germination unknown" (Karling, *loc. cit.*).

Saprophytic on chitinous substrata in soil and water, UNITED STATES.

About 18 per cent of the sporangia and resting spores were formed from thalli which had developed from the germ tube of the zoospore and not by expansion of the zoospore body itself. The type of development seemed dependent upon the behavior of the nucleus of the encysted zoospore. If it remained in the cyst a *Rhizidium*-like development ensued, whereas if it passed into the germ tube the less typical method of development was undergone. The sporangia are quite variable in shape and may have one to three apophyses.

As noted by Karling (1947d) in other species of *Chytriomyces*, a single nucleus is present in the sporangial rudiment until the latter reaches full size.

AMPHICYPELLUS Ingold
Trans. Brit. Mycol. Soc., 27: 96. 1944
(Fig. 33 F-G, p. 564)

Thallus monocentric, eucarpic, extramatrical, consisting of an operculate sporangium and an apophysis with a rhizoidal system arising from it; only the tips of the rhizoids entering the substratum; zoospores finally delimited in a vesicle formed upon the dehiscence of the operculum; resting spore not observed.

A monotypic genus, members occurring on planktonic species of *Ceratium* and *Peridinium*.

Although the generic description states that the fungus is operculate, the actual method of discharge was not seen by Ingold. Canter, who has observed considerable material of *Amphicypellus*, states (comm., 1954) that she believes it to be inoperculate and to possess a type of sexuality precisely like that in *Rhizoclosmatium*. R.A. Paterson (comm.), however, who recently studied abundant material in Michigan, has found sporangial discharge to be constantly operculate. Furthermore, the zoospores in his material were simultaneously delimited in a vesicle formed at the sporangial orifice. Here they underwent a period of motility before being liberated, as is typical for species of *Chytriomyces*. Although the two genera strongly resemble one another, there are several points of difference. *Amphicypellus* is constantly apophysate, only the tips of its rhizoids enter the substratum and these always arise laterally from the apophysis, final cleavage of zoospores occurs in the vesicle. In *Chytriomyces*, the apophysis is evidently not a constant feature, the rhizoids are entirely endobiotic (in some species, for example the non-apophysate *C. appendiculatus*, their position is not clear) and may arise from any position on the apophysis and the zoospores are completely formed at the time of discharge into the vesicle. No resting spore has been found in *Amphicypellus*. It is epibiotic in *Chytriomyces*.

Pertinent information necessary for the proper disposition of this genus was too late in forthcoming to place it in the key to genera.

AMPHICYPELLUS ELEGANS Ingold [1]
Trans. Brit. Mycol. Soc., 27: 96, figs. 1-3, pl. 9. 1944

Sporangium spherical, 6–16 μ in diameter, with a globose, 3–5 μ

[1] See Paterson in *Mycologia*, 50:91. 1958.

broad by 2–3 μ high apophysis from which two to four main rhizoidal axes arise laterally and become distally divided into numerous delicate branches the tips of which penetrate the substratum; zoospores ten to thirty, spherical, 3.5–4.5 μ in diameter, with an eccentric globule and posterior flagellum, completing maturation and initiating motility in a vesicle formed at the discharge pore upon the dehiscence of a subapical operculum; resting spore not observed.

On dead cells of *Ceratium hirundinella, Peridinium sp.*, from Windermere, Ingold (*loc. cit.*), *P. cinctum, C. hirundinella*, Canter (1951: 151; 1953: 294), Great Britain; *Ceratium hirundinella*, Canter (1951: 153), Denmark; *Ceratium hirundinella*, Canter (*loc. cit.*), Sweden; *Ceratium hirundinella*, Canter (*loc. cit.*), Italy; *Ceratium hirundinella*, Paterson (comm.), United States.

Paterson (*loc. cit.*) has recently made a limno-mycological study of this species. Among other things, he determined that not only is water temperature a limiting factor but also total alkalinity. The maximum numbers of the fungus occurred between 19–21.5 degrees C. and within an alkalinity range of 98–105.5 parts per million.

ZYGORHIZIDIUM Löwenthal

Arch. Protistenk., 5: 228. 1905

(Figs. 4 P-Q, p. 72; 11 A-G, p. 110; 31 R, p. 496)

Ectochytridium Scherffel, Arch. Protistenk., 53: 7. 1925.

Thallus epi- and endobiotic, monocentric, eucarpic, the epibiotic part forming either the rudiment of the sporangium or a receptive or contributing thallus; sporangium operculate, epibiotic, sessile, predominantly formed from the enlarged body of the encysted zoospore; zoospores posteriorly uniflagellate; rhizoidal system endobiotic, consisting usually of a subsporangial apophysis with or without an unbranched or branched broad rhizoid; resting spore epibiotic, sessile, thick-walled, formed from the body of the receptive thallus after conjugation with a usually smaller contributing thallus by means of a conjugation tube produced by the smaller plant, germination not observed.

A genus the species of which are known only as parasites of green algae and diatoms.

Scherffel (*loc. cit.*) proposed the name *Ectochytridium* for this genus, as a subgenus of *Chytridium*, but used the name in a generic sense ("*E. willei* [Löwenth.] Scherff.").

The concept of the genus has been somewhat enlarged to include nonapophysate forms. Salient features are the epibiotic operculate sporangia and the epibiotic resting spores which develop after the receptive thallus receives the contents of a small male thallus through a conjugation tube. It is not unlikely that forms will be found in which this tube is either very short or altogether lacking. If so, the genus as now constituted, can well accommodate them.

KEY TO THE SPECIES OF ZYGORHIZIDIUM

Sporangium formed solely from the body of the encysted zoospore
  Sporangium apophysate; on Conjugatae
    Resting-spore wall smooth .... *Z. willei*, p. 548
    Resting-spore wall verrucose .... *Z. verrucosum*, p. 550
  Sporangium lacking an apophysis; on diatoms
    Conjugating thalli of like size; on *Ankistrodesmus*
                                  Z. parallelosede, p. 550
    Conjugating thalli of dissimilar size; on diatoms
      Male cell not enlarged, that is, essentially same size as a zoo-
        spore; resting spore ovate; on *Melosira* .... *Z. melosirae*, p. 551
      Male cell somewhat enlarged; resting spore subspherical to oval;
        on *Synedra* .... *Z. planktonicum*, p. 551
Sporangium formed from both the cyst and germ tube of the zoospore
                                     Z. parvum, p. 552

ZYGORHIZIDIUM WILLEI Löwenthal
Arch. Protistenk., 5: 228, pl. 8, figs. 8-43. 1905
(Figs. 4 P-Q, p. 72; 31 R, p. 496)

Ectochytridium willei (Löwenthal) Scherffel, Arch. Protistenk., 53: 7, pl. 1, figs. 11-24. 1925.

Sporangium sessile, single or in groups, spherical, subspherical, or broadly or narrowly pyriform, with a single apical, subapical, or lateral broad operculum (rarely two), wall smooth, stout, colorless, somewhat refractive, not giving a cellulose reaction, typically about 15 μ in diameter, dwarf sporangia 4–5.4 μ in diameter; endobiotic system consisting of a knoblike centrally depressed or irregular structure 1–2 μ in diameter, from the center of which one or two tenuous generally feebly developed branched rhizoids emerge; zoospores from four to forty in a sporangium, asymmetrically ovoid, sharply acuminate posteriorly, with a single anterior colorless refractive globule and a long flagellum, emerging after the dehiscence of the strongly convex operculum, movement hopping; "male" thallus (dwarf sporangia?) pyriform, 4–5.4 μ in diameter, the expanded endobiotic part with or without rhizoids, copulation tube basal or lateral, usually one (rarely two), up to 45 μ long by 1–2 μ in diameter, refractive, with a narrow lumen, making contact with the lower half of the receptive thallus, if not conjugating functioning as a sporangium; receptive thallus large, spherical or subspherical, the knob-like endobiotic part with or without rhizoids, after conjugation forming a subspherical resting spore 8–11 μ in diameter by 7–10 μ high, with a thick smooth colorless or brownish wall, contents with numerous large refractive often centrally disposed globules, germination not observed.

On *Cylindrocystis brebissonii*, possibly only saprophytic, Löwenthal (*loc. cit.*), NORWAY; *Mougeotia parvula*, *Mougeotia sp.*, Scherffel (*loc. cit.*), *Spirogyra longata*, *Mougeotia sp.*, *Zygnema sp.*, Domján (1936: 51, pl. 1, figs. 128–129, 138), HUNGARY; *Mougeotia sp.*, Canter (1947c: 128, fig. 2, pl. 11, figs. 1–2), GREAT BRITAIN; *Zygnema sp.*, Sparrow and Barr (1955: 554), UNITED STATES.

The nonsexual thalli observed by Scherffel on *Mougeotia* differed from those on *Cylindrocystis* in that they lacked an endobiotic knob and formed instead a group of very short rodlike rhizoids. They also differed in that they caused a marked bending of the long host cell and stimulated it to form a protective plug of wall material. It is possible that this reaction of the host may account for the absence of the characteristic knob.

Scherffel's contention that the fungus called *Rhizophydium sphaerocarpum* Zopf by Atkinson (1909a) was *Zygorhizidium willei* is open to question (see Sparrow, 1943: 365).

Zygorhizidium willei was investigated cytologically by Löwenthal. He found the young thallus to be uninucleate at first and the cytoplasm strongly alveolate. As the plant increases in size the plasma becomes denser and the spherical (0.5–0.1 μ in diameter) generally homogeneous nuclei are more numerous as well as smaller and less distinct. Mitotic figures are obscure and observed with difficulty. Around each of the nuclei a portion of the protoplasm is cleaved out and the resultant zoospores are uninucleate, the nucleus lying posterior to the oil droplet. (See also under "Sexual Reproduction," p. 78.)

ZYGORHIZIDIUM VERRUCOSUM Geitler

Arch. Protistenk., 96: 116, figs. 1, 2. 1942

Sporangium sessile, nearly spherical, transversely ellipsoidal or somewhat pyriform, up to 10 by 12 μ, mostly smaller, with a somewhat lateral or apical broad operculum, wall smooth and thin; endobiotic system consisting of an at first small nearly spherical swelling, 0.5–1 μ in diameter, which later becomes finger-like, irregular, hemispherical or clavate and often somewhat lobed, 2–2.5 μ in diameter, without rhizoids; zoospores up to 64 in a sporangium, sometimes fewer, those from large sporangia somewhat elongate and almost reniform or grape-seed-like, dorsiventrally flattened, 3–3.5 μ long by 1.5–2.2 μ broad, those from smaller sporangia more spherical and 2–3 μ in diameter, with a flagellum laterally inserted near forward end of spore but directed backwards during motility, with a single anterior globule; male plant 2 by 3 μ, with 1–3 often very long conjugation tubes, 0.5 μ in diameter; receptive thallus larger, the endobiotic part lacking rhizoids, after conjugation forming a broadly ellipsoidal resting spore 5–5.5 by 6–6.5 μ, rarely up to 7 μ broad, with a thick wall covered by coarse warts about 4.5 μ high, contents with several large oil globules, germination not observed.

Parasitic on *Mesotaenium caldariorum*, AUSTRIA.

The two types of zoospores produced suggest some sort of sexual differentiation.

ZYGORHIZIDIUM PARALLELOSEDE Canter

Trans. Brit. Mycol. Soc., 37: 128, figs. 8-9, pl. 5, figs. 5-6. 1954

(Fig. 11 F-G, p. 110)

"Thallus monocentric, eucarpic sporangium developed from body of an encysted zoospore. Rhizoid a fairly thick unbranched or little branched thread. Sporangium broadly cylindrical to cigar shaped, 3–6 μ high and 8–26 μ long; oblong to oval, 3–4 μ high and 4–5.5 μ long; operculate, not collapsing after dehiscence. Zoospores 4–40, fully formed in the sporangium, spherical (2 μ in diameter, posterior flagellum 11 μ long), with a latero-basal globule and greyish protoplasm with a few minute granules. Resting spore sexually formed. Male oval to elongate oval (2 × 3.5–2 × 6 μ) makes contact with a female of more or less similar size by means of a conjugation tube up to 16 μ long. Resting spore elongate oval, 5.5–17 μ long and 3–6 μ high. Wall thick, smooth, colourless, content when mature a single large globule. Both male and female bearing rhizoids. Germination unknown" (Canter, *loc. cit.*).

Parasitic on *Ankistrodesmus sp.*, *Elaktothrix gelatinosa*, in plankton, GREAT BRITAIN.

Here, the zoospore makes its way through the very broad gelatinous colonial envelope and comes to rest on the host cell. In sexual reproduction the male may sometimes be nearly adnate to the female. Conjugating thalli seemed always to be originally of the same size.

ZYGORHIZIDIUM MELOSIRAE Canter

Ann. Bot. London (N.S.), 14: 283, fig. 13. 1950

"Thallus epibiotic, stalked or sessile, sporangium ovate, 7–14 μ high by 5–10 μ in diameter with 6 to 30 zoospores, dehiscing by a lid. Zoospores spherical, 2.8–3.3 μ in diameter, with a large oil globule (0.9 μ), and posterior flagellum. Intramatrical rhizoid unbranched or sparingly branched, not tapering. Resting spores ovate, 9.5–10 μ high by 6–7.5 μ broad, wall smooth, the content with a few large globules; arising from fusion of the contents of a small male with a larger female cell by a conjugation tube, 0.7–7.5 μ long. Germination unknown" (Canter, *loc. cit.*).

Parasitic on *Melosira italica* subsp. *subartica*, GREAT BRITAIN; *Melosira sp.*, Paterson (comm।)., UNITED STATES.

Whenever a gelatinous sheath surrounds the host filament, the zoospore rests on the outer surface and germinates. Hence, sporangia from such zoospores are stalked.

ZYGORHIZIDIUM PLANKTONICUM Canter [1]

Trans. Brit. Mycol. Soc., 36: 34, fig. 1 E-M, fig. 5 M-X. 1953

(Fig. 11 A-B, p. 110)

"Thallus monocentric consisting of an epibiotic obpyriform [pyriform] sporangium (4–9 μ high; 3–8 μ broad) whose apex functions as an oper-

[1] Paterson (*Trans. Brit. Mycol, Soc.*, 41: 457. 1958) considers this species synonymous with the preceding one.

culum (2–3 μ diameter) which often remains adherent after dehiscence; there is a short richly branched internal rhizoidal system. Sporangium developed by direct enlargement of the zoospore. Resting spore [subspherical to oval] (7–8 × 6.5–7.5 μ) with a thick, smooth wall and containing several refractive globules; formed by the fusion of two thalli through a conjugation tube (to 10 μ long). Empty male thallus (2.5–4 × 4–4.5 μ). Rhizoidal system of male and female thallus identical with that of sporangia" (Canter, in Canter and Lund, *loc. cit.*).

On *Synedra acus* var. *angustissima*, Canter and Lund (1953: 34), SWITZERLAND, ITALY; ? *Asterionella formosa* (*loc. cit.*), GREAT BRITAIN; *Synedra sp.*, Paterson (1956: 276), (MICHIGAN), UNITED STATES.

Eighty per cent of the Swiss diatoms were infected and 50 per cent of the Italian.

Paterson's studies of this and the preceding species led him to conclude that there were no striking morphological differences between the two. The smaller sizes of the parts of the present species, recorded by Canter, might well be due, he argues, to measuring preserved material. He found the sizes of all parts in living material of both species to be essentially the same.

ZYGORHIZIDIUM PARVUM Canter

Ann. Bot. London (N.S.), 14: 287, figs. 14-15, Pl. 8 C. 1950

(Fig. 11 C-E, p. 110)

"Thallus monocentric, eucarpic, consisting of a sporangium developed from the body of an encysted zoospore and the whole or a part of the original germ tube. Sporangia pear-shaped, cylindrical, or oval, varying in size from 5 to 13 μ high by 2.5 to 8 μ broad. Zoospores from 4 to 40 fully formed within the sporangium, emerging after the detachment of a lid. Zoospores, 2 μ in diameter, posteriorly uniflagellate, with an anterior lateral globule and a minute shining granule. Rhizoid a short, unbranched thread. Resting spore sexually formed, male thallus (resembling an encysted zoospore and its germ-tube) makes contact with a slightly larger female thallus by means of a conjugation tube which arises as a lateral branch from the germ-tube of the male. Resting spore spherical, 6–8 μ in diameter, or elongate-oval, 5–15 μ × 3.5–8 μ. Wall smooth, hyaline, content composed of small globules. Germination unknown" (Canter, *loc. cit.*).

Parasitic on *Sphaerocystis schroeteri* and *Kirchneriella obesa*, GREAT BRITAIN.

Canter (*loc. cit.*) points out that the sporangium and resting spore of this species develop from both the cyst of the zoospore and its germ tube, a parallel situation to that in the inoperculate genus *Dangeardia* (p. 319). While she recognizes that to include the species in *Zygorhizidium* strains the concept of that genus, until other related forms are discovered, she prefers to leave it there.

RHOPALOPHLYCTIS KARLING

Amer. J. Bot., 32: 363. 1945

(Fig. 32 B, p. 554)

"Thallus monocentric, eucarpic, consisting of an extramatrical sporangium and an intramatrical rhizoidal system. Sporangia operculate, stalked or sessile, septate or continuous. Zoospores posteriorly uniflagellate, emerging from sporangium and swarming in a vesicle. Resting spores unknown" (Karling, *loc. cit.*).

A monotypic genus, the species of which has been found only on chitinous substrata.

Although not exhibiting the type of development found in *Podochytrium*, mature plants of *Rhopalophlyctis*, with their basal sterile part, resemble those of that genus. *Rhopalophlyctis* may be distinguished from the similar-appearing *Cylindrochytridium* by its extramatrical sporangium, which develops from the body of the encysted zoospore, and by the absence of an apophysis.

RHOPALOPHLYCTIS SARCOPTOIDES Karling

Amer. J. Bot., 32: 363, figs. 1-26. 1945

"Thalli numerous, up to 500 on one host. Sporangia hyaline, smooth with fairly thick (1.5 μ) walls, obpyriform (10–70 × 15–90 μ), clavate (12–40 × 35–180 μ), spherical (8–40 μ), or elongate, continuous or septate, sessile or stalked, base of stalk sometimes expanded irregularly

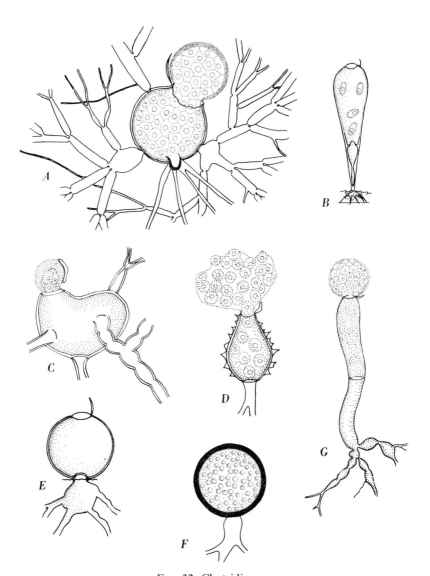

Fig. 32. Chytridiaceae

to form a foot; operculum shallow, saucer-shaped, 6–12 μ in diam. Zoospores oval, 5 × 6.5–7.5 μ, with a refractive globule 3 μ in diam. near posterior end; flagellum 25-28 μ long; zoospores swarming in a hyaline vesicle outside of sporangium for 2–8 minutes before breaking out and swimming away; vesicle continuous with interior of sporangium. Rhizoids arising as a tuft of fine threads from base of thallus and extending for a distance of 200 μ; threads simple or branched. Resting spores unknown" (Karling, *loc. cit.*).

Saprophytic on exuviae, BRAZIL; exuviae (*loc. cit.*), UNITED STATES.

CATENOCHYTRIDIUM BERDAN

Amer. J. Bot., 26: 460. 1939

(Figs. 8 A-E, p. 97; 33 A-B, p. 564)

"Thallus intra- and extramatrical, predominantly monocentric,eucarpic. Zoosporangium extramatrical, operculate, delimited by a cross wall at maturity. Development of zoosporangium endo-exogenous. Apophysis intramatrical, [usually] compound, consisting of linear series of constricted, catenulate segments subtended by an extensive, richly branched rhizoidal system. Zoospores posteriorly uniciliate, emerging in a globular mass and lying quiescent for a few moments before swimming away; method of swimming rapid and darting. Resting spore extramatrical, usually formed in the same position as the zoosporangium, a segment of apophysis sometimes encysting and becoming a resting spore; germination unknown" (Berdan, *loc. cit.*).

Explanation of Figure 32

A. Truittella setifera Karling, thallus on cellulosic substratum showing central operculate sporangium, main axes of rhizoidal system, and zoospore cyst bearing setae. *B. Rhopalophlyctis sarcoptoides* Karling on insect exuviae, empty basally septate sporangium. *C. Karlingiomyces dubius* (Karling), comb. nov., on chitinous substratum. *D. Chytriomyces spinosus* Fay on vegetable debris, discharging sporangium. *E–F. Chytriomyces aureus* Karling on insect exuviae: *E*, empty epibiotic sporangium; *F*, epibiotic resting spore. *G. Cylindrochytridium johnstonii* Karling in vegetable debris, discharging sporangium.

(*A*, Karling, 1949b; *B*, *E–F*, 1945c; *C*, 1949e; *D*, 1947d; *G*, 1941a)

Saprophytes on vegetable debris.
Distinguished from *Chytridium* by the catenulate secondary apophyses.

KEY TO THE SPECIES OF CATENOCHYTRIDIUM

Apophysis always compound; zoospore with a single globule
  Persistent zoospore cyst near apex of sporangium; the latter variable
    in shape .... *C. carolinianum*, p. 556
  Persistent zoospore cyst near base of sporangium; the latter regu-
    larly citriform .... *C. kevorkianii*, p. 557
Apophysis simple or compound; zoospore with several refractive glob-
  ules .... *C. laterale*, p. 558

CATENOCHYTRIDIUM CAROLINIANUM Berdan

Amer. J. Bot., 26: 461, fig. 1. 1939

(Fig. 33 A, p. 564)

"Zoosporangia hyaline, spherical, sub-spherical, pyriform, obovoid, ovoid, elliptical, kidney-shaped or convoluted with pointed lobes, 8–40 × 8–75 μ. Operculum apical to sub-apical in position, hinged to and persistent on the empty sporangium; orifice circular, 6–20 μ in diameter. Catenulate segments of apophysis 2–30 in number, arranged in 1–4 linear series attached to the primary apophysate cell; primary apophysate cell commonly spherical to ovoid, 5.5–22 μ; other segments of apophysis spherical, ovoid, elliptical or irregularly elongate, joined by protoplasmic connection through the wall or by an elongated isthmus. Rhizoidal system (including apophysis) 55–800 μ in extent; rhizoids from .5–3 μ in diameter, becoming very finely branched; branching somewhat dichotomous. Zoospores hyaline, spherical, 5–6 μ, uninucleate, with a single highly refractive globule about 2.5 μ in diameter; cilium 35–40 μ in length. Infecting zoospores commonly attached laterally to wall of host cell. Old zoospore case usually persistent on the zoosporangium or resting spore, flattened, hyaline or amber and thick-walled, about 8 μ in diameter. Treatment with chlor-iodide of zinc producing a pale mauve color in the sporangium wall, a deep mauve in the old spore case, a deep pinkish-mauve in the segments of the apophysis, magenta in the primary apophysate cell, barely affecting the rhizoids. Resting spore smooth, spherical to ovoid, 8–40 μ, thick-walled, light to dark brown, with one large globule and a parietal layer of smaller ones; germination unknown" (Berdan, *loc. cit.*).

Saprophytic in leaves of wheat, corn, rye, oats, and various grasses, Berdan (*loc. cit.*; 1941b), UNITED STATES, CANADA; vegetable debris, Karling (1941a: 387; 1941b: 108; 1942c: 620; 1948c: 509), UNITED STATES.

Catenochytridium carolinianum Berdan f. *marinum*
Kobayasi and Ookubo
Bull. Nat. Sci. Mus. (Tokyo), 33: 57, fig. 4. 1953

"Zoosporangium extramatrical, hyaline, spherical, ovoid oi kidney-shaped, 40–60 μ high, 15–36 μ in diameter, somewhat thick-walled (1.5–2 μ in thickness) with two or more papillae; orifice circular, 5–10 μ in diameter. Apophyses composed of two or three linear series; each series composed of catenulate 2–6 segments; basal segment ovoid or oblong, other segments ovoid, fusoid or irregularly elongate, terminally attenuated. Rhizoids originated from apical and intermediate segments of apophyses, simple or dichotomously branched, not so long, length of rhizoidal system (including apophyses) 40–60 μ. Zoospores not observed" (Kobayasi and Ookubo, *loc. cit.*).

On *Cladophora japonica* (marine), JAPAN.

Differing from the type in being marine and parasitic on an alga. A further study of this form will no doubt show it to be a distinct species.

CATENOCHYTRIDIUM KEVORKIANII Sparrow
Rev. Soc. Cubana Bot., 9: 70, figs. A-E. 1952

Sporangium predominantly citriform at maturity, 40–43 μ high by 35–36 μ in diameter, with a smooth colorless or faintly amber-colored wall, a basal, thick-walled, dark amber-colored protrusion, 5–8 μ in diameter, and an apical hyaline papilla about 12 μ in diameter; primary apophysate cell irregularly pyramidal, 12–21 μ in greatest width, its broadest face usually adjacent to the base of the sporangium; catenulate rhizoidal segments thin-walled, variable in size and number, arising from one or opposite faces of the primary apophysis and terminating distally in a main branching rhizoidal axis; zoospores ellipsoidal, 9 by 5 μ, with a conspicuous hyaline globule and posterior flagellum, escaping through a broad pore formed upon the dehiscence of an operculum 12–13 μ in diameter, and remaining in a compact quiescent group before assuming motility; resting spore not observed.

Saprophytic on cellophane bait, roadside soil, CUBA.

Differing from the following species in the shape of its primary apophysate cell, regularly citriform sporangium and always compound apophysis.

CATENOCHYTRIDIUM LATERALE Hanson

Torreya, 44: 32. 1944

(Figs. 8 A-E, p. 97; 33 B, p. 564)

"Zoosporangia hyaline, smooth, oval, 16–46 × 21–62 μ, spherical, 12–44 μ, pyriform, 12–48 × 18–71 μ, cylindrical, 15–25 × 61–93 μ, and lobed, 28–63 × 88–160 μ, when developed intramatrically; operculum apical, sub-apical, or lateral, 7.5–15 μ in diameter, generally persistent on the empty sporangium. Primary apophysate cell always predominant, spherical, ovoid, or lobed, up to 27–30 μ in diameter. Catenulate segments of the apophysis 1–7 in number, arranged in 1–4 linear series attached to the primary apophysate cell laterally or apically, so that they emerge between the primary apophysate cell and the sporangium, rarely emerging from the base of the primary apophysate cell, often completely lacking. Rhizoidal system (including primary apophysis) up to 224 μ in extent, becoming finely branched; branching dichotomous. Zoospores hyaline, spherical, 2.9–4.5 μ, with two, three, four (rarely one), refractive globules; flagellum 26–30 μ long. Zoospore case always persistent on the zoosporangium, thickened, bulbous, never flattened, amber to dark brown in color, rarely apical or lateral, but remaining like a basal protuberance on the sporangium. Resting spores not observed" (Hanson, *loc. cit.*).

Saprophytic on grasses, bleached corn leaves, onion, and cellophane, UNITED STATES.

See Hanson (1946a) for figures and developmental details.

KARLINGIOMYCES, GEN. NOV.[1]

(Fig. 32 C, p. 554)

Thallus predominantly monocentric, eucarpic, consisting of a reproductive rudiment usually formed from the body of the encysted zoospore and several to many branched rhizoidal axes; sporangium usually with more than one discharge papilla each surmounted by an operculum, and in some instances, with an endooperculum as well; zoospores formed within the sporangium, posteriorly uniflagellate, with one or more globules, at discharge forming a compact motionless group and sometimes undergoing a period of collective swarming before dispersing; resting spore asexually formed, thick-walled, borne like the sporangium on the thallus, upon germination functioning as a prosporangium.

Saprophytes on vegetable debris and chitinous substrata.

The genus as established here includes those species of *Karlingia* Johanson with exoopercula (cf. *Rhizophlyctis*, p. 435). The type species of her genus is here retained in *Rhizophlyctis*.

The genus is named for J. S. Karling, well-known student of chytridiaceous fungi.

KEY TO THE SPECIES OF KARLINGIOMYCES

Zoospore with a single globule
  Resting spores abundantly formed; fungus strongly chitinophilic
    Resting spore wall bearing straight or curved spines; rhizoids not constricted
      Spines straight, blunt, peglike.............. *K. asterocystis*, p. 560
      Spines curved, hooklike, very numerous.... *K. curvispinosus*, p. 560
    Resting-spore wall smooth to rugose or verrucose; rhizoids irregularly constricted, thick-walled .... *K. dubius*, p. 561
  Resting spores lacking; fungus cellulosic .... *K. marilandicus*, p. 562

[1] *Karlingiomyces*, gen. nov. — Thallus praecipue monocentricus, eucarpicus, ex rudimento reproductivo oriens, eodem ab zoospora cystoidea et axibus pluribus ramosis derivato. Sporangium plerumque pluribus papillis emittientibus operculatis praeditum; etiamque interdum endooperculatum. Zoosporae postice uniflagellatae, noviciae in massa compacta immobiles post demum gregatim natantes vel cito dispersae. Spora perdurans in thallo asexualiter originata, crasse circumvallata, germinatione prosporangium simulans.

Saprophyticus in substratis chitinosis vel putrescentibus partibus vegetabilium.

Species typica: *Karlingiomyces asterocystis*, primum descripta ex "Charles County, Maryland" in Mycologia, 41: 509, figs. 9-19, 1949.

Zoospore with numerous globules
    Resting spore spherical or oval, brown, with a somewhat rough wall
        K. granulatus, p. 563
    Resting spore deeply lobed or irregular, hyaline, with a smooth wall
        K. lobatus, p. 563

KARLINGIOMYCES ASTEROCYSTIS (Karling), comb. nov.

Karlingia asterocysta Karling, Mycologia, 41: 509, figs. 9-19. 1949.

Sporangium hyaline, smooth-walled, spherical (20–110 μ in diameter), pyriform (12–40 by 29–75 μ), oblong, elongate, fusiform, or irregular, in large sporangia with one to four low, barely perceptible discharge papillae (8–14 μ in diameter) surmounting a broad hyaline hemispherical area up to 15 μ wide and 16 μ deep, papillae in small sporangia fairly conspicuous and up to 11 μ high; rhizoids for the most part emerging from several places on the sporangium, the main axes attaining a diameter of 18 μ, branching and extensive; operculum hyaline, shallowly convex, 14 μ in diameter, terminating the papilla; zoospores hyaline, spherical, 4.2–4.6 μ in diameter, with a hyaline refractive globule, 0.7–1.2 μ in diameter, and a flagellum, 24–26 μ long, after discharge swarming for a short time in a quickly evanescent vesicle; resting spore subspherical (15–30 μ in diameter), oval (12–16 by 14–22 μ), oblong, angular, or irregular, the dark greenish-brown wall covered with blunt to sharp-pointed, occasionally curved conical pegs, 4–8 μ high by 2–4 μ broad at base, rarely verrucose, contents hyaline and finely granular, germination not observed.

Saprophytic on chitinous substrata, in soil and water, UNITED STATES.

Resting spores were formed in greater abundance than sporangia in this species. The discharge papilla of the sporangia were scarcely discernible and their position was usually determined by the conspicuous hyaline material beneath them.

KARLINGIOMYCES CURVISPINOSUS (Karling), comb. nov.

Karlingia curvispinosa Karling, Mycologia, 41: 511, figs. 20-35. 1949.

Sporangium usually sessile, rarely stalked, hyaline, smooth-walled, variable in shape and size, subspherical (10–120 μ in diameter), oval

(10–80 by 15–140 μ), pyriform (8–70 by 18–160 μ), obclavate, oblong, or elongate, with one to three low and inconspicuous or cone- or dome-shaped and prominent exit papillae; rhizoids for the most part emerging from several places on the sporangium, main axes coarse and up to 16 μ in diameter, much branched and extensive; operculum surmounting the discharge papilla, quickly disappearing after dehiscence, 6–18 μ in diameter; zoospores hyaline, spherical, 3.8–4.2 μ, with a hyaline refractive globule, 0.6–0.8 μ in diameter, and a flagellum 10–13 μ long, not swarming in a vesicle after discharge; resting spore spherical (6–21 μ in diameter), oval (8–12 μ by 11–16 μ), or slightly angular and irregular, covered with numerous curved, somewhat hooked-shaped pegs or spines, occasionally verrucose, rarely echinulate or smooth, dark amber or brown, contents evenly granular with a small central vacuole, at germination functioning as a prosporangium.

Saprophytic on chitinous substrata in soil and water, UNITED STATES.

This species resembles *Karlingiomyces asterocystis* in the type of resting spores, but differs from it in having spores with more numerous, curved or hooked, spines on them. It also has smaller zoospores with a shorter flagellum which do not swarm in a vesicle. Karling points out that in *K. curvispinosus* the developing spiny resting spores are surrounded by a relatively clear zone of material as they are in species of *Rozella* and *Olpidiopsis*.

KARLINGIOMYCES DUBIUS (Karling), comb. nov. [1]

(Fig. 32 C, p. 554)

Karlingia dubia Karling, Mycologia, 41: 513, figs. 36–51. 1949.

Sporangium smooth-walled, hyaline, subspherical (20–240 μ in diameter), oval (45–65 by 60–75 μ), pyriform (15–35 by 40–78 μ), or oblong, with one to four exit papillae, 12–34 μ in diameter, below which is a hemispherical area up to 12 μ in diameter that may extend to a depth of 16 μ into sporangium; rhizoids for the most part emerging from several places on the sporangium, main axes attaining a diameter of 16 μ, much branched and extensive, usually thick-walled with many regular or irregular constrictions which may extend almost completely

[1] See also Willoughby (1957).

across the lumen; operculum surmounting the discharge papilla, shallowly convex, 10–30 μ in diameter; zoospores hyaline, spherical, 6–6.5 μ in diameter, with a basal hyaline globule 2–2.3 μ in diameter, and a flagellum 32–35 μ long, emerging in a mass imbedded in a matrix with the flagellum coiled around the body, the flagellum soon uncoiling and assuming motility; resting spore spherical (8–20 μ), oval (9–14 by 12–17 μ), narrowly elongate, or angular, with coarse granular contents, the dark-brown wall usually smooth, occasionally rugose or verrucose, germination not observed.

Saprophytic on chitinous substrata, UNITED STATES.

Distinguished by its large operculum and smooth to rugose or verrucose resting spores. In having nearly catenulate rhizoids the species resembles one of *Catenochytridium*. The dehiscing of the operculum sometime prior to zoospore discharge and its elevation on the inner hyaline papilla is occasionally seen in other chytrids.

KARLINGIOMYCES MARILANDICUS (Karling), comb. nov.

Karlingia marylandia Karling, Mycologia, 41: 518, figs. 70-78. 1949.

Sporangium with a smooth 1.8–2.6 μ thick wall, spherical (20–60 μ in diameter), oval (20–72 by 30–85 μ), pyriform (20–28 by 40–60 μ), oblong, elongate, or irregular, with one or two nearly sessile exit papillae or discharge tubes, 10–26 by 15–204 μ; rhizoids for most part emerging from several places on the sporangium, the main axes usually coarse, attaining a diameter of 12 μ, irregularly constricted, with thick walls, much branched and extensive; operculum surmounting the discharge papilla or just beneath the apex, no hyaline plugs formed, shallowly convex, up to 17 μ in diameter; zoospores hyaline, spherical, either 5.5–6.0 μ or 2.0–3.5 μ in diameter (in same sporangium) with a single hyaline, refractive globule 2.3–2.8 μ in diameter, upon emergence forming a temporary globular mass in a slimy matrix; resting spore not observed.

Saprophytic on cellulosic substrata in soil and water, UNITED STATES.

Similar to *Karlingiomyces granulatus* and *K. lobatus* in having endo- and exopercula and constricted rhizoids, but differing from them in possessing a single large hyaline refractive globule in the zoospore and only one to two exit papillae without hyaline plugs. *K. marilandicus* also may occasionally form very long exit tubes on its thicker walled sporangia.

KARLINGIOMYCES GRANULATUS (Karling), comb. nov.

Karlingia granulata Karling, Mycologia, 39: 57, figs. 1-22. 1947.

Sporangium hyaline, smooth-walled, spherical (8–240 μ in diameter), pyriform (6–50 by 10–120 μ), oval (8–60 by 10–90 μ), elongate, or irregular; with one to five exit papillae or tubes (5–8 by 7–110 μ); rhizoids emerging usually from several places on the sporangium, principal axes for most part coarse, up to 12 μ in diameter, often constricted and irregular in outline with conspicuous internal trabeculae, the walls becoming thick and brown with age; operculum hyaline, delicate, apical or submerged in the discharge papilla or tube, slightly convex, 15 μ in diameter; zoospores hyaline, spherical, 5.5–6.5 μ, bearing 10–40 minute granules in their plasma, flagellum 35–40 μ long; resting spore smooth or rugose, brownish, with a thick wall 2.0–3.5 μ thick ("diam."), spherical (6–25 μ) or oval (10–20 by 13–25 μ), at germination functioning as a prosporangium.

Saprophytic on vegetable debris, in moist soil, Karling (*loc. cit.*), BRAZIL; isolated from moist soil, Karling (1948c: 509), UNITED STATES; from soil, substrate ?, Gaertner (1954b: 22), EGYPT, EQUATORIAL EAST AFRICA, SOUTH AFRICA.

A few (five) thalli (of the great many studied) were polycentric. As in *Septochytrium*, they had a large primary sporangium and one to three secondary ones.

KARLINGIOMYCES LOBATUS (Karling), comb. nov.

Karlingia lobata Karling, Mycologia, 41: 515, figs. 52-69. 1949.

Sporangium hyaline, spherical (15–180 μ in diameter), pyriform (12–40 by 20–160 μ), oval (9–80 by 14–98 μ), oblong, elongate, or irregular, with one to four exit papillae, wall in large as well as in old sporangia thick and wrinkled or ridged, extending sometimes to the concomitant rhizoids; rhizoids for the most part emerging from several places on the sporangium, main axes usually coarse, fairly thick-walled, irregular-

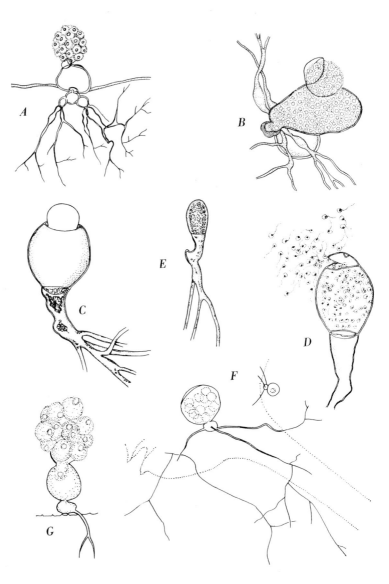

FIG. 33. *Catenochytridium*, *Macrochytrium*, and *Amphicypellus*

ly constricted, almost catenulate, up to 20 μ in diameter, much branched and extensive; operculum apical or submerged, shallowly convex, up to 20 μ in diameter; zoospores hyaline, spherical, 5.2–6.2 μ in diameter, bearing eight to twenty hyaline refractive granules and a flagellum 30–32 μ long, emerging in a compact mass and soon dispersing; resting spore hyaline, smooth-walled, deeply lobed, angular, and irregular in shape, rarely slightly irregular, 7–38 μ in diameter with numerous hyaline refractive globules, functioning as a prosporangium at germination.

Saprophytic on cellulosic substrata, UNITED STATES.

Resembles *Karlingiomyces granulatus* in its digitate or irregularly stellate sporangial stage but differs in having strongly lobed resting spores.

MACROCHYTRIUM MINDEN

Centralbl. f. Bakteriol., Parasitenk. u. Infektionskrankh., Abt 2, 8:824. 1902; Kryptogamenfl. Mark Brandenburg, 5: 385. 1911 (1915); Falck, Mykolog. Untersuch. Berichte, 2(2): 249. 1916

(Fig. 33 C-E, p. 564)

Thallus epi- and endobiotic, monocentric, eucarpic, the epibiotic part

---

Explanation of Figure 33

A. Catenochytridium carolinianum Berdan on decaying wheat; epibiotic operculate sporangium, on upper part of which is attached a portion of spore case, discharging zoospores; catenulate compound apophysis and rhizoids are in substratum. *B. Catenochytridium laterale* Hanson, discharging sporangium bearing basal cyst and large primary apophysate cell and catenulate segments of apophysis which emerge between sporangium and primary apophysate cell. *C–E. Macrochytrium botrydioides* Minden on submerged fruits: *C*, empty sporangium with large persistent operculum; *D*, discharging operculate zoosporangium; *E*, resting spore (?); primary apex appears as kneelike projection on left terminating rhizoidal axis. *F–G. Amphicypellus elegans* Ingold: *F*, young and mature individuals on theca of *Ceratium* (dotted line); *G*, discharging sporangium showing hinged operculum at left of cluster of zoospores.

(*A*, Berdan, 1939; *B*, Hanson, 1946a; *C–E*, Minden, 1916; *F*, Ingold, 1944; *G*, Paterson, *in ed.*)

forming subapically the rudiment of the sporangium or the resting spore, the endobiotic giving rise to a system of broad wide-lumened branched rhizoids; sporangium operculate; zoospores posteriorly uniflagellate; resting spore thick-walled, epibiotic, borne like the sporangium, germination not observed.

A monotypic genus, saprophytic on vegetable debris in fresh water.

Although early stages in the development of this remarkable chytrid were not observed Minden did determine that the young plant consisted of a short somewhat cylindrical or irregular thick-walled main axis that gave rise basally to coarse rhizoids. Beneath the apex of this axis a lateral outgrowth appeared which soon expanded to form a spherical, at first oblique but later nearly upright, body—the rudiment of the sporangium. As this rudiment continued to expand the true apex of the axis was pushed aside and appeared as a blunt or rather angular process on the mature thallus. The whole thallus was one-celled and filled with dark, brownish, granular protoplasm, which was mostly collected in the distal expanded part. The latter was then cut off by a cross wall from the rest of the thallus and its contents cleaved into zoospores. At maturity the sporangia were so large as to be visible to the naked eye. Minden was in doubt as to whether or not he observed the resting spore (Fig. 33 E).

The genus is an interesting one from a phylogenetic standpoint, since in its thallus development it approximates *Blastocladiella*, a member of the Blastocladiales. It seems probable, however, that there will be found in the future an inoperculate *Macrochytrium*-like chytrid which will even more closely connect these two orders than does Minden's fungus.

Macrochytrium botrydioides Minden

Centralbl. f. Bakteriol., Parasitenk. u. Infektionskrankh., Abt. 2, 8: 824. 1902; Kryptogamenfl. Mark Brandenburg, 5: 386, fig. 30 a-c. 1911 (1915); Falck, Mykolog. Untersuch. Berichte, 2(2): 249, pl. 8, figs. 76-85. 1916

Sporangia broadly ellipsoidal, with a broad rounded apex, subspherical or somewhat long-cylindrical, variable in size, the smaller ones 300–350 μ long by 200–250 μ in diameter, and the larger up to 800 μ long by 650 μ in diameter, wall smooth, fairly thick, the outer layer cuticularized, the inner colorless, cut off from the broad apex of the rhizoidal axis by a concave cross wall; rhizoidal axis stout, 400–450 μ long by 60–90 μ in diameter, divided basally into a rootlike complex of coarse wide-lumened thick-walled richly branched rhizoids which are imbedded in the substratum; zoospores up to a thousand in large sporangia, spherical, with a long flagellum, emerging through a broad apical pore formed upon the dehiscence of a broad convex smooth operculum that occasionally bears at the center of its inner wall a short peglike outgrowth, the emerged spores surrounded by a delicate vesicle which ruptures when about one half the size of the sporangium, movement of zoospores at first amoeboid, later, when free of the surrounding bacterial mass, swimming; resting spore (?) borne like the sporangium, contents with globules, germination not observed.

Saprophytic on rotting fruits, especially apples, possibly also on old submerged twigs, Minden (*loc. cit.*), GERMANY; twigs of various trees (*Quercus, Abies, Fraxinus, Alnus, Aesculus*), Lund (1934: 56. fig. 29), DENMARK; submerged pears, coll. B. B. Kanouse, in Sparrow (1943: 368), UNITED STATES.

Lund noted that his fungus, which was 100–558 μ long, was usually collected in pools of stagnant water where there was much decaying vegetable material and where the surface was frequently covered by aquatic angiosperms. It occurred in tufts on the twigs in company with *Blastocladia, Rhipidium*, and the like, always covered by bacteria. From these facts he concluded that it did not require much oxygen for its existence. Kanouse frequently found it in the vicinity of Ann Arbor, Michigan, on submerged pears. *Macrochytrium* is the largest of the monocentric chytrids.

The fungus studied physiologically by Crasemann (1954) has been identified in our laboratories as probably a species of *Cylindrochytridium* and not a *Macrochytrium*.

SUBFAM. ENDOCHYTRIOIDEAE

Sporangium, rhizoids, and resting spore endobiotic; epibiotic part an evanescent or persistent cyst.

ENDOCHYTRIUM Sparrow

Amer. J. Bot., 20: 71. 1933

(Fig. 34 A-E, p. 571)

Thallus endobiotic, monocentric, eucarpic, mono- or polyphagous, consisting of the rudiment of the sporangium and the branched rhizoidal system emerging from it, the cyst and penetration tube evanescent or persistent; sporangium operculate, with a discharge tube the tip of which at least is extramatrical; zoospores formed in the sporangium, posteriorly uniflagellate, with a single globule; resting spore thick-walled, endobiotic, borne like the sporangium, apparently asexually formed, upon germination functioning as a prosporangium, the sporangium epibiotic, operculate.

The species are weakly parasitic or saprophytic in fresh-water green algae or saprophytic in decaying plant tissues.

Morphologically, the genus is the operculate counterpart of *Entophlyctis*.

KEY TO THE SPECIES OF ENDOCHYTRIUM

Sporangia predominantly ovoid or pyriform, smooth
  Resting spore filling container; case of the infecting zoospore not persistent
    Resting spore entirely smooth-walled .... *E. ramosum*, p. 568
    Resting spore warty .... *E. operculatum*, p. 569
  Resting spore lying loosely in the container, the outer wall scaly; case
    of the infecting zoospore persistent ..... *E. pseudodistomum*, p. 570
Sporangia predominantly elongate, obclavate, or triangular and basally lobed, often somewhat apophysate .... *E. digitatum*, p. 572

ENDOCHYTRIUM RAMOSUM Sparrow

Amer. J. Bot., 20: 72, pl. 2, figs. A-G. 1933

(Fig. 34 A-E, p. 571)

Sporangium ovoid, subspherical, or sometimes pyriform, up to 35 μ in diameter, with a short broad discharge tube which just penetrates the wall of the substratum, wall thin, smooth, colorless; rhizoids extensive, irregularly and profusely branched, ramifying through many cells, often broad (up to 10 μ in diameter) at the basal or somewhat lateral place of attachment on the sporangium wall; zoospores spherical or somewhat elongate, 3–5 μ in diameter, posteriorly uniflagellate, with a colorless centric globule, escaping upon the dehiscence of an operculum 7 μ in diameter and forming for a few moments at the orifice an ellipsoidal motionless mass; resting spore spherical, 20–35 μ in diameter, with a smooth faintly brownish wall 2.5–3 μ thick, contents with a large central and several small peripheral globules, germination not observed.

Weakly parasitic or saprophytic in *Cladophora sp.*, UNITED STATES; vegetable material, Shanor (1944: 331), MEXICO; saprophytic on grass-leaf bait, from soil, Sparrow (1952b: 69), CUBA.

Resting spores were found in abundance in old cultures in dead *Cladophora*. These were associated in filaments with the nonsexual stage and were even formed inside evacuated sporangia.

Karling (1937a) has identified the species with one found by him that is saprophytic in various algae and cysts of monads, and considers both to be identical with *Rhizophlyctis operculata* de Wildeman and *Entophlyctis maxima* Dangeard. On the basis of the sporangial stage alone this is justifiable. In Karling's fungus, however, the spherical, ovoid, or slightly ellipsoidal resting spores are 4.5–18 μ in diameter or 5 by 7 to 12 by 16 μ, and the wall is predominantly rough or warty, only occasionally smooth (Hillegas, 1940). In *Endochytrium ramosum*, on the other hand, the resting spores are spherical and larger (20–35 μ), and the wall is always smooth. Since the character of the wall of the resting spore is ordinarily remarkably constant in a particular species of chytrid and, indeed, in the Phycomycetes as a whole, variation in this respect is unusual and worthy of further study.

To which of these two fungi de Wildeman's *Rhizophlyctis operculata* belonged is problematical, since only the sporangia were found. The same may be said of Dangeard's *Entophlyctis maxima*, which Karling considers synonymous with de Wildeman's and his own fungi.

ENDOCHYTRIUM OPERCULATUM (de Wild.) Karling

Amer. J. Bot., 24: 353, figs. 1-53. 1937

Rhizophlyctis operculata de Wildeman, Ann. Soc. Belge Micro. (Mém.), 19: 108, pl. 4, figs. 1-9. 1895.

(?) *Entophlyctis maxima* Dangeard, Le Botaniste, 24: 242, 1 fig. 1932.

"Zoosporangia hyaline, smooth, almost spherical, 4–140 μ, broadly and narrowly pyriform, 5 × 7—60 × 150 μ, ovate, egg- or spindle-shaped, elongated, tubular and cylindrical, occasionally obclavate or irregular and plurilocular with one to several thick exit papillae or tapering tubes of varying length, 15–75 μ, and diameter, 5–20 μ; operculum spherical, 4–8 μ, or oval, 4 × 5—6 × 7 μ. Zoospores hyaline, spherical or slightly oval, 3–5 μ, with a clear refractive globule in the center. Rhizoidal system usually extensively developed, branched, coarse and irregular, often invading several adjacent host cells and attaining a diameter of from 2–10 μ at its point of insertion on the sporangium. Resting spores hyaline or occasionally with a faint yellow tinge, predominately spherical, 4.5–18 μ, oval or slightly ellipsoidal, 5 × 7 μ—12 × 16 μ, smooth, rough, or warty; germination unknown" (Karling, *loc. cit.*).

In various algae, tissues of higher plants, and cysts of Monadineae, dead *Chara*, onion skin, bleached grass leaves, soil and water, Karling (*loc. cit.*, 1941a: 387; 1941b: 108; 1942c: 620; 1948c: 509), in decayed maize stem, Sparrow (1952d: 768), UNITED STATES; saprophytic in tissues of higher plants, de Wildeman (*loc. cit.*), FRANCE; rotifer eggs and nematodes, Karling (1946b: 2, pl. 2, fig. 46), BRAZIL.

Successful cultivation on solidified media as well as on a variety of cooked algae and plant tissues has been reported by Karling.

The inclusion of Dangeard's *Entophlyctis maxima* in the synonymy is open to question, since no zoospore discharge was observed; his fungus may, in fact, be inoperculate and hence a species of *Entophlyctis*.

ENDOCHYTRIUM PSEUDODISTOMUM (Scherffel) Karling

Mycologia, 33: 357. 1941

Entophlyctis pseudodistoma Scherffel, in Domján, Folia cryptogam., 2: 24, pl. 1, figs. 64, 66, 68, 70, 76-81, 85-87, 99, 100, 111. 1936.

Sporangium endobiotic, somewhat ellipsoidal, 17.5–25.4 μ high by 15–25.4 μ broad, with a smooth colorless wall, the extramatrical case of the infecting zoospore persistent, discharge tube 5–15 μ long by 5–7.5 μ in diameter, generally formed on upper part of the sporangium near the place of attachment to the spore case, rarely lateral; rhizoids stout,

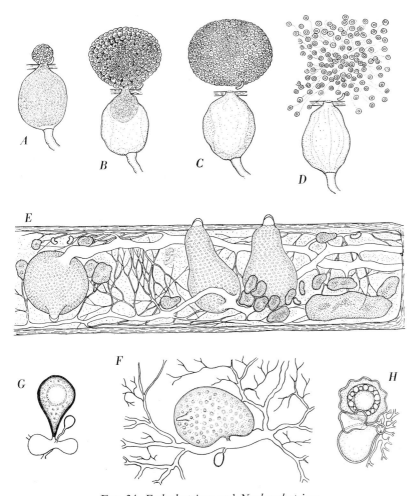

FIG. 34. *Endochytrium* and *Nephrochytrium*

A–E. Endochytrium ramosum Sparrow in *Cladophora sp.*: *A–D*, stages in discharge out into the water of zoospores of endobiotic sporangium; *E*, three plants within alga, bearing mature zoosporangia. *F–G. Nephrochytrium appendiculatum* Karling in *Chara* and *Nitella*: *F*, portion of thallus bearing mature sporangium; latter is connected by a short isthmus to a long apophysis; persistent thick-walled case of zoospore is attached to apophysis by a short narrow tube; *G*, resting spore of same species. *H. Nephrochytrium stellatum* Couch, stellate resting spore.

(*A–E*, Sparrow, 1933a; *F–G*, Karling, 1938a; *H*, Couch, 1938a)

emerging from the base of the sporangium, strongly developed, much branched, polyphagous, the tips at times becoming extramatrical; zoospores spherical, 5–7.5 μ in diameter, posteriorly uniflagellate, with a colorless centric or eccentric oil drop 1.2–2.5 μ in diameter in the granular vacuolate plasma, escaping upon the dehiscence of a circular operculum which terminates the discharge tube and remaining in a motionless group before the orifice, the group slowly moving away and losing coherency and the individuals assuming motion; resting spore endobiotic, nearly spherical, brown, thick-walled, the outer surface provided with irregularly disposed thick slightly reflexed scales, contents bearing a large eccentric oil drop 11 μ in diameter, formed asexually and endogenously in a sporangium-like structure which it partly or completely fills and, like the sporangium, bearing extramatrically the persistent cyst of the infecting zoospore, germination not observed.

Saprophytic in *Spirogyra, Zygnema,* HUNGARY.

The presence of an operculum distinguishes this as a species of *Endochytrium* rather than of *Entophlyctis.*

ENDOCHYTRIUM DIGITATUM Karling

Mycologia, 30: 307, text figs. 20-37. 1938

"Thalli numerous, intramatrical, monocentric, eucarpic. Zoosporangia hyaline and smooth except for one to several blunt digitations at or near the base; formed as an enlargement on the germ tube and delimited from the rhizoidal system by a cross wall at maturity; elongate and obclavate 11 × 44 μ—18 × 35 μ, pyriform, 15 × 22 μ—71 × 120 μ, obpyriform, irregular, subspherical, somewhat triangular and lobed, with 1–4, usually one, single or branched, straight, curved, undulating, or coiled, tapering exit tubes, 5–18 μ in diameter and 10–275 μ in length, which may occasionally extend 88 μ beyond the surface of the host wall. Operculum spherical or slightly oval, 3.3–5.5 μ. Zoospores hyaline with a clear refractive globule 1.6–2.2 μ in diameter, spherical, 4.4–5.5 μ, posteriorly uniciliate; emerging fully formed and singly, and lying quiescent in a globular mass a short while before becoming actively motile, intermittently amoeboid. Rhizoidal system well developed and richly branched, extending sometimes for a distance of 550 μ, smooth or irregular in contour, 2.7–5 μ in diameter and occasionally digitate at the base. Resting spores smooth, light to medium brown, oval, subspherical, 16 × 18 μ—10 × 15 μ, spherical, 20 μ, obpyriform, with a 1.75–2.5 μ thick wall and a large refractive globule usually surrounded by several small ones; germination unknown" (Karling, *loc. cit.*).

Saprophytic in dead internodes of *Chara coronata, Nitella flexilis,* and other algae, Karling (*loc. cit.*; 1942c: 621) (?), UNITED STATES.

IMPERFECTLY KNOWN SPECIES OF ENDOCHYTRIUM

? ENDOCHYTRIUM OOPHILUM Sparrow

Amer. J. Bot., 20: 72, text fig. 1 r-s. 1933

Sporangium endobiotic, ovoid, 50 μ long by 30–35 μ wide, with a short papilla which barely penetrates the wall of the egg and which terminates in an operculum about 6 μ in diameter; zoospores spherical or somewhat elongate, 3 μ in diameter, formed in the sporangium, posteriorly uniflagellate, with a single globule, liberated with great rapidity upon the dehiscence of the operculum; resting spore not observed.

Parasitic in rotifer eggs, UNITED STATES.

If further observations confirm that no vegetative system is ever formed the fungus should be removed from *Endochytrium* and placed in a new genus, which would be the operculate counterpart of *Olpidium.* (See Karling, 1946b, pl. 2, fig. 46).

NEPHROCHYTRIUM KARLING

Amer. J. Bot., 25: 211. 1938

(Fig. 34 F-H, p. 571)

"Thallus intramatrical, monocentric, eucarpic. Zoosporangia variously shaped, apophysate, with one or more exit papillae or tubes of varying length; formed as an outgrowth from the apophysis and delimited from the latter by a cross wall at maturity. Rhizoidal system coarse, richly branched, and extensive, with occasional elongate, spindle-shaped, intercalary enlargements. Zoospores uniguttulate, posteriorly uniciliate. Resting spores variously shaped, apophysate, thick-walled; formed as an outgrowth from the apophysis; germination unknown" (Karling, *loc. cit.*).

Saprophytic in Characeae and grasses.

Nephrochytrium superficially resembles *Diplophlyctis*. It differs from this genus in that "the sporangia and resting spores [of *Diplophlyctis*] are formed as enlargements of the germ tube [whereas] in the present species [*N. appendiculatum*] they develop as protuberances or outgrowths from a transverse, fusiform, spindle-shaped, medianly constricted apophysis. Furthermore, occasional intercalary, spindle-shaped swellings occur in the rhizoidal system, while the zoospore case becomes thickened, amber in color, and persists on the surface of the host cell as an appendage to the sporangia and resting spores" (Karling, *loc. cit.*).

Unfortunately, the critical point as to whether the sporangium is operculate or inoperculate has not been determined in *Nephrochytrium appendiculatum*, the type species. Couch (1938a) has identified with Karling's genus an operculate form with a similar type of development. Because of the frequent parallelisms in body structure known to exist in these fungi, it is impossible to say without a reëxamination of Karling's fungus whether Couch's *N. stellatum* and Whiffen's *N. aurantium* should be placed here or in a genus of their own.

KEY TO THE SPECIES OF NEPHROCHYTRIUM

Globule of zoospore colorless
　　Apophysis elongate, transverse, spindle-like; resting spore smooth-
　　　　walled .... *N. appendiculatum*, p. 574
　　Apophysis globose, ovoid, or lobed; resting spore with a stellate wall
　　　　　　　　　　　　　　　　　　　　　　　N. stellatum, p. 575
Globule of zoospore orange .... *N. aurantium*, p. 576

NEPHROCHYTRIUM APPENDICULATUM Karling

Amer. J. Bot., 25: 211, figs. 1-2. 1938

(Fig. 34 F-G, p. 571)

"Zoosporangia numerous, hyaline, smooth, sub-spherical, flattened, depressed, usually somewhat kidney-shaped, 8×14 μ—18×30 μ, with 1–3 exit papillae or tubes of varying length. Zoospores hyaline, spherical, 3.5–4.5 μ, with a large clear refractive globule; cilium approximately 40 μ long; zoospore case becoming thick-walled, amber colored, and persisting on the surface of the host cell after germination. Apophysis elongate, transverse, usually spindle-shaped and medianly constricted; rhizoids arising as branches of its ends, extending occasionally over a radius of 600 μ and often attaining a diameter of 5–6 μ; intercalary swellings 4–8 μ in diameter. Resting spores smooth, light to dark amber, usually somewhat kidney-shaped, flattened, depressed, occasionally obpyriform, 10 × 18 μ—17 × 26 μ, thick-walled with one or more refractive globules" (Karling, *loc. cit.*).

Saprophytic in cells of *Chara coronata, C. delicatula, Nitella flexilis, N. gracilis,* Karling (*loc. cit.*), *Chara coronata,* Karling (1941b: 108), moribund cells of *Chara sp.,* Sparrow and Barr (1955: 555), UNITED STATES.

NEPHROCHYTRIUM STELLATUM Couch

Amer. J. Bot., 25: 507, 509, text figs. 1-34. 1938

(Fig. 34 H, p. 571)

"Thallus endophytic beneath the cuticle of *Nitella* or sometimes on inner side of cell membrane, monocentric. Each thallus consisting at maturity either of a richly developed rhizoidal system, a more or less spherical apophysis and a zoosporangium, or of a resting body with rhizoids and apophysis. Sporangia roughly disc-shaped from pressure, usually circular in outline in face view but sometimes irregular in outline, particularly when growing with *Coleochaete,* usually with a basal columella which bulges into sporangium; 26–50 × 29–50 μ; with a basal, globose, ovoid, or sometimes lobed apophysis, the latter being connected to the sporangium by a narrow isthmus, apophysis 8.4–12.8 × 14.7–20 μ. The sporangium and apophysis, connected by a narrow isthmus, have an hour-glass-like appearance, the sporangium being much the larger part of the hour glass. Emergence pore formed near columella, usually not tubular but penetrating through the cuticle of the *Nitella,* bursting irregularly but always with a distinct cap. Spores emerging slowly in a spherical mass and remaining quiet for a few seconds at the sporangial mouth; spherical, about 5 μ thick, with a large refractive globule and a very long cilium, 35–40 μ long; zoospore case pyriform, becoming thick-walled, yellowish, and persisting on the surface of the *Nitella*, attached to the apophysis at the isthmus. Rhizoids elaborately developed, much branched, the ultimate branches with blunt tips, attached to the apophysis near the isthmus or more frequently to the isthmus by one main trunk. Resting spores near amber brown, nearly spherical but slightly wider than tall, usually with 8–12 large, rounded protuberances, rarely smooth, wall 2.8–4 μ thick, when ripe with one large oil (?) globule surrounded by a layer of smaller spherical bodies, 10–30 μ wide × 11–29 μ long, usually 18–21 μ wide × 16–19 μ long; spore with an empty, basal, usually barrel-shaped, or sometimes irregular apophysis, the walls of which are hyaline or nearly so; barrel-shaped part about 12–19 μ wide × 8–15 μ long, but much smaller in depauperate specimens, wall about 2.5 μ thick beneath the spore but thinning to a mere membrane at the basal rhizoidal end. The empty zoospore case becoming thick-walled and yellowish and remaining attached to the base of barrel-shaped part. Germination not observed" (Couch, *loc. cit.*).

Saprophytic in cells of *Nitella hyalina*, UNITED STATES.

Distinguishable from *Nephrochytrium appendiculatum* "by the more or less disc-shaped sporangia connected with the nearly spherical apophysis by a narrow isthmus, the columella-like structure at the sporangial base, the irregularly shaped pore through which the spores emerge, and the stellate resting spores..." (Couch, *op. cit.*).

NEPHROCHYTRIUM AURANTIUM Whiffen

Amer. J. Bot., 28: 41, figs. 1-26. 1941

"Thallus monocentric, consisting at maturity of a much branched rhizoidal system, an empty apophysis and an orange-colored zoosporangium. Zoosporangia spherical, cylindrical, or much lobed, 12–54 μ × 16–62 μ. Exit papillae, one or more in number, closed by a circular cap, which is pushed out by the emerging zoospores. Apophysis, 6–23 μ × 7–30 μ, typically spherical, developing as an enlargement of the unbranched portion of the germ tube. Rhizoidal system, colorless, extensive, much branched, continuous with the apophysis. Zoospore case orange-brown in color, attached to the apophysis by its germ tube. Zoospores, 4–4.8 μ, spherical, posteriorly uniciliate, each with a single orange-colored oil globule, emerging in a spherical mass and remaining quiescent at the mouth of the exit papilla for several seconds before swimming away. Resting spores unknown" (Whiffen, *loc. cit.*).

Saprophytic on grass leaves, Whiffen (*loc. cit.*), Karling (1941a: 387; 1942c: 620), UNITED STATES.

CYLINDROCHYTRIDIUM KARLING

Bull. Torrey Bot. Club, 68: 382. 1941

(Fig. 32 G, p. 554)

Siphonochytrium Couch, nom. nud., J. Elisha Mitchell Sci. Soc., 55: 208. 1939.

"Thallus monocentric and eucarpic. Zoosporangia usually stalked and cylindrical, occasionally sessile, operculate. Zoospores posteriorly uniflagellate, emerging fully formed and lying quiescent in a globular mass at the orifice of the sporangium for a few minutes before swimming away. Rhizoidal system extensive, branched with numerous catenulate spindle-shaped swellings. Resting spores unknown" (Karling, *loc. cit.*).

Saprophytes in vegetable debris.

Although not mentioned in his diagnosis, Karling (1945c: 367) later, in differentiating *Rhopalophlyctis* from the present genus, noted that *Cylindrochytridium* is usually intramatrical, whereas *Rhopalophlyctis* is extramatrical, save for the rhizoids.

Whiffen (1941b: 324, pl. 8, fig. 13) points out that *Siphonochytrium* Couch, which is undescribed, is *Cylindrochytridium johnstonii*.

CYLINDROCHYTRIDIUM JOHNSTONII Karling

Bull. Torrey Bot. Club, 68: 383, figs. 1-16. 1941

"Zoosporangia hyaline, smooth, thin-walled, usually tubular, cylindrical or slightly clavate, 12–25 μ × 30–800 μ, occasionally oval, pyriform and sessile; stalk or basal portion usually of the same shape and diameter as the sporangium, but sometimes inflated, vesicular, irregular and apophysis-like. Operculum oval, ellipsoidal, 4 × 6 μ–8 × 10 μ, spherical, 4–17 μ; remaining attached to the sporangium or lying loose nearby. Zoospores spherical, 5.6–7 μ, with a large highly refractive globule; flagellum 22–26 μ long. Rhizoidal system arising from one to several points on the base of the stalk, extending over a radius of 100–1200 μ; spindle shaped swellings 8 × 12 μ–20 × 30 μ, rarely lacking entirely" (Karling, *loc. cit.*).

Saprophytic in decaying vegetable debris, Karling (*loc. cit.*), onion skin and bleached grass leaves, from moist soil, Karling (1942c: 621; 1948c: 509), cellulose, Couch (1939a: 212), Whiffen (1941b: 329, pl. 8, fig. 13), R.M. Johns (comm.), Crasemann (1954), UNITED STATES; cellulose substratum, Shanor (1944: 331), MEXICO.

It is probably this fungus, not *Macrochytrium*, whose nutritional requirements Crasemann (1954) determined.

Shanor (*loc. cit.*) described the resting spores as nearly spherical, thick-walled, smooth, with light-brown or amber-colored walls, and with a large yellow globule in the contents.

TRUITTELLA KARLING

Amer. J. Bot., 36: 454. 1949

(Fig. 32 A, p. 554)

"Thallus predominantly monocentric, eucarpic; sporangia, rhizoids and resting spores developing from the germ tube or an outgrowth of the zoospore; sporangia operculate, variable in size and shape; rhizoids usually arising at several points on the surface of the sporangium; resting spores formed by encystment of segments of the rhizoids" (Karling, *loc. cit.*).

Saprophytes on cellulosic substrata.

Resembling *Catenochytridium* but differing in that the rhizoids arise from several places on the sporangium and the sporangium develops from the tip of the germ tube of the zoospore and not from the body of the spore.

TRUITTELLA SETIFERA Karling

Amer. J. Bot., 36: 455, figs. 1-44. 1949

"Sporangia spherical (22–70 μ), oval (20–35 × 28–65 μ), angular, irregular or lobed with a smooth, hyaline to light brown, 1.8–2.3 μ, thick wall, and a low exit papilla; operculum saucer- or bowl-shaped, 10–17 μ diam. Zoospores spherical (4.2–6 μ) with a conspicuous hyaline refractive body, 2.5–2.8 μ diam., flagellum 30–34 μ long. Persistent zoospore cyst usually thick-walled, bearing 1–20 simple or branched, long (30–300 μ) or short (15–12 μ), cylindrical setae, up to 3 μ diam. Rhizoids typically constricted at intervals and usually branching dichotomously and sometimes extending for a distance of 320 μ; rhizoidal segments predominantly cylindrical (7–10 × 20–42 μ) and thick-walled at maturity. Resting spores spherical (19–25 μ), oval (15–20 × 17–30 μ), oblong (20–24 × 30–32 μ), occasionally lobed or constricted with a smooth, 2–3 μ thick, dark, reddish-brown wall and coarsely granular refractive content; germination unknown" (Karling, *loc. cit.*).

Saprophytic in cellulosic substrata, UNITED STATES.

In thallus development, the rudiments of the rhizoidal system were laid down first, and succeeded by that of the sporangium.

IMPERFECTLY KNOWN GENUS OF THE CHYTRIDIACEAE

? HAPLOCYSTIS SOROKIN

Bull. Soc. Nat. Kazan, 4 (3): 11. 1874

Thallus epibiotic, monocentric, obpyriform, with a short narrow stalklike base, apparently without a vegetative system, superficially attached to the substratum, the contents divided by successive cleavage into thirty-two parts which rotate within the operculate sporangium and conjugate in pairs; swarmers (planozygotes) biflagellate, emerging upon the dehiscence of a broad operculum, movement hopping; resting stage not observed.

A monotypic marine genus on submerged wood.

? HAPLOCYSTIS MIRABILIS Sorokin

Bull. Soc. Nat. Kazan, 4 (3): 11, pl. 1, figs. 44-55. 1874

Sporangium 117 μ high, wall thin, smooth, swarmers sixteen, spherical, 11 μ in diameter, with a refractive globule, upon germination enlarging to form a new sporangium.

On wood, ITALY (VENICE).

A fungus with such a remarkable life history is not improbable, but it certainly needs validation.

MEGACHYTRIACEAE

Thallus epi- and endobiotic, or free in the medium, only the tips entering the substratum, polycentric, either rhizoidal, extensive, and much branched, with intercalary swellings, or broadly tubular, hypha-like, not distinctly rhizoidal, with swellings or constrictions and sometimes septae; zoosporangia operculate, formed from terminal or intercalary swellings; zoospores posteriorly uniflagellate; resting spores thick-walled, apparently asexually formed, upon germination producing zoospores or functioning as a prosporangium.

Saprophytes in vegetable debris, members of one genus (*Megachytrium*) saprophytic and possibly parasitic on *Elodea*.

This family includes all polycentric operculate chytrids except those in *Tetrachytrium* and *Zygochytrium*. These genera are placed at the end of this family, although not belonging in it (see pp. 599-601). When further observations validate the two (particularly *Tetrachytrium*), each should, perhaps, be put in a family of its own, since they possess radically different types of sexual reproduction (see "Sexual Reproduction," p. 79).

KEY TO THE GENERA OF THE MEGACHYTRIACEAE

Thallus forming tenuous strongly tapering rhizoids
  Rhizoids septate only where delimiting the reproductive organs
  NOWAKOWSKIELLA, p. 580
  Rhizoids septate and constricted at intervals as well as where
    delimiting the reproductive organs .... SEPTOCHYTRIUM, p. 592
Thallus forming a broadly tubular vegetative system not tapering
    strongly distally .... MEGACHYTRIUM, p. 596

NOWAKOWSKIELLA SCHROETER

Engler and Prantl, Natürlichen Pflanzenfam., 1 (1): 82. 1892 (1893)

(Fig. 35, p. 583)

Cladochytrium Nowakowski, pro parte, in Cohn, Beitr. Biol. Pflanzen, 2: 92. 1876.

Thallus eucarpic, polycentric, endobiotic, extramatrical, or both, extensive, branched, rhizoidal, bearing irregular swellings, occasionally septate turbinate cells, and the rudiments of the zoosporangia and

resting spores; zoosporangium operculate, generally apophysate, intra-
or extramatrical, internally proliferous; zoospores posteriorly uniflagellate, with a single globule, escaping through a sessile pore or a discharge
tube, generally undergoing a period of rest at the orifice before swimming away; resting spore borne like the sporangium, thick-walled,
germination not observed.

A genus containing species saprophytic in the decaying parts of higher
plants and in the gelatinous sheath of *Chaetophora*.

The vegetative system is ordinarily very extensive and profusely
branched and bears numerous irregularities. It may be entirely within the
substratum or, more often, form an extensive extramatrical growth.
The commonest species, *N. elegans*, may generally be collected by
baiting aquatic sites, or even water cultures containing vegetable trash,
with bits of grass or corn stem.

KEY TO THE SPECIES OF NOWAKOWSKIELLA

Sporangia and vegetative swellings smooth-walled
  Zoospores less than 10 μ in diameter; operculum always external
    Sporangia spherical, subspherical, oval, ovoid, ellipsoidal or
      pyriform; rhizoidal system highly variable in diameter,
      branching, and extent
      Resting spore borne in a one-celled container
        Rhizoidal swellings usually not septate, never pseudoparen-
          chymatous; resting spore where known smooth-walled
          .... *N. elegans*, p. 582
        Rhizoidal swellings frequently forming variously oriented
          cross walls and becoming pseudoparenchymatous; rest-
          ing spores with low verrucae, occasionally smooth-
          walled............................... *N. ramosa*, p. 586
      Resting spore typically formed in the upper half of a two-celled
        container from the fused contents of the two halves......
        .... *N. hemisphaerospora*, p. 587
    Sporangia predominantly cylindrical or clavate, borne on a once-
      or several-septate stalk.................. *N. elongata*, p. 588
  Zoospores more than 10 μ in diameter; operculum slightly sunken
    in discharge tube or external............... *N. macrospora*, p. 589
Sporangia and turbinate cells bearing setae.......... *N. atkinsii*, p. 591

NOWAKOWSKIELLA ELEGANS (Nowak.) Schroeter

Engler and Prantl, Natürlichen Pflanzenfam., 1 (1): 82.1892 (1893)

(Fig. 35 A-G, p. 583)

Cladochytrium elegans Nowakowski, pro parte, in Cohn, Beitr. Biol. Pflanzen, 2: 95, pl. 6, figs. 14–17. 1876.

Nowakowskiella endogena Constantineanu, Revue Gén. Bot., 13: 387, fig.83. 1901.

Sporangium terminal, occasionally intercalary, when free being spherical, ovoid, pyriform, or oblong, when endobiotic often assuming the shape of the confining cell, 16–40 μ or more in width, apophysate or nonapophysate, with or without a discharge tube, wall thin, smooth, colorless, proliferating, operculum smooth or umbonate; rhizoidal system highly variable in nature and extent, strongly polycentric, with irregular expansions, up to 10 μ or more in width, tips delicate, septate turbinate cells occasionally formed; zoospores spherical, 5.0–7.5 μ in diameter, with a large colorless globule and a long flagellum, escaping upon the dehiscence of the operculum, 5–7 μ in diameter, and forming a temporary motionless compact mass at the orifice, imbedded in or surrounded by mucilaginous material, movement swimming or amoeboid; resting spores, where known, with a smooth, thick wall, completely filling their container.

Saprophytic in the gelatinous sheath of *Chaetophora*, Nowakowski (*loc. cit.*), GERMANY, decaying leaves of *Alisma plantago-aquatica*, Constantineanu (*loc. cit.*), RUMANIA; boiled grass culms, Matthews (1928: 229, pl. 34), cultivated on seeds and corn stem, Sparrow (1933a: 70, fig. 2), grass leaves, Couch (1939a), Karling (1941a: 387; 1942c: 620), rotting oat leaves, Karling (1941b: 108), on cellophane, from moist soil, Karling (1948c: 510), decaying maize stem, Sparrow (1952d: 768), UNITED STATES; in leaves of *Elodea* and in grass, Sparrow (1936a: 453, pl. 17, fig. 17), GREAT BRITAIN; soil, Karling (1944b: 388), BRAZIL; Shanor (1944: 331), MEXICO; cellophane bait and vegetable debris, Sparrow (1952b: 69), CUBA; soil, Remy (1948: 214), Reinboldt (1951: 178), GERMANY; corn leaves, Shen and Siang (1948: 185), CHINA; from soil, substrate?, Gaertner (1954b: 22), EGYPT, EQUATORIAL EAST AFRICA, SOUTH AFRICA.

Constantineanu's fungus is said to differ from *Nowakowskiella elegans*

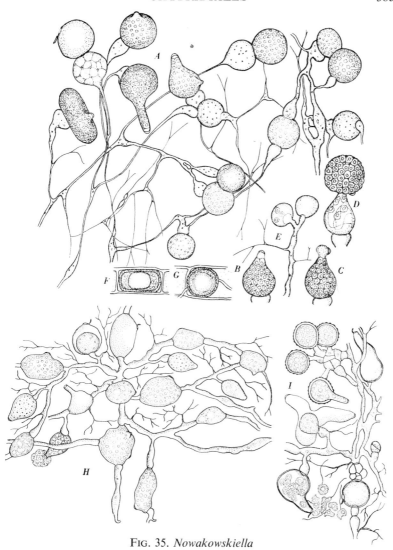

Fig. 35. *Nowakowskiella*

A–G. Nowakowskiella elegans (Nowak.) Schroeter: *A*, portion of extramatrical part of strongly polycentric plant; *B–D*, stages in discharge of sporangium; *E*, portion of small plant with two sporangia; *F–G*, endobiotic resting spores associated with sporangial plants. *H. Nowakowskiella profusa* Karling, portion of polycentric thallus bearing sporangia. *I. Nowakowskiella ramosa* E. J. Butler, portion of thallus bearing sporangia and resting spores, the latter arising as outgrowths from the "pseudoparenchyma."

(*A–G*, Sparrow, 1933a; *H, I*, Karling, 1944b)

in that it is endobiotic and the sporangium has a discharge tube. Both of these are variable characters and of questionable taxonomic worth in distinguishing species. The form called *N. endogena* by Domján (1936: 51) appears from the character of its resting spores more nearly related to *N. ramosa*.

Thick-walled spherical or ellipsoidal apophysate colorless resting spores with fatty contents were associated with the sporangia in the British material. From the fact that they were borne on a polycentric rhizoidal system it is possible that they may belong to the species, but further observations are necessary to determine this point with certainty.

The three following species appear to be indistinguishable from *Nowakowskiella elegans* except for regular formation of resting spores. No striking and significant unvarying characters of thallus, sporangia, zoospores, or resting spores separate them from that species and the sizes of parts intergrade. Until the limits of variation of the rhizoidal systems of the species are established, it cannot be said what reliance can be placed upon them for differentation at the species level. The situation is further complicated by the fact that while Karling, the author of two of these species, has reported *N. elegans* many times, he has never described or figured his conception of it. Since, however, future observations may clearly indicate the limits of *N. elegans* and prove that the three are distinct from it, their descriptions are given here and they are not placed in synonymy.

? Nowakowskiella delica Whiffen

J. Elisha Mitchell Sci. Soc., 59: 37, pl. 2. 1943

"Rhizomycelium, intra- and extramatrical, much branched with numerous elongated swellings, which give rise to zoosporangia or resting bodies. Zoosporangia, terminal or intercalary, $12.5 \times 15.0 \mu$ to $22.5 \times 28.8 \mu$, spherical, ovoid, or pyriform; with a single exit pore, usually laterally but often apically placed, operculate; apophysis variable in shape, $2.5 \times 15.0 \mu$ to $11.5 \times 17.5 \mu$. Zoospores hyaline, spherical, $5.7–7.5 \mu$, posteriorly uniflagellate, flagellum 30μ long, uniguttulate. Resting bodies, terminal or intercalary, usually intramatrical, ovoid to spherical, $10.0 \times 15.0 \mu$, to $26.2 \times 29.9 \mu$, apophysate, hyaline, containing one to many oil globules. Germination of resting bodies not observed" (Whiffen, *loc. cit.*).

Saprophytic on a grass leaf in soil, UNITED STATES.

? Nowakowskiella profusa Karling

Bull. Torrey Bot. Club, 68: 386, 1941; 71: 382, figs. 45–68. 1944

(Fig. 35 H, p. 583)

Rhizomycelium very profuse, extensive, and richly branched, hyaline, 1–9 µ rarely 6–15 µ in diameter, well-defined, septate, spindle-shaped and oval swellings rare or lacking; rhizoids abundant; zoosporangia terminal or intercalary, hyaline, smooth, rarely apophysate, spherical (10–45 µ in diameter), ovoid, ellipsoid (8 by 12–20 by 35 µ), clavate, obclavate (10–22 µ by 15–40 µ), pyriform, obpyriform, elongate, cylindrical (8 by 25–10 by 50 µ), lobed and irregular; operculum apical, subapical or lateral, oval and spherical, 4.4 µ–7 µ, remaining attached to the sporangium or lying nearby; zoospores hyaline, spherical, 4 µ–5.5 µ with a small refringent globule, 0.7–2 µ; resting spores terminal or intercalary, spherical (14–25 µ), ovoid, ellipsoid (10 by 15–14 by 22 µ), truncate, spindle-shaped, and rarely irregular, with a fairly thick, yellowish brown, smooth wall, content granular with numerous refractive globules, germinating after a short rest period, forming a simple or branched, tapering, thin-walled, operculate exit tube and producing zoospores directly within, or functioning as a prosporangium and forming a thin-walled zoosporangium on the surface.

Saprophytic in decaying vegetable debris, Karling (1944b: 382), rotting oat leaves, Karling (1941b: 108), Karling (1942c: 620), on cellophane and onion skin, from soil, Karling (1948c: 510), J. Roberts (1948: 147, fig. 2), UNITED STATES; soil, Reinboldt (1951: 178), GERMANY.

J. Roberts (1948) reported that the optimum temperature for growth on solid cellulosic media of his isolate assigned to this species was 24–28° C. He noted that in the same layer the walls showed a predominance of chitin mixed with cellulose.

? Nowakowskiella crassa Karling

Bull. Torrey Bot. Club, 76: 294, figs. 1–15. 1949

Rhizoidal system hyaline, profuse, branched, usually large and coarse, 6–18 μ in diameter, with numerous nonseptate subspherical (14–21 μ in diameter), oval (12–18 by 16–22 μ) fusiform (14–16 by 25–28 μ) or irregular enlargements; zoosporangia terminal or intercalary, hyaline, smooth, spherical (15–40 μ in diameter), oval (18–30 by 22–38 μ), fusiform, clavate or irregular, operculum 10–15 μ in diameter, zoospores spherical, 4.5–5 μ in diameter with a single refractive globule 0.8–1.2 μ in diameter and flagellum 24–26 μ long; resting spore hyaline, smooth, spherical (12–23 μ in diameter), oval (18–20 by 22–24 μ), germination not observed.

Saprophytic in vegetable debris, UNITED STATES.

NOWAKOWSKIELLA RAMOSA E. J. Butler

Mem. Dept. Agr. India, Bot. Ser., 1: 141, pl. 10, figs. 3–10. 1907

(Fig. 35 I, p. 583)

"Rhizomycelium hyaline, profuse, richly-branched, occasionally septate; tenuous portions 1.5–8 μ in diameter, occasionally anastomosing; spindle organs oval 4–6 × 6–10 μ, or broadly fusiform 5–7 × 12–16 μ, or almost spherical 6–9 μ, or elongate. Sporangia terminal or intercalary, apophysate or non-apophysate, apophysis when present usually subspherical and up to 11 μ in diameter; sporangia spherical 20–50 μ, or pyriform 15–30 × 25–40 μ, or oval 15–20 × 22–30 μ, or elongate or slightly irregular, with 1–3 low exit papillae or exit tubes up to 100 μ long. Opercula oval or circular in outline, 4–6 μ in diameter. Zoospores spherical 6.6–8.8 μ, with a large (3 μ) plastic refractive globule and a flagellum 36–40 μ long; frequently becoming amoeboid; forming a globular mass at the exit orifice immediately after emerging but soon separating and dispersing. Resting spores formed from proliferated spindle organs and short lateral branches; spherical or slightly angular, 15–26 μ, hyaline to yellowish in color, with numerous small refractive globules or a large central one surrounded by smaller globules; wall 1.8–2.6 μ thick, smooth or slightly verrucose (?); resting spores usually functioning as prosporangia in germination and giving rise to thin-walled zoosporangia on their surface; occasionally germinating directly as sporangia with an exit tube which bursts through the spore wall" (Karling, 1944b).

Saprophytic on rotting stems of *Triticum vulgare*, Butler (*loc. cit.*), INDIA; tissues of *Typha* (*angustifolia?*), Domján (as *Nowakowskiella endogena*; 1936: 51, pl. 1, figs. 89, 98, 108–109, 112–124, 126–127, 133–136, 143–150, 156–159, 166, 168–169, 175–179), HUNGARY; rotting oat leaves, Karling (1941b: 107), bleached grass leaves and cellophane from moist soil, Karling (1948c: 510), Karling (1942c: 620), J. Roberts (1948: 154, fig. 1), R. M. Johns (comm.), nucules of moribund *Chara sp.*, Sparrow and Barr (coll. Paterson) (1955: 555), UNITED STATES; Karling (1944b: 384, fig. 69), BRAZIL; from soil, substrate ?, Gaertner (1954b: 22), EGYPT, SOUTH AFRICA.

Preference is given to Karling's description because it is more complete than Butler's.

Domján's fungus differs from Butler's only in that the resting spores were occasionally somewhat angular.

Butler (*loc. cit.*) described the development of the resting spores as follows: "Certain hyphae commence to proliferate, either at their ends, or laterally, growing out into large, irregular cells. New cells are formed from these, both by proliferation, and by division of existing cells. In this manner a thin-walled mass of angular cells is formed, sometimes of considerable size. The marginal cells of this swell up into spherical bodies, which thicken their walls to become resting spores. As the process advances, the first formed cells are emptied of their contents, which apparently go to form new cells. As a final result, a group of resting spores is produced, joined together by the thin-walled parenchymatous tissue of the mass." This peculiar process was also observed by Domján (1936) and Karling (1944b) and by us. Karling remarked that resting spores may originate from short lateral branches which enlarge distally, divide, and form pseudoparenchyma. According to J. Roberts (1948), the optimum temperature for growth in solid cellulosic media is 16–18 degrees C. (see also "Cytology," p. 99).

NOWAKOWSKIELLA HEMISPHAEROSPORA Shanor

Amer. J. Bot., 29: 174, figs. 1–38. 1942

(Fig. 36 D–F, p. 590)

"Rhizomycelium much branched, extensive, hyaline, filaments quite variable in diameter, spindle shaped or oval swellings numerous or very much scattered. Zoosporangia usually terminal on short lateral branches or occasionally intercalary, smooth, hyaline, operculate, quite variable in shape and size but commonly ovoid, ellipsoid, or pyriform, usually 7.5–14.2 μ × 9.5–28.4 μ (commonly 11.5 × 17.2 μ) with one to several exit papillae (or tubes), apical, subapical, or lateral, varying in length up to 18 μ and usually about 4.0–4.7 μ in diameter; operculum circular, 3.1–3.5 μ in diameter, either remaining attached to the sporangium or lying loose nearby. Zoospores hyaline, spherical or ovoid, 4.4–6.3 μ in diameter, with a single refractive globule; cilium attached posteriorly, 32.5–40.0 μ in length. Resting bodies terminal or intercalary, usually somewhat ellipsoidal, containing one to four thick-walled hyaline resting spores and a corresponding number of empty cells. Resting spores rather uniform in size, 8.5–12.6 μ × 11.6–15.6 μ (commonly 11.0 × 14.2 μ) usually somewhat hemispherical in shape; refractive globule in mature resting spores large with several smaller ones commonly surrounding it. Germination unknown" (Shanor, *loc. cit.*).

On cellophane, Shanor (*loc. cit.*), Karling (1942c: 620), on cellophane, from soil, Karling (1948c: 510), on cellophane, Sparrow (1952d: 768), UNITED STATES; leaf bait, Shanor (1944: 331), MEXICO; cellophane, Haskins (1946: 135), GREAT BRITAIN; cellophane bait, from soil, Sparrow (1952b: 69), CUBA.

The species appears to be a common one in both soil and water. Its peculiar method of resting-spore formation (Fig. 36 D-F) parallels that found in *Septosperma* (p. 225) and *Nephrochytrium stellatum* (p. 575).

NOWAKOWSKIELLA ELONGATA Karling

Bull. Torrey Bot. Club, 71: 375, figs. 30–44. 1944

(Fig. 36 C, p. 590)

Rhizoidal system hyaline, profuse, copiously branched, 1–6 μ in diameter, with nonseptate swellings, oval (5–13 by 7–15 μ), broadly fusiform (4–8 by 8–17 μ), or globose (5–15 μ in diameter), with refractive globules; sporangia terminal or intercalary, rarely apophysate, sometimes with a basal 1–3 septate sterile portion, straight, elongate-clavate (8–40 by 20–820 μ), cylindrical with swollen apex, curved or coiled

(5–20 by 30–900 μ), pyriform (15–44 by 20–70 μ), globose (10–70 μ in diameter), or irregularly oval, with an apical convex operculum 4–8 μ in diameter which is rarely persistent, occasionally proliferating; zoospores globose, 5–6 μ in diameter, with a single, rarely two refractive globules 2–2.5 μ in diameter, upon discharge forming a temporary globular mass at the orifice of the discharge pore; resting spore formed from the intercalary enlargements of the rhizoidal system, hyaline, smooth, globose (16–24 μ in diameter), oval (14–16 by 18–22 μ), citriform, with a large refractive globule up to 15 μ in diameter or sometimes completely filling the spore, wall thickened, upon germination functioning as a prosporangium and forming a thin-walled evanescent sporangium.

Saprophytic on vegetable debris, Karling (*loc. cit.*), BRAZIL; cellophane, R. M. Johns (comm.), UNITED STATES.

As Karling said, this species bears an astonishing resemblance to the monocentric *Cylindrochytridium johnstonii*.

NOWAKOWSKIELLA MACROSPORA Karling

Amer. J. Bot., 32: 29, figs. 1–30. 1945

"Rhizomycelium profuse, richly-branched, fairly coarse, tenuous portions 2–6 μ in diameter; spindle organs nonseptate, oval (8–16 × 12–15 μ), broadly spindle-shaped (5–7 × 12–15 μ), elongate and fusiform (6–10 × 15–30 μ), or slightly irregular. Sporangia terminal or intercalary, hyaline, smooth, usually apophysate, often slightly flattened and elongated transversely to apophysis, spherical (14–40 μ), oval (18–25 × 23–30 μ), pyriform (8–30 × 18–55 μ), or elongate (10–20 × 30–60 μ), often with an elongate neck, 5–8 × 20–60 μ; apophysis oval or nearly spherical, 8–20 μ in diameter, oblong, clavate or elongate; operculum usually slightly sunken, often apiculate and somewhat hat-shaped, 5–8 μ in diameter; sporangia sometimes becoming brown, thick-walled and dormant in old cultures, functioning as sporangia or prosporangia in germination. Zoospores slowly oozing out and forming a globular mass at exit orifice, spherical, 10–12 μ, with a large (3–5 μ), somewhat disc-shaped refractive globule, and numerous minute granules at posterior end; flagellum 38–42 μ long.

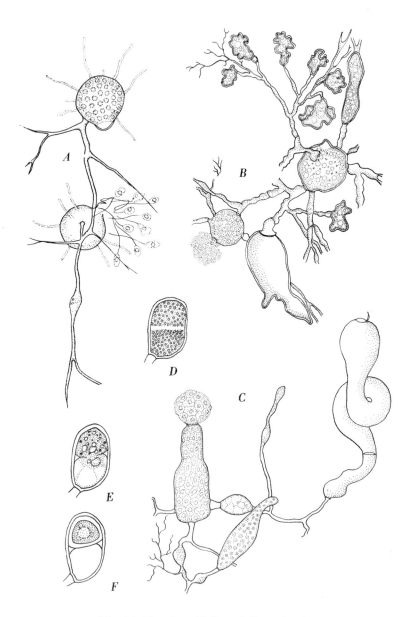

Fig. 36. *Nowakowskiella* and *Septochytrium*

Resting spores spherical (12–22 μ), oval (15–18 × 20–25 μ), with a large refractive globule surrounded by numerous smaller ones, wall smooth, 1.5–2 μ thick, faintly yellowish-brown in color; functioning as prosporangia in germination" (Karling, *loc. cit.*).

Saprophytic in decayed vegetable debris, BRAZIL; soil, Reinboldt (1951: 178), GERMANY; vegetable debris, cellulosic substrata, Shen and Siang (1948: 186), CHINA; bleached grass leaves from soil, Karling (1948c: 510), R. M. Johns (comm.), (TEXAS) UNITED STATES.

Disposition of this species is difficult. Karling (1945a) points out clearly that the typical method of discharge is by a slightly sunken (and presumably endo-) operculum. Sometimes, however, a true operculum is formed. Although Shen and Siang (1948) mention an operculum, they do not indicate whether it is a true operculum or an endooperculum. We have studied a form which in every respect but one corresponds exactly with this species. In it no operculum of any kind whatever is formed. The resolving of this puzzle awaits further study. Meanwhile, since some true opercula were observed in the type material, the present species is retained tentatively in *Nowakowskiella*.

NOWAKOWSKIELLA ATKINSII Sparrow

J. Wash. Acad. Sci., 40: 52, figs. 25, 26. 1950

(Fig. 36 A, p. 590)

Thallus extensive, much branched, bearing occasional irregular swellings and rarely very large (35–40 μ by 18–25 μ) setigerous one-or two-celled turbinate organs; sporangia at the tips of more or less elongated branches, rarely intercalary, predominantly spherical and 13–20 μ in diameter or somewhat pyriform, often apophysate; the wall bearing a variable number of somewhat thickened flexuous setae, 9–16 μ long; zoospores slightly ovoid, 5 by 3 μ with a single hyaline globule and

---

Explanation of Figure 36

A. *Nowakowskiella atkinsii* Sparrow. B. *Septochytrium plurilobum* Johanson; thallus showing resting spores and sporangia. C. *Nowakowskiella elongata* Karling. D-F. *Nowakowskiella hemisphaerospora* Shanor; stages in development of resting spore.

(A, after Sparrow, 1950; B, after Johanson, 1943; C, after Karling, 1944b; D-F, after Shanor, 1942b)

posterior flagellum; emerging through a lateral or subbasal slightly elevated pore upon the dehiscence of an operculum 8 μ in diameter and remaining in a compact quiescent group before assuming motility; resting spore not observed.

Saprophytic on cellophane, in soil, Sparrow (*loc. cit.*; 1952b: 69), CUBA.

The species has a remarkably similar inoperculate counterpart in *Cladochytrium setigerum* Karling (p. 466).

SEPTOCHYTRIUM BERDAN

Amer. J. Bot., 26: 461. 1939

(Fig. 36 B, p. 590; fig. 37 C, p. 598)

"Rhizomycelium intramatrical, predominantly polycentric, consisting of elongate, septate and constricted filaments, intercalary swellings and finely branched rhizoids. Zoosporangia variously shaped, operculate, terminal and intercalary, with one (occasionally several) neck of variable length. Zoospores posteriorly uniciliate, emerging in a globular to ovoid mass and lying quiescent for a few moments before swimming away; method of swimming rapid and darting. Resting spores terminal or intercalary, formed in the same position as the sporangia or from the intercalary swellings; germination through a pore in the wall directly into an operculate zoosporangium similar to the evanescent one or into a tube at whose tip the contents are concentrated and cut off by a cross wall to form the zoosporangium" (Berdan, *loc. cit.*).

Saprophytic on various plant parts.

In her 1942 paper (in which the development is described) Berdan comments (p. 260) that, "So many variations occur in the development of this chytrid that it is very difficult to describe any one type as definitely representing the normal."

KEY TO THE SPECIES OF SEPTOCHYTRIUM

Zoospores up to 8.7 μ in diameter; septations and trabeculae commonly formed in the rhizoids
  Sporangium extremely irregular in shape; zoospore with a single
    globule. . . . . *S. variabile*, p. 593

Sporangium oval, spherical, ellipsoidal, or pyriform; zoospore with
   numerous granules, lacking a main globule
Sporangium bearing a long (up to 1400 μ) unbranched or
   branched discharge tube; resting spores lacking...........
   .... *S. marilandicum*, p. 594
Sporangium bearing one to several short broad discharge tubes;
   resting spores abundantly formed, very deeply lobed.......
                                   S. plurilobulum, p. 595
Zoospores 11–13 μ in diameter; septations and trabeculae rare or
   absent................................ *S. macrosporum*, p. 595

SEPTOCHYTRIUM VARIABILE Berdan

Amer. J. Bot., 26: 461, fig. 2. 1939

(Fig. 37 C, p. 598)

"Zoosporangia hyaline to pale brown, spherical, 4–150 μ in diameter
(often 75–150 μ, average 45–60 μ) with a very short, broad papilla or
neck, ovate, egg-shaped, broadly pyriform, 10 × 15 μ—180 × 220 μ
(commonly 100 × 150 μ) with neck 4 μ–60 μ wide, obclavate to flask-
shaped, 2 × 6—35 × 360 μ, bell-shaped, irregular, flattened and depressed with one (rarely several) broad exit papilla or neck of varying
diameter and length; zoosporangia delimited by true septa at maturity,
sporangial wall smooth when young, striated or layered at maturity,
wrinkled when empty; orifice of operculum circular, 1–16 μ in diameter,
or slightly oval, 4 × 6—6 × 10 μ. Zoospores hyaline, spherical to oval,
4–6 μ, with a single refractive globule, .7–3 μ (usually 2 μ) in diameter;
cilium 30–45 μ long. Rhizomycelium coarse, extensive (20 μ—1 cm.),
richly branched, with constrictions and septations or trabeculae extending partially or entirely across the rhizoids; inserted on the sporangia
at 1–12 points; diameter at point of insertion .4–10 μ. Intercalary swellings usually persistent as empty or partially empty enlargements of the
rhizomycelium but often becoming enlarged and transformed into
secondary or tertiary zoosporangia or into resting spores, occasionally
acting only as a very large, primary centre of organization of the thallus
and sometimes seeming to divide into 2 cells one of which enlarges and
becomes a zoosporangium or resting spore while the other remains as
a sort of apophysis. Treatment with chlor-iodide of zinc giving a pronounced violet colour in the sporangial walls and intercalary swellings.

Resting spore light to dark amber, spherical 4–60 μ diameter, ovoid 4 × 6—50 × 65 μ, or elongated, 10×35 μ, thick-walled, smooth, layered, or with outer coat rather irregular, usually with one large refractive globule and numerous smaller ones; zoosporangia formed by direct germination of the resting spore, spherical, pyriform, ovate, etc., usually smaller than the resting spore, those formed indirectly at the end of a tube oval, round, pyriform or clavate; tube wide and saccate or narrow and long with twists and coils, 7–26 μ × 10–450 μ" (Berdan, *loc. cit.*).

Saprophytic on various grasses, wheat, rye, oats and corn leaves and narcissus root tips, UNITED STATES, CANADA; Karling (1941a: 387; 1942 c: 620; 1948c: 510), UNITED STATES; grass-leaf bait, from soil, Sparrow (1952b: 69), CUBA.

SEPTOCHYTRIUM MARILANDICUM Karling

Bull. Torrey Bot. Club, 78: 39, figs. 9–30. 1951

Rhizomycelium profuse, much branched, coarse, rarely septate or trabeculate, 8–17 μ in diameter, with large broadly or narrowly fusiform or variously shaped intercalary enlargements, bearing slender rhizoids, with occasional anastomoses; sporangia predominantly oval, 30–60 by 40–80 μ, broadly pyriform, sometimes spherical, 25–60 μ, rarely apophysate, usually with their long axis at right angles to the concomitant rhizoidal axis, with a long (up to 1400 μ) curved, coiled or contorted, simple or branched, occasionally very short discharge tube; operculum slightly sunken, 6–18 μ in diameter; zoospores spherical, 3.8–4.7 μ, with numerous minute refractive granules and 24–27 μ long flagellum; resting spores not observed.

In vegetable debris, UNITED STATES.

The species merits distinction by reason of its usually well-developed discharge tubes. While Karling emphasizes, as a differentiating feature, the numerous granules (instead of a single large one) in the zoospore, this is also true of *Septochytrium plurilobulum*. Although *S. marilandicum* is said to be endooperculate, the figures show a true operculum, surrounded by a narrow collar of wall material. From the great rarity of the septae and trabeculae the fungus gives the appearance of being a species of *Nowakowskiella*.

SEPTOCHYTRIUM PLURILOBULUM Johanson

Amer. J. Bot., 30: 621, fig. 1. 1943

(Fig. 36 B, p. 590)

"Rhizomycelium extensive and coarse with septations and trabeculae extending partly or completely across the irregular tenuous portions. Zoosporangia terminal or intercalary, hyaline, smooth, spherical, (11–113 μ in diameter, average 45–55 μ), oval, ellipsoidal, broadly pyriform, with one to several short broad (7 μ), or long (33–38 μ) exit tubes; operculum oval, spherical, 3.75 to 7 μ in diameter. Zoospores oval to spherical, (7–8 μ, average 7.7 μ) with numerous minute refractive globules which impart a grayish granular appearance to the spores; emerging fully developed and lying quiescent for a few moments in a globular mass at the mouth of the exit tube before swimming away. Resting spores usually terminal, irregular, and deeply lobed, 15–43.5 μ in greatest diameter; of a greenish gray color, with a dark, smooth, thick wall 2.62–7 μ in thickness; containing one to several small or large refractive globules; content emerging slowly in germination and developing into an evanescent, thin-walled zoosporangium on the surface of the spore" (Johanson, *loc. cit.*).

Saprophytic in leaves of the striped maple, corn, and other grass leaves, UNITED STATES.

SEPTOCHYTRIUM MACROSPORUM Karling

Amer. J. Bot., 29: 616, figs. 1–15. 1942

"Thallus predominantly polycentric, occasionally monocentric. Rhizomycelium unusually coarse, richly branched, rarely septate, with thick walls which stain brick-red to reddish-lavender with chloro-iodide of zinc; tenuous portions apart from rhizoids 5 to 15 μ in diam.; rhizoids numerous and richly branched; intercalary enlargements broadly or narrowly spindle-shaped, elongate, fusiform, and irregular. Zoosporangia terminal or intercalary, delimited from remainder of thallus by cross septa, non-apophysate, spherical, 15–280 μ, pyriform, 30–50 μ × 70–190 μ, obpyriform, broadly fusiform, obclavate, uteriform [*sic*], and sometimes irregular; hyaline and smooth; opercula 9–16 μ in diam. Zoospores spherical, 11–13 μ, average 12.2 μ, with one larger, 2.5–3.5 μ, and three to six minute refractive globules; emerging fully formed and lying quiescent for a few moments in a globular mass at the exit orifice before swimming away; intermittently amoeboid. Resting spores intercalary, oval, 30–50 × 50–75 μ, spherical, 25–115 μ, amber, and yellow to light-brown in color, smooth or covered with coarse, simple or branched pegs or filamentous extensions, 4–18 μ long; wall 4–6 μ thick, content coarsely granular with one to several large refractive granules; germination unknown" (Karling, *loc. cit.*).

Saprophytic in vegetable debris, Karling (*loc. cit.*; 1942c: 620; 1948c: 510), UNITED STATES.

This species is left in *Septochytrium*, as is *S. marilandicum*, with grave misgivings since it is only rarely septate. It might better be regarded as a species of *Nowakowskiella*. The ornamented resting spores are suspected by Karling to possibly be encysted sporangia bearing abortive rhizoids.

MEGACHYTRIUM SPARROW

Occ. Papers Boston Soc. Nat. Hist.., 8: 9. 1931; Amer. J. Bot., 20: 73. 1933

(Fig. 37 A–B, p. 598)

Thallus epi- and endobiotic, strongly polycentric, eucarpic, consisting of much-branched broad tubular occasionally septate hypha-like filaments bearing at frequent intervals the swollen rudiments of the sporangia or resting spores; sporangia operculate, intercalary or borne at the tips of short lateral branches; zoospores posteriorly uniflagellate, with a single globule, formed in the sporangium; resting spore thickwalled, usually intercalary, contents with globules, upon germination functioning as a prosporangium and forming externally an operculate zoosporangium.

A monotypic genus, found thus far only on *Elodea*.

By reason of its tubular polycentric vegetative system the genus represents a chytridiaceous counterpart of the anteriorly uniflagellate *Hyphochytrium*. The complete development of the thallus is not known. Because of the opaque character of the host difficulty was encountered in tracing it. The zoospore upon germination gives rise to a rather broad undulating "hypha" which, as it grows over the host surface, expands and branches. The "mycelium" ultimately produced varies greatly in diameter, is markedly undulate, and shows in the younger stages of development a tendency to follow the region of juncture of the host cell walls. The latter fact would seem to suggest some type of pectin relationship. Further growth and branching are profuse. The contents of the thallus are finely granular and refractive, with large vacuoles, and are occasionally separated by narrow cross walls. The ultimate branches are extremely refractive, often fusing laterally with one another in a very characteristic manner. It is particularly noteworthy that, in contrast to other chytridiaceous forms having a well-developed thallus, such as *Nowakowskiella*, the vegetative system never becomes rhizoidal, that is, strongly tapering. In heavily parasitized leaves it is endobiotic as well as epibiotic, although the method whereby the fungus gains entrance to the host has not been ascertained. On the stouter portions of the threads large broadly fusiform or irregular swellings delimited by cross walls are produced (Fig. 37 A). These may develop either into sporangia or resting spores. The latter may germinate after little or no resting period. In this process the wall is partly assimilated and a sporangium is formed on the outside of the resting spore (Fig. 37 B). Zoospores arise in the usual manner. The ordinary sporangia originate as somewhat pyriform terminal enlargements of the filaments. When mature they are variable in shape and sometimes have a slightly inflated apophysis. Proliferation has been noted in a few instances.

MEGACHYTRIUM WESTONII Sparrow

Occ. Papers Boston Soc. Nat. Hist., 8: 9. 1931; Amer. J. Bot., 20: 73, pl. 3, figs. A–E. 1933

Thallus at first entirely epibiotic, later also endobiotic, consisting of a profusely branched extensive tubular undulating hypha-like vegetative system whose main axes are up to 5–7 μ in diameter and whose smaller ones are about 3 μ, and of numerous terminal or intercalary swellings; sporangia spherical or clavate but more often irregular, with or without a single short discharge tube, varying greatly in size, usually about 15–50 μ long by 10–30 μ wide, sometimes apophysate, rarely proliferating, wall thin, smooth, colorless; zoospores spherical, 5 μ in diameter,

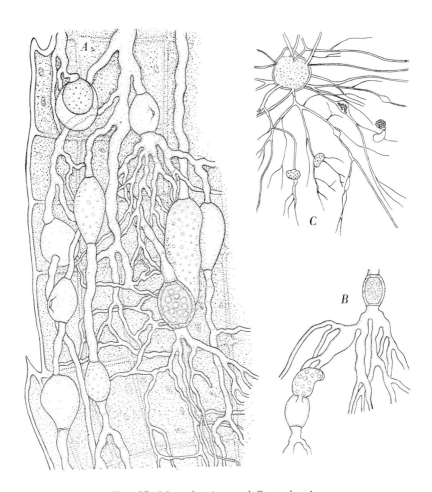

FIG. 37. *Megachytrium* and *Septochytrium*

A-B. Megachytrium westonii Sparrow on *Elodea: A,* portion of thallus bearing zoosporangia, swellings and resting spores, on *Elodea* leaf; *B,* portion of thallus bearing two resting spores; lower one has germinated and produced an operculate zoosporangium. *C. Septochytrium variabile* Berdan, portion of mature thallus showing large central primary operculate zoosporangium and swellings and small secondary sporangia.

(*A-B,* after Sparrow, 1933a; *C,* after Berdan, 1939)

with a small colorless centric globule and a long flagellum, escaping upon the dehiscence of a convex operculum 3–5 μ in diameter; resting spore broadly ovoid with truncate ends, with a thick smooth wall, 20 μ long by 15 μ wide, contents with globules, germ sporangium operculate.

Parasitic on *Elodea canadensis*, UNITED STATES.

This remarkable fungus caused a pronounced discoloration and disintegration of the leaves of *Elodea*.

GENERA OF DOUBTFUL AFFINITY

TETRACHYTRIUM SOROKIN

Bot. Zeitung, 32: 311. 1874; Bull. Soc. Nat. Kazan, 4(3): 15. 1874

(Fig. 38 F–M, p. 600)

Zoospores upon germination developing at one pole a cylindrical axis which forms distally a single short reflexed lateral sterile branch and three terminal ones, each of which bears a single operculate sporangium, developing at the opposite pole a lobed holdfast which anchors the plant to the substratum; the thallus polycentric, eucarpic, hypha-like; zoospores (gametes?) four, with a central vacuole (?), posteriorly uniflagellate, matured outside the sporangium in a delicate evanescent vesicle which envelops the extruded protoplasm after the dehiscence of the operculum, conjugating in pairs to form a new sporangial plant; no resting stage formed.

Primarily saprophytic on submerged decaying wood and grass stems.

TETRACHYTRIUM TRICEPS Sorokin

Bot. Zeitung, 32: 311, pl. 6, figs. 23–35. 1874; Bull. Soc. Nat. Kazan, 4 (3): 15, pl. 2. figs. 23–35. 1874

Thallus 39–94 μ long, main axis 19–78 μ long by 5–9 μ in diameter, protoplasm bluish; sporangium spherical or subspherical, 15–17 μ in diameter, with a terminal colorless operculum having a prolonged conical umbo; zoospores spherical, 11 μ in diameter, bluish with a colorless centric spot, flagellum two to three times as long as the diameter of the body, movement lively, never amoeboid.

Saprophytic on wood, grass stems, and the like, cadaver of Coleoptera, EUROPEAN RUSSIA (southern part).

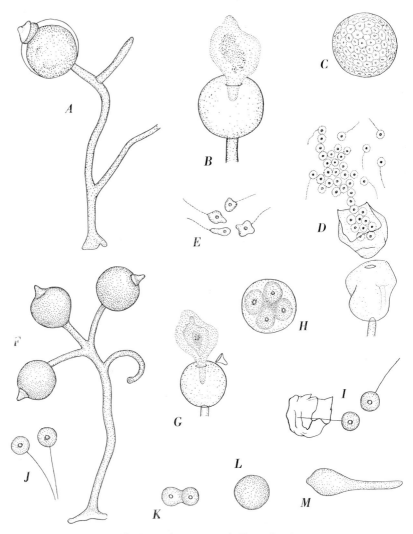

Fig. 38. *Zygochytrium* and *Tetrachytrium*

A-E. Zygochytrium aurantiacum Sorokin on insect cadavers: *A*, base and one of the two zoosporangium-bearing branches; *B*, discharge of uncleaved contents of sporangium; *C*, contents undergoing cleavage in vesicle at orifice of sporangium; *D*, liberation of mature zoospores from vesicle; *E*, mature zoospores. Protoplasm in *Zygochytrium* is golden, with granules of vermilion,

Like *Zygochytrium*, which it closely resembles in its development, thallus, and nonsexual reproduction, the species has never been observed since its discovery by Sorokin and doubts as to its authenticity have been freely expressed by mycologists. The blue coloration of the protoplasm has without question added to this skepticism. Other water fungi occurring on woody substrata occasionally show this bluish color and specimens of *Monoblepharis* have been observed in which it has been very pronounced (Sparrow, 1933b). This would not, however, explain the coloration presumably found also in *Tetrachytrium* growing on the Coleoptera cadaver.

Sorokin considered the "conjugation" of the zoospores (Fig. 38 J-L) to form a zygote to be a very simple type of fertilization. A somewhat similar occurrence was reported by Sparrow (1936a: 434) to take place in *Chytridium lagenaria*, where, under poor conditions of nutrition, the receptive thallus, after fusion of the contents of two encysted spores (there was no merging of the bodies), underwent considerable vegetative development. In the *Chytridium*, however, it was unfused spores rather than fused (as in *Tetrachytrium*) that were capable of germination.

Further search will probably yield this fungus again and its true relationships can then be established.

ZYGOCHYTRIUM Sorokin

Bot. Zeitung, 32: 308. 1874; Bull. Soc. Nat. Kazan, 4 (3): 12. 1874

(Fig. 38 A–E, p. 600; also, Fig. 4, R–T, p. 72)

Zoospore upon germination forming at one pole a cylindrical axis which branches dichotomously, at the opposite pole producing a broad

---

and zoospores have a golden plasma with a vermilion globule. *F-M. Tetrachytrium triceps* Sorokin saprophytic on bits of wood: *F*, complete plant with three sporangia and a recurved appendage; *G*, discharge of uncleaved protoplasm from sporangium; *H*, formation of four zoospores within vesicle at orifice of sporangium; *I*, two of the four zoospores which have escaped at rupture of vesicle; *J-L*, fusion of swarmers in pairs to form zygote; *M*, germination of zygote to form new plant. Color of cytoplasm in *Tetrachytrium triceps* is bluish.

(After Sorokin, 1874a)

irregularly lobed holdfast which anchors the plant to the outer surface of the substratum, mature thallus polycentric, eucarpic, hypha-like consisting of the holdfast, main axis, and two dichotomously branched secondary axes, one of the branches of each secondary axis terminating in an operculate sporangium, the other remaining sterile; zoospores posteriorly uniflagellate, with a single globule, formed outside the sporangium in a delicate evanescent vesicle which envelops the extruded protoplasm after the dehiscence of the operculum; resting spore surrounded by an epispore and an endospore, formed after the conjugation of the tips of two short lateral opposite branches of the same thallus which became walled off from the branches, germinating by means of a hypha.

On submerged cadavers of insects.

Because of the remarkable combination of chytridiaceous sporangia and zoospores (Fig. 38 A-E,) and the zygomycetous type of sexual reproduction (Fig. 4 R-T), Sorokin's genus has been almost universally rejected by monographers and mycologists in general. This rejection has been strengthened by the lack of further observations on the organism. Sorokin's description and figures of the development and reproductive processes are unusually clear and distinct, and there seems no reason for doubting them. Since it is now apparent that the chytrids have evolved a variety of types of sexual reproduction it is not surprising to find a form having a method like that observed in another group of Phycomycetes. Such parallelism is frequent in all types of biological material. No one doubts the relationship of *Polyphagus* to the chytrids, and yet it possesses an unmistakably "zygomycetous" type of sexual reproduction. Such instances, however, do not mean that *Polyphagus* and *Zygochytrium* are related to the Zygomycetes or are even in the same line of fungous evolution.

Repeated collections on the same substrata at the same time of year at the same locality will probably result in the rediscovery of *Zygochytrium*.

Zygochytrium aurantiacum Sorokin

Bot. Zeitung, 32: 308, pl. 6, figs. 1–22. 1874; Bull. Soc. Nat. Kazan, 4(3): 12, pl. 2, figs. 1–22. 1874

Thalli occurring in orange-red gelatinous masses on the surface of the substratum, each 78–97 μ high, the main axis 58 μ long by 5–7 μ in diameter, protoplasm golden with numerous vermilion granules, wall fairly stout, colorless; zoosporangium ovoid, 19 μ in diameter, bearing an apical somewhat flattened refractive operculum with a prominent conical umbo, wall collapsing after discharge; zoospores spherical, 5 μ in diameter, golden with a centric red globule, escaping from the vesicle by rupturing of the wall, movement lively, shortly becoming amoeboid; resting spore somewhat spherical, 17–19 μ in diameter, exospore blood-red, covered with irregular protuberances, endospore nearly colorless, smooth, contents golden with red granules, resting spore germinating readily (even twenty-four hours after formation) by the cracking open of the exospore and the elongation of the endospore into a long irregular thick tube (with colorless contents?).

On submerged insect cadavers (gnats, flies, wasps), EUROPEAN RUSSIA.

After the formation of sporangia the rest of the plant still contains protoplasm, but there is no evidence that this is eventually used up, even in sexual reproduction.

BLASTOCLADIALES

THE order Blastocladiales was founded in 1909 by H. E. Petersen to accommodate a single genus, *Blastocladia*, which had been established in 1878 by Reinsch and which up to 1909 had been included in the Saprolegniales. It was apparent to Petersen, even from fragmentary evidence, that the two fungi included in *Blastocladia* differed in several important features from those comprising the Saprolegniales, for they exhibited no cellulose whatsoever in the walls of the thallus and no sexual reproduction, both well-marked characters of the Saprolegniales. Furthermore, Thaxter (1896a) had already shown that the type of zoospore produced by them was quite different in both its internal structure and its method of attachment of the flagella from that found in the older order, although this fact was not stressed by Petersen. In addition, Thaxter's reinvestigation of Reinsch's species confirmed the presence in *B. pringsheimii* Reinsch of highly peculiar thick-walled punctate resting spores, which were apparently asexually formed. *Blastocladia* remained a monotypic genus until 1896, when Thaxter, in connection with his observations on Reinsch's species, described a second species, *B. ramosa*. Scarcely two years after the establishment of Petersen's small order Butler (1911) added to it a second genus, *Allomyces*, which differed in several striking features from *Blastocladia*. The distinctiveness of *Allomyces* further justified the segregation of these fungi from the Saprolegniales. Since then, other genera, *Blastocladiella* (Matthews, 1937), *Catenaria* Sorokin (Couch, 1945a), *Coelomomyces* Keilin (Couch, 1945b), *Blastocladiopsis* Sparrow (1950), and *Catenomyces* Hanson (1944b) have been added to the Blastocladiales.[1] Monographs of the order have been published by Kanouse (1927), Indoh (1940), and Sparrow (1943). As it stands today the group is composed of clearly related fungi. Furthermore, as a result of a series of discoveries concerning

[1] The names of two genera, *Sphaerocladia* (Stüben 1939) and *Clavochytridium* (Cox, 1939), which were included in this order in the first edition, are now regarded as synonyms of *Blastocladiella*.

604

sexuality in these forms, this hitherto little understood group has been raised to a place of high biological importance among the Thallophyta. Until 1929 no type of sexual reproduction had been convincingly demonstrated in any blastocladiaceous fungus. Hitherto, sexuality, wherever found in any mycelium-forming zoosporic phycomycete, had been clearly oögamous, with the diploid phase represented by a thick-walled resting oöspore directly formed from the zygote. It is now apparent that as early as 1919 Weston (see Emerson, 1941) had noted in a species of *Allomyces*, which he collected in the Philippines, that two types of "sporangia" and "zoospores" were produced. He suspected them to be gametangia and gametes, respectively. In 1929 and 1930 Hans Kniep published accounts of the morphology and life cycle of *A. javanicus* in which he showed clearly that there existed in this fungus a type of reproduction and life history previously unknown among any of the fungi. Kniep's fungus produced posteriorly uniflagellate gametes of two sizes, borne in gametangia of two types on a sexual plant. These free-swimming gametes fused in pairs in the water and the biflagellate zygote instead of becoming a thick-walled resting structure, as in all other known "Oomycetes," germinated at once to form a second thallus. The new plant, though resembling the sexual one, bore (instead of gametangia) thin-walled zoosporangia and thick-walled punctate resting spores. The zoospores upon discharge from these zoosporangia formed new thalli like the parent, whereas the resting spores at germination gave rise to swarmers which reproduced only sexual plants.

Kniep, then, was able to prove that instead of lacking sexuality, the Blastocladiales, or at least one member of it, actually possessed anisogamous planogametic sexual reproduction and an alternation of isomorphic (like) generations. The stimulus provided by his researches had far-reaching results. It led to intensive studies by others of the morphology, sexuality, and life histories of various members of the order. These investigations have been unusually fruitful; they have revealed the existence of isogamous planogametic reproduction (Harder and Sörgel, 1938) and in species of *Allomyces*, *Blastocladiella*, and *Catenaria* of various types of life cycles (Emerson, 1938a, 1939, 1941; McCranie, 1942; Couch and Whiffen, 1942; Teter, 1944; Couch, 1945a).

Further, they resulted in the recognition of a series of thallus types (Matthews, 1937; Stüben, 1939), which, together with the reproductive structures, unquestionably link the Blastocladiales to the Chytridiales on the one hand and possibly to the Monoblepharidales on the other.

So far as known, species of the order are either parasites of aquatic larvae of insects, eggs of liver flukes, adult nematodes, and aquatic fungi or they are saprophytes in fresh water or in soil. The saprophytes in water occur most commonly on rosaceous fruits, twigs of ash, birch, oak, and horse chestnut, or on bits of animal debris. The precise character of the substratum of only a few of the terricolous species is known, since these forms are ordinarily obtained through methods of indirect culture.

The astute observations of Couch (1945b) led him to the discovery that the curious group of parasites of mosquito larvae first described by Keilin (1921) as *Coelomomyces* and long of problematical relationship belonged in the Blastocladiales.

Members of the Blastocladiales are in general characterized morphologically by the possession of posteriorly uniflagellate zoospores with a prominent nuclear cap (Fig. 46 F, p. 680) and bipolar mode of germination, dark-colored resting spores with minutely punctate thick walls, and a more or less well-defined basal cell anchored to the substratum by a series of strongly tapering, branching, chytrid-like rhizoids. These rhizoids not only act as holdfasts, but by their extensive growth and profuse branching undoubtedly provide the developing thallus with a well-organized and effective nutrient-gathering system.

DEVELOPMENT AND MORPHOLOGY

THE THALLUS

The character of the thallus differs widely among members of the Blastocladiales. It varies in complexity from a simple unwalled and almost plasmodial type (in the Coelomomycetaceae) to one resembling that of a monocentric or polycentric chytrid (Fig. 44 A, G, I, p. 651) or one produced by a true mycelial fungus. Indeed, the order is remarkable because it provides examples of parallelism of body form with the Chytridiales, the Leptomitales, and the higher fungi. If the thallus is simple, it may consist either of an anchored reproductive rudiment (Fig. 45 A) or a basal cell and the rudiment of one or more reproductive structures (Figs. 45 E, p. 661; 46 D, p. 680). In other forms it is more elaborate with the basal cell bearing distal branches (Fig. 46 A) or pseudoseptate branched hyphae of unlimited powers of growth (Fig. 40 G, p. 616). The walls give a reaction for chitin rather than for cellulose (Harder, 1939a, 1939b; Nabel, 1939; Ritchie, 1947; Frey, 1950). They are lacking in *Coelomomyces*, although a filamentous habit is maintained (Couch, 1945b).

The nature of the cytoplasm is changeable, differing markedly in the same plant under altered conditions of environment and at various ages. Often finely granular and homogeneous, it may contain dispersed in it minute globules or large clodlike bodies of fatty nature. Again, it may be either densely packed with irregular refractive granules or reticulately or alveolately vacuolate. The cytoplasm is colorless except in the male gametangia, in the immature resting spores of certain species of *Allomyces*, and in the sporangia of *A. moniliformis* and in *Catenomyces*. Although true cross walls are formed primarily to delimit reproductive structures, in the Catenariaceae they are also developed sparingly on the vegetative system. In *Allomyces* peculiar sievelike pseudosepta which resemble true cross walls also occur at intervals along the hyphae.

REPRODUCTION

Nonsexual Reproduction

Nonsexual reproduction is accomplished by posteriorly uniflagellate zoospores which are formed within thin-walled zoosporangia. In *Blastocladiella stubenii* and in most specimens of *B. microcystogena*, the sporangium arises from an enlarged reproductive rudiment, which is derived (as it is in such a chytrid as *Rhizidium*) from the swollen body of the encysted zoospore (Fig. 45 A, p. 661). Other species of *Blastocladiella* have a single sporangium formed at the apex of the basal cell (Fig. 45 E, p. 661). *Catenaria* and *Catenomyces* possess intercalary sporangia, typically separated from one another by sterile isthmuses delimited by septa (Fig. 44 A, G, I, p. 651). *Blastocladia* (Fig. 46 E, p. 680) for the most part has the sporangia sessile, whereas in

Allomyces they are terminally or laterally placed on hyphal branches arising from the basal cell. In all species of the latter genus secondarily formed sporangia may develop in basipetal succession (Fig. 40 E, G, p. 616).

In members of the order the zoospores are matured within the sporangium and are liberated through one or more pores formed upon deliquescence of the discharge papillae. Under certain environmental conditions the first zoospores to emerge are surrounded by a temporary vesicle (Fig. 40 E, p. 616); under others they emerge individually. In *Catenomyces*, as in some chytrids, an endooperculum is formed (Fig. 44 I, p. 651). In some species of *Blastocladia* a peculiar peglike structure which appears to be endogenously produced by the distal wall of the sporangium has been found (Minden, 1916; Sparrow, 1932b). The function of this plug is unknown, but Lloyd (1938) observed that it is divided into an inner and an outer part and she suggests that it is the inner part which gives rise to the temporary vesicle often surrounding the zoospores at their emergence. Indoh (1940) considered the papillae on the sporangium of *Allomyces* to be projections of the inner sporangium wall. Internal proliferation of the sporangia takes place in two species of *Blastocladia* (*B. prolifera* and *B. sparrowii*) (Fig. 46 C, p. 680).

The zoospores of all members of the order, with the exception of *Blastocladiella stomophilum*, are very much alike in appearance, internal organization, and type of motility. Although many are spherical when first escaping from the sporangium, they become ovoid during active swarming. The plasma may contain a few anterior, minute, colorless, or occasionally colored, globules and it always bears near the center a dull-gleaming top-shaped or subtriangular structure, the so-called "food body" or "nuclear cap" (Fig. 46 F). In certain species of *Blastocladiella* and *Allomyces* and in *Catenaria allomycis*, there is also present a lachrymose lateral structure ("side body") of the same refractivity as the food body (Fig. 45 D, p. 661), whereas in *Blastocladiella stomophilum* there is a ring of small oil globules (Fig. 45 I). At the point of emergence of the long slender posterior flagellum of the zoospore, a bright refractive granule, probably the blepharoplast, is often visible. The spore moves in a deliberate and relatively even fashion when swimming. Pronounced amoeboid movement is frequently resorted to, particularly when the zoospores are emerging from the sporangium and when they are nearing the end of their period of swarming. The body of the spore at these times may elongate slightly, become strongly vacuolate, and produce broad irregular anterior and lateral pseudopodia.

The flagellum of the zoospore in *Allomyces*, already determined by Couch (1941) to be of the whiplash type, has been carefully examined by Manton, *et al.* (1952), see p. 10. They confirmed Ritchie's (1947) observations as to the flagellum's fibrillar nature.

Cantino and Horenstein (1954) have presented careful experimental and observational evidence to the effect that a cytoplasmic transfer may take place between swarmers of *Blastocladiella*. In a pigmented mutant strain of *B. emersonii* a certain minimum percentage of its swarmers would pair up and undergo some sort of exchange with normal, color-less swarmers of the species. Furthermore, such mutant swarmers might then repeat the process with other swarmers of *B. emersonii*, so that a single normal swarmer of the latter may be successively approached, in turn, by several from the mutant. These investigators were also able to demonstrate that cytoplasmic bridges formed between such swarmers but that no changes occurred in their nuclei. Cantino and Horenstein conclude that if the bridges were functional, a cytoplasmic rather than a nuclear exchange mechanism was involved. They postulate that this transfer of cytoplasmic factors may chiefly be a unilateral one, either from the mutant to the normal *B. emersonii* or vice versa. Further, they also discuss the significance of this paramecium-like behavior to the distribution of a physiologically active cytoplasmic material which they believe governs the growth pattern in *Blastocladiella* as earlier described by Cantino and Hyatt (1953a). Their hypothesis lends support to the contentions by Emerson (1950) and Cantino and Hyatt (*op. cit*). that the expression of "sex" in *Blastocladiella* is not genotypically controlled.

The zoospores after a varying period of motility come to rest, round off, and apparently absorb the flagellum into the body. Eventually a slender germ tube appears, which branches distally to form the first elements of the holdfast system. The body of the spore enlarges, the region opposite the point of origin of the rhizoids elongates rapidly, and there is either produced the reproductive rudiment or the basal cell. In contrast to the Chytridiales, germination is bipolar in nature. Subsequent development of the thallus differs with each genus and even with species of the same genus.

The peculiar, often pitted, resting spores so characteristic of this order are unquestionably a device for tiding the plant over unfavorable environmental circumstances. Unlike other parts of the fungus they can withstand drying and freezing and probably high temperatures. Although found for the most part on the zoospore-bearing plant they are occasionally observed on the gametophyte, if it is formed. Their structure in practically all instances is identical. In the early stages of development they resemble in position and shape ordinary zoosporangia. The increasing density and darkening of the protoplasm and the thickening and pigmentation of the wall, however, together with the lack of formation of discharge papillae, soon distinguish them from developing zoosporangia (Fig. 40 F, p. 616). The brownish pigment characteristic of these resting spores has in several species of *Allomyces* been found by Emerson and Fox (1940) to belong to the melanin group. At maturity the obpyriform, ovoid, clavate, beaked, or sometimes spherical resting spore is more or less closely enveloped by the thin wall of the container within which it lies. The outer wall of the spore is thick, of varying shades of brown, and usually perforated by innumerable minute inwardly directed cone-shaped pits or pores. The apices of these pores are in contact with a second, thinner, smooth colorless wall which surrounds the cytoplasm. The living contents, although considerably masked by the pigmented outer wall, are composed of numerous large .fat globules imbedded in a finely granular matrix. The resting spores vary somewhat in shape in the different species, but they frequently have a narrow truncate base and, for the most part, are broadest slightly above the equatorial region (Fig. 40 D,F). Although the container or hyphal sheath may burst to liberate its resting spore, more commonly it persists around the resting spore and is shed with it. If persistent, upon germination the container bursts and the thick outer wall of the resting spore cracks open along a preformed line. Discharge papillae develop on the bulging, exposed, thin, inner wall and deliquesce to form pores through which the posteriorly uniflagellate planonts emerge (Fig. 42 B, p. 626). In certain forms a somewhat prolonged discharge tube is produced. What type of plant is subsequently developed from these swarmers depends upon the particular organism involved.

Resting-spore formation in *Blastocladia pringsheimii* was induced in pure culture by Emerson and Cantino (1948) when the fungus was grown in an atmosphere high in CO_2 (99.5 per cent) or in a medium containing carbonate.

Machlis and Ossia (1953a) showed that maturation of resting spores in *Allomyces* was markedly affected by the conditions under which the fungus was cultured. In nutrient broth the maturation period was reduced by 70 per cent over that necessary when the fungus was grown on agar slants. They also (1953b) present evidence indicating that certain auxins, particularly IAA under certain cultural conditions, influence the development and maturation of the resting spores in two ways: (1) by a reduction in the time necessary for chromosphere disappearance (as an indicator of maturation, see p. 621) and (2) a marked increase in the proportion of resting spores which will germinate.

The germination of the resting spores among members of the order has long presented a puzzling situation. Dormancy of several weeks is evidently necessary in some, whereas in others immediate germination can occur. Cantino (1951a) studied this process in blastocladiaceous fungi growing in pure culture under controlled conditions. In *Blastocladiella*, when precautions were taken to eliminate in culture inhibitory factors, salts for example, all of the resting spores in a population of same age would germinate immediately after maturation and within a few moments of one another. Cantino (*op. cit.*) further points out that resting-spore germination is a two-step mechanism, the first step terminating with the cracking of the wall, the second with the discharge of the zoospores. Relatively low concentrations of anions as well as different temperatures exert a pronounced differential influence on these two processes.

Sexual Reproduction and Alternation of Generations

Sexual reproduction occurs in certain species of *Catenaria*, *Blastocladiella*, and *Allomyces* (in which it was first observed), but it has not thus far been convincingly demonstrated in *Blastocladia* (Lloyd, 1938; Blackwell, 1940: see, however, E. A. Bessey, 1939; Blackwell, 1939). In *Blastocladiella* (see Fig. 39, diagram) and *Catenaria* (Fig. 44 C-F, p. 651) fusion of isogamous posteriorly uniflagellate planogametes has been observed, whereas in those species of *Allomyces* exhibiting sexuality, fusion of isogamous and anisogamous planogametes is the rule. Isomorphic alternation of generations is found in all species manifesting anisogamous sexual reproduction. In those with isogamous reproduction, the gametophyte may resemble the sporophyte (*Blastocladiella*) or it may be represented by haploid zoospores which quickly

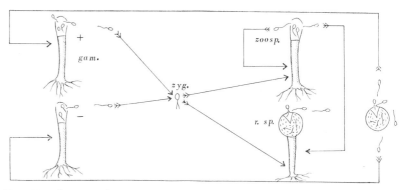

FIG. 39. Diagram of life cycle of *Blastocladiella variabilis* Harder and Sörgel

At the left are two gametophyte plants (*gam.*), each bearing a single gametangium from which are emerging isogamous planogametes. Gametes in one gametangium bear an orange pigment, those in the other are colorless. Gametes of opposite signs fuse in pairs to form a biflagellate zygote (*zyg.*), which germinates at once to produce the sporophyte plant. This may be either a zoosporangial plant (*zoosp.*) or one bearing a single thick-walled golden-brown resting spore (*r. sp.*). Zoospores of zoosporangial plant reproduce new sporophyte plants of either type; resting spore upon germination forms planonts which give rise at germination either to + or — gametophyte plants. (Modified from Harder and Sörgel, 1938)

encyst and function as gametangia, forming four gametes each (*Catenaria allomycis, Blastocladiella cystogena, Allomyces neo-moniliformis*). In *Allomyces* male and female gametangia are developed on the same gametophyte thallus (Fig. 40 A-B, p. 616), whereas in "long-cycled" genera which are monocentric, the gametophyte thallus bears either a + or a — gametangium (Fig. 39, p. 612). A further discussion of the types of life cycles typical of *Blastocladiella* and *Allomyces* is given on page 624.

The elaboration of the life cycle in the *Blastocladiales* has been thought by some investigators to indicate relationship with the algae. The affinities of members of the order with the Chytridiales are so much more pronounced, however, that one is forced to conclude, merely, that the Blastocladiales and the algae have, in the course of their evolution, arrived at similar methods for insuring the beneficial effects of cross fertilization. Although in all the Blastocladiales in which distinct sexual vegetative plants have been discovered similar sporophytes and gametophytes are produced, species may yet come to light which, like certain brown algae, develop dissimilar ones.

CYTOLOGY AND PHYSIOLOGY

Little is known of the cytology of any of the Blastocladiales with the exception of *Allomyces* (Barrett, 1912a; Lugg, 1929; Hatch, 1935, 1938; Ritchie, 1947; Emerson and Wilson, 1949: Wilson, 1952).

Cytological preparations of the zoospores of *Blastocladiella simplex* are figured by Matthews (1937) and of *Blastocladia pringsheimii* and *Blastocladia globosa* by Cotner (1930a, b). Since *Allomyces* differs markedly in several respects from other members of the order, its cytology (Fig. 41, p. 622) is not representative of the group as a whole and is discussed separately.

Information is being rapidly accumulated concerning the physiology of members of the order. Species of *Allomyces* and *Blastocladiella* have been cultivated on a variety of solid and liquid media. A series of papers has been published on their physiology: see Stüben, 1939; Emerson and Cantino, 1948; Cantino, 1948, 1949a, 1950, 1951a, 1952; Barner and Cantino, 1952; Cantino and Hyatt, 1953a, 1953b, 1953c; Cantino and Horenstein, 1955, 1956a,b; Brown and Cantino, 1955; Machlis and Ossia, 1953a, 1953b; Machlis, 1953 a, b, c, 1957; Machlis and Crasemann, 1956; Cantino, Lovett and Horenstein, 1957; Turian, 1952.

INVESTIGATIONS ON ALLOMYCES

Results of several extensive investigations of the morphology, development, cytology, life cycle, and distribution of *Allomyces* have not only revealed facts of great general biological interest but have also increased knowledge of this genus to a point far beyond that attained for any other member of the order. For example, it is now safe to say that far more is understood concerning the geographic occurrence of *Allomyces* than of any other aquatic phycomycete. By the use of water cultures prepared with soil samples collected from various localities throughout the world and baited with split hempseed, the known distribution of the species has been enormously increased (see especially the work of Emerson [1941],F. T. Wolf[1941a], and Gaertner [1954b]).

MORPHOLOGY AND DEVELOPMENT

The sequence of development of the thallus in *Allomyces*, whether asexual or sexual, follows a single pattern. The swarmer, be it zoospore, zygote, or flagellated planont from the resting spore, comes to rest after a period of motility, loses its flagellum, and encysts. A germ tube is then produced at one pole, which branches to lay down the first elements of the rhizoidal system. Soon after, a second, much broader, germ tube grows from the spore body at the pole opposite the point of origin of the rhizoids (Fig. 41 G, p. 622). This second tube ultimately forms the basal cell, from which arises distally in regular dichotomous fashion a fan-shaped extraordinarily symmetrical complex of hyphae. At occasional intervals along the branches of the young thallus and near the primary diverticulum of the basal cell there are formed discontinuous rings of refractive material which project inwardly from the hyphal wall. These, by centripetal accretion, elongate to produce wheel-like pseudosepta (Coker, 1930). Additional material may be laid down to form a plate punctuated by large radiating triangular openings. Constrictions of the hyphae frequently occur wherever the pseudosepta are located and give a jointed appearance to the thallus. The primary reproductive organs, whether zoosporangia, resting spores, or gametangia, are formed at the tips of hyphal branches, from which they are separated by true cross walls. Secondarily formed zoosporangia and resting spores terminate hyphal branches which, in sympodial fashion, have grown up from beneath the primary organ. Zoosporangia and, rarely, resting spores may also develop in basipetal succession along a hypha.

On the sexual plant the primary gametangia ordinarily appear in pairs, a male and a female, at the tips of the hyphae (Fig. 40 A-C, p. 616), but as growth proceeds, secondary ones, male and female, are alternately formed on sympodial branches or in basipetal succession. The gametangia produce and liberate their gametes in the same manner as do the zoosporangia. During gametogenesis, however, the changes which occur in the aspect of the cytoplasm differ from those found in the zoosporangia. [1] Hatch (1935) states that in *Allomyces arbuscula* the dense cytoplasm of the contents of the hyphal tip which will give rise to gametangia is gray black, and that this color persists until after the septa delimiting the terminal female and subterminal male gametangia are laid down. The lateral walls of the maturing structures then distend and the color of the male gametangium grows lighter, at first becoming yellowish and later assuming a rusty hue. The female becomes dull gray. With the appearance of the papillae of discharge the contents of the male gametangium turn salmon-pink, whereas those of the female remain unchanged. In both *A. arbuscula* and *A. javanicus* the larger, female, gametes are colorless and resemble zoospores. The male, however, is small, more active than the female, and, so far as is known, always pigmented. Its contents vary with age from faint orange to brick-red, depending on the amount of coloring matter accumulated (Emerson, 1941). The pigment was determined by Emerson and Fox (1940) to be composed of gamma-carotene, a relatively rare isomere of carotene. It is located in minute lipoid granules, which in the early stages of development of the gametes are dispersed throughout the cytoplasm of the gametangium. At maturity the colored material becomes more or less localized in the gametes but is never in single globules as in the zoospores of such an aquatic chytrid as *Rhizoclosmatium aurantiacum*. Emerson and Fox (1940) pointed out the relationship of carotene to reproduction in both algae and higher plants and suggest that "such compounds may play important biochemical roles in sexuality and the processes involved in the metabolism of reproduction."

Chance alone seems to decide whether or not male and female gametes, once discharged, will meet and fuse. There is no evidence to indicate that gametes from the same thalli are incapable of doing so. In fact, Emerson and Wilson (1954) reveal that fusion between gametes of the same species of plant is immediate, whereas that between gametes

[1] See Turian's important paper on this process in *Bull. Soc. bot. suisse*, 67: 458. 1957.

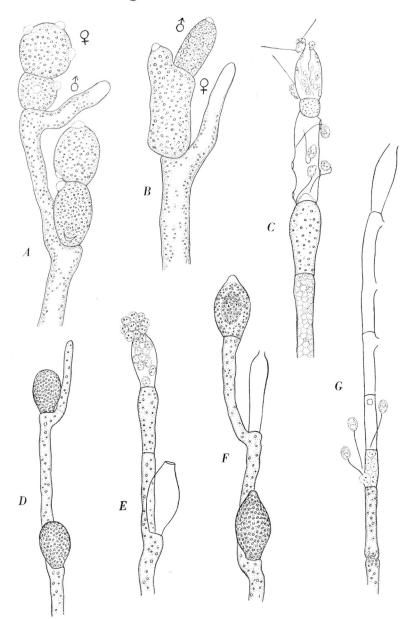

Fig. 40. Reproductive structures in *Allomyces*

of different species is much slower. Hatch (1938) assumed that age plays a part in determining whether fusion will take place. He asserts that it is achieved most readily between recently emerged gametes, but becomes increasingly difficult as time elapses. Conjugation most frequently occurs when either one or both of the gametes is temporarily quiescent or exhibiting amoeboid movement. Actual fusion is preceded by a more or less protracted period of intense pseudopodial activity on the part of both gametes. During this period the plasma of the two often becomes strongly vacuolate, and the flagella may wave feebly. Eventually, more or less complete fusion takes place, after which the zygote swims vigorously about for a time or undergoes a period of amoeboid movement before coming permanently to rest. It then rounds off and encysts; the flagella (according to Hatch, *op. cit.*) are dehisced; germination then ensues. Cytological investigations by Hatch (*op. cit.*) of stages in the fusion of the gametes indicate that actual fusion takes place only when the flagella-bearing ends are in opposition. This observation may explain, at least in part, the often prolonged preliminary amoeboid activity. Hatch did not believe that the male plasma is engulfed by that of the female but, rather, that both empty toward a common point of rupture to form the new zygote. He found that nuclear fusion does not occur in most instances until after the flagella of the zygote are cast off and the nuclear caps have dissociated, that is, at the time of germination (Fig. 41 R-V, p. 622). Fused nuclei were seen in zygotes which still bore their flagella. This, Hatch thought, can be explained

Explanation of Figure 40

A. *Allomyces arbuscula* E. J. Butler, tip of hypha of gametangial plant bearing terminal colorless female gametangia and subterminal golden-orange male gametangia. B. *Allomyces javanicus* Kniep, tip of hypha of gametangial plant bearing a terminal golden-orange male gametangium and a subterminal colorless female one. C. *Allomyces macrogynus* (Emerson) Emerson and Wilson, male and female gametes being discharged and conjugating. D-E. *Allomyces anomalus* Emerson; D, hypha bearing resting spores; E, zoosporangia, the terminal one discharging zoospores. F-G. *Allomyces moniliformis* Coker and Braxton: F, tip of hypha bearing discharged zoosporangium, terminal immature resting spore, and, at base, a mature beaked one; G, empty basipetal zoosporangia and discharging one.

(Sparrow, 1943)

by the fact that the orientation of the gamete nuclei in the zygote is such that their still intact nuclear caps do not, as is ordinarily the case form a barrier to fusion. In most instances the nuclear caps of the two gametes merge soon after conjugation. The initiation of zygote germination is apparently not dependent upon the fusion of the gamete nuclei, since in about one half of the specimens examined karyogamy had occurred at this time and in the remainder it had not. It is, however, dependent upon dissociation of the fused nuclear cap, for germination is never initiated until this is completed. He asserted, therefore, that the fragmentation of the nuclear cap is the factor causing the zygote to start its development.

In summarizing the results of a cytological study of gametogenesis in *Allomyces arbuscula*, Hatch (1935) stated:

1. In the hyphal tips of *A. arbuscula* there are numerous nuclei, lipoid granules, and chondriosomes. Nuclei and lipoid granules are distributed at random; the chondriosomes are concentrated in the tip. The nuclei have six chromosomes; the lipoid granules are grey-black in colour, small and spherical; the chondriosomes are long and filamentous.

2. When the male and female gametangia are cut off from a hyphal tip the nuclei and lipoid granules are distributed between the male and female gametangium in approximately equal numbers. The chondriosomes segregate unequally, a disproportionately large number going to the terminal, female gametangium.

3. In early gametogenesis the nuclei divide more often in the male gametangium, so that it contains roughly twice as many nuclei as the female. These male nuclei are one-half the size of the female nuclei. The chromosome count, however, is six in the nuclei of both gametangia. These nuclei become the "organization centres" in the formation of gametes, and each collects about itself a sheath of lipoid granules and a tangled mass of fine, filamentous chondriosomes.

4. In late gametogenesis the lipoid granules in the male gametangium change colour, becoming salmon-pink, while those in the female remain grey. The chondriosomes fragment into a cloud of small granules, and these granules subsequently enlarge and fuse to form, first, a reticulate mantle about the nucleus, and finally, a single large mass which becomes appressed to the nucleus in the form of a nuclear cap.

5. The female gamete is two to three times as large as the male; its nucleus is twice, and its nuclear cap three to four times, as large as that of the male. Its lipoid granules are grey, while those of the male are of a brassy colour.

6. Since the nuclei in the hyphae are genetically the same and are segregated

in male and female gametangia in equal number, there appears to be here a peculiar type of differentiation in which the distribution of chondriosomes is of primary importance in the determination of sex.

7. In the visible expression of sexual differences there is a definite quantitative factor in the amount of chondriosomes (nuclear cap) and a qualitative factor in the colour of the lipoid granules.

8. The extranuclear nature of the nuclear cap found in the gametes and zoospores of *A. arbuscula* is demonstrated and its chondriosomal origin described.

Ritchie (1947), as well as Wilson (1952), disagrees with Hatch's views concerning the mitochondrial origin and the composition of the nuclear cap (see above). [1]

On the asexual plant the thin-walled zoosporangia form uninucleate zoospores which are liberated through several pores. The development and cytology were studied first by Barrett (1912a) and then by McCranie (in Sparrow, 1943), (Figs. 41 A-F, p. 622; 42 L, p. 626) and, more recently, by Ritchie (1947). The latter investigated the formation and structure of the zoospores of *Allomyces arbuscula*, *A. javanicus*, and *A. anomalus*.

According to Ritchie, in living material a hyphal tip swells and is soon cut off by a septum. After the sporangium attains mature size, spore origins appear. These at first are never distinct and they soon fade out completely. A period ensues in which nothing is visible in the cytoplasm but the lipoid droplets outlining the positions of the nuclei. This phase may last several days and is terminated by the reappearance of the spore origins. The nuclei then move to the surface and the lipoid droplets collect between them. Fissures cleave out uninucleate polyhedral blocks of protoplasm and within a minute or two nuclear caps develop. The exit papillae (one to six) become distended and when the spores are completely delimited one and then others open. The first spores to emerge remain massed for a few moments before dispersal; the later ones, after a period of amoeboid movement, swim off individually. It was noted by Ritchie that when maximum size is attained, the sporangium decreases suddenly and sharply in volume. A second, even sharper, shrinkage takes place just prior to spore release.

---

[1] See Turian and Kellenberger (1956) who believe ribonucleic acid is concerned in its composition.

Fixed and stained sections showed that in zoosporogenesis cleavage progresses centrifugally and the spores become delimited before the nuclear caps are deposited. The mitochondria, conspicuous in living hyphae, disappear in the young sporangium. When the nuclear caps are about to form, deep-staining granules appear in the cytoplasm. These, which have been interpreted as mitochondria by some investigators, flow together into larger masses until finally they form a single, crescent-shaped cap attached to the nucleus.

On the basis of the staining reactions Ritchie indicates that the nuclear cap cannot be mitochondrial in origin. Furthermore, the cap cannot be dissolved by certain solvents as would probably be true if this were the case. He concludes that it is partly from condensed material in the cytoplasm and partly from material extruded from the nucleus. Although its eventual fate is undetermined, it has not been seen to break up into mitochondria.

Unusual features of zoospore structure and behavior were noted by Teter (1944) in Sparrow's strain of *Allomyces moniliformis* from Trinidad. Teter reported that in this material the zoospores from the sporangia were always devoid of flagella. Following a period of amoeboid movement the spores encysted. The cysts either gave rise to new aflagellated zoospores, which crept out and in their turn became quiescent, or developed rhizoids after which an undersized swarmer emerged. The forming of a second zoospore is a clear case of repeated emergence, the only well-authenticated instance so far recorded for *Allomyces*. None of the planonts (zoospores or gametes) of the Trinidad strain possessed flagella. Teter carried along parallel cultures under similiar conditions of a consistently flagellated strain of *A. moniliformis*. The control strain continued to form flagella. Lack of them, therefore, in the Trinidad strain was not due to poor developmental conditions.

The resting spore in *Allomyces*, which is generally formed only on the asexual thallus, may at its maturity fall from the plant, still surrounded by its persistent outer hyphal wall, or this hyphal sheath may burst and the spore drop from it. At germination the contents of the resting structure swell, the outer thick, pitted wall cracks, and the inner thin membrane surrounding the living contents bulges out. This thin-walled protruding sporangium then produces several discharge papillae, which deliquesce to form pores through which the planonts emerge (Fig. 42 A-B, p. 626). Emerson (1941) states that the whole process of germination may take place within an hour if environmental conditions are favorable.

The cytological sequence of events in the maturation and germination of the resting spore was followed by Wilson (1952). He discovered that certain internal changes apparently determine maturity and capacity for germination and that, in fact, such changes must occur before the latter process can take place.

Young resistant sporangia soon after delimitation possess a clear homogeneous protoplasm, nonstainable with aceto-orcein. Concurrent with the thickening, pitting, and pigmentation of the wall, spherical bodies appear which take this stain. These "chromospheres" persist until near the end of the maturation period, when the diploid nuclei enter the prophase of Meiosis I, at which time they become eroded and disintegrate. The spore is now mature. The interval during which chromospheres exist corresponds to the maturation period. Their disappearance signals the changes that make germination possible.

External conditions also affect germination. For example, Wilson found that temperatures of 20 to 25 degrees C. produced most uniform germination. In some species meiosis is an integral part of germination and metaphases of Meiosis I were abundant 55 to 65 minutes after resting spores were placed in water. Metaphases of Meiosis II appeared in 80 to 110 minutes and after two hours the haploid planonts escaped. Time for germination varied somewhat according to the temperature, strain, and age of the culture.

After the second division of meiosis, bodies resembling the aforementioned chromospheres were seen. They collected around the nuclei in cuplike fashion and became the nuclear caps. Whether the premeiotic and postmeiotic chromospheres are chemically alike is not known. Wilson thinks it unlikely that they are chondriosomal in origin, since they withstand strong acid solutions. He notes that such nuclear caps are present only in the motile stages, which gives weight to Kusano's (1912) suggestion that they are concerned with food metabolism and thus are analogous to the macronucleus of the Ciliata.

Basic haploid chromosome numbers are given by Wilson (1952) and by Emerson and Wilson (1954) for the following species of *Allomyces*:

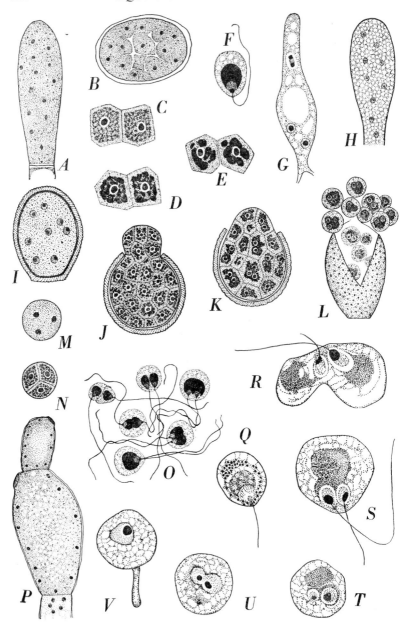

FIG. 41. Cytology of *Allomyces*

Explanation of Figure 41

A-J. Allomyces javanicus Kniep: *A*, immature zoosporangium, some of whose nuclei are dividing; *B*, tangential section of more mature sporangium showing cleavage furrows in center; *C*, two zoospore initials, each bearing a single nucleus; chromatic material which will eventually become aggregated around nucleus to form conspicuous nuclear cap has appeared in cytoplasm; *D-E*, further stages in concentration of nuclear-cap material; *F*, mature zoo-spore showing large nuclear cap, granular nucleus, and small deep-stained nucleolus, which is connected by a delicate thread to a minute peripheral blepharoplast, to which, in turn, the single posterior flagellum is attached; sequence of formation of nuclear cap and internal organization of swarmer are the same in all the swimming bodies (i.e. zoospores, gametes, etc.) in *Allomyces*; *G*, very young sporophyte plant showing portion of first-formed rhizoids at base and, at tip, germ tube which will produce hyphae; contents are strongly vacuolate and bear two resting nuclei and a dividing one; *H*, hyphal tip forming rudiment of resting spore; note characteristic vacuolization; *I*, very early stage in germination of resting spore; abundant chromatic material characteristically found in cytoplasm of resting spore prior to incep-tion of germination has by now almost disappeared; *J*, germinated resting spore showing enlarged sporangium which has burst resting-spore wall, and nearly mature planonts; latter are in same stage of maturation as are the two zoospores in *D*. *K-O. Allomyces neo-moniliformis* Indoh; *K*, germinating rest-ing spore; note that here, in contrast to *J* (*A. javanicus*), protoplasm has been cleaved into segments bearing from one to several nuclei; *L*, germinated resting spore with cysts bearing from one to several nuclei; *M*, "primary R. S. zoospore," bearing three nuclei; nuclear cap has disappeared; according to McCranie, these zoospores bear no flagella; *N*, segregation of "secondary R. S. zoospores," showing usual aggregation of chromatic material around nucleus; *O*, stages in fusion of swarmers (isogamous gametes) liberated from cysts to form biflagellate zygote, which gives rise to new sporophyte plant. *P. Allomyces javanicus* Kniep, gametangia showing nuclei in terminal male and subterminal female arranged around periphery. *Q-V. Allomyces arbuscula* Butler: *Q*, female gamete stained with Janus green; with the exception of deep-staining lipoid granules in cytoplasm surrounding nucleus and nuclear cap, structure is like zoospore shown in *F*; *R*, stage in conjugation of male (small) and female gametes; here nuclei are coming to lie side by side without nuclear cap material (dark) between them; *S*, planozygote with two nuclei, as yet unfused, and fused nuclear caps; *T*, resting zygote; flagella have been lost; *U*, zygote in which nuclei are beginning to fuse, the nucleoli still being distinct; nuclear cap has almost completely dissociated; *V*, germinating zygote in which fusion of nucleoli is complete.

(*A-P*, McCranie, in Sparrow, 1943; *Q-V*, Hatch, 1938)

A. neo-moniliformis (*cystogenus*) 14
A. arbuscula 8
A. macrogynus 14

Polyploidy was found by Emerson and Wilson in both *A. arbuscula* and *A. macrogynus* (see p. 632).

Certain features in the cytology of various species of *Allomyces* are shown and explained in Figure 41.

LIFE CYCLES

Comparative investigations by Emerson (1938a, 1939, 1941) of a large number of isolates of *Allomyces* from various parts of the world and the work of McCranie (1942) and Teter (1944), have revealed some extraordinary facts concerning the life history of these organisms. As may be recalled, Kniep (1929) had discovered that in *A. javanicus* the planonts[1] emerging from resting spores gave rise to sexual plants upon germination. The male and female gametes produced by these plants fuse to form zygotes which, upon germination, develop into asexual thalli. It was clear that an alternation of generations was present (Kniep, 1930).

This "long-cycled" life history (Fig. 42, p. 626), which was observed by Kniep in *Allomyces javanicus*, Emerson designated "Euallomyces." Certain of the strains with which he worked, however, failed to exhibit a sexual phase. Closer scrutiny revealed that in them two other different life cycles existed. Of these, the one exemplified by *A. moniliformis*, *A. cystogenus*, and *A. neo-moniliformis* (Fig. 43, p. 629) he called "Cystogenes" and the other represented by *A. anomalus*, "Brachyallomyces." [2]

At this point it should be drawn to the reader's attention that the Euallomyces, Cystogenes, and Brachyallomyces life cycles have, subsequent to the early work on *Allomyces*, also been found in various

---

[1] Called "R.S. zoospore" by Emerson (1941; 89). Emerson and Wilson (1954) refer to the resting spore (except in Brachyallomyces) as a "meiosporangium" and to its swarmers as "meiospores."

[2] "Euallomyces," "Cystogenes," and "Brachyallomyces" are used as subgeneric names by Emerson (see *Allomyces*, pp. 670-678).

other genera of the Blastocladiales. For example, the Cystogenes type [1] is present in *Catenaria* (*C. allomycis*) (Fig. 44 B-F, p. 651) and all three occur in *Blastocladiella*. For this reason use is here made of Euallomyces, and the other terms, in keys and elsewhere, even when such application precedes the treatment of the genus *Allomyces* itself.

In the Cystogenes life cycle (Fig. 43, p. 629) characteristic of *Allomyces moniliformis*, *A. cystogenus*, and *A. neo-moniliformis*, the zoospores from the resting spore are large, sluggish, and usually posteriorly bi-flagellate. According to McCranie (1942) and Teter (1944), in some, flagella are present, in others they are apparently lacking. Teter assumed two flagella to be normal. Wilson's (1952) cytological study confirmed both Teter's observations and his own contention that the number of flagella present will conform to that of the number of nuclei in the spore. The zoospores encyst at once and from each, four small gametes emerge which may or may not have a flagellum. These gametes fuse in pairs to form a zygote which gives rise to the sporophyte plant.

Wilson (1952) not only clarified certain of McCranie's (1942; also in Sparrow, 1943) observations but the homologies between the Cystogenes and Euallomyces life cycles as well. There are approximately the same number of nuclei in resting spores of both. In Cystogenes and Euallomyces the two meiotic divisions occur in the germinating resting spore. In the former, before cleavage of the cytoplasm into resting-spore zoospores ("meiospores") its nuclei pair, members of each pair being held together by a common nuclear cap. At cleavage binucleate spores are formed; these emerge, each with two flagella, and encyst. During encystment the only haploid mitotic division in the life cycle takes place and by it the nuclei in the cyst are increased to four. Individual nuclear caps are now formed and four gametes are produced in each cyst. The cyst in Cystogenes is considered homologous with the game-tophyte plant in Euallomyces. Wilson thinks it probable that in the Cys-togenes group the cyst is homothallic as is the gametophyte of Euallo-myces. He also infers from the pairing of nuclei in the resting spore that the gametes in the cyst are at least physiologically differentiated as to sex.

In the *Brachyallomyces* life cycle neither sexual plants nor cysts are

[1] In all likelihood it occurs in some species of the chytrid genus *Micromyces* (p. 192).

produced. Emerson (1941) placed his isolates of this type in what might be called a "form species" and gave it a binomial, *Allomyces anomalus* (Fig. 40 D-E, p. 616). The resting-spore zoospores upon emergence germinate directly into new asexual plants like the parents. In the majority of these isolates further manipulation resulted in the induction of a gametophyte phase similar to either that in *Allomyces javanicus* or that in *A. arbuscula*. Some isolates, however, even after two years of obser-

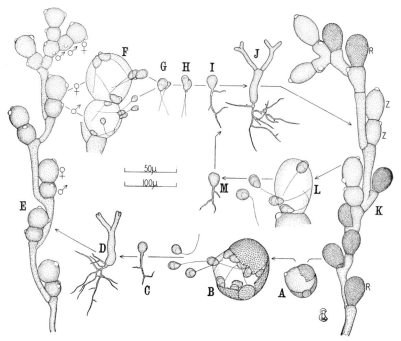

FIG. 42. Life cycle of Euallomyces illustrated by *Allomyces arbuscula* E.J. Butler

"*A*, germinating resistant sporangium with outer wall split and a papilla of discharge already formed on the inner membrane; *B*, R.S. zoospores emerging from the germinated resistant sporangium; *C*, germinating R. S. zoospore; *D*, young gametophytic plant; *E*, mature gametophytic hypha bearing female and male gametangia; *F*, female and male gametes emerging from a pair of gametangia; *G*, copulating gametes; *H*, planozygote; *I*, germinating zygote; *J*, young sporophytic plant; *K*, mature sporophytic hypha bearing thin-walled zoosporangia (*Z,Z*) and heavy-walled resistant sporangia (*R,R*); *L*, zoospores emerging from a zoosporangium; *M*, germinating zoospore" (Emerson, 1941).

vation, failed to produce sexual plants. Recalling the situation found in *Blastocladia pringsheimii* by Blackwell (1940), in which precisely the same life cycle was observed, Emerson suggested that there are "brachy-" or "short-cycled" forms in nature in which the asexual thallus alone is produced.

Wilson (1952), who examined the situation in *Allomyces anomalus* cytologically, determined that, although there is an increase in nuclear size during maturation of the resting spores (thus resembling prophase stages of other species before meiosis), the chromosomes either completely or partly fail to pair. Ensuing divisions in the resting spores are consequently mitotic and not meiotic and the zoospores eventually formed are diploid. They only give rise, of course, to sporophyte plants; hence, a gametophyte phase is lacking. Wilson concludes from this that an inhibiting factor is operative which may, by some as yet unknown mechanism, suppress meiosis in long-cycled forms over long periods. The potentiality for production of a haploid generation continues to exist, however, and is expressed whenever such "inhibition" is released.

Besides the three types of life cycles that are a regular and characteristic feature of certain isolates, variations or "departures" from the normal have been described in some isolates of species belonging to the Euallomyces type. One such departure is the capacity of the female gamete to develop parthenogenetically. Kniep (1929, 1930) had observed that the female gamete in *Allomyces javanicus* could, on occasion, come to rest, germinate, and form a new sexual thallus, thus simulating a zoospore in function. Sörgel (1937b) and Emerson (1941) have confirmed this both for Kniep's species and for *A. arbuscula*. Sörgel found that in some instances the female gamete might also give rise directly to *asexual* plants, a fact verified by Emerson (1941) and by Emerson and Wilson (1954). No instances of germination of the male gamete, however, have ever been observed nor have such gametes ever been seen to fuse with each other.

A second departure noted by Sörgel and Emerson in both the long-cycled species mentioned is the formation of asexual plants by planonts from the resting spores. Emerson found that certain of his strains did not regularly produce sexual plants under aquatic conditions and that certain others were induced to do so only after very special treatment. He points out that on this physiological basis we have a series in both *Allomyces arbuscula* and *A. javanicus* grading from those which regularly produce a sexual stage to those which produce one only after manipulation. The reason for this variation from the long-cycled type is not known but Wilson (1952) postulates an inhibiting factor (p. 627). Sörgel and Emerson both speculate that it may be linked up with environmental conditions, particularly with the amount of nutriment immediately available to the planont on its emergence from the resting spore. No evidence for the fusion of these planonts with each other has ever been observed.

A third departure, but by no means uncommon, is the formation of the dark, pitted resting spores on the sexual as well as on the asexual thallus. Sörgel (1937b) attempted to prove by volumetric studies of the nuclei of plants showing this peculiarity that there are mixtures of gametophyte and sporophyte nuclei within the hyphae. Emerson believes, however, that until there is definite cytological evidence from chromosome counts to confirm the existence of such "mixed hyphae" it is better to assume that both sexual and asexual plants may form resting spores rather than that such structures are restricted to the asexual generation alone. Although Hatch (1935) stated that the planonts from these resting spores produce sexual thalli, Emerson feels that this is still a matter of doubt.

Beneke and Wilson (1950) found that in *Allomyces macrogynus* sodium nucleate treatment of germinating zygotes increased the frequency with which resting spores from resultant sporophytes gave rise at germination to planonts which developed into *sporophytes* as well as gametophytes. Colchicine appeared to have a similar effect (see Sost, 1955). These authors suggested that such treatment of the zygotes induced some nuclei to become polyploid and the resulting asexual thalli mixoploid. Hence, at reduction division in the germinating resting spores, some of the resulting planonts would be haploid and some diploid or even polyploid. Only the first-named would give rise to sexual thalli, the others would be asexual.

Whiffen (1951) noted that when cycloheximide (Acti-dione), an antibiotic substance, was added to media on which *Allomyces arbuscula*

sporophytes were grown, hyphal outgrowths appeared bearing gametangia. These outgrowths, when transplanted, gave rise to mixed sporo-
phyte-gametophyte mycelia which eventually became either entirely

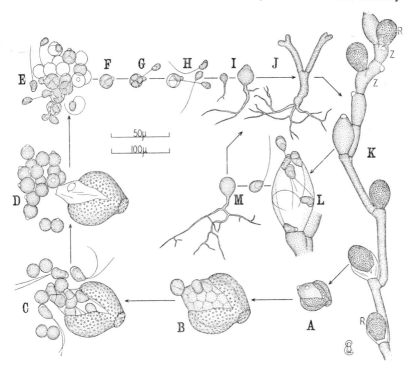

FIG. 43. Life cycle of Cystogenes illustrated by *Allomyces neo-moniliformis*
Indoh

A, germinating resistant sporangium with outer wall split and two papillae
of discharge formed on the inner membrane; *B*, the same (enlarged) just
starting to release R. S. zoospores; *C*, primary R. S. zoospores emerging
from the germinated resistant sporangium, some still motile, others already
encysted and lacking flagella; *D*, cysts (gametangia), clustered at the mouth
of the empty resistant sporangium and each with a single papilla; *E*, isogamous
gametes emerging from cysts; *F-H*, stages in the emergence of a quartet of
gametes from a cyst; *I*, germinating zygote; *J*, young sporophyte; *K*, hypha
of a mature plant bearing thin-walled zoosporangia (*Z,Z*) and heavy-walled
resistant sporangia (*R,R*); *L*, zoospores emerging from a zoosporangium;
M, germinating zoospore.

(Modified from Emerson, 1941)

sporophyte or gametophyte. She suggested the chemical may cause separation of the chromosomes into two groups during mitosis without their splitting.

The genetics of *Allomyces* has been investigated experimentally. The major part of the work up to the present has been done by Emerson (1941) and by Emerson and Wilson (1954) and deals especially with hybridization and inheritance among members of the Euallomyces group. It will be seen from Figure 40 A-B (p. 616) that a well-marked and opposing arrangement of the gametangia may exist on the gametophyte plant, that is, in *A. arbuscula* the male is hypogynous and the female epigynous, whereas in *A. javanicus*, on the contrary, the male is epigynous and the female hypogynous. Interspecific crosses were successfully made and the inheritance of the gametangial arrangement followed in the haploid (gametophyte) generation. This particular procedure was necessary because the sporophytes of the two species showed no striking differences. In this respect the studies, therefore, differ from those carried out on higher plants in which the inheritance of characters of the diploid generation is followed. The interested reader is referred directly to the extensive and careful elucidation of the methods given in Emerson and Wilson's paper, which will undoubtedly serve as a model for future work of a similar character.

Emerson and Wilson summarize their findings as follows:

Reciprocal matings made between four strains of *A. arbuscula* and three of *A. javanicus* in various combinations show that the reaction of the gametes and the percentage of "takes" vary according to the particular parents used. Counts of epigyny (E) and hypogyny (H) in the gametophytes derived from over a hundred F_1 sporophytes have demonstrated that, in addition to both the parental types (E and H), a whole series of intermediate strains (I) segregate out. From these results it is concluded that the arrangement of gametangia is controlled either by more than one pair of independently segregating alleles or by a single pair of duplicated alleles that segregate independently. The viability of meiospores from F_1 sporophytes is shown to be reduced to less than one tenth that of the parents.

In about one-fifth of the crosses *all* of the progeny exhibited pure hypogyny (H). For the following reasons we believe that hybridization failed to occur in these instances, the (F_1) sporophyte having arisen by parthenogenetic development of the female gamete. (1) The female parent was always *A. arbuscula*. (2) Apomictic formation of sporophytes, accompanied by chromosome doubling, characterizes certain strains of *A. arbuscula*, and it was from "crosses" of just such strains that the purely H-type progeny arose. (3) The reaction of the gametes in these crosses was atypical and zygotes were not seen.

Second and third generation progeny from the true crosses generally exhibit high meiospore viability and perpetuation of the characters (E, H, or I) of the F_1 gametophytes from which they were derived.

Studies of chromosome number and behavior in parental and hybrid strains have provided a precise basis for understanding and interpreting the genetic experiments just summarized. A polyploid series consisting of natural strains with 8, 16, 24, and 32 haploid chromosomes exists in *A. arbuscula*, and counts of 14, 28, and 50+ (probably 56) have been established in *A. javanicus* var. *macrogynus* [*A. macrogynus*]. The parental strains originally selected for hybridization have 16 and 28 chromosomes respectively in their gametophytic nuclei, and hence the sporophytes, with 32 and 56 chromosomes, represent a tetraploid condition.

Two patterns of chromosome number and behavior have been observed at the first meiosis in F_1 hybrids obtained by crossing these tetraploid parents. In Type A nuclei, there are $16 + 28 = 44$ chromosomes, but only very few bivalents, and the univalents are distributed randomly to the poles. In Type B nuclei approximately 55 chromosomes have been detected; about half of them form bivalents, and again many univalents go to the poles at random. The irregular distribution of chromosomes in both types accounts for the greatly reduced viability of F_1 meiospores. More precise determinations within the hybrid population show, furthermore, a direct correlation between the degree of pairing and the percent meiospore viability: Type A, few pairs and *ca.* 0.1% viability; Type B, many pairs and *ca.* 3% viability. From the observed number of chromosomes, the amount of pairing, and the fact that Type B hybrids always have *A. arbuscula* as the female parent, it is concluded that Type B nuclei arise by doubling of the *arbuscula* complement of chromosomes during or just prior to syngamy, i. e., $2 \times 16 + 28 = 60$ (55 detected).

The irregular distribution of univalents in the F_1 explains the variable haploid chromosome numbers (20–44) which are found to occur in the F_2 and F_3 progeny and also gives insight into the mechanism whereby E and H types, as well as a series of intermediates, I, segregate out. Chromosome pairing is usually regular and complete again in F_2 and F_3 meioses, and meiospore viability returns to the high level of the parents.

All of the evidence, morphological, genetic, and cytological, points to the conclusion that *Allomyces javanicus* var. *javanicus* is a natural hybrid of *A. arbuscula* × *A. javanicus* var. *macrogynus*. Gametophytes are characterized by an intermediate condition in which epigyny and hypogyny occur on the same plant; this intermediacy has been exactly duplicated by crosses made in the laboratory; and the chromosome numbers of natural isolates range from 13 to 21, just as those of the F_2 and F_3 from artificial crosses vary, though over a somewhat higher and wider range.

The genetical data given above are of special interest, as Emerson has pointed out, in connection with the location of the reduction division in the life cycle of the Euallomyces group. Kniep (1930) had approached the question by way of volumetric studies of the nuclei of the sexual and the asexual plants. He found that in *Allomyces javanicus* a well-marked ratio of 1 : 2.12 exists between the average volumes of the nuclei of the sexual and the asexual phases and from this concluded that meiosis occurs in the resting spore.[1] His observations were abundantly confirmed by Sörgel (1936) for *A. arbuscula* ("*A. kniepii*"). Indeed, even in plants of this species which Sörgel considered to be heteroploid, he obtained the same constancy in ratio of nuclear volume between the two phases. Sörgel mentions that there are six chromosomes in the gametophyte and twelve in the sporophyte. The only cytological study dealing with the reduction division in *Allomyces* prior to the reports of Emerson and Wilson (1949, 1954) and Wilson (1952), was one by Hatch (1938). From his investigations on nuclear behavior in the zygote, Hatch came to the conclusion that meiosis takes place at the first division of the fusion nucleus, at which time the chromosomes are reduced from twelve to six.

Wilson's (1952) and Emerson and Wilson's (1954) studies, utilizing the aceto-orcein smear technique, have yielded definitive information on meiosis, as well as on chromosome numbers, not only in members of Euallomyces but of Cystogenes. They have also afforded light on the nuclear situation in Brachyallomyces. The haploid chromosome count for the Euallomyces group shows that hypogyny (*Allomyces arbuscula*) is associated with a basic chromosome number of 8 or of simple multiples of 8, that is, 16, 24, and 32. Since in most natural isolates of *A. arbuscula* the gametophyte has 16 chromosomes and the sporophyte 32, they are considered tetraploid. Among the epigynous forms the one later termed *A. macrogynus* (*A. javanicus* var. *macrogynus* = *A. javanicus* var. *japonensis* Indoh) seems to possess the basic number of chromo-

---

[1] See, also, Sost's (1955) work on the induction of polyploidy, in which he utilized nuclear volume as a criterion.

somes, namely 14. This is the only purely epigynous form and polyploids of it bearing 28 and 50+ (56?) chromosomes are known. As for Kniep's isolate, on which *A. javanicus* was erected, Wilson (1952) and Emerson and Wilson (1954) conclude from its chromosome complement of 21 that it is a natural hybrid (*A. arbuscula* × *A. macrogynus*). The nuclear situation in Cystogenes (see p. 625), and Wilson's findings and interpretation of Brachyallomyces (p. 627) have already been discussed.

SYSTEMATIC ACCOUNT
BLASTOCLADIALES

MICROSCOPIC fresh-water and terricolous saprophytic or parasitic fungi; the thallus, usually walled, coenocytic, eucarpic, sometimes with pseudosepta, true cross walls formed for the most part only to delimit the reproductive organs, composed of a system of branched rhizoids that anchor it to the substratum and either a single reproductive rudiment or, more commonly, a basal cell which bears one or more reproductive structures directly on its surface or on lobes or on extensive nonseptate or pseudoseptate dichotomously, sympodially, or umbellately branched hyphae, sterile setae present or absent, the walls sometimes giving a reaction for chitin, never for cellulose, protoplasm variable in aspect, frequently alveolately or reticulately vacuolate; plant sometimes differentiated into similar sporophyte and gametophyte phases, the *asexual* plant bearing one or more inoperculate, uni- or multiporous thin-walled zoosporangia and thick-walled, usually punctate, generally brownish resting spores borne singly within and usually completely filling the terminal segments of the hyphae, the *sexual* plant monoecious or dioecious, bearing one or more thin-walled inoperculate uni- or multiporous gametangia; zoospores posteriorly uniflagellate, with a conspicuous subtriangular nuclear cap, and sometimes a side body, movement swimming or amoeboid, germinating directly and bipolarly to form the asexual plant; resting spores upon germination producing either (*a*) posteriorly uniflagellate planonts which give rise directly to new asexual plants or to sexual plants, or (*b*) posteriorly biflagellate planonts which immediately encyst, each of the cysts functioning as a gametangium and forming endogenously four uniflagellate isogamous gametes that, after emerging from the cyst, conjugate to form zygotes which germinate to produce asexual plants; gametes posteriorly uniflagellate, isogamous or anisogamous, if anisogamous the smaller gamete always containing carotinoid pigment, fusing in pairs to form a biflagellate planozygote, which, without a period of rest, germinates to form an asexual plant.

Three families are now recognized in the order. These are:

1. The Coelomomycetaceae, in which the thalli lack demonstrable walls and are without rhizoids. No reproductive structures save thick-walled resting spores and their planonts are known. The family comprises a highly specialized group of parasites primarily of mosquito larvae.

2. The Catenariaceae, in which the tubular, walled thallus bears rhizoids and forms cross walls which delimit reproductive structures or sterile isthmuses. Zoosporangia and resting spores are produced and *Catenaria allomycis* has a Cystogenes type of life cycle (p. 625).

3. The Blastocladiaceae, members of which, so far as now recognized, fall into two well-marked groups: the one contains the genera *Blastocladiella*, *Blastocladiopsis*, and *Allomyces*; the other is coextensive with the genus *Blastocladia*.

The first group is typified (1) by having sporangia with several discharge pores and (2) by sexual reproduction (where observed) accompanied (except in Cystogenes types) by alternation of isomorphic generations. In *Blastocladiella* hyphal branches are lacking; in *Blastocladiopsis* the hyphae are without pseudosepta and limited in growth; and in *Allomyces*, the hyphal branches of the often poorly defined basal cell are pseudoseptate and unlimited in growth.

The second group (*Blastocladia*) is characterized by the possession of sporangia that develop a single papilla, often with an inwardly projecting plug and an apical pore. Branches of the hyphae, if any, lack pseudosepta and are slight in extent. No sexual reproduction has yet been observed in any of its members.

Further investigations of the two groups of the Blastocladiaceae may justify their segregation into separate families or may show that many intermediate forms exist.

COELOMOMYCETACEAE

Obligate parasites within the body cavity of insects; mycelium naked, without rhizoids; thick-walled, resistant sporangia only present, the entire mycelium used up in their formation; sporangial and zoospore structure much as in other Blastocladiales; sporangia dehiscing by the cracking of the outer wall along a preformed groove, the inner wall and the contents swelling and pushing outward through this crack; spores discharged by the gelatinization of the exposed surface of the inner wall.[2]

In erecting a new family to accommodate this group of highly special-ized parasites, primarily of mosquito larvae, Couch (1945b) pointed out that they are more closely related to the Blastocladiales than to the Chytridiales, the order in which these organisms were placed by Keilin (1921) and others.

Similarity with blastocladiaceous fungi is to be found in the coarse, well-developed, dichotomously branched mycelium, the character of the resting spore wall and its preformed line of dehiscence, and the structure of the zoospore and its discharge and manner of swimming. Couch noted, furthermore, that the parasitic habit of these fungi has been accompanied by striking structural changes in the vegetative thallus. No hyphal walls can be demonstrated, nor are there specialized food-absorbing structures such as rhizoids. Evidently the whole naked, branch-ed thallus functions vegetatively. Where hyphal bodies are formed, they too are unwalled, a condition analogous to that in at least

---

[1] See also the recently described genus *Oedogoniomyces* (p. 694), possibly belonging in the Eccrinales.

[2] Revised for this treatise by J.N. Couch.

one other entomogenous fungus (*Entomophthora colorata* Sorokin).

Although, as Couch emphasized, in other members of the *Blasto-cladiales* a period of drying is usually necessary for resting-spore germination, there is considerable variation within this curious group of parasites in this respect. This has come about, probably, by adaptation to the different habitats in which various mosquitoes breed. Certain mosquitoes, *Psorophora ciliata* for example, breed in temporary pools and their eggs are capable of withstanding prolonged drought. The spore of a *Coelomomyces* parasitizing their larvae needs and apparently has a capacity to remain viable under like conditions. Indeed, they may actually require desiccation to germinate. Other mosquitoes habitually deposit their eggs in permanent or semipermanent bodies of water. Eggs of such species are less resistant to drying and the coelomomycetaceous spores of their parasites are similarly vulnerable. Thus, the resting spores of *C. dodgei* will germinate without desiccation and may even be killed if subjected to it.

The life histories of members of the Coelomomycetaceae are still incompletely known. As Couch says, many questions need to be answered: (1) is the resting-spore zoospore the agent of infection; (2) what is the method of infection; (3) is infection congenital; (4) which parts of the insect's body are attacked; (5) is a particular species of fungus host specific or does it have an alternation of hosts; (6) within the life cycle does alternation of generations occur, as in certain species of *Allomyces*; (7) can the fungi be cultivated on artificial media; and (8) is it possible to use any of these parasites for artificial biological control of the insects? The last point is of special significance to the medical entomologist. As yet only conflicting evidence is available.

COELOMOMYCES Keilin, emend. Couch

J. Elisha Mitchell Sci. Soc., 61: 128. 1945
(Fig. 44 L–M, p. 651)

Coelomomyces Keilin, Parasitology, 13: 226. 1921.
Zografia Bogoyavlensky, Russkii arkhiv protistologii (Arch. Russian Protistol. Soc.), 1: 113. 1922.

Obligate parasites within the body cavity of insects; mycelium coenocytic, aseptate, dichotomously or irregularly branched, without rhizoids or cell walls; reproducing by thick-walled, smooth or variously sculptured, resistant sporangia which develop in the insect's hemocoele; sporangia at first covered by a thin membrane formed from the old plasma membrane, the wall proper consisting of two layers, the outer thick, smooth or usually sculptured, and brownish in color, the inner smooth and hyaline; in germinating, the outer membrane cracking along a preformed groove much as in *Allomyces*, the inner wall and the contents swelling and protruding through this slit; spores discharging later by the gelatinization and disintegration of the exposed surface of the inner wall; zoospores posteriorly uniflagellate, with a nuclear cap as in *Allomyces*; sporangial walls without cellulose. [1]

Germination of the resting spores in *Coelomomyces* was first observed by de Meillon and Muspratt (1943). It was these workers that noted, as had earlier been predicted by Keilin (1921), that the spore wall cracks along a preformed line of dehiscence and that the contents (surrounded by a membrane) over a day or more gradually extrude to the outside. The most complete description of this process, as it occurs in *C. lativittatus*, is furnished by Couch and Dodge (1947)(Fig. 44 L-M, p. 651). They state:

None of the material was dried and six days after it had been collected some of the sporangia had started germinating..... [A] few sporangia were seen to have a slight bulge on one side, and in others the swelling had gone far enough to split the outer wall along the preformed line, exposing the inner sporangial membrane. By this time the lipoid granules, which had been more or less evenly dispersed throughout the cytoplasm, had aggregated in spherical groups, each group destined to be the center of a spore origin, a stage characteristic of other members of the Blastocladiales. About six to twelve hours after the opening appeared in the outer wall the contents of the sporangium, surrounded by the thin inner membrane, had pushed out through the slit to form a dome-shaped extension. At this stage the spherical aggregates of lipoid granules were very distinct.....

The swelling of the internal contents of the sporangium continues until it reaches its maximum, when the slit in the outer wall extends from one-half to two-thirds the length of the sporangium and is broadly elliptical in outline. The protoplasm, surrounded by the inner wall layer, protrudes through this opening as a slightly flattened hemispheric mass in side view, but is really about twice as long as wide. At this stage the spore outlines are distinct and are polygonal from pressure....the nuclear cap and nucleus, with the lipoid

[1] Revised for this treatise by J. N. Couch.

granules beside it in a clump, are readily seen. The first indication that the spores are about to emerge is the gelatinization of the wall surrounding the protruding spore mass. This takes about ten minutes, during which the membrane increases to four or five times its original thickness. About three to four minutes before the spores emerge, those in the protrusion begin a rocking motion which in a few seconds spreads throughout the sporangium; and in a few seconds more the whole mass begins a slow motion which soon becomes cyclic, so that the entire mass is moving round and round in the sporangium. Suddenly at one end of the elongated, protruding mass the outer part of the gelatinous membrane breaks and the inner part seems to dissolve, and through this opening the spores rush out and swim away. In less than a minute the entire gelatinous wall disappears and all the spores emerge except for a few. These one by one find the slit, which has now become smaller, and creep through to the outside.

KEY TO THE SPECIES OF COELOMOMYCES [1]

Outer wall smooth, pitted, with or without faint striae or crinkles
  Outer wall without striae or crinkles
    Outer wall with straight or diagonal rows of pits 1.5–3 μ apart
    Pits large, 1.5–3 μ apart; resting spores 37 by 63 μ..........
    .... *C. stegomyiae*, p. 639
    Pits small, less than 1.5 μ apart; resting spores 37–67 by 46–100 μ
    .... *C. psorophorae*, p. 640
    Outer wall with dispersed rounded or elongate pits, 2–4 μ apart
             C. punctatus, p. 640
  Outer wall with faint striae or crinkles
    Outer wall with faint striae as well as pits; pits elongate, stellately
    arranged............................... *C. keilini*, p. 641
    Outer wall with crinkles and dispersed pits...... *C. africanus*, p. 641
Outer wall with bands or ridges; usually pitted
  Outer wall with low bands
    Bands seven to ten, indistinct; wall sometimes pitted .. *C. dodgei*, p. 642
    Bands five to eight, narrow; wall very rarely pitted ....
    .... *C. lativittatus*, p. 643
  Outer wall with prominent ridges
    Ridges not anastomosing; similar in height, longitudinal
    Ridges numerous......................... *C. indiana*, p. 643
    Ridges four to six
      Ridges four, rarely more; pits transversely striate; wall not
      unusually irregular
      Sporangia 12–21 by 19–40 μ.......................
      .... *C. quadrangulatus* var. *quadrangulatus*, p. 644

[1] Key not strictly dichotomous.

COELOMOMYCES STEGOMYIAE Keilin

Parasitology, 13: 226, figs. 1–7. 1921

Mycelium scanty in the body cavity, well developed around the viscera, anterior intestinal coeca, and beneath the hypoderm; branched, the branches 2-6 μ in diameter, irregular with terminal swellings 30–35 μ long by 20–22 μ in diameter which fragment from the mycelium and become hyphal bodies free in the visceral fluid where they increase to 32–65 μ in length; resting spores formed from the hyphal bodies, oval, flattened on one side, 37.5 by 20 μ–57 by 30 μ, inner wall smooth, 0.7 μ thick, outer wall 1.7–2 μ thick, yellowish with minute pores and a fine line of dehiscence from pole to pole on the convex side, germination not observed.

In larvae of the yellow fever mosquito *Aëdes aegypti* (syn. *Stegomyia scutellaris*), coll. Lamborn, FEDERATED MALAY STATES.

Keilin rightly conjectured that the resting spores of this species rupture along the fine line of cleavage and probably give rise to flagellated spores. Since he was dealing with preserved material he could not ascertain this stage.

A second type of resting spore with thinner walls than in the majority was associated with those of *Coelomomyces stegomyiae*. They may possibly belong with the sporangia described by Couch and Dodge (1947) from Keilin's type slide as *C. quadrangulatus* var. *lamborni* (p. 645).

COELOMOMYCES PSOROPHORAE Couch

J. Elisha Mitchell Sci. Soc., 61: 129, pl. 1, figs. 5–6. 1945

Hyphae 7.5–10 μ thick, not well developed but breaking up into hyphal bodies which spread the infection through the host or develop into resting sporangia; resting sporangia oval, frequently slightly flattened on one side, rarely spherical, 37–67 by 46–119 μ when oval, 40–78 μ thick when spherical, wall 3–10 μ thick, consisting of two distinct layers, the inner smooth, the outer with vast numbers of minute anastomosing pits and a longitudinal groove, both wall layers deep brown; germination not observed. [1]

In larvae of *Psorophora ciliata, P. howardii, Aëdes vexans, Culiseta* (syn. *Theobaldia*) *inornata,* UNITED STATES.

Variations in size of the resting spore on the different hosts are given in Couch and Dodge (1947).

The species is similar to *Coelomomyces stegomyiae* Keilin in wall structure but differs from it in having the pits in the wall closer together (less than "1.5 μ" apart as compared with "1.5–3 μ.")

Couch (1945b) pointed out that the wall of the resting spore of this species is the thickest known and is likely an adaptation to the very transient aquatic environment of the host.

COELOMOMYCES PUNCTATUS Couch and Dodge

J. Elisha Mitchell Sci. Soc., 63: 72, pl. 16, figs. 5–6. 1947

Mycelium as in *C* [*oelomomyces*] *dodgei;* sporangia oval, slightly flattened on one side, rarely subglobose, 32–41 × 42–75 μ, most 32–34 × 46–54 μ; wall 1.5–3.8 μ thick, consisting of an outer, pale yellow to brown layer and an inner hyaline layer, outer layer slightly thicker than inner and set with minute rounded or elongated pits which are about 0.5 μ in diameter when rounded and 0.5 × 4 μ or more when elongated, about 2–4 μ apart; outer wall layer with a preformed longitudinal groove extending half to two-thirds the length of sporangium on one

[1] Revised for this treatise by J. N. Couch.

side, along which dehiscence occurs permitting zoospore discharge. Zoospores as in *C. dodgei*. [1]

In larvae of the malaria mosquito *Anopheles quadrimaculatus*, UNITED STATES.

"Recognized by its occurrence on *An* [*opheles*] *quadrimaculatus* and by the pitted walls. *C*[*oelomomyces*] *dodgei*, to which it is closest, occurs only on *A. crucians* and has sporangial walls that are furnished with pits and bands and hence may easily be distinguished from *C. punctatus*" (Couch and Dodge, *op. cit.*).

COELOMOMYCES KEILINI Couch and Dodge

J. Elisha Mitchell Sci. Soc., 63: 74, pl. 20, figs. 2–5. 1947

Hyphae fairly abundant and conspicuous though less so than in *C* [*oelomomyces*] *quadrangulatus*, consisting mostly of rather short subdichotomously branched pieces, 5–25 μ, usually 10–12.6 μ thick and 60–170 μ long or sometimes longer, and many smaller irregularly-shaped pieces. Sporangia oval in outline, usually slightly flattened on one side, 34–46 by 58–71 μ; wall consisting of three layers, the outer, very thin, hyaline membrane derived from the old plasma membrane and the wall proper which is 3–7 μ thick, the outer part up to 5 μ thick, the inner up to 2 μ. In the thinner-walled sporangia, the outer wall smooth or with minute striae; in the thicker-walled ones, the outer wall pitted, the mouths of the pits slit-like and the pits appearing somewhat star-like as one focuses down; in sectional view spindle-shaped, with parallel striae between the pits. In some of the thick-walled sporangia, the protoplasm having shrunken from the first-formed wall layers at one end and forming an additional wall with the old walls. Sporangia with a preformed longitudinal groove. [1]

In larvae of *Anopheles crucians*, UNITED STATES.

COELOMOMYCES AFRICANUS Walker

Ann. Trop. Med. and Parasitol., 32: 231, pl. 3, fig. 3. 1938

Mycelium from 3–8 μ in diameter, branched; resting spore ellipsoidal, 14–18 by 25–35 μ in length, with a crinkled pitted wall.

[1] Revised for this treatise by J. N. Couch.

In larvae of *Anopheles gambiae* (syn. *A. costalis*), SIERRA LEONE.

Four types of resting spores were found by Walker (*op. cit.*) in material obtained from various places in Sierra Leone. To the most common (his "Type 3") he gave the name *Coelomomyces africanus*. Although the others are without significant descriptions, it is evident from the the photomicrographs that at least one of them (Pl. 3, fig. 4 "Type 4") is distinctive. It will no doubt prove to be new. The resting spores of Walker's types 1 and 4 were 45–60 μ long; those of his types 2 and 3 varied from 25–35 μ.

Walker unsuccessfully attempted to infect larvae with undried resting spores of *Coelomomyces*. As Couch (1945b) explained, it is likely Walker's negative results were due to the fact that he was dealing with a species requiring drying of the resting spores before germination.

COELOMOMYCES DODGEI Couch

J. Elisha Mitchell Sci. Soc., 61: 129, pl. 1, figs. 1–4. 1945. Emend. Couch, in Couch and Dodge, J. Elisha Mitchell Sci. Soc., 63: 71, pl. 16, fig. 1, pl. 20, fig. 1. 1947

Hyphae 7–14 μ thick irregularly branched and anastomosing; sporangia 27–42 by 37–65 μ, oval, sometimes slightly flattened on one side, wall deep brown, rarely hyaline, 1.5–4.2 μ thick, consisting of an outer thickened hyaline to brown part (2–3 μ thick) and an inner thin hyaline layer (1–2 μ thick); outer part of wall with rounded or elongated pits or with narrow bands separated by grooves; not infrequently with narrow bands on one side and pits on the other; the grooves extending lengthwise or arranged in variously curved patterns; bands about 3.6 μ wide and not very distinct, with 7–10 visible on surface view; wall with a preformed longitudinal groove along which dehiscence occurs to permit spore discharge; germinating in water and without previous drying after the death and partial disintegration of the larva, the process occupying 24 to 36 hours; when ready to germinate, the contents swelling, producing a lateral bulge and thus causing the thick outer wall to crack open at the longitudinal groove; twenty-four to thirty-six hours later, the spores emerging through this crack, surrounded by a gelatinous material which after three to five minutes disappears, allowing the spores to escape; spores posteriorly uniflagellate, elongated and broadest at the posterior end, 2.6–3.8 × 5.2–6.3 μ when swimming, 4–5 μ when quiescent and rounded, with several lateral lipoid granules and a nuclear cap. [1]

In larvae of *Anopheles crucians*, UNITED STATES.

"*Coelomomyces dodgei* as first understood (Couch, 1945 [b]) included resting sporangia with pits and narrow bands, with only pits, and with wide bands. . . .[It] has been found that these three sporangial types are constant and rather strictly limited as to host. . . . .[The] form with pits and narrow bands occurring on *An[opheles] crucians* is herein retained as *C. dodgei* emend., the form with only pits, restricted almost exclusively to *An[opheles] quadrimaculatus*, and the form with wide bands, occurring on *An[opheles] crucians*, are described as new species." (Couch and Dodge, *op. cit.*).

COELOMOMYCES LATIVITTATUS Couch and Dodge

J. Elisha Mitchell Soc., 63: 72, pl. 15; pl. 16, figs. 2–4. 1947

(Fig. 44 L–M, p. 651)

Hyphae much as in *C [oelomomyces] dodgei*, 4–10 μ thick; resting bodies oval, in cross-sectional view usually rounded, rarely flattened on one side, with wide, very distinct, longitudinal bands on one side and irregular or transverse bands on the other, very rarely with a few pits; longitudinal bands five to eight on a side, bands 4–6.3 μ wide; the preformed longitudinal groove of dehiscence between the two median longitudinal bands; 29–35 by 40–58 μ, rarely 36 × 77 μ, averaging 32 by 48 μ; wall 1.5–4 μ thick, consisting of the outer, brownish layer with ridges 2–3 μ thick and the inner, smooth, pale or hyaline layer, about 1–2 μ thick; zoospores as in *C. dodgei*. [1]

In larvae of *Anopheles crucians*, UNITED STATES.

Occurring on the same host (*Anopheles crucians*) as *Coelomomyces dodgei*, with which it was at first included.

COELOMOMYCES INDIANA Iyengar

Parasitology, 27: 446, figs. 1, 3–4. 1935

"Mycelium unicellular, fragile, very thin-walled and filled with dense

[1] Revised for this treatise by J. N. Couch.

protoplasm and numerous nuclei; pear-shaped in early stages, later tubular. Branches short, never anastomosing. Thickness of mycelium 7–14 μ, sometimes more, especially at apex. Mycelium attached to fat-body apparently by very minute hyphae.

"Early sporangium globular or oval, thin-walled and measuring 20 × 30–28 × 40 μ. Vacuolated sporangium nearly same size, oval and thin-walled. Sporangium of the next stage with thick refractile wall, dense protoplasmic contents and numerous nuclei. Size 20 × 30–28 × 42 μ, sometimes larger. In the mature sporangium, the wall is thick, opaque and yellow, and has thick ribs running lengthwise from one end of the sporangium to the other. Sometimes the ribs branch considerably to form a net-like sculpturing on the wall. The sculpturing on the sporangial wall varies to some extent. . . . Size of sporangium 25 × 38–36 × 60 μ. The sporangium is typically oval in shape. Wall of sporangium in section shows alternating yellow and brown striae. Thickness of wall at the ribs 2.5–3 μ and between the ribs 1 μ. Inner wall of sporangium corresponding to that observed in *C.stegomyiae* absent"(Iyengar, *loc.cit.*).

Parasitic in larvae of the following species of *Anopheles*: *A. barbirostris*, *A. nigerrimus*, *A. subpictus*, *A. aconitus*, *A. varuna*, *A. ramsayi*, *A. annularis*, and *A. jamesi*, INDIA.

COELOMOMYCES QUADRANGULATUS var. QUADRANGULATUS Couch

J. Elisha Mitchell Sci. Soc., 61: 130, pl. 2, figs. 8–10. 1945

"Hyphae 9.6–25 μ thick; sporangia roughly oval in outline but with numerous angularities, usually somewhat flattened on one side, 12–21 × 19–40 μ, in end or cross section view squarish or with four lobes; entire wall 3–5 μ thick, consisting of two layers: the outer layer pale brown with four longitudinal ridges which give the spore the four-angled or lobed appearance in end or cross section view, with very minute, closely set pits which are frequently arranged in rows, and thus give the impression of transverse striations as in a diatom shell; the inner layer hyaline, circular; dehiscence by a preformed longitudinal furrow which runs along one of the ridges. Germination not observed" (Couch, *loc. cit.*).

In larvae of *Anopheles sp.*, UNITED STATES.

This species is discussed by Couch and Dodge (1947).

COELOMOMYCES QUADRANGULATUS var. LAMBORNI
Couch and Dodge

J. Elisha Mitchell Sci. Soc., 63: 75. 1947

Sporangia 26–31 × 36–58 μ, wall transversely striate in surface view, four-angled in cross section, wavy in longitudinal section; with a distinct preformed longitudinal groove in the outer wall layer on one side.

In one larva of *Stegomyia scutellaris*, with *C* [*oelomomyces*] *stegomyiae*, collected by Dr. Lamborn in the Federated Malay States.[1]

In larva of *Aëdes aegypti* (syn. *Stegomyia scutellaris*).

Found by Couch on a slide of the type material of *Coelomomyces stegomyiae* Keilin, from which it differs in shape and in larger size.

COELOMOMYCES QUADRANGULATUS var. IRREGULARIS Couch and Dodge

J. Elisha Mitchell Sci. Soc., 63: 75, pl. 19, figs. 4,5. 1947

Mycelium well developed, much as in the typical species; sporangia roughly oval in outline but with the outer wall crenulated and very irregular, 15–21 by 23–41 μ, with 4–6 irregular longitudinal ridges between which are numerous transverse lines; very minutely punctate; inner wall layer in longitudinal sectional view oval in outline, slightly flattened on one side; outer wall with 4–6 ridges in cross section, inner wall nearly rounded in the same view; outer wall with a distinct longitudinal groove on one of the ridges. [1]

In larvae of *Anopheles punctipennis*, UNITED STATES.

Considered to be an intermediate form between *Coelomomyces quadrangulatus* and *C. pentangulatus* but distinct from either by reason of the very irregular walls of the resting spore.

COELOMOMYCES PENTANGULATUS Couch

J. Elisha Mitchell Sci. Soc., 61: 130, pl. 1, fig. 7, pl. 2, figs. 11, 12. 1945

Hyphae 4.2–10 μ thick, hyphal bodies very abundant and mostly

---

[1] Revised for this treatise by J. N. Couch.

round when first formed, 12–15 μ thick; sporangia oval, elongated or wheat-seed shaped; 12–18 by 18–40 μ, most about 14–31 μ; wall 2–3 μ thick; the outline of the sporangia in longitudinal section is usually smooth, though at times it may be slightly angular, the inner wall smooth or frequently undulating, with one to three or several wave crests on each side in section view; the two wall layers frequently separating at the two ends, or sometimes on the side, leaving clear spaces; surface with five to six elevated longitudinal ridges distinctly visible in cross section view as five or six elevations; wall apparently very finely pitted, and with a distinct longitudinal groove on one of the ridges; germination not observed. [1]

In larvae of *Culex erraticus*, UNITED STATES.

The species is characterized by small resting spores which in cross-sectional view usually have five or six angles or elevations.

COELOMOMYCES BISYMMETRICUS Couch and Dodge

J. Elisha Mitchell Sci. Soc., 63: 73, pl. 17, figs. 5–7, pl. 18, figs. 1–4. 1947

Mycelium not so thick or well-developed as in *C. dodgei*, hyphae 3–10.5 μ thick, usually about 6–9 μ thick, sparingly branched and each thread of uneven diameter; young sporangia oval with an irregular outline, outer zone of young sporangium hyaline, the central part with dense protoplasm; mature sporangia 23–28 by 34–48 μ, averaging 25 by 40 μ, oval; wall pale brown, the outer layer with alternating high and low ridges and one conspicuous mammate structure, the ridges typically encircling the cell in such fashion as to give the wall a bilateral symmetry with a long ridge bordering one edge and thus appearing smooth, and the "ends" of the wide and narrow ridges with the mammate structure in the center on the other edge; not infrequently, the ridges irregularly arranged; in median cross section with two wall layers, the outer typically with six wide and high elevations (sections of the large ridges) alternating with six smaller elevations (sections of the small ridges), the number of each type of elevation varying from five to seven, variations from this usual regular pattern frequently occurring;

---

[1] Revised for this treatise by J. N. Couch.

wall with a preformed longitudinal groove on the wide ridge opposite the mammate structure. Germination not observed. [1]

In larvae of *Anopheles crucians*, UNITED STATES.

COELOMOMYCES CRIBROSUS Couch and Dodge

J. Elisha Mitchell Sci. Soc., 63: 74, pl. 17, fig.3, pl. 18, fig. 5. 1947

Hyphae 6–11 μ thick; resting sporangia 24–42 by 42–71 μ, oval or slightly allantoid, i.e., appearing flattened on one side in longitudinal outline, mostly circular in outline in cross sectional view; wall 2–4.2 μ thick, pale yellow under microscope, consisting of an inner, smooth, hyaline layer and an outer layer which is variously sculptured or rarely smooth; wall typically with 3–20 or more circular or oblong thin areas on each side, the circles being thin areas in the wall between thicker ridges or bands, usually with several small, rounded or elongated pits in the thin areas; circles usually 2–6.4 μ wide; wall sometimes with minute rounded or elongated pits, these small pits scattered over the entire surface or sometimes arranged in two bands which border the dehiscence groove, or with thick and thin irregular bands; all resting sporangial types with interconnecting forms; in median cross sectional view wall showing several (usually seven to nine) more or less conspicuous rounded elevations, between each two of which is a smaller elevation, the larger ones being sections of the bands and the smaller the thin, circular areas between the bands; each resting sporangium with a preformed longitudinal groove located in the middle of the most conspicuous band.[1]

In larvae of *Anopheles crucians* and *A. punctipennis*, UNITED STATES.

Related to *Coelomomyces bisymmetricus* but with larger resting spores whose walls, though variable in their markings, are characterized by large, thin, circular or oblong areas, bordered by thicker bands.

COELOMOMYCES ANOPHELESICA Iyengar

Parasitology, 27: 447, figs. 2, 5. 1935

"Closely allied to *C* [*oelomomyces*] *indiana*. Mycelium similar, measuring 7–12 μ thick, short and branched, non-anastomosing and attached

---

[1] Revised for this treatise by J. N. Couch.

to fat-body of host. Mycelium like that of *C. indiana* is very fragile and extremely thin-walled. Formation of sporangium similar to *C. indiana*. Early sporangium with dense protoplasm, globular or oval, measuring 19×28–$23 \times 37 \mu$. Vacuolated sporangium 20×30–$24 \times 40 \mu$, oval, or with one side flat and the other side convex. The next stage of sporangium with a thick refractile wall and dense contents and large number of nuclei. Mature sporangium asymmetrical, circular in shape, with one side flat and the other side strongly convex; thickness of sporangium less than breadth. Size 28×34–$40 \times 44 \mu$. Thickness 16–23μ. Wall of sporangium with many raised ribs running in concentric or eccentric circles, the middle ribs branched and irregular. . . . When viewed at the edge, the sporangium is somewhat oval with ribs running parallel to each other.

"Structure of sporangial wall similar to *C. indiana* and composed of alternating light and dark striae. Inner spore-wall of *C. stegomyiae* absent. Thickness of wall at the rib 2.6–3.4μ, and between the ribs 1.3μ." (Iyengar, *loc. cit.*).

In larvae of the following species of *Anopheles: A. subpictus, A. vagus, A. annularis,* and *A. varuna,* INDIA.

COELOMOMYCES URANOTAENIAE Couch

J. Elisha Mitchell Sci. Soc., 61: 130, pl. 2, figs 13–15. 1945

"Hyphae 4–12μ thick, elongated, branched and anastomosing, rather sparse and poorly developed, frequently encased in a thick transparent sheath; hyphal bodies spherical, oval or pyriform; enlarging to an irregularly oval body, 27–35×30–55μ, the protoplasm becoming differentiated into an inner, dense, oval, granular zone and an outer, wide hyaline zone; inner granular part 12–31×29–35μ, outer zone 4–12μ wide; the resting sporangia developing from these bodies; resting sporangia oval in outline, 21–30×29–45μ, with a very distinctive wall. The inner wall is smooth, hyaline and 1.5–2.5μ thick; the outer wall pale brown or yellow and 2–3μ thick, extending out to form seven or eight longitudinal, anastomosing, steep ridges, about 4–5μ tall and spaced 7–9μ apart; wall between ridges with very fine transverse striations and entire sporangium covered with remains of the hyaline envelope which surrounded the structure when immature. In cross section view the ridges appear as seven or eight spines" (Couch, *loc. cit.*).

In larvae of *Uranotaenia sapphirina*, UNITED STATES.

Further observations by Couch and Dodge (1947: 76, pl. 17, fig. 4) indicate that the mycelium is enclosed by a hyaline sheath.

COELOMOMYCES SCULPTOSPORUS Couch and Dodge

J. Elisha Mitchell Sci. Soc., 63: 73, pl. 17, figs. 1, 2; pl. 18, figs. 6–9. 1947

Mycelium much as in other species; hyphae 4–17 μ thick, resting sporangia 22–31 $\times$ 33–58 μ, most about 27 $\times$ 45 μ, oval, wall consisting of two layers, an inner, smooth one and an outer, variously sculptured one; outer wall with high, wide ridges (4.2–6.3 μ wide), usually in the form of an irregular net, the meshes rarely circular, usually oblong or elongated, rarely with the high ridges parallel on one side (usually three to a side) and irregular on the other; in longitudinal section the ridges standing out as distinct, rounded elevations, which may appear over the margin of the entire oval or on one side only, with the opposite side smooth; in median cross section the inner wall circular and smooth, the outer showing five to seven wide, high, rounded elevations with a smaller elevation 2–4 μ wide between each pair; a preformed longitudinal groove extending along the middle of one of the ridges, which may be the only longitudinal ridge. [1]

In larvae of *Anopheles punctipennis* and *A. crucians*, UNITED STATES.

Differing from *Coelomomyces bisymmetricus* in that the pattern of the ridges on the wall is never the same on both sides, and from *C. cribrosus* in having resting spores bearing a few circles on only one side.

IMPERFECTLY KNOWN SPECIES

? COELOMOMYCES NOTONECTAE (Bogoyavlensky) Keilin

Parasitology, 19: 366. 1927

Zografia notonectae Bogoyavlensky, Russkii arkhiv protistologii (Arch. Soc. Russe Protist.), 1: 118, pl. 10. 1922.

Mycelium branching, the branches anastomosing. Resting spores ovoid with a thick smooth, unpitted (?) wall.

In adult back swimmers, *Notonecta sp.*, RUSSIA.

[1] Revised for this treatise by J. N. Couch.

? COELOMOMYCES SP. Couch and Dodge

J. Elisha Mitchell Sci. Soc.., 63: 75. 1947

Resting spores oval, flattened on one side, with the usual longitudinal groove, 31–38 by 42–60 μ, with a pale brown, smooth to minutely pitted wall, the pits scattered or arranged in transverse lines, thus giving a striated appearance.

In larvae of *Anopheles crucians*, UNITED STATES.

Intermingled with typical *Coelomomyces dodgei*.

CATENARIACEAE [1]

Thallus intra- and extramatrical, cylindrical, branched or unbranched, septate, the septa delimiting the rudiments of reproductive organs or sterile isthmuses, bearing numerous rhizoids; zoosporangia formed as enlargements of the axes of the thallus, frequently in linear series connected by narrow septate isthmuses, variable in shape; zoospore formation, structure, and discharge as for order; resting spores formed singly and loosely within a zoosporangium-like structure or in segments of the hypha, their wall somewhat thickened, smooth or very minutely pitted, pale brown, upon germination developing a discharge tube and functioning as a sporangium, the uniflagellate swarmers giving rise either directly to new asexual plants or encysting, each of the cysts serving as a gametangium and forming endogenously four uniflagellate isogamous gametes which fuse in pairs to produce a biflagellate zygote, the zygote upon germination establishing a nonsexual thallus.

Parasites of microscopic worms and of fungi; also, saprophytes on a variety of plant and animal substrata.

As a result of careful observation of *Catenaria*, Couch (1945a) raised the subfamily Catenarioideae (Sparrow, 1943) to a family and moved it from the Chytridiales to the Blastocladiales. He cited as reasons the resemblance in structure, manner of discharge, movement, and germination of the zoospores, and the similarity in place of formation of the resting spore, the kind of septation, and the type of life history.

On much the same grounds, *Catenomyces* Hanson is included in this family of the Blastocladiales rather than placed in one of the Chytridiales.

[1] Couch, *Mycologia*, 37: 187. 1945.

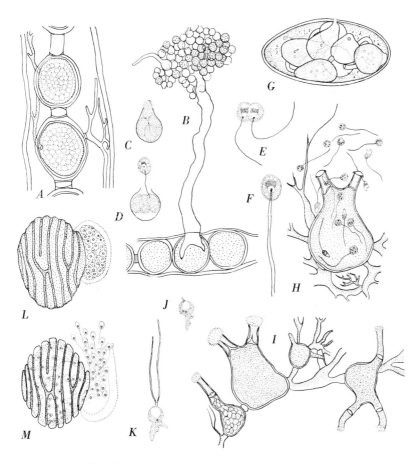

FIG. 44. Catenariaceae and Coelomomycetaceae

A-F. Catenaria allomycis Couch: *A*, resting spores and rhizoids in hypha of *Allomyces*; *B*, germinated resting spore showing cysts at orifice of discharge tube, one of the cysts has apparently germinated; *C-D*, discharge of gametes from cysts; *E*, fusion of gametes; *F*, zygote. *G. Catenaria anguillulae*, in liver-fluke egg. *H-K. Catenomyces persicinus* Hanson: *H*, discharging endoöperculate sporangium; *I*, portion of a thallus bearing several sporangia; *J-K*, bipolar germination of zoospore. *L-M. Coelomomyces lativittatus* Couch and Dodge in mosquito larva: *L*, beginning of germination of resting spore; *M*, escape of the zoospores.

(*A-G*, Couch, 1945a; *H-K*, Hanson, 1945a; *L-M*, Couch and Dodge, 1947)

KEY TO THE GENERA OF THE CATENARIACEAE

Thallus usually with strongly defined major axes along which in linear
  series are reproductive structures alternating with sterile isthmuses;
  sporangia with one discharge tube.............. CATENARIA, p. 652
Thallus much branched, diffuse; sporangia often with more than one
  discharge tube, endooperculate................ CATENOMYCES, p. 658

CATENARIA SOROKIN

Ann. Sci. Nat. Bot., VI, 4: 67. 1876

(Fig. 44 A–G, p. 651)

Thallus endobiotic, eucarpic, predominantly strongly polycentric,
branched or unbranched, septate, the septa delimiting the rudiments of
the sporangia, resting spores, or sterile isthmuses; sporangia generally
with a single discharge tube; zoospores posteriorly uniflagellate with
one or more globules, formed in the sporangium; resting spores thick-
walled, borne like the sporangia, upon germination functioning as a
sporangium, the planonts either giving rise directly to new asexual
plants or encysting at once, the cysts gametangia, each producing four
posteriorly uniflagellate isogamous gametes which fuse in pairs to form
biflagellate zygotes, zygotes reëstablishing the sporophyte thalli.

Parasitic or saprophytic in the eggs of small or microscopic animals,
Anguillulae, liver flukes, mites, and adult rotifers, in *Allomyces*, and
so on; saprophytic in fresh-water algae and vegetable debris.

Species of the genus develop highly specialized, often extensive, polycentric thalli.

Much has become known in recent years about the morphology and
method of development in *Catenaria anguillulae*. Sorokin (1876) states
that the young thallus was septate and said that certain segments expanded to produce the sporangia, while others remained narrow and
formed two-celled isthmuses. Dangeard (1884–85b), on the other hand,
did not believe that segmentation took place until after the appearance
of the branches and sporangial rudiments. He also detected the presence
of the rhizoids and observed the lack of constancy of the two-celled
character of the isthmus. J. B. Butler and Buckley (1927), E. J. Butler
(1928), Buckley and Clapham (1929), Karling (1934a; 1938b), and
Couch (1945a) have all verified the segmentation sequence described by
Dangeard.

The most important contribution to our knowledge of this genus has been Couch's (1945a) discovery of a Cystogenes type of life cycle in *Catenaria allomycis* Couch, entirely similar to that found in *Allomyces* and *Blastocladiella* (see p. 625).

Members of *Catenaria* occur on a wide variety of substrata. *C. anguillulae* is outstanding among them in its ability to live as a saprophyte in vegetable materials as well as a parasite of nematodes (this has been confirmed by Couch, *op. cit.*). On the other hand, Couch reported that *C. allomycis*, which will parasitize all species of *Allomyces*, would attack only *Blastocladiella simplex*, of the four species of that genus tested, and would not infect *Blastocladiopsis parva, Catenaria anguillulae, Achlya caroliniana,* or *Saprolegnia parasitica.*

The resting spores of all the species have been observed. In *Catenaria anguillulae* and *C. allomycis* they lie somewhat loosely in their container; in *C. sphaerocarpa*, they completely fill it. Those of *C. anguillulae* seem simply to be encysted sporangia with the contents somewhat contracted and thick-walled. Karling (1938b) voiced a similar opinion regarding the resting spores of *C. sphaerocarpa*. At germination, where this has been seen, a tube is formed through which the swarmers emerge.

KEY TO THE SPECIES OF CATENARIA

Zoospores with numerous globules; sporangia variable in shape
    Parasitic in microscopic animals and their eggs and saprophytic in
        vegetable debris; sporangia pyriform, subglobose, or irregular;
            with a Brachyallomyces type of life cycle..... *C. anguillulae*, p. 653
    Parasitic in *Allomyces*; sporangia and resting spores somewhat
            globose; with a Cystogenes type of life cycle.... *C. allomycis*, p. 655
Zoospores with a single conspicuous globule; sporangia predomi-
    nantly globose.......................... *C. sphaerocarpa*, p. 657

CATENARIA ANGUILLULAE Sorokin

Ann. Sci. Nat. Bot., VI, 4: 67, pl. 3, figs. 6–28. 1876

(Fig. 44 G, p. 651)

"Parasitic or saprophytic in nematodes, liver fluke eggs, and saprophytic on cooked grass leaves, etc., and various kinds of nutrient agar. Thallus composed at first of a branched or unbranched nonseptate or sparingly septate hypha, with rhizoids. Hypha 4–15 μ thick, swelling at more or less regular intervals to form zoosporangia or resting bodies connected by narrow one- or two-celled isthmuses and thus catenulate. Zoosporangia pyriform or subpyriform in fluke eggs, 25–36 × 38–71 μ or considerably smaller when crowded, emergence papillae 5–8.6 × 8- several hundred microns long, connecting isthmuses 5–5.4 × 4–14 μ; in nematodes zoosporangia oval or elliptic, 9–20 × 12–34 μ, the emergence papilla only projecting through the nematode skin; on liver agar zoosporangia subglobose with very long emergence tubes, up to a mm. long; zoospores completely formed within the sporangium, usually showing rocking motion before discharge; first spores usually emerging to form a spherical mass enclosed by a gelatinous substance at the tip; this gelatinous envelope soon dissolves and the first spores swim away, the rest of the spores swim away as soon as they reach the exit, or first spores may swim away immediately; zoospores 3.8–5.4 × 6.7–8 μ tapering toward the anterior end, with 3–4 anterior fat (?) globules, a distinct nuclear cap and nucleus to one side of which is a side body and several fat ? globules; with one posterior whiplash cilium; rounding up and encysting before germinating, 4.6–5.4 μ; germinating in water or nutrient agar by sending out a delicate rhizoid and then forming a tubular growth from the opposite pole, which may form a dwarf sporangium with a small, sterile basal part, or may grow into a new mycelium if sufficient food is available [on fluke eggs, zoospore leaves empty cyst on outside of egg membrane (Butler and Buckley, 1927)]. Resting bodies formed on nematodes, fluke eggs, leaf tissue, and nutrient agars; formed within zoosporangial membrane and conforming somewhat to its shape, resting spore protoplasm retreating from the old sporangial wall and forming a new thick pale brownish wall of its own; on nematodes oval or oblong ovate, 16–18 × 20–33 μ, in fluke eggs spherical, subspherical, ovoid or irregular in shape, 21–42 μ when spherical, 20–33 × 40–55 μ when subspherical; on boiled leaves spherical, pyriform, lobed, or cylindrical with rounded ends frequently conforming to the leaf cells except for a cone-shaped part through which the emergence tube sprouts, 30–50 × 38–100 μ; on agar spherical or subspherical, except for a small or large cone-shaped elongation up to over 100 μ long, on agar No. 5[1] up to 138–176 μ thick when spherical or subspherical; wall

[1] See Couch, 1945a.

smooth except for a short papilla apparently always present and always directed towards emergence pore of zoosporangium, wall about 2–3 μ thick. Resting sporangium germinating by the irregular cracking of the outer thicker wall and the emergence of a long or short tube through which the zoospores emerge as in the zoosporangium. Zoospores in resting sporangia as in zoosporangia" (Couch, 1945a).

In exuviae of *Gordius spp.*, Villot (1874, pl. 6, figs.13–18), Anguillulae, *Nitella*, Dangeard (1884–85b: 126; 1886a: 307, pl. 14, figs. 12–16), FRANCE; Anguillulae, Sorokin (*loc. cit.*; 1883: 39, fig. 50), EUROPEAN RUSSIA, ASIATIC RUSSIA; Anguillulae, Constantineanu (1901: 389, fig. 84), RUMANIA; nematodes, Seurat (1920: 189) (?), ALGERIA; eggs of *Fasciola hepatica*, J. B. Butler and Buckley (1927: 497, pl. 23–26), E. J. Butler (1928: 817, figs. 1–19), J. B. Butler and Humphries (1932: 301, pl. 13–18), IRELAND; helminth and mite eggs, Buckley and Clapham (1929: 1, pl. 1, figs. 1–21), GREAT BRITAIN; rotifers and nematodes, Karling (1946b:10, pl. 2, figs. 48–53), BRAZIL; eggs of microscopic animals, snake-skin bait, soil, Sparrow (1952b: 71), CUBA; roots of *Panicum* and sterilized green algae, characeans, liverworts, eggs of rotifers, infusoria, insects, and so forth, Karling (1934a: 528, figs. 1–3, pl. 57–58); Karling (1942c: 620), sheep liver-fluke eggs, Couch (*op. cit.*: 173), eggs of an undetermined microscopic animal, snake-skin bait, Sparrow (1952d: 769), UNITED STATES.

The fungus in eggs of *Nais* described by Carter (1858: 99, pl. 4, fig.45) probably belongs here.

Couch (1945a) critically evaluated the fungi referred to this species and he gives sufficient latitude in his description to accommodate all authentic records. Seurat's record is retained here only tentatively since it was not considered by Couch.

Catenaria anguillulae has been cultivated on various agar media containing extracts of liver, fluke ova, or the like. Couch carried it in stock culture on 0.3 per cent "Difco" meat extract with 1.5 per cent agar. It has frequently been isolated from soil by the use of snake-skin bait.

CATENARIA ALLOMYCIS Couch

Mycologia, 37: 171, figs. 1–41. 1945

(Fig. 44 A–F, p. 651)

"Thallus parasitic in the threads of *Allomyces* and *Blastocladiella*;

consisting when mature of a simple or branched catenulate hypha with a few stubby rhizoids; usually 300–600 μ long, consisting of 6–15 zoosporangia or resting bodies or both, sometimes much longer and at times much shorter, being composed of only one zoosporangium or resting body; the swellings in the thallus connected by one-celled very rarely 2-celled short isthmuses, 5–9.2 × 7–16 μ. Septations incompletely formed, bumpy, pitted, or ridged. The first developed thalli forming zoosporangia, the later ones zoosporangia and resting bodies, and the last thalli only resting bodies. Zoosporangial development much as in *Allomyces* or *Blastocladiella simplex*. Zoospores with numerous fat bodies or lipoid granules, a conspicuous nuclear cap and a side body (visible only when stained), posteriorly uniflagellate. First zoospores emerging in a gelatinous envelope, the later ones emerging and swimming away upon reaching the exit; swimming smoothly as in *Blastocladiella*. Zoosporangia globose, subglobose, or pyriform to long elliptic or oblong elliptic, usually oval or ovoid; 15–30 × 30–55 μ; emergence tube 5–6 μ thick × 10–100 μ long. Zoospores oval, 5–6.3 × 6.3–7 μ, cilium about 17 μ long and tail piece 6.3 μ long. Resting bodies pale brown to pinkish; usually globose or subglobose, ovoid, elliptic, pyriform, rarely somewhat irregular in shape. On *Allomyces anomalus* 16–51 μ when globose, 30–41 × 34–42 when subglobose; on *A. javanicus* considerably larger, up to 63 μ thick when globose; wall of resting body 1–3 μ thick, smooth or very minutely rough; the whole spore surrounded by a thin-walled case which it almost completely fills. Resting body germinating by irregular cracking of the outer thick wall and the emergence of a germ tube which varies from 50–several hundred μ in length. Resting body zoospores uniciliate when discharged and capable of a little feeble movement, encysting almost immediately near the emergence pore in an irregular mass. Cysts spherical, 5.4–6.4 μ thick. After a rest period of about 2 hours germinating to form four uniciliate gametes which emerge through a pore to fuse in pairs, gametes 3 × 4.4–4.7 μ. Zygotes biciliate, 3.5–7.6 μ. Germinating and penetrating the host to form a zoosporangial thallus" (Couch, *loc. cit.*).

Parasitic in *Allomyces anomalus*, in soil; capable of infecting *Allomyces arbuscula*, *A. javanicus*, *A. moniliformis*, and *Blastocladiella simplex*, UNITED STATES.

The parasite attacked and destroyed both sporophyte and gameto-phyte stages of *Allomyces arbuscula* and *A. javanicus*. On the latter host it was particularly voracious and completely destroyed the sporophyte even before resting spores of the host could be formed. As Couch remarks, it is doubtful if the parasite could survive in nature on this plant, presumably "eating itself out of house and home." Although *Blastocladiella simplex* was successfully inoculated, none of the other three species of that genus or species of *Achlya* or *Saprolegnia* was attacked.

CATENARIA SPHAEROCARPA Karling

Amer. J. Bot., 25: 328, figs. 1–34. 1938

"Thallus predominantly polycentric, occasionally monocentric. Zoo-sporangia hyaline, smooth, usually spherical, 8–50 μ, oval, 8 × 10 μ—30 × 33 μ, and sometimes spindle-shaped, 7 × 14 μ—15 × 25 μ, with 1–3 straight, curved, or irregular exit tubes, 5–600 μ long and 2.5–4 μ in diameter, which may end flush with the surface of the host cell or extend 3–200 μ beyond it. Zoospores spherical, 4–4.8 μ with a single, large hyaline refractive globule; cilium approximately 25 μ long; emerging singly in succession and after a momentary pause swimming away. Isthmuses between sporangia of variable length, rarely inflated and spindle-shaped. Rhizoids numerous, well developed and branched, arising from the isthmuses as well as from the sides and ends of the sporangia. Resting spores usually spherical and oval, 10–25 μ, occa-sionally spindle-shaped and elongated with a heavy brown wall 1.5–2.5 μ thick, and an evenly granular content; apparently developed in the same manner as the zoosporangia; germination unknown" (Karling, *loc. cit.*).

Saprophytic in cells of *Hydrodictyon reticulatum*, *Chara coronata*, *Nitella flexilis*, *Cladophora glomerata*, *Pithophora sp.*, *Spirogyra crassa*, *Elodea canadensis*, and root tips of *Zea mays* and *Allium cepa*, Karling (*loc. cit.*), dead *Cladophora*, Sparrow (1943: 320), UNITED STATES; snake-skin bait, from soil, Sparrow (1952b: 71), CUBA.

Couch (1945a) has rejected this as a species of *Catenaria* because of the chytridiaceous nature of the zoospore. It possibly belongs in *Sep-tochytrium* but is retained here provisionally.

CATENOMYCES Hanson

Torreya, 44: 30. 1944

(Fig. 44 H-K, p. 651)

"Thallus usually polycentric, rarely monocentric, intra- and extramatrical; intramatrical portion branched or unbranched, septate; septa delimiting the rudiments of the sporangia or sterile isthmuses; extramatrical portion branched, aseptate and sterile. Sporangia with one to several exit tubes in which opercula develop beneath mucilaginous plugs. Zoospores posteriorly uniflagellate. Resting spores unknown or doubtful" (Hanson, *loc. cit.*).

Saprophytic on vegetable debris.

See remarks, p. 650.

CATENOMYCES PERSICINUS Hanson

Torreya, 44: 30. 1944

"Protoplasm of intramatrical hyphae developing golden refractive globules, while the protoplasm of the extramatrical hyphae remains hyaline. Zoosporangia smooth, with peach-colored spore plasm at maturity, variable in shape, uteriform [*sic*], $21-71 \times 25-82 \mu$, pyriform, $12-45 \times 19-82 \mu$, ovoid, $17-63 \times 28-97 \mu$, cylindrical, $6-15 \times 19-75 \mu$, spherical, $17-57 \mu$, elliptical, $21-62 \times 37-159 \mu$, rectangular, $43-55 \times 59-83 \mu$, triangular, $35-59 \times 44-65 \mu$, or irregular, $26-67 \times 35-193 \mu$, with 1-9 exit canals, $3.7-16 \times 7.5-112 \mu$, frequently branched, and of which only one functions. Tips of exit papillae or canals softening at maturity and becoming filled with a plug of mucilaginous material; granular protoplasm receding downward and forming an operculum beneath the plug. Opercula extremely thin, shallow saucer-shaped, circular or oval in outline, $2.2-2.9 \mu$, in diameter. Zoospores spherical, $3.7-4.5 \mu$, with many golden refractive globules, flagellum approximately 30μ long, emerging singly and forming a temporary group near the orifice, intermittently amoeboid. Resting spores doubtful" (Hanson, *loc. cit.*).

Saprophytic on grasses, bleached corn (maize) leaves, onions, and cellophane, from water and soil containing animal and vegetable debris, Karling (1949c: 299), UNITED STATES.

BLASTOCLADIACEAE

Thallus walled, highly variable in extent, usually with a basal cell anchored to the substratum by branched rhizoids, nonseptate or pseudoseptate, sometimes with sterile setae, of determinate or indeterminate growth; reproductive rudiments one or more, sessile or variously borne on the basal cell or its branches or on hyphae, delimited from the thallus by true cross walls at maturity; sometimes differentiated into similar sporophyte and gametophyte phases; zoospores borne in thin-walled sporangia, emerging through one or more pores; resting spores punctate; smooth-walled or variously ornamented, in a thin-walled container, upon germination producing planonts; sexuality isogamous, anisogamous, or lacking; plants monoecious or (in *Blastocladiella*) dioecious; life history of the Euallomyces, Cystogenes, or Brachyallomyces type.

Saprophytes in water and soil on a variety of plant and animal debris.

KEY TO THE GENERA OF THE BLASTOCLADIACEAE [1]

Thallus consisting of a single reproductive rudiment from which the rhizoids emerge directly, or of a reproductive rudiment borne at the apex of an unbranched basal cell anchored by rhizoids to the substratum............................. BLASTOCLADIELLA, p. 660
Thallus bearing an indeterminate number of reproductive rudiments on the basal cell or on its branches
   Thallus consisting of a basal cell and a few depauperate, distal, dichotomously branched hyphae, without pseudoseptae, one of the dichotomies usually rudimentary; resting spore loose within its container, unpitted............ BLASTOCLADIOPSIS, p. 668
   Thallus consisting either of a basal cell from which arise strongly developed dichotomously branched, pseudoseptate hyphae which bear the reproductive rudiments, or of a basal cell alone, the reproductive rudiments sessile or on lobes or extensions of the basal cell
      Thallus with an unlobed or unbranched basal cell which gives rise distally and usually dichotomously to cylindrical pseudoseptate branches, setae never formed; zoosporangium with one or more discharge papillae; gametophytes known.. ALLOMYCES, p. 669

---

[1] Sörgel (1952) gave fragmentary accounts of certain soil fungi which he assigned to this family as new genera, viz., *Ramocladia*, *Allocladia*, *Brevicladia*, and *Leptocladia*. It is hoped that more complete descriptions will be forthcoming, so that these forms may be properly evaluated.

Thallus with a simple, lobed, or branched basal cell; secondary axes present and lacking pseudosepta, or absent, setae present or absent; zoosporangium with a single apical discharge papilla; gametophytes unknown.......... BLASTOCLADIA, p. 678

BLASTOCLADIELLA MATTHEWS

J. Elisha Mitchell Sci. Soc., 53: 194. 1937

(Figs. 39, p. 612; 45, p. 661)

Rhopalomyces Harder and Sörgel, Nachrichten Gesell. Wiss. Göttingen, Math.-Physik. Kl., Fachgruppe VI (Biol.), (N. F.), 3(5): 123. 1938. Non Corda et alii.

Clavochytridium Couch and Cox, in Cox, J. Elisha Mitchell Sci. Soc., 55: 389. 1939.

Sphaerocladia Stüben, "Planta," Archiv. wiss. Bot., 30(3): 364. 1939

Thallus consisting either of a simple spherical swelling with a basal complex of rhizoids or a more or less elongate unbranched basal cell without pseudosepta, forming distally a single reproductive organ, the whole anchored to the substratum by a system of branched holdfasts, walls not giving a cellulose reaction; sporophyte plant bearing terminally either a zoosporangium with thin walls, which discharges the fully matured posteriorly uniflagellate zoospores through one or more pores produced by deliquescence of papillae, or a resting spore having thick two-layered walls (outer one variously sculptured) that completely fills a thin-walled case; resting spore germinating to form posteriorly uniflagellate planonts which either give rise directly to new asexual or sexual plants or at once encyst, cysts each developing endogenously four posteriorly uniflagellate isogametes which emerge through a pore and fuse in pairs, the resulting biflagellate zygote producing upon germination an asexual plant; gametophyte plant similar to the sporophyte, dioecious, giving rise to posteriorly uniflagellate isogamous planogametes.

Thus far collected primarily only as saprophytes in soils from southerly latitudes.

KEY TO THE SPECIES OF BLASTOCLADIELLA

Life cycle of the Euallomyces type, that is, involving isomorphic generations, sexual and asexual

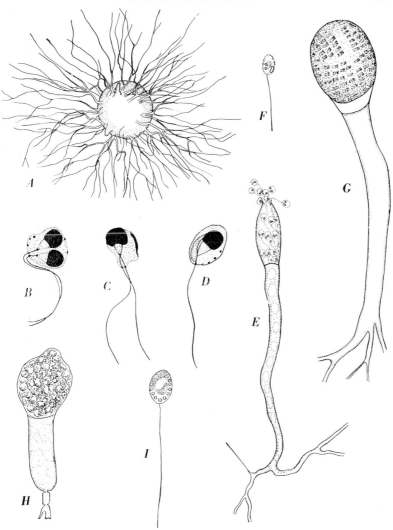

FIG. 45. *Blastocladiella*

A-D. Blastocladiella stubenii Couch and Whiffen: *A*, mature sporangium with two discharge papillae; rhizoids beneath plant not shown; *B-D*, cytological preparations of swarmers, *B*, two recently fused isogamous gametes, *C*, a zygote, and *D*, a zoospore showing lateral body as well as nuclear cap. *E-G. Blastocladiella simplex* Matthews: *E*, small plant with discharging sporangium; *F*, single zoospore (drawn freehand); *G*, plant bearing resting spore. *H-I. Blastocladiella stomophilum* (Couch and Cox) Couch and Whiffen: *H*, basal cell and sporangium; *I*, zoospore.

(*A-D*, Stüben, 1939; *E-G*, Sparrow, 1943; *H-I*, Cox, 1939).

Sporangia and gametangia usually sessile; both gametangia color-
less.. *B. stubenii*, p. 662
Sporangia and gametangia usually stalked; male gametangia orange-
colored................................ *B. variabilis*, p. 663
Life cycle of the Cystogenes type, that is, the gametophyte represented
by a cyst bearing four isogamous gametes
Resting-spore wall faintly areolate; cysts 8–10 μ in diameter......
.... *B. cystogena*, p. 663
Resting-spore wall smooth; cysts 4–6 μ in diameter..............
.... *B. microcystogena*, p. 664
Life cycle of the Brachyallomyces type, that is, involving only resting-
spore and zoosporangial plants
Both zoosporangia and resting spores present
Plants derived from planonts from resting spores all colorless
Thalli more than 500 μ in height; resting sporangia areolate...
.... *B. simplex*, p. 664
Thalli less than 500 μ in height
Resting-spore wall verrucose............*B. asperosperma*, p. 665
Resting-spore wall smooth..............*B. laevisperma*, p. 666
Plants derived from planonts from resting spores over 98 per cent
colorless and less than 2 per cent orange-colored..........
.... *B. emersonii*, p. 666
Only zoosporangia present; thalli up to 300 μ high, usually stalked
when on leaves.........................*B. stomophilum*, p. 667

Blastocladiella stubenii Couch and Whiffen

Amer. Journ. Bot., 29: 588. 1942
(Fig. 45 A–D, p. 661)

Sphaerocladia variabilis Stüben, "Planta," Archiv wiss. Bot., 30 (3): 364,
figs. 1–12. 1939.

Sporangium with a thin smooth wall, spherical or more or less ovoid
or ellipsoidal, averaging 60 μ in diameter when on flies, 140 μ on peptone
agar; rhizoids profusely developed; zoospores emerging through one or
several papillae, ellipsoidal, 3.5 by 4.8 μ, the contents bearing in addition to a "food body," a lateral tear-shaped structure; resting spore
either ovoid, 13 by 17 μ (the brownish wall 0.5 μ thick), or spherical,
110 μ in diameter (the wall 2.5 μ thick); planohaplonts one-half the size
of the zoospores, emerging through a prominent papilla which protrudes
through a crack in the resting-spore wall; gametophytes similar to

the zoosporangial plants but smaller, averaging 106 μ on peptone agar, the + or — gametes similar to the zoospores but smaller; zygote biflagellate and germinating at once to form a sporophyte.

In soil, coll. Ulmcke, MEXICO.

BLASTOCLADIELLA VARIABILIS Harder and Sörgel

Deutsch-Dominik. Tropenforschungsinstituts, Hamburg-Ciudad Trujillo
D.S.D., 1: 123. 1939

(Fig. 39, p. 612)

Rhopalomyces variabilis Harder and Sörgel, Nachrichten Gesell. Wiss. Göttingen, Math.-Physik. Kl., Fachgruppe VI (Biol.) (N.F.), 3(5): 123, figs. 1–3, fig. 4 B–E. 1938.

Basal cell cylindrical, holdfasts delicate, much branched, wall thin, smooth; sporangium clavate, colorless, wall chitinous, thin, smooth, with several discharge papillae; zoospores ovoid, with a refractive saddle-shaped "food body" and a long posterior flagellum; resting spore borne like the sporangium, spherical, with a thick dark-brown several-layered wall (sculptured?), cracking upon germination and allowing papillae to protrude, which upon dissolution form pores for the escape of numerous posteriorly uniflagellated planonts; planonts upon germination giving rise to thalli that resemble the zoosporangial plants, on each of which is produced either a colorless or an orange-colored clavate gametangium (+ or —); gametes isogamous (+ or —) fusing in pairs to form a zygote, which at once produces a sporophyte plant.

Saprophytic in soil, coll. Ulmcke, DOMINICAN REPUBLIC.

By analogy with long-cycled species of *Allomyces* the pigmented gametangium could be regarded as the male and the colorless one as the female.

BLASTOCLADIELLA CYSTOGENA Couch and Whiffen

Amer. Journ. Bot., 29: 589, figs. 1–14, 49–57, 58–63. 1942

"Zoosporangial thalli lacking in life cycle. Resting sporangial thalli when on leaves usually extramatrical, spherical or pyriform and sessile or with a very small and inconspicuous stalk, frequently intramatrical on leaves and then subspherical ovoid or lobed; on hemp seed usually tubular, the case that encloses the resting sporangium globose to sub-cylindrical. Rhizoids well developed, attached basally if sporangium is extramatrical, or attached to several places on the sides if intramatrical. Resting sporangia when spherical 16–342 μ thick, when subspherical 37–142 × 35–209 μ; stalk when present very variable in size, 30–116 × 39–564 μ; usually filling the case in which it is formed; wall two–layered, very faintly areolate, 1.5–6.1 μ thick, nearly hyaline to dull yellow or orange brown. Germination as in the genus. Zoospores uniciliate when discharged, encysting almost immediately near the sporangial mouth in an irregular mass. Encysted spores (gametangia) 8.2–10.2 μ thick, spherical. After one to two hours each cyst gives rise to four uniciliated gametes which emerge through a minute pore to fuse in pairs near the empty cysts; gametes 4.1 × 4.9 μ. Zygotes bi-ciliated, 6 × 8 μ, swimming for an hour or more before germinating to form resting sporangia" (Couch and Whiffen, *loc. cit.*).

On grass leaves, from soil, coll. Philip Couch, UNITED STATES.

BLASTOCLADIELLA MICROCYSTOGENA Whiffen

J. Elisha Mitchell Sci. Soc., 62: 57, pl. 7, figs. 1–5. 1946

"Thallus of resting sporangium sessile or stalked; spherical to ovoid, 12–68 μ in diameter; wall of resting sporangium smooth, hyaline to light yellow brown, 1.3–4.5 μ thick. Germination of resting sporangium by cracking open of wall and formation of one exit papilla, through which uniflagellate zoospores are discharged. Zoospores encysting al-most immediately; encysted zoospore (gametangium) spherical, 4.8–6.2 μ in diameter; each gametangium discharging four uniflagellate gametes, 2.5 × 2.9 μ, which fuse in pairs. Zygote biflagellate, encysting and germinating to form a plant bearing a resting sporangium" (Whiffen, *loc. cit.*).

On grass-leaf bait, from soil, coll. J. N. and P. Couch, UNITED STATES.

BLASTOCLADIELLA SIMPLEX Matthews

J. Elisha Mitchell Sci. Soc., 53: 194, 1 text fig., pls. 20–21. 1937
(Fig. 45 E–G, p. 661)

Basal cell cylindrical, holdfasts delicate, branched, wall thin, smooth; whole thallus, including rudiment of reproductive structure, 30–1005 μ long by 8–40 μ in diameter; sporangium cylindrical to globose, 15–105 μ in diameter, wall thin, smooth, with from one to three discharge papillae; zoospores ovoid to ellipsoidal, 5.5–7 μ long by 3–4 μ wide, with a long posterior flagellum and an anterior ring of refractive globules, emerging in a quickly evanescent vesicle; resting spore borne like the sporangium, 15–180 μ in diameter, surrounded by the thin wall of the container, clavate, with a rounded apex and a truncate base, wall dark brown, thick, coarsely and irregularly reticulate, upon germination forming posteriorly uniflagellate planonts which give rise to zoospore- or resting-spore-bearing thalli, sexuality not known.

On fly cadaver, Matthews (*loc. cit.*), hempseed bait, bog soil, coll. G. R. LaRue, Sparrow (1943: 418), UNITED STATES; Sörgel (1952: 388), FRANCE.

BLASTOCLADIELLA ASPEROSPERMA Couch and Whiffen

Amer. Journ. Bot., 29: 588, figs. 29–35, 41, 43–45, 66. 1942

"Thalli consisting of extramatrical stalked or sessile zoosporangia and resting sporangia anchored to the substratum by rhizoids; single or caespitose. Zoosporangial thalli spherical, ovoid, pyriform or nearly cylindrical; sporangia spherical, pyriform, ovoid, sub-cylindrical or irregular; 25–100 μ thick when spherical, up to 88 × 155 μ when ovoid or pyriform; stalk when present varying from a small basal part to a long tube 30 × 150 μ, usually thickest just below the sporangium, frequently with one to several rings just below sporangium. Sporangia with one to several (up to 11) emergence papillae. Zoospores usually becoming active in sporangium before emergence. The first spores emerging in a spherical vesicle formed from the gelatinized tip. After the vesicle bursts the spores remaining in the sporangium emerge slowly and swim away immediately upon reaching the outside. Zoospores 3.6–4.6 × 6–7 μ. Resting sporangial thalli similar in shape, size and early development to the zoosporangial thalli; resting sporangia not completely filling the case in which they are formed; spherical, ovoid, pyriform or sub-cylindrical; outer wall yellow brown and distinctly warted; 14–80 μ thick on grass when spherical, somewhat larger on hemp seed and spherical to oval in shape. Germinating after several weeks' rest to form zoospores as in zoosporangia" (Couch and Whiffen, *loc. cit.*).

On boiled grass leaves, from soil, coll. Philip Couch, UNITED STATES.

BLASTOCLADIELLA LAEVISPERMA Couch and Whiffen

Amer. Journ. Bot., 29: 589, figs. 15–28, 36–39, 40, 42, 46, 65. 1942

"Zoosporangial and resting sporangial thalli much as in *B. asperosperma* except resting sporangia usually fill the case and have a smooth wall except for a few ridges. Zoosporangia usually sessile on leaves and stalked on hemp seed; 25–117 μ when spherical; stalk up to 26 × 105 μ. Zoospores 3.8–4.6 × 6–6.5 μ when active, 5–5.4 μ when rounded up. Resting sporangial case as a rule stalked on hemp seed but usually sessile on leaves; rarely two resting sporangia may be formed on the same stalk; spherical, ovoid, pyriform or sub-cylindrical, sometimes constricted in the middle, at times lobed; 25–140 μ thick when spherical, up to 63 × 95 μ when ovoid; stalk 30 × 155 μ, broadest at the top; resting sporangia usually completely filling the case and conforming to its shape, up to 126 μ thick when spherical; wall 1.5–2.8 μ thick, reddish brown or pale dull yellow, smooth except for one or several conspicuous ridges. Germinating after a few weeks' rest to form zoospores which are similar to those from zoosporangia" (Couch and Whiffen, *loc. cit.*).

Obtained from the same soil collection as *Blastocladiella asperosperma*, UNITED STATES.

BLASTOCLADIELLA EMERSONII Cantino and Hyatt

A. v. Leeuwenhoek, 19: 67, figs. 1–14. 1953

"Thalli with short stalks, anchored to substratum by rhizoids, and bearing single apical resistant sporangia [R. S.], thin-walled colorless spore-sacs, or thin-walled spore-sacs with orange pigmentation. Under controlled conditions on agar media, resistant sporangia, spherical, of very uniform dimensions, sculpturing, and deep-brown pigmentation; *ca.* 120 to 180 μ diameter, depending on media used, with wall 2.5 μ thick, and containing pits and depressions (similar to those in *B. simplex*) which function as preformed dehiscence ridges. Stalk always thickest just beneath sporangium. R. S. germinate when mature and liberate spores, $7 \times 9 \mu$, through several papillae. Submerged in water, on the usual ill-defined natural substrata, or under crowded conditions on agar media, R. S. vary from 18 to 170 μ diameter, with or without pits, or with pits confluent in irregular depressions, and with degree of pigmentation varying from light yellow to deep brown; stalk may be pyriform or cylindrical; in liquid culture often with 1 to 4 septa below sporangium. *Ca.* 99% of plants derived from R.S. spores bear apical reproductive units which are thin-walled, colorless and spherical to ovoid-pyriform, with constant dimensions under controlled conditions on agar media, but with great variation in size and shape on natural substrata. Swarmers, mostly $7 \times 9 \mu$, discharged through one to several papillae. *Ca.* 1% of R.S. spores yield thin-walled plants bearing apical reproductive units with orange pigmentation, similar to those of colorless plants in shape and size, but swarmers are $4 \times 6 \mu$. No one type of swarmer is capable of fusing with any other. On media containing bicarbonate, *ca.* 95–100% of R.S. spores give rise directly to R.S. plants rather than thin-walled plants" (Cantino and Hyatt, *loc. cit.*).

On silica-gel agar, submerged in fresh-water pond, UNITED STATES.

BLASTOCLADIELLA STOMOPHILUM (Couch and Cox) Couch and Whiffen
Amer. J. Bot., 29: 587. 1942
(Fig. 45 H–I, p. 661)
Clavochytridium stomophilum Couch and Cox, in Cox, J. Elisha Mitchell
Sci. Soc., 55: 390, fig. 1, pls. 45–46. 1939.

"Thallus monocentric; each thallus at maturity consisting of a coarse intramatrical rhizomycelium and an extramatrical zoosporangium. Rhizoids more or less profusely branched, sometimes constricted or ovoid, ellipsoid or cylindrical, sessile or stalked, the length of the stalk variable (up to 320 μ). Spores escaping singly from one or more exit papillae, remaining motionless or becoming amoeboid for a few seconds at the mouth of the sporangium and then swimming away. Spores posteriorly uniciliate (length of cilium 35 to 50 μ), $3.5 \times 6.5 \mu$, ovoid or elliptical, with two to twelve small eccentric refractive bodies. Empty sporangium hyaline, persisting on the surface of the dead host. Resting spores unknown" (Couch and Cox, in Cox, *loc. cit.*).

Saprophytic on boiled corn (maize) and grass leaves used as bait, UNITED STATES.

BLASTOCLADIOPSIS Sparrow

J. Wash. Acad. Sci., 40: 52, 1950

(Fig. 47 G–J, p. 682)

Thallus filamentous, without a well-defined basal cell, nonseptate except where reproductive organs are delimited, dichotomously or subdichotomously branched; anchored to the substratum by a system of coarse-branched rhizoids; zoosporangia irregular or somewhat cylindrical, with one to six discharge papillae; zoospores posteriorly uniflagellate, with several oil globules and a conspicuous nuclear cap; resting spores usually spherical or somewhat ellipsoidal, with a thin, golden to amber-colored, smooth nonpunctate wall, borne singly and loosely within their container, upon germination cracking open to discharge posteriorly uniflagellate zoospores through one or more pores; gametophyte unknown.

So far as known, a monotypic genus, in soil.

Blastocladiopsis parva (Whiffen) Sparrow

J. Wash. Acad. Sci., 40: 53, figs. 27–30. 1950

Blastocladia parva Whiffen, J. Elisha Mitchell Sci. Soc., 59: 40, pl. 4, figs. 17–36. 1943.

Thallus 300 μ or more in length, unbranched or more commonly dichotomously or subdichotomously branched; hyphae 12–50 μ in diameter, somewhat irregular; zoosporangia rare, terminal on the hyphae, irregular or somewhat cylindrical, 40 by 65.6 to 41.3 by 90.2 μ, with one to six discharge papillae; resting spore lying loosely in a smooth-walled or occasionally apically papillate container, spherical, ellipsoidal or ovoid, 36.8 by 41 μ to 35.2 by 77.1 μ, with a golden to pale amber-colored smooth, nonpunctate wall, upon germination the wall cracking open and posteriorly uniflagellate zoospores escaping through one or two discharge pores.

Saprophytic in soil, coll. J. N. and P. Couch, Whiffen (1943), United States; on snake skin, grass used as bait, in soil, Sparrow (1950), Cuba.

The measurements are those for Whiffen's Texan material. In the Cuban fungi, the zoosporangia, also very rarely formed, ranged from 55 to 70 μ long by 22 to 25 μ broad. They developed a lateral as well as an apical discharge pore. Occasionally, the resting-spore container bore an apical papilla.

Although *Blastocladiopsis parva* approaches certain species of *Blasto-cladia* in similarity of thallus structure, it is readily distinguished. Its resting spores are completely smooth-walled and not punctate. Further-more, they are loose in their containers, rather than filling them (Fig. 47 G, I, J) and the zoosporangia may have more than one discharge pore.

Development of the fungus is remarkably rapid. Within two or three days after the start of a new culture from dried material, plants with mature resting spores are obtained. Sporangia are evidently exceedingly rare (Fig. 47 I). Whiffen suggests that temperature may be a factor inducing their formation. In her material, at 24–25 degrees C. only resting spores formed, but at 21 degrees C. about twelve zoosporangia appeared.

The complete life history is not yet known. From the scarcity of spo-rangial plants it is not likely that they are gametangial in function. If a sexual stage exists, one possibility is that the resting spores liberate gametes directly and that these fuse and form new sporophytes. No such fusion, however, was noted by Whiffen, and she observed zoospores (from resting spores) develop into plants that bore other resting spores.

ALLOMYCES E. J. Butler[1]
Ann. Bot. London, 25: 1027. 1911
(Figs. 40–43, pp. 616, 622, 626, 629)

Septocladia Coker and Grant, J. Elisha Mitchell Sci. Soc., 37: 180. 1922.

Thallus consisting of a cylindrical more or less differentiated trunklike basal cell which gives rise distally to cylindrical dichotomously, sub-dichotomously, or sympodially branched, blunt-tipped successively more slender pseudoseptate hyphae of indefinite extent on which are borne the reproductive organs, contents often alveolately or reticulately vacuolate, anchored to the substratum by a system of endobiotic

---

[1] A great number of isolates of the various species of this genus have been collected. It is impossible to include them all in the sections devoted to geographic distributions. Consequently, only the source of the original isolate or isolates on which the two phases of the particular species are founded or of those pertinent to its interpretation (ones giving rise to synonyms) is noted. More complete data on all isolates are avail-able in Emerson (1941) and F. T. Wolf (1941a).

branched strongly tapering rhizoids; asexual plant bearing terminally, sympodially, or in basipetal succession thin-walled zoosporangia which discharge their fully formed posteriorly uniflagellate zoospores through one or more pores produced upon the deliquescence of prominent papillae, and persistent or deciduous resting spores with a thick brown punctate outer wall and a thin inner one, the resting spores upon germination producing either (*a*) posteriorly uniflagellate planonts which give rise directly to new asexual plants or to sexual plants, or (*b*) posteriorly flagellate planonts which immediately encyst, each of the cysts forming endogenously four isogamous uniflagellate gametes which, after emerging from the cyst through a pore, fuse in pairs, the zygote germinating to form asexual plants; sexual plant similar to the sporophyte, monoecious, bearing male and female gametangia terminally in pairs or alternating in basipetal succession, gametes anisogamous, posteriorly uniflagellate, the small male always pigmented, the larger female colorless, the planozygote posteriorly biflagellate and germinating to form the asexual plant.

In water and soil on plant and animal remains.

Emerson (1938a, 1941) established three subgenera, based on the type of life cycle exhibited. His groupings have been adopted here (but not as subgenera). They are more fully discussed under "Life Cycles" (see pp. 624–627).

KEY TO THE SPECIES OF ALLOMYCES

Life cycle of the Euallomyces type; pits on resting spore closely spaced
    Gametangia when first formed developing in pairs, with the female
        terminal .... *A. arbuscula*, p. 671
    Gametangia when first formed developing in pairs, with the male
        usually terminal
        Primary male gametangia sometimes hypogynous; female game-
            tangium slightly longer than male .... *A. × javanicus*, [1] p. 673
        Primary male gametangia always terminal; female gametangium
            two to four times longer than male .... *A. macrogynus*, p. 674
Life cycle of the Cystogenes type; pits on resting spore widely spaced
    Resting spores mostly beaked or fusiform, cytoplasm often pigment-
        ed .... *A. moniliformis*, p. 676

[1] Natural hybrid between *A. arbuscula* and *A. macrogynus*.

Resting spores with broadly rounded apex, cytoplasm colorless....
.... *A. neo-moniliformis*, p. 677
Life cycle of the Brachyallomyces type.............. *A. anomalus*, p. 678

GROUP EUALLOMYCES

With alternation of isomorphic asexual and sexual generations; resting spore persistent on plants, pits on wall closely spaced, germinating to form planonts which give rise to sexual plants.

ALLOMYCES ARBUSCULA E. J. Butler

Ann. Bot. London, 25: 1027, figs. 1–18. 1911. Emend. Hatch, J. Elisha Mitchell Sci. Soc., 49(1): 163. 1933
(Fig. 40 A, p. 616; Fig. 41 Q-V, p. 622; Fig. 42, p. 626)

(?) *Blastocladia strangulata* Barrett, Bot. Gaz., 54: 367, pl. 18–20. 1912.
(?) *Allomyces strangulata* (Barrett) Minden, in Falck, Mykolog. Untersuch. Berichte, 2(2): 214. 1916.
(?) *Septocladia dichotoma* Coker and Grant, J. Elisha Mitchell Sci. Soc., 37: 180, pl. 32. 1922.
(?) *Allomyces arbuscula* forma *dichotoma* (Coker and Grant) Kanouse, Amer. J. Bot., 14: 303. 1927.
Allomyces kniepii Sörgel, Nachrichten Gesell. Wiss. Göttingen, Math.-Physik. Kl., Fachgruppe VI (Biol.) (N. F.), 2(10): 155. 1936; Zeitschr. Bot., 31: 402, figs. 2–10. 1937.
Allomyces arbuscula var. *arbuscula* Emerson, Lloydia, 4: 136. 1941.
Allomyces arbuscula var. *minor* Emerson, Lloydia, 4: 136. 1941.

Basal cell conspicuous, 100–200 µ long by 60–100 µ in diameter, hyphae copiously sympodially or dichotomously branched, the pseudo-cells up to 250 µ long by 15–25 µ in diameter; sporangia single or catenulate, broadly ellipsoidal or ovoid, with rounded or truncate ends, 40–70 µ long by 30–40 µ in diameter, forming from one to four discharge papillae; zoospores ovoid, oblong, or ellipsoidal, 12 µ long by 6 µ in diameter; resting spores abundant, ovoid, with rounded apex and truncate base, 28–67 µ long by 16–45 µ in diameter,[1] exospore thick-walled, tawny to reddish brown, minutely punctate, upon germination forming posteriorly uniflagellate planonts; sexual thallus similar to the asexual, gametangia at first terminal in pairs, later catenulate, alternating, the

[1] From Emerson's data (1941) on this strain, "North Carolina No. 2."

large globose, clavate, or ovoid colorless female gametangium terminal, 40–60 μ long by 16.5–30 μ in diameter, subtended by a short to long cylindrical or barrel-shaped male gametangium 6.6–56 μ long by 13–24 μ in diameter, with faintly golden or salmon-pink contents, female gamete colorless, ovoid, 10–12 μ long by 3.6–7 μ wide, male gamete ovoid or nearly spherical, 6–8 μ long by 4–8 μ in diameter, planozygote biflagellate, upon germination forming the sporophyte.

On insect cadavers (sporophyte only), Butler (*loc. cit.*), INDIA; Barrett (*loc. cit.*), North Carolina No. 2 isolate, gametophyte, coll. A. B. Couch, Coker and Grant (*loc. cit.*), North Carolina No. 1 isolate, coll. W. C. Coker, Emerson (1941), UNITED STATES; Kniep (1930), BALI; CENTRAL AMERICA: MEXICO, GUATEMALA, CANAL ZONE; WEST INDIES: DOMIN-ICAN REPUBLIC, HAITI; SOUTH AMERICA: BRAZIL, ARGENTINA; EU-ROPE: PORTUGAL; AFRICA: BELGIAN CONGO, NYASALAND, UGANDA, CAPE PROVINCE; INDIA (further isolations by Emerson): CEYLON, BURMA; JAPAN; CHINA; PHILIPPINE ISLANDS; FIJI ISLANDS.

Recent records: Cejp (1947), CZECHOSLOVAKIA; Remy (1948), GER-MANY; Shen and Siang (1948), CHINA; Sparrow (1952b), CUBA; Gaertner (1954b), AFRICA; Kobayashi and Ookubo (1952a; 1954b), JAPAN.

Specific distinctions in the Euallomyces group depend in great measure on the arrangment of the gametangia. Only the asexual plant of *Allomyces arbuscula* was described by Butler and there are now no living cultures of his fungus; hence, it is impossible to say just what he had. Coker and Matthews (1937) associated with this species a game-tophyte stage described by Hatch (1933), from the North Carolina No. 2 isolate, in which the female gametangium like that of Kniep's from Bali is terminal. It is entirely possible that Kniep's *A. javanicus* was iden-tical with Butler's fungus. Indeed, of four isolates obtained by Emerson (1941) from the type locality of Butler's fungus, three turned out to be *A. javanicus* and one *A. anomalus*. Since Kniep described both asexual and sexual phases of his Java isolate, however, his species (subse-quently shown to be a hybrid) should remain distinct.

As here understood, *Allomyces arbuscula* is based on Butler's asexual plant and on the North Carolina No. 2 strain, the gametophyte of which was studied by Hatch. Most of the synonyms are questioned, because they are based on asexual plants only. Emerson (1941) treated the relation of *A. kniepii* Sörgel to *A. arbuscula* in detail. He also established two varieties of *A.arbuscula* that depend on differences in size of the resting spores. Since intergrades between the varieties occur, this separation was mainly for convenience. In *A. arbuscula* var. *arbuscula* the resting structures average 32–45 μ in width; in var. *minor*, 24–31 μ. These varieties are not maintained here, as Emerson and Wilson (1954) doubt their validity on the basis of size alone.

ALLOMYCES × JAVANICUS Kniep (pro sp.)[1]

Berichte Deutsch. Bot. Gesell., 47: 211, figs. 1–7. 1929
(Figs. 40 B, p. 616; 41 A–J, P, p. 622)

Allomyces javanicus var. *javanicus* Emerson, Lloydia, 4: 135. 1941.
Allomyces javanicus var. *perandrus* Emerson, Lloydia, 4: 135. 1941.

Basal cell conspicuous, variable in size, hyphae copiously sympodially or dichotomously branched; zoosporangia ovoid or barrel-shaped, terminal or catenulate, 60–80 μ long by 27–50 μ in diameter, with one or several discharge papillae, zoospores ovoid, 11–12.5 μ long by 8–10 μ in diameter; resting spores ovoid or subspherical, with rounded apex and truncate base, 34.5–60 μ long by 23.5–35 μ in diameter, the exospore thick, olivaceous brown to tawny or reddish brown,[2] minutely punctate, upon germination forming posteriorly uniflagellate planonts; sexual plant similar to the asexual, gametangia somewhat irregularly arranged, terminal, single, in pairs or catenulate and alternating, the male terminal or, rarely, subterminal, cylindrical, with narrow apex, usually about 34.5 μ long by 23.5 μ broad when terminal, subtended by the somewhat larger, more ovoid female gametangium, which is usually about 51 μ long by 33 μ in diameter, male gamete 4.8–6.3 μ long by 3.4–4.4 μ wide, faintly orange to reddish, female gamete 9–11.5 μ long by 7.5–8.5 μ wide, colorless, the biflagellate planozygote coming to rest to form the new asexual plant.

In soil, Kniep (*loc. cit.*), JAVA; UNITED STATES; MEXICO; TANGANYIKA; BURMA; FIJI; JAPAN.

[1] Demonstrated by Emerson and Wilson (1954) to be *Allomyces arbuscula* × *A. macrogynus*, see p. 631.
[2] According to Emerson (1941).

New records: Sparrow (1952b), Cuba; Sörgel (1952: 388), France. The description is based in the main on Kniep's Java No. 1 isolate. Emerson and Wilson (1954) demonstrated experimentally that this "species" is a natural hybrid between *Allomyces arbuscula* and *A. macrogynus* (see p. 631).

Allomyces macrogynus (Emerson) Emerson and Wilson

Mycologia, 46: 429. 1954
(Fig. 40 C, p. 616)

Allomyces javanicus var. *japonensis* Indoh, Sci. Rept. Tokyo Bunrika
  Daigaku, Sect. B, 4: 265, figs. 1b, 24–28, 29 a–d, 30 a–c. 1940.
Allomyces javanicus var. *macrogynus* Emerson, Lloydia, 4: 135. 1941.

Vegetative structures resembling *Allomyces arbuscula*; gametangia, particularly on young hyphae, regular in shape and arrangement, the primary and often the secondary ones very regularly paired, the males always terminal, the females markedly elongate in the primary pairs, often nearly cylindric, strikingly longer than the males (averaging about twice and not seldom three to four times as long); female gametes, mean diameter 9–12 μ; male gametes 4–6 μ; resistant sporangia 32–85 μ long by 26–53 μ wide, always formed in abundance even on young hyphae; pits usually very fine, sometimes almost indistinguishable. (Slightly modified from Emerson, 1941.)

Indoh (1940), Japan; Sparrow, coll. W. R. Taylor (1943: 426), Venezuela. For other isolations see Emerson, 1941.

There seems little doubt that Emerson's and Indoh's varieties were established on identical forms. Emerson and Wilson (1954) show conclusively that *Allomyces macrogynus* should be segregated at the specific level from the hybrid represented by *A. javanicus*. Furthermore, their cytogenetical proof that *A. macrogynus* is one of the basic parental types of that complex is decisive.

So far as known Indoh had not prior to 1954 raised his variety to specific rank. Hence, Emerson and Wilson's species name would be valid because of the change of status from variety to species.

As a result of Emerson and Wilson's (1954) work, it is anticipated that the variety immediately following will prove to be of hybrid origin.

Allomyces javanicus var. *allomorphus* Indoh

Nagaoa, 2: 28, figs. 1–4. 1952

"Mycelium [in] white tuft[s], reaching about 7.8 mm. in length, attached by rhizoids to substrata. Hyphae with pseudosepta 25–34 μ, sometimes up to 42 μ thick at base, 13–23 μ, av. 18.2 μ at apices, branching dichotomously or subdichotomously.

"Zoosporangia terminal, sympodially arranged, sometimes 2–6 in chains. Primary ones clavate, oval to fusiform, 29–45 × 84–118 μ, av. 37.3 × 97.0 μ, catenate ones cylindrical, barrel-shaped 29–45 × 50–88 μ, av. 32.3 × 66.7 μ, occasionally *Y*- or *T*-shaped. Zoospores similar [in] shape and size to *All. javanicus* var. *japonensis* Indoh.

"Chlamydocysts terminal on asexual mycelia, spherical to ovoid, 42–67 × 67–109 μ, av. 49.7 × 86.1 μ, sympodially arranged, but in old cultures many of them crooked ovoid, some ones arranged in catenate [manner], subcylindrical to long barrel-shaped, occasionally *L*- or *T*-shaped. Appearing yellow orange [in] color, with two layers of membranes, outer one thick conspicuously and finely pitted as *All. javanicus* var. *japonensis* Indoh.

"Sexual reproduction by means of anisogamic gametogamy. Primary gametangia terminal on sexual mycelia arranged sympodially, consisting of an epigynous male gametangium and a hypogynous female gametangium. Later arranged in catenate [manner]. Male gametangia salmon-orange globose, 3.5–5.5 × 7.5–10.5 μ, female gametangia cylindrical to barrel-shaped 7.5–9.5 × 12–16 μ, the length of female gametangium is 2 to 3 times of the length of the paired male gametangium. But in old cultures, occurs [*sic*] various sizes and forms of male and female gametangia, subglobose, narrow cylindrical, long or short barrel-shaped, *Y*-shaped. Male and female gametes and zygotes, of similar form and behaviors, to *All. javanicus* var. *japonensis* Indoh" [=*A. macrogynus*] (Indoh, *loc. cit.*).

Isolated from paddy soil with boiled hempseed, JAPAN.

GROUP CYSTOGENES

With asexual phase dominant, the gametophyte represented by a cyst; resting spore deciduous, pits on wall widely spaced, germinating to form planonts which encyst and produce isogamous gametes.

ALLOMYCES MONILIFORMIS Coker and Braxton

J. Elisha Mitchell Sci. Soc., 42: 139, pl. 10. 1926. Emend. Emerson, Mycologia, 30: 127. 1938
(Fig. 40 F–G, p. 616)

Basal cell up to 150 μ or more in length by 17–48 μ in diameter, hyphae tapering, 12–18 μ in diameter, slightly but distinctly constricted at the pseudosepta, dichotomously branched, the pseudocells up to 655 μ long, contents in old cultures becoming slightly pink; primary sporangia narrowly clavate or cylindrical, 62–135 μ long by 20–32 μ in greatest diameter, with an apical papilla, secondary sporangia formed predominantly in basipetal succession, ovoid to nearly spherical, with truncate ends and from one to four lateral papillae, successively diminishing in size, the proximal ones as small as 20 μ in diameter, contents pink, becoming browner as the zoospores approach maturity; zoospores ovoid, 10–15 μ long by 5–8 μ broad, with a long posterior flagellum, capable of repeated emergence; resting spores narrowly to broadly ovoid, with truncate base and pronounced apical beak, usually 43–75 μ long by 21–43 μ in greatest width, generally slipping out of their containers at maturity, the exospore thick-walled, dark orange-brown, with widely spaced pits, germination of the Cystogenes type, primary biflagellate planonts and cysts 11–15 μ in diameter, isogamous gametes from the cysts 8–9 μ in mean diameter.

In moist sand and loam, Coker and Braxton (*loc. cit.*), UNITED STATES; MEXICO; CUBA; PUERTO RICO (doubtful); TRINIDAD; BOLIVIA.

Allomyces moniliformis is unique because it is the only member of the genus to have carotinoid pigment in structures other than the male gamete. Emerson (1938a) established the occurrence of cyst formation in the species, using an isolate obtained from J. N. Couch. Although not the type isolate, this was probably the one Teter (1944) compared with Sparrow's Trinidad strain. In general aspect, Sparrow's strain, which Teter studied carefully, is similar to Couch's *A. moniliformis*. The Trinidad strain is alone, however, of any of the Blastocladiales, in having all motile bodies devoid of flagella; movement is amoeboid only. By running parallel cultures with the North Carolina strain, Teter proved that this was not merely due to environment. The North Carolina isolate always bore flagellate bodies whereas the Trinidad strain never did. Since the phenomenon is probably caused by some flagellum-suppressing factor and since in most other respects the form resembles *A. moniliformis*, the Trinidad strain will not be segregated here.

Another interesting feature of the Trinidad strain was the frequency with which repeated emergence of the zoospores occurred. Coker and Braxton (1926) had figured this process in *Allomyces moniliformis*, but Emerson (1941) doubted their explanation. Emerson thought they had confused the phenomenon with the emergence of cyst-forming planonts from resting spores. In view of this tendency, it would not be surprising to find other members of the Cystogenes group exhibiting repeated emergence, since essentially the same process gives rise to the isogametes from the cysts.

ALLOMYCES NEO-MONILIFORMIS Indoh

Sci. Rept. Tokyo Bunrika Daigaku, Sect. B, 4: 271, figs. 2 d, 31–33, 34. 1940
(Figs. 41 K–O, p. 622; 43, p. 629)

Allomyces cystogenus Emerson, Lloydia, 4: 136, figs. 7, 10 A, 15, 1941; Mycologia, 30: 120, figs. 1–11. 1938.
Allomyces cystogenus var. *cystogenus* Emerson, *loc. cit.*, p. 136. 1941.
Allomyces cystogenus var. *elongatus* Emerson, *loc. cit.*, p. 136. 1941.

Basal cell 25–43 μ in diameter at base, anchored by rhizoids to substratum, the hyphae with pseudoseptae and indeterminate in length, subdichotomously branched, contents colorless; sporangia terminal, cymose or catenulate, the terminal ones clavate to somewhat cylindrical and 50–124 μ long by 20–40 μ in diameter, the catenulate ones barrel-shaped; zoospores with a mean diameter of 10–12 μ; resting spores terminal or cymose, oval to elongate to almost clavate, 34–95 μ long by 24–49 μ broad, with broadly rounded apex and scattered pits (about 3.5 μ apart); planonts from resting spores aflagellate or bearing two posterior flagella, 9–12 μ in diameter, quickly encysting, the cysts (reduced gametophytes) giving rise to four isogamous posteriorly uniflagellate gametes which fuse in pairs, the resultant zygote producing upon germination the sporophyte plant.

In soil, Indoh (*loc. cit.*), JAPAN; soil, Emerson (1941); BURMA, VENEZUELA, CHINA.

The description has been drawn from those by Indoh and Emerson.

There is but little doubt that their species were identical. Neither observed sexuality in his fungus. This phase was first established by Mc-Cranie (1942) and confirmed by Teter (1944).

Emerson's varieties are not maintained as distinct.

GROUP BRACHYALLOMYCES

With asexual phase only; resting spore persistent or deciduous, upon germination producing planonts which give rise to asexual plants.

ALLOMYCES ANOMALUS Emerson

Lloydia, 4: 133. 1941
(Fig. 40 D–E, p. 616)

"Characters of the subgenus [*Brachyallomyces*]. (A problematical subgenus and species tentatively established to include those few isolates in which repeated attempts to obtain sexual plants have been unsuccessful)" (Emerson, *loc. cit.*).

UNITED STATES; MEXICO; INDIA; CUBA.

Wilson's (1952) cytological studies show (see p. 627) that in *Allomyces* the omission of a sexual phase is the result of mitotic (and not meiotic) divisions occurring at germination of the resting spore.

REJECTED SPECIES OF ALLOMYCES

* ALLOMYCES MONSPELIENSIS Arnaud

Bull. Soc. Mycol. de France, 68: 184, fig. 1 E–H. 1952

On eggs of batrachian, FRANCE.

Too little information is given to define this species. From the beaked appearance of the resting spore, as shown in Arnaud's illustration (Fig. 1 F), affinity with one of the Cystogenes group is indicated.

BLASTOCLADIA REINSCH

Jahrb. wiss. Bot., 11: 298. 1878
(Figs. 46, p. 680; 47 A–F p. 682)

Thallus consisting of a cylindrical more or less elongate trunk-like basal cell which is either expanded at its apex or gives rise to broad distally

expanded lobes or short clavate branches or to cylindrical slightly tapering dichotomously, subdichotomously, or sympodially arranged branches on which the reproductive organs are borne, septa only delimiting
the reproductive organs, the whole anchored to the substratum by a
system of branched holdfasts; zoosporangia sessile, with a single apical
discharge papilla and, often projecting downward from this, a refractive
peglike plug; zoospores posteriorly uniflagellate, with a hyaline often
conspicuous subtriangular nuclear cap, formed in the sporangium, after
the deliquescence of the papilla emerging individually or in an evanescent vesicle, the papilla and peg sometimes persistent; resting spore with
a thick minutely punctate wall, persistent or deciduous, rounded or
beaked, with a truncate base, completely filling the thin-walled case in
which it is borne, formed on the same or on different plants from the
sporangia, upon germination producing planonts; gametophyte apparently not formed.

Saprophytes on decaying twigs and fruits, on which they form crisp
hemispherical pustules. Some species may occur alone, but usually they
are found growing with other water molds such as *Rhipidium, Gonapodya,* and the like. One species, *Blastocladia pringsheimii,* is undoubtedly
extremely common in all fresh-water habitats and it has been collected
from soils.

No absolutely conclusive evidence for the occurrence or nonoccurrence
in this genus of sexuality or of a gametophyte phase has yet been
presented. This has been due largely to the difficulty in obtaining germination of the resting spores. Minden (1916) observed early stages of
germination, but evidently did not follow the fate of the swarmers.
Miss Blackwell (1937) secured abundant germination of the resting
spores in *Blastocladia pringsheimii.* The results of her investigations on
the further development of the swarmers (Blackwell, 1940) indicate that
there is no gametangial plant or alternation of generations in this species.
The zoospores from germinating resting spores formed small thalli on
which were produced ordinary sporangia and zoospores. The latter were
never observed to fuse, but, rather, gave rise to thalli similar to the parent plant. The function, if any, of the sterile setae formed on some plants
has not been determined.

As elsewhere noted, Emerson and Cantino (1948) and Cantino (1948,

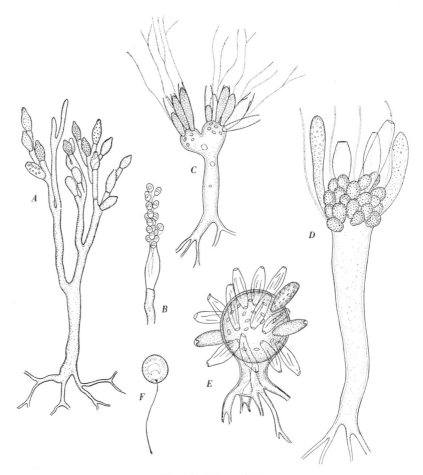

FIG. 46. *Blastocladia*

A-B. Blastocladia rostrata Minden: *A*, habit of plant bearing zoosporangia and beaked resting spores; *B*, sporangium discharging its zoospores. *C. Blastocladia sparrowii* Indoh, plant bearing setae, proliferated zoosporangia, and lobed basal cell. *D. Blastocladia pringsheimii* Reinsch plant bearing setae, zoosporangia, and resting spores. *E. Blastocladia globosa* Kanouse, plant with spherical basal cell and zoosporangia. *F. Blastocladia sp.*, living zoospore, showing internal structure.

(*E*, Kanouse, 1927; all others, Sparrow, 1943)

1949a) have grown *Blastocladia pringsheimii* and *B. ramosa* in pure culture on a medium composed of glucose, yeast extract, and certain inorganic salts, and have studied their nutrient and (in *B. pringsheimii*) vitamin requirements. One of the most interesting results of their experiments was the fact that resting spores of *B. pringsheimii* were produced in culture only when a 99.5 per cent carbon dioxide atmosphere was maintained or when the plants were grown in media containing carbonate.

The "*ramosa*" group of *Blastocladia* approximates *Allomyces* in the habit of the thallus. No pseudosepta are formed, however, and in plants as found in nature the zoospores are discharged through only a single apical papilla.

Identification of species is complicated by the diverse shapes which the basal apparatus may assume, and in some instances specific characters based on this feature will probably be shown in the future to be of questionable value. In general, however, reliance can be placed on the shapes of the resting spores and the sporangia and, to a lesser degree, on the presence or absence of a distal swelling of the basal cell or its branches. A study of the variations on different substrata of strains originating from single-spore cultures is greatly needed to clarify specific concepts.

A few studies of the development of the thallus indicate that the holdfast system, which here as in *Allomyces* is considered the homologue of the rhizoids of the chytrids, is derived from the primary germ tube of the zoospore. The basal cell represents the expanded body of the spore itself, and the reproductive organs originate as papilla-like outgrowths from its surface. Although resembling *Rhipidium*, *Mindeniella*, and *Araiospora* of the Leptomitales in superficial aspect, exhibiting, in fact, evolutionary parallelism with these genera, *Blastocladia* differs in bearing sessile sporangia, resting spores rather than oöspores, and posteriorly uniflagellate zoospores.

KEY TO THE SPECIES OF BLASTOCLADIA

Sporangia predominantly cylindrical, at least four times as long as wide; thallus variable in habit
Basal cell clavate or globose, with lobes or clavate branches

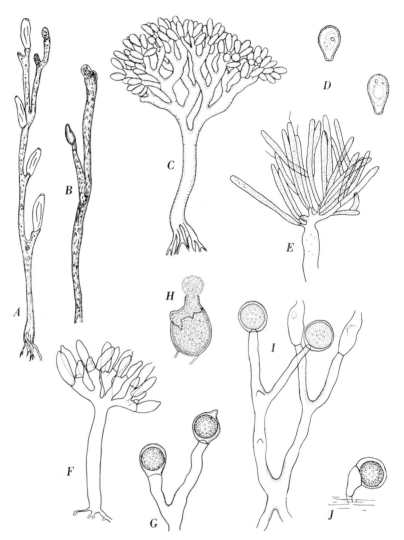

Fig. 47. Blastocladiaceae

Basal cell distinctly clavate, the branches, when formed, always clavate

Sporangia not proliferating .... *B. pringsheimii*, p. 684

B. aspergilloides, p. 686

Sporangia proliferating .... *B. sparrowii*, p. 686

Basal cell globose the cylindrical part very short or absent

B. globosa, p. 687

Basal cell cylindrical throughout only slightly, if at all, clavate, branched or unbranched

Sporangia proliferating .... *B. prolifera*, p. 688

Sporangia not proliferating

Sporangia about nine times as long as wide; borne on short branches of the basal cell .... *B. angusta*, p. 688

Sporangia about from three to four times as long as wide; arranged subracemosely, corymbosely, cymosely, or subdichotomously on short branches

Sporangia cylindrical to broad-clavate .... *B. incrassata*, p. 689

Sporangia long-cylindrical .... *B. gracilis*, p. 690

Sporangia predominantly narrowly or broadly ovoid, fusiform, beaked, or broadly ellipsoidal or dome-shaped and truncate

Sporangia narrowly or broadly ovoid or fusiform, appearing beaked; thallus cylindrical throughout

Walls of the thallus smooth

Sporangia and the thick-walled brown resting spores appearing beaked .... *B. rostrata*, p. 690

Sporangia beaked; resting spores with rounded apex, thin-walled, colorless .... *B. ramosa*, p. 691

Explanation of Figure 47

A. Blastocladia gracilis Kanouse, habit of plant bearing racemosely arranged empty zoosporangia. *B. Blastocladia tenuis* Kanouse, plant showing sculptured wall. *C-D. Blastocladia ramosa* Thaxter: *C*, habit of plant; *D*, optical sections of two resting spores from type material, showing canals of pits in outer walls. *E. Blastocladia angusta* Lund, habit of upper part of plant. *F. Blastocladia incrassata* Indoh, habit of plant. *G-J. Blastocladiopsis parva* (Whiffen) Sparrow: *G*, terminus of a dichotomy showing two smooth-walled resting spores lying loosely in their containers; *H*, resting spore producing zoospores upon germination; *I*, thallus bearing two resting spores and two empty zoosporangia each with two discharge pores; *J*, dwarf plant consisting of a few rhizoids in substratum and short basal cell and single resting spore.

(*A*, Kanouse, 1927; *B*, after Kanouse, 1927; *C*, after Thaxter, 1896a; *E*, Lund, 1934; *F*, Indoh, 1940; *G*, after Sparrow, 1950; *H*, Whiffen, 1943; *I-J*, Sparrow, 1950)

Walls bearing ridged markings .... *B. tenuis*, p. 692
Sporangia broadly ellipsoidal or dome-shaped and truncate
    Sporangia broadly ellipsoidal in dense clusters, basal cell wide,
        tapering distally, branching apically .... *B. glomerata*, p. 692
    Sporangia dome-shaped and truncate, few, basal cell cylindrical,
        only slightly expanded distally .... *B. truncata*, p. 693

BLASTOCLADIA PRINGSHEIMII Reinsch

Jahrb. wiss. Bot., 11: 298. 1878
(Fig. 46 D, p. 680)

Basal cell variable in habit and size, generally cylindrical, 400–1000 μ long by 30–90 μ in diameter, wall smooth or rough, up to 8 μ thick, expanded distally and simple or giving rise to cylindrical, apically expanded, subdichotomously, subumbellately, or irregularly arranged branches or broad lobes up to 240–400 μ long by 80–160 μ in diameter, setae present or absent, 2–6 μ in diameter, generally bulbous at the base, holdfasts richly branched, the whole thallus up to 2000 μ long, contents with many globules; sporangia borne along the tips of the branches or over the surface of the swollen lobes, predominantly cylindrical or narrowly clavate, often somewhat curved, also narrowly ellipsoidal, fusiform, long ovoid, or siliquiform, 70–350 μ long by 13–70 μ in diameter, usually at least from three to five or more times as long as broad, the discharge papilla often bearing an endogenous plug, zoospores ovoid and 6–9 μ long by 5–6 μ in diameter, or spherical and 12–15 μ in diameter, emerging individually or in a columnar or pyriform group surrounded by an evanescent vesicle bearing an apical, persistent plug (the remains of the discharge papilla), empty sporangia often deciduous; resting spores usually borne among the sporangia, ellipsoidal, ovoidal, or spherical with truncate base, 40–99 μ long by 30–50 μ in diameter, wall thick, brownish, punctate, upon germination the wall splitting and the contents becoming divided into planonts.

Forming dense pustules on apples, Reinsch (*loc. cit.*), fruits and twigs, Minden (1902: 823; 1915: 603, fig. 13 [p. 580]; 1916: 189, 211, text figs. 15–17, pl. 4, figs. 25–33), substratum (?), Laibach (1927), Behrens (1931), GERMANY; apples and other plant materials, Thaxter (1896a: 51, pl. 3, figs. 1–13), fruits of apple, crab apple, rose, *Crataegus*, Kanouse (1927: 297, pl. 33, figs. 8–13), apples, Cotner (1930a: figs. 1–4), apples, twigs,

Sparrow (1932b: 291, pl. 7, fig. H; 1933c: 529), Emerson and Cantino (1948); twigs, Sparrow and Barr (1955: 555), apples and twigs, Ziegler and Linthicum (1957), UNITED STATES; apples and ash twigs, H. E. Petersen (1909: 395; 1910: 532, fig. 10), Lund (1934: 40, fig. 18), Sparrow, DENMARK; apple, Valkanov (1931a: 366), BULGARIA; twigs, Barnes and Melville (1932: 94), rose fruits, Cook and Forbes (1933: 641), Forbes (1935a: 237, pl. 10, fig. 10), twigs and apples, Sparrow (1936a: 455, pl. 20, fig. 5), tomato fruits, Blackwell (1937: 933; 1940: figs. 1–9), Lloyd (1938: figs. 1–3), Emerson and Cantino (1948), Waterhouse (1942), GREAT BRITAIN; fruits of rose, banana, apples, *Japonica*, winter cherry, *Cotoneaster*, Crooks (1937: 222, fig. 8), AUSTRALIA; *Pirus* fruits, Indoh (1940: 250, figs. 9 a–e), JAPAN; apples, Sparrow, HOLLAND; tomato fruits, Shen and Siang (1948: 188), CHINA; in soil, coll. Hansford, Emerson and Cantino (1948), UGANDA.

The commonest species of the genus. Since the habit of the plant is extremely variable, considerable observation on cultures derived from single-spore strains growing on various twigs and fruits will be necessary before the species can be adequately delimited. A glance at the figures of what various authors consider this species will show that all plants with somewhat cylindrical sporangia and resting spores which are thick-walled and not beaked have been termed *Blastocladia pringsheimii*. Certain specimens showing more pronounced variations in thallus habit have been segregated as distinct species (*B. globosa, B. aspergilloides, B. angusta*, and so on). Attempts have also been made (Lloyd, 1938) to arrange the thallus types in groups, the extremes being on the one hand a globose type with a short cylindrical axis and on the other a slender ramose type. Unfortunately, significant data can only be accumulated by resort to single-spore cultures. Lloyd's observations over a period of time on gross cultures of what was considered a single species showed that there was no periodicity in the shape of the thallus, the frequency of resting spores, or the presence or absence of setae. The lobed type with definite cylindrical axis and the branched type with swollen apices predominated. It is important to bear in mind that the latter type was figured by Reinsch as typical of his species.

The sizes given for the thallus are probably of very little significance. Crooks (1937) has determined from a study of the size of the sporangia in 265 individuals that there was wide variation in this respect, the structures ranging from 70 to 270 μ in length and from 15 to 75 μ in diameter; sporangia 100–210 μ in length by 25–55 μ in diameter were in the majority, whereas those 150–159.9 by 30–39.9 μ occurred with the greatest frequency.

BLASTOCLADIA ASPERGILLOIDES Crooks

Proc. Roy. Soc. Victoria (N. S.), 49(2): 228, text fig. 11c, pl. 10, figs. 1, 4. 1937

"Plant attached to substratum by means of a few fairly stout rhizoids —up to 5 μ in diameter; plant consists of a single cell, cylindrical in the lower part 25–45 μ in diameter, but expanded at the apex to form a swollen head—60–85 μ in diameter; branched forms were not observed; plants 140–200 μ high, dark in color due to dark brown protoplasm, wall of basal cell fairly thick, 3.5–5 μ; sterile hairs usually present, only 1–2 μ in diameter; sporangia long, narrow, cylindrical, arising from the swollen head, 85–150 × 8–15 μ. Zoospores emerge through a terminal opening; resting spores not observed" (Crooks, *loc. cit.*).

On rose hips, apples, AUSTRALIA.

This is only very doubtfully distinct from *Blastocladia pringsheimii;* it has been seen many times by the author. Generally regarded as a dwarf form of that species, it has in one unusual instance (Sparrow, 1932b: pl. 7, fig. H) been figured attached to a typical plant of *B. pringsheimii.*

BLASTOCLADIA SPARROWII Indoh

Science Rep. Tokyo Bunrika Daigaku, Sect. B, 4: 259. 1940
(Fig. 46 C, p. 680)

"Basal body cylindrical, 13–31 × 312–468 μ; distal portion of basal body greatly swollen, lobed, or more often, unlobed, 47–374 μ in diam., bearing sessile sporangia and sterile setae. Sterile setae branched or unbranched, up to 260 μ long.

"Zoosporangia cylindrical, 13–21 × 73–143 μ. Internal proliferation of the sporangia frequent and very evident. Zoospores spherical, 5.2 μ diam., posteriorly uniciliate.

"Chlamydocyst not observed" (Indoh, *loc. cit.*, modified from Sparrow, 1936a: 458, pl. 20, figs. 3, 13).

Saprophytic on twigs of *Fraxinus sp.*, Sparrow (*loc. cit.*), GREAT BRITAIN; fruits, Das-Gupta and John (1953: 166, fig. 1), rotting turnip, Lacy (1955: 208), INDIA.

Founded on a fungus identified by Sparrow (*loc. cit.*) as *Blastocladia prolifera* Minden. Because of the apically swollen basal cell and the sterile setae Indoh considers it distinct from Minden's species. In view of the variations found in both the shape of the basal cell and the presence or absence of setae in the closely related *B. pringsheimii*, the validity of the segregation on these bases may be open to question.

BLASTOCLADIA GLOBOSA Kanouse

Amer. J. Bot., 14: 298, pl. 32, figs. 1–4. 1927
(Fig. 46 E, p. 680)

Basal cell globose or subglobose, the proximal cylindrical part very short and 36–60 μ in diameter or absent, distally entire or with large irregular expanded lobes or branches up to 200 μ in diameter by 120–350 μ high, wall thick (up to 10 μ), brittle, laminate, smooth or slightly roughened, contents colorless or brownish, holdfasts stout, much branched, setae present or absent, whole thallus 120–400 μ long and up to 200 μ or more in diameter; sporangia cylindrical or broadly cylindrical, 55–160 μ long by 15–60 μ in diameter, numerous, zoospores posteriorly uniflagellate, spherical or somewhat elongate, 12–14 μ (long?) or 7–9 μ long by 5–6 μ wide; resting spores borne with the sporangia, subspherical, ovoid or subpyriform, with rounded apex and truncate base, 25–70 μ long by 27–50 μ in diameter, wall thick, brownish, punctate, germination not observed.

Forming minute white pustules, particularly on hard fruits. Fruits of crab apple, *Crataegus*, Kanouse (*loc. cit.*), apples, Cotner (1930a: 297, figs. 5–10), Sparrow (1933c: 529), UNITED STATES; apple, Sparrow (1936 a: 458), GREAT BRITAIN; fruits of *Solanum pseudo-capsicum* Crooks (1937: 228, text fig. 10C, pl. 10, fig. 2), AUSTRALIA; fruits of *Cornus officinalis*, Indoh (1940: 249, fig. 8), JAPAN; fruits, Das-Gupta and John (1953: 167, fig. 3), INDIA.

If, as is possible, this is only a variety of *Blastocladia pringsheimii*, growing on hard fruits, it is nonetheless a well-marked and readily identifiable form. As Miss Kanouse points out, the species differs from

B. pringsheimii in having a more conspicuously globose basal cell, the cylindrical stalk often being almost entirely absent. When it is present, however, the habit of the plant closely approximates small specimens of *B. pringsheimii.*

Miss Kanouse describes the zoospores as 12–14 μ in diameter, kidney-shaped to ovoid when swimming, and biflagellate. Only posteriorly uniflagellate ones have been observed by Cotner (*loc. cit.*) and by Sparrow.

BLASTOCLADIA PROLIFERA Minden

Kryptogamenfl. Mark Brandenburg, 5: 606. 1912 (1915); Falck, Mykolog. Untersuch. Berichte, 2(2): 213, text figs. 20–22. 1916

Basal cell cylindrical, 100–300 μ long by 24–80 μ in diameter, apically divided into subdichotomously or irregularly arranged short branches, setae absent, holdfasts branched; primary sporangia numerous, straight-cylindrical or somewhat curved, basally truncate, 60–150 μ long by 13–35 μ in diameter, with a prominent apical papilla, internally proliferous (up to five times), secondary sporangia successively smaller; zoospores spherical, posteriorly uniflagellate, 5.2 μ in diameter; resting spore not observed.

On dead plant parts, Minden (*loc. cit.*), GERMANY; fruits of apple and *Japonica*, Crooks (1937: 225, fig. 10 A–B), AUSTRALIA; fruits of *Cornus officinalis* Indoh (1940: 254, fig. 11), JAPAN.

Certain plants mentioned by Crooks (*loc. cit.*) may be referable to *Blastocladia sparrowii.*

BLASTOCLADIA ANGUSTA Lund

Kgl. Danske Vidensk. Selsk. Skrift., Naturv. Math., Afd. IX, 6 (1): 44, fig. 21. 1934
(Fig. 47 E, p. 682)

Basal cell cylindrical, slender, up to 150 μ long by 10–35 μ in diameter, the distal part branched (occasionally unbranched), the branches remaining cylindrical, holdfasts slender, branched, whole thallus 160–500 μ long, contents sometimes brownish, setae usually present; sporangia borne at the tips of the branches, narrowly cylindrical, 60–210 μ long by 6–25 μ in diameter; zoospores not observed (?), apparently liberated through an apical pore; resting spore broadly ovoid and beaked, base narrow and truncate, 25–45 μ long by 16–26 μ wide, wall thin, colorless, possibly pitted on inner face, germination not observed.

Forming small whitish pustules. On apple fruits, Lund (*loc. cit.*), DENMARK; rose fruits, Crooks (1937: 227, text fig. 11 D–G, pl. 10, fig. 5), AUSTRALIA.

The resting spores found by Crooks resemble in shape those of *Blastocladia rostrata*, but if these were actually mature specimens the wall is much like that of the resting structures of *B. ramosa*.

Cejp (1947) has separated the Australian fungus from *Blastocladia angusta* as *B. crooksae* but, fortunately, has not validated this segregation. If the fungus is distinct from Lund's species, then it was misidentified by Crooks and is a new species requiring a diagnosis.

BLASTOCLADIA INCRASSATA Indoh

Science Rep. Tokyo Bunrika Daigaku, Sect. B, 4: 252, text fig. 10. 1940
(Fig. 47 F, p. 682)

"Fungus-colony small, white, in compact tufts; basal body cylindrical, rather broad at upper end, closely branched in dichotomous or racemose manner, at lower end attached by scanty rhizoids. Whole fungus 200–500 μ high, 15–50 μ diam. at base. Cell wall smooth, hyaline, thin, about 2 μ thick. Plasm granulous with oil drops.

"Zoosporangia terminal on branches, sessile, single, racemosely or cymosely arranged, cylindrical to broad clavate, 18–28 × 50–88 μ, with truncate base, having apically a single dehiscence papilla about 3 μ high.

"Chlamydocyst not observed" (Indoh, *loc. cit.*).

On submerged fruits of *Cornus officinalis*, Indoh (*loc. cit.*), JAPAN; Minden (1916: pl. 4, fig. 26), GERMANY; Sparrow (1936a: 455, pl. 20, fig. 7), GREAT BRITAIN.

Erected to include certain forms described by Minden as *Blastocladia pringsheimii*, the organism identified by Sparrow as *B. ramosa*, and the Japanese fungus. Doubtfully distinct from *B. gracilis*. Waterhouse (1942) has suggested that it is merely a variety of *B. ramosa*.

BLASTOCLADIA GRACILIS Kanouse

Amer. J. Bot., 14: 300, pl. 33, figs. 14–16. 1927
(Fig. 47 A, p. 682)

Blastocladia ramosa var. *luxurians* Kanouse, Papers Mich. Acad. Sci., Arts, Letters, 5: 113, pl. 1, fig. 1. 1926.

Basal cell slender, 20–80 μ in diameter, cylindrical throughout, distally racemosely or subdichotomously branched, walls 2.5–4 μ thick, smooth, contents colorless, setae present or absent, holdfasts few, poorly developed, whole thallus 600–1500 μ long; sporangia racemosely or corymbosely arranged along the branches, long-cylindrical, 70–220 μ long by 20–34 μ in diameter, with a prominent discharge papilla; zoospores ovoid 9 by 8 μ, or subspherical, 8 to 9 μ, escaping through an apical pore; resting spores borne with the sporangia, usually terminal, ovoid, subspherical or spherical with truncate base, 40–66 μ long by 20–40 μ in diameter, wall thick, brownish, punctate, upon germination forming zoospores which give rise to new plants.

In loose tufts or mats with other water molds, particularly *Blastocladia pringsheimii* and *Rhipidium*. On fruits of apple, Kanouse (*loc. cit.*), UNITED STATES; apples, Lund (1934: 43, fig. 20 a–b), DENMARK; apples, rose fruits, Crooks (1937: 226, fig. 11 A–B), AUSTRALIA; Waterhouse (1942: 317, fig. 1, I), GREAT BRITAIN; tomato fruits, Shen and Siang (1948: 188), CHINA.

Whether or not this is a form of *Blastocladia pringsheimii* is open to question. Plants of that species when growing in dense stands in long slits on apple fruits frequently assume the habit of *B. gracilis*. Waterhouse (1942) considers the species distinct from *B. pringsheimii* because the resting spores are more constantly oval and have a more transparent wall and less conspicuous pits. A further distinction is the rapid and prolific development of the resting spores.

BLASTOCLADIA ROSTRATA Minden

Kryptogamenfl. Mark Brandenburg, 5: 604. 1912 (1915); Falck, Mykolog. Untersuch. Berichte, 2: 211, text figs. 18–19, pl. 4, figs. 34–35. 1916
(Fig. 46 A–B, p. 680)

Basal cell narrowly or broadly and irregularly cylindrical, 140–150 μ long by 15–63 μ in diameter, profusely branched and rebranched dichotomously, pseudodichotomously, or sympodially, cylindrical throughout, holdfasts stout, branched, setae absent, entire thallus 500-1500 μ long; sporangia spirally arranged, terminal or intercalary and sessile or on short lateral branches, cylindrical, subcylindrical, predominantly distinctly long-fusiform, basally truncate, with a prominent apical papilla, 45–100 μ long by 17–40 μ in greatest diameter; zoospores spherical or slightly elongate, posteriorly uniflagellate, 7.5–10 μ in diameter, emerging in a compact column before dispersal; resting spores broadly fusiform or ellipsoidal, with a pronounced apical beak and a truncate slightly elongate base, 30–53 μ long by 15–30 μ in greatest diameter, contents with globules, wall moderately thick, brown, punctate, occurring alone or with the sporangia, at maturity falling out of the thin-walled enveloping case, germination not observed.

Forming a fairly loose turf on the surface of the substratum or mixed with other water molds in pustules. On fruits, Minden (*loc. cit.*), GERMANY; twigs of *Aesculus*, Lund (1934: 42, fig. 19), DENMARK; twigs of *Aesculus sp.*, Sparrow (S.) (1936a: 455, pl. 20, fig. 14), GREAT BRITAIN; fruit, Das-Gupta and John (1953: 168, fig. 4), rotting turnip, Lacy (1955: 208), INDIA.

BLASTOCLADIA RAMOSA Thaxter

Bot. Gaz., 21: 50, pl. 3, figs. 14–16. 1896
(Fig. 47 C–D, p. 682)

Basal cell cylindrical, up to 400 μ long by 14–80 μ in diameter, divided distally dichotomously or subdichotomously into from two to several secondary slightly tapering axes which branch and rebranch sympodially or somewhat irregularly, holdfasts delicate, sparingly branched, wall thin, smooth, setae absent, whole thallus delicate, with an open ramose habit, up to 260–1000 μ high; sporangia terminal and subterminal, on short branches, either narrowly or broadly ovoid with a narrow truncate base or broadly fusiform, 30–85 μ long by 7–24 μ in diameter, papilla apical; zoospores ellipsoid to pyriform, 5–6 × 6–7 μ, posteriorly uniflagellate; resting spores borne like the sporangia, broadly ovoid, narrowly clavate or spatulate, with a rounded apex and a narrower truncate base, 18–38 μ long by 11–28 μ in diameter, wall colorless or faintly brown, slightly thickened, minutely punctate, germination not observed.

Among other water molds or forming minute pustules. On twigs, Thaxter (F.) (*loc. cit.*), twigs of *Populus trichocarpa*, Graff (1928: 169), apple, Sparrow (S.) (1932b: 293, pl. 8, fig. J), Emerson and Cantino (1948), UNITED STATES; fruits, Minden (1915: 605; 1916: 197, pl. 4, figs. 36–37), GERMANY; fruits of banana, Crooks (1937: 226, fig. 11 H–I), AUSTRALIA; *Pirus* fruits, Indoh (1940: 250, fig. 9 a–e), JAPAN; Waterhouse (1942: 318, fig. 1, III), GREAT BRITAIN; pear and tomato fruits, Shen and Siang (1948: 189), CHINA; fruit, Das-Gupta and John (1953: 167, fig. 2), rotting turnip, Lacy (1955: 209), INDIA.

In general aspect the thallus resembles that of *Allomyces*. Study of the resting spores of the type material shows them to be faintly brownish and minutely punctate (Fig. 47 D).

Emerson and Cantino have secured this species in pure culture.

BLASTOCLADIA TENUIS Kanouse

Amer. J. Bot., 14: 301, pl. 33, figs. 5–7. 1927
(Fig. 47 B, p. 682)

Basal cell narrowly cylindrical throughout, if at all branched then only once or twice near the middle, 300–1000 μ long by 30–60 μ in diameter, wall thin (3–4 μ), golden brown, very brittle, sculptured throughout with ridged markings, setae absent, holdfasts delicate, few, branched; sporangia few, terminal at the apices of the basal cell or its branches, somewhat fusiform with beaklike apex, 27 μ long by 11 μ in diameter; zoospores not observed; "oögonia" borne singly or in clusters at the apex of the basal cell, irregularly pyriform or broadly dome-shaped, mature resting spore not observed. (Modified from Kanouse.)

Forming tufts on fruits of rose and *Crataegus* in stagnant water, UNITED STATES.

Although the character of its wall distinguishes this species from others of the genus further observations are needed on the reproductive organs.

BLASTOCLADIA GLOMERATA Sparrow

J. Linn. Soc. London (Bot.), 50: 456, text fig. 5 f–j, pl. 20, figs. 4, 9. 1936

Basal cell stout, very broad at the base, often strongly tapering, 312–364 μ long by 104–162 μ in diameter, rarely unbranched, usually giving rise distally to from two to six broad somewhat clavate branches 195–556 μ long by 52–111 μ in diameter, setae branched or unbranched, holdfasts stout, branched, whole thallus exclusive of holdfasts and setae 693–1020 μ long; sporangia occurring in dense clusters at the tips of the branches, predominantly broadly ellipsoidal, often slightly curved, resting on a truncate, collar-like base, 63–169 μ long (majority 88–100 μ) by 34–63 μ in diameter (majority 42–52 μ), ratio of length to width 1.3–2.3: 1; zoospores spherical, 10 μ in diameter, posteriorly uniflagellate; resting spores borne among the sporangia, nearly spherical, ovoid or somewhat elongate, basally truncate, 39–52 μ long by 36–49 μ in diameter (average 46 by 39.6 μ), wall thick, punctate, dark brown, germination not observed.

Forming large coarsely granulated pustules on twigs of *Aesculus sp.*, Sparrow (S., B.M.), tomato fruits, Waterhouse (1942: 318, fig. 1, II), Sparrow (1957a), GREAT BRITAIN.

Certain forms of *Blastocladia pringsheimii* figured by Minden (1916: fig. 15) and Lund (1934: fig. 18b) resemble *B. glomerata* to a degree. Though its resting spore is practically identical with that of *B. pringsheimii*, *B. glomerata* differs from this species in the shape of the basal cell and more especially in the ratio of length to width of the sporangia (1.3–2.3: 1 as compared to 6.4–8: 1).

BLASTOCLADIA TRUNCATA Sparrow

Mycologia, 24: 293, pl. 7, fig. G. 1932

Basal cell narrowly cylindrical, unbranched, slightly expanded at the apex, 250–286 μ long by 7.7–26 μ in diameter; setae lacking, holdfasts slightly branched; sporangia borne on the apex of the basal cell, truncate, nearly as broad as long, 10.4–15 μ long by 10.4–12 μ in diameter, appearing more acuminate after discharge; zoospores spherical, 3.5 μ in diameter; resting spores formed.

Occurs mixed with other water molds in pustules on fruits of apple, UNITED STATES.

Although this species does not appear to be simply a form of *Blastocladia pringsheimii*, further observations on it and particularly on the character of the resting spores would be desirable. Waterhouse (1942) reported finding several plants with resting spores but she does not describe them.

IMPERFECTLY KNOWN SPECIES OF BLASTOCLADIA

? BLASTOCLADIA SP. Indoh

Science Rep. Tokyo Bunrika Daigaku, Sect. B, 4: 259. 1940

"Fungus-body arbuscule, consisting of broad cylindrical trunklike basal body and thin, well ramified branches, 700–800 μ high. Basal body 60–100 × 400–700 μ, attached to substrata by means of sparsely branched rhizoids, branches dichotomous to irregular, 20–25 μ diam.

"Zoosporangia (?) terminal, sympodially arranged on the branches, cylindrical, 19–20 × 22–30 μ, with a single dehiscence papilla, apically. Zoospores not observed.

"Chlamydocysts sympodially arranged on the branches, elliptical to pyriform, 40–47 × 45–85 μ, with attenuated base, yellowish, containing many oil drops; two membraned, the outer conspicuously pitted. Spore-dehiscence not observed" (Indoh, *loc. cit.*).

Saprophytic on submerged twigs of *Morus sp.*, JAPAN.

Indoh considers this incompletely observed fungus to be most closely related to *Blastocladia gracilis* and *B. incrassata* but different from them in that "(1) the basal body is thicker than that of *Bl. gracilis* and longer than that of *Bl. incrassata*, (2) the zoosporangia (?) are shorter than those of the two, (3) the chlamydocysts are longer than those of *Bl. gracilis*, and not truncated, but somewhat attenuated basally."

RECENTLY DESCRIBED TAXA [1]

OEDOGONIOMYCES KOBAYASHI AND OOKUBO

Bull. Nat. Sci. Mus. (Tokyo) (N.S.) 1, No. 1 (34) : 62. 1954

"Thallus apparently saprophytic on shells or other vegetable debris in fresh water, eucarpic, composed of simple hypha, cylindric, hyaline, with chitinous membrane, attached to substratum with appressorium, without rhizoid, at first continuous, then transverse septa appear one by one at the upper part of hypha, bringing forth zoosporangial cell.

[1] Not included in the key.

Zoosporangium produced basipetally from the end of hypha, short cylindric with truncate ends, cut off in two parts by transverse cleavage line, sometimes with exit-pore on the upper side, containing numerous zoospores, without discharge tube or papilla. Zoospores with one posterior cilium, escaping separately or in mass from cleavage line or exit-pore of zoosporangium, with nuclear cap. Gemmae and chlamydocysts present. Sexual organ unknown." (Kobayashi and Ookubo, *loc. cit.*).

OEDOGONIOMYCES LYMNAEAE Kobayashi and Ookubo

Bull. Nat. Sci. Mus. (Tokyo) (N.S.) 1, No. 1 (34): 63, figs. 1–6, pls. 21–22. 1954

"Thallus fasciculate or single, composed of simple hypha. Hyphae cylindric 0.5–1 cm. long, 20–37 μ thick at upper part, hyaline, pointed at terminal, membrane 2–3 μ thick in adult stage, basal part attenuated or discoid or stellate. Zoosporangium short cylindric 20–37 μ thick, 10–60 μ long, containing 100–200 zoospores, with one cleavage line or exit-pore. Zoospores globose, ovoid or ellipsoid, 6–9 μ in diameter, commonly 6 μ, with 18–25 μ long cilium. Gemmae chained at the upper part of hypha, short cylindric, apparently cuboid in lateral view, separated in adult stage, very thick walled, producing several zoospores when matured. Chlamydocysts ellipsoid or broad fusiform, 19.5–49 × 15.3–23.8 μ, thick walled, finely pitted, with or without pedicel, single or clustered on the end or lateral side of hypha which is simple or with short lateral branches and remotely septate" (Kobayashi and Ookubo, *loc. cit.*).

Forming clusters of thalli on the shells of living *Lymnaea ollula*, *L. reticulata*, occasionally on vegetable debris, JAPAN.

Emerson (comm.) has found a similar fungus which he believes belongs in the Eccrinales. The resting spores of the Japanese fungus strongly resemble those of *Allomyces*.

MONOBLEPHARIDALES

IN 1871 Cornu published his discovery of a new genus of aquatic fungi which, in contrast to all other known oögamous forms, possessed motile sperms. Three species, *Monoblepharis* (now *Gonapodya*) *prolifera*, *M. sphaerica*, and *M. polymorpha*, were briefly characterized at that time. The following year, in his classic *Monographie des Saprolégniées* (1872a), he described the last two fungi more completely and illustrated them; he also included a brief description, without figures, of the first, *M. prolifera*. This species he figured two years later in the 1874 edition of van Tieghem's *Traité de Botanique* (French edition of Sachs's *Lehrbuch*).

Many years elapsed before any members of the genus were again observed. Indeed, as Thaxter (1895a), presumably the second person to find these organisms, suggested (1903), mycologists had been doubtful whether or not a group of fungi with such unique characters actually existed. With the appearance of Thaxter's 1895 paper all doubts were dispersed, and information concerning the genus *Monoblepharis* was considerably increased. Further investigations, especially those of Lagerheim (1900), Woronin (1904), Sparrow (1933b; 1940b), Beneke (1948), Johns and Benjamin (1954), and Perrott (1955) have greatly extended this knowledge, as has the work by Laibach (1926, 1927) on the cytological aspects of the group.

Monoblepharis was regarded by Cornu as a member of the Saprolegniaceae. The genus was placed in a separate family, the Monoblepharidaceae, by Fischer (1892). Schroeter (1893), Minden (1915), and later authors segregated it in a distinct order, the Monoblepharidales, which, as pointed out previously (Sparrow, 1933b), is closely related to the Blastocladiales.

The most interesting feature of the order is its method of sexual reproduction. In one genus, *Monoblepharis*, the zygote is converted immediately after fertilization into an oöspore, whereas in the genera *Gonapodya* and *Monoblepharella* it undergoes a period of motility propelled by the persistent flagellum of the male gamete before coming to rest and encysting (see p. 708).

Most members of the order may be obtained from a single favorable situation. Their supposed rarity appears due largely to lack of information concerning proper methods of collection and of subsequent treatment of material.

Species of *Monoblepharis* are primarily inhabitants of dead, entirely submerged twigs in permanent fresh-water habitats. In the collection of such twigs several factors should be borne in mind:(1) The pool must be relatively quiet and free from silt and from an excess of products of organic decomposition. (2) The twigs must not be decorticated and should preferably be waterlogged. (3) Certain twigs, notably those of birch, oak, and ash, seem particularly suited to the requirements of the fungus.

Other types of substrata, such as insect cadavers, twigs of broad-leaved trees, needles, twigs, and sap of coniferous trees, submerged lichens and fungi, and fruits, have also been described as favorable to the development of *Monoblepharis*.[1]

Material of the fungus is rarely found on twigs brought in from the field and immediately subjected to examination. If, however, such twigs are placed in sterile distilled water and maintained at 8–15°C. for from three to seven days, the fungus, if it is present on the substratum, will often by then have produced an abundance of growth. In such cases there will appear tufts or pustules of very delicate pale-gray rather flexuous hyphae, which may cover the twig or be confined to the openings of the lenticels. If, subsequently, the material thus obtained is maintained at 8–11°C. only sporangia will develop, whereas if it is placed at room temperature (21°C.) sexual reproduction will ensue.

Monoblepharella has thus far only been recovered from soils in warm latitudes by means of water cultures baited with vegetable material. Species of this genus form sporangia at 13–36°C. and sex organs between 26–32°C., thus both may be produced simultaneously at certain temperatures (Springer, 1945b).

Species of *Gonapodya* are frequently found on twigs along with *Monoblepharis*. They are much more common on submerged fruits, however, particularly on those of apple and rose. On these substrata

---

[1] See Perrott (*Nature*, 182:1322. 1958), where directions are given for growing *Monoblepharis* in pure culture on agar media and 1 per cent tryptone broth.

the fungus will form a loose filmy mass, or, more often, it will occur in definite pustules on the surface of the fruit in association with *Blastocladia* and *Rhipidium*. The surest method of obtaining such fruit-inhabiting fungi is to construct traps of galvanized wire screening, place the fruits inside, and submerge them in some likely aquatic habitat. Such traps when left for at least a month will usually yield an abundance of *Gonapodya* and other Phycomycetes. After examination the fruits may be placed in jars with a relatively large amount of water, left at a low temperature (3–8°C.), and examined at intervals. Further details of these culture methods may be found in papers by Kanouse (1926, 1927).

DEVELOPMENT AND MORPHOLOGY

THE THALLUS

Since more is known about the development and morphology of *Monoblepharis* than about that of any other member of the order, emphasis is placed on it throughout this section.

The zoospore of *Monoblepharis* upon germination may produce two germ tubes, one giving rise to the holdfast system which anchors the plant to the substratum, the other producing the main body of the plant. According to Lagerheim (1900), holdfasts may also be formed by the ramifying hyphae.

Once the fungus is established there results, under favorable conditions, an abundant mycelial growth, the nature and extent of which appear to depend somewhat on the particular species. For example, in *Monoblepharis macrandra* the growth and branching may be exceedingly profuse and may result in a solid mat of interlocking tangled hyphae covering the substratum, whereas in the other species the filaments seem more rigid and less branched, and tend to remain separated from one another. The finely granular content of the hyphae, in which are occasional refractive granules, is usually disposed, because of the regularly placed vacuoles, in a reticulate or foamy manner. The striking effect produced by this type of vacuolization makes it comparatively easy for one to recognize, even in the vegetative state, a member of the Monoblepharidales. Under changing environmental conditions the protoplasm may temporarily assume a nonvacuolate homogeneous texture.

The thallus and sporangia of *Monoblepharella taylori* resemble in superficial aspect those of *Monoblepharis regignens* and *M. ovigera*. The mycelium, which forms a lustrous pearly-gray halo around the substratum, is composed of delicate moderately branched hyphae 2–3 μ in diameter. Near the base, where the plant is anchored by a system of holdfasts to the substratum, the hyphal axes may attain a diameter of 5 μ. Catenulate series of swellings are formed on the hyphae of some, but not of all, isolates. The hyphal contents are characteristically arranged in a rich network or reticulum, within which somewhat coarse refractive granules of irregular size may be seen moving. A preliminary cytological examination of the hyphae shows the minute nuclei to be disposed at more or less uniform intervals.

REPRODUCTION

Nonsexual Reproduction

In most species of *Monoblepharis*, at about 8–11°C., only nonsexual reproductive organs are formed. These are usually terminal, slightly swollen, cylindrical portions of the hyphae, with homogeneous contents. Each sporangium is finally separated by a cross wall from its adjacent hypha. According to Laibach (1927), the nuclei are at first more or less regularly placed in the hyphae (Fig. 48 F, p. 700). As the rudiment of the sporangium begins to develop there is an increase in the number of nuclei in that body (Fig. 48 G–H). No mitotic figures were observed in the process of sporangial formation by either Lagerheim (1900) or Laibach. It remains a question, therefore, whether this increase is due to a migration into the sporangium or to the division of a few nuclei. As the cross wall is laid down the nuclei become more or less equidistant from one another (Fig. 48 I). A central vacuole appears during differentiation of the zoospores (Fig. 48 J). Coincident with spore cleavage there is a marked increase in the size of the individual nucleus, which now exhibits around its periphery masses of dark-staining material. Laibach suggests that this material may be connected with flagella formation.

The cleavage planes of the spores appear in most instances to be at right angles to the long axis of the sporangium, although many may be obliquely placed (Fig. 48 K, p. 700). The spore initials are at first angular

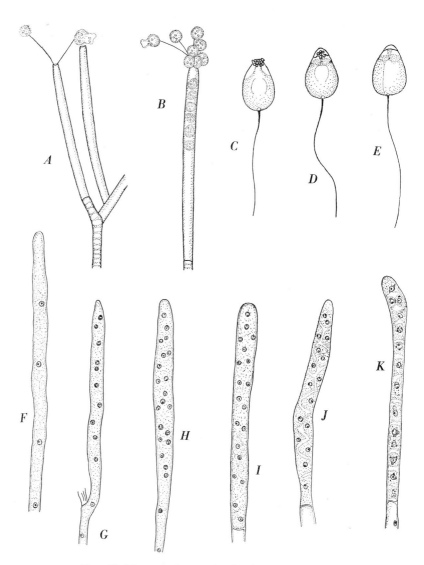

Fig. 48. Nonsexual reproduction in *Monoblepharis*

but gradually become more rounded. During this process of cleavage all the protoplasm may not be used up in the formation of the spores, and small bits may remain in the sporangium after discharge. By the deliquescence of the tapering apex of the sporangium a circular, sometimes angular, pore is formed, through which the swarmers creep in amoeboid fashion to the outside medium. The zoospore remains adherent by its flagellum to the mouth of the sporangium for a varying length of time and may oscillate for some little while before finally becoming disengaged. In the meantime other spores may continue to emerge, and it is not uncommon to see three or more thus attached to the orifice of the sporangium (Fig. 48 A–B). The zoospore at this stage exhibits an almost homogeneous content, in which are imbedded a few refractive granules. Ultimately, by a quick succession of vigorous jerks it becomes entirely free from the sporangium, and either immediately darts away or floats for a time, feebly lashing its flagellum. This appendage, which is about four or five times the length of the diameter of the spore body, slowly increases its rate of vibration and, trailing behind, propels the spore in a smooth gliding but lively fashion through the water. After complete discharge of the zoospores further sporangia may be formed by cymose branching of the hypha or, in *Monoblepharis regignens* and occasionally in *M. sphaerica* and *M. ovigera*, by proliferation through the empty sporangium.

Recently discharged zoospores undergo a remarkable transformation, for the internal structure, at first nearly homogeneous, assumes such a

---

Explanation of Figure 48

A-B. Discharging zoosporangia of *Monoblepharis macrandra* (Lagerheim) Woronin. *C-E*. Freehand drawings of moving zoospores of *Monoblepharis polymorpha* Cornu, showing internal structure. *F-K*. Cytological preparations of developing sporangia in *Monoblepharis macrandra* (Lagerheim) Woronin: *F*, tip of hypha before initiation of sporangium formation; *G-H*, young sporangia before formation of basal cross walls; nuclei have increased in number and some are paired, possibly as a result of a recent division; *I*, sporangium with basal cross wall laid down, separating it from hypha; nuclei are more regularly distributed in cytoplasm; *J*, vacuole formation delimiting spore initials; *K*, further differentiation of zoospores; dark-staining material is present in cytoplasm in vicinity of nuclei.

(*A-E*, Sparrow, 1933b; *F-K*, Laibach, 1927)

definite, characteristic arrangement that it enables one to recognize free-swimming spores of this genus, as well as those of *Monoblepharella* and *Gonapodya*. When the spore is in motion the refractive granules in the cytoplasm come to occupy the most distal portion of the now more cylindrical spore body and, indeed, often appear to protrude from the somewhat acuminate slightly quivering apex (Fig. 48 C, p. 700). Sometimes they seem to be fused into a single broadly conelike structure (Fig. 48 D–E). Immediately beneath them is a space entirely devoid of granular material. A narrow band or strand connects the granules with the rest of the spore body or possibly with the nucleus. The greater part of the spore is of a very finely granular slightly refractive protoplasm, which appears in some views to be a band the two ends of which have fused (Fig. 48 E). At the point of insertion of the flagellum a highly refractive body may usually be found. The little-known figures of zoospores and antherozoids given by Cornu in van Tieghem's *Traité de Botanique* indicate that he was well aware of this characteristic internal structure. It is essentially like that observed in the swarmers of *Blastocladia*, *Allomyces*, and such chytrids as *Nowakowskiella* and *Cladochytrium*, although *Blastocladia* and *Allomyces* lack the well-organized nearly centric globule found in the other two genera.

In *Monoblepharella* nonsexual and sexual reproductive organs may occasionally be formed simultaneously on the same plant. Apparently, as earlier indicated, this occurs when favorable temperatures for the production of each overlap. The zoosporangia are ordinarily formed at the periphery of the colony, at the tips of delicate, sparingly branched hyphae. By subsequent sympodial branching of the hypha they appear lateral. The difference in width of the sporangium and its attendant hypha is so striking that the sporangia frequently resemble long slender fusiform or siliquiform highly refractive conidia lying free in the tangled mycelial complex. The zoospores are fully matured before discharge, and emerge through a small pore formed upon the deliquescence of the sporangial apex, in the same manner as in species of *Monoblepharis*. They are ovoid or somewhat cylindrical, and have a single long posterior flagellum. The internal organization is exactly like that in *Monoblepharis*. Secondary sporangia are produced by sympodial branching.

It can reasonably be supposed that the development of the sporangial plant of *Gonapodya* and its method of anchorage are essentially similar to those of *Monoblepharis*. Whether temperature or some other external factor governs gametangial and sporangial formation is at present not known. Further study of these processes, and especially of the origin of the pseudosepta, is greatly needed. In its cytological aspects the sporangium of *Gonapodya prolifera* (Laibach, 1927) resembles that of *Monoblepharis*. As has been pointed out previously, the type of zoospore and method of formation are also similar to those of *Monoblepharis*.

Sexual Reproduction

The extraordinary type of sexual reproduction found among members of this order has made the group one of greatest interest to the mycologist as well as a never-failing source of stimulation to the student of phylogeny.

Details of the sexual reproduction of *Monoblepharis* were accurately portrayed by Cornu, and the observations of the few subsequent workers have added little except cytological data. In such species as *Monoblepharis polymorpha*, *M. fasciculata*, *M. bullata*, and *M. insignis* the antheridia appear at first glance to be inserted on the oögonia (epigynous). A study of their development, however, indicates that the oögonium is formed beneath the antheridium and is an intercalary structure. In such a typical epigynous form as *M. polymorpha* the antheridium originates as a walled-off terminal portion of the hypha, the contents of which are rather homogeneous (Fig. 49 A, p. 704). The more proximal portion of the hypha just beneath the antheridial cross wall then gradually becomes distended and forms a lateral somewhat oblique projection (Fig. 49 B). This lateral distention continues, and a clavate body eventually separated from the hypha by a basal cross wall is formed (Fig. 49 C–D). Often, before the formation of the septa, the antheridium has discharged its antherozoids. The oögonium thus delimited gradually becomes more rotund (Fig. 49 D).

Monoblepharis sphaerica, *M. hypogyna*, and *M. macrandra*, though having essentially the same type of sex organs as does *M. polymorpha*, differ from it in their methods of development.

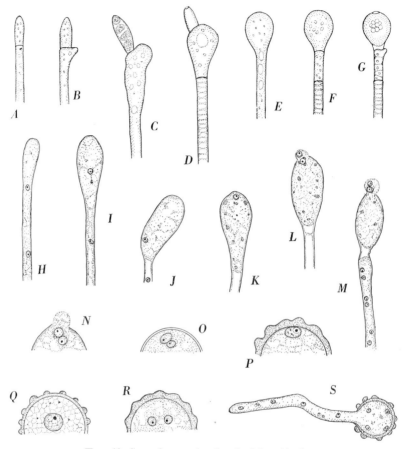

Fɪɢ. 49. Sexual reproduction in *Monoblepharis*

A-D. Method of development of sex organs in *Monoblepharis polymorpha* Cornu : *A*, terminal antheridium cut off by basal cross wall; *B*, same, showing beginning of formation of oögonial rudiment beneath antheridium; *C*, further expansion of oögonial rudiment; antherozoids have matured and are about to be discharged; *D*, nearly mature oögonium, now separated by basal cross wall from hypha; antherozoids have been discharged from antheridium, which appears to be placed on oögonium. *E-G*. Method of development of sex organs in *Monoblepharis hypogyna* Perrott : *E*, oögonial rudiment forming terminally on hypha; *F*, nearly mature oögonium cut off by basal cross wall; a cylindrical section immediately beneath, the antheridial rudiment, has been

In *Monoblepharis sphaerica* and *M. hypogyna* the oögonial rudiment is formed first in a terminal position (Fig. 49 E, p. 704). After the oögonium is delimited another more proximal hyphal segment is blocked off, which becomes the hypogynous antheridium (Fig. 49 F). Within it, sperms are produced (Fig. 49 G) which escape in the usual manner from a slightly exserted tubelike outgrowth immediately below the oögonial septa. In *M. macrandra* the antheridia and oögonia first formed are produced terminally on different hyphal branches (Fig. 53 E, p. 730). As growth and reproduction proceed the diclinous habit is lost, and oögonia and antheridia occur in various positions. If both organs are formed on a single hyphal branch, however, alternating groups of one or the other type of structure are usual.

Maturation and escape of the antherozoids are accomplished in the manner described for the zoospores. The antheridia, in contrast to the sporangia, bear relatively few motile bodies (from four to eight). In their shape, internal structure, and flagellation, these resemble the zoospores (Fig. 50 G, p. 708). They are smaller, however, and, unlike them, exhibit a pronounced tendency toward amoeboid movement.

Further maturation of the oögonium involves the development of a highly refractive apical receptive papilla (Fig. 50 A, p. 708). Coincident with, or often before, the formation of this structure the minute evenly

---

Explanation of Figure 49

delimited; *G*, mature oögonium and antheridium. *H-S*. Cytological preparations of developing oögonia, fertilization process, and formation and germination of oöspores of *Monoblepharis macrandra* (Lagerheim) Woronin (all?): *H-I*, beginning of formation of oögonium; single egg nucleus is already clearly distinguishable; *J*, oögonium delimited by cross wall; enlarged nucleus has not as yet migrated to apex of oögonium; *K*, mature oögonium with apical nucleus; *L*, mature egg in act of being fertilized by antherozoid; nuclei of the two gametes are clearly visible; deeper-stained areas may be seen in oöplasm, as in preceding figure; *M*, beginning of emergence of zygote from oögonium; the two nuclei lie in close proximity but are not as yet fused; *N*, the two nuclei lying side by side in fertilized egg; *O*, portion of young oöspore before fusion of nuclei; *P*, old oöspore with single diploid nucleus; *Q*, oöspore after winter rest period with resting diploid nucleus; *R*, binucleate stage previous to germination; *S*, germinated oöspore with multinucleate germ tube.

(*A-G*, Sparrow, 1933b; *H-S*, Laibach, 1927)

disposed oil droplets in the oöplasm combine to form a number of large refractive globules. These, as the ripening of the egg progresses, may come to occupy a central position in the oögonium. Both Lagerheim and Laibach have shown that the egg is uninucleate, and that the nucleus ultimately attains a terminal position in the oögonium (Fig. 49 H–K, p. 704).

Apparently fertilization is possible only after the egg has reached the proper stage of development. It was frequently observed that antherozoids creeping over immature eggs could not fertilize them. Often, too, they seemed unable to fertilize ova which, by their appearance, were fully mature. Whether this was due to the fact that the eggs were only seemingly mature or to the circumstance that the antherozoids from androgynous antheridia were unable to fertilize their own oösphere is in need of further investigation. The latter explanation does not seem to suffice in all instances, however, for numerous examples of self-fertilization may be found.

When an antherozoid approaches the apex of an oögonium the peripheral collar of the wall of the latter, until then contiguous with the papilla (Fig. 50 B, p. 708), dilates slightly (Fig. 50 C–D). The sperm resting on the mucilaginous papilla, which seems to be an integral part of the oöplasm, is immediately engulfed (Fig. 50 E–F), and both sperm and papilla become relatively indistinguishable from the egg. The flagellum of the sperm may protrude for a few moments, but it, too, is finally absorbed. After fertilization, the egg, which has previously become more compact and has moved toward the apex of the oögonium, retreats slightly and remains motionless for from three to five minutes. It then expands, and in some species there is initiated a gradual evacuation from the oögonium (Fig. 50 H–J). The time required for this process varies, but it usually takes at least two minutes. The wall of the oögonium is again dilated as the egg commences to emerge. In rare instances the protoplasm of the antherozoid may still be distinguishable at this time.

Outside, the egg remains attached by a narrow hyaline collar to the mouth of the oögonium. A pellicle soon forms around it, which gradually thickens and on which in most species there appear regularly placed protuberances (Fig. 50 J–K). These grow in size and become the bullations so characteristic of the oöspore of most species of the genus. Lagerheim (1900) states that in *Monoblepharis macrandra* the zygote may occasionally move away from the oögonium and exhibit amoeboid changes of shape. Rarely the flagellum of the male persists for a short time, but always for a briefer period than in *Monoblepharella* and *Gonapodya*. This behavior has also been noted by Barnes and Melville (1932), although they do not believe as did Lagerheim that fertilization may occur outside the oögonium. Woronin (1904) found the oöspore to be composed of two main layers, exospore and endospore. The exospore, in turn, had two parts. Of these the inner, in "*M. sphaerica*," was thick and colorless and was raised to form the bullations; the outer part was thin, brown, and did not cover the warts. In *M. macrandra*, however, the outer, brown layer covered the bullations. Within the exospore the living protoplasm was surrounded by a thin, nearly colorless, elastic wall (endospore).

In *Monoblepharis sphaerica*, *M. fasciculata*, *M. insignis*, and *M. bullata*, in contrast to all the others in which it is typically exogenous, the zygote remains within the oögonium and becomes converted endogenously into an oöspore.

As Lagerheim and later Laibach (1927) observed, the male and female nuclei in the egg do not fuse at once, but remain side by side (Fig. 49 L-O, p. 704) until wall formation has reached an advanced stage and the bullations, if any, are beginning to take shape. Fusion then occurs and the mature oöspore is uninucleate (Fig. 49 P–Q).

Only a few instances of germination of the oöspore have been observed. In several oöspores which were estimated to be not more than a month old the wall of the spore had cracked open and a single hyphal tube had been produced (Sparrow, 1933b.) Under the existing conditions only mycelium was formed (Fig. 53 H, p.730). No other type of germination was reported by Lagerheim or Laibach, nor has it been by Perrott (1955). In *Monoblepharis macrandra*, according to Laibach, the large resting nucleus of the oöspore (Fig. 49 Q, p. 704) may divide into as many as sixteen perceptibly smaller ones. No mitotic figures were apparent. It was supposed that reduction took place during the first division (Fig. 49 R). Upon the formation of the germ tube the nuclei migrated into it, and the vegetative mycelium was established (Fig. 49 S).

Further cytological work is greatly needed on this and other critical points in the life cycle, particularly of an epigynous species.

Occasionally one finds smooth-walled endogenous resting structures (Fig. 53 C, p. 730). Whether or not these are always unfertilized eggs which have developed parthenogenetically, as has been suggested by Perrott (1955) and others, awaits confirmation. Lagerheim described the formation of "gemmae" consisting of somewhat rounded chains of hyphal segments in *Monoblepharis polymorpha*.

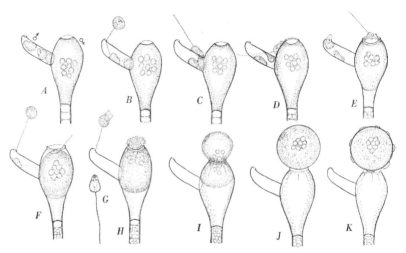

FIG. 50. Sexual reproduction in *Monoblepharis polymorpha* Cornu

A-B. Emergence of antherozoid from antheridium. *C-D.* Antherozoid creeping toward receptive spot of oögonium; oögonial wall around receptive papilla has begun to dilate. *E-F.* Antherozoid being engulfed by oöplasm, after which oöplasm retreats into oögonium. *G.* Antherozoid in motion; note difference in internal structure from that of amoeboid antherozoid. *H-J.* Emergence of fertilized egg from oögonium; protoplasm of antherozoid may still be distinguished. *K.* Early stage in formation of bullate wall of oöspore. (Sparrow, 1933b)

In *Monoblepharella*, oögonia and antheridia are frequently formed on somewhat shorter branches of the thallus than are the zoosporangia. The clavate or obpyriform oögonium may, like the sporangium, be at first terminal, but after sympodial branching of the hypha it may appear lateral. In *M. taylori* both oögonium and antheridium develop in the same manner as do those of *Monoblepharis hypogyna*, that is, the rudiment of the terminal oögonium is formed first. After this is delimited another, more proximal, segment is separated from the supporting hypha by a cross wall. In most instances this basal segment has, before its delimitation, formed beneath the oögonium a short branch, which continues to increase in size as maturation proceeds. In *Monoblepharella elongata* a similar sequence of development of the first-formed gametangia is found, whereas in *M. mexicana* and *M. laruei* the reverse is typical (Springer, 1945b). *Monoblepharella endogena* is devoid of antheridia (Sparrow, 1953a); the oöspores are evidently parthenogenetic and they remain within the gametangium.

In *Monoblepharella taylori* the mature oögonium is thin-walled and apparently without a prominent receptive papilla, although further observations are needed on this point. The contents of the large broadly ellipsoidal egg are highly characteristic and conspicuous by reason of the numerous prominent colorless refractive globules imbedded in the clear cytoplasm (Fig. 51 A–B, p. 710). Although usually only a single egg is formed in the oögonium, from two to six have occasionally been found. The mature antheridium, which may be produced singly or in basipetal series beneath the oögonium, consists of a cylindrical portion and a large lateral beaklike outgrowth formed from the previously mentioned branch. From two to five strongly amoeboid posteriorly uniflagellated antherozoids are produced and escape through a pore at the tip of the beak. These may creep about after discharge or, like the zoospores, which they resemble in all but size, swim about in the medium. The early stages in the process of fertilization are like those of *Monoblepharis*. The antherozoid after reaching the apex of the fully mature oögonium becomes strongly amoeboid. Its contents assume a watery consistency and spread over the oögonial apex (Fig. 51 C). Numerous small vacuoles appear and disappear so rapidly as to give an appearance of cytoplasmic "boiling." The flagellum waves feebly above the body of the sperm and, as the cytoplasm of the male gamete gradually sinks into the oöplasm (Fig. 51 D–E), becomes more hyaline in appearance. During absorption of the male gamete the oöplasm expands and for a short time fills the oögonium (Fig. 51 F). In none of the many instances

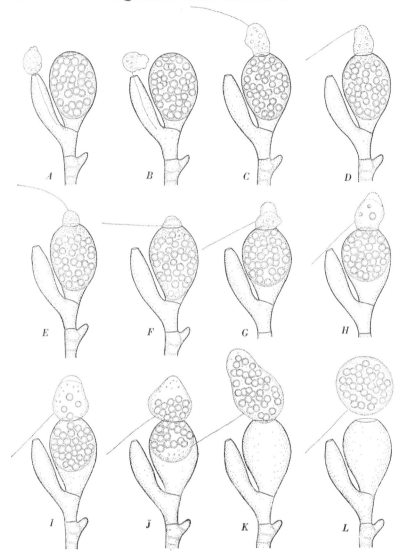

Fig. 51. Sexual reproduction in *Monoblepharella taylori* Sparrow

A-B. Mature oögonium and last of four antherozoids emerging from hypogynous antheridium. *C.* Antherozoid making contact with egg. *D-E.* Stages in absorption of male gamete by egg. *F.* Zygote immediately before emergence; a small part of body of male gamete and its flagellum persist, the flagellum having assumed a lateral position. *G.* Beginning of emergence of zygote. *H-K.* Further stages in emergence of zygote. *L.* Zygote rounding off and about to swim away from oögonium.

(Sparrow, 1940b)

of fertilization observed was the body of the male gamete completely absorbed by the oöplasm. There was always a small papilla-like part which persisted at the apex and from which protruded the flagellum of the antherozoid (Fig. 51 F). The remainder of the male gamete could be detected for a time as a slightly more granular material in the anterior part of the egg, but it was soon lost to view. Almost instantly after the absorption of the major part of the antherozoid the papilla-like residue of this structure on the surface of the egg started to increase in size (Fig. 51 G). This marked the initiation of evacuation of the zygote from the oögonium. More definite evidence of emergence could then be seen in the migration of the conspicuous globules into the enlarging papilla (Fig. 51 H–J). These continued to flow out with the cytoplasm of the zygote. Meanwhile, the flagellum remained passive, but slowly assumed a lateral position with respect to the orifice of the oögonium as the zygote oozed out. The completely emerged zygote was at first rather pyriform, with the flagellum nearly basal and extending at a right angle or more to the long axis of the body (Fig. 51 K). The zygote rounded off, remained quiescent for a few seconds, and then began to rock gently (Fig. 51 L). A trembling movement of increasing intensity was soon initiated, which frequently carried the zygote somewhat away from the oögonial orifice. Lateral vibration of the hitherto quiescent flagellum followed, and vacuoles appeared in the anterior part of the now more ovoid body. After a few violent tugs, accompanied by rapid vibration of the dark-appearing flagellum, the zygote began to rotate on its long axis as well as to progress forward; finally it swam slowly off. Under poor environmental conditions the zygote may fail to emerge, and the oöspore is formed in the oögonium. Cytological preparations of motile zygotes (Sparrow, 1953b) indicate that the nucleus of the male gamete (not a fusion nucleus) presides over the activities of the flagellum.

After a period of motility of unknown duration, frequently punctuated by intervals of quiescence and strong amoeboid crawling, the zygote comes to rest. Its flagellum is apparently absorbed and it is surrounded by a thickened wall. The globules persist for a time, but eventually these are assimilated and the oöspore undergoes a period of dormancy, far removed from the oögonium. The two gamete nuclei remain distinct at least in the early stages of oöspore maturation. In fully mature oöspores, however, only a single, presumably fusion nucleus, can be observed (Sparrow, 1953b). How long the encysted oöspores remain viable is not known. Fully mature spores dried for three months on cover slips have germinated when placed in water, and soil samples baited four years after collection have yielded the fungus (Springer, 1945b). It is probable, therefore, that the oöspore can remain alive in the soil during ordinary periods of tropical drought. Upon germination

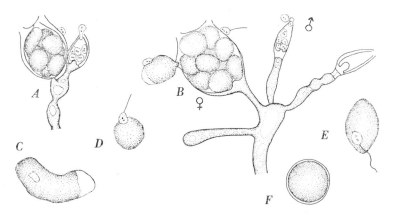

FIG. 52. Sexuality in *Gonapodya polymorpha*

A. Large internally proliferated female gametangium with nonflagellated gametes and smaller proliferated male gametangium from which gametes are emerging. *B.* Tip of plant showing a discharging female gametangium with male gamete adherent, a discharging male gametangium and an empty proliferated male gametangium. *C.* Amoeboid female gamete free in water. *D.* Nearly complete fusion of a male and a female gamete. *E.* Same; flagellum of male gamete active. *F.* Encysted zygote free in water.

(Contributed by Robert M. Johns)

a single small pore is formed in the oöspore wall, through which a hypha emerges. The hypha elongates indefinitely, branches, makes contact with bits of organic material, and reëstablishes the fungus. Reproductive organs of either type develop, or the mycelium may continue its vegetative growth.

In *Gonopodya*, sexual reproduction, according to Johns and Benjamin (1954), is effected by posteriorly uniflagellate male and nonflagellate female gametes. These are borne in terminal gametangia, both types of which may be renewed by internal proliferation (Figs. 52 A, p. 712; 54 B, p. 738). The small male gametes, which contain a conspicuous apical cluster of refractive granules, are discharged as in *Monoblepharis* and *Monoblepharella*. The female gametes (Fig. 52 C) may be distinguished by their lack of flagella, their relatively larger size, and the presence within them of many minute refractive granules which impart a brownish color (Fig. 52 B). Since the latter gametes may, or may not, be discharged, gametic fusion can occur either within or outside the female gametangium. In either case it is incomplete and part of the body of the male cell with its flagellum is always evident upon the surface of the female gamete (Fig. 52 D, E). After a variable period of amoeboid movement, the zygote swims about propelled, as in *Monoblepharella*, by the persistent flagellum of the male. Following the motile stage, which may last as long as three hours, the zygote comes to rest, assumes a spherical shape, and develops into a smooth-walled, brownish oöspore (Fig. 52 F). Its germination has not been observed.

SYSTEMATIC ACCOUNT

MONOBLEPHARIDALES

MICROSCOPIC eucarpic fungi with a well-developed filamentous mycelium, the contents disposed in a reticulate or foamy manner, nonseptate save when reproductive organs are formed, or possessing pseudosepta; nonsexual reproduction by means of posteriorly uniflagellate zoospores borne in sporangia; zoospores usually with an anterior group of refractive granules; sexual reproduction oögamous, by means of posteriorly uniflagellate antherozoids borne in antheridia and nonflagellate oöspheres, one or more borne in each oögonium; the fertilized oösphere becoming a thick-walled oöspore, upon germination forming a hypha.

As originally conceived by Cornu, *Monoblepharis* (including *Gonapodya*) embraced *Saprolegnia*-like organisms which had uniflagellate zoospores. With the advent of more accurate observations on the zoospores of various filamentous Phycomycetes, there can be little question that this idea was a correct one. The only other group of true mycelial fungi with similar zoospores, the Blastocladiales, is undoubtedly allied to the Monoblepharidales. This relationship is strikingly illustrated in *Allomyces* and *Blastocladiella*, where the vacuolization of the hyphal cytoplasm and the development of the gametangia may at times exactly resemble those of certain species of *Monoblepharis*. Presumably, both orders stemmed from chytridiaceous ancestry but developed independently, with one line differing from the other particularly in method of sexual reproduction and in growth habit.

Members of *Monoblepharis* and *Gonapodya* are quite variable in nature. It is frequently a difficult and puzzling matter to separate the species. Even in *M. hypogyna*, one of the best-defined species of *Monoblepharis*, forms very like those of *M. polymorpha* or the closely related *M. macrandra* are occasionally found. In *Gonapodya* individual variations and intergradations between the two known species may be so extensive as to make specific determination impossible. Wide divergences in size are common, and often a single plant will bear organs approaching or reaching the recorded limits for the species. Size, therefore, is not considered especially significant. The fact that all their features are subject to variation and that many forms are often found growing together, is strong evidence that in this group (as in *Allomyces*) hybridization has occurred between species.

Of the two families of the order now recognized, the Gonapodyaceae and Monoblepharidaceae, the former, containing *Gonapodya* and *Monoblepharella*, is clearly the more primitive. In the Gonapodyaceae, more than one female gamete may be found in an oögonium and it (in *Gonapodya*) may actually creep out and be fertilized at some distance from the parent cell as happens in anisogamous planogametic reproduction. Furthermore, the gametangia in that family are not so uniformly in intimate contact with one another as they are in the Monoblepharidaceae and the zygote undergoes a period of motility before encystment. In the Monoblepharidaceae, sexuality is more strongly oögamous. A single egg is formed in the gametangium, within which it is fertilized. No period of motility is undergone by the zygote other than to ooze to the mouth of the oögonium, and the sex organs (except in *Monoblepharis macrandra*) are borne in intimate contact with one another.

GONAPODYACEAE [1]

Mycelium with or without pseudosepta and catenulations; zoosporangia elongate or ovoid; gametangia with or without internal proliferation, the female gametangium forming one or more female gametes, at fertilization the male gamete only partially engulfed by the female, its flagellum propelling the female away from the oögonium; oöspore at maturity lying free in the water.

Saprophytic on fruits and twigs in water or on organic material in tropical and subtropical soils.

GONAPODYA FISCHER

Rabenhorst. Kryptogamen-Fl., 1(4): 382. 1892
(Figs. 52, p. 712; 54 B–D, F, p. 738)

Mycelium irregularly or dichotomously branched, varying in extent of development, frequently profuse, method of attachment to the substratum probably by rhizoids, composed of cylindrical, often moniliform hyphal segments delimited by hyaline constricted pseudosepta, hyphae

[1] The family has been suggested from time to time, most recently by Cejp (1957).

with a reticulate or foamy or sometimes homogeneous disposition of the protoplasm; zoosporangia terminal, occurring singly or in fascicles, internally proliferous, varying in shape; zoospores completely formed within the sporangium, escaping upon the deliquescence of sporangial apex, ovoid to cylindrical, posteriorly uniflagellate, possessing an internal organization similar to that of *Monoblepharis*; sexual reproduction oögamous, male and female gametangia borne terminally in fascicles, internally proliferous, the female bearing up to twenty amoeboid gametes, the male bearing numerous small posteriorly uniflagellate sperms which fertilize the female gametes either outside of or within the oögonium; the zygote propelled by the persistent flagellum of the male gamete, after a period of motility encysting, germination of the thick-walled resting spore unknown.

Saprophytic primarily on submerged twigs and fruits.

The main features of Johns and Benjamin's account (1954) of the long-sought sexual stage of this genus are given under the discussion of the order (see "Sexual Reproduction, p. 712). Their work, however, leaves certain questions unanswered, particularly with reference to the sporangial stage. If, as is true of other members of the Monoblepharidales, the sexual and nonsexual structures are borne on the same thallus,[1] what, for example, are the factors that determine which of the stages will be produced? No doubt, as in *Monoblepharis* and *Monoblepharella*, temperature plays an important role. In *Gonapodya polymorpha*, R. M. Johns (comm.) says that the sporangia are morphologically distinct and that, although they resemble the female gametangia, they differ from them in the size of the structures produced. Johns further observed that in contrast to unfused male and female gametes the zoospores germinated.

KEY TO THE SPECIES OF GONAPODYA

[1] Benjamin presents convincing evidence that they do (*Mycologia*, 50: 789. 1958).

GONAPODYA PROLIFERA (Cornu) Fischer

Rabenhorst. Kryptogamen-Fl., 1(4): 382. 1892
(Fig. 54 B, D, F, p. 738)

Monoblepharis prolifera Cornu, Bull. Soc. Bot. France, 18: 59. 1871; Ann. Sci. Nat. Bot., V, 15: 16. 1872; in van Tieghem, Traité de Botanique (1874 ed.), fig. 167 B, 5. Paris.
Saprolegnia siliquaeformis Reinsch, Jahrb. wiss. Bot., 11: 293, pl. 15, figs. 12–13. 1878.
Gonapodya siliquaeformis (Reinsch) Thaxter, Bot. Gaz., 20: 480, pl. 31, figs. 6–10. 1895.
Gonapodya bohemica Cejp, Bull. Soc. Mycol. France, 62(3–4): 10. 1946. (Separate)

Mycelium composed of hyphae more or less regularly divided by pseudosepta into short-elliptical to long-clavate segments, copiously and successively subumbellately branched, the branches diverging in a dense tuft from a common base; sporangia once to many times proliferous, the secondary sporangia only slightly exserted, long, pod-shaped, inflated below, the sometimes very elongate distal portion tapering gradually to a blunt apex, borne sessile on the terminal cell of a branch or separated from it by a clearly defined constriction; zoospores variable in number, up to fifty or more in a sporangium, posteriorly uniflagellate, elliptical, or somewhat cylindrical; male and female gametangia once to at least five times proliferous, successive gametangia progressively smaller, borne singly or in small groups on the terminal cell of a branch and separated from it by clearly defined constrictions; female gametangia elongate-ovoid, inflated below, tapering abruptly or gradually to a blunt apex, forming a single discharge papilla, 60–180 by 25–35 μ, female gametes variable in number, up to twenty in a gametangium, globose, nonflagellate, 15–19 μ in diameter; male gametangia smaller and more slender than the female, forming a single discharge papilla, 40–107 by 10–15 μ, male gametes variable in number, up to forty in a gametangium, posteriorly uniflagellate, elliptical or somewhat cylindrical, with a conspicuous anterior cluster of refractive granules, 7–10 by 3–6 μ, flagellum 22–24 μ in length; zygote retaining the flagellum of the male gamete, at first amoeboid and with varying shape, characteristically with a hyaline anterior pseudopodium, finally actively motile, posteriorly uniflagellate, ovoid, often reverting to the amoeboid condition, 20–25 by 11–15 μ, encysting to form a smooth-walled, spherical resting spore surrounded by a hyaline envelope, germination not observed. (Adapted in part from Johns and Benjamin, 1954.)

On decaying fruits and twigs of various types in water. Cornu (*loc. cit.*), twigs, Barbier (1950: 35, figs. 13–20), FRANCE; Reinsch (*loc. cit.*), Minden (1915: 577, fig. 12a; 1916: pl. 6, fig. 56), Laibach (1927: 599, fig. 11), GERMANY; Thaxter (F.) (*loc. cit.*), Kanouse (1927: 304), Sparrow (S.) (1932b: 291, pl. 7 A; 1933b: 535, pl. 20, figs. 30, 32; 1933c: 530), apples, etc., Sparrow (1943: 473), Beneke (1948: 30), oak twigs, Benjamin (in Johns and Benjamin, 1954: 201), twigs, Sparrow and Barr (1955: 555), UNITED STATES; Petersen (1909: 397; 1910: 533, fig. 11), Lund (1934: 39), DENMARK; Valkanov (1931a: 366), BULGARIA; Apinis (1930: 236), LATVIA; Barnes and Melville (1932: 93), Sparrow (1933b: 535; 1936a: 459, pl. 20, fig. 1), tomato, Waterhouse (1942: 320), GREAT BRITAIN, Crooks (1937: 220, fig. 7 b–d), AUSTRALIA; twigs of *Pyrus pashia*, Shen and Siang (1948: 190), CHINA; Kobayasi and Ookubo (1952a: 104; 1954b: 570), Ookubo (1954: 55), JAPAN; Cejp (1946: 10; 1947: 47, pl. 2, figs. 3–4), CZECHOSLOVAKIA; fruits, Das-Gupta and John (1953: 168, fig. 5), Lacy (1955: 209), INDIA.

This is actually the first monoblepharid described by Cornu (1871) and is a rather common and variable species, generally forming small white pustules on rosaceous fruits under very foul environmental conditions. Variations in the shape of the sporangium are extensive and may approach those typical of *Gonapodya polymorpha*.

Cornu (1877b) reported that in his fungus the oval colorless oöspores were borne in oögonia similar in shape to zoosporangia and derived from an oösphere fertilized by a sperm. He gave no further information or figures.

Cejp's (1946; 1947: 48, pl. 2, fig. 14) fungus termed *Gonapodya bohemica* is a common form of *G. prolifera*. To make separate species of the many growth forms encountered would result in confusion.

Of the two species of the genus, this is the most readily recognizable. In some collections, however, intergrades between the two occur.

GONAPODYA POLYMORPHA Thaxter

Bot. Gaz., 20: 481, pl. 31, figs. 11–16. 1895
(Figs. 52, p. 712; 54 C, p. 738)

Hyphae irregularly or more frequently dichotomously branched, more or less uniformly divided into short-oval or irregular segments, the segmented portion either arising directly from the substratum or, more often, confined to tufts of branchlets borne subumbellately on the ends of slender elongate hyphae in which the segmentation is indistinct or obsolete, the segmentation frequently ill-defined or obsolete throughout the whole vegetative body; sporangia variable in size and form, long-oval, tapering rather abruptly to the blunt tip, terminal and solitary or sometimes several arising from a single segment, once to many times proliferous, the hyphae sometimes traversing and growing beyond the empty sporangium; zoospores somewhat variable in size and number, usually about 6–10 μ long by 7 μ in diameter; male and female gametangia terminal and solitary or several arising from a single segment, up to three times proliferous, hyphae sometimes growing through and beyond discharged gametangia; female gametangia subspherical to short-ovoid, forming one to four discharge papillae, 20–60 by 15–25 μ, female gametes variable in number, up to 16 (usually six to eight in a gametangium, spherical, nonflagellate, 11–18 μ in diameter; male gametangia smaller than the female, short-elliptical to ovoid, forming a single, terminal discharge papilla, 20–25 by 10–15 μ, male gametes variable in number, up to eighteen in a gametangium, posteriorly uniflagellate, elliptical or somewhat cylindrical, with a conspicuous anterior cluster of refractive granules, 7–9 by 3–5 μ, flagellum 21–23 μ in length; zygote retaining the flagellum of the male gamete, at first amoeboid, then actively motile, posteriorly uniflagellate, ovoid, 16–25 by 10–15 μ, encysting to form a smooth-walled, spherical resting spore, germination not observed. (Adapted in part from Johns and Benjamin, 1954.)

On submerged fruits of various types, especially those of the Rosaceae; submerged twigs of fir, spruce mucilage, and twigs of deciduous trees. Thaxter (F) (*loc. cit.*), Sparrow (1932b: 290, pl. 7, fig. L; 1933b: 537, pl. 20, fig. 34; 1933c: 530), Matthews (1935: 309, pl. 63, figs. 1–3), Beneke (1948: 30), Johns and Benjamin (1954: 201), Sparrow and Barr

(1955: 555), United States; Petersen (1909: 398, figs. 12–14; 1910: 534, figs. 12–14), Lund (1934: 39), Denmark; Apinis (1930: 236), Latvia; Minden (1915: 578), Germany; Barnes and Melville (1932: 93, fig. 6), Sparrow (1933b: 537; 1936a: 459, pl. 20, fig. 8), Great Britain; Crooks (1937: 221, fig. 7a), Australia; Beverwijk (1948: 231, fig. 2), Holland; Kobayasi and Ookubo (1952a: 103; 1954b: 570), Ookubo (1954: 55), Japan; Cejp (1947: 46, pl. 2, fig. 2), Czechoslovakia; fruits, Das-Gupta and John (1953: 168, figs. 6,7), apples, Lacy (1955: 209), India.

In general habit this species is more open and ramose than *Gonapodya prolifera* and it usually grows under less foul environmental conditions. Whether or not the difference in environment is responsible for the distinctions between the two fungi awaits further investigation.

MONOBLEPHARELLA Sparrow

Allan Hancock Pacific Expeditions, Publ. Univ. So. Calif., 3(6): 103. 1940

(Fig. 51, p. 710)

Mycelium pearly gray in aggregate, the hyphae branched, delicate, often catenulate, nonseptate, with very thin walls, contents disposed in a reticulate, scalariform, or foamy manner; zoosporangia cylindrical or somewhat siliquiform, cut off from the hyphae by cross walls, secondary ones sympodially developed; zoospores fully formed within the sporangium in one or several rows, with an anterior group of refractive granules, escaping after dissolution of the tip of the sporangium; antheridia and oögonia when first formed usually associated in pairs, sperm posteriorly uniflagellate with an anterior group of refractive granules, oöspheres nonflagellate, containing large refractive globules usually one (rarely more than three), borne in an oögonium which lacks a conspicuous papilla; sperm not completely engulfed by the egg at fertilization; zygote at once emerging and swimming away by means of the persistent flagellum of the sperm; oöspore formed free in the water, with a smooth, thickened wall, upon germination forming a mycelium.

Saprophytic in soil or in fresh water; primarily tropical and subtropical.

KEY TO THE SPECIES OF MONOBLEPHARELLA

Male and female gametangia both formed; oöspores typically exogenous

First formed gametangium of a pair female, the male gametangium hypogynous or terminal on a short branch subtending the female

Male gametangium hypogynous, less than five times as long as wide; female gametangium bearing a single oösphere, rarely more .... *M. taylori,* p. 721

Male gametangium hypogynous or terminal on a short branch subtending female, more than five times as long as wide; female with one to three oöspheres, rarely more . . *M. elongata,* p. 722

First formed gametangium of a pair male, female terminal on a short branch subtending male or directly beneath it, or intercalary; male terminal or epigynous, never hypogynous

Female gametangium always terminal on a short branch subtending the male; male gametangium predominantly more than 15 μ in length .... *M. mexicana,* p. 723

Female gametangium frequently formed directly beneath the male, male gametangium then appearing epigynous, and less than 15 μ in length .... *M. laruei,* p. 724

Male gametangium apparently lacking; oöspores typically endogenous

M. endogena, p. 725

MONOBLEPHARELLA TAYLORI Sparrow

Allan Hancock Pacific Expeditions, Publ. Univ. S. Calif., 3(6): 103, pls. 16–17. 1940
(Fig. 51, p. 710)

Monoblepharis taylori Sparrow, Mycologia, 31: 737. 1939.

Mycelium well developed, consisting of tenuous flexuous branched hyphae mostly 2–5 μ in diameter, often with swellings of various shapes, the contents reticulately vacuolated; sporangia narrowly siliquiform or fusiform or cylindrical, with a tenuous wall, variable in size, 18–115 μ long by 5–20 μ in diameter, with a very narrow (2.5–4 μ) base, occurring singly or in pairs at the tips of the hyphae or after sympodial branching of a hypha appearing lateral; zoospores ovoid or somewhat cylindrical, 7–10 μ long by 4.5–6 μ wide, the posterior flagellum from two to three times the length of the body; oögonium at first terminal or, after sympodial branching of the supporting hypha, often appearing lateral, clavate or obpyriform, with rounded apex and narrow cylindrical base 10–22 μ long by 7–16 μ wide tapering to 2–3 μ at the base, the contents at maturity forming one or occasionally up to four eggs, containing numerous large refractive globules; antheridia hypogynous, often several developed in basipetal succession, consisting of a cylindrical segment of the suboögonial hypha and a beaklike lateral outgrowth 4–15 μ long by 4–7 μ wide (terminal ones 8–25 μ by 4–8 μ); antherozoids two to five, strongly amoeboid, posteriorly uniflagellate, ovoid when swimming, about 5.6 μ long by 3.4 μ wide, escaping through a pore formed at the tip of the beak; zygote broadly ovoid to nearly spherical, 10–13 μ long by 8–10 μ wide, posteriorly uniflagellate, free-swimming, the contents bearing numerous large refractive globules; oöspore formed free in the water, spherical, 8–13 μ in diameter, with a slightly thickened light-brown smooth wall, contents bearing globules, forming a mycelium upon germination.

In soil, hempseed bait, coll. W. R. Taylor, BRITISH WEST INDIES, PANAMA; coll. C. D. LaRue, NICARAGUA.

MONOBLEPHARELLA ELONGATA Springer

Mycologia, 37: 206, figs. 1–23, 47. 1945

"Mycelium well developed; hyphae sparingly branched, the branches usually arising at right angles to the main axes, 1.5–4 μ in diameter, the stouter basal portions up to 7 μ; vacuolization reticulate or scalariform; hyphae usually with many irregular swellings. Sporangia narrowly cylindrical or siliquiform, 40–120 μ in length by 5–13 μ in diameter at the widest point, tapering to 2–4 μ at the base, terminal, or after sympodial branching of the hyphae, appearing lateral, usually with one or occasionally several lateral papillate outgrowths near the base. Zoospores emerging through a pore at the apex of the sporangium and through the apices of outgrowths; zoospore with an anterior group of small refractive globules, ovoid or subcylindrical, 6.5–10.5 μ long by 4–6 μ wide, the single posterior flagellum up to 26 μ long. Oogonium at first terminal or, after sympodial branching of the supporting hypha, appearing lateral, narrowly obpyriform, 17–35 μ long by 7–12 μ in diameter at the widest point, with rounded apex and a cylindrical base 2–4 μ in diameter, the contents at maturity forming one to three or rarely up to eight eggs containing numerous large refractive globules.

Antheridium either terminal on a branch subtending the oogonium and cylindrical, 20–45 μ long by 3–5 μ wide, or hypogynous and geniculate, consisting of a cylindrical section of the suboogonial hypha 2–19 μ long and a beaklike lateral outgrowth 10–35 μ long by 3–5 μ wide. Antherozoids four to seven, emerging through a pore at the apex of the antheridium, strongly amoeboid, ovoid when swimming, 5–6 μ long by 3–4 μ wide, with an anterior group of small refractive globules, posteriorly uniflagellate, the flagellum up to 20 μ in length. Zygote spherical or broadly ovoid, 9–13 μ long by 8–10 μ wide, posteriorly uniflagellate free swimming or during rest periods strongly amoeboid, containing large refractive globules. Oospore formed free in the water, or occasionally retained within or at the orifice of the oogonium, 9–12 μ in diameter, with a light brown, smooth wall up to 1 μ in thickness, contents bearing globules, upon germination forming a mycelium" (Springer, *loc. cit.*).

In soil, hempseed bait, coll. C. D. LaRue, MEXICO; soil, coll. M. E. Springer, UNITED STATES.

MONOBLEPHARELLA MEXICANA Shanor

Mycologia, 34: 242, figs. 1–20. 1942

"Mycelium well developed, hyphae delicate, 1.5–5.5 μ in diameter, much branched, branches usually growing almost at right angles to the main hyphae, contents reticulately vacuolated; sporangia narrowly cylindrical or siliquiform, variable in size, 40–95 μ in length by 6.5–10 μ in diameter [23–92 μ × 9.4 μ][1] at the widest point, occurring singly or in clusters due to marked sympodial branching of the supporting hypha; zoöspores ovoid to subcylindrical, 6.6–10 μ long by 4–5 μ in diameter, posteriorly uniciliate, cilia up to 36 μ long; oögonia at first terminal but often becoming lateral due to the sympodial branching of the supporting hypha, obpyriform with somewhat rounded apex and a narrow cylindrical base, 14–17 μ long by 9–15 μ in diameter, tapering to 2–4 μ at the base, containing usually a single egg in which there are numerous large refractive globules; antheridia terminal or after sympodial branching of the supporting hypha appearing lateral, narrowly cylindrical or fusiform, 14–16 μ long by 4–6.5 μ in diameter [11–25 ×

---

[1] Springer (1945b).

4–8 μ][1]; antherozoids 2–8, amoeboid, posteriorly uniciliate, ovoid when swimming, 4–6 μ long by 2.5–3.7 μ in diameter, normally containing 2–4 strongly refractive globules; zygote broadly ovoid to nearly spherical, 10.5–13.6 μ long by 8–10 μ in diameter, free swimming or becoming stationary at oögonial orifice; oöspores formed free in the water or within oögonium or at its mouth, normally spherical, 10–13 μ in diameter with a slightly thickened, amber to light brown, smooth wall, contents containing many large refractive globules, upon germination forming a mycelium" (Shanor, *loc. cit.*).

In soil, hempseed bait, Shanor (*loc. cit.*; 1944: 332), MEXICO.

Springer (1945b) experienced considerable difficulty in her attempts to induce sex-organ formation in this species. They developed only at 36°C. and then sporadically. Their sequence of development is just the reverse of that in *Monoblepharella taylori* and *M. elongata*. In old heavily contaminated cultures the two types of sex organs tend to form in clusters and the eggs are usually abnormal.

MONOBLEPHARELLA LARUEI Springer

Mycologia, 37: 212, figs. 24–46, 51. 1945

"Mycelium well developed; hyphae sparingly branched, the branches usually arising at right angles to the main axes, delicate, 1.5–4 μ in diameter, the stouter basal portions up to 7 μ; vacuolization reticulate or scalariform; hyphae with occasional swellings. Sporangia cylindrical or siliquiform, 28–82 μ long by 7–15 μ in diameter at the widest point, occurring at the tips of hyphae, or several often developed in basipetal succession, later sporangia sometimes geniculate. Zoospores emerging through a pore at the apex of the sporangium, ovoid or somewhat cylindrical, 7–9 μ long by 5–5.5 μ in diameter, with an anterior group of small refractive globules, posteriorly uniflagellate, the flagellum up to 27 μ in length. Oogonium terminal on a branch subtending the antheridium, or formed by a swelling of the hypha below the antheridium, after sympodial branching of the hypha appearing lateral, obpyriform, 11–20 μ long by 7–12 μ in diameter at the widest point, with rounded apex, and, if terminal, with narrowly cylindrical base tapering to 2–4 μ,

----

[1] Springer (1945b).

the contents at maturity forming one or rarely up to three eggs bearing numerous large refractive globules. Antheridium always formed terminally on the hypha, later often epigynous, 8–19 μ long by 4–7 μ in diameter at the widest point. Antherozoids two to five, emerging through a pore at the apex of the antheridium, strongly amoeboid, ovoid when swimming, 4–5 μ long by 3–3.5 μ wide, with an anterior group of small refractive globules, posteriorly uniflagellate, the flagellum up to 19 μ in length. Zygote spherical or broadly ovoid, 10–13 μ long by 8–10 μ wide, posteriorly uniflagellate, free swimming, amoeboid during rest periods, the contents bearing numerous large refractive globules. Oospore formed free in the water, spherical, 9–13 μ in diameter, with a light brown, smooth wall up to 1 μ in thickness, contents bearing globules, germination not observed" (Springer, *loc. cit.*).

In soil, hempseed bait, coll. C. D. LaRue, NICARAGUA.

The strong tendency for basipetalous development of secondary sporangia is distinctive for this species. Although the sex-organ arrangement here resembles that of the previous species, it differs in the frequent basipetalous development of the oögonia. Sex organs are produced at all temperatures between 26° and 32°C.

MONOBLEPHARELLA ENDOGENA Sparrow

Mycologia, 45: 593, fig. 1. 1953

Mycelium well developed, of tenuous flexuous branched hyphae 2.5–6 μ in diameter, with many irregular swellings up to 9 μ in diameter, contents reticulately vacuolate; sporangia siliquiform, 34–47 μ long by 5–8 μ in diameter, occurring singly or in pairs at tips of the hyphae or after sympodial branching appearing lateral; zoospores ovoid or subcylindrical, 8 μ long by 5 μ wide, the posterior flagellum two to three times the length of the body; oögonium at first terminal or after sympodial branching of hypha appearing lateral; clavate or obpyriform with rounded apex and narrow cylindrical base, 10–15 μ long by 7.5–8.75 μ wide, tapering to 2.5 μ at base, the contents at maturity forming one, rarely up to four eggs bearing numerous large refractive globules; antheridium and antherozoids unknown; oospore spherical, 7.5–10 μ in diameter, endogenous, with a slightly thickened light-brown smooth wall, contents bearing globules.

In soil, hempseed bait, Sparrow (*loc. cit.*), Johns (comm.) (NORTH CAROLINA), T. W. Johnson, Jr. (comm.), (MISSISSIPPI), UNITED STATES.

No antheridia have ever been found in this species although the possibility of their occurrence cannot be disregarded. Apparently, the oöspores are typically parthenogenetic.

MONOBLEPHARIDACEAE

Mycelium lacking pseudosepta; zoosporangia always elongate; gametangia not proliferous; oögonium typically forming a single oösphere, the entire male gamete engulfed by the female at fertilization, female gamete converted without an intervening swarm period into a usually bullate oöspore which remains in intimate contact with the oögonium.

One genus, *Monoblepharis*.

Saprophytic primarily on twigs in cool, clear water.

MONOBLEPHARIS CORNU

Bull. Soc. Bot. France, 18: 59. 1871
(Figs. 48–50, pp. 700, 704, 708; 53, p. 730; 54 A, E, p. 738)

Diblepharis Lagerheim, Bih. Klg. Svensk. Vetensk.-Ak. Handl., 25, Afd. 3, No. 8: 39. 1900.

Monoblephariopsis Laibach, Jahrb. wiss. Bot., 66: 603. 1927.

Mycelium nonseptate, branched or unbranched, colorless or with a slightly brownish tinge, attached by rhizoids to the substratum, contents of the hyphae disposed in a reticulate or foamy manner; zoosporangia usually terminal, narrowly cylindrical or somewhat irregular in shape, cut off from the hyphae by cross walls, renewed by branching of the hyphae or by internal proliferation; zoospores fully formed within the sporangium, escaping after the dissolution of its apex, posteriorly uniflagellate; oögonia intercalary or terminal, usually narrowly pyriform to spherical, cut off from the attendant hyphae by cross walls, each oögonium exhibiting upon maturity a well-defined receptive papilla and a single egg; antheridia of differing shapes, usually somewhat cylindrical, variously placed, forming a small number of uniflagellate sperms entirely similar, save for their smaller size, to the zoospores; oöspheres after fertilization remaining in the oögonia or emerging, in either case developing into thick-walled oöspores; oöspore upon germination producing a new thallus.

Saprophytic primarily on vegetable debris, particularly twigs, and on animal remains.

The genus *Diblepharis* was established by Lagerheim to include *Monoblepharis fasciculata* and *M. insignis* Thaxter, which were described as having biflagellate zoospores. See, however, the remarks under the descriptions of these species (pp. 735, 737).

Monoblephariopsis Laibach was erected to include *Monoblepharis regignens* and *M. ovigera*, sporangial forms differing from other species of *Monoblepharis* in having more slender hyphae and smaller sporangia, which proliferated, and in lacking sex organs.

KEY TO THE SPECIES OF MONOBLEPHARIS [1]

Sexual reproduction known; sex organs generally formed in abundance
  Oögonia without beaks, spherical, subspherical or narrowly pyriform; oöspores exogenous, that is, extruded from the oögonium, or endogenous, that is, retained within the oögonium, generally spherical; antheridia variously borne; hyphae delicate, not often exceeding 5 μ in diameter; usually flexuous and much branched
    Oöspores endogenous; antheridia hypogynous, that is, formed immediately below oögonium, usually strongly exserted...
    .... *M. sphaerica*, p. 728
  Oöspores exogenous; antheridia variously borne
    Antheridia usually hypogynous, or on separate branches
      Antheridia scarcely exserted, in young plants hypogynous, nearly always accompanying oögonia ... *M. hypogyna*, p. 729
      Antheridia conspicuously exserted, in young plants occurring on separate branches from the oögonia, in older ones formed in groups with the oögonia.
        Oöspores bullate .... *M. macrandra*, p. 731
        Oöspores smooth .... *M. laevis*, p. 733

---

[1] Perrott (1955) has taken up Lagerheim's (1900) division into the subgenera *Monoblepharis*, containing the coarse endogenous species with cylindrical oögonia (except *M. sphaerica*), and *Exoospora*, embracing the delicate exogenous forms with more or less pyriform oögonia. To separate *M. sphaerica* in this manner from its morphologically similar allies in the *Exoospora* seems somewhat extreme but may prove practical.

Antheridia epigynous, that is, appearing to be inserted on the
  oögonia . . . .   *M. polymorpha*, p. 733
Oögonia always conspicuously beaked, mostly cylindrical; oöspores
  constantly endogenous, generally ellipsoidal; antheridia always
  epigynous; hyphae generally coarse, straight, rigid and scarcely
  branched, up to 23 μ in diameter
Oöspores smooth; sex organs in fascicles, linearly arranged or
  singly at tips of the hyphae
Sex organs in fascicles
  Oöspores 21–25 μ by 18 μ . . . .   *M. fasciculata*
                                                var. *fasciculata*, p. 735
  Oöspores 28–32 μ by 23 μ . . . . . .   *M. fasciculata* var. *magna*, p. 736
Sex organs linearly arranged, basipetal, or single at the tips of
  the hyphae
  Oöspores 30–40 μ by 23–32 μ . . .   *M. insignis* var. *insignis*, p. 737
  Oöspores 23–25 μ by 20–21 μ . . . . .   *M. insignis* var. *minor*, p. 737
Oöspores bullate; sex organs in fascicles, linearly arranged or
  singly at the tips of the hyphae . . . .   *M. bullata*, p. 740
Sexual reproduction unknown [1]
Sporangia narrowly cylindrical, frequently proliferating . . . .
  . . . .   *M. regignens*, p. 741
Sporangia more ovate, rarely proliferating . . . .   *M. ovigera*, p. 741

MONOBLEPHARIS SPHAERICA Cornu

Bull. Soc. Bot. France, 18: 59. 1871; Ann. Sci. Nat. Bot., V, 15: 82, pl.2, figs.1–6
1872

Non *Monoblepharis sphaerica* Cornu emend. Woronin, Mém. Acad. Sci
St. Pétersb., Phys.-Math. Cl. VIII, 16: 1–24. 1904.

Mycelium well developed, consisting of cylindrical, somewhat rigid,
rather frequently branched hyphae, 1–2 mm. long by 4–6 μ in diameter;
oögonia subspherical to spherical, usually arranged singly at the tips
of the hyphae and their branches, occasionally borne in fascicles at the
tips of the branches, less frequently in a series alternating with hypogynous antheridia, varying in length from 21 to 31 μ (majority 23 μ),
diameter 19–27 μ (majority 21 μ); antheridia narrowly cylindrical,
hypogynous, always present, usually opening by a slightly exserted tube
approximately 2 μ long, formed just below the oögonial cross wall

---

[1] The two following species may belong in *Monoblepharella* or they may be
distinct from that genus as well as from *Monoblepharis*. Final disposition will depend on their type of sexual reproduction, if any.

(this tube occasionally curved and reaching 4–10 μ in length), 10–23 μ long (majority 15 μ) by 4–6 μ in diameter; antherozoids amoeboid, uniciliate, 3.5 by 2 μ, four to seven in a single antheridium; usually protandrous; oöspores single, spherical, endogenous, germinating *in situ*, thick-walled, golden brown, covered when mature with closely arranged, colorless to pale-yellow bullations 1–2 μ in height, diameter varying from 12.5 to 23 μ (majority 17–19 μ). (Modified from Perrott.)

On submerged twigs, Cornu (1871: 59), FRANCE; twigs of *Quercus robur*, Perrott (1955: 270, pl. 11, figs. 3–4, text fig. 12), GREAT BRITAIN.

Perrott (1955) has pointed out that Woronin (1904) and later authors who followed him were in error in ascribing to Cornu's species a form having exogenous oöspores. As is clearly shown by both Cornu and Perrott these spores are characteristically borne endogenously in *Monoblepharis sphaerica*.

An attempt is made here to separate the citations of occurrence referring to the true *Monoblepharis sphaerica* from those incorrectly ascribed to it in the past, and now belonging under *M. hypogyna*.

MONOBLEPHARIS HYPOGYNA Perrott

Trans. Brit. Mycol. Soc., 38: 272, fig. 13. 1955
(Fig. 49 E–G, p. 704; 53 C, p. 730)

Monoblepharis sphaerica Cornu emend. Woronin, Mém. Acad. Sci. St. Pétersb., Phys.-Math. Cl. VIII, 16: 1–24. 1904, pro parte.

"Mycelium well developed, consisting of cylindrical, somewhat rigid, usually sparingly branched hyphae 1–2 mm. long, and varying in diameter from 7.5 μ in the stouter basal portions to 2 μ at the tip (average 3–5 μ).

"Oogonia narrowly pyriform, occurring singly and terminally or occasionally in a series alternating with antheridia, or in a fascicle, at a hyphal tip; rarely intercalary. Length 21–45 μ (majority 25–34 μ); diameter 8–19 μ (majority 13 μ).

"Antheridia narrowly cylindrical, hypogynous, opening by a slightly exserted tube just beneath the oogonial cross-wall. Length, 9–27 μ; diameter 4–9 μ. An antheridium is nearly always present at the base of each oogonium, except in the case of some series of oogonia and anther-

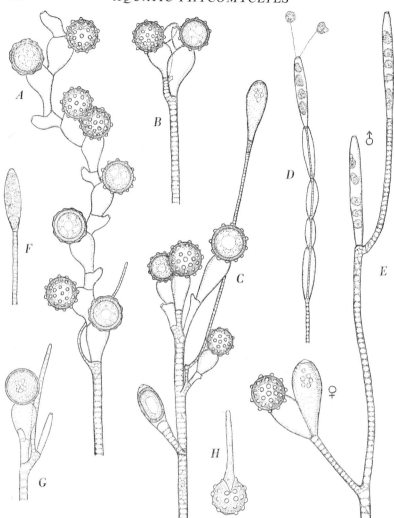

FIG. 53. *Monoblepharis*

A-B. Monoblepharis polymorpha Cornu. *C. Monoblepharis hypogyna* Perrott. *D.* Proliferating zoosporangia of *Monoblepharis regignens* Lagerheim. *E.* Antheridia and oögonia of *Monoblepharis macrandra* (Lagerheim) Woronin. *F.* Mature sporangium of *Monoblepharis ovigera* Lagerheim. *G. Monoblepharis laevis* Sparrow. *H.* Germinating oöspore of *Monoblepharis polymorpha* Cornu.
(Sparrow, 1933b)

idia, where the hypha will occasionally give rise to two oogonia without the alternation of an antheridium. A single antheridium usually contains 4–7 amoeboid uniflagellate antherozooids approximately 3.5 μ by 1.5–2 μ.

"Each oogonium produces a single spherical oospore, 13–23 μ in diameter (majority 17 μ), and is nearly always exogenous when mature. These oospores are spherical in shape, thick-walled, golden brown in colour, and covered at maturity with light yellow, transparent bullations, 2 μ in height. When the oospore reaches the outside of the oogonium it remains attached to the oogonial mouth for some time before it falls away. When endogenous oospores are found, the oospore is seen to fill the diameter of the oogonium, and bullations are to be found only upon those surfaces of the oospore which are not adpressed to the walls of the oogonium. Oospores produce a vegetative hypha on germination...

"Zoosporangia are narrowly cylindrical, 72–104 μ in length by 5–7 μ in diameter when borne singly in a terminal position, or 21–38 μ in length by 5 μ in diameter when borne in a row. Occasionally borne in an intercalary position. Zoospores, amoeboid, uniflagellate, 4–9 μ by 3–5 μ, arranged in a single or double row, inside the sporangium" (Perrott, *loc. cit.*).

On submerged twigs of *Quercus robur*, Perrott (*loc. cit.*); twigs, Barnes and Melville (1932: 84, fig. 1), Sparrow (1933b: 528; 1936a: 459), GREAT BRITAIN; Woronin (1904: 1–24, pl. 1, figs. 1–16, pl. 2, figs. 17–19, 21–27, pl. 3, figs. 50–53), FINLAND; Laibach (1927: fig. 8), Höhnk (1935), GERMANY; Thaxter (F.), Sparrow (S.) (1932b: 290, pl. 7, fig. F; 1933b: 528, pl. 20, figs. 1–4, 29; 1933c: 530), coll. Linder, Sparrow (1933b), Wolf (1944: 18), Beneke (1948: 30), R. M. Johns (comm.), (NORTH CAROLINA) UNITED STATES; Apinis (1930: 237), LATVIA.

See remarks under *Monoblepharis sphaerica*, p. 729.

MONOBLEPHARIS MACRANDRA (Lagerheim) Woronin

Mém. Acad. Impér. Sci. St. Pétersb., Phys.-Math. Cl., VIII, 16: 13, pl. 2, figs. 32–46, pl. 3, figs. 47–49, 54–70. 1904
(Fig. 53 E, p. 730)

Monoblepharis polymorpha Cornu, pro parte, Ann. Sci. Nat. Bot., V, 15: 84, pl. 2, figs. 10–32. 1872; van Tieghem, Traité de Botanique (1874 ed.), figs. 167 C, 7 p–q. Paris.

Monoblepharis polymorpha var. *macrandra* Lagerheim, Bih. Kgl. Svensk. Vetensk.-Ak. Handl., 25, Afd. 3, No. 8: 35, pl. 1, figs. 2, 4, 21–24, 36–46, 48–51, 54, 63, 67–68, pl. 2, figs. 11–26. 1900.

Mycelium filamentous, exceedingly well developed, consisting of rather flexuous nearly isodiametric profusely branched hyphae which under excellent conditions for growth may interlock and completely envelop the substratum, hyphae 5 μ tapering distally to 1.5–2 μ in diameter, bearing occasional irregular swellings; sporangia narrowly cylindrical, 107–346 μ in length by 4.5–6 μ in diameter, occurring singly at the tips of the hyphae or grouped in sympodial or fasciculate fashion, occasionally proliferating; zoospores 7.8 μ in diameter by 9–12 μ in length; oögonia broadly cylindrical to narrowly pyriform, at first formed singly in a terminal or intercalary position, later occurring sympodially or more commonly in fascicles associated with antheridia; antheridia cylindrical, at first formed at the tips of hyphal branches other than those bearing oögonia, later occurring with them, always strongly exserted, variable in size, usually about 12.5–59 μ long by 5–7 μ in diameter; antherozoids from five to fourteen in an antheridium, about 6 μ in length by 4 μ in diameter; oöspores normally exogenous, having a tendency to fall away from the oögonium, 13–25 μ in diameter, the brown wall covered by lighter-colored bullations 1.5–2 μ in height, germination not observed.

Saprophytic on submerged twigs of various types. Lagerheim (*loc. cit.*), SWEDEN; Woronin (*loc. cit.*), FINLAND; Cornu (*loc. cit*), FRANCE; Tiesenhausen (1912: 266), SWITZERLAND; Petersen (1909: 399; 1910: 535, fig. 15c), Lund (1934: 45), DENMARK; Minden (1915: 476), Laibach (1926: figs. 1–3; 1927: figs. 5, 7b, 9–10, pl. 12, figs. 1–19, 28–35, pl. 13, figs. 36–47), Höhnk (1935: 219), GERMANY; Wettstein (1921), AUSTRIA; Thaxter (F.), Sparrow (S.) (1933b: 530, fig. 1 s–u, pl. 20, figs. 5–6, 25, 31; 1933c: 530), twigs, Beneke (1948: 30), Sparrow (1952d: 769), R. M. Johns (comm.), (NORTH CAROLINA), UNITED STATES; Scherffel (1931: 137), HUNGARY; Barnes and Melville (1932: 86, figs. 2–5), Sparrow (1933b: 530; 1936a: 459), twigs of *Quercus robur*, *Fraxinus excelsior*, *Ulmus sp.*, Perrott (1955: 275, pl. 13, figs. 1–2, 14–15), GREAT BRITAIN.

If one combines the description of variations found in *Monoblepharis polymorpha* given at the top of page 84 of Cornu's monograph with the figures shown by him in this paper and in van Tieghem's *Traité de Botanique*, there seems little question that he had observed *M. macrandra*. Lagerheim considered the species to be a variety of *M. polymorpha*, but because of the position of the antheridium, its strong exsertion, and the tendency of one or the other of the sex organs to be formed in groups little chance exists of confusing this with others of the genus. Forms are occasionally found, however, which produce antheridia approximating those of the closely related *M. sphaerica* and *M. hypogyna*, and, rarely, epigynous ones are observed. The determination of whether or not these variations are due to hybridism, as has been suggested, awaits further study.

MONOBLEPHARIS LAEVIS (Sparrow), stat. nov.

(Fig. 53 G, p. 730)

Monoblepharis macrandra var. *laevis*, Ann. Bot. London, 47: 531, pl. 20, figs. 14–16. 1933.

Thallus and reproductive organs like those of *Monoblepharis macrandra*; oöspore spherical, 25 μ in diameter, dark brown, smooth-walled, contents bearing numerous globules.

On rose fruits, Sparrow (*loc. cit.*), twigs, Beneke (1948: 30), UNITED STATES; twig of *Aesculus sp.*, Sparrow (1936a: 459), twigs of *Quercus robur, Fraxinus excelsior*, Perrott (1955: 277, pl. 12, fig. 4, text-fig. 16), GREAT BRITAIN; twigs of *Fraxinus sp.*, Sparrow (1936a: 459), DENMARK.

MONOBLEPHARIS POLYMORPHA Cornu

Bull. Soc. Bot. France, 18: 59. 1871; Ann. Sci. Nat. Bot., V, 15: 83, pl. 2, figs. 7–9. 1872; van Tieghem, Traité de Botanique (1874 ed.), fig. 167 B, 4 (sporangia), and fig. 167 C, 7 l–n, and 9. Paris

(Figs. 48 C–E, p. 700; 49 A–D, p. 704; 50, p. 708; 53 A–B, H, p. 730)

Monoblepharis brachyandra Lagerheim, Bih. Kgl. Svensk. Vetensk.-Ak. Handl., 25, Afd. 3, No. 8: 37, pl. 1, figs. 1, 3, 5–10, 14–20, 35–45, 47, 52–53, 55–62, 64–66, pl. 2, figs. 6–10. 1900.

Monoblepharis brachyandra var. *longicollis* Lagerheim, *loc. cit.*, p. 38, pl. 1, fig. 53, pl. 2, figs. 1–5. 1900.

Mycelium filamentous, well developed, consisting of somewhat rigid cylindrical rather frequently branched hyphae which, in their stouter, basal portions attain a diameter of 12–15 μ, tapering distally to 1.5–2 μ; sporangia narrowly cylindrical, rarely somewhat irregular, 130–234 μ in length by 10.4–13 μ in diameter, occurring singly, terminally, or occasionally in clusters sympodially arranged; zoospores 10.4–13 μ in length by 7.8–10.4 μ in diameter; oögonia in young material broadly to narrowly pyriform, in older plants differing somewhat in shape, the even contour often being notched at the point of insertion of the antheridium, variable in size, usually 20–28 μ long by 20–28 μ tapering proximally to 5–7 μ in diameter; antheridia epigynous but often in a series of incompletely developed sex organs appearing hypogynous, when terminal, somewhat cylindrical, when intercalary, somewhat geniculate with a broadly conical apex, varying greatly in size, usually about 10–35 μ in length by 5–10 μ in diameter; antherozoids from five to seven, each about 5.2 μ in length by 2.6 μ in diameter; oöspores spherical, nearly always exogenous, with a thick brown wall beset with bullations 1.5–2 μ in height, or oftentimes with light-colored undulations, 12–25 μ in diameter; oöspore germinating by means of a hypha.

Saprophytic on submerged twigs of various types and on animal remains. Cornu (*loc. cit.*), FRANCE; Lagerheim (*loc. cit.*), SWEDEN; Woronin (1904), FINLAND; Tiesenhausen (1912: 265, fig. 1), SWITZERLAND; Petersen (1909: 400; 1910: 535, fig. 15 a–b), Lund (1934: 46, fig. 22d), Sparrow, DENMARK; Claussen (1912), Minden (1902: 806), Laibach (1927: 601, fig. 2), GERMANY; Apinis (1930: 237), LATVIA; Wettstein (1921), AUSTRIA; Thaxter (F.), Sparrow (S.) (1933b: 529, fig. 1 a–m, r, text fig. 2 a–k, pl. 20, figs. 7–13, 19–20, 28 [this species?], 36, 38–39; 1933c: 530), twigs, Wolf (1944: 18), Beneke (1948: 30), R. M. Johns (comm.), (NORTH CAROLINA) *Betula* twigs, Sparrow and Barr (1955: 555), UNITED STATES; Barnes and Melville (1932: fig. III, 3), twigs of *Quercus robur, Fraxinus excelsior*, Perrott (1955: 278, pl. 12, figs. 1–3. text-figs. 15 c–h. 17), GREAT BRITAIN; *Pyrus pashia* twig, Shen and Siang (1948: 189, fig. 7), CHINA.

Monoblepharis brachyandra is said to be distinct from *M. polymorpha* chiefly in the uneven contour of the oögonium at the place of insertion of the shorter stouter antheridium and in the frequently intercalary position of the latter, or, when epigynous, its tendency to be formed on the lower third of the oögonium. The oöspores differ in being smaller and in having flatter broader bullations, which may, in some specimens, be only slight undulations. Such differences are readily apparent when one has only a limited amount of material, in early stages of development. If large amounts of the fungus are available, however, and if the plants are observed over a long period of time, these differences become less distinct. One finds that whereas in the sex organs first formed the antheridia and oögonia are often disposed in a definite manner and possess definite, uniform shapes, in subsequent "generations" of such organs on the same hypha these characters vary considerably. Indeed, one may find combinations of *polymorpha* and *brachyandra* characters on a single plant. Such combinations are evident in Lagerheim's figures of his species. These remarks apply also to the variety *longicollis*, which is based chiefly on slight differences in size, shape, and position of the sex organs and stronger bullations on the somewhat smaller oöspore. Variations are so prevalent in plants with a profuse development of sex organs that nearly every group might be considered a variety if based on such slight differences. Gemmae have been described by Lagerheim as occurring in *M. polymorpha*.

As originally described by Cornu *Monoblepharis polymorpha* was sufficiently inclusive to embrace *M. macrandra*.

MONOBLEPHARIS FASCICULATA var. FASCICULATA Thaxter

Bot. Gaz., 20: 439, pl. 29, figs. 8–12. 1895
(Fig. 54 E, p. 738)

Diblepharis fasciculata (Thaxter) Lagerheim, Bih. Kgl. Svensk. Vetensk.-
Ak. Handl., 25, Afd. 3, No. 8: 40. 1900.

Hyphae straight, rigid, cylindrical, simple or (rarely) simple or sympodially branched at the tips, 1–2 mm. long by 5–12.5 µ in diameter; zoosporangia narrowly cylindrical, zoospores posteriorly uniflagellate, 7–9 µ in diameter; antheridia narrow, cylindrical, tapering slightly, straight, not divergent, 10.5–27 µ long by 5–12.5 µ in diameter; antherozoids five to sixteen (usually five to eight) in an antheridium, 3 µ in diameter; oögonia oval-oblong, elliptical or cylindrical, with a straight or slightly curved neck or beak which is shorter than the antheridium, 23–46 µ long by 15–27 µ in diameter, arranged singly or in fascicles of two to eight at the tips of the hyphae; oöspores subspherical, broadly ellipsoidal or oval-oblong, golden-brown, smooth-walled, 17–27 μ long by 13–25 μ in diameter, germinating *in situ*.

On submerged twigs, Thaxter (F.) (*loc. cit.*), R. M. Johns (comm.) (NORTH CAROLINA), Benjamin (comm.) (MASSACHUSETTS), UNITED STATES; Thomas [Perrott] (1939: 124, fig. 1), twigs of *Quercus robur*, Perrott (1955: 258, pl. 9 and fig. 3), GREAT BRITAIN.

R. M. Johns observed the true zoosporangia of this species and says that they are narrowly cylindrical. The zoospores are posteriorly uniflagellate not biflagellate (see Sparrow, 1943: 467).

MONOBLEPHARIS FASCICULATA var. MAGNA Perrott

Trans. Brit. Mycol. Soc., 38: 260, fig. 4, 1955

"Mycelium well developed, consisting of straight, rigid, cylindrical, vacuolated hyphae, which are often pale brown, especially in the basal portions, and hyaline near the tips; rarely branched, except near the tip, 1–2 mm. long by 7–12.5 μ in diameter (average 7–10.5 μ); attached to the substratum by branching rhizoids.

"Oogonia arranged singly or in fascicles at the tips of hyphae, cylindrical, contain a single oosphere, and open by a tube termed the 'neck' which is usually shorter than the antheridium and curved toward it. Occasionally this tube is as long as the antheridium. Oogonia vary in length from 32 to 54 μ (majority 39–50 μ); diameter 21–36 μ (majority 25 μ).

"Antheridia long, cylindrical, and tapering at the tip, rarely sub-conical, usually straight, but occasionally slightly curved towards the neck of the oogonium; length 14–29 μ (majority 21–25 μ); diameter 5–11 μ (majority 7–9 μ tapering to 6–7 μ); always present, borne on the oogonium (epigynous) to one side of the neck, which they always exceed in length. Antherozooids 4–5 μ in diameter, amoeboid and uniciliate; usually 6 or 7 in each antheridium. Protandry is well marked.

"Each oogonium contains a single oospore which matures and germinates *in situ* (endogenous). Oospores pale brown in colour, walls smooth, spherical, widely ellipsoid and cylindrical; length 24–36 μ (majority 28–32 μ), diameter 17–29 μ (majority 23 μ)" (Perrott, *loc. cit.*).

On submerged twigs of *Quercus robur*, GREAT BRITAIN.

Resembling var. *fasciculata* in everything but its larger size. Since both varieties were found on the same twig, environmental factors (except nutrition) are ruled out as a reason for size.

MONOBLEPHARIS INSIGNIS var. INSIGNIS Thaxter

Bot. Gaz., 20: 438, pl. 29, figs. 1–7. 1895
(Fig. 54 A, p. 738)

Diblepharis insignis (Thaxter) Lagerheim, Bih. Kgl. Svensk. Vetensk.-Ak. Handl., 25, Afd. 3, No. 8: 40. 1900.

Hyphae straight, rigid, hyaline or very pale reddish brown, nearly cylindrical 1.5–2.5 mm. in length by 9–16 μ in diameter, rarely branched; antheridia broad, subconical to subcylindrical, straight or slightly curved, the rounded tip often bent slightly inward, nearly symmetrical, epigynous and to one side of the oögonial beak, 9–13 μ in diameter at the base, tapering distally, 20–27 μ long, bearing four to six uniflagellate antherozoids 5–6 by 3–5 μ; oögonia single and terminal or in series of two to eight in basipetal succession, occasionally intercalary, cylindrical or irregular in shape, with a prominent lateral straight or slightly curved beak, which is often as long as the antheridium, 39–54 μ long by 25–35 μ in diameter; oöspores broadly ellipsoidal, spherical or irregular, 30–45 μ long by 22–33 μ in diameter, the wall smooth and golden brown or amber brown; zoosporangia long cylindrical, the same diameter as their concomitant hyphae; zoospores posteriorly uniflagellate.

On submerged twigs in pools and ditches. Thaxter (F.) (*loc. cit.*), R. M. Johns (comm.) (NORTH CAROLINA), Benjamin (comm.) (MASSACHUSETTS), UNITED STATES; Thomas [Perrott] (1939: 124, figs. II, III), twigs of *Quercus robur*, Perrott (1955: 261, figs. 5–6), GREAT BRITAIN.

True zoosporangia and zoospores of this species have been observed by R. M. Johns (comm.).

MONOBLEPHARIS INSIGNIS var. MINOR Perrott

Trans. Brit. Mycol. Soc., 38: 263, pl. 10, text fig. 7. 1955

"Mycelium well developed consisting of straight, rigid, cylindrical, hyaline, sometimes tinged with brown, vacuolated hyphae, which are simple or branch sympodially. Each hypha bears one oogonium or a

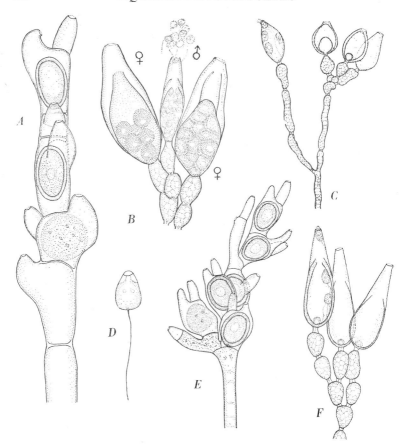

Fig. 54. *Monoblepharis* and *Gonapodya*

A. *Monoblepharis insignis* Thaxter, tip of hypha bearing epigynous antheridia and beaked oögonia, within which are endogenous oöspores (type material). B. *Gonapodya prolifera* (Cornu) Fischer, showing two lateral female gametangia and a central discharging male gametangium; all internally proliferating. C. *Gonapodya polymorpha* Thaxter, part of plant showing a discharging sporangium and proliferated ones. D. Zoospore of *Gonapodya prolifera* (Cornu) Fischer. E. *Monoblepharis fasciculata* Thaxter, tip of hypha showing arrangement of sex organs, and endogenous oöspores (type material). F. *Gonapodya prolifera* (Cornu) Fischer, part of plant, showing hyphal segments and proliferated zoosporangia.

(*A, C-F*, Sparrow, 1933b; *B*, Johns and Benjamin, 1954, redrawn from photomicrograph)

superimposed series of oogonia at its tip. Length of hypha 1–2 mm., diameter varying from 5 to 14 μ (majority 7–9 μ); attached to the substratum by branching rhizoids.

"Oogonia arranged singly, or in rows of 2–16 (average 9), formed in basipetal succession, at the tips of the hyphae. The long chains of superimposed oogonia are very characteristic of this variety. Occasionally intercalary oogonia are formed. Oogonia are usually cylindrical in shape, but occasionally irregular, opening when the oosphere is formed by a tube or 'neck' which may be curved or straight. The neck is very variable, long- and short-necked forms being found in the same series of oogonia. The oogonia vary in length from 25 to 54 μ (majority 36–43 μ), diameter 14–36 μ (majority 21–25 μ).

"Antheridia normally, but not always, present, varying from subconical to cylindrical in shape, tapering at the tip, narrow, usually straight, but occasionally slightly curved; length 7–29 μ (majority 14–21 μ); diameter 5–14 μ (majority 7–9 μ). The majority of antheridia are longer than the neck of the oogonium, although some may be equal in length or shorter than it; as a rule borne upon the terminal wall of the oogonium (epigynous), to one side of the neck, but occasionally hypogynous and intercalary in position, opening by an exserted tube formed just beneath the oogonial cross-wall. A single antheridium usually contains 5–7 amoeboid and uniflagellate antherozooids which measure 3.5–7 μ by 3.5 μ. Protandry is well marked.

"Each oogonium contains a single oospore which matures and germinates *in situ* (endogenous). Oospores golden brown, smooth, and very variable in shape, spherical, cylindrical, irregular, and widely ellipsoid forms being found (ellipsoid form the most typical); length 18–32 μ (majority 23–25 μ); diameter 11–25 μ (majority 20–21 μ). Much variation in oospore size is found, even among oospores contained in oogonia borne on the same filament" (Perrott, *loc. cit.*).

On submerged twigs of *Quercus robur, Fraxinus excelsior,* GREAT BRITAIN.

Resembling var. *insignis* in every way except for smaller size and frequently parthenogenetic oöspores. Var. *minor* was also found living on the same twig as the typical var. *insignis.*

MONOBLEPHARIS BULLATA Perrott

Trans. Brit. Mycol. Soc., 38: 266, pl. 11, figs. 1–2, text figs. 8–11. 1955

"Mycelium of straight, rigid hyaline or pale brown, cylindrical, rarely branched hyphae, 1.5–2.5 mm. long; attached to the substratum by branching rhizoids. Diameter 5 μ (in narrowest parts) to 23 μ (at the tips which are expanded to bear fascicles of sexual reproductive organs); average for intermediate portions 9 μ.

"Oogonia arranged singly, in superimposed series of 2–12 or in fascicles of 2–8, borne at the tips of the hyphae or their sympodial branches. Sometimes combinations of these three arrangements are to be found on one hypha; occasionally intercalary. Oogonia usually cylindrical, opening when the oosphere is formed at the tip of the prominent neck, which may be straight or curved, with its tip pointing towards the antheridium. Oogonia occasionally exhibit irregularities of form and size. Length 25–53 μ (majority 34–43 μ), diameter 16–42 μ (majority 21 μ).

"Antheridia tapering at the tips, and varying from subconical to cylindrical. Narrow, straight or slightly curved, with the tip bent inwards towards the neck of the oogonium. Much variation in length even among those in the same group. 10.5–25 μ long (majority 14–21 μ) by 6–14 μ diameter (majority 7–9 μ tapering to 5–7 μ). Not always present, but usually so. Borne upon the terminal wall of the oogonium (epigynous), to one side of the neck. Occasionally hypogynous and intercalary. Each usually contains 5–6 amoeboid and uniflagellate antherozooids which measure 4–6 μ by 4–5 μ. Protandry is well marked.

"Each oogonium contains a single oospore which matures and germinates within the oogonium (endogenous). The oospores have thick, golden brown walls covered with small, pale yellow, transparent bullations which are 1 μ in height. They vary in shape from spherical to widely ellipsoid, and are occasionally irregular in outline; length 19–32 μ (majority 21–25 μ), diameter 12–27 μ (majority 18–21 μ). Much variation in size is often seen in the same series" (Perrott, *loc. cit.*).

On submerged twigs of *Quercus robur* and *Fraxinus excelsior*, GREAT BRITAIN.

The only species of the genus with cylindrical oögonia and endogenous, bullate oöspores.

MONOBLEPHARIS REGIGNENS Lagerheim

Bih. Kgl. Svensk. Vetensk.-Ak. Handl., 25, Afd. 3, No. 8: 39, pl. 1, figs. 11–13.
1900
(Fig. 53 D, p. 730)

Monoblephariopsis regignens (Lagerheim) Laibach, Jahrb. wiss. Bot., 66: 603,
text fig. 4, pl. 12, figs. 20–27. 1927.

Mycelium exceedingly tenuous, sparingly branched, hyphae about 5
μ at the base, tapering to 1.8–2 μ, in diameter; sporangia narrowly
cylindrical, but distinctly broader than the hyphae, on which they are
usually terminally placed, 18–36 μ, in length by 5.4–7.2 μ in diameter,
new sporangia formed by proliferation partly or wholly through the
apex of the old one or occasionally by cymose branching; zoospores 8
μ long by 5 μ in diameter; sexual reproduction not observed.

Saprophytic on submerged twigs of various types. Lagerheim (*loc.
cit.*), SWEDEN; Thaxter (F.), Sparrow (1933b: 534, pl. 20, fig. 26; 1933c:
530), UNITED STATES; Laibach (*loc. cit.*), Höhnk (1935: 220, fig. 1 a–b),
GERMANY; Sparrow (1933b: 534), GREAT BRITAIN.

This and the following species may belong in *Monoblepharella*.
See note, p. 728 n.

MONOBLEPHARIS OVIGERA Lagerheim

Bih. Kgl. Svensk. Vetensk.-Ak. Handl., 25, Afd. 3, No. 8: 39, pl. 1, figs. 69–70.
1900
(Fig. 53 F, p. 730)

Monoblephariopsis ovigera (Lagerheim) Laibach, Jahrb. wiss. Bot., 66: 609.
1927.
Monoblephariopsis oblongata Höhnk, Abhandl. Naturwiss. Vereins Bremen,
29(3): 221, fig. 1 c–h. 1935.

Mycelium often profuse, composed of very delicate occasionally
branched hyphae 3–4 μ in diameter; zoosporangia terminal or intercalary, ovoid, 10–13 μ in diameter by 23–33 μ in length, rarely proliferating; zoospores often formed in two rows, 8 μ long by 6 μ in diameter;
sexual reproduction not observed.

Saprophytic on submerged twigs of various types. Lagerheim (*loc.
cit.*), SWEDEN; Sparrow (1933b: 535, pl. 20, figs. 23, 33, 35, 37; 1933c:

530), Beneke (1948: 29, pl.1, fig. 18), UNITED STATES; Sparrow (1933b: 535; 1936a: 459), GREAT BRITAIN; Höhnk (1935: 221, fig. 1 c–h), GERMANY.

Höhnk's species appears to differ in no essential features from *Monoblepharis ovigera*. Though proliferation of the sporangium in the latter is rare it is by no means lacking. It is possible that the very small structures resembling sexual organs and the smooth-walled spherical cysts found by Sparrow (1933b: pl. 20, figs. 21–22, 24, 27) among sporangial plants of this species indicate that it has a type of sexual reproduction similar to that of *Monoblepharella taylori*.

See note, p. 728 n.

EXCLUDED SPECIES OF MONOBLEPHARIS

* MONOBLEPHARIS LATERALIS Hine

Amer. Quart. Micro. Journ., 1: 141, pl. 7, figs. 4–21. 1878–79

This is doubtless a saprolegniaceous fungus, probably infected by a flagellate, a situation also found in *Archilegnia* (see p. 796).

REJECTED GENUS OF THE MONOBLEPHARIDALES

* MYRIOBLEPHARIS THAXTER

Bot. Gaz., 20: 482, pl. 31, figs. 1–5. 1895

After many years, Minden's (1915) astute conclusions have been verified concerning this paradoxical form. Waterhouse (1945) has proved conclusively that *Myrioblepharis paradoxa* Thaxter either is a *Pythium* or a *Phytophthora* parasitized by a ciliate, probably a species of *Prorodon*.

HYPHOCHYTRIALES

UNTIL 1884 the only Phycomycetes that had been described possessed posteriorly uniflagellate or either apically biflagellate or laterally biflagellate zoospores (or both). That year two papers were published (Zopf, 1884; Fisch, 1884a) which indicated the existence of yet another type of swarmer, namely, one bearing a single anterior flagellum. Since then there were occasional reports of fungi with anteriorly uniflagellate zoospores, but the number remained small.

Confirmation of the anteriorly uniflagellate character of the zoospore in *Rhizidiomyces* by Coker (1923) and in *Hyphochytrium* by Valkanov (1929b) and Karling (1939b) made necessary the segregation of these fungi of obscure relationships from the true chytrids (Sparrow, 1935b, 1942, 1943), with whom they were associated by older writers. On the strength of the hypothesis that the zoospore represents the most primitive condition, it is supposed that the members of the Hyphochytriales arose from anteriorly uniflagellate monad ancestors and underwent an apparently limited (so far as diversity of types is concerned) but nonetheless parallel evolution with the posteriorly uniflagellate chytridiaceous series. There is, however, another possible explanation. It has been suggested by E. A. Bessey (1942) that these forms may have arisen from anteriorly biflagellate ancestors through the loss of one flagellum.

Because of their small number, the anteriorly uniflagellate species were grouped together as a family of uncertain affinities and placed immediately after the chytrids in the first edition (1943) of the *Aquatic Phycomycetes*. Later, but in that same year (1943), the group was raised to ordinal rank by Karling who gave it the name Anisochytridiales. It seems more appropriate here to make use of the long-existing family name.

Karling divided the order into three families: (1) Anisolpidiaceae, including holocarpic predominantly monocentric forms, comparable (as a group) to the Olpidiaceae of the Chytridiales; (2) Rhizidiomycetaceae, containing two genera of eucarpic monocentric forms, comparable to the Phlyctidiaceae; and (3) Hyphochytriaceae, composed of a

743

single polycentric genus, comparable to the Megachytriaceae. Separation at the family level of so few forms is open to criticism but does seem justified. The small number of accredited species is probably due either to insufficient or inaccurate observations on zoospore structure or to their actually being of limited diversity, or possibly to the fact that many as yet unknown species occupy habitats thus far unexplored for fungi.

The establishment and development of the thallus differs little from that found in the true chytrids. Both chitin and cellulose are present in the walls of some forms (Nabel, 1939), in others there is no evidence of cellulose. During thallus development in the holocarpic *Anisolpidium ectocarpii*, the nuclei divide mitotically and simultaneously, forming intranuclear spindles (Karling, 1943).

Zoospore production apparently differs somewhat among members of the group. In *Anisolpidium* spores are cleaved out within the sporangium (Karling, *op. cit.*). Furrows extend from the border of a large irregular central vacuole outward, cutting out segments of contents of various sizes. Further cleavage in a centrifugal direction gives rise to the rudiments of the zoospores. Soon after delimitation these initiate movement. This increases in intensity until the tips of the earlier-formed discharge tubes open, whereupon the spores escape and aggregate in an oscillating mass at the mouth of the tube. No vesicle surrounds them and after several minutes they swim away.

In *Canteriomyces* the protoplasmic contents of the sporangium emerges as one or several naked masses and undergoes complete maturation into zoospores outside in the water. In *Rhizidiomyces* the undifferentiated contents usually issues to form a spherical or hemispherical mass at the orifice of the discharge tube. It quickly divides and the zoospores are delimited. In this genus Zopf (1884) and others have also noted some differentiation of the zoospores prior to discharge. The rapidity with which these mature after liberation certainly suggests some previous cleavage. Evidence concerning the presence of a vesicle around the spore mass in *Rhizidiomyces* is conflicting. Nabel (1939) states definitely that in *R. bivellatus* there is such a membrane, but Karling (1944d) failed to find one in his material of this species. In *Rhizidiomycopsis* the spores mature completely within the sporangium and emerge individually without formation of a vesicle.

The zoospore is somewhat elongate, pyriform or obpyriform, with a single flagellum of the tinsel type attached at the forward, narrower end (see "Zoospore," p. 9). In most species of the order there is a small lateral, more or less refractive body near this same end. Movement is even and deliberate and is punctuated by sudden stops and changes of direction, quite different from the behavior of the zoospore of a true chytrid.

Resting spores have been reported in some genera. In *Anisolpidium*, where they are somewhat like sporangia in their early developmental stages, a thickened wall soon forms about the contents which lacks a large reserve globule.[1] In *Rhizidiomyces* only structures that have been interpreted as encysted sporangia have been found. Zopf (1894) described *Latrostium comprimens* as having very thick-walled resting spores. In *Hyphochytrium hydrodictii*, according to Valkanov (1929b), they are thick-walled, terminal or intercalary, and function directly as sporangia upon germination. No resting spores have been seen in *Canteriomyces* or in *Rhizidiomycopsis*. In no instance, save in the problematic genus *Reessia*, is there any evidence of sexuality preceding resting-spore formation[1]. In *Reessia*, Fisch (1884a) says a fusion of isogamous plano-gametes takes place, after which the zygote enters the host cell and becomes a resting spore.

Canter (1950b) points out that two series exist within the order, one, in which the zoospores are formed within the sporangium, and another, in which they are developed outside from presumably undifferentiated protoplasm. Because these two methods are completely distinct, they constitute differences of generic significance and are so regarded here.

SYSTEMATIC ACCOUNT
HYPHOCHYTRIALES

Microscopic aquatic fungi with a body plan resembling that of the Chytridiales, inoperculate, holocarpic or eucarpic, monocentric or polycentric, the vegetative system rhizoidal or hypha-like with intercalary swellings; zoospores anteriorly uniflagellate, maturing inside or outside

---

[1] See Johnson (1957a) where these are shown to be sexually formed by endobiotic isoaplanogametes fusing in pairs.

the sporangium; resting spore asexually or sexually formed, upon germination functioning as a sporangium.

Parasites of fresh-water and marine algae, aquatic Phycomycetes, ascocarps of Discomycetes, and saprophytes on dead plant material and insect remains.

KEY TO THE FAMILIES AND GENERA OF THE HYPHOCHYTRIALES

ANISOLPIDIACEAE

Thallus endobiotic, holocarpic, without a specialized vegetative system, converted as a whole into a zoosporangium or resting spore; zoospores formed within or outside the sporangium, anteriorly uniflagellate, with a more or less refractive globule or granule, discharged through one or more tubes; resting spore thick-walled, endobiotic, asexually or sexually formed, germination not observed.

Only three marine and one fresh-water fungus can be regarded as valid members of the family. Karling (1943) included the fresh-water *Reessia* (p. 764), but Fisch's (1884a) contradictory and unconfirmed accounts of his fungi inspire no confidence in the accuracy of his observations.

ANISOLPIDIUM Karling

Amer. J. Bot., 30: 637. 1943

(Fig. 55 J–L, p. 752)

"Thallus intramatrical, monocentric, olpidioid and holocarpic, variable in size and shape. Zoosporangia similar in size and shape to thalli, with one or more exit tubes of variable length. Zoospores anteriorly uniflagellate. Resting spores similar in size and shape to thalli, thick-walled; germination unknown" (Karling, *loc. cit.*).

Parasitic in marine algae.

KEY TO THE SPECIES OF ANISOLPIDIUM

Parasitic in *Cladostephus, Sphacelaria,* and *Chaetopteris* ....
.... *A. sphacellarum,* p. 747
Parasitic in *Ectocarpus* .... *A. ectocarpii,* p. 748
Parasitic in *Pylaiella* .... *A. rosenvingii,* p. 749

Anisolpidium sphacellarum (Kny) Karling [1]

Amer. J. Bot., 30: 641. 1943

Chytridium (Olpidium) sphacellarum Kny, Sitzungsber. Gesell. Naturforsch.
  Freunde Berlin, 1871: 97; Hedwigia, 11(6): 87. 1872.
Olpidium sphacellarum (Kny) Fischer, Rabenhorst. Kryptogamen-Fl., 1 (4):
  26. 1892.
Pleotrachelus sphacellarum (Kny) H. E. Petersen, Oversigt Kgl. Danske
  Vidensk. Selskabs. Forhandl., 1905: 452, fig. II, 5–8.
? *Olpidiopsis sphacellarum* (Kny) Sparrow, Aquatic Phycomycetes, p. 629.
  1943.

Sporangia single or up to nine in a cell, frequently attacking the terminal or other cells of the lateral branches and occasionally the apical cell of the main axis, as well as the setae, causing swelling of the infected cell, spherical, subspherical, or oblong, variable in size, 35–45 μ long by 17–52 μ in diameter, wall thin, smooth, colorless, bearing from one to three short stout discharge tubes 8–10 μ in diameter; zoospores somewhat pyriform, 4 μ long by 2 μ in diameter, with a colorless granule near the broader posterior end and an anterior flagellum, ini-

---

[1] According to Professor H. H. Bartlett, this species name should have been "*sphacelariarum.*" Note that the host name has only one "l."

tiating movement within the sporangium and emerging rapidly through the dissolved tip of the discharge tube, movement even, with sudden stops and changes of direction; resting spore not observed.

Parasitic in cells of *Cladostephus spongiosus*, Kny (*loc. cit.*), GREAT BRITAIN; *C. spongiosus*, Magnus (1875: 77, pl. 1, figs. 17–20), HELIGO-LAND; *Sphacelaria tribuloides*, Pringsheim (1855: 153, fig. 25)?, ITALY; *Sphacelaria cirrhosa*, Magnus (*loc. cit.*), *Chaetopteris plumosa*, Petersen (1905: 452, fig. II, 5–8), DENMARK; *Sphacelaria cirrhosa*, *Sphacelaria sp.*, Seymour (1929), *Sphacelaria cirrhosa*, Sparrow (1936b: 250, figs. 9–11, pl. 1, fig. 3, pl. 2, fig. 5), UNITED STATES; *Chaetopteris plumosa*, *Sphacelaria sp.*, Aleem (1953: 8, figs. 9–12), SWEDEN; *Sphacelaria cirrhosa*, Feldmann (1954: 133), FRANCE.

On the basis of Sparrow's (1936b) studies of the zoospores, Karling (1943) transferred this species to *Anisolpidium*. If, as Karling states, the biflagellate spores described by Pringsheim (*loc. cit.*) do not belong to the fungus, this is a logical procedure. The movement of the zoospores seen by Sparrow was certainly like that noted in other members of the order.

Observations on American material indicate that the zoospore effects penetration of the cell by means of a tube through which the contents pass. The young thallus often very quickly attaches itself to the nucleus of the host. When cells of the lateral branches are attacked, they soon exhibit pronounced swelling. The fungus was a true parasite and became inactive under abnormal conditions prevailing in the laboratory.

ANISOLPIDIUM ECTOCARPII Karling

Amer. J. Bot., 30: 637, figs. 1–21. 1943

(Fig. 55 J–L, p. 752)

"Thalli one to five in a cell, single thallus occasionally occupying two cells; spherical, oval, oblong, cylindrical and irregular; transformed directly into sporangia or resting spores. Zoosporangia hyaline and smooth; spherical, 8–17 μ; or oval, 15–20 $\mu \times$ 20–28 μ; or elongate, 10–13 $\mu \times$ 20–35 μ; or cylindrical with concave ends, 15 $\times$ 30 μ; or irregular with one to several tapering exit tubes, 3–5 $\mu \times$ 10–40 μ, which may open within the host, or end flush with the outer surface of the wall or extend greatly beyond it. Zoospores pyriform, slightly clavate, 1.8–2.3 μ × 3–3.5 μ, hyaline to greyish granular in appearance with one small slightly refringent globule; flagellum 5–6.5 μ long. Resting spores [1] hyaline and smooth, spherical, 10–14 μ, or oval, 8 × 12 μ, or oblong; content coarsely granular, germination unknown" (Karling, *loc. cit.*).

Parasitic in *Ectocarpus mitchellae* and *E. siliculosus*, killing and destroying the contents of infected cells, UNITED STATES.

Some cytological details of the species are given by Karling (*op. cit.*).

ANISOLPIDIUM ROSENVINGII (H. E. Petersen) Karling

Amer. J. Bot., 30: 641. 1943

Pleotrachelus rosenvingii Petersen. Oversigt Kgl. Danske ¦Vidensk Selskabs. Forhandl., 1905: 453, fig. III, 1, 5, 6.

Sporangium completely filling the host cell and assuming its shape or lying free in it and somewhat spherical, with faintly yellow wall and contents, wall not reacting to chloriodide of zinc, 10–31 μ long by 18–36 μ in diameter, with one to three discharge tubes up to 25 μ in length; zoospores elliptical or pyriform, 2–3 μ long, with a single anterior flagellum.

In *Pylaiella littoralis*, H. E. Petersen (*loc. cit.*), Sparrow (1934c: 19, pl. 4, fig. M), DENMARK; Aleem (1953: 7, pl. 1, fig. 1), SWEDEN.

The description is based entirely on the living material studied by Petersen and Sparrow. A form from Greenland studied only in preserved condition by Petersen may also belong here. Petersen characterized it as follows:

"Sporangia colorless, smooth-walled, turning violet with chloriodide of zinc, filling or nearly filling the host cell, 20–68 μ long by 24–41 μ in diameter, with from 1–4 discharge tubes 4–6 μ long by 4–5 μ in diameter; zoospores not observed."

In *Pylaiella littoralis*, coll. A. Jessen, GREENLAND.

---

[1] See Johnson (1957a) where these are shown to be sexually formed.

CANTERIOMYCES GEN. NOV. [1]

(Fig. 55 N–O, p. 752)

Thallus endobiotic, holocarpic, lying loosely in the host cell or completely filling it, at maturity converted into a sporangium; zoospores anteriorly uniflagellate, formed at the orifice of the discharge tube; resting spores not observed.

Parasitic in the fresh-water algae *Stigeoclonium* and *Draparnaldia*.

The method of zoospore formation, that is, outside the sporangium, is sufficient grounds for separating de Wildeman's and Canter's fungus from the marine ones with endogenously formed zoospores. Although the protoplasm is typically discharged as a single mass from the sporangium, it may emerge as several.

The genus is named in honor of Dr. Hilda Canter (Mrs. J. W. G. Lund).

CANTERIOMYCES STIGEOCLONII (DE WILD.), comb. nov.

Olpidium stigeoclonii de Wildeman, Mém. Herb. Bossier, 1900 (15): 3; Bull. Acad. Roy. Belg. (Sci.), V, 17: 297, pls. 1–2. 1931.
Anisolpidium stigeoclonii (de Wildeman) Canter, Trans. Brit. Mycol. Soc., 33: 343, pl. 24–26, text figs. 1–6. 1950.

"Thalli 1–4 partly or completely filling hypertrophied host cell; hyaline smooth spherical 13–23 μ in diameter or oval, 9 × 21–21 × 46 μ with one exit tube (very rarely two) elongate, 3–70 μ long; 3–8 μ broad, wall thinner at apex. Content of thallus emerging as one or several undifferentiated naked protoplasmic masses which undergo cleavage into zoospores. Motile zoospores obpyriform 5 μ long × 2.5 μ wide at the apex, broad anterior end with single anterior flagellum 7.5 μ long; content granular with a bright lateral granule" (Canter, *loc. cit.*).

[1] *Canteriomyces*, gen. nov. Thallus endobioticus, holocarpicus, maturitate in sporangium transformatus. Zoosporae antice uniflagellatae, in orificio tubi efferentis orientes ex massa (plerumque una sed interdum 2 vel 3) protoplasmatis nondum differentiata. Sporae perdurantes nondum observatae.

Parasiticus in generibus aquae dulcis Chlorophycearum *Stigeoclonio* et *Draparnaldia*.

Originatione zoosporarum extrasporangiali valde differt a fungis similibus aquae salsae sed zoosporis intrasporangialibus praeditis.

Nomino id genus honoris causa pro Dr. Hildam Canter.

Parasitic in *Stigeoclonium subuligerum, Stigeoclonium sp.*, and *Draparnaldia plumosa* Canter (*loc. cit.*), GREAT BRITAIN; *Stigeoclonium sp.*, Karling (1941c: 357), *Stigeoclonium sp.* (MICHIGAN), UNITED STATES. As indicated by Canter, the zoospores take a relatively long time to become delimited and to mature (up to 30 minutes). Even longer times have been noted in the Michigan material.

RHIZIDIOMYCETACEAE

Thallus eucarpic, monocentric, composed of an extramatrical fertile part and an intramatrical apophysate or nonapophysate part bearing a branched rhizoidal system, walls containing both cellulose and chitin; zoospores anteriorly uniflagellate, usually with one or more small refractive globules or granules formed within the sporangium, or discharged in a more or less amorphous mass and completing maturation, sometimes in a vesicle, at the orifice of the discharge tube; resting spore, where known, thick-walled, like the sporangium in position and rhizoidal system, germination not observed.

Parasitic on oögonia and eggs of Phycomycetes, on algae, and saprophytic in soil.

Separation at the family level of the fungi with endogenously formed zoospores from those in which they are developed at the orifice of the discharge tube may in the future prove feasible.

RHIZIDIOMYCES Zopf

Nova Acta Acad. Leop.-Carol., 47: 188. 1884

(Fig. 55 E–G, p. 752)

Thallus monocentric, eucarpic, composed of an extramatrical part, converted at maturity into an apophysate or nonapophysate sporangium, and an intramatrical branched rhizoidal system; sporangium sessile, inoperculate, with a pronounced discharge tube; zoospores possibly delimited in part within the sporangium, discharged as an amorphous mass and undergoing maturation at the orifice of the discharge tube where they may be surrounded by a vesicle, somewhat ovoid or spherical, often bearing a refractive globule, anteriorly uniflagellate; resting spore not observed.

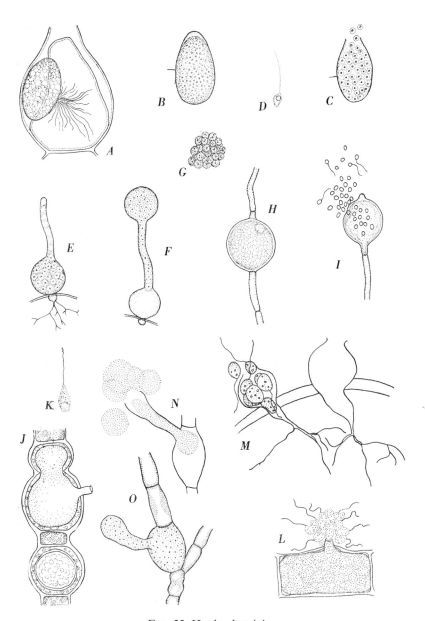

Fɪɢ. 55. Hyphochytriales

Parasitic on eggs and oöspores of aquatic Phycomycetes and on green algae; saprophytic on pollen bait in soil.

KEY TO THE SPECIES OF RHIZIDIOMYCES

Sporangium wall persistent after discharge; on eggs and oöspores of
    other aquatic Phycomycetes or saprophytic in soil on pollen bait
    Sporangium apophysate; on eggs and oöspores of other aquatic
        Phycomycetes .... *R. apophysatus*, p. 754
    Sporangium nonapophysate; saprophytic in soil
        Wall of sporangium smooth
            Zoospores 5.5–6 by 7–8 μ; protoplasm colorless ....
                                  R. bivellatus, p. 754
            Zoospores 4–4.5 by 5.5–6.5 μ; protoplasm yellowish to orange
                                  R. hansonii, p. 755
        Wall of sporangium covered by unbranched setae .. *R. hirsutus*, p. 756
Sporangium wall evanescent after discharge; on *Chlamydomonas* ...
                                  R. ichneumon, p. 756

Explanation of Figure 55

A-D. *Latrostium comprimens* Zopf in oögonia of *Vaucheria*: *A*, sporangium within oögonium, resting on surface of egg of host; the delicate rhizoids are within egg; *B*, sporangium with large papilla laterally placed with respect to rhizoidal axis; *C*, discharging sporangium; *D*, anteriorly uniflagellate zoospore. *E-G*. *Rhizidiomyces apophysatus* Zopf on oögonia of *Achlya*: *E*, mature apophysate sporangium with discharge tube; *F*, sporangium with contents emerging into vesicle formed at tip of discharge tube; *G*, mature zoospores formed outside sporangium. *H-I*. *Hyphochytrium infestans* Zopf on ascocarp of *Helotium*: *H*, intercalary sporangium, showing discharge papilla; *I*, terminal apiculate sporangium discharging its anteriorly uniflagellate zoospores through a lateral pore. *J-L*. *Anisolpidium ectocarpii* Karling in *Ectocarpus*: *J*, resting spore and empty sporangium in hypertrophied host cells; *K*, zoospore; *L*, zoospores emerging. *M*. *Rhizidiomycopsis japonicus* (Kobayashi and Ookubo) Sparrow on oögonium of *Aplanes sp.*, empty sporangium and one discharging fully formed zoospores. *N-O*. *Canteriomyces stigeoclonii* (de Wild.), comb. nov., in *Stigeoclonium*: *N*, emergence of protoplasm from sporangium; *O*, protoplasm starting to emerge.

(*A-D*, Zopf, 1894; *E-I*, Zopf, 1884; *J-L*, Karling, 1943; *M*, Kobayashi and Ookubo, 1954b; *N-O*, Canter, 1950b)

RHIZIDIOMYCES APOPHYSATUS Zopf

Nova Acta Acad. Leop.-Carol., 47: 188, pl. 20, figs. 1–7. 1884

(Fig. 55 E–G, p. 752)

Sporangium spherical, subspherical, or broadly pyriform, 18–45 μ in diameter, wall of cellulose, stout, smooth or with short spines, colorless or faintly golden brown, with an apical or subapical long cylindrical discharge tube; rhizoids richly branched, arising from one or two stout main axes at the base of a pyriform, or occasionally spherical or fusiform, subsporangial apophysis up to 18.5 μ in diameter; zoospores formed outside at the apex of the discharge tube, ovoid or oblong with rounded ends, 3.7–6 μ (long?), with a few minute gleaming granules and a short anterior flagellum, movement swimming or feebly amoeboid; resting spore not observed.

Parasitic on oögonia of *Saprolegnia ferax, S. asterophora, Achlya polyandra,* Zopf (*loc. cit.*), GERMANY; *Achlya conspicua, A. apiculata,* Coker (1923: 186, pl. 63), "Saprolegnian," cultivated on pollen of *Liquidambar,* nutrient agar, Couch (1939a), *Achlya sp.,* Sparrow (1932b: 282, fig. 3e), *A. flagellata,* Karling (1943: 644), UNITED STATES; *Achlya flagellata,* Tokunaga (1934b: 391, pl. 11, fig. 10), JAPAN; host (?), Forbes (1935b: 3), GREAT BRITAIN; *Achlya klebsiana,* Chaudhuri and Kochhar (1935: 150, pl. 12, figs. 24–29), INDIA; oögonia of *Saprolegnia* and *Achlya,* Cejp (1934: 228), CZECHOSLOVAKIA; oögonia of *Achlya flagellata,* Karling (1944d: 392, figs. 1–34), BRAZIL; ? *Vaucheria sp.,* Bérczi (1940: 84, pl. 2, figs. 23, 24), HUNGARY; from soil, pine pollen, Gaertner (1954b: 22), NORTHWEST AFRICA, WEST AFRICA, EQUATORIAL EAST AFRICA, SOUTH AFRICA.

Whether or not a discrete vesicle is formed around the maturing spore mass is open to question. Karling (1944d) believes that only a thickened plasma membrane is around the periphery.

RHIZIDIOMYCES BIVELLATUS Nabel

Arch. f. Mikrobiol., 10: 537, figs. 1–7. 1939

Sporangium spherical, 80–100 μ in diameter, wall smooth, light brown, becoming dark and rough with age, in young plants consisting of two layers, the inner wall of chitin and evanescent and the outer of cellulose and persistent, the cellulose discharge tube apical, up to 300 μ long by 10 μ in diameter; rhizoids richly branched, arising from one or more axes at the base of the sporangium; apophysis apparently lacking; zoospores oblong-ellipsoidal, 8 μ long by 6 μ broad, with a single anterior flagellum about 20 μ long, formed in a vesicle produced at the tip of the discharge tube; resting spore not observed.

In soil, "flies," Nabel (*loc. cit.*), HAITI, VENEZUELA, MEXICO, JUGO-SLAVIA; insect cases, Karling (1943: 644), UNITED STATES; insect wings and legs, Karling (1944d: 393, figs. 20–34), BRAZIL.

The fungus was recovered by Nabel on different types of bait (primarily fruit flies) in water cultures to which soil had been added. It was cultivated on agar but failed to form zoospores.

Karling (1944d) found that in the majority of instances a single rhizoidal axis was developed. Occasionally, completely extramatrical, *Rhizophlyctis*-like thalli were formed and in one case the plant was polycentric. Contrary to Nabel's observations, he found no vesicle formed at spore discharge.

RHIZIDIOMYCES HANSONII Karling

Amer. J. Bot., 31: 396, figs. 35–64. 1944

"Sporangia extramatrical, non-apophysate, with smooth, light to dark brown walls, and yellowish to orange-tinted protoplasm; spherical (10–60 μ), oval or ellipsoidal (8–20 × 12–38 μ), or oblong (12–22 × 18–35 μ); content emerging through an exit tube, 20–150 μ long, and undergoing cleavage outside the sporangium; vesicular membrane around spore mass lacking. Zoospores oval to slightly elongate, 4–4.5 × 5.5–6.5 μ, with numerous yellowish to orange-tinted granules and one or two minute globules; flagellum 8–10 μ long. True resting spores unknown. Sporangia in old cultures often becoming dark brown, thick-walled, 2–3 μ, and dormant; later giving rise to zoospores in the same manner as the more evanescent sporangia" (Karling, *loc. cit.*).

Saprophytic in soil containing vegetable debris, chitinous material, BRAZIL.

See remarks on spore discharge under the species that follows.

Rhizidiomyces hirsutus Karling

Bull. Torrey Bot. Club, 72: 47, figs. 1–19. 1945

Sporangium extramatrical, nonapophysate, hyaline, globose (6–180 μ in diameter), oval (8–20 × 26–60 μ), pyriform, obpyriform, oblong or irregular, provided with 3–47 coarse elongate setae 15–190 μ long by 2–3 μ wide; rhizoidal system in solid substratum much branched, arising mostly from a single axis at the base of the sporangium, in liquid media lacking, or composed of several radiating axes from which arise branched rhizoids; zoospores oval, oblong or elongate, 3–4 × 6–8 μ, with a single minute refringent granule and a flagellum 14–18 μ long; resting spore not observed.

On hempseed bait, leaf mold, Karling (*loc. cit.*), BRAZIL; pollen of *Cucurbita sp.* (MICHIGAN), UNITED STATES.

As in *Rhizidiomyces hansonii*, Karling could not demonstrate a vesicle around the developing spore mass. Sometimes in liquid culture no rhizoidal system was produced, only setae. These were supposed to function as absorbing organs. The formation of abundant setae on the sporangia renders this a highly characteristic species. The Michigan material was densely covered with setae, which were sometimes branched.

Rhizidiomyces ichneumon Gobi

Scripta Bot. Horti Univ. Imper. Petro., 15:251, pl. 6, figs. 1–28, pl. 7, figs.29–39. 1900

Sporangium consisting of two intercommunicating parts, an epibiotic sessile spherical or rarely flattened portion 9–16 μ high, with a smooth thin colorless wall which collapses after zoospore discharge and a more or less elongate apical discharge tube, and (in previously uninfected host cells) a smaller endobiotic spherical, rarely pyriform or fusiform, portion 3–5 μ high, from the base of which emerges a system of delicate falsely dichotomously branched rhizoids; zoospores formed by progressive cleavage in an evanescent vesicle, from four to sixty, subspherical or ovoid, about 3 μ long, with fine or coarsely granular plasma and an anterior flagellum, movement slow and even.

Parasitic on actively moving and encysted *Chlamydomonas globulosa*, RUSSIA.

Because of the curious lack of a cross wall between the endobiotic and epibiotic parts the sporangium is two-lobed. No cross walls were noted separating the rhizoids from the apophysis. In thalli forming on already infected cells of *Chlamydomonas* the rhizoids arose directly from the base of the epibiotic part, no apophysis being developed. This suggests that the apophysis possibly aided the immature parasite in maintaining its position on the moving host. With chloriodide of zinc the walls of the sporangium turned violet, the rhizoids, golden.

RHIZIDIOMYCOPSIS GEN. NOV. [1]

(Fig. 55 M, p. 752)

Thallus monocentric, eucarpic, composed of an epibiotic part which at maturity becomes converted into a sporangium, and an endobiotic apophysis from which a branched rhizoidal system arises; sporangium sessile, inoperculate, without a discharge tube; zoospores completely delimited within the sporangium, emerging individually, somewhat ovoid with several refractive globules and a single anterior flagellum; resting spore not observed.

Parasitic on oögonia of water molds.

The genus is erected to accommodate a *Rhizidiomyces*-like fungus in which the zoospores are completely formed within the sporangium (not outside as in *Rhizidiomyces*) and liberated through a pore.

RHIZIDIOMYCOPSIS JAPONICUS (Kobayashi and Ookubo), comb. nov.

Rhizidiomyces japonicus Kobayashi and Ookubo, Rept. Osegahara Gen. Sci. Surv. Comm., 1954: 573, fig. 17. 1954.

Sporangia gregarious, epibiotic, globose, 10–15 μ in diameter, with a thin, smooth, hyaline wall, at maturity forming a sessile pore, without

---

[1] *Rhizidiomycopsis*, gen. nov. Thallus monocentricus, eucarpicus divisus in partes duas, primam partem epibioticam maturitate in sporangium transformatam, alteram partem endobioticam (vel apophysin), ramosam, ramis rhizoidalibus. Sporangium sessile, exoperculatum et sine tubo efferenti. Zoosporae separatim maturantes in sporangio et singulatim dispersae, ovoideae, globulis refractivis pluribus et flagello uno anteriori praeditae. Sporae perdurantes nondum visae.
Parasiticus in oogoniis mycetum aquaticorum.
Species typica *Rhizidiomycopsis japonicus*.

a discharge tube, endobiotic part a globose, obconical or pyriform apophysis 4–5 μ in diameter from the tip of which a rhizoidal system branches; zoospores ovoid or ellipsoid, 3–6 μ in diameter, with three to six refractive globules and an elongate anterior flagellum, completely formed within the sporangium and swimming away individually; resting spore not observed.

Parasitic on oögonia of *Aplanes sp.*, JAPAN.

LATROSTIUM ZOPF

Beitr. Physiol. Morph. niederer Organismen, 4: 62. 1894

(Fig. 55 A–D, p. 752)

Thallus resting on and in the contracted oöplasm within the oögonium of the host, monocentric, eucarpic, consisting of the rudiment of the sporangium, which is sessile on the oöplasm, and a complex of extremely delicate much-branched rhizoids arising laterally at one place on the sporangial rudiment and penetrating the oöplasm; sporangium inoperculate, forming a broad discharge papilla; zoospores anteriorly uniflagellate, with a single globule, escaping fully formed through a broad apical pore which does not penetrate the host wall; resting spore borne like the sporangium, with a thick smooth radially striated exospore and a thin smooth endospore, contents with an extremely large globule, germination not observed.

Parasitic in oögonia of *Vaucheria*.

The genus is founded on a species so like the debatable *Rhizophydium decipiens* in habitat, shape of the sporangium, method of discharge, and structure of the resting spore, that it seems hardly probable that two organisms can be so alike in all characters except for the flagellation of the zoospore and not be identical. Since the observations on zoospore flagellation come from so high an authority as Zopf, however, we are forced to assume their correctness, at least until further investigations disprove them. If development is of the *Entophlyctis* type the genus should be segregated in its own family.

LATROSTIUM COMPRIMENS Zopf

Beitr. Physiol. Morph. niederer Organismen, 4: 62, pl. 3, figs. 6–19. 1894

Sporangia from one to six in a host cell, broadly lenticular, with a delicate smooth colorless wall which collapses after discharge of the zoospores and a broad apical papilla; rhizoids extremely delicate, much branched; zoospores irregularly ovoid, 2.5–3 μ in diameter, with a large colorless globule, the broader, anterior end bearing a long flagellum, escaping individually through a wide apical pore, movement evenly swimming, not hopping; resting spore broadly lenticular, 30–50 μ in diameter, outer wall thick, colorless, smooth, radially striated, giving a cellulose reaction, inner wall thin, homogeneous, contents with an extremely large globule that nearly fills the lumen, rhizoids delicate, much branched, germination not observed.

In oögonia of *Vaucheria sessilis*, *V. terrestris*, GERMANY.

De Wildeman (1895a: 63) described ovoid resting spores with striated walls found in oögonia of *Vaucheria sessilis* from Belgium and Switzerland as belonging to this species. Since the sporangia were not observed, however, it is equally possible that these organisms belong to *Rhizophydium decipiens*. Scherffel (1926a: 221) claims that the resting spores of the two species, which in all other respects are identical (no rhizoids, however, have been observed as yet in *R. decipiens*), may be distinguished by the fact that in *Latrostium comprimens* there is a giant globule in the contents, whereas in *R. decipiens* there are numerous small ones. The validity of this fine distinction can only be determined after both forms have been thoroughly investigated. Resting spores of both types have been found in the same oögonium in *Vaucheria terrestris* in Michigan.

HYPHOCHYTRIACEAE

Thallus eucarpic, polycentric, consisting of relatively broad, branched hyphae with occasional cross walls; sporangia inoperculate, terminal or intercalary; zoospores partly or fully formed within the sporangium or cleaved out at the orifice of the discharge tube; resting spore thick-walled.

On algae, higher fungi, and vegetable debris.

It may be practicable in the future to segregate *Hyphochytrium catenoides* Karling from that genus, since its zoospores typically are cleaved out after discharge of the contents from the sporangium, and not endogenously produced.

See remarks under the species, p. 762.

HYPHOCHYTRIUM Zopf

Nova Acta Acad. Leop.-Carol., 47: 187. 1884

(Fig. 55 H–I, p. 752; Fig. 56, p. 761)

Hyphophagus (Zopf) Minden, Kryptogamenfl. Mark Brandenburg, 5: 420. 1911 (1915).

Mycelium isodiametric, relatively broad, branched, extensive, with occasional cross walls, ramifying within the substratum; sporangia arising as terminal or intercalary swellings of the mycelium, from which they are cut off by cross walls; zoospores anteriorly uniflagellate, plasma without a prominent globule, either escaping fully or partly formed through a pore produced upon the deliquescence of a portion of the sporangium wall or cleaved out at the orifice of a discharge tube; resting spore thick-walled.

On fresh-water algae, ascocarps of Discomycetes, and moribund stems of maize.

Zopf's fungus was considered by Vuillemin (1907) to be a filamentous fungus parasitized by a chytrid. On this basis Minden placed it in a new genus, *Hyphophagus* of the Cladochytriaceae, retaining, however, the name Hyphochytriaceae Schroeter for a family including *Macrochytrium*, *Zygochytrium*, and *Tetrachytrium*. No valid reason exists for the substitution of Minden's generic name for Zopf's, particularly since Valkanov (1929b) and Karling (1939b) have reaffirmed in related species Zopf's observations on the flagellation of the zoospore and ascertained that the sporangial and vegetative stages belong to the same organism.

KEY TO THE SPECIES OF HYPHOCHYTRIUM

Vegetative system richly branched; in ascocarps of *Helotium*, in moribund tissues of maize, or in internodes of *Chara* and *Nitella*
   Sporangium with an apiculus, discharging fully formed zoospores
      through a lateral pore; in *Helotium* .... *H. infestans*, p. 761
   Sporangium without an apiculus, zoospores formed outside the sporangium, the protoplasmic mass discharged through a tube; in
      moribund tissue of maize and internodes of *Chara* and *Nitella*
                        H. catenoides, p. 762
Vegetative system sparingly branched; in *Hydrodictyon*.. *H. hydrodictii*, p. 763

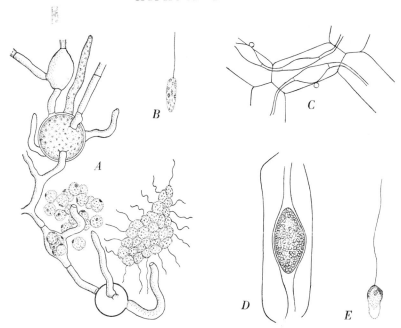

FIG. 56. *Hyphochytrium*

A-B. Hyphochytrium catenoides Karling on decaying maize: *A*, portion of thallus showing (lower right) formation of zoospores at orifice of discharge tube, group of quiescent spores, sporangium with its discharge tube, and (at top) empty segments from which contents have migrated; *B*, anteriorly uniflagellate zoospore. *C-E. Hyphochytrium hydrodictii* Valkanov in *Hydrodictyon: C*, parts of thalli in alga, showing epibiotic cysts of zoospore and primary and secondary swellings; *D*, resting spore; *E*, anteriorly uniflagellate zoospore. (*A-B*, Karling, 1939b; *C-E*, Valkanov, 1929b)

HYPHOCHYTRIUM INFESTANS Zopf

Nova Acta Acad. Leop.-Carol., 47: 187, pl. 18, figs. 13–20. 1884

(Fig. 55 H–I, p. 752)

Hyphophagus infestans (Zopf) Minden, Kryptogamenfl. Mark Brandenburg, 5: 420. 1911 (1915).

Vegetative system ramifying throughout the substratum, richly branched; sporangium, when intercalary fusiform or ovoid, when terminal spherical with a small apiculus, wall smooth, stout, colorless, collapsing after discharge; zoospores from sixty to one hundred in a sporangium, very small, spherical or ovoid, anterior flagellum fairly long, movement amoeboid, discharged with great speed from a lateral pore; resting spore not observed.

In ascocarp of a *Helotium*-like member of the Pezizaceae, on damp poplar stump, GERMANY.

HYPHOCHYTRIUM CATENOIDES Karling

Amer. J. Bot., 26: 513, figs. 1–18. 1939

(Fig. 56 A–B, p. 761)

"Thallus predominantly polycentric and intramatrical; usually hyphal-like, and consisting of a linear series, up to 500 μ in extent, of inter-calary and terminal swellings and sporangia connected by tubular hyphae or isthmuses 1 to 138 μ in length and 2.2 to 4 μ in diameter; occasionally monocentric, oval, elongate, spherical and *Olpidium*-like. Zoosporangia terminal or intercalary, delimited by cross septa, hyaline, smooth, spherical, 10–35 μ, oval, 10 × 12 μ—18–22 μ, broadly spindle-shaped 6 × 10 μ—9 × 18 μ, elongate and sometimes slightly irregular with 1–4 single or branched, straight, curved, coiled, or irregular exit tubes, 5–250 μ in length and 3–6 μ in diameter. Content of sporangium usually emerging as a naked spherical mass on the outside and under-going cleavage into zoospores; occasionally undergoing complete or partial cleavage in the sporangium whereafter the segments glide out in succession. Zoospores anteriorly uniciliate, slightly flattened, oval, and elongate, 1.5 × 3.5 μ—2 × 3 μ, with several small, slightly refractive granules. Sexuality and resting spores unknown" (Karling, *loc. cit.*).

Weakly parasitic and saprophytic in *Zea mays*, *Nitella flexilis*, and *Chara coronata*, Karling (*loc. cit.*), UNITED STATES; air contaminant, Siang (1949), CANADA.

Since there is sometimes partial or complete cleavage of the zoospores within the sporangium, this species is retained in *Hyphochytrium*, but see remarks under the family (p. 759).

HYPHOCHYTRIUM HYDRODICTII Valkanov

Arch. Protistenk., 67: 122, figs. 1–11. 1929

(Fig. 56 C–E, p. 761)

Vegetative system arising as a lateral outgrowth from opposite sides of the rudiment of the sporangium, broad, tubular, not tapering, rarely branched, extending through many cells; sporangia endobiotic, intercalary, from one to several (up to three) on the thallus, when single, sporangium formed from the primary swelling produced by the infecting zoospore, the cyst of which is persistent, when several, sporangia formed as well from secondary swellings of the vegetative system from which they are cut off by cross walls at maturity, broadly fusiform or occasionally somewhat irregular and gibbose, with a smooth, thin, colorless wall, forming a single functional papilla which pierces the host wall (rarely two or more nonfunctional papillae), method of opening not observed; zoospores ovoid with a broad rounded apex, a single eccentric colorless globule, and a long anterior flagellum, capable of amoeboid motion, from fifty to one hundred or more in a sporangium, individual motion initiated within sporangium; resting spore terminal or intercalary, fusiform, with a thicker inner wall, contents charged with numerous droplets of uniform size, upon germination forming a single discharge papilla.

Parasitic on young cells of *Hydrodictyon reticulatum*, BULGARIA.

According to Valkanov the development of the fungus is as follows: The zoospore, after coming to rest on the host and encysting, penetrates the wall and produces within the alga a spherical outgrowth. This growth as it expands elongates parallel to the long axis of the *Hydrodictyon* cell (usually in opposite directions from the point of infection) and results in the formation of a broad tubular hypha-like generally unbranched structure (Fig. 56 C). The rudiment of the sporangium is recognizable from the beginning as the rather broad fusiform structure that is first laid down by the parasite and from the opposite sides of which the rhizoidal elements emerge. Later, other sporangia may be produced by secondary swellings of the "hyphae." It is probable that the primary reproductive structure absorbs host material, in much the same fashion as does an *Olpidium*, at least until the vegetative organs are formed. Eventually the sporangial rudiment, which has grown more in thickness than in length, is cut off by cross walls from the rest of the thallus and one or more papillae are formed. The droplets within its contents coalesce to form the globules of the mature zoospores. Discharge of the spores already moving within the sporangium was not observed with certainty.

IMPERFECTLY KNOWN GENUS OF THE HYPHOCHYTRIALES

? REESSIA Fisch

Sitzungsber. Phys.-Med. Soc. Erlangen, 16: 41. 1884

"Thallus intramatrical, monocentric, holocarpic; more or less naked (but immiscible with, and distinct from, the enveloping host protoplasm) when young, but becoming invested with a distinct wall at maturity; amoeboid or stationary during the vegetative developmental stages. Zoosporangia usually solitary, hyaline and smooth, oval or spherical with one elongate cylindrical exit tube which may project considerably beyond the surface of the host cell. Zoospores oval or spherical and hyaline with a conspicuous refractive globule; emerging fully formed and swimming directly away or lying quiescent for a few moments in a mass at the mouth of the exit tube. Gametes when present similar to the zoospores, fusing in pairs to form biflagellate motile zygotes which infect the host cell, grow in size, and become resting spores. Resting spores spherical or oval, yellowish or light brown, with a smooth thick double-layered wall and one to several large refractive globules; transformed directly into a zoosporangium in germination" (Karling, 1943: 642).

Parasitic in species of *Lemna*.

In addition to the two *Lemna* parasites described in the following pages, Fisch cited a third species, *Reessia cladophorae*, about which practically nothing is known. It has been referred to *Olpidium* by Fischer (1892) and Minden (1915).

The genus *Reessia* (*R. amoeboides*) was established by Fisch (1884a: 41) for an organism inhabiting *Lemna*. The zoospore was said to penetrate the cell of the host by its flagellum. Inside the cell the thallus remained amoeboid for a time, then surrounded itself with a wall, enlarged, and became a sporangium. After discharge from such sporangia, the anteriorly uniflagellate zoospores often conjugated in pairs to form a zygote, the unfused ones developing into new sporangia. The zygote eventually entered a *Lemna* cell and became transformed into a brownish, thick-walled resting spore, with from one to three or more large globules. This spore upon germination gave rise to zoospores which were surrounded by an evanescent vesicle. Fischer (1892: 28) considered *R. amoeboides* synonymous with *R. lemnae*.

All these observations need confirmation, particularly those referring to zoospore flagellation.

? REESSIA AMOEBOIDES Fisch

Sitzungsber. Phys.-Med. Soc. Erlangen, 16: 32, pl. 1, figs. 1–6. 1884

"Thallus amoeboid with several pseudopods during the vegetative developmental stages. Zoosporangia solitary, hyaline, smooth with an elongate straight or curved cylindrical exit tube which may often penetrate several host cells. Zoospores large, hyaline, spherical or oval with a conspicuous refractive globule; frequently fusing in pairs and forming biflagellate motile zygotes which infect the host cell and develop into dormant spores. Resting spores oval or spherical with a smooth light brown exospore and a hyaline endospore; containing one to several large refractive globules; endospore expanding out of the ruptured exospore during germination and forming a vesicle in which zoospores are eventually developed" (Karling, 1943: 642).

Parasitic in the epidermal cells of *Lemna minor* and *L. polyrhiza*, GERMANY.

? REESSIA LEMNAE (Fisch) Karling

Amer. J. Bot., 30:642. 1943

Chytridium lemnae Fisch, Sitzungsber. Phys.-Med. Soc. Erlangen, 16: 43, pl. 1, figs. 7–9. 1884.
Olpidium lemnae (Fisch) Schroeter, Kryptogamenfl. Schlesien, 3 (1): 181. 1885.

Sporangium spherical, thin-walled, with a thin smooth colorless wall and a long narrow slightly irregular discharge tube; zoospores spherical, with a small colorless globule and an anterior flagellum from two to three times as long as the body, remaining for a short time at the mouth of the discharge tube, motion lively; resting spore spherical, with a double wall, the outer thin and cuticularized, the inner refractive, contents with from one to two large globules and a peripheral bright spot, upon germination producing zoospores.

In cells of *Lemna minor, L. polyrrhiza,* Fisch (*loc. cit.*), *L. trisulca,* coll. Hieronymus, Schroeter (1885: 181), GERMANY.

EXCLUDED GENUS OF THE HYPHOCHYTRIALES
* CATENARIOPSIS COUCH, NOM. NUDUM
Amer. J. Bot., 28: 707. 1941

Mentioned only by name. Considered by Karling (1943) as probably a *Hyphochytrium.*

SPECIES OF DOUBTFUL AFFINITY
? CHYTRIDIUM MESOCARPI (Fisch) Fischer
Rabenhorst. Kryptogamen-Fl., 1(4): 126. 1892

Euchytridium mesocarpi Fisch, Sitzungsber. Phys.-Med. Soc. Erlangen, 16: 101. 1884.

Sporangium epibiotic, flasklike, resting on the broad base, the upper part prolonged into a short tube, with a brownish stout smooth wall; rhizoid delicate, extending to the middle of the host cell, rarely branched; zoospores somewhat large, with the fine granular plasma containing an oil droplet, not over eight formed in a sporangium, with a single anterior flagellum attached to the somewhat narrower forward end of the body, emerging suddenly from the tip of the sporangium after the dehiscence of a circular operculum, after a period of swarming coming together in pairs and fusing at the flagella-bearing poles; the zygote containing two oil globules which fuse into one, its motion slow, soon coming to rest on the surface of the host and penetrating it by means of a small outgrowth, through which the content of the zygote is discharged into the host, where it enlarges, eventually surrounds itself with a double wall, and becomes a resting spore; the resting spore germinating after a short period, producing zoospores which penetrate other host cells and form new sporangia.

On *Mougeotia sp.*, GERMANY.

Fisch says all the zoospores from the sporangia fused and that the unconjugated ones never formed new sporangia, as they do in *Reessia* (p. 764). If this is so then only zoospores from germinated resting spores can form new sporangia (gametangia). It should be noted that the zoospores are *anteriorly* uniflagellate, a point not mentioned by Fischer and Minden, who, on the basis of Zopf's observations on *Rhizophydium pollinis-pini*, doubt their conjugation. The lack of figures greatly weakens Fisch's account. He does not state whether an epibiotic or endobiotic sporangium is formed at the germination of the resting spore.

The fungus is not referred to by Karling (1943) in his synopsis of anteriorly uniflagellate fungi. If it is rediscovered and the observations of Fisch confirmed it should be placed, on the basis of the flagellation of the zoospores, operculum, and the apparent lack of true sporangia, in a new genus.

A form mentioned by Cornu (1872a : 121) as "near *Chyt. acuminatum*," which has an operculate sporangium and an endobiotic spherical smooth-walled resting spore with a single globule, and which is parasitic on zygospores of *Mougeotia scalaris*, France, has been referred tentatively to this species by Fischer and Minden, apparently on the basis of the similarity of hosts.

BIFLAGELLATAE

PLASMODIOPHORALES

ALTHOUGH the Plasmodiophorales is not ordinarily considered a group of primarily aquatic fungi, over half the species in Cook's (1933b) and Karling's (1942d) accounts of the order, and in subsequent literature, are obligate parasites of aquatic vascular plants, Characeae or aquatic fungi. The discovery in recent years of plasmodiophoraceous fungi on Phycomycetes has proved particularly fruitful in clarifying the concepts of life histories and relationships. On such hosts their development, reproductive activity, and so forth, can most readily be followed. Some have regarded the Plasmodiophorales as Phycomycetes (Fitzpatrick, 1930; Sparrow, 1943). Others assigned them a vague position between the Myxomycetes, Protozoa, and Phycomycetes. Still others classed them as a family of the Myxomycetes. Schroeter (1885, 1893) placed them in the Phytomyxinae, a group of organisms more animal-like than plant-like. Gaumann (1926) and Gaumann and Dodge (1928) originally thought them to be Archimycetes, a group separate and coequal with the Phycomycetes (see Martin, 1932, 1940; Karling, 1942d).

While the Plasmodiophorales are not chytrids, their inclusion in the Phycomycetes seems increasingly justified by the evidence. A phycomycetous sporangial stage has been clearly demonstrated in species of *Sorodiscus* (Goldie-Smith, 1951), *Spongospora* (Kole, 1954), *Woronina* (Goldie-Smith, 1954), *Octomyxa* (Couch, Leitner, and Whiffen, 1939; Pendergrass, 1948, 1950), and *Polymyxa* (Ledingham, 1939; Sparrow, 1947b). Protomitosis [1] and the formation of a heterocont type of zoospore (one with two unequal flagella) have been proven typical for valid members of the order. The presence of these in *Woronina polycystis* (Goldie-Smith, 1954) substantiates, therefore, the earlier transfer of that genus (and family) to the Plasmodiophorales (Sparrow, 1943).

Karling (1942d), while he did not commit himself specifically as to

[1] See Nawaschin (1899) and Horne (1930).

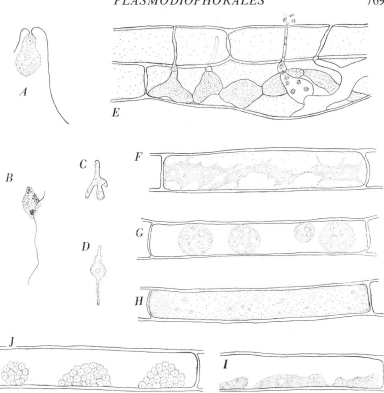

FIG. 57. *Polymyxa graminis* Ledingham in roots of wheat

A. Free-swimming zoospore with a long and a short flagellum, both of which are here directed anteriorly. *B.* Zoospore immediately after release. *C-D.* Shapes assumed by zoospores during amoeboid movement; flagella have now been lost. *E.* Septate thalli, some segments of which have become converted into zoosporangia; each sporangium bears a discharge tube which reaches the outside medium. *F.* Naked myxamoebae during active vegetative growth; it is in such thalli that the nuclei divide by protomitosis. *G.* Meronts formed by division of myxamoebae. *H.* Same meronts coalesced. *I.* Myxamoebae just prior to segmentation into resting spores. *J.* Spore clusters beginning to be formed from myxamoebae. (Ledingham, 1939)

the precise relationships of the Plasmodiophorales, admitted to their "closer affinity with the simple fungi than was formerly believed to exist."

Unfortunately, the whole group still so urgently requires a thorough study that no significant account of the aquatic species, save for the parasites of Phycomycetes, can presently be given. The need applies in particular to the obligate parasites of vascular plants, both aquatic and terrestrial; for that reason and because such fungi do not fall within the defined limits of this treatise they are not considered here. It is not necessary to enumerate all the existing elements of confusion concerning this group of fungi. They are discussed in the previous edition of this book and by Karling (1942d). It is sufficient to emphasize that with respect to a very important diagnostic feature, the type of zoospore, the investigations of Ledingham (1939), Ellison (1945), and Kole (1954) show beyond question that species of *Plasmodiophora*, *Spongospora*, *Sorosphaera*, and *Polymyxa*, parasites of vascular plants, possess two apically attached flagella of very different lengths. Moreover, the flagella, in contrast to those of all other biflagellate zoospores, are both of the whiplash type. Practically the same type of zoospore is formed by the plasmodiophoraceous parasites of water molds, species of *Octomyxa* (Couch, Leitner, and Whiffen, 1939; Pendergrass, 1948, 1950), *Sorodiscus* (Goldie-Smith, 1951), and *Woronina* (Goldie-Smith, 1954, 1956a). A heterocont zoospore is also typical of many of the true Myxomycetes (Elliot, 1949), which gives weight to the theory that this group has affinities with the Plasmodiophorales.

The life-history studies of Ledingham (1939) on *Polymyxa graminis* led him to lay considerable emphasis on the sporangial stage, so long overlooked. Although not able to establish the precise connection between the resting and sporangial stages by direct observation, he furnishes abundant evidence that they are, indeed, phases of the same organism. The following taken from his account substantiates this.

If wheat plants are grown in sterilized soil which has been inoculated with finely pulverized roots containing resting spores of *Polymyxa*, great numbers of thin-walled, septate, multinucleate thalli, which even in their youngest stages are surrounded by a delicate wall, develop in the roots. At maturity each of these segments becomes converted into a zoosporangium that is provided with a discharge tube (Fig. 57 E, p. 769). This tube eventually reaches the exterior, and through it numerous biflagellate zoospores (Fig. 57 A–D), exactly like those produced at the germination of the resting spore, are discharged. Their further fate could not be determined, although the evidence indicated that they penetrate the host cell. A few resting spores are formed early in the course of the infection, but by far the greater number are produced somewhat later, when the roots are very heavily diseased. The plasmodium which eventually produces the resting spores is unwalled, in contrast to that forming the zoosporangia. As it grows and becomes multinucleate by protomitosis it gives rise to long radiating threadlike pseudopodia, which may be retracted after a time (Fig. 57 F). The thallus then may fragment into a group of secondary thalli or "meronts" (Fig. 57 G). Occasionally, fusion of distinct plasmodia occurring in the same host cell was observed (Fig. 57 H). It could not be determined whether these plasmodia were meronts derived from the same or from different thalli. As the plasmodium matures, its contents become denser (Fig. 57 I), lines of cleavage form around each nucleus, and the walls of the resting spores are laid down (Fig. 57 J). Investigations of the nuclear condition in the maturing thallus before resting-spore formation indicated that the akaryote stage was recognizable. By the use of certain stains (Newton's iodine-gentian-violet) it could be demonstrated, however, that the chromatin was not, in fact, extruded, but that it merely failed to react to the usual stain (iron-alum haematoxylon). No nuclear fusions, as reported by Webb (1935) in *Sorosphaera* were observed. Just previously to cleavage of the cytoplasm ordinary division figures (not of the promitotic type) were formed, but whether meiosis took place could not be determined.

In summing up Ledingham's results, it is evident that he regarded the formation of the thin-walled zoosporangia as an essential and integral part of the life history of *Polymyxa*. He also intimated that they precede the production of resting spores. Further, he showed from his own studies on *Polymyxa* and *Spongospora* and from those of Cook (1926) and Cook and Schwartz (1930) on *Ligniera* and *Plasmodiophora*, that differences in the zoosporangial stages of these genera are well marked and may, in fact, prove of greater taxonomic worth than the method of aggregation of the resting spores (Palm and Burke, 1933; Wernham, 1935). Although earlier Cook had discovered the sporangial stage and mentioned it in connection with those species in which it occurs, he made little taxonomic use of it, nor did he incorporate it into the life cycle of the Plasmodiophoraceae.

Kole (1954) reinvestigated the morphology, cytology, and life history

of *Spongospora subterranea* on the potato. His results, although concerned with a terrestrial parasite, are of significance here. The resting
spores only germinate in the presence of the potato roots and previous
drying stimulates the process. Resting-spore zoospores penetrate the
root hairs and root epidermal cells and form multinucleate plasmodia.
The plasmodial nuclei are of the wheel type and divide protomitot-
ically. Zoosporangia are formed by segmentation of the plasmodium
into uninucleate or multinucleate units, which then undergo an akaryote
stage and give rise to zoospores after at least one mitotic division of the
nuclei. If free moisture is present, the biflagellate and heterocont zoospores are discharged into the water, where they may fuse either in pairs
or in threes. No nuclear fusion, however, has been observed.

In the early stages of infection myxamoebae and plasmodia are
present in the cells beneath the periderm of the host, whence they
proceed to infect the more deeply layered ones of the cortex. Infected
cells are stimulated to continuous cell division, producing wartlike outgrowths. During these divisions the fungus may be passively distributed
among the newly formed cells. As long as host-cell division continues
the fungus remains in the vegetative stage, the nuclei dividing by
protomitosis. When host-cell division ceases, the myxamoebae fuse to
form plasmodia whose nuclei undergo an akaryote stage. Subsequently
there are two or three or more consecutive mitotic nuclear divisions, after
which the plasmodia develop into the spore balls typical of the fungus.

With respect to the parasites of aquatic fungi, the studies by Couch,
Leitner, and Whiffen (1939) on *Octomyxa achlyae* and of Goldie-Smith
(1951) on *Sorodiscus cokeri* are of interest. The first-named group of
investigators summarize their findings as follows:

"The species is an obligate parasite on the hyphae of *Achlya glomerata*, causing the formation of gall-like swellings on the hyphal ends.
Infection is by single spores which enter the hyphae without leaving a
cyst. The spore is carried to the hyphal tip where it develops into a
multinucleate plasmodium. Vegetative nuclear divisions are of the
protomitotic type characteristic of the Plasmodiophoraceae. The early
formed plasmodia develop into sori of zoosporangia, which in turn
give rise to zoospores. The zoospores are biciliate with one long and
one short cilium. The later formed plasmodia form sori of resting

spores. These are found as a rule in groups of eight, each group being made up of two tetrads of resting spores."

Goldie-Smith in her study of a *Pythium* parasitized by a *Sorodiscus* (*cokeri*) reports that, "The plasmodia develop chiefly in the sporangia of the host, causing little or no hypertrophy. Cruciform nuclear divisions take place during vegetative growth. At maturity, a sorus of zoosporangia or resting spores is formed. The zoosporangia are thin-walled, spherical or ellipsoid, forming heterokont zoospores, each with a long posterior and a short anterior flagellum. Exit papillae are formed only by some of the sporangia on the periphery of the sorus. The zoospores formed in the interior of the sorus escape by passing through narrow pores formed in contiguous walls, from one sporangium to another, and thus to the outside. In its developmental stages this organism closely resembles *Octomyxa*. It is characterized, however, by its cystosori, which are composed of one-layered discs of resting spores. Usually there are two discs in a cystosorus, closely associated to form a spore-cake. Frequently there are three or four, forming *Y*- and *H*- shaped figures, respectively, in sectional view. This species is limited in its host range to *Pythium*, of which three other species have been successfully infected."

SYSTEMATIC ACCOUNT

PLASMODIOPHORALES

MICROSCOPIC parasitic aquatic or semiaquatic fungi, frequently producing hypertrophy of the host; the thallus endobiotic, holocarpic, without specialized vegetative structures, naked and more or less amoeboid or surrounded by a delicate wall, sometimes dividing into several daughter thalli (meronts, schizonts), the membranated thallus forming at maturity one or more thin-walled zoosporangia (gametangia?), the unwalled thallus becoming fragmented into a cluster or aggregation of thick-walled resting spores which produce zoospores at germination; zoospores biflagellate, with one long posteriorly directed flagellum and a short anteriorly directed one, both of the whiplash type; sexuality, in species in which it is known, by fusion of motile amoeboid or biflagellated isogamous gametes, the zygote becoming a naked thallus, which at maturity forms the resting spores.

This order contains only one family, the Plasmodiophoraceae, parasites of terrestrial and aquatic flowering plants and fresh-water algae, Phycomycetes, and *Isoetes*.

PLASMODIOPHORACEAE

Characters those of the order.

As in the first edition the Plasmodiophoraceae includes *Woronina*, which was placed by Minden (1915) and later authors in a separate family of the Chytridiales, the Woroninaceae. *Rozella septigena* Cornu, in the sense of Fischer (1882), and *R. simulans* Fischer may yet be found to be referable to the Plasmodiophoraceae (see the delineation of the zoospores of *R. septigena* by Tokunaga, 1933a). They are, however, given here under *Rozellopsis* (pp. 924, 925) of the Olpidiopsidaceae.

No original taxonomic treatment of the genera and species of the parasites of aquatic vascular plants can be attempted. The reader is referred to the monographs by Cook (1933b) and Karling (1942d) for details of these and other species.

KEY TO THE AQUATIC GENERA OF THE PLASMODIOPHORACEAE [1]

Parasitic in the hyphae of aquatic Phycomycetes and in filaments of
    Vaucheria; zoosporangia globose
    Infected parts of the host segregated by cross walls; resting spores
        either linearly or irregularly grouped or aggregated to form a
        somewhat globose mass .... WORONINA, p. 775
    Infected parts of the host not segregated by cross walls; resting spores
        grouped predominantly in eights .... OCTOMYXA, p. 782
Parasitic in aquatic vascular plants and *Chara*; zoosporangia variously
    shaped
    Resting spores scattered, without definite arrangement in the host
        cells; infected parts of the host strongly hypertrophied ....
        .... PLASMODIOPHORA, p. 783
    Resting spores more definitely aggregated; infected parts of the host
        with or without hypertrophy
    Resting spores in irregular groups; host not hypertrophied ......
        .... LIGNIERA, p. 784
    Resting spores in groups of two and four; host hypertrophied ...
        .... TETRAMYXA, p. 785
    Resting spores in two layers, forming a flat ellipsoidal plate; host
        hypertrophied .... SORODISCUS, p. 787
    Resting spores forming spherical or ellipsoidal, usually hollow
        masses; host hypertrophied .... SOROSPHAERA, p. 790

[1] Note that the key is not strictly dichotomous.

WORONINA Cornu

Ann. Sci. Nat. Bot., V, 15: 176. 1872

(Figs.58 A–E, K–M, p. 778; 59 E–H, p. 786)

Thallus unwalled, endobiotic, holocarpic, in walled-off portions of the host (the walls those of the host), forming the rudiment of the sporangia, sorus, or cystosorus; sporangia grouped, each forming a pore through which the biflagellate heterocont zoospores emerge; cysts thick-walled, angular or spherical, generally closely aggregated into cystosori, each upon germination functioning as a zoosporangium.

Parasites of other Phycomycetes and green algae.

Members of the genus are very animal-like in some of their features. If Zopf's observations on the behavior of the plasmodium in *Woronina glomerata* are unquestionably confirmed and extended the species will provide a remarkable connecting link with *Proteomyxa*-like protozoa.

The best-known species, *Woronina polycystis*, is a common parasite in *Saprolegnia* and *Achlya*. The observations of Fischer (1882) indicated that the linear sequence of thallus development found in heavily infected hyphae was not due to successive fractionation of a single thallus but to multiple infection. A single zoospore gave rise to a single thallus and the transverse septa were formed by the host, not the parasite. Cook and Nicholson (1933), on the other hand, declare that the multinucleate "plasmodium" may, at the time of septation by the host, be divided and that the segments produced may develop into full-sized thalli. In this manner a series of plasmodia may be formed. They also noted that the thallus feeds mainly upon the globules of oil present in the host cells.

The most recent study of *Woronina polycystis* is one by Goldie-Smith (1954). Her most pertinent findings are the occurrence of protomitotic nuclear figures (Fig. 58 K, p. 778) and the existence of the heterocont zoospores that are typical of the Plasmodiophorales.

She states that the zoospores, after a period of amoeboid activity on the outside wall of the host cell, encyst and produce a curved germ tube which effects penetration (Fig. 58 M, p. 778). She does not say whether the numerous young plasmodia in the hypertrophied parts of the host are each derived from a single zoospore or by the fragmentation of a single plasmodium. In view of the many encysted zoospores found outside the infected parts the former seems the more likely. The plasmodia retain their individuality within the host and their nuclei multiply by protomitosis which is characterized by the formation of cruciform figures, and so forth. Each plasmodium then becomes transformed into a sorus (sometimes hollow) composed of somewhat spherical sporangia. Certain of the peripheral sporangia may each produce an exit tube, or two may combine to form a single one (Fig. 58 L). Akaryote stages in mitoses precede zoospore formation. Cleavage furrows divide the contents of each sporangium into ten or more elongate zoospores. Each spore contains several granules, a refractive elongate body, and a short anterior and long posterior flagellum. Sporangia in the interior of the sorus evidently connect by means of a system of intercommunicating pores with those more peripherally located, and their zoospores are eventually liberated through the latter's discharge tubes.

In older cultures cystosori are produced. They arise from plasmodia that appear darker than those which yield zoosporangial sori and usually occupy a more central position in the gall. Cleavage lines divide the dark plasmodium into polygonal blocks which thereupon subdivide into angular thick-walled golden-brown resting spores. These are loosely associated in a spherical or cylindrical group—the cystosorus. No germination of the resting spores was observed.

KEY TO THE SPECIES OF WORONINA

Parasitic in aquatic Phycomycetes; resting spores in compact masses
  or separate
  Parasitic in members of the Saprolegniaceae
    Cystosorus composed of globular compact masses of angular
      resting spores .... *W. polycystis*, p. 776
    Cystosorus composed of linear groups of unconnected spiny resting spores .... *W. asterina*, p. 779
  Parasitic in *Pythium* .... *W. pythii*, p. 781
Parasitic in fresh-water algae; the resting spores separate, in linear
  groups .... *W. glomerata*, p. 779

WORONINA POLYCYSTIS Cornu

Ann. Sci. Nat. Bot., V, 15: 176, pl. 7. 1872

(Fig. 58 A–C, p. 778)

Sporangia sorus terminal or intercalary in segments (often swollen) of the host, sometimes in linear series, the segments up to 476 μ long by 60 μ in diameter; sporangia varying in number according to the size of the sorus, spherical, 8–33, mostly 15–21 μ in diameter, wall thin, smooth, colorless, with a short discharge papilla; zoospores unequally biflagellate, 3–4 μ long by 2 μ wide, emerging through a pore formed upon the dissolution of the papilla; cystosorus borne like the sporangia sorus, dark, variable in size and shape, predominantly somewhat ovoid or ellipsoidal or linear; cysts (cystosporangia) golden-brown, thick-walled, 4–8 μ wide, somewhat angular, each upon germination becoming more spherical, longer, thin-walled, and functioning as a zoosporangium.

Parasitic in *Achlya polyandra, A. racemosa, Saprolegnia spiralis*, Cornu (*loc. cit.*), *Achlya sp., S. monoica*, Dangeard (1890–91b: 86, pl. 4, figs. 1–4), FRANCE; *Saprolegnia sp.*, Fischer (1882), Minden (1915: 275), GERMANY; *Achlya racemosa*, Sorokin (1883: 39, fig. 51), EUROPEAN RUSSIA, ASIATIC RUSSIA; *Saprolegnia sp.*, Maurizio (1895), SWITZERLAND; *Saprolegnia sp., Achlya sp.*, H. E. Petersen (1909: 425; 1910: 556, fig. 27 a–b), DENMARK; *Achlya sp., Saprolegnia sp.*, Cook and Nicholson (1933: 851, figs. 1–16), host (?), Forbes (1935b), *Achlya spp.*, Sparrow (1936a: 425), *Saprolegnia ferax* (?), Goldie-Smith (1954: 441, figs. 1–29), GREAT BRITAIN; *Achlya spp.*, Sparrow (1933c: 515), *Saprolegnia sp.*, (MICHIGAN) UNITED STATES; in vegetative hyphae and reproductive organs of *Achlya americana, Achlya sp.*, Shen and Siang (1948: 190), CHINA.

The fungus in *Oedogonium sp.* referred by Cook (1932a: 133, figs. 1–6) to this species cannot be identified with it.

Cook and Nicholson (*loc. cit.*) described the zoospores as spherical and the resting cysts as oval or ellipsoid. Earlier, Fischer had stated that the zoospores were elongate, often flattened on one side, and that the cysts were polygonal.

The fungus with posteriorly uniflagellate zoospores described by Pringsheim (1860: 205, pl. 23, figs. 1–5) and commonly ascribed to this species, has been placed in a separate genus, *Pringsheimiella*, by Couch (1939b), see p. 157.

Goldie-Smith's strain was confined to *Saprolegnia*. It was experimentally induced to parasitize *Isoachlya* but not certain species of *Achlya, Aphanomyces, Thraustotheca, Pythium, Apodachlya*, or *Allomyces*. In

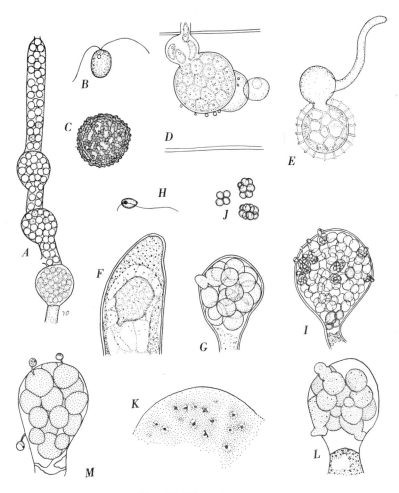

FIG. 58. Woroninaceae

A-C. Woronina polycystis Cornu in Saprolegniaceae: *A*, portion of hypha of *Achlya*; most of the many spherical sporangia in upper part have discharged their zoospores; in basal segment sporangia are just beginning to form; *B*, interpretation of zoospore according to Cook and Nicholson (1933); *C*, cystosorus of small angular resting spores. *D-E. Woronina glomerata* (Cornu) Fischer in *Vaucheria: D*, zoosporangium discharging its zoospores through tube opening to outside of alga; *E*, germinating resting spore on which discharge tube has been formed. *F-J. Octomyxa achlyae* Couch, Leitner, and

view of the preponderance of records for occurrence on *Achlya*, rather than *Saprolegnia*, it is quite possible that different races of the species occur in nature.

WORONINA ASTERINA Tokunaga

Trans. Sapporo Nat. Hist. Soc., 13: 26, pl. 2, figs. 15–16. 1933

Sporangia sorus linear, 96–216 μ long by 18–30 μ in diameter; zoosporangia 4–20, in one or two rows, spherical, 12–19 μ in diameter, with a thin smooth colorless wall and a short papilla; zoospores spherical or ovoid, 3–4 μ in diameter; cystosorus like the sporangia sorus in size and shape, cysts spherical, 12–22 μ in diameter, golden, the thick wall covered with large conical spines, germination not observed.

Parasitic in hyphae of *Achlya americana*, JAPAN.

This is a doubtful species according to Karling (1942e).

WORONINA GLOMERATA (Cornu) Fischer

Rabenhorst. Kryptogamen-Fl., 1(4): 67. 1892

(Fig. 58 D–E, p. 778)

Chytridium glomeratum Cornu, Ann. Sci. Nat. Bot., V, 15 : 187, pl. 7, figs. 20–22. 1872.

Sporangia sorus cylindrical, variable in size, 70–300 μ long by 50–96 μ in diameter; sporangia varying in number, spherical, 10–33 μ in diameter, with a smooth colorless wall and a narrow discharge tube, zoospores ellipsoidal to cylindrical, 3.6 by 2.4 μ, biflagellate; cystosorus

---

Whiffen in *Achlya*: *F*, thallus of parasite in tip of host hypha; *G*, group of nearly mature zoosporangia; *H*, zoospore bearing short anterior flagellum and long posterior one; *I*, hypertrophied tip of host hypha bearing numerous zoosporangia, some of which are discharging their zoospores; *J*, several groups of resting spores, which, like the sporangia, are formed in great numbers in swollen hyphal tips. *K-M. Woronina polycystis* Cornu on *Saprolegnia sp.*: *K*, fixed and stained plasmodium with nuclei at cruciform stage of division; *L*, zoosporangial sorus with peripheral sporangia forming discharge tubes; *M*, similar stage showing encysted zoospores on outside of host.

(*A*, Sparrow, 1943; *B*, Cook and Nicholson, 1933; *C*, Cornu, 1872a; *D-E*, after Zopf, 1894; *F-J*, Couch, Leitner, and Whiffen, 1939; *K-M*, Goldie-Smith, 1954)

borne like the sporangia sorus, cysts spherical or ellipsoidal, 12–22 μ in diameter, thick-walled, the outer wall reticulate with minute spines, upon germination forming a flasklike tube which pierces the algal wall and through which the zoospores presumably escape.

Parasitic in *Vaucheria terrestris*, *V. sessilis*, Cornu (*loc. cit.*), FRANCE; *Vaucheria terrestris*, *V. sessilis*, Zopf (1894: 43, pl. 2, pl. 3, figs. 1–3), Minden (1915: 275), GERMANY; *Vaucheria sessilis*, Voronichin (1920: 10), RUSSIA; *Vaucheria sp.*, Valkanov (1931a: 361), BULGARIA; *Vaucheria sessilis*, Tokunaga (1933a: 26, pl. 2, figs. 17–18), JAPAN.

On the basis of Zopf's observations on the vegetative stage this curious organism seems more animal-like than fungoid. According to Zopf, the swarmer from the overwintering spore penetrates the *Vaucheria* filament in early spring and, once inside, becomes amoeboid. The "amoebae" feed upon the chlorophyll of the host—ingesting it as solid particles into the plasma—increase in size, and sometimes fuse together to form an extensive netlike plasmodium. After the plasmodium has fragmented the chlorophyll residue is expelled and each of the fragments rounds off, surrounds itself with a thin wall, and forms a sporangium. In each sporangium, zoospores are produced which are discharged through a tube into the water, thus spreading the infection. Upon the advent of unfavorable conditions later in the season the plasmodium, which may be so large as to fill the whole algal tube, divides into segments ("Teilplasmodium") and from each is formed a sorus of cysts.

It is important that observations be made on the method of infection. If this occurs by encystment and by the formation of a penetration tube, relationship with *Woronina* is strengthened; if the swarmer enters as a whole, without encystment, its animal-like nature is emphasized.

The imperfectly known *Woronina aggregata* Zopf (*op. cit.*, p. 60) in *Mougeotia* has a round cluster of from ten to twenty spore cysts which discharge their zoospores through a tube. No resting spores were observed. Here, as in *W. glomerata*, the plasmodium ingests the chlorophyll and starch and expels material before encysting. What is probably another species is mentioned by Zopf as occurring in *Pilobolus*.

RECENTLY DESCRIBED TAXON
WORONINA PYTHII Goldie-Smith

J. Elisha Mitchell Sci. Soc., 72: 348, figs. 1–8, 16–35. 1956

(Fig. 59 E–H, p. 786)

"Obligate parasite in species of *Pythium*, causing galls which are always delimited by septa, often in catenulate series. Nuclei undergoing cruciform divisions during vegetative stages of plasmodium. Mature plasmodium forming a sorus of zoosporangia, or a cystosorus composed of resting spores. Zoosporangia thin-walled, spherical or ovoid, about 4.9–8.8 μ in diam. Zoospores biflagellate, with one long posterior and one short anterior flagellum; discharged through papillae formed only on some sporangia on the periphery of the sorus; encysting on the hyphae and other organs of the host, and germinating with a short, swollen penetration tube. Resting spores about 3.7–5.6 μ in diam., smooth, thick-walled, loosely associated in a cystosorus, forming a sphere or flattened spheroid with its greatest diameter usually less than the diameter of the gall containing it, golden-brown in color. Sporangial and resting spore membranes without cellulose, as shown by a negative reaction with chlor-iodide of zinc" (Goldie-Smith, *loc. cit.*).

Isolated from soil, UNITED STATES.

IMPERFECTLY KNOWN SPECIES OF WORONINA
? WORONINA ELEGANS (Perroncito) Fischer

Rabenhorst. Kryptogamen-Fl., 1(4):66. 1892

Chytridium elegans Perroncito, Centralbl. f. Bakteriol., Parasitenk. u. Infektionskrankh., Abt. 2, 4: 295. 1888.

Sporangia sorus spherical or somewhat stellate, filling the body cavity of the animal, 60–110 μ in diameter, with rose-red contents; sporangia 8–20 or more, spherical or pyriform, 20–30 μ in diameter, discharge tube 5–100 μ or more long by 3–4 μ in diameter; zoospores 30–50, ovoid, reddish, 4–5 μ long by 2–3 μ thick, with two long oppositely directed flagella.

Parasitic in adults and eggs of *Philodina roseola*, in a thermal spring, ITALY.

From the color of the zoospores it appears possible that here, as in *Woronina glomerata*, solid particles are ingested.

OCTOMYXA Couch, Leitner, and Whiffen
J. Elisha Mitchell Sci. Soc., 55: 400. 1939
(Fig. 58 F–J, p. 778)

"Parasitic on *Achlya* causing hypertrophy of host. The infecting zoospore giving rise to a naked protoplast, which at maturity forms a large spherical sorus of zoosporangia or resting spores. Vegetative nuclear divisions of the 'cruciform type.' Zoosporangia thin-walled, spherical, ovoid, or slightly flattened by pressure, zoospores with one long and one short flagellum. Resting spores spherical and with a slightly thickened wall; aggregated in groups of eight, each group not enclosed in a common membrane" (Couch, Leitner, and Whiffen, *loc. cit.*).

Parasitic in members of the Saprolegniaceae.

KEY TO THE SPECIES OF OCTOMYXA
Parasitic on *Achlya glomerata* .... *O. achlyae*, p. 782
Parasitic on *Brevilegnia sp.*, *Geolegnia inflata* ...... *O. brevilegniae*, p. 783

OCTOMYXA ACHLYAE Couch, Leitner, and Whiffen
J. Elisha Mitchell Sci. Soc., 55: 400, pls. 47–48. 1939
(Fig. 58 F–J, p. 778)

"Obligate parasite on *Achlya glomerata* Coker, causing spherical galls mostly on ends of hyphae. Galls 50–150 μ thick. Plasmodium at maturity partially or completely filling the gall and segmenting into either zoosporangia or resting spores. Zoosporangia globose to ovoid, thin-walled, variable in size, 6 μ to 16 μ thick. Spores discharged through small papillae which are formed only on some of the sporangia next to the host wall, the other peripheral sporangia as well as those deeper within the sorus discharging their spores through the peripheral ones; zoospores biciliate with one long posterior and one short anterior flagellum, 6–14 in a zoosporangium. Resting spores smooth-walled, 2.4 μ to 3.2 μ, aggregated in groups of eight. Sporangial and resting spore membranes without cellulose as shown by a negative reaction with chlor-iodide of zinc" (Couch, Leitner, and Whiffen, *loc. cit.*).

Parasitic in *Achlya glomerata*, coll. F. Foust, UNITED STATES.
Some cytological details are given by Whiffen (1939).

OCTOMYXA BREVILEGNIAE Pendergrass

J. Elisha Mitchell Sci. Soc., 64: 133, pl. 15. 1948

"Obligate parasite in *Brevilegnia linearis* Coker and *Geolegnia inflata* Coker and Harvey, causing spherical galls mostly on the ends of the hyphae of the host. Mature galls 30–90 μ thick. Plasmodia of the parasite at maturity completely filling the galls and segmenting into zoosporangia; plasmodia developed later segmenting into resting spores in clusters of eight. Zoosporangia globose to ovoid, 5.2–7.6 μ mostly 7 μ, in diameter, thin-walled. Spores discharged through papillae which are formed only on some of the sporangia next to the host wall, the other peripheral sporangia and those deeper within the sorus discharging their spores through those furnished with papillae; zoospores biflagellate with one long posterior and one short anterior flagellum, 4–6 in a zoosporangium. Resting spores 2.8–4.9 μ, mostly 3.5 μ in diameter, with smooth, somewhat thickened walls; germination unknown" (Pendergrass, *loc. cit.*).

Parasitic on *Brevilegnia sp.*, *Geolegnia inflata*, not capable of infecting *Achlya*, *Saprolegnia*, *Aplanes*, *Dictyuchus*, *Isoachlya*, *Allomyces*, or *Apodachlya*, UNITED STATES.

Details of the development and structure of this species were described later by Pendergrass (1950: 279, figs. 1–29). Although *Geolegnia* was infected artificially, attempts to inoculate representatives of other saprolegniaceous genera were unsuccessful.

PLASMODIOPHORA WORONIN

Arbeit. St. Petersburg Naturf. Gesell., 8: 169. 1877; Jahrb. wiss. Bot., 11: 548. 1878

Ostenfeldiella Ferdinandsen and Winge, Ann. Bot. London, 28: 648. 1914.

"Resting spores lying free in host cell, not united in cystosori, variable in size and shape, usually producing one zoospore in germination. Zoospores anteriorly biflagellate and heterocont, becoming intermittently amoeboid, infecting the host as an amoeba (?), dividing and budding (?), and eventually forming multinucleate plasmodia, which cleave into uninucleate segments. Cleavage segments developing into small zoosporangia which produce few zoospores. Secondary zoospores reinfecting host and forming additional plasmodia. Sporogenous plasmodium partly or completely filling host cell, moving slowly in amoeboid fashion within the host cell and in migrating from cell to cell; occasionally undergoing schizogony into uni- and multinucleate meronts; rarely encysting; cleaving into resting spores at maturity" (Karling, 1942d: 22).

Type species: *Plasmodiophora brassicae* Woronin.

Parasites of terrestrial and aquatic vascular plants. The known aquatic species are all parasites on marine hosts, on which they produce swellings of various types.

SPECIES IN AQUATIC VASCULAR PLANTS

PLASMODIOPHORA DIPLANTHERAE (Ferdinandsen and Winge) Cook

Hong Kong Naturalist (Suppl.), No. 1: 34. 1932; Arch. Protistenk.,80: 194, text fig. 9, pl. 6, figs. 5–6. 1933

Parasitic in *Diplanthera wrightii*.

PLASMODIOPHORA HALOPHILAE Ferdinandsen and Winge

Centralbl. f. Bakteriol., Parasitenk. u. Infektionskrankh., Abt. 2, 37; 167, 3 figs. 1913

Parasitic in *Halophila ovalis*.

PLASMODIOPHORA BICAUDATA Feldmann

Bull. Soc. d'Hist. Nat. de l'Afrique du Nord, 31: 173, figs. 1–2. 1940

Parasitic in *Zostera nana*.

LIGNIERA MAIRE AND TISON

C. R. Acad. Sci. Paris, 152: 206. 1911

"Resting spores not consistently aggregated in cystosori of characteristic shape and structure; variously-shaped with relatively thin hyaline or colored, smooth or verrucose walls. Plasmodium relatively small, partly or completely filling the host cell; segmenting into either zoosporangia or one or more cystosori; schizogony reduced or lacking (?). Zoosporangia numerous in a cell and usually grouped together, small and variously-shaped; opening by a rupture of the wall. Zoospores from sporangia pyriform. Germination of resting spores doubtful or unknown at present" (Karling, 1942d: 58).

Type species: *Ligniera junci* (Schwartz) Maire and Tison.

In roots of aquatic and marsh plants.

A poorly defined genus erected to include plasmodiophoraceous fungi with loosely and variously aggregated resting spores that develop within a single host cell and do not cause host hypertrophy. As Karling (1942d) rightly conjectured, it appears "to be scarcely more than a convenient dumping ground for species which cause little or no hypertrophy." Cook (1933b) indicated that the zoospores are anteriorly uniflagellate and that they function as isogametes. Both of these features are questionable and are in need of further study.

SPECIES IN AQUATIC VASCULAR PLANTS

LIGNIERA JUNCI (Schwartz) Maire and Tison

C. R. Acad. Sci. Paris, 152: 206. 1911

Parasitic in *Juncus spp.*, and a wide variety of aquatic, marsh, and terrestrial plants.

LIGNIERA ISOETES Palm

Svensk. Bot. Tidsskrift, 12: 228, figs. 1–3. 1918

Parasitic in *Isoetes lacustris.*

TETRAMYXA GOEBEL

Flora, 67: 517. 1884

Thecaphora Setchell, Mycologia, 16: 243. 1924.

"Resting spores usually in tetrads but often separating and lying singly, or in diads and triads; variously shaped, giving rise to a single nonflagellate (?) and amoeboid cell in germination. Plasmodia usually small, becoming parietal in the host cell at maturity and cleaving into uninucleate spore-mother cells or sporonts which usually divide twice

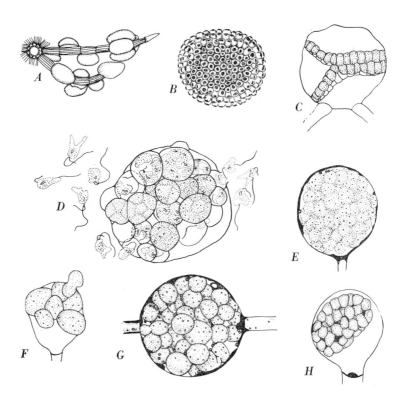

Fig. 59. Plasmodiophoraceae

A-B. Sorodiscus karlingii Cook in *Chara:* *A*, two of a whorl of leaves showing strongly hypertrophied corticating cells on each leaf; *B*, sorus of resting spores composed of approximately two hundred cells. *C-D. Sorodiscus cokeri* Goldie-Smith in *Pythium:* *C*, two convex cystosori; *D*, discharging sorus of zoosporangia, the zoospores passing from inner to outer sporangia and thence through pores to the outside, the zoospores undergoing amoeboid change of shape before swimming away; the zoospore body bears a contractile vacuole, scattered droplets, and a long refractive body. *E-H. Woronina pythii* Goldie-Smith in *Pythium proliferum:* *E*, young zoosporangial sorus; *F*, zoosporangial sorus, one sporangium of which has a swollen exit tube; *G*, mature zoosporangial sorus with peripheral refractive residual host material; *H*, mature cystosorus.

(*A-B*, Karling, 1928c; *C-D*, Goldie-Smith, 1951; *E-H*, Goldie-Smith, 1956a.)

to form tetrads of resting spores. Zoosporangia and zoospores unknown" (Karling, 1942d: 37).

A monotypic genus, members of which are parasitic on and cause hypertrophy (galls) of marine vascular plants.

SPECIES IN AQUATIC VASCULAR PLANTS

TETRAMYXA PARASITICA Goebel

Loc. cit.

Parasitic in *Ruppia spp.*, *Zannichellia spp.*, and *Potamogeton panormitanus* (see recent paper by Luther, 1950, for numerous records of occurrences and hosts).

SORODISCUS LAGERHEIM AND WINGE

Arch. f. Botanik, 12(9): 23. 1913

(Fig. 59 A–D, p. 786)

Membranosorus Ostenfeld and Petersen, Zeitschr. Bot., 23: 17. 1930.

Cystosori usually flat, oval, disc-shaped and composed of one or two layers of spores pressed closely together, often variable in size and shape, rarely hollow spheres, occasionally an elongate and irregular linear series of spores or reduced to tetrads, triads, diads and rarely monads; soral membrane doubtful or lacking; resting spores polygonal, angular and urn-shaped or oval and almost hemispherical with hyaline smooth or spiny outer walls, apical collar and cap present or lacking, remaining attached or separating at maturity, producing one or possibly more than one zoospore in germination; zoosporangia thin-walled, spherical or ovoid (in *S. cokeri*); zoospores with one short anterior flagellum and a long posterior one, discharged after the deliquescence of papillae; plasmodia one to several in a cell, large or small, schizogony lacking or doubtful in some species. (Modified from Karling, 1942d: 46.)[1]

Parasites of aquatic vascular plants, Characeae, and *Pythium*.

Karling's (*loc. cit.*) diagnosis of the genus was sufficiently broad to allow for the inclusion of *Sorodiscus* (*Membranosorus*) *heterantherae*, a species which is somewhat variable with respect to type of spore mass.

---

[1] Modified in the light of Goldie-Smith's (1951) findings.

Even in it, however, a considerable number of the cystosori are some-what circular in outline and one- or two-layered. The answer to the question of what is the correct generic concept of *Sorodiscus* still awaits critical study and evaluation.

KEY TO THE SPECIES OF SORODISCUS

SORODISCUS KARLINGII Cook
Arch. Protistenk., 80: 207. 1933
(Fig. 59 A–B, p. 786)

"Cystosori numerous, up to 400 in a cell, quite variable in size and shape, often oval, elongate and disc-shaped, 15–30 μ × 45–70 μ, occa-sionally almost spherical, 10–35 μ in diameter, irregular, or reduced to tetrads, triads, diads and rarely monads; consisting of from 1 to 200 spores; enveloping membrane unknown. Resting spores polygonal and angular, 4–9 μ, when pressed together in large sori, spherical, oval and ellipsoidal when single or in small groups, 5–23 μ in diameter, uni- or multinucleate with hyaline smooth walls and surmounted by one and occasionally two fairly thick caps; germination unknown. Plasmodia one to several in a cell, multinucleate, and up to 90 μ in diameter; schizogony unknown. Zoosporangia and zoospores unknown" (Kar-ling, 1942d).

Parasitic in *Chara contraria* and *C. delicatula*, causing marked hyper-trophy, Karling (1928c: 485, figs. 1–9; 1942d: 50, pl. 8), *Chara sp.*, (MICHIGAN) UNITED STATES.

The species may be quite abundant in the lakes in Lower Michigan in some years.

Because of the variations in shape of the cystosori and the lack of a common surrounding membrane, Karling (1942d) retains the species in *Sorodiscus* only provisionally. The Michigan material in spite of var-iations in the shape and size of the cystosori fits well enough into *Sorodiscus* as now defined.

SORODISCUS COKERI Goldie-Smith [1]

J. Elisha Mitchell Sci. Soc., 67: 108, pls. 1, 2. 1951

(Fig. 59 C–D, p. 786)

"Obligate parasite on species of *Pythium*, in swellings homologous with the sporangia of the host, causing little or no hypertrophy. Naked plasmodium undergoing cruciform nuclear divisions during vegetative growth; at maturity partly or occasionally wholly filling the swelling, and dividing into zoosporangia or resting spores. Zoosporangia thin-walled, spherical to ovoid, 5.3–8.8 μ in diameter. Zoospores biflagellate, with one long posterior and one short anterior flagellum; 4–11, usually 8 or 9, in a sporangium; discharged through papillae formed only on some sporangia on the periphery of the sorus. Resting spores 3.1–4.1 μ in diameter, smooth, thick-walled, closely pressed together in circular or ovoid discs one spore thick. Discs usually paired, forming curved, two-layered plates; occasionally in threes or fours, giving an appearance in section of *Y*- or *H*- shaped figures respectively.

"Sporangial and resting spore membranes without cellulose, as shown by a negative reaction with chlor-iodide of zinc" (Goldie-Smith, *loc.cit.*).

Parasitic on *Pythium proliferum*, Goldie-Smith (*loc. cit.*), UNITED STATES; from soil, substrate?, Gaertner (1954b: 22), EGYPT, WEST AFRICA.

Inoculation experiments involving such hosts as *Callitriche*, *Nitella*, and species of various genera of the Saprolegniaceae and of *Pythium* by Goldie-Smith were all negative except for *Pythium irregulare*, *P. undulatum*, and *P. elongatum*.

SPECIES IN AQUATIC VASCULAR PLANTS

SORODISCUS CALLITRICHIS Lagerheim and Winge

Arch. f. Botanik, 12(9):23, pl. 1, figs. 9–10; pl. 2; pl. 3, figs. 43–64. 1914

Parasitic in *Callitriche spp.*

SORODISCUS HETERANTHERAE Wernham

Mycologia, 27: 272, figs. 1–2, pls. 17–18. 1935

Parasitic in *Heteranthera dubia*.

[1] Emended (1956a) to include hypertrophy of host and more than four spore discs in a cystosorus.

SOROSPHAERA Schroeter

In Cohn, Kryptogamenfl. Schlesien, 3(1): 135. 1885–89

"Cystosori one to several in a cell, predominantly of the shape of hollow spheres or ellipsoids, but often extremely variable in size and shape; presence of common enveloping membrane doubtful. Resting spores oval, ellipsoidal, pyriform, pyramidal and urn-shaped with yellowish-brown to brown, thin, smooth or verrucose walls; with or without apical collar; producing a single biflagellate, heterocont zoospore in germination. Evanescent thin-walled zoosporangia small. Plasmodia one to several in a cell, large or small; schizogony present (?) or lacking; producing a single cystosorus" (Karling, 1942d: 41).

Type species: *Sorosphaera veronicae* Schroeter.

SPECIES IN AQUATIC VASCULAR PLANTS

Sorosphaera veronicae Schroeter

In Cohn, Kryptogamenfl. Schlesien, 3(1): 135. 1885–89

Parasitic in *Veronica spp.*

Sorosphaera radicalis Cook and Schwartz

Ann. Bot., 43: 86, pl. 2, figs. 1–6. 1929

Parasitic in root hairs of aquatic grasses.

IMPERFECTLY KNOWN GENUS OF THE PLASMODIOPHORACEAE

? PYRRHOSORUS Juel

Bih. Kgl. Svensk. Vetensk.-Ak. Handl., 26, Afd. 3, No. 14: 12. 1901

Pyrrhosorus marinus Juel

Op. cit., p. 12, pl. 1

Thallus at first plasmodial, later fragmenting into free ellipsoidal or fusiform naked uninucleate cells; sori from larger rounded mother cells, about 8 μ in diameter, which occur with the sterile fusiform cells; sporangia naked, with orange granules, divided by three successive divisions into a naked mass of eight rounded cells, which become the zoospores; zoospores about 4.5 μ long by 2.5 μ wide, pyriform with an orange pigment spot and two lateral oppositely directed flagella.

Saprophytic in *Cystoclonium purpurascens*, in aggregate causing bright orange spots, SWEDEN.

There are a number of puzzling features about this fungus. From the description it is difficult to understand the relationship of the plasmodial thallus, which fragments into the spindle-shaped cells, to the sori of sporangia. There is a possibility that two organisms are involved, a *Labyrinthula*—often found, as was *Pyrrhosorus*, in decaying algae in marine aquaria—and a *Woronina*-like fungus to which the sori and zoospores belong. Winge (1913), who points out the resemblance of *Pyrrhosorus* to *Sorolpidium*, a parasite of beets, gives the following account of the life history: Infection is presumably caused by the zoospore, which penetrates the alga. Inside the host several myxamoebae are found, some small with a single large nucleus, others larger with many small nuclei. Juel thought it possible that the large multinucleate thalli have arisen either by divisions of the single nucleus of the smaller thalli or by the fusion of uninucleate plasmodia. The single large nucleus of the smaller thallus, he believed, has simply enlarged after establishment in the alga. The multinucleate plasmodium may be extensive and penetrate a great number of cells. Eventually it becomes walled and within it are formed either a close aggregation of numerous small uninucleated spindle-shaped cells, which round off and become the "spore mother cells," or scattered spindle-shaped cells, which sometimes also eventually become spore mother cells. The closely aggregated, uninucleated, naked spore mother cells may frequently have intermixed with them sterile cells which degenerate. Each of the spore mother cells and its nucleus undergoes three successive divisions. In this manner the cell becomes divided into eight biflagellate zoospores, each with two lateral flagella.

Aleem (1953) identified amoeboid bodies in *Ceramium rubrum* from Sweden with this fungus but offers no new clues as to its relationships.

SAPROLEGNIALES[1]

THE order Saprolegniales includes what are probably the best and most widely known species of aquatic Phycomycetes. Its members have long been the object of extensive morphological, physiological, and taxonomic studies. Indeed, the terms "water mold" and "fish mold" as ordinarily used refer only to members of one family, the Saprolegniaceae. Most of the species belonging to the order are saprophytic on plant and animal debris in fresh water or in soil. A few are parasitic on fresh-water and marine algae, especially diatoms, and on the roots of terrestrial flowering plants. *Sommerstorffia spinosa* is a predaceous parasite of microscopic animals, particularly rotifers. Tiffany [2] (1939a, 1939b) reviewed the relationship of species of *Saprolegnia* to diseases of fish and amphibia and added new experimental evidence on the parasitism of these fungi.

More recently Vallin (1951) has given a clear account of an epidemic in the northern Baltic, among members of a single species of copepod, *Eurytemara hirundoides*, that is caused by a saprolegniaceous fungus, probably a species of *Leptolegniella* or *Leptolegnia*.

Nearly all the members of the largest family, the Saprolegniaceae, may be grown in pure culture on artificial media.

Although the designation "water mold"[3] suggests that the Saprolegniaceae occur exclusively in water, investigations have shown otherwise. Numerous species have been isolated from the soil and some are thus far known only from that habitat. This leads naturally to the speculation: are they not primarily soil organisms and merely adventitious

---

[1] The Saprolegniaceae has not been treated here in full. A key to the genera, the diagnoses of genera, and references to any new taxa (except for *Achlya*) published since Coker (1923) and Coker and Matthews (1937) are included. A comprehensive study of *Achlya* has recently appeared (Johnson, 1956) and for complete accounts of other genera, see the two aforementioned monographs. The original generic descriptions are mostly cited from recognized authors. The others lay no claim to be critical analyses. It is hoped the keys and figures are sufficiently informative to be of service for identification at the generic level.

[2] See also Vishniac and Nigrelli (1957).

[3] See Bock (1956).

inhabitants of the water? The general structure of the thallus and the fact that the free-swimming zoospore is ordinarily the nonsexual propagative unit, however, argues for their being primarily aquatic.

DEVELOPMENT AND MORPHOLOGY

THE THALLUS

The thallus in members of the Saprolegniaceae is a richly branched coenocytic aggregation of hyphae, usually with unlimited capacity for growth. This aggregation may be pustular or form a dense turf; it is easily visible macroscopically on the substratum. In the other two families, the Ectrogellaceae and Thraustochytriaceae, however, the body is of very simple structure, of limited growth, saccate, and distinctly chytrid-like.

Characteristically, the thallus walls in all members of the order give a pronounced cellulose reaction with chloriodide of zinc. In the hypha-forming species there does not appear to be, as in the Leptomitales, a strong differentiation of the lower part of the thallus into a basal cell and a holdfast system. The multinucleate contents are not highly refractive except in actively growing regions. Frequently they are somewhat thin and watery in appearance, with the granules arranged in a loose longitudinally disposed reticulum around the periphery of a central vacuole. Cross walls are laid down in normal material of eucarpic species only to delimit the reproductive organs and "gemmae" (chlamydospores). The latter are simply distended parts of the hyphae, of somewhat variable shape and often formed in catenulate series, within which the protoplasm accumulates. They may eventually disarticulate and, upon the advent of favorable conditions, germinate to produce either hyphae or short-stalked zoosporangia.

REPRODUCTION

Nonsexual Reproduction

Nonsexual reproduction is ordinarily accomplished by means of zoospores borne in zoosporangia. The zoospores, after escape, swarm, but eventually come to rest and germinate to form a new mycelium.

The uninucleate swarmers are cleaved out within the sporangium and discharged after a highly characteristic and distinctive series of cytoplasmic changes (see Büsgen, 1882; Hartog, 1887; Rothert, 1888; Humphrey, 1893; Schwartze, 1922; Couch, 1924). Briefly, these changes as noted by Hartog and, particularly, by Humphrey are as follows:

1. The protoplasm in the young sporangium at first surrounds a central axial vacuole.

2. Irregular lines of cleavage extend outward from the central vacuole. These increase in number, connect with one another, and delimit the spore initials as irregularly polygonal uninucleate masses. At this time, if at all, the discharge papilla makes its appearance.

3. A homogeneous stage develops abruptly, accompanied by a loss of turgidity of the sporangium. The cleavage lines or extensions of the central vacuole now suddenly become invisible because of the increase in size of the zoospore initials. Small vacuoles appear and disappear in these initials, the contents of which become less granular. Fluid, possibly of vacuolar origin, is probably expelled at this time.

4. The small vacuoles vanish, the cytoplasm again becomes granular, and the zoospore initials contract and separate into rounded individuals.

The structure of the zoospores is discussed in the "Introduction," p. 9. Their behavior differs depending on which genus is involved. In the Saprolegniaceae, the method of liberation and subsequent activity after escape are relatively constant for a given fungus and are of great diagnostic importance in distinguishing genera. Diplanetism (dimorphism [1]) is present in *Isoachlya, Saprolegnia, Leptolegnia*, and in certain species of *Ectrogella*. Vestiges of it, according to most interpretations,

---

[1] Bessey's (1950: 106) statements concerning terminology are pertinent. He says: "It is customary to refer to the characteristic of forming primary zoospores only, as monoplanetic and of the formation of two successive types of zoospores as diplanetic. More correctly these two terms should be *monomorphic* and *dimorphic* (italics ours). Properly speaking monoplanetic means wandering once, or with only one swimming stage, while diplanetic means with two swimming stages. Since in *Pythiopsis* the primary type of zoospores may swim and encyst several times and in *Achlya*, *Dictyuchus*, and other genera, the secondary type of zoospore may also do the same thing the customary terms are not used in their correct etymological sense."

Unfortunately, Bessey has not given us a proper term to apply to an almost universal condition found in higher aquatic Phycomycetes, formation of the secondary type of zoospore only.

are to be found in all members of the order. Monoplanetism (monomorphism) occurs only in the genus *Pythiopsis*, in which the emerging zoospores are of the primary type described below; that is, after encystment they usually germinate directly to form a mycelium. Diplanetism, as here understood, is the successive formation by a single fungus of *two different types of zoospores*. The "primary" zoospore is pyriform or "pip-shaped," with two apical flagella. It encysts after swarming and gives rise to a "secondary" zoospore. This is reniform or grape-seed-like and bears two laterally attached oppositely directed flagella. Further encystments of the secondary zoospore have been observed, for example, in *Dictyuchus* by Weston (1919) and in *Achlya* by Salvin (1940). When they occur, the succeeding swarmer is always of the secondary type. The number of such "repeated emergences" (Weston, *op. cit.*) or "repetitional diplanetism" is, as Salvin has emphasized, no doubt often influenced by the environmental conditions (lack of food, cool temperature, aeration, and so on) prevailing in the medium. Coker and Matthews (1937) apply the term "monocystic" to zoospores which encyst once before germinating and "dicystic" to those which encyst twice.

Sexual Reproduction

Sexual reproduction is accomplished in most genera by the formation of oögonia and antheridia. One or several eggs (oöspheres), usually devoid of periplasm, are formed from the contents of the oögonium. This structure, as well as the egg, is at first multinucleate. At maturity, however, only a single nucleus is present in each egg. The antheridial branches, at the tip of which the antheridia develop, may arise from the same or different thalli. If only antheridia are formed by one thallus and oögonia by another (*Dictyuchus monosporus* [J. N. Couch, 1926b], *Achlya bisexualis* [Coker and A. B. Couch, in Coker, 1927]) the species is heterothallic. If both types of sex organs are produced on a single thallus it is homothallic. In some instances antheridia occur only on a small percentage of oögonia or are completely lacking. When they are not formed the eggs mature parthenogenetically (apogamously). Monandrous or polyandrous conditions occur. In some species well-developed fertilization tubes are formed by the antheridia. Whether or not fertilization always takes place if antheridia are present has been a matter of considerable discussion in the past (Coker, 1923; Fitzpatrick, 1930). The male gamete is never flagellate and, like the female, never makes contact with the outside medium. [1]

The mature oöspore is surrounded by a thick wall. The contents consist of a finely granular matrix within which are formed, typically, numerous small fatty droplets which surround wholly or in part a single large globule or several smaller ones. The structure of the egg in the Saprolegniaceae is of considerable taxonomic importance. According to Coker (1923: 10), there are two main types:

In all cases the fatty reserve is on or near the periphery, but in one type it is in the form of small droplets entirely surrounding the protoplasm, while in the other it is collected into one or a few larger drops on one side. The first of these types is called centric, the second eccentric, but intergrading types occur which connect the two extremes, and for certain of these I have found it useful to introduce the word subcentric. The three terms may be defined as follows:

A *centric* egg has one or two layers of small fat droplets entirely surrounding the central protoplasm.

A *subcentric* egg has the protoplasm surrounded by one layer of droplets on one side and two or three layers on the other, or rarely with the droplets entirely lacking on part of one side as in *Achlya oblongata*; this last condition connecting directly with such eccentric structure as is shown by *Pythiopsis cymosa*. [2]

An *eccentric* egg has one large drop on one side either outside the protoplasmic surface or barely enclosed by a thin layer of protoplasm, or several large drops enclosed in the protoplasm on one side, or a lunate row of small drops (in optical sections) on one side, as in *Pythiopsis cymosa*.

After a period of rest the oöspore germinates to produce a tube which either elongates and reëstablishes the thallus or forms a sporangium at

[1] Apinis (1935) described as *Archilegnia latvica*, a saprolegniaceous fungus in which the eggs are said to be fertilized by minute uniflagellate free-swimming male gametes. As has been pointed out by Coker and Matthews (1937), recognition of such an aberrant organism must be withheld until a further study is made. From the figures given, it is entirely possible that the material carried a persistent monad infection.

[2] Johnson (1956) has recognized three types of subcentric eggs in *Achlya*: I, with one layer of small oil droplets on one side of the oöplasm and two or three on the opposing side; II, as in Type I but with the single layer of droplets not formed, thus giving a lunate grouping of droplets partially surrounding the oöplasm; III, with a single circular layer of small droplets located eccentrically to the oöspore wall.

its tip. The plant body presumably is always haploid, the only diploid structure being the oöspore.

Couch (1926b) established the existence of heterothallism or, better, dioecism in the ubiquitous water mold *Dictyuchus monosporus*.[1] When the oögonial and the antheridial plants bearing sexual organs were isolated and grown separately oöspore formation did not occur. When, however, the two strains were grown together sex organs were formed and mature oöspores were produced wherever the hyphae of the two intermingled. Contact of the two strains was necessary and seemed to be the only type of stimulation concerned in the process. Environmental conditions had only a secondary and variable effect. Intercrosses between the four species of the genus then recognized were successful, and the resulting variations in morphological characters, hitherto supposed to be of specific significance, were so marked as to invalidate all but the type species, *D. monosporus*. Male, female, and neutral strains were found to occur in nature, as well as one which formed its oöspores parthenogenetically. Oöspores of this last strain were germinated and the mycelium thus produced was crossed (1) with a male strain, which was, as a consequence, stimulated to the formation of (functional?) antheridia that applied themselves to the oögonia produced by the parthenogenetic strain; (2) with an oögonial strain, in which experiment oögonia were formed on both strains and, in addition, functional antheridia were also produced on the parthenogenetic strain. Thus the latter strain was shown to be inherently monoecious. Germination of the oöspores formed by dioecious strains disclosed an interesting fact, namely, that parts of the mycelium arising from the germ hypha were male, parts female, and parts mixed. This suggests that sexual segregation took place early in the process of germination. If the germ hypha gave rise to a sporangium, the segregation probably occurred in the cleaving-out of the zoospores, since some of the latter produced male, some female, and some mixed mycelia.

Homothallism or monoecism has been definitely proved in *Leptolegnia* and in certain species of *Saprolegnia*, *Achlya*, and *Protoachlya* (Schlösser, 1929). Schlösser also gave some interesting details of regeneration and "reversal" in the isolated diclinous sex organs of certain homo-

---

[1] Also termed "gynandromixis" (Raper, 1940b).

thallic species. At all stages in their development before actual fertilization the antheridia and the oögonia can, by alterations in the environment, be made to reverse the sequence of their protoplasmic changes and hence to become again vegetative in character. Further, if sex organs are placed under conditions favorable for sporangial formation they may, if the process of fertilization has not been initiated, be converted into sporangia and produce functional zoospores. Also, in certain groups of *Saprolegnia*, in which species are differentiated mainly on the number of oögonia supplied with antheridia, this character can be modified considerably in a single form by changing the temperature at which growth takes place. A number of other valuable observations are made in Schlösser's excellent paper.

Between 1936 and 1949 J. R. Raper conducted a remarkable series of investigations on species of *Achlya*. He proved (1939b, 1940a) that in *A. ambisexualis* and *A. bisexualis* hormones play an essential part in the initiation and coordination of the stages of the sexual process. Emerson (1950) reviewed his work as follows:

[Raper] demonstrated conclusively that at least four distinct hormones are involved. Table II summarizes succinctly the action of these substances.

TABLE [II]

THE ACTION OF HORMONES IN COORDINATING THE SEXUAL PROCESSES OF GYNANDROMICTIC *Achlya* SPS.*

Hormone	Produced by	Affecting	Specific Action(s)
A	♀-Vegetative hyphae	♂-Vegetative hyphae	Induces the formation of antheridial branches
B	♂-Antheridial branches	♀-Vegetative hyphae	Initiates the formation of oogonial initials
C	♀-Oogonial initials	♂-Antheridial branches	(1) Attracts antheridial branches (2) Induces, in connection with a thigmotropic response, the delimitation of antheridia
D	♂-Antheridia	♀-Oogonial initials	Brings about the delimitation of the oogonium by the formation of a basal wall.

* From Raper [1939b].

Matings were made in both liquid and solid media. Diffusion of the hormones across cellophane membranes was shown and the sequence of steps and the timing of each was ingeniously demonstrated by many different types of experiments. Reciprocal matings between *A. ambisexualis* and *A. bisexualis* revealed the nonspecificity of certain of the hormones and the specificity of others, the latter providing a precise explanation for the sexual incompatibility of these two species. It was shown that both hormone A and hormone B are stable at 100°C. Intensive studies of the properties and action of hormone A followed [1942a]. It was found that the number of antheridial hyphae produced was proportional to the concentration of hormone A applied and could be used as an accurate index of reaction intensity. Optimal conditions of temperature, hydrogen ion concentration, and other factors were determined, and standard conditions for bioassay of hormone A were described. In 1942, Raper & Haagen-Smit [1942] refined the method of assay still further and succeeded in obtaining, by a complex series of chemical fractionations, a preparation of hormone A 70,000 times more active than the starting material. Unfortunately, despite intensive effort, the substance was not isolated in a pure state, but many of its physical and chemical properties were established. Subsequently, Raper [1942b, 1949] discovered that the initial response of the male vegetative plant to the female vegetative plant depends upon a complex of interactions between two substances, A and A^2, produced by the female, and two substances, A^1 and an inhibitor, produced by the male.

PHYSIOLOGICAL INVESTIGATIONS

The classic physiological investigations of Klebs (1896, 1898, 1899, 1900) on *Saprolegnia*, which were followed by those of Kauffman (1908), Obel (1910), Pieters (1915), and others, have furthered enormously our knowledge of the underlying factors determining the growth and reproduction of members of the Saprolegniales and of aquatic Phycomycetes in general. The conditions necessary to growth have been summarized by Coker from Klebs as follows (see Coker, 1923):

1. Uninterrupted continuous growth:—in all good nutrient media, so long as fresh unaltered nutrient is present, e.g., in water with peas, in weak meat extract (1–2%), in gelatin with peptone, in mixtures of water with albumen, casein, etc.

2. Prompt and complete transformation of the mycelium into sporangia and zoospores:—by placing a well-nourished mycelium in fresh water.

3. Growth with continuous formation of zoospores:—in very weak solution of certain nutrients, e.g. 0.005% haemoglobin, also in mycelium on agar-albumen jelly that is put in running water.

4. Active formation of oogonia with limited growth:—by putting a well-nourished mycelium in agar-agar.

5. Active growth, then active formation of oogonia:—

    (*a*) oogonia with antheridia:—in solution of leucin (0.1 %) with tricalcium phosphate (0.1 %).

    (*b*) oogonia without antheridia:—in solution of haemoglobin (0.05–0.1 %).

6. Growth, then formation of sporangia, then of oogonia:—by placing the mycelium in water from gelatin-meat extract; or by culture on dead insect in water.

7. Growth and simultaneous formation of sporangia and oogonia:—in water with some fibrin or syntonin.

8. Growth, then formation of oogonia and later sporangia:—after strong nutrition of the mycelium transfer to 0.01 % haemoglobin.

9. Active formation of gemmae:—by putting a well-nourished mycelium in 0.6 % tricalcium phosphate, or 1 % sodium chloride, etc.

10. Growth with sporangia, then gemmae; or growth with oogonia, then gemmae; or growth with sporangia and oogonia and then gemmae:—in the items 3, 5 and 6 above, when the culture is continued to the complete exhaustion of the nutrient material.

General conclusions in regard to conditions for the formation of sex organs are summarized as follows (Coker, *loc. cit.*, p. 566):

1. In a mycelium which is constantly given fresh nourishment no oogonia are ever formed. Young, just formed oogonia were, by means of fresh, soluble food, induced to vegetative growth. The old were, however, killed.

2. If a strongly nourished mycelium is changed to a medium of low nutritive value (in which the formation of sporangia is rare or absent) oogonia are formed in a few days.

3. In a good soluble food, preferably at such concentration that the sporangia cannot be formed, the mycelium begins to form oogonia as soon as the solution is chemically changed on account of its growth, and has lost its nutritive value.

4. The formation of oogonia is particularly encouraged through phosphate, which is likewise necessary to the formation of the antheridia. In a soluble food that is poor in phosphate oogonia are formed, but no antheridia; particularly abundant are such oogonia in a pure solution of haemoglobin.

5. In many soluble foods, for example in peptone, gelatine, etc. are excreted certain products of assimilation of the mycelium which hinder the formation of oogonia.

Since the work of the early investigators on the physiology of the Saprolegniales, numerous modern studies concerning this aspect have been made on members of the group. References to most of them are given by Cantino (1950, 1955).

SYSTEMATIC ACCOUNT

SAPROLEGNIALES

MICROSCOPIC, saprophytic or parasitic, aquatic or terricolous fungi; the thallus endobiotic or more commonly partly within and partly outside the substratum; holocarpic or eucarpic; when eucarpic the hyphae without constrictions and of unlimited growth; septa formed only in eucarpic species, where they delimit reproductive organs; walls turning blue with chloriodide of zinc; contents granular, refractive only in growing tips; gemmae present or absent; zoospores formed in sporangia, which in certain genera may be internally proliferous; zoospores biflagellate or (in *Geolegnia*) lacking flagella, mono- or diplanetic (mono- or dimorphic), if diplanetic the primary zoospore somewhat pyriform or pip-shaped, with two anterior flagella, the secondary zoospore reniform or grape-seed-like with two lateral or subapical oppositely directed flagella, capable in some individuals of repeated encystments and emergences before germination; sexual reproduction oögamous, plants homo- or heterothallic, gametes never flagellate nor set free in the medium; oögonium producing one or more eggs without periplasm[1]; antheridium (occasionally nonfunctional or lacking) usually forming a fertilization tube; oöspore thick-walled, characteristically with a large reserve globule (partly or completely surrounded by one or more layers of minute globules) and a lateral bright spot, upon germination forming a mycelium or a short hypha terminated by a zoosporangium.

The order as here defined excludes the Leptomitaceae of older authors, which was raised by Kanouse (1927) to ordinal rank.

The Saprolegniales consists of three families, the Ectrogellaceae, Thraustochytriaceae, and Saprolegniaceae. The Ectrogellaceae includes simple endobiotic holocarpic fungi which strongly resemble endobiotic true chytrids in their body characteristics. The Thraustochytriaceae, based on a eucarpic marine form, *Thraustochytrium proliferum*, saprophytic on *Bryopsis*, approximates in its bodily organization species of the chytridiaceous genera *Rhizophydium* and *Phlyctochytrium*, the sporangia being epibiotic and the vegetative system within the alga rhizoidal. The members of both these families, however, show unmistakable

---

[1] Except *Pythiella*.

affinities with the Saprolegniaceae. In the Ectrogellaceae features such as the sequence of changes in the maturing sporangium, the diplanetic (dimorphic) character of the biflagellate zoospores, and the cellulose wall are all saprolegniaceous. Although the affinities of *Thraustochytrium* are as yet somewhat obscure, its methods of zoospore discharge, the biflagellate zoospores, and internal proliferation of the zoosporangium of *T. proliferum* all point to a relationship with the Saprolegniaceae. The newer members of the family, added in recent years, further confirm this (Kobayasi and Ookubo, 1953).

KEY TO THE FAMILIES OF THE SAPROLEGNIALES

Thallus holocarpic, endobiotic during development, more or less extramatrical at maturity; zoospores mono- or diplanetic (mono- or dimorphic), behaving variously after discharge; primarily parasites of fresh-water and marine diatoms and Phaeophyceae

ECTROGELLACEAE, p. 802

Thallus eucarpic, intra- and extramatrical; saprophytic or parasitic on a wide variety of substrata

Thallus resembling that of a monocentric chytrid, the reproductive rudiment epibiotic, the vegetative system rhizoidal

THRAUSTOCHYTRIACEAE, p. 828

Thallus consisting of a more or less well developed complex of tubular hyphae without constrictions, the extramatrical parts of which bear numerous reproductive organs . . SAPROLEGNIACEAE, p. 833[1]

ECTROGELLACEAE

Thallus endobiotic, sometimes more or less extramatrical at maturity, one-celled, unbranched or sparingly branched, holocarpic, walls turning blue with chloriodide of zinc, contents at first vacuolate, later coarsely granular; sporangium inoperculate with one or more discharge pores which are sessile or at the tips of tubes; zoospores segmented within the sporangium, diplanetic (dimorphic), primary zoospores biflagellate, after discharge either undergoing a short period of motility before encysting or encysting at once, secondary zoospores laterally biflagellate; resting spore thick-walled, filling or lying loosely in a thin-walled

---

[1] See note, p. 792. See also Vishniac, in *Mycologia*, 50: 66, 1958, where a new family of holocarpic marine fungi, the Haliphthoraceae (*Haliphthoros milfordensis*), is established.

containing structure, contents with globules, germination not observed, antheridial cell present or absent.

Endobiotic holocarpic saprolegniaceous parasites of fresh-water and marine diatoms, of marine Phaeophyceae and Rhodophyceae, and of Phycomycetes.

KEY TO THE GENERA OF THE ECTROGELLACEAE

Sporangium unbranched
  Zoospores generally encysting outside the sporangium; cysts spherical; parasitic in diatoms and Phycomycetes
    Parasitic in diatoms; antheridial cell, where known, not forming a fertilization tube .... ECTROGELLA, p. 803
    Parasitic in Phycomycetes; antheridial cell forming a well-defined fertilization tube .... PYTHIELLA, p. 812
  Zoospores encysting within the sporangium or outside; cysts angular; parasitic in marine Phaeophyceae and Rhodophyceae
    Sporangium becoming partly extramatrical at maturity, with one or two broad discharge tubes; zoospores encysting within the sporangium ("net–sporangium") or emerging at once
                                             EURYCHASMA, p. 814
    Sporangium remaining completely endobiotic at maturity, with numerous narrow discharge tubes; zoospores encysting outside .... EURYCHASMIDIUM, p. 820
Sporangium branched .... APHANOMYCOPSIS, p. 824

ECTROGELLA ZOPF

Nova Acta Acad. Leop.-Carol., 47:175. 1884. Emend. Scherffel, Arch. Protistenk., 52:5. 1925

(Fig. 60 A–C, G–J, p. 806)

Thallus endobiotic, tending to force apart the valves of the host and to become partly extramatrical, holocarpic, without a specialized vegetative system, tubular or occasionally rounded, unbranched, contents at first vacuolate, later coarsely granular; sporangium bearing from one to many short conical discharge tubes; zoospores formed in the sporangium, diplanetic, primary spores biflagellate or nonflagellate, swimming directly away or encysting at the orifice, secondary spores, where known, biflagellate; resting spore endobiotic, thick-walled, completely filling or lying loosely in a saclike containing structure, accompanied (in one species) by a companion cell, germination not observed. Parasites of fresh-water and marine diatoms.[1]

A relatively poorly known group of minute parasites. Zopf stated that the zoospores were posteriorly uniflagellate, but Scherffel has shown them to be biflagellate and diplanetic. The genus as understood here is confined to parasites of diatoms. Scherffel (*loc. cit.*), however, suggested the inclusion of the phaeophycean parasite *Eurychasma* in *Ectrogella*.

The discharge tubes of *Ectrogella*, rather than boring through the siliceous wall of the diatom, gain access to the outside by expansion of the thallus, which forces apart the valves of the host.

KEY TO THE SPECIES OF ECTROGELLA [2]

Sporangium narrowly tubular, with or without an equatorial swelling, discharge tubes short
   Sporangium predominantly narrowly tubular throughout, discharge tubes numerous; primary zoospores flagellated and undergoing a short period of motility before encysting
       E. bacillariacearum, p. 805
   Sporangium predominantly tubular, with an equatorial swelling, discharge tube single; primary zoospores nonflagellate, encysting at the orifice after discharge . . . .*E. monostoma*, p. 807
Sporangium predominantly broadly cylindric-oblong, flattened ellipsoidal, or ovoid, or lenticular or spherical, discharge tubes of variable length
   Sporangium broadly cylindric-oblong, or ovoid; primary zoospores nonflagellate, encysting at the orifice after discharge
      Sporangium predominantly broadly cylindric-oblong, discharge tubes short, generally two, placed near one end of the sporangium; in *Gomphonema* . . . . *E. gomphonematis*, p. 807
      Sporangium predominantly ovoid, discharge tubes slightly prolonged, from two to ten, often opposite, formed at any place on the sporangium; in *Licmophora* . . . .*E. licmophorae*, p. 808
   Sporangium predominantly spherical or lenticular or flattened ellipsoidal; zoospores swimming directly away after escape
      Sporangium predominantly spherical or lenticular; in marine species of *Licmophora* . . . . *E. perforans*, p. 809
      Sporangium predominantly flattened ellipsoidal; in fresh-water *Eunotia* . . . . *E. eunotiae*, p. 810

[1] See, however, *Ectrogella marina* on *Chlorodendron subsalsum* (J. and G. Feldmann, 1955: 238), p. 811.
[2] See also recently described taxa, p. 811.

ECTROGELLA BACILLARIACEARUM Zopf

Nova Acta Acad. Leop.-Carol., 47: 175, pl. 16, figs. 1–24. 1884. Emend.
Scherffel, Arch. Protistenk., 52: 5, pl. 1, figs. 1–9. 1925

(Fig. 60 A, p. 806)

Sporangium tubular, fusiform, ellipsoidal or occasionally spherical, variable in size, up to 200 μ or more in length, unbranched, generally forcing apart the valves of the host, wall thin, smooth, colorless, discharge tubes short, thick-walled, from one to ten, arranged in one or two files corresponding in position to the girdle bands of the host cell; primary zoospores moving within the sporangium, pyriform, 4 μ long by 2 μ wide, with two equal, laterally inserted flagella 4 μ long, cysts spherical, not grouped compactly at the orifice, secondary zoospores ovoid, with an anterior broad oblique cleft, flagella unequal, movement darting, with pauses and frequent changes of direction; resting spore not observed.

Parasitic in *Synedra sp., S. lunularis, Gomphonema sp., Pinnularia sp.,* Zopf (*loc. cit.*), GERMANY; *Synedra ulna, Meridion circulare,* Scherffel (*loc. cit.*; 1902b), Domján (1936: 52, pl. 1, fig. 167), HUNGARY; *Synedra sp., Gomphonema sp.* (coll. de Wildeman, Marchal), de Wildeman (1890: 26), BELGIUM; diatoms, de Wildeman (1894: 155), FRANCE; diatoms, de Wildeman (1895a: 65), SWITZERLAND; diatoms, Atkinson (1909a: 338), *Pinnularia sp.,* Sparrow (1933c: 531), *Nitzschia sigmoidea,* Karling (1942e: 20), *Pinnularia sp.,* coll. Bartsch, Wolf (1944: 43), UNITED STATES; *Synedra capitata,* Friedmann (1952: 200), AUSTRIA.

The species has generally been found in the early spring. Zopf observed that in nature about 75 per cent of the diatoms were infected, and under laboratory conditions nearly 100 per cent. He concluded that this was due to the enormous numbers of zoospores produced.

When more than one thallus is formed in the host cell (occasionally as many as thirty appear there), its tubular shape is lost and it tends to become more ellipsoidal or spherical. Aside from differences already noted in the zoospore, Scherffel observed that the primary swarmer does not contain the solitary globule characteristic of the chytrid spore, but, rather, bears posteriorly several refractive granules. The secondary spore, on the other hand, contains dense hyaline plasma anteriorly and

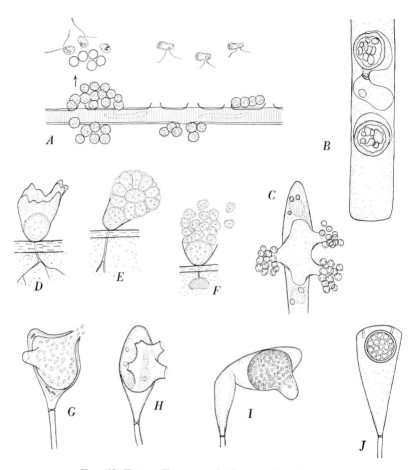

Fɪɢ. 60. Ectrogellaceae and Thraustochytriaceae

A. Ectrogella bacillariacearum Zopf, portion of the diatom *Synedra*, within which part of a discharged sporangium is shown; outside the host, near orifice of discharge tubes of fungus, are groups of encysted primary zoospores; above arrow are secondary zoospores which have emerged from cysts, and above to the right are primary zoospores with rudimentary flagella. *B-C. Ectrogella licmophorae* Scherffel in *Licmophora: B*, two resting spores, upper one apparently formed after a sexual process; supposed antheridial cell is empty save for single globule; *C*, discharged zoosporangium with groups of encysted primary zoospores at orifices of discharge tubes; base of each of latter structures is thick-walled, forming a "forcing apparatus"; frustule of diatom

one or more large refractive droplets posteriorly. In the behavior of the zoospores the species is said by Scherffel to resemble *Saprolegnia*, that is, the primary zoospores undergo a period of motility before encysting,

ECTROGELLA MONOSTOMA Scherffel

Arch. Protistenk., 52: 8, pl. 1, figs. 10–19. 1925

Sporangium long, tubular, 4–8 μ wide, with a pronounced equatorial swelling, unbranched, wall extremely thin, colorless, smooth, discharge tube single, short, 2–3 μ in diameter, formed on the swelling; primary zoospores few, not swarming in the sporangium, without flagella, after escape encysting in a group at the orifice, cysts 6–8 μ in diameter, secondary zoospores grape-seed-like, with a ventral furrow, 8 μ long, with two lateral oppositely directed flagella; resting spore not observed.

Parasitic in *Synedra ulna*, Scherffel (*loc. cit.*), HUNGARY; *Pinnularia sp.*, Sparrow (1933c: 531), UNITED STATES; *Synedra sp.*, Sparrow (1936a: 461, fig. 4p), GREAT BRITAIN.

The valves of the host are forced apart by means of the equatorial swelling, and the discharge tube protrudes free in the medium.

ECTROGELLA GOMPHONEMATIS Scherffel

Arch. Protistenk., 52: 9, pl. 1, figs. 20–21. 1925

Sporangium broadly cylindric-oblong, about 21 μ long by 6 μ wide (calculated), unbranched, forcing apart the valves of the host, wall thin, smooth, colorless, discharge tubes broad, short, thin-walled, lateral,

---

abnormally swollen. *D-F. Thraustochytrium proliferum* Sparrow on *Bryopsis plumosa:* D, discharged primary sporangium with secondary sporangium beginning to enlarge within it; E, mature primary sporangium showing basal body which will become rudiment of secondary sporangium; F, liberation of spores after deliquescence of upper part of wall of primary sporangium; each of the spores later becomes biflagellate. *G-J. Ectrogella perforans* H. E. Petersen in *Licmophora:* G, abnormally swollen diatom with zoospores of fungus escaping through one of the two visible discharge tubes; H, empty sporangium with four visible discharge tubes; I, hypertrophied diatom with unopened sporangium within which is peripheral layer of quiescent zoospores; J, resting spore.

(*A-C*, Scherffel, 1925a; *D-F*, Sparrow, 1936b; *G-J*, Sparrow, 1934c)

generally two, placed near one end; primary zoospores from fifteen to eighteen, swarming within the sporangium, ovoid, 3 μ long, with a single refractive granule and two equal subapical posteriorly directed flagella longer than the body, encysting at the orifice in a group, cysts 3 μ in diameter, with a large refractive globule, secondary zoospores not observed; resting spore not observed.

Parasitic in *Gomphonema micropus*, HUNGARY.

Differing from *Ectrogella bacillariacearum* primarily in having an *Achlya*-like rather than a *Saprolegnia*-like type of spore discharge.

ECTROGELLA LICMOPHORAE Scherffel

Arch. Protistenk., 52: 10, pl. 1, figs. 22–30. 1925

(Fig. 60 B–C, p. 806)

Sporangium predominantly ovoid and olpidioid, occasionally irregularly saccate, 7–25 μ long by about 7 μ in diameter (calculated), wall smooth, thin except at the base of the discharge tube, where it is thickened to form a "forcing apparatus," discharge tubes from two to ten (rarely one), slightly prolonged, broadly conical, often emerging from opposite sides and giving a starlike appearance; primary zoospores pyriform, 3 μ long, with two apical posteriorly directed flagella, assuming motility within the sporangium, upon emergence encysting in a group at the orifice of the discharge tube, cysts 3.5 μ in diameter, secondary zoospores not observed; oöspore (one instance) subspherical, 12 μ in diameter, with a thick smooth colorless wall, contents with large irregular fat clods, not filling the oögonium, the latter spherical, thin-walled, 14 μ in diameter, germination not observed; antheridium consisting of a single saclike structure almost equal in size to the oögonium, attached to the latter by a narrow tube.

Parasitic in *Licmophora sp.*, ITALY (the Adriatic, near Rovigno).

Ectrogella licmophorae occurs in the same host as *E. perforans*. It differs from Petersen's species in several particulars but primarily in the encystment of the zoospores after discharge, the presence of the "forcing apparatus," the more irregular shape of the sporangium, and the fact that the oöspore lies loose in the oögonium, to which the saccular antheridium is attached by a beaklike process (Fig. 60 B, p. 806).

ECTROGELLA PERFORANS H. E. Petersen

Oversigt Kgl. Danske Vidensk. Selskabs. Forhandl., 1905(5): 466, fig. VII, 1–5

(Fig. 60 G–J, p. 806)

Sporangium spherical, lenticular, or rarely irregularly saccate, 26–40 μ long by 20–35 μ in diameter, with a thin colorless wall, discharge tubes from one to five, broadly conical, 8–10 μ long by 9–12 μ in diameter; zoospores pyriform, 3 μ long by 2 μ wide, somewhat curved, with an anterior refractive droplet, the two flagella anteriorly (?) attached and oppositely directed, emerging individually through the large orifice of the discharge tube and swimming away immediately, movement an uneven rotation; resting spore spherical, 14–19 μ in diameter, with a smooth colorless double wall, 2.5–3 μ thick, the outer wall thin, the inner thicker, contents with globules, germination not observed.

Parasitic in *Licmophora lyngbyei* (*abbreviata?*), *Synedra ulna* (?), Petersen (*loc. cit.*), *Licmophora sp.*, Sparrow (1934c: 19, pl.4, figs. T–Y), DENMARK; *Striatella unipunctata*, *Licmophora abbreviata*, Sparrow (1936b: 239, pl. 3, fig. 2), *Licmophora abbreviata*, *L. flagellata*, Karling (1942e: 21), UNITED STATES; *Licmophora spp.*, *Striatella unipunctata*, *Podocystis adriatica*, and probably *Thalassionema nitzschioides*, Aleem (1950c: 713, figs. 1–2), *Licmophora spp.*, *Striatella unipunctata*, *Podocystis adriatica*, Aleem (1950d: 423, figs. 1–4), FRANCE; *Licmophora abbreviata*, *L. gracilis*, *Striatella unipunctata*, *Lauderia borealis*, *Synedra tabulata*, Aleem (1953: 18, figs. 34–42, pl. 1, fig. 4), SWEDEN.

With respect to zoospore flagellation, Aleem (1953) agreed with Petersen that in the moving spore only a single posteriorly directed flagellum is present. Earlier, Höhnk (1939) had insisted that the normal zoospore is posteriorly uniflagellate, although he admittedly had seen biflagellate ones. All this is at variance with the present author's repeated observations that the spores are biflagellate. It is, of course, entirely possible that two different fungi are involved, both of which were attacking the same host simultaneously. If so, the uniflagellate fungi reported by Petersen, Aleem, and Höhnk belong to *Pleotrachelus* and the biflagellate forms to a species of *Ectrogella*.

In most instances the discharge tubes gain access to the outside because the valves of the host are forced apart by the thallus of the fungus. Occasionally (Sparrow, 1934c; Aleem, 1953), however, the diatom frustule was considerably distorted, so much so in fact as to suggest that the fungus had dissolved the siliceous material and produced hypertrophy of the cell (Fig. 60 G, I, p. 806). One unopened sporangium, presumably of this species, was found in which the mature zoospores were loosely disposed around the periphery of a large central vacuole, exactly as in *Eurychasma* (Fig. 60 I). No traces of a net sporangium could be detected. This observation lends some support to the contention of Scherffel (1925a) that *Eurychasma* should be merged with *Ectrogella*. In the Danish material a resting spore was found to which was attached a small hemispherical cyst, suggesting the occurrence here of an *Olpidiopsis*-like type of sexuality.

Stages in the penetration of the fungus into the diatom were observed in the American material. Many frustules bore quiescent zoospores on the outer surface. In several diatoms a needle-like penetration tube from the cystospore had pierced the cell wall. Actual passage of the fungous material was not, however, observed, although empty epibiotic cysts were found. Inside the cell the parasite assumed a central position, possibly attaching itself to the nucleus of the alga. Once established within the diatom it caused disarrangement of the chloroplasts and eventually their total destruction. At maturity the sporangium was surrounded by a few chestnut-brown residual granules, all that remained of the host contents.

Observations consistently showed that the fungus alone initiated the infection and, unaided by other biological agencies, brought about the complete disintegration of the diatom. During July infection of the diatoms assumed epidemic proportions, as many as 88 per cent of a population being invaded by the fungus.

ECTROGELLA EUNOTIAE Friedmann

Österr. Bot. Zeitschr., 99: 200, fig. 4, a–s. 1952

Sporangium flattened ellipsoidal, assuming somewhat the shape of the host cell, 11–21 μ broad by 17–52 μ long by 5–7 μ high, wall thin, smooth, colorless, discharge tube single, occasionally two opposite ones, 4–15 μ long by 3.5–4.5 μ in diameter, with a broad, conical base, usually breaking through the dorsal side of the host and extending to the outside; primary zoospores moving within the sporangium, pyriform, flattened and grooved on one side, 3.5 by 2.5–2.8 μ, with numerous fat drops, one or two vacuoles and two nearly equal, about 5.5 μ long, oppositely directed flagella that are inserted in the groove, after a period of motility encysting, cysts spherical, 3.5 μ in diameter; secondary zoospores not observed; resting spore not observed.

Parasitic in *Eunotia arcus*, AUSTRIA.

A few cytological observations are given by Friedmann.

RECENTLY DESCRIBED TAXA [1]

ECTROGELLA EURYCHASMOIDES J. and G. Feldmann

Rev. Mycologique, 20: 238, fig. 1. 1955

Sporangium ovoid, 35–40 μ by 20–25 μ, nearly filling the host cell, mostly with two broad discharge tubes of unequal length, one behind the other, which penetrate the siliceous connective face of the host; zoospores dimorphic, the primary ones elongate-ovoid, asymmetrical, biflagellate, 2.5–3 μ long, and undergoing swarming within the sporangium after which they encyst, secondary zoospores not seen; resting spore spherical, 16–18 μ in diameter, with a stratified wall 3–3.5 μ thick, contents with a large eccentric vacuole and oil globule, germination not observed.

Parasitic on *Licmophora lyngbyei* (marine), FRANCE.

ECTROGELLA MARINA (Dang.) J. and G. Feldmann

Rev. Mycologique, 20: 238, fig. 2. 1955

Olpidium marinum, Dangeard, Le Botaniste, 12:XVI, figs. 23, 24. 1912.

Sporangium, when occurring singly within the cell, ovoid, 8–12 μ by 7–8 μ, when several, spherical and 5–6 μ in diameter, with a single lateral cylindrical discharge tube which extends 5–8 μ beyond the host wall; zoospores eight to sixteen in a sporangium, ovoid, somewhat elongate, sometimes reniform, 3–4 μ long, biflagellate (?), upon emergence forming a moving compact cluster near the orifice of the discharge

---

[1] Not included in the key.

tube, after about five minutes suddenly coming to rest and encysting, the cysts 2–2.5 μ in diameter; other stages unknown.

Parasitic in *Chlorodendron subsalsum*, Dangeard (*loc. cit.*); J: and G. Feldmann (*loc. cit.*), FRANCE.

Since no zoospores were seen by Dangeard, whether or not his fungus and that of the Feldmanns were identical cannot be determined.

PYTHIELLA COUCH

Mycologia, 27: 160. 1935

(Fig. 63 A–B, p. 824)

Thallus endobiotic, holocarpic, without specialized vegetative system, spherical, subspherical, or (in *Pythiella besseyi*) ellipsoidal and irregularly tubular, causing hypertrophy of the host; sporangium with one or more tubes; zoospores formed after a sequence of protoplasmic changes similar to that found in mycelial members of the order, primary zoospores upon emergence encysting at the orifice of the discharge tube, each cyst giving rise after a period of quiescence to a laterally biflagellate secondary zoospore; oögonium a spherical cell bearing a single egg; antheridial cell single, adnate to the oögonium, forming a well-defined fertilization tube; oöspore endobiotic, thick-walled, sexually formed, with distinct periplasm, lying loose within the oögonium; germination not observed.

Parasites of aquatic Phycomycetes.

The type species (*Pythiella vernalis*) is an endobiotic holocarpic parasite in the hyphae of algae-inhabiting species of *Pythium*.

Pythiella is of great interest because its members resemble in habitat and appearance those of *Olpidiopsis*, a genus composed primarily of parasites of other Phycomycetes. In *Olpidiopsis* the zoospores exhibit no well-defined diplanetism and the sex organs are less highly specialized, that is, the protoplasm of the contributing thallus is conveyed into the receptive structure through a pore. The resting-spore wall consists, in part at least, of the wall of the receptive thallus and there is no differentiation at maturity (except in *O. oedogoniarum*) between the spore and its container. In *Pythiella*, on the contrary, there is well-defined diplanetism (Fig. 63A), a fertilization tube is formed by the contributing thallus (Fig. 63B), and the protoplasm of the receptive thallus is differentiated into periplasm and oöplasm. At maturity the resting spore has a distinct wall of its own and is loose within the container.

The sequence of protoplasmic changes preceding zoospore formation exhibited by *Pythiella* is similar to that in *Ectrogella*, in which strong vacuolization, "balling," and homogeneous and segmented stages occur. Because of this Couch (*op. cit.*) concluded that the two genera are closely related. There is no doubt that placing the genus in the Saprolegniales expresses its proper relationship, rather than the former alliance with *Olpidiopsis* in the Lagenidiales (Sparrow, 1943).

Although some doubt will exist until a sexual stage is found, *Ectrogella besseyi* Sparrow and Ellison, both in structure and host plant, exhibits a closer affinity to *Pythiella* than to *Ectrogella*. For this reason, the original generic description of *Pythiella* has been made somewhat more general (but not modified in essentials) to include species on hosts other than *Pythium*.

KEY TO SPECIES OF PYTHIELLA

Sporangium spherical or rarely subspherical; in hyphae of *Pythium*

Sporangium somewhat tubular, often lobed; in *Olpidiopsis*

PYTHIELLA VERNALIS Couch

Mycologia, 27: 160, figs. 1–27. 1935

(Fig. 63 A–B, p. 824)

"Sporangia developing in the threads of *Pythium*, spherical or rarely subspherical when mature, without mycelium and rhizoids; causing the formation of a distinct gall in the *Pythium* thread, usually one sporangium in each gall though two, three, or four may not uncommonly occur; 10–30 μ thick, emptying through a long tube up to 50 μ long and about 4 μ thick; on some sporangia several tubes may be formed (as many as five), some of which may be branched. Spores diplanetic, encysting after discharge, at the tip of the sporangial tube, emerging from the cysts after about an hour, elongated with a longitudinal groove and with two cilia; spores 3.7–4 μ thick. In swimming the active cilium is directed forward while the posterior one is dragged along behind. Sexual reproduction is by oogonia and antheridia; oogonia 11–18.5 μ thick, spherical, containing one egg, which does not completely fill the oogonium; eggs 9–15 μ thick, spherical, when mature surrounded by a thick wall and a small amount of periplasm; antheridium spherical, about 5 μ thick, emptying its entire contents through a delicate tube into the egg" (Couch, *loc. cit.*).

Parasitic in the hyphae of *Pythium gracile* and *P. dictyosporum*, UNITED STATES.

The type species of the genus. See remarks under *Pythiella*.

PYTHIELLA BESSEYI (Sparrow and Ellison), comb. nov.

Ectrogella besseyi Sparrow and Ellison, Mycologia, 41: 33, figs. H–M. 1949.

Sporangium irregularly tubular, often lobed, sometimes ellipsoidal, 27–42 μ long by 13–17 μ in diameter, one to several in a host cell, forming one to several discharge tubes of varying length; zoospores numerous, delimited within the sporangium, upon discharge from the sporangium encysting and forming motionless clusters at the orifice of the discharge tube, emerging from the cyst as a laterally biflagellate zoospore, 5 by 2.5 μ; resting spores not observed.

Parasitic in thalli and sporangia of *Olpidiopsis schenkiana*, UNITED STATES.

See remarks under *Pythiella*.

EURYCHASMA MAGNUS

Hedwigia, 44: 347. 1905

(Fig. 61, p. 818)

Thallus at first wholly endobiotic, at maturity bursting the distended host wall and becoming partly extramatrical, holocarpic, unbranched; sporangium with from one to several extramatrical discharge tubes, zoospores encysting within the sporangium or directly on emerging, laterally biflagellate; resting spore not observed.

So far as is known, this fungus occurs exclusively on marine algae. See the remarks under *Ectrogella*, above.

EURYCHASMA DICKSONII (Wright) Magnus

Hedwigia, 44: 347. 1905

(Fig. 61, p. 818)

Rhizophydium dicksonii Wright, Trans. R. Irish Acad. Dublin (Sci.), 26: 374, pl. 6. 1879.
Olpidium dicksonii (Wright) Wille, Vidensk. Selsk. Skr. Christiana (Mat.-Nat. Kl.), 1899, No. 3: 2.
Ectrogella dicksonii (Wright) Scherffel, Arch. Protistenk., 52: 4. 1925.

Sporangium at maturity generally protruding from the host cell, extremely variable in shape and size, generally irregularly saccate, 25–80 μ high by 20–40 μ in diameter, with one or two broad short discharge tubes, wall thin, smooth, colorless; zoospores somewhat gibbose-pyriform, 5 μ long by 3 μ in diameter, with two unequal, subapically attached, oppositely directed flagella, emerging without encystment (?) or coming to rest and encysting within the sporangium ("net sporangium"), from which they eventually escape; resting spore not observed.

Parasitic in *Ectocarpus granulosus*, Wright (*loc. cit.*), IRELAND; *Ectocarpus confervoides*, *E. crinitus*, *E. pusillus*, Hauck (1878: 321), ITALY; *Ectocarpus siliculosis*, Rattray (1887: 589, pls. 147–148), SCOTLAND; *Ectocarpus constanciae*, Hariot (1889: 176), KERGUELEN; *Striaria attenuata*, Wille (*loc. cit.*), *Pylaiella littoralis*, Löwenthal (1905: 225, pl. 7, figs. 3–7), NORWAY; *Punctaria sp.*, *Stictyosiphon tortilis*, *Pylaiella littoralis*, *Ectocarpus sp.*, coll. K. Rosenvinge, Petersen (1905: 476), GREENLAND; *Ectocarpus confervoides*, coll. Börgesen, Petersen (1905: 477), FAROE ISLANDS; *Ectocarpus sp.*, *Stictyosiphon tortilis*, coll. K. Rosenvinge, *Akinetospora sp.*, *E. confervoides*, *E. sandrianus*, *Striaria attenuata*, *Stictyosiphon tortilis*, *Pylaiella littoralis*, Petersen (1905: 477, fig. VIII, 1–7), *Striaria attenuata*, Sparrow (1934c: 5, pl. 1, figs. A–S), DENMARK; *Ectocarpus sp.*, Pierre Dangeard (1934: 69, pl. 8, figs. A–E), *Stictyosiphon soriferus*, Pierre Dangeard (1934), *Ectocarpus sp.*, Aleem (1950d: 434, figs. 24–25), *Ectocarpus sp.*, *Pylaiella littoralis*, J. Feldmann (1954: 133), FRANCE; *Ectocarpus granulosus*, Aleem (1950a: 239; 1950b:119, fig. 1), GREAT BRITAIN; *Ectocarpus granulosus*, Aleem (1950a: 239, figs., 1–9), *Pylaiella littoralis*, *Striaria attenuata*, Aleem (1953: 22, figs. 43–48, pl. 2, fig. 3), SWEDEN.

This appears to be the most common and widespread of the marine fungi. Considerable information has been collected with respect to its development and something is known of its cytology. Further study of the behavior of the zoospores is needed, however, particularly to ascertain whether or not they are diplanetic when they swarm directly from the sporangium without previous encystment.

Aleem (1950a) has indicated that the zoospores are more or less rounded or slightly pyriform, with two unequal flagella, one about four times the diameter of the zoospore in length, the other two to three times. The flagella arise at the same end of the cell (anterior?) and are inserted slightly apart.

The zoospore (Sparrow, 1934c) upon coming to rest on the surface of *Striaria* encysts and produces a tenuous germ tube which penetrates the wall of the host and through which the protoplasm of the zoospore flows (Fig. 61 A, p. 818). After discharge the empty cyst of the spore remains adherent, at least for a time, to the wall of the alga. Once infection is accomplished, the amoeboid-appearing plasma of the fungus increases in size and, though at first irregular in shape and scarcely distinguishable from the algal protoplasm, ultimately becomes a somewhat spherical refractive mass, which often occupies the center of the cell of the *Striaria* (Fig. 61 B–F). The cell is apparently stimulated to abnormal growth very early in the course of the infection.

The chloroplasts of the infected cell soon become discolored and disintegrate, and the residue of such material not utilized by the fungus may usually be observed as a peripheral brownish-green layer around the outside of the thallus. The wall of the host is eventually ruptured by the constantly enlarging fungus, which then protrudes into the outside medium (Fig. 61 K–M, p. 818). This liberation of the parasite from a wholly endobiotic existence is initiated by the formation on the thallus of one or, usually, two broad apical or subapical papillae which penetrate the algal wall (Fig. 61 G–J). Subsequent expansion and elongation of the parasite, if more than one papilla is formed, causes a part of the algal wall between the papillae to be carried up between the protuberances. The remainder of the wall persists around the more proximal portion of the sporangium.

The thallus is at first uninucleate according to Löwenthal (1905).

Petersen (1905) has described the sequence of changes which occur in the protoplasm of the developing thallus as follows:

1. Stage of ordinary protoplasm: Protoplasm dense with few vacuoles; nuclei in process of division.

2. Globular stage: Division of nuclei has been achieved as well as differentiation of zoospores. Little globular bodies closely packed in sporangium.

3. Foamy stage: Protoplasm with numerous large vacuoles. Zoospores invisible. Nuclei appear in large numbers in protoplasmic bridges between vacuoles. (Fig. 5 of Löwenthal.)

4. Stage at which zoospores are regularly disposed against the wall. (Distinguishable from stage 2 only in the older condition of the sporangium and the more regular arrangement of zoospores against the wall.)

After the foamy stage there occurred a very strong contraction of the plasma, which lasted twenty minutes and during which protoplasmic threads united it to the host wall. Dilation then occurred and the foamy aspect disappeared. Differentiation of the zoospores took place during the period of dilation. When this was half over a certain number of zoospores had already assumed motility, and when dilation was at maximum all the zoospores were in motion. After a period of swarming, the zoospores again became immobile and encysted, forming a layer against the wall. Presumably they eventually escaped from their cysts and emerged through the open discharge tube, leaving behind a reticulum (net sporangium) of cyst walls. As has been previously indicated, it is not certain that encystment of the zoospores within the sporangium necessarily precedes emergence. In both open and unopened sporangia the mature zoospores form a thin peripheral layer around a large central vacuole (Fig. 61 M, S, p. 818). Possibly under favorable conditions the zoospores may emerge at once upon the deliquescence of the papilla (Fig. 61 O–Q), whereas if external conditions are unfavorable they encyst and only escape after the return of suitable environmental circumstances (Fig. 61 R). The earlier observations of Rattray (1887) on the zoospores indicated that they were negatively phototropic.

The presence of a net sporangium in *Eurychasma* (Fig. 61 N, p. 818) was believed by Petersen to be of considerable taxonomic import and led him to establish the family Eurychasmaceae. Scherffel (1925a: 4) and

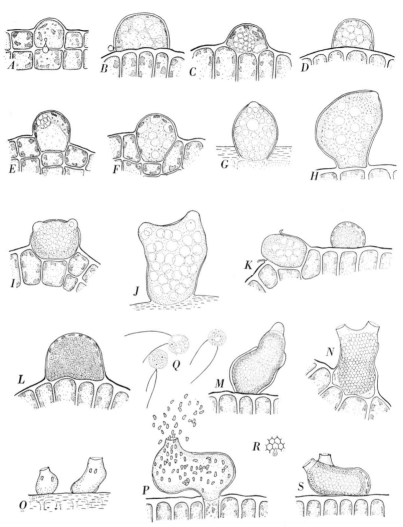

FIG. 61. Development of *Eurychasma dicksonii* (Wright) Magnus in *Striaria*

A. Zoospore infecting vegetative cell of *Striaria*; hypertrophy of host cell is evident. *B.* Empty cyst and infection tube of zoospore on hypertrophied host cell; thallus of fungus appears as irregular, somewhat refractive mass. *C–E.* Infected host cells showing spherical shape assumed by thallus of fungus; latter contains a number of highly refractive granules. *F.* Infected cell showing peripheral disposition of disintegrating chloroplasts. *G–I.*

Coker and Matthews (1937: 59) describe this type of spore discharge as *Dictyuchus*-like. The characterization seems hardly accurate, however, since in *Eurychasma* the secondary zoospores never penetrate the sporangium wall, but emerge through the orifice.

IMPERFECTLY KNOWN SPECIES OF EURYCHASMA

? EURYCHASMA SACCULUS H. E. Petersen

Oversigt Kgl. Danske Vidensk. Selskabs. Forhandl., 1905 (5): 477, fig. VIII, 5, 8–9

Sporangium irregularly saccate, epibiotic part 48–184 μ long, with two short discharge tubes, endobiotic part 40-192 μ long, contorted and lobed, constricted where it passes through the superficial layer of host cells; other characters unknown.

In *Halosaccion ramentaceum*, coll. A. Jessen, *Rhodymenia palmata*, coll. H. P. Sörensen, GREENLAND.

Found most frequently in host cells beneath the superficial layer, rarely in the central cells.

Petersen (conversation, 1933) does not regard the species as distinct from *Eurychasma dicksonii*. If the lobed nature of the endobiotic part of *E. sacculus* is not due to the action of preservatives, however, this character as well as the nature of the host plants (Rhodophyceae) may separate it from the inhabitant of phaeophyceans.

Formation of papillae by fungus during vacuolate stage. *J*. Extrusion of fungus from host cell by bursting of confining wall of latter; more distal portion of host wall may be seen between the two papillae. *K*. Two infected host cells; fungus to the left has burst host wall. *L*. Sporangium in which zoospores have been formed before extrusion from host cell; papillae were present but were not seen in this view. *M*. Extruded sporangium showing single broad papillae and, within, peripheral layer of zoospores. *N*. A "net sporangium"; all but two zoospores have evacuated their cysts; walls of latter appear as network of polygonal cells. *O*. Two dwarf sporangia. *P*. Zoospores being discharged from sporangium; no evidence of previous encystment of these spores could be observed. *Q*. Zoospores killed with 1 per cent osmic acid and stained with fuchsin. *R*. Portion of "net sporangium" showing partial emergence of zoospore from its cyst. *S*. Sporangium with two open discharge tubes, showing peripheral layer of spores.

(Sparrow, 1934c)

? EURYCHASMA SP. Kobayasi and Ookubo

Bull. Nat. Sci. Mus. (Tokyo), (N.S.), 1 (2) No. 35:70, fig. 9. 1954

"Zoosporangium endobiotic at first, gregarious in host-cell, then protruding from the distended host wall and occasionally becoming partly extramatrical by the collapse of the latter, ellipsoid, subglobose or pyriformed, 25–50 μ in diameter, hyaline, thin-walled, with 5–10 distinctly protruding papillae, tip of which becoming perforated at maturity by the dehiscence of wall. Rhizoid none. Zoospores not swimming in the sporangium, without flagella, after escape encysting in a loose group at the orifice of papilla. Cysts globose, not angular. Secondary zoospores not observed. Resting spore endobiotic, spheroid, about 50 μ in diameter, hyaline, thick-walled, further development not observed" (Kobayasi and Ookubo, *loc. cit.*).

On *Bryopsis sp.*, JAPAN.

This unnamed species resembles *Eurychasmidium* in the behavior of its zoospores and *Eurychasma* in being partly intramatrical and partly extramatrical. It differs from *Eurychasma dicksonii* in having more numerous discharge papillae. If the endobiotic resting spore really belongs to the fungus, as seems probable, and if the relationship of the zoospores to either of the aforementioned genera is proved, then this will be one of the few instances in which resting structures have been found in marine members of the Ectrogellaceae.

EURYCHASMIDIUM SPARROW

Biol. Bulletin, 70: 241. 1936

(Fig. 62, p. 821)

Thallus endobiotic, plasmodial, holocarpic, without a specialized vegetative system, completely or almost filling the distended host cell; sporangium with many discharge tubes which pierce the host wall; zoospores formed within the sporangium, biflagellate, encysting near the sporangium after discharge, ultimately emerging as motile swarmers; resting spore not observed.

Parasitic in marine Rhodophyceae.

The precise method of entrance of the fungus into the host cell is not known. Magnus (1872: 87) stated that he observed in one instance that the zoospore came to rest on the wall of the alga, penetrated it, and passed into the contents. Sparrow, on the other hand, presented evidence that the zoospore encysts on the surface and then produces a penetration

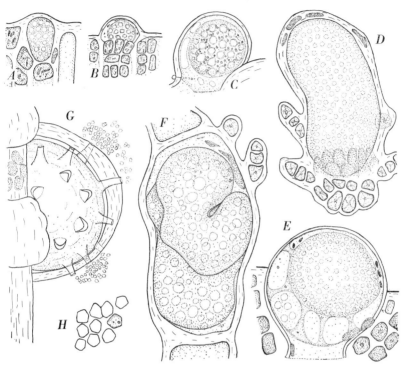

Fig. 62. *Eurychasmidium tumefaciens* (Magnus) Sparrow in *Ceramium diaphanum*

A–B. Early stages in formation of thallus; host cells are beginning to hypertrophy. *C.* More mature thallus, showing at bottom of left-hand side the remains of infecting zoospore and its penetration tube. *D–F.* Strongly hypertrophied host cells with vacuolate thalli of fungus in them. *G.* Empty sporangium showing the many discharge tubes and a few of the discharged, encysted, zoospores; latter are so numerous as to form a dense cloud around infected region. *H.* Angular cysts produced by discharged zoospores, from all but one of which spores have emerged.

(Sparrow, 1936b)

tube through which the contents pass (Fig. 62 C, p. 821). The subsequent sequence of development is similar to that in *Eurychasma*, save that the whole body of the fungus with the exception of the tips of the discharge tubes remains endobiotic (Fig. 62 A–G). Further, the zoospores of *Eurychasmidium* encyst outside the sporangium (Fig. 62 H). There is also a marked tendency for infected swollen regions of the algal frond to produce adventitious lateral branches.

EURYCHASMIDIUM TUMEFACIENS (Magnus) Sparrow

Biol. Bulletin, 70: 241, text figs. 14–21, pl. 1, fig.1. 1936

Chytridium tumefaciens Magnus, Sitzungsber. Gesell. Naturforsch. Freunde Berlin, 1872: 87; Wissensch. Meeresunters. Abt. Kiel, 2–3: 76, pl. 1, figs. 1–16. 1875.
Olpidium tumefaciens (Magnus) Wright, Trans. R. Irish Acad. Dublin (Sci.), 26: 360. 1879.
Pleotrachelus tumefaciens (Magnus) H. E. Petersen, Oversigt Kgl. Danske Vidensk. Selskabs. Forhandl., 1905(5): 456.

Sporangia spherical and 100–110 µ in diameter or irregular, lobed, and 110 µ wide by 200 µ long, from one to six, nearly or completely filling the abnormally enlarged host cell, the alga being stimulated to form clusters of lateral branches in the infected region, wall thin, smooth, colorless; zoospores very numerous, escaping through as many as thirty short narrowly cylindrical sessile discharge tubes, encysting outside, the loosely disposed cysts angular and 4 µ in greatest width, emerging from the cysts after a period of quiescence as ellipsoidal biflagellate zoospores 5 µ long by 3 µ in diameter; resting spore not observed.

Parasitic in *Ceramium flabelligerum, C. acanthonotum,* Magnus (*loc. cit.*), SCOTLAND; *Ceramium spiniferum,* coll. Cramer, Magnus (*loc. cit.*), ITALY; *Ceramium acanthonotum,* Wright (1879a: 360), IRELAND; "Floridées," coll. Massart, de Wildeman (1900b: 4), FRANCE; *Ceramium rubrum,* H. E. Petersen (1905: 456), DENMARK; *Ceramium diaphanum,* coll. C. Jao and Sparrow, Sparrow (1936b: 241, figs. 14–21, pl. 1, fig. 1), UNITED STATES.

The American material was found only in the nodal cells of the alga. The earliest developmental stages observed showed an already well-established spherical thallus easily distinguishable from the host contents by its numerous irregular refractive bodies. As growth proceeded the disintegrated chloroplast material became more granular, whereas the algal protoplasm assumed a vacuolate character. Coincident with the increase in size of the fungus there was a strong distention of the host cell accompanied by a pronounced thickening of the wall. In addition, certain adjacent nodal cells were stimulated to divide, and there was produced in the vicinity of the infected cell a number of curved stunted lateral branches which gave a "bushy" appearance to the region. Such places could easily be detected with a hand lens. Apparently, some sort of substance was produced in infected cells which diffused to adjacent ones and stimulated them to abnormal growth. Apical cells infected with what was presumably the same fungus showed little hypertrophy.

It is not known whether the myriad of zoospores produced in a single sporangium emerge by action of the flagella or are forced out. Once discharged, they form a dense cloud around the infected part of the filament, each spore being surrounded by an angular wall (Fig. 62 G, p. 821). These cystospores are not connected with one another as in *Eurychasma* but are loosely disposed in the medium (Fig. 62 H). After a varying period of quiescence the protoplasm of each of the cysts emerges, probably through a small pore; it exhibits a rocking motion near the empty shell and undergoes fashioning which terminates with the production of the fully formed biflagellate zoospore. Further observations are needed on the orientation, length, and place of attachment of the two flagella.

The fungus is apparently a true parasite but, unlike certain other marine fungi, does not seem able to continue its destruction of the alga after the latter has been noticeably weakened or killed. The remainder of the host plant, save in the immediate vicinity of the infected cell, appears unaffected by the incursion of the fungus.

See remarks under *Olpidiopsis magnusii* (p. 953), where J. and G. Feldmann (1955) have segregated the fungi found by Magnus in the rhizoids of *Ceramium* from those in the nodal and cortical cells.

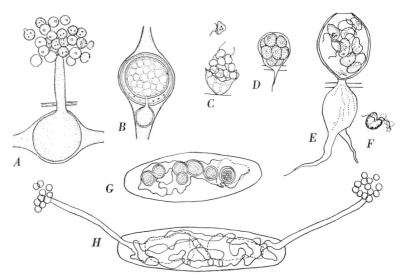

FIG. 63. Ectrogellaceae and Thraustochytriaceae

A–B. Pythiella vernalis Couch: *A*, discharged sporangium in hypha of *Pythium*; secondary zoospores beginning to emerge from cysts; *B*, resting spore with small antheridial cell and fertilization tube. *C–D. Thraustochytrium globosum* Kobayasi and Ookubo on ulotrichaceous marine alga. *E–F. Japonochytrium marinum* Kobayasi and Ookubo: *E*, discharging sporangium; *F*, biflagellate zoospore. *G–H. Aphanomycopsis desmidiella* Canter, in *Netrium digitus*: *G*, resting spores in thallus; *H*, empty sporangium with two discharge tubes, the latter with cysts of primary zoospores.

(*A–B*, Couch, 1935a; *C–F*, Kobayasi and Ookubo, 1953; *G–H*, Canter, 1949d)

APHANOMYCOPSIS Scherffel

Arch. Protistenk., 52: 11. 1925

(Figs. 63 G–H, p. 824; 64, p. 826)

Thallus endobiotic, holocarpic, branched or unbranched, broad, tubular, one-celled, transformed into a single sporangium; zoospores diplanetic, the primary spores emerging singly without swarming motion through one or more evacuation tubes and forming at the orifice a cluster of cysts, the secondary zoospores laterally biflagellate, emerging from the cysts through discharge tubes usually provided at their bases with thick walls which spread apart the valves of the host; resting spores (oöspores?) thick-walled, with eccentric globules and peripheral refractive spots, without periplasm, one or several formed, apparently asexually, in an expanded part of the thallus, germination not observed.

In fresh-water diatoms and desmids.

Tokunaga (1934a: 232) proposed the transference of the genus to the Lagenidiaceae on the following grounds: "...(1) absence of a typically [well-?] developed mycelium. (2) Thallus completely transformed into the reproductive organs at maturity." While it is unquestionably true that the thallus of *Aphanomycopsis* is of limited extent and that all of it is transformed into a reproductive structure, the method of zoospore formation is markedly different from that found in the Lagenidiaceae, with one exception (noted by Scherffel, 1925a: 112). Further, the cytoplasm is typically saprolegniaceous, rather than lagenidiaceous. Then, too, the form studied by Tokunaga is quite different from Scherffel's in that the thallus is septate (see discussion under *Aphanomycopsis bacillariacearum*). Hence, Karling's (1942e) expansion of the genus to include Tokunaga's fungus is not followed here.

KEY TO THE SPECIES OF APHANOMYCOPSIS

Parasitic in diatoms; thick-walled forcing apparatus at base of discharge tube usually present .... *A. bacillariacearum*, p. 825
Parasitic in desmids; forcing apparatus absent ..... *A. desmidiella*, p. 827

APHANOMYCOPSIS BACILLARIACEARUM Scherffel

Arch. Protistenk., 52: 14, pl. 1, figs. 31–35, pl. 2, figs. 36–48. 1925

(Fig. 64, p. 826)

Sporangium 6–10 μ in diameter, unbranched or, more frequently, richly branched, the branches of variable length, discharge tubes one or several, slightly tapering, occasionally branched, up to 240 μ long; cysts of the primary zoospores variable in number, 8–10 μ in diameter, secondary zoospores grape-seed-like in shape, 10–12 μ long by 7–8 μ broad, anterior flagellum short and active, posterior one long and passive, movement even, in a zigzag line; oöspores one or several, lying loosely in an expanded part of the thallus, spherical (20 μ in diameter) or broadly ovoid (24 by 20 μ), colorless, wall thick, smooth, germination not observed.

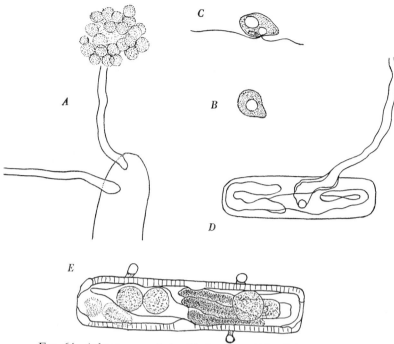

FIG. 64. *Aphanomycopsis bacillariacearum* Scherffel in diatoms

A. Two discharge tubes emerged from a frustule of *Pinnularia*, one with a group of encysted primary zoospores. *B.* Cyst of primary zoospore from which secondary zoospore is beginning to emerge. *C.* Side view of secondary zoospore. *D.* Diatom cleared to show endobiotic thallus, and thick-walled "forcing apparatus" at base of long extramatrical discharge tube. *E.* Diatom on outer surface of which are three encysted zoospores; within a somewhat swollen tubular rudimentary oögonium are two immature oöspores, and a third oöspore to the right is partly masked by disintegrating host contents. (Scherffel, 1925a)

Parasitic in *Pinnularia viridis*, *Epithemia turgida*, rarely in *Cymbella gastroides*, *Nitzschia sigmoidea*, Scherffel (*loc. cit.*), HUNGARY; *Pinnularia sp.*, Sparrow (1933c: 530, pl. 49, fig. 14), pennate diatom, Sparrow and Barr (1955: 555), UNITED STATES; *Synedra sp.*, Sparrow (1936a: 461), GREAT BRITAIN; *Pinnularia viridis*, Friedmann (1953: 7), AUSTRIA.

Tokunaga (1934a: 230, fig. 3 a–c) identified with this species a parasite of diatoms in Japan which, though resembling it in its sporangial stage and resting spore, differs in two important features: (1) in having a septate thallus and (2) in lacking the "Spriezapparat," or thick-walled spreading apparatus at the base of the evacuation tube which forces the valves apart.

Because of its septate thallus his fungus cannot be included in the Ectrogellaceae as defined by Scherffel (1925a: 6) and probably represents the type of a new genus. Tokunaga's description is quoted here:

Thallus endobiotic, at first consisting of a cylindrical, unbranched tube, later richly branched, provided with long or short, often somewhat inflated twigs, septate at indefinite intervals into a number of cells at maturity, without prominent constriction at the septum, each component cell functioning as a sporangium or an oogonium; sporangia cylindrical or tubular, unbranched, or irregularly branched, often lobed, widely variable in length, up to 150 μ long, 4.8–16.8 μ in diameter; exit-tubes single for a sporangium, very long, up to 150 μ in length, about 4.8 μ in breadth; zoospores on leaving the sporangium coming to rest at once in a hollow sphere at the mouth of the exit-tube, encysting there as in *Achlya*, later swimming away leaving their cyst behind, in encysting globular, 6–7.2 μ in diameter, in swimming kidney-shaped, narrower in front, provided with two cilia near the hilum, containing an oil drop; oogonia (?) intermixed with sporangia in a thallus, terminal or intercalary, cylindrical, medially expanded, 15.6–21.6 μ in breadth, provided with no periplasm; antheridia absent; oospores (?) one or two, lying loosely in an oogonium, spherical, 14.4–19.2 μ in diameter, with smooth, thick membrane and a large oil globule, germination unknown.

Tokunaga's fungus occurs on *Surirella sp.* and *Navicula sp.*, JAPAN.

The septate fungus figured by West and West (1906: 99, pl. 11, fig. 9) on *Pleurotaenium ehrenbergii* from Ireland and the Outer Hebrides resembles Tokunaga's fungus in structure and *Aphanomycopsis desmidiella* in host. West and West say that it was this organism which caused Archer (1860: 215) to claim that zoospores were formed by desmids.

A lone specimen of the fungus described by Friedmann (1952: 200, fig. 5, k) on *Pinnularia viridis* from Austria, possessed a cross wall in the thallus. He speculated that it might be transitional between the typical nonseptate condition and the much-septate Japanese form.

APHANOMYCOPSIS DESMIDIELLA Canter

Trans. Brit. Mycol. Soc., 32: 166, figs. 2–3. 1949

(Fig. 63 G–H, p. 824)

Thallus endobiotic, branched, holocarpic, nonseptate, 410 μ long by

5–15 µ in diameter; sporangium 5–15 µ in diameter, with one or two discharge tubes 10–185 µ long by 5–8.5 µ in diameter contracted to 2.5 µ where it passes through wall of the host; primary zoospores probably nonflagellate, forming ten to sixty spherical cysts 6–8 µ in diameter at the mouth of the discharge tube, secondary zoospores 8 µ long by 7 µ broad, kidney-shaped with two lateral flagella; resting spores 3–17 formed within the thallus, spherical to subspherical, 9–20 µ in diameter, with a thick colorless probably punctate wall, numerous small refractive globules in the contents, germination not observed.

Parasitic in *Netrium digitus*, Canter (*loc. cit.*), GREAT BRITAIN; *Pleurotaenium trabecula*, Friedmann (1952: 203, fig. 5, 1), AUSTRIA.

Canter's species differs from *Aphanomycopsis bacillariacearum* in its host, the character of the resting-spore wall, the size of the secondary zoospores, and the lack of a "Spriezapparat" where the discharge tube penetrates the host wall. Friedmann remarks that the desmid parasite figured by Petersen (1910: 556, fig. 26, b) is probably this species.

IMPERFECTLY KNOWN SPECIES OF APHANOMYCOPSIS

? APHANOMYCOPSIS SP. Friedmann

Österr. Bot. Zeitschr. 99: 201, figs. 5 a–i. 1952

Sporangium 3.2–8.5 µ in diameter, up to 200 µ long, the main axis lying the length of one of the valves of the host, bearing numerous lateral branches that bend and anastomose to produce a ladder-like structure, wall extremely delicate, quickly disorganizing after spore discharge through one to several 7–8 µ diameter (tapering to 5 µ distally) discharge tubes; primary zoospore cysts 6.5–7 µ in diameter; other features not observed.

Parasitic in *Nitzschia sigmoidea*, AUSTRIA.

Differs from *Aphanomycopsis bacillariacearum* in the delicate walls and ladder-like aspect of the thallus and in the smaller cysts of the primary zoospores.

THRAUSTOCHYTRIACEAE, EMEND.

Thallus epi- and endobiotic, monocentric, eucarpic, chytridiaceous in character, the epibiotic part composed of the sporangium, the endobiotic part, of the rhizoidal system and sometimes an apophysis as well; zoospores formed in the sporangium, liberated as flagellated or non-flagellated bodies, laterally biflagellate when motile; resting stage not observed. [1]

Members of this family are unique in combining a typically *Chytridium*-like thallus structure with a saprolegniaceous kind of zoospore. Although so far they are known only from the marine habitat, undoubtedly fresh-water forms occur.

Two new species have recently been discovered by Kobayasi and Ookubo (1953), one, the type of a new genus, and the other an addition to *Thraustochytrium*. Thus, after two decades there comes confirmation of the existence of these bizarre fungi.

KEY TO THE GENERA AND SPECIES OF THE THRAUSTOCHYTRIACEAE

Zoospores liberated upon the bursting and dissolution of the distal
    part of the sporangium wall . . . . THRAUSTOCHYTRIUM, p. 829
  Zoospores at discharge nonflagellated; sporangium internally pro-
     liferous . . . . *T. proliferum*, p. 831
  Zoospores at discharge emerging as flagellated bodies; sporangium
     not proliferating . . . . *T. globosum*, p. 831
Zoospores liberated upon the formation of an apical sporangial pore;
    sporangium apophysate . . . . JAPONOCHYTRIUM (*marinum*), p. 832

THRAUSTOCHYTRIUM SPARROW, EMEND. [2]
Biol. Bulletin, 70: 259. 1936
(Figs. 60 D–F, p. 806; 63 C–D, p. 824)

Thallus epi- and endobiotic, monocentric, eucarpic, consisting of the epibiotic rudiment of the sporangium derived from the enlarged body of the encysted zoospore and the endobiotic unbranched or branched rhizoidal vegetative system; sporangium liberating the spores upon the bursting and dissolution of the distal part of the wall, internally proliferous; zoospores formed within the sporangium, liberated as nonflagellate, somewhat angular bodies, becoming flagellate after a period of rest, or as flagellated bodies, the flagella oppositely directed and anteriorly or laterally attached; resting spores epibiotic, thick-walled, with endobiotic rhizoidal system.

[1] See Johnson (1957c).
[2] See also *T. pachydermum* Scholz, *Arch. f. Mikrobiol.*, 29: 359, 1958.

Known only on marine algae.

The establishment and development of the thallus are of the *Chytridium* type (see p. 47).

Observations on zoospores of *Thraustochytrium proliferum* have revealed that approximately three hours after liberation, the spores in the freed clumps separate from one another. Individual movement of the spore body is initiated, and it loses its angularity and becomes more ellipsoidal. After a few preliminary twists it then leaves the group as a free-swimming body. The motile spore is somewhat gibbose-pyriform, with a small refractive anterior granule and a central vacuole. Movement is slow and even rather than hopping and chytridiaceous.. No evidence of encystment of the zoospore during the period of quiescence succeeding discharge can be found.

A peculiarity of *Thraustochytrium proliferum* is its method of internal proliferation. After cleavage of the zoospores (Fig. 60 E, p. 806) there can generally be seen in the sporangium a larger basal protoplasmic unit. This persists after spore liberation, enlarges, and becomes the new secondary zoosporangium (Fig. 60 D). Thus, in contrast to the proliferating sporangia of *Saprolegnia*, *Phytophthora*, and so on, the rudiment of the secondary sporangium of *Thraustochytrium* appears to be delimited at the time of zoospore cleavage in the primary body rather than after discharge of the spores (Fig. 60 E–F). Furthermore, it is formed as part of the contents of the primary sporangium, not as an outgrowth from the base. The subsequent enlargement of the secondary sporangium undoubtedly occurs as a result of materials received from the vegetative system.

In *Thraustochytrium globosum* Kobayasi and Ookubo (1953) the zoospores become completely mature within the sporangium and move about actively inside prior to liberation. Once the wall breaks, the spores remain together for a few minutes before swimming away. After a swarming period of about five hours, they come to rest on the algal wall and germinate. No internal proliferation of the sporangium occurs in this species.

Watson (in Vishniac, 1955b) has studied certain physiological aspects of *Thraustochytrium proliferum* in pure culture. [1]

[1] See also Adair and Vishniac (1958).

THRAUSTOCHYTRIUM PROLIFERUM Sparrow

Biol. Bulletin, 70: 259, text figs. 22–28, pl. 1, fig.2. 1936

(Fig. 60 D–F, p. 806)

Sporangium sessile, obpyriform, 15.6–18 μ high by 10–13 μ in diameter, very thin-walled, smooth, colorless; rhizoid branched or unbranched; zoospores few, somewhat angular at liberation, later more spherical, 4 μ in diameter, when motile gibbose-pyriform and 3 μ long by 2.5 μ wide, with an anterior refractive colorless granule and two flagella, movement an even swimming; resting spore not observed.

Saprophytic on *Bryopsis plumosa*, *Ceramium diaphanum*, UNITED STATES.

The zoospores are strongly attracted by the disintegrating chlorophyll of the *Bryopsis* and swarm around the outside of the portions of the cell containing it. As a result, dense clusters of sporangia may be formed in these regions.

THRAUSTOCHYTRIUM GLOBOSUM Kobayasi and Ookubo

Bull. Nat. Sci. Mus. (Tokyo), 33: 60, fig. 6. 1953

(Fig. 63 C–D, p. 824)

Zoosporangia gregarious on host cell, sessile, globose or ellipsoid, sometimes conic at the base, never proliferating, smooth, hyaline, thin-walled, without a papilla, 5–10 μ high, 5–20 μ in diameter, containing eight to twenty-four to thirty zoospores, at maturity bursting, the upper half of sporangial wall irregularly torn away; rhizoid single and simple, moderately long; zoospores polyhedral in the immature stage, becoming nephroid at maturity, 3–4 by 2.5 μ, with two oppositely directed, lateral flagella, containing two or three granules, initiating movement within the sporangium; resting spore not observed. (Modified from Kobayasi and Ookubo.)

On green algae (Ulotrichales), JAPAN.

Differing markedly from *Thraustochytrium proliferum* in the behavior of the zoospores and lack of internal proliferation (see discussion under the genus).

JAPONOCHYTRIUM Kobayasi and Ookubo

Bull. Nat. Sci. Mus. (Tokyo), 33: 57. 1953

(Fig. 63 E–F, p. 824)

Thallus epi- and endobiotic, monocentric, eucarpic; zoosporangium epibiotic, smooth, inoperculate, at maturity forming an apical discharge pore, never bursting; endobiotic part composed of an apophysis and rhizoids, the apophysis connected with the sporangium by a somewhat long neck, spheroid, smaller than the sporangium, rhizoids short, branched; zoospores few within the sporangium, liberated through a pore one by one as flagellate bodies, the two flagella laterally attached and oppositely directed; resting spore not observed. (Modified from Kobayasi and Ookubo.)

Inhabitants of marine algae.

The genus differs from *Thraustochytrium* primarily in the formation of a subsporangial apophysis and in liberation of the zoospores through a discrete pore, not by bursting of the sporangial wall.

Japonochytrium marinum Kobayasi and Ookubo

Bull. Nat. Sci. Mus. (Tokyo), 33: 60, fig. 5. 1953

Sporangia scattered on the host cell, shortly stipitate or sessile, spheroid or more ovoid, 16–30 μ high by 10–20 μ in diameter, somewhat thick-walled, smooth, hyaline, distinct from the cylindrical, 3–5 μ long by 3–4 μ thick, stalk; apophysis vesicular or ovoid, smaller than the sporangium, 10–13 μ long, 5–10 μ in diameter, thin-walled, hyaline, rhizoids usually arising from one or two axes produced at the base of the apophysis, generally stout, up to 3 μ in diameter at the point of origin, branched; zoospores ten or more formed in one sporangium, at first spheroid, then reniform, 4–5 μ in diameter, with two laterally attached flagella, containing one to several refractive globules, slowly swimming away through the apical pore of sporangium, varying in form when swimming; resting spore not observed. (Modified from Kobayasi and Ookubo.)

On *Gracilaria confervoides*, *Cladophora japonica* (in culture dish), JAPAN.

SAPROLEGNIACEAE

Thallus eucarpic, mycelial, without constrictions, of unlimited growth, bearing numerous reproductive organs, homo- or heterothallic; zoosporangia, varied in character, usually terminal; zoospores mono- or diplanetic (mono- or dimorphic), the secondary zoospores sometimes capable of repeated emergence; antheridia from one to many, hypogynous, androgynous, or diclinous, sometimes nonfunctional or entirely lacking; oögonium with smooth or pitted wall, eggs from one to many, formed from the entire contents of the oögonium; oöspores sexually or apogamously formed, thick-walled, partly or nearly completely filling the oögonium, upon germination forming hyphae or a hyphal stalk bearing a zoosporangium.

Primarily saprophytic on plant and animal debris in fresh water or soil; some species parasitic on microscopic animals or on fish, amphibia and their eggs, and on the roots of higher plants.

The following key to the genera is based mainly on Coker and Matthews (1937).

KEY TO THE GENERA OF THE SAPROLEGNIACEAE

Zoospores of the primary type only, monoplanetic (monomorphic); sporangia spherical to somewhat elongate .... PYTHIOPSIS, p. 835
Zoospores exhibiting varying degrees of diplanetism (dimorphism)
  Zoospores normally emerging from the sporangium without previous encystment
    Primary zoospores bearing flagella at discharge and swimming away
      Zoospores in more than one row in the sporangium
        Sporangia renewed primarily by internal proliferation
                              SAPROLEGNIA, p. 835
        Sporangia renewed by cymose branching as well as by internal proliferation .... ISOACHLYA, p. 838
      Zoospores in one row in the sporangium
        Sporangia for the most part unbranched, eggs borne singly in a distinct oögonium .... LEPTOLEGNIA, p. 839
        Sporangia usually branched; resting structures asexually formed in undifferentiated portions of the hyphae, numerous .... LEPTOLEGNIELLA, p. 840
    Primary swimming stage partly or wholly suppressed, the primary zoospores after emergence mostly at once encysting

[1] For an explanation of the terms used in describing the structure of the mature egg (oöspore) of the Saprolegniaceae see p. 796.

Encysted spores for most part more than 15 μ in diameter, in a
single row, wall thick, never giving rise to motile zoospores .... GEOLEGNIA, p. 850

PYTHIOPSIS DE BARY

Bot. Zeitung, 46: 609. 1888

(Fig. 65 C, p. 836)

Hyphae slender, branched; sporangia typically short and plump,
spheric, oval, pyriform with a distinct apical papilla, or varying to
elongate and irregular, the primary ones terminal, the secondary ones
multiplied from lateral stalks below the old ones to form more or less
dense clusters; spores emerging and swimming as in *Saprolegnia*, pip-
shaped with two apical cilia, sprouting after the first encystment
(monoplanetic); gemmae resembling the sporangia, formed plentifully,
often in chains, producing zoospores after a rest; oögonia borne like
the sporangia and gemmae and resembling them in youth, typically
spheric, oval, or pyriform, with unpitted, smooth, wavy, or papillate
walls; eggs one or few, eccentric; antheridia short and thick, typically
androgynous from the close neighborhood of the oögonia, rarely
diclinous. (Modified from Coker and Matthews, 1937.)

Type species: *Pythiopsis cymosa* de Bary.

TAXA NOT IN COKER (1923) OR COKER AND MATTHEWS (1937)

PYTHIOPSIS INTERMEDIA Chaudhuri and Banerjee

Proc. Indian Acad. Sci., Sect. B, 15: 221, pl. 2. 1942

PYTHIOPSIS PAPILLATA Ookubo and Kobayasi

Nagaoa, 5: 8, fig. 6. 1955

SAPROLEGNIA C. G. NEES

Nova Acta Acad. Leop.-Carol., 11: 513. 1823

(Fig. 65 D–E, p. 836)

Diplanes Leitgeb, Jahrb. Wiss. Bot., 7: 374. 1869.

"Saprophytic on animal or plant remains, or in some species parasitic
on aquatic animals as fish, frog-eggs, etc.; exposed hyphae branched

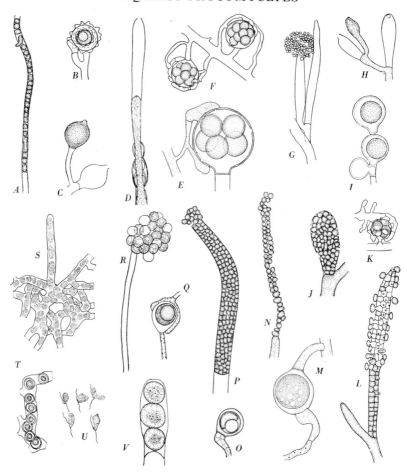

FIG. 65. Saprolegniaceae

A–B. Leptolegnia eccentrica Coker: *A*, sporangium; *B*, oögonium with mature oöspore and androgynous antheridium. *C. Pythiopsis humphreyana* Coker, globular sporangia. *D–E. Saprolegnia ferax* (Gruith.) Thuret: *D*, proliferating sporangium; *E*, sex organs. *F–G. Achlya americana* Humphrey: *F*, sex organs; *G*, sporangium. *H–I, Isoachlya unispora* Coker and Couch: *H*, sporangia renewed as in *Achlya*; *I*, oögonia in chain. *J–K. Thraustotheca clavata* (de Bary) Humphrey: *J*, encysted spores within sporangium; *K*, sex organs. *L–M. Dictyuchus monosporus*: *L*, zoospores escaping through wall of sporangium; *M*, sex organs. *N–O. Brevilegnia unisperma* var. *delica* Coker: *N*, unwalled sporangium with spores dispersing; *O*, apogamous oögonium

or more or less simple, straight or crooked, usually tapering gradually outward, more or less pointed, springing from an intricately branched, in part rhizoid-like mycelium within the substratum; hyphae not septate nor constricted until the approach of reproductive stages. Sporangia at first terminal on main hyphae, typically long-clavate and thicker toward the distal end, or at times slender-fusiform, often irregular and polymorphic in older cultures, typically proliferating within the older ones in a "nested" fashion, but often also as in *Achlya*; at maturity opening typically by an apical mouth. Spores emerging rapidly one by one through pressure from within, diplanetic, at first pip-shaped with two apical cilia and swimming away as soon as discharged, soon coming to rest and encysting, after a few hours emerging from the cyst and swimming again more actively in a somewhat kidney-shaped form with two lateral cilia, finally coming to rest and germinating; gemmae (chlamydospores) of variable shape and size formed in greater or less number, often in chains, after resting a few days either becoming sporangia directly or indirectly or sprouting into a mycelium. Oogonia terminal on main hyphae or on lateral branches, or in some species intercalary singly or in chains, spheric or oval or pyriform or when intercalary sometimes fusiform, the wall smooth or papillate, often pitted; eggs one or many in an oogonium, smooth, the protoplasm entirely surrounded by one or two layers of fatty food material (centric or subcentric), undergoing a rest period before sprouting. Antheridia present or absent, androgynous or diclinous, usually terminating slender antheridial branches which are short or long, simple or branched; antheridia when present often forming one or more slender tubes, these entering the oogonia through thin places and reaching the eggs" (Coker and Matthews, 1937).

Type species: *Saprolegnia ferax* (Gruith.) Thuret.

---

with mature oöspore. *P. Calyptralegnia achlyoides* (Coker and Couch), Coker; discharging sporangium. *Q–R. Aphanomyces laevis* de Bary: *R*, tip of sporangium with cluster of encysted zoospores; *Q*, sex organs. *S–U. Leptolegniella keratinophilum* Huneycutt: *S*, intricate sporangial apparatus; *T*, resting spores; *U*, zoospores. *V. Geolegnia septisporangia* Couch, multinucleate spores in sporangium.

(*A–B, N–O*, Coker, 1927; *C–K, Q, R*, Coker, 1923; *L–M*, Couch, 1926b; *P*, Coker and Couch, 1923; *S–U*, Huneycutt, 1952; *V*, Couch, 1927)

838   *AQUATIC PHYCOMYCETES*

SAPROLEGNIA BERNARDENSIS Harvey

J. Elisha Mitchell Sci. Soc., 58: 22, pl. 3. 1942

SAPROLEGNIA LATVICA Apinis

Acta Horti Bot. Univ. Latv., 4: 211, pl. 1, figs. 1–12.
1930

SAPROLEGNIA PSEUDOCRUSTOSA Lund

Kgl. Danske Vidensk. Seldk. Skrift., Naturv. Math., Afd. IX, 6: 9, fig.2. 1934

SAPROLEGNIA TERRESTRIS Cookson

Proc. Roy. Soc. Victoria (N. S.), 49(2): 235, figs. 1–2, pl. 11. 1937

SAPROLEGNIA TOKUGAWANA Emoto

Bot. Mag. (Tokyo), 37: 15, pl. 1, figs. 1–12. 1923. (In Japanese). *In* Nagai, J. Fac. Agric., Hokkaido Imp. Univ., Sapporo, 32: 8. 1931

SAPROLEGNIA ULIGINOSA Johannes

Archiv für Mikrobiol., 14: 596, fig. 1. 1950

ISOACHLYA KAUFFMAN [1]

Amer. J. Bot., 8: 231. 1921

(Fig. 65 H–I, p. 836)

"Hyphae rather stout or slender. Sporangia formed from tips of the hyphae, oval, pyriform, ventricose-clavate, elongate-pyriform to clavate or cylindric-clavate, the later ones arising either by cymose or pseudo-cymose arrangement, as in *Achlya*, or by internal proliferation as in *Saprolegnia*, both modes occurring earlier or later in the development of one and the same species, or frequently on the same main hypha. Spores diplanetic, their form and behavior as in *Saprolegnia*. Gemmae present. Oogonia terminal or torulose, occasionally intercalary; eggs

[1] See *Cladolegnia* Johannes, 1955.

centric or eccentric, not filling the oogonium. Antheridia present or few to none" (Coker and Matthews, 1937).

Type species: *Isoachlya toruloides* Kauffman and Coker.

TAXA NOT IN COKER (1923) OR COKER AND MATTHEWS (1937)

ISOACHLYA ANISOSPORA var. INDICA Saksena and Bhargava

Current Science, 13: 79. 1944.

ISOACHLYA SUBTERRANEA Dissmann

Beihefte Bot. Centralbl., II, 48: 110, figs. 1-7. 1931.

ISOACHLYA TORULOIDES var. PAUCISPORA Moreau

Bull. Soc. Mycol. France, 64: 227, fig. 2. 1948

LEPTOLEGNIA DE BARY

Bot. Zeitung, 46: 609. 1888

(Fig. 65 A–B. p. 836)

"Hyphae long and delicate, sparingly branched. Sporangia long, apical, cylindric, of the same size as the hyphae, at times multiplied by growth through empty ones, rarely branched; spores formed in a single row, elongate on emerging, then changing their form to pip-shaped and swarming with two apical cilia, encysting and swimming again as in *Saprolegnia*. Gemmae lacking. Oogonia borne on short lateral branches, small, smooth or warted, subspheric, not pitted; eggs single, completely or nearly filling the oogonium, eccentric. Antheridia when present pyriform, diclinous or androgynous" (Coker and Matthews, 1937).

Type species: *Leptolegnia caudata* de Bary.

TAXON NOT IN COKER (1923) OR COKER AND MATTHEWS (1937)

LEPTOLEGNIA MARINA Atkins

J. Mar. Biol. Asˢ. U. K., 33: 622, figs. 1–5. 1954

LEPTOLEGNIA SP. Vallin

See Vallin (1951) for report of an epidemic among copepods caused by this fungus (or possibly a *Leptolegniella*).

LEPTOLEGNIELLA Huneycutt

J. Elisha Mitchell Sci. Soc., 68: 109. 1952

(Fig. 65 S–U, p. 836)

"Mycelium developing mostly intramatrically, hyphae very irregular, much branched, occasionally septate. Rhizoids slender and branching. Zoosporangia branched, not differentiated from the vegetative mycelium. Zoospores emerging incompletely formed, as in *Leptolegnia*, diplanetic. Resting bodies formed within the hyphae by rounding up of portions of the protoplasm, asexually formed.

"With chloro-iodide of zinc the old hyphal walls give a reddish-purple reaction" (Huneycutt, *loc. cit.*).

Type species: *Leptolegniella keratinophilum* Huneycutt.

TAXON NOT IN COKER (1923) OR COKER AND MATTHEWS (1937)

Leptolegniella piligena Ookubo and Kobayasi

Nagaoa, 5: 4, fig. 3. 1955

PROTOACHLYA Coker

Saprolegniaceae, 90. 1923

(Fig. 66 A–B, p. 842)

"Hyphae more delicate than in *Achlya*. Sporangia subcylindric to clavate or flask-shaped, blunt and usually thickest beyond the middle, proliferating like a cyme, as in *Achlya*, and also less frequently by growth through the empty sporangia as in *Saprolegnia*. Spores diplanetic, on emerging ciliated and all or some showing sluggish or less often active motion, some remaining attached in an irregular clump to the tip of the sporangium. Gemmae spheric to pyriform or elongate. Oogonia borne singly, the great majority on short lateral stalks from the main hyphae and with or without a few pits; eggs usually few, centric. Antheridia androgynous or diclinous, typically pyriform with their tips applied to the oogonia" (Coker and Matthews, 1937).

Type species: *Protoachlya paradoxa* Coker.

TAXA NOT IN COKER (1923) OR COKER AND MATTHEWS (1937)

PROTOACHLYA HYPOGYNA Shanor and Conover

Amer. Midl. Nat., 28: 747. 1942

PROTOACHLYA POLYSPORA (Lindstedt) Apinis

Acta Horti Bot. Univ. Latv., 4: 224, pl. 3, figs. 1–15. 1930

ACHLYA C. G. NEES

Nova Acta Acad. Leop.-Carol., 11: 514. 1823

(Fig. 65 F–G, p. 836)

Hydronema Carus, Nova Acta Acad. Leop.-Carol., 11: 491. 1823

"Thalli monoecious or dioecious. Hyphae stout or slender, more or less branched, straight or flexuous, gradually tapering from base to apex; variable in length. Gemmae, when present, formed by segmentation of the hyphae; variable in size and shape; functioning as zoosporangia or germinating by one or more slender hyphae which usually terminate in a small zoosporangium. Zoosporangia filiform, fusiform, naviculate, or clavate; renewed sympodially or by basipetalous development and cymose branching. Zoospores usually dimorphic; primary ones on discharge encysting at once to form a more or less spherical, hollow mass at the zoosporangial orifice and occasionally provided with two quickly evanescent, apically attached flagella during emergence; secondary zoospores reniform, laterally biflagellate, germinating after encystment by a slender hypha; in a few species, aplanoid, dictyoid, or thraustothecoid discharge also present. Oögonia borne variously, being lateral on stalks of variable length, terminal, intercalary, or sessile; in some species, the immature ones proliferating; variously shaped, predominantly spherical or pyriform. Oögonial walls with or without ornamentations; pitted or unpitted. Antheridial branches diclinous, monoclinous, androgynous, or exigynous, in one species hypogynous; in a few species lacking. Antheridial cells predominantly tubular and clavate; laterally or apically appressed to the oögonial wall or attached by finger-like projections; fertilization tubes usually present. Oöspheres generally maturing. Oospores one to many; centric, subcentric, or eccentric; germination, when present, usually accom-

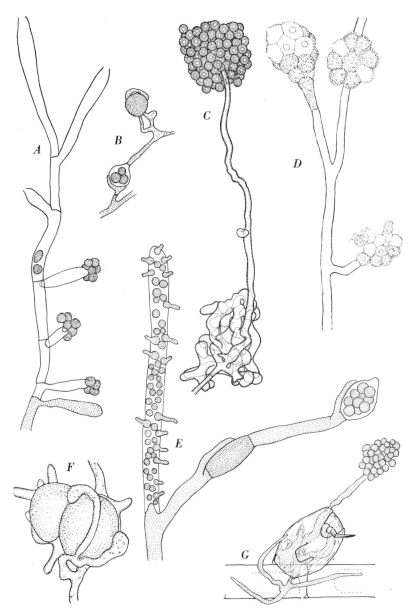

Fig. 66. Saprolegniaceae

plished by a slender germ tube ultimately terminating in a zoosporangium" (Johnson, 1956).

Type species: *Achlya prolifera* C. G. Nees.

The recognized[1] species are those treated by Johnson (1956).

APHANOMYCES DE BARY

Jahrb. Wiss. Bot., 2: 178. 1860

(Fig. 65 Q–R, p. 836)

"Hyphae very delicate, long, sparingly branched. Sporangia formed from unchanged hyphae, long to very long, not proliferating within old ones and rarely laterally from below. Spores borne in a single row, emerging apically in elongate form, then rounding up and encysting in a clump at end of the sporangium as in *Achlya*, then emerging and swimming again as in that genus. Specialized gemmae lacking. Oogonia terminal on short or long branches, smooth, warted, or spiny; wall thin or thick and irregular; eggs single, not filling the oogonium (nearly so in some species), of various structure. Antheridia diclinous or androgynous, not always present" (Coker and Matthews, 1937).

Type species: *Aphanomyces stellatus* de Bary.

TAXA NOT IN COKER (1923) OR COKER AND MATTHEWS (1937) [2]

APHANOMYCES ACINETOPHAGUS Bartsch and Wolf

Amer. J. Bot., 25: 394, figs. 1–9. 1938

Explanation of Figure 66

A–B. Protoachlya paradoxa Coker: *A*, sporangia; *B*, sex organs. *C. Plectospira myriandra* Drechsler, discharged lobulate sporangium. *D. Aphanodictyon papillatum* Huneycutt, sporangia, one of which is discharging zoospores. *E. Aplanes androgynus* (Archer) Humphrey, sporangium and sex organs. *F. Aphanodictyon papillatum* Huneycutt, sex organs. *G. Sommerstorffia spinosa* Arnaudow, thallus epiphytic on an alga, bearing three capturing organs and a parasitized rotifer from which a zoosporangium emerges.

(*A–B*, Coker, 1923; *C*, Drechsler, 1927; *D*, *F*, Sparrow, 1950; *E*, de Bary, 1888; *G*, Sparrow, 1929)

---

[1] Vishniac and Nigrelli (1957) do not accept Johnson's reduction to synonymy with *A. racemosa* of *A. sparrowii* Reischer (1949b).

[2] See also Benisch (1940), and Ziegler in *Mycologia*, 50: 403, 1958 (*A. mucronata*).

APHANOMYCES AMPHIGYNUS Cutter

Mycologia, 33: 230, figs. 13 a–f. 1941

APHANOMYCES APOPHYSII Lacy

Indian Phytopathol., 2: 137, figs. 2D, 3. 1949

APHANOMYCES ASTACI Schikora

Fischerei-zeitung, 6: 353. 1903 (see also Schikora, 1906)

APHANOMYCES DAPHNIAE Prowse

Trans. Brit. Mycol. Soc., 37: 22, figs. 1–3. 1954

APHANOMYCES LAEVIS de Bary f. KERATINOPHILUS Ookubo and Kobayasi

Nagaoa, 5: 6, figs. 4–5. 1955

APHANOMYCES HYDATINAE Valkanov

Arch. Protistenk., 73: 366; 74: 5, figs. 1–16. 1931

APHANOMYCES MAGNUSII Schikora

Verhandl. Bot. Vereins Prov. Brandenberg, 63: 87. 1922

APHANOMYCES OVIDESTRUENS Gicklhorn

Lotos, 71: 143, figs. 1–8. 1923

APHANOMYCES SPARROWII Cutter

Mycologia, 33: 233, figs. 15 c–g. 1941

SOMMERSTORFFIA Arnaudow

Flora, 116: 109. 1923

(Fig. 66 G, p. 842)

Mycelium delicate, of limited complexity, parasitic in bodies of rotifers and extending out into the water, some branches with sharp tips covered with mucilage for capturing rotifers; sporangia long and slender, zoospores in a single row, encysting at mouth of sporangium, then emerging as biflagellate spores; sexual reproduction by means of oögonia containing one egg; antheridia not observed. (Modified from Coker and Matthews, 1937.)

Type species: *Sommerstorffia spinosa* Arnaudow.

Prowse (1954a) describes smooth-walled oögonia with one to seven eggs and an antheridial system composed of four branches closely applied to the oögonial wall. Since only one such instance was observed, he feels that abnormal material may be involved. Even if the material was normal, this fungus is certainly not *Sommerstorffia spinosa*. Karling (1952) gives a brief account of another possible species which lacks specialized capturing organs and adheres to the substratum by a basal flattened holdfast.

PLECTOSPIRA Drechsler

J. Agr. Res., 34: 294. 1927

(Fig. 66 C, p. 842)

"Mycelium slender, sparingly or moderately branched. Zoosporangia composed of inflated elements, often compacted into an irregular complex, within which zoospores are differentiated in two or more series, together with a prolonged filamentous element within which zoospores are formed in one series and by which the entire organ is evacuated. Zoospores encysting at the mouth of the efferent hypha, later escaping from their cysts and swarming. Oogonia intercalary or terminal. Antheridia absent or present. Oospores single and somewhat eccentric (subcentric) in internal structure" (Drechsler, *loc. cit.*).

Type species: *Plectospira myriandra* Drechsler.

A genus whose undoubted members have thus far only been reported as root parasites of flowering plants. Whether or not *Plectospira dubia* Atkins (1954b), parasitic on various crustacea, belongs here is, as its author indicates, questionable.

TAXON NOT IN COKER (1923) OR COKER AND MATTHEWS (1937)

Plectospira dubia Atkins

J. Mar. Biol. Ass. U.K., 33: 731, figs. 1–5. 1954

See *Sirolpidium zoophthorum*, p. 968.

APLANES DE BARY

Bot. Zeitung, 46: 613. 1888

(Fig. 66 E, p. 842)

"Mycelium as in *Achlya*. Sporangia extremely scarce, often entirely absent for long periods in culture, cylindric, renewed as in *Saprolegnia* and perhaps also as in *Achlya*; spores at times escaping as in *Achlya* or *Saprolegnia*, at times retained in the sporangium and sprouting there, their behavior not well known in all species. Oogonia abundant, in chains or single and terminal, barrel-shaped, spheric, or pyriform, their walls very thick (more so than in other water-molds) and heavily pitted; eggs centric or subcentric, spheric or at times elliptic from pressure. Antheridial branches arising from immediately below the oogonia, or when the oogonia are in chains arising from the top of one oogonium and attached to the next above, simple or branched; antheridia with their sides attached to the oogonia" (Coker and Matthews, 1937).

Type species: *Aplanes braunii* de Bary.

Johnson (1956) has demonstrated that the best-known species, *Aplanes treleaseanus*, is in fact an *Achlya*. If, as is possible, the others belong either in *Achlya* or *Saprolegnia*, the genus can be suppressed. Its validity now rests on two doubtful criteria: (1) rarity of sporangia and (2) germination of the zoospores *in situ*.

THRAUSTOTHECA HUMPHREY

Trans. Amer. Phil. Soc. (N.S.), 17: 131. 1893

(Fig. 65 J–K, p. 836)

"Primary threads in greater part stout, branching. Sporangia clavate to subcylindric, often irregular, proliferating from below as in *Achlya*; spores always or in great majority encysting within the sporangium when formed and later, in more or less angular form, swelling and escaping by irregular rupture or disintegration of the sporangial wall, not escaping at once by an apical papilla except in the *Achlya*-like primary sporangia of one species. Eggs eccentric, usually multiple. Antheridia present" (Coker and Matthews, 1937).

Type species: *Thraustotheca clavata* (de Bary) Humphrey.

CALYPTRALEGNIA Coker

J. Elisha Mitchell Sci. Soc., 42: 219. 1927

(Fig. 65 P, p. 836)

Mycelium composed of hyphae of usual achlyoid type; sporangium opening by the dehiscence of an apical, caplike segment; zoospores encysting within the sporangium, somewhat angular, emerging intermittently by swelling of consecutive groups in basipetalous succession, the free cysts each giving rise to a laterally biflagellate zoospore which may encyst and emerge again; oögonia with one to eight eggs, centric, subcentric, or eccentric; antheridia usually androgynous rarely diclinous. (Modified from Coker and Matthews, 1937.)

Type species: *Calyptralegnia achlyoides* (Coker and Couch) Coker.

TAXON NOT IN COKER (1923) OR COKER AND MATTHEWS (1937)

Calyptralegnia riparensis Höhnk

Veröff. Inst. Meeresforsch. Bremerhaven, 2: 232, 1 pl. 1953

APHANODICTYON Huneycutt

J. Elisha Mitchell Sci. Soc., 64: 279. 1948

(Fig. 66 D, F, p. 842)

"Mycelium of limited growth, hyphae very slender as in the more delicate species of *Aphanomyces*, much branched; sporangia variable in shape but predominantly globose to subglobose; spores encysting within the sporangium, emerging separately from their cysts as in *Dictyuchus*, leaving a net of empty cysts, and swimming in the laterally biflagellate form or germinating *in situ* by germ tube. Oogonia abundant, containing from one to several thick-walled eggs. All mature cell walls give a cellulose reaction with chloroiodide of zinc" (Huneycutt, *loc. cit.*).

Type species: *Aphanodictyon papillatum* Huneycutt. On keratin substrata.

See also Sparrow (1950).

DICTYUCHUS Leitgeb

Bot. Zeitung. 26: 503. 1868

(Fig. 65 L–M, p. 836)

"Mycelium usually quite vigorous, reaching a diameter of 2–3 cm. on hempseed; threads branched, up to 100 μ thick at the base, straight at first except where branched, becoming eventually quite zigzag by the continual formation of apical sporangia from the base of which the thread continues its growth. Sporangia formed in great abundance, at first around the outer margin of the culture, later scattered over the entire surface; first sporangia long-cylindric, often thicker in the distal half than in the proximal; sporangia in the *D. monosporus* group with spores included, in large part breaking away from the hyphae and floating on the surface of the water; the greater part of hyphae often becoming sporangia, even including the oogonial and antheridial branches; sporangial wall persistent in the *D. monosporus* group, quickly disappearing in the false-net group, but the encysted spores sticking together to retain the sporangial shape; spores encysting within the sporangia, emerging later in the laterally biciliate form, leaving their empty cysts in the form of a true or false net; primary sporangia in some species of the *Achlya* type. Gemmae lacking or, in one species, rarely present. Plants heterothallic, homothallic, parthenogenetic, or apparently sexually sterile. Oogonia when present with a single eccentric egg" (Coker and Matthews, 1937).

Type species: *Dictyuchus monosporus* Leitgeb.

TAXON NOT IN COKER (1923) OR COKER AND MATTHEWS (1937)

DICTYUCHUS PSEUDOACHLYOIDES Beneke

J. Elisha Mitchell Sci. Soc., 64: 263, pl. 30, figs. 1–13. 1948

BREVILEGNIA Coker and Couch

J. Elisha Mitchell Sci. Soc., 42: 212. 1927

(Fig. 65 N–O, p. 836)

"Mycelium depauperate, dense and opaque, never aerial. Sporangia in the great majority behaving about as in *Thraustotheca*, the wall soon disappearing; in some species sporangia of *Achlya* type also present; spores very variable in size and shape in the same culture, larger ones multinucleate, encysting in position except in the achlyoid type, and only slowly separating after the disintegration of the sporangial wall; after encystment under usual conditions either emerging and swimming once (dicystic and monoplanetic) or not swimming, or some swimming and some not, depending on the species (in all but one species they have been induced to swim by special treatment). Gemmae present or wanting. Oogonia small, with a single eccentric egg. Antheridia present or wanting, androgynous or diclinous" (Coker and Matthews, 1937). Type species: *Brevilegnia subclavata* Couch.

TAXA NOT IN COKER (1923) OR COKER AND MATTHEWS (1937)[1]

BREVILEGNIA CRASSA Rossy-Valderrama

J. Elisha Mitchell Sci. Soc., 72: 130, figs. 1–13. 1956

BREVILEGNIA IRREGULARIS Rossy-Valderrama

J. Elisha Mitchell Sci. Soc., 72: 133, figs. 14–22. 1956

BREVILEGNIA LONGICAULIS Johnson

Mycologia, 42: 244. fig. 1. 1950

BREVILEGNIA MEGASPERMA var. BREVICAULIS Rossy-Valderrama

J. Elisha Mitchell Sci. Soc., 72: 133, figs. 23–29. 1956

BREVILEGNIA MINUTANDRA Höhnk

Veröff. Inst. Meeresforsch. Bremerhaven, 1: 77, pl. 13. 1952

BREVILEGNIA PARVISPORA Höhnk

Veröff. Inst. Meeresforsch. Bremerhaven, 1: 67, pl. 9. 1952

BREVILEGNIA VARIABILIS Indoh

Mag. Nat. History, Tokyo, 38: 87, fig. 1. 1941 (In Japanese.)

[1] See also *B. globosa* Ziegler in *Mycologia*, 50: 405, 1958.

GEOLEGNIA Coker

Harvey, Elisha Mitchell Sci. Soc., 41: 153. 1925

(Fig. 65 V, p. 836)

"Mycelium of very limited growth, forming a dense, opaque mat; hyphae slender. Spores in a single row, very large, and multinucleate, encysting within the sporangium with a thick wall and without any motile stage, escaping by decay of the thin-walled sporangium and sprouting by a germ-tube. Oogonia abundant, even, containing a single eccentric egg not filling the cavity. Antheridia always present and androgynous" (Coker and Matthews, 1937).

Type species: *Geolegnia inflata* Coker and Harvey.

TAXON NOT IN COKER (1923) OR COKER AND MATTHEWS (1937)

Geolegnia intermedia Höhnk

Veröff. Inst. Meeresforsch. Bremerhaven, 1: 81, pl. 14. 1952

IMPERFECTLY KNOWN GENERA OF THE SAPROLEGNIACEAE

? HAMIDIA Chaudhuri

Proc. Indian Acad. Sci., Sect. B, 15: 227. 1942

"Hyphae hyaline, generally racemosely branched, delicate, sparsely septate, bearing oogonia and sporangia both in racemose and cymose manner; best seen in natural condition. Oogonia borne singly or in clusters (of usually 3). Oogonia when borne singly have long stalks which break at the slightest disturbance. Oogonium with a single large egg entirely filling it. Egg with smooth wall; emerges gradually and imperceptibly. Apandrous; sporangia resembling oogonia also formed, each with 2–7 swarm spores. Discharge tube may or may not be present. Swarm spores, without a properly differentiated wall and non-ciliate (monoplanetic) germinate soon after discharge. Undischarged swarm spores germinate inside the sporangium, putting forth unilaterally or bilaterally produced germ tubes. Gemmae also formed. Growth on fresh potato stalks most luxuriant; egg yolks and insects unsuitable for growth" (Chaudhuri, *loc. cit.*).

Type species: *Hamidia indica* Chaudhuri, on submerged decaying twigs.

From the description and figures, the species is apparently based upon abnormal material, possibly pythiaceous in character.

? APLANOPSIS Höhnk

Veröff. Inst. Meeresforsch. Bremerhaven, 1: 85. 1952

Mycelium intra- and extramatrical, hyphae slender, resembling *Leptolegnia*, *Geolegnia*, and *Brevilegnia* in part; zoosporangia not observed; oögonium with a single centric to subcentric oöspore which does not completely fill it; antheridia very rare, androgynous.

Type species: *Aplanopsis terrestris* Höhnk, on animal substrata, saline soil.

See also Höhnk, 1953a.

LEPTOMITALES

THE establishment of the Leptomitales as an order coequal with the Saprolegniales (Kanouse, 1927) has proved eminently feasible and its division in the first edition of the *Aquatic Phycomycetes* into two families, the Leptomitaceae and Rhipidiaceae, has received general acceptance. Members of these two families are all fresh-water saprophytes which usually form tangled or flocculent mats of hyphae or small whitish pustules on the substratum. They occur primarily on vegetable debris, particularly twigs and fruits. Some species seem to prefer cool clear water, whereas others grow under exceedingly foul environmental conditions. While the pustules are occasionally composed of a single species, more often they consist of a mixture with other Phycomycetes such as *Blastocladia* and *Gonapodya*. Most of them appear, at least from published records, to be of infrequent occurrence.

The Leptomitales constitute a rather closely related group having in common well-marked characters. Generally speaking, these are the presence of a more or less well-defined basal cell, segmentation of the thallus, cellulose walls, pedicellate reproductive structures, and oögamous sexual reproduction. When Kanouse (1927) separated the order from the Saprolegniales, she pointed out that the members of the Leptomitales show definite affinities with the Saprolegniales on the one hand and with the Peronosporales on the other. Like the Saprolegniales they lead an aquatic life, have the same general thallus structure, and form numerous zoosporangia which produce biflagellate zoospores. Furthermore, as is true in the Saprolegniales, the zoospores of two genera of the Leptomitales (*Leptomitus* and *Apodachlya*) exhibit diplanetism (dimorphism) or show evidences of it (Zopf, 1888; Coker, 1923). The Leptomitales resemble the Peronosporales in the nature of their reproductive organs and processes, but are unlike them in habitat and in their lack of parasitic tendencies. As in the Peronosporales, the members of the Leptomitales (with the exception of *Apodachlyella completa*) form a single oöspore in the oögonium. Except in *Apodachlya* the contents of the oögonium are differentiated into oöplasm and periplasm, and a coenocentrum is distinguishable in the oöplasm (Kevorkian, 1935). In the Rhipidiaceae a functional antheridium is formed which is applied at a definite region on the oögonial wall, and a well-defined, functional fertilization tube is produced.

Zoospores of the primary type are formed in *Leptomitus* and *Apodachlya brachynema*. These encyst, as in *Saprolegnia*, and give rise to swarmers of the secondary type. In the Rhipidiaceae the primary stage is apparently completely suppressed and only secondary zoospores are produced, a further point of resemblance to the Peronosporales.

In spite of the fact that the body structure is obviously similar to that typical of the Blastocladiales (strikingly exemplified by a comparison of *Blastocladia pringsheimii* with *Mindeniella spinospora*) and in the Monoblepharidales (as illustrated by the segmented hyphae of *Gonapodya* and *Apodachyla*), there is abundant evidence to show that there is no close relationship between them. This is indicated primarily in the structure of the zoospore, the aspect of the protoplasm, the composition of the walls, and the radically different methods of sexual reproduction. These dissimilarities are apparent when the diagnoses of the three orders are compared (cf. pp. 633, 713, and 871). Here again it can be pointed out that a resemblance in the body plan of various fungi has given rise to faulty ideas of relationships.

DEVELOPMENT AND MORPHOLOGY

THE THALLUS

The thalli of the two families of the order are unlike in certain features, particularly in the degree of differentiation of the basal cell and the extent of the development of the hyphal branches.

In the Leptomitaceae there appears to be little or no specialization of the proximal portion of the thallus; further investigation of this feature, however, is desirable. Apparently no specialized system of holdfasts anchors the plant to the substratum, although Dangeard (1890–91b: 120) briefly mentions that such structures are formed in *Leptomitus*. The hyphae of members of this family are well developed and seemingly have unlimited powers of continued growth and branching. They are conspicuously constricted at more or less regular intervals (Fig. 69 E, p. 875), the constrictions being partly plugged by pseudosepta consisting of a somewhat refractive material termed "cellulin" by Pringsheim (1883a). These constrictions of the main hyphae, and of the branches which may arise immediately beneath them, give a characteristic jointed or segmented appearance to the whole thallus. The contents, at least in *Apodachlya*, are rather lustrous and, in both this genus and *Leptomitus*, possess occasional conspicuous refractive discs of cellulin. These discs, according to Radais (1898), may sometimes act as "corks" to plug up accidental tears in the hyphal walls.

In the Rhipidiaceae the thallus is always somewhat arborescent and more or less strongly differentiated into a basal cell, derived from the body of the germinated zoospore (Minden, 1916), and into hyphal branches which arise from its distal portion (Fig. 70 C, p. 890). The basal cell is anchored in the substratum by a system of tubular sometimes locally expanded holdfasts. These evidently perform the same function as the rhizoids of the Chytridiales and Blastocladiales, that is, anchorage and absorption, but they appear to lack the characteristic strongly tapering "chytrid-like" aspect. In some species the basal cell may be slender and scarcely differentiated from the hyphae, as in *Sapromyces* (Fig. 70 A). In others, such as *Rhipidium*, it may be very trunklike, with a "monstrously developed," strongly expanded, lobed and gnarled distal part which forms a platform from which the hyphae and reproductive organs arise. The walls of the basal cell are frequently of considerable thickness, colorless or somewhat brownish (especially with age), and occasionally roughened on the outer surface (Kanouse, 1927). Whatever the extent of development of the basal apparatus, the hyphae arising from it (except in *Mindeniella*) are always marked off at their point of origin by a constriction containing a more or less well developed pseudoseptum of cellulin. As in the Leptomitaceae, these hyphae have occasional constrictions along their length (Fig. 70 A). They may remain simple or be sympodially branched.

This curious differentiation of the thallus into rootlike holdfasts, trunklike basal cell, and branches is clearly evident in *Rhipidium* and *Araiospora*, and to a lesser degree in *Sapromyces*. Although branches are lacking in *Mindeniella* (Fig. 72, p. 902), the holdfast and basal-cell development is as pronounced as in the other three genera (Kanouse, 1927; Sparrow and Cutter, 1941; Johnson, 1951b). Why this particular arborescent habit of growth should appear in wholly unrelated groups of aquatic Phycomycetes is as yet little understood. It can be assumed, however, that such differentiation of the thallus is well adapted to the type of substratum on which all these fungi are commonly found, namely, somewhat spongy decaying fruits and twigs.

REPRODUCTION

Nonsexual Reproduction

In nonsexual reproduction the zoosporangia are either single or in whorls or umbels. In all instances they are separated from the vegetative part of the plant by a constriction within which there is a cellulin plug, the whole forming a short pedicel (Fig. 70 B, p. 890). In *Leptomitus* (Pringsheim, 1883a; Coker, 1923), slightly modified segments of the hyphae are simply transformed into sporangia, the terminal one maturing first, and then others in basipetal succession (Fig. 69 A, p. 875). In the remaining genera, however, the sporangia are well-defined broadly or narrowly ovate structures. They are smooth-walled in all except *Araiospora* and *Mindeniella*. In these genera sporangia ornamented with spines, as well as the more common smooth-walled type, are formed (Fig. 70 E–F, H, p. 890). In *Mindeniella* (Kanouse, 1927; Sparrow and Cutter, 1941), the spiny sporangia (Fig. 72 B, D, p. 902) have a tendency to appear after the colonies have become well established on the substratum, which suggests a possible relationship to the amount of nutrition available (see also Webster, 1943), but Emerson (comm.), by means of pure-culture studies, has shown their formation to be related to near absence of oxygen. The spiny sporangia give rise to the same kind of zoospores as do the smooth-walled ones.

The zoospores are cleaved out within the sporangium in a manner similar to that in the Saprolegniaceae. Considerable differences are apparent between the members of the Leptomitaceae and the Rhipidiaceae with respect to the type of zoospore produced at discharge and its subsequent behavior. In the Leptomitaceae definite evidences exist for the diplanetic (dimorphic) nature of the zoospore. Thus, in *Leptomitus lacteus* and *Apodachlya brachynema* the first swarmers to emerge are of the primary, apically biflagellate type (Hartog, 1887; Coker, 1923; Shen and Siang, 1948; Indoh, 1953) (Fig. 69 B, I, p. 875). These quickly come to rest and encyst, and from each cyst a laterally biflagellate secondary zoospore eventually issues (Fig. 69 J–K). In *A. pyrifera* (Zopf, 1888; Shen and Siang, 1948), however, there is a pronounced tendency for the immediate encystment of the primary swarmers at the orifice of the sporangium (Fig. 69 E). In the Rhipidiaceae the primary swarm stage is apparently suppressed, although it is possibly represented by the exceedingly ephemeral vesicle which is sometimes formed (Thaxter, 1896b) (Fig. 71 B, p. 894). The zoospores of this family are exclusively of the laterally biflagellate type (Fig. 71 F). There have been no reports except in *Mindeniella spinospora* (Sparrow and Cutter, 1941) of the repeated emergence of the secondary zoospores.

The zoospores of most species of the order show no unusual features. In *Araiospora spinosa*, *Rhipidium*, and *Mindeniella*, however, they are unique and striking objects by reason of the presence within the contents of great numbers of colorless refractive globules (Fig. 71 F, p. 894; Fig. 72 C, p. 902). The body of the zoospore, although differing somewhat in the various genera, conforms for the most part to the "kidney-shaped" or "bean-shaped" configuration common to all zoospores of the secondary type. The flagella are apparently of equal length, oppositely directed, and attached in a shallow groove.

Sexual Reproduction

Sexual reproduction is known to occur in the majority of species. It is apparently lacking, however, in *Leptomitus lacteus*, *Rhipidium parthenosporum*, and *Mindeniella spinospora*, the oöspore in the last two species being supplanted as the resting structure by a parthenogenetically developed resting spore (Kanouse, 1927). Where known, sexual reproduction is oögamous. The oögonia originate in the same manner as the zoosporangia and either terminate hyphal segments or are borne on the basal cell on short pedicels. Except in the aberrant species *Apodachlyella completa* (Humphrey, 1893; Indoh, 1939) only a single egg is formed in the oögonium. In the Leptomitaceae the contents of the oögonium are not differentiated into periplasm and oöplasm, as in the more highly evolved Rhipidiaceae.

The type of sexual reproduction found among members of the Leptomitaceae appears less highly specialized than that among the Rhipidiaceae. In *Apodachlya brachynema* (Coker, 1923; Sparrow, 1932b; Indoh, 1953), which is characterized by the production of numerous lateral moniliform branches, the oögonium arises as a terminal outgrowth of the most distal segment of the branch. This continues to increase in size by the flow of materials to it from the proximal segments. At maturity it is a large globular structure filled with dense homogeneous mottled protoplasm and subtended by the hypogynous cell from which it had its origin. Like the oögonium, the smaller subterminal cell contains densely granular protoplasm. A light spot (probably a pore) now appears in the base of the oögonium and the contents of the hypogynous antheridial cell slowly pass into the female gametangium. After a short rest period this bright spot disappears and the contents of the fertilized egg become organized into an oöspore of typically saprolegniaceous character. The wall thickens and one or more oil globules are formed. The oöspore, together with its attendant antheridial cell, may frequently be abscissed from the remainder of the thallus. The mature resting structure, the wall of which is distinctly thickened, nearly or, more often, completely fills the oögonium (Fig. 69 C, p. 875). Kanouse (1927: 338) described the oöspore wall of *A. brachynema* as consisting of three parts, an outer and an inner thin layer, and a middle thick one. In *A. punctata* the wall is punctate as in the resting spore of the Blastocladiales (Minden, 1912 [1915]; Sparrow, 1933c) (Fig. 69 G–H). A more specialized antheridium is formed in *A. minima* (Coker and Leitner, 1938). Here the hypogynous cell gives rise to a branch, the tip of which is applied to the oögonium (Fig. 69 D). The cell and the branch continuous with it function as an antheridium. No fertilization tube is formed. Germination of the oöspore of *A. brachynema* by several multinucleate germ tubes has been mentioned by Kevorkian (1935), but no details were given. Coker and Leitner (*loc. cit.*), who followed the process as it occurs in *A. minima*, describe it essentially as follows: At the inception of germination the contents of the oöspore gradually become granular throughout, with the exception of the large oil droplet, which persists. The oöspore enlarges and cracks open the surrounding oögonial wall. One or two somewhat irregular thick germ tubes protrude through the wall of the oöspore. These tubes elongate, become constricted at intervals, and eventually establish the new mycelium. A plug is formed in the first constriction which prevents the backflow of materials into the now empty oöspore. Frequently the oöspore after cracking open the oögonial wall slips out of its container and falls to the bottom of the culture dish.

In *Apodachlyella completa*, Humphrey (1893) and Indoh (1939) have shown that the sex organs are of a most peculiar type (Fig. 69 F, p. 875). The contents of the oögonium divide into from two to twelve (usually from four to seven) oöspheres, which eventually become oöspores. The suboögonial segment gives rise to from one to three branches, which are constricted and segmented like the ordinary vegetative hyphae. The terminal segment functions as the antheridium and is applied laterally to the wall of the oögonium. The contents then fragment into from four to ten small spheres, each of which produces a short germ tube and simulates a germinating zoospore. According to Indoh, these tubes penetrate the antheridial and oögonial walls and accomplish fertilization. It is not clear whether all the antheridial spheres discharge their contents into the oögonium. Indoh's observations on this extraordinary phenomenon closely follow those of Humphrey. The latter noted, however, that although the tubes usually grew toward the oögonium there were occasional exceptions, which appear from Indoh's figures to have been present in his material also. These exceptions, together with the occurrence of a few empty terminal segments devoid of such cysts and tubes, led Humphrey to suspect that his material was parasitized.

The sex organs of the Rhipidiaceae are in several ways more highly specialized than those of the Leptomitaceae. The oögonium always bears a single egg, the contents of which during maturation are strongly differentiated into a large somewhat dense mass of oöplasm and a thin vacuolated peripheral layer of periplasm. A single well-defined antheridium is formed which is usually fairly constant as to its point of application to the oögonial wall and which always produces a conspicuous fertilization tube. The wall of the oöspore is generally roughened or ornamented, presumably by periplasmic material.

The oögonia originate singly or in whorls in the same manner as the zoosporangia. They are frequently distinguishable from the latter, however, by their more spherical shape. A constriction is always present beneath the oögonium which divides it from its concomitant hypha. After the oögonium has received its complement of protoplasm and nuclei from the thallus it is separated by a plug of wall material. Details of the protoplasmic changes which then occur are discussed under "Cytology" (p. 861). The antheridium in some species is monoclinous; in others, diclinous. It is borne at the tip of a more or less extended slender branch, and its broad apex is applied to a well-defined spot on the oögonial wall. A cross wall separates the expanded antheridium from the slender sometimes branching hypha which bears it. The oöspore proper never completely fills the oögonium. It has an inner smooth wall of moderate thickness and an outer one derived from the periplasm. In *Rhipidium* (Fig. 71 C, p. 894) this outer wall is folded into a series of anastomosing ridges which give it an irregular stellate appearance, whereas in *Sapromyces* (Fig. 70 B, p. 890) the wall is almost but not completely smooth, the degree of undulation differing with the species. The oöspores of *Araiospora* (Fig. 70 D, G) are striking objects. Here the living contents, bearing one or more brilliantly golden globules, are surrounded by a thick smooth wall, which in turn is enveloped by a single layer of thin-walled hexagonal cells. Germination of the oöspores has not been observed in any member of the family.

An interesting series of investigations of sexuality in one of the Rhipidiaceae, *Sapromyces elongatus*, was carried on by Jordan (in Weston, 1938) and Bishop (1940). The almost complete agreement among the relatively few observers of this species that its antheridia were diclinous in origin (Fig. 70 B) naturally raised the question as to whether or not it was actually heterothallic in the sense in which that term had been applied to the Mucorales (Blakeslee, 1904). Preliminary studies by Jordan on single isolated basal cells of either oögonial or antheridial plants showed that when these were transplanted to sterile water cultures baited appropriately and grown alone no sex organs were produced. There was, however, one exception, a female strain which formed oögonial initials. When sterile plants, developed from isolated male and female basal cells, were placed in the same culture in such a manner that their branches were interwoven, an abundance of sex organs resulted. Plants forming antheridia could be traced to male basal cells, whereas those forming only oögonia had developed from the female basal cells. In addition to the aberrant female strain previously mentioned, certain of Jordan's gross cultures were composed of strains which never produced sex organs. Some of these when isolated and paired with strains of known sexual potentiality proved to be male, others, female, but there remained a few which showed no sexual potentiality whatsoever. Jordan's preliminary work, therefore, established experimentally what had been suspected as being the reason for the sterile strains reported from time to time by various investigators and so frequently found in nature, that is, that *S. elongatus*, like *Dictyuchus* of the Saprolegniaceae (Couch, 1926b), was heterothallic. It also showed that there existed in nature a female strain which could form oögonial initials without contact with the opposite sex, as well as other strains which under ordinary conditions showed no reactions to either sex.

Bishop (1940), starting from single-zoospore isolations, extended the study of this fungus and grew it in pure artificial culture. Thirty-nine pure cultures derived from single zoospores were obtained. Of these, seventeen were intensively studied. Four were found to be strongly male and could be distinguished not only by the formation of antheridial branches but by their greater rate of growth. One was classified as "weakly male," five were neuter or neutral, one "weakly female," and six "strongly female." The strongly male and strongly female strains when mated formed reproductive organs (the former, antheridia, the latter, oögonia); the eggs were fertilized, and normal oöspores were developed. There was some evidence that the formation and direction of growth of the antheridial branches were positive responses to substances diffusing from the female; this suggests a hormone-control mechanism similar to that found in *Achlya* by J. Raper (1939a, 1939b, *et seq.*, see p. 798). Evidence derived from various combinations indicated also that, whereas the male strains never showed signs of latent femaleness when grown alone, all female strains under such conditions exhibited undoubted latent maleness, could form antheridial branches, and could even fertilize their own oögonia. Since all the cultures used for critical experimental work were derived from single zoospores, which have been shown by Kevorkian (1935), using cytological methods, to be uninucleate, the older theory postulating that each nucleus possesses the potentialities of but one sex could not be applied here to explain the sexual phenomena found in *Sapromyces elongatus.* On the basis of the results of these investigations Bishop concluded that the theory of "relative sexuality" proposed by Hartmann (1925), rather than the "heterothallism" of Blakeslee, best explained the observed facts. He pointed out that heterothallism implied the strict unisexuality of the individual, whereas relative sexuality postulated that there were:

> ...even in single nuclei, male potencies (A) and female potencies (G) under the control of male realisators (alpha) and female realisators (gamma). In the male strains of haplogenotypic, heterothallic organisms, the male realisator (alpha) is at once the means of activation of the male potency (A) and the inhibition of the female potency (G). The reverse is true in the female strains of such organisms, where the female realisator (gamma) activates the female potency (G) at the expense of the male potency (A).....

On this hypothesis Bishop has indicated that the following types of sexuality may be present in *S. elongatus:* pure male (*MM*), male with latent femaleness (*Mf*), neutral, strongly sexed (*MF*), neutral, weakly sexed (*mf*), female with latent maleness (*mF*), and pure female (*FF*). Of the seventeen single-zoospore cultures studied by Bishop, there were five of the *MM* type, seven of the *mF* type, and five of the *mf* type. He suggests that further collections may reveal the *FF*, *Mf*, and *MF* types.

CYTOLOGY

Representatives of all genera of the Leptomitales save *Mindeniella* have been studied cytologically and their nuclear behavior, consequently, is well known.

In the types examined (*Leptomitus lacteus*, *Apodachlya brachynema*, *Sapromyces elongatus*, *Araiospora pulchra*, and *Rhipidium interruptum*) the thallus is multinucleate, with the nuclei scattered throughout a peripheral layer of cytoplasm lining a central vacuole. Nuclei are especially abundant in the growing apices. Kevorkian (1935) states that the numerous nuclei found in the basal cell of *S. elongatus* result from the repeated mitotic divisions of the single nucleus of the zoospore during its germination. In the basal cell of *Rhipidium*, which is even more developed than that of *Sapromyces*, Behrens (1931) noted that the many nuclei formed migrate into the developing hyphal branches, which as a result become nucleated.

The nuclei appear to flow with the protoplasm into the rudiments of the zoosporangia, for no division figures have been observed. Once the sporangium attains its full size it is cut off from its attendant hypha by a basal hyaline plug. The nuclei are at first irregularly arranged in the

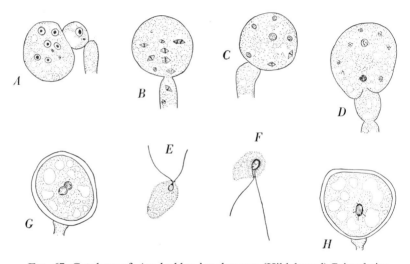

FIG. 67. Cytology of *Apodachlya brachynema* (Hildebrand) Pringsheim

A. Immature terminal oögonium and hypogynous antheridium, showing arrangement of nuclei. *B*. Simultaneous mitoses in oögonium and antheridium. *C*. Oögonium with nuclei in peripheral position prior to their degeneration. *D*. Oögonium and antheridium, showing gamete nuclei and a number of degenerating peripheral nuclei. *E*. Primary zoospore with the two anterior flagella each connected to a distinct basal granule, which in turn is connected to nucleus by a delicate strand. *F*. Secondary swarmer, with the two laterally placed flagella each attached to a distinct basal granule, which in turn is attached to nucleus. *G*. Oögonium with thickened wall (oöspore?), with the two gamete nuclei closely associated but not yet fused. *H*. Oögonium bearing nearly completely fused nuclei, from which a few astral rays emanate.

(*A–D, G–H*, Kevorkian, 1935; *E–F*, Cotner, 1930b)

rudiment, but eventually a central vacuole forms, around which, at least in certain species, they become regularly disposed in one or two layers. Lines of cleavage then extend from the vacuole outward (Behrens, 1931) and divide the contents into uninucleated segments of approximately equal size. These segments, the zoospore initials, become flagellate before their discharge from the sporangium. The precise method of formation of the delicate whip-like flagella is, however, understandably obscure.

In the motile primary pip-shaped zoospores of *Apodachlya* the nucleus is in the anterior part of the body. The two apical flagella are connected to separate "basal granules" of nuclear origin (Cotner, 1930b), and these, in turn, by delicate fibrillar structures to the tip of the beaked nucleus (Cotner, *loc. cit.*; Kevorkian, 1935) (Fig. 67 E). The secondary swarmers in all genera of the order appear to be nearly uniform in internal structure and organization of the nucleus, which is more centrally disposed than in the primary zoospore. In all secondary types of zoospores the nucleus is somewhat beaked. Occasionally two opposite beaks are formed (Cotner, *loc. cit.*). In *A. brachynema* there emerge from the tip of the beak, which is usually darker-staining, either two delicate fibrillar strands or a single one. The latter is supposedly composed of two fused fibrils (Cotner, *loc. cit.*) connecting with basal granules from which the oppositely directed flagella have their origin (Fig. 67 F). In the secondary zoospore of *Rhipidium interruptum* (Cotner, *loc. cit.*) the basal granules are united with a more massive chromatic body which is adjacent to the nucleus. Cotner considers these basal granules of nuclear origin, and intimately connected with the formation and control of the flagella. He points out that they are present wherever flagella are found and that if more than the usual number of granules are formed a corresponding number of flagella appear. He describes the "basal apparatus" as consisting of several granules, two of which usually remain within the nucleus to form its dark-staining beak, whereas the third is on the periphery of the cytoplasm at the base of the flagellum. Cotner also asserts that even though the granules are of nuclear origin, once formed they appear to function even after separation from the nucleus. He thus indicates that the flagella may arise from and be controlled by differentiated parts of the nuclear material rather than by the whole nucleus.

The well-coördinated movement of these swarmers through the water seems, however, to indicate that there is some central controlling body, most likely the main body of the nucleus, of which the granules are, after all, an integral part.

It is in the sexual stage that the most interesting nuclear phenomena are to be found. Since members of the two families differ somewhat from each other in this phase they will be considered separately.

In the Leptomitaceae sexuality is known in *Apodachlya* and *Apodach-lyella*. Only *Apodachlya brachynema*, however, has been investigated cytologically. In this species (Kevorkian, 1935) the oögonium is terminal and the antheridium is the hyphal segment immediately below it (Fig. 67 A, p. 862). The male organ at maturity contains from three to four spherical nuclei which are scattered in the protoplasm. These undergo a simultaneous mitotic division, after which one nucleus enlarges and the remainder degenerate. Meanwhile a simple pore has been formed on the membrane separating the two gametangia, through which the contents pass into the oögonium. No specialized fertilization tube is produced. The developing oögonium possesses at first from ten to twenty nuclei, which have been carried into it by the inflow of proto-plasm prior to the formation of the basal septum separating it from the antheridial cell. These nuclei are at first more or less evenly distributed in the protoplasm. When the oögonium achieves its maximum size and is separated from the antheridium a single simultaneous mitotic division of these nuclei occurs. This division is coincidental with that in the antheridium (Fig. 67 B). The nuclei of the two organs may not, however, all be at the same stage of division. All but one of the nuclei in the oögonium make their way, possibly by means of vacuolar activity, to the periphery of the oösphere. The single favored nucleus assumes a central position and enlarges, attaining ultimately from two to three times its original size (2.5–3.5 μ in diameter). The peripheral nuclei then degenerate (Fig. 67 C). A poorly defined irregular coenocentrum sur-rounds the egg nucleus. The male nucleus, upon its entrance into the oögonium by way of the pore, migrates toward the nucleus of the egg (Fig. 67 D) and makes contact with it. Both then enlarge. A few astral rays emanate from the region of the nuclei. Actual fusion, however, may not take place until the oöspore wall is in the process of thickening

(Fig. 67 G–H). No cytological details of germination are given. Reduction division presumably occurs at germination, at which time the multinucleate germ tubes are formed.

In the Rhipidiaceae the sexual process is of a higher type, although the general sequence of nuclear activity is essentially the same as that in *Apodachlya*. In *Sapromyces elongatus* (Kevorkian, 1935) the oögonia and the antheridia are formed on different branches and usually on separate thalli. The antheridium contains from four to six nuclei, which are similar to those found in the sporangia and the oögonia. These undergo a single simultaneous mitotic division, after which all but one degenerate. Meanwhile a fertilization tube has been produced which penetrates the wall of the oögonium and reaches the oösphere. One male nucleus is discharged through this tube into the egg. The developing oögonium contains from ten to twelve spherical nuclei, which have been carried into it with the inflowing protoplasm. It is not clear when the basal cross wall is laid down. The contents of the oögonium become vacuolate, however, and the nuclei undergo a single simultaneous mitotic division. All save one favored nucleus now migrate to the periphery and degenerate. Occasionally degeneration of the supernumerary nuclei may occur without their migration. The gamete nucleus then enlarges and occupies the center of the egg. At some time before fertilization the oögonial contents become differentiated into a large central mass of oöplasm and a thin peripheral layer of periplasm into which the supernumerary nuclei have migrated. The periplasm continues to become less granular than the oöplasm, and a thin membrane eventually separates the two. Evidently during or prior to the delimitation of the inner periplasmic membrane (the time is not mentioned) the male nucleus is discharged into the oöplasm through the fertilization tube. As in *Apodachlya brachynema* a coenocentrum and a few astral rays are developed. Nuclear fusion is delayed, but, from the figures given, it seems to occur before formation of the oöspore wall.

The investigations of King (1903) on *Araiospora pulchra* and particularly those of Behrens (1931) on *Rhipidium interruptum* give the most complete accounts of the cytology of members of the Rhipidiaceae. In *R. interruptum* the oögonium originates in exactly the same fashion as the sporangium, the two structures being indistinguishable at first. About

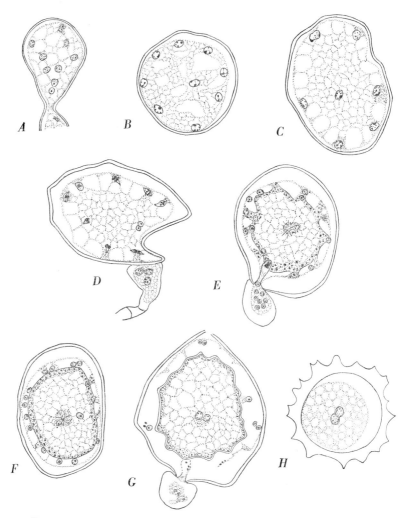

FIG. 68. Cytology of sexual organs of *Rhipidium interruptum* Cornu

A. Young oögonium; cytoplasm is vacuolate and nuclei have already begun to move toward periphery; cross wall has not as yet cut off oögonium from hypha; the two basal, lighter-stained nuclei have probably just recently entered oögonium. *B.* Mature oögonium; nuclei have all, with one exception, assumed a peripheral position; cytoplasm is alveolate and contains large vacuoles. *C.* Oögonium shortly before nuclear division; differentiation into periplasm and

thirty or thirty-five nuclei migrate into the developing oögonium before it is separated from its hypha by a cross wall (Fig. 68 A, p. 866). In the mature oögonium all save one of the nuclei are arranged around the periphery (Fig. 68 B). No single large central vacuole is formed, as is characteristic of the sporangium, but, rather, several large irregularly disposed ones appear.

Each of the nuclei has a fairly prominent dark-stained nucleolus and several dark-stained peripheral granules. Differentiation of the content of the oögonium then ensues. The peripheral material forms numerous polygonal vacuoles, whereas the inner, main content develops a fairly regular meshwork of smaller vacuoles. The supernumerary nuclei are arranged in the protoplasmic meshwork in a thin vacuolate layer of periplasm or between the periplasm and the oöplasm, and the single oögonial nucleus is in approximately the center of the somewhat denser oöplasm (Fig. 68 C, p. 866). There follows an almost simultaneous mitotic division of all the nuclei (Fig. 68 D). The spindles produced during this process have no definite orientation and are intranuclear. After division the periplasm in which the now paired smaller supernumerary nuclei lie becomes more deeply stained. Evidences of nuclear degeneration are apparent. One of the two central nuclei becomes the egg nucleus; the other, like the periplasmic nuclei, degenerates.

The antheridium, the broad apex of which is applied near the base

---

oöplasm is completed. *D.* Nuclear division in oögonium; the three visible nuclei of antheridium have not as yet divided. *E.* Oögonium, showing a single central beaked egg nucleus with a centrosome from which radiate striae; resorption of periplasm is in progress and strongly stained inclusions have made their appearance around periphery of egg; first indications of wall formation are visible; antheridium has produced fertilization tube, its nuclei have divided, and one gamete nucleus has just entered base of tube; deep-staining material at tip of tube indicates that deliquescence of apex has begun. *F.* Oögonium in which male nucleus is shown approaching larger egg nucleus; degeneration of supernumerary nuclei and resorption of periplasm is in progress; dark-staining peripheral material is clearly defined, as is wall. *G.* Egg with large, nearly like-sized, paired male and female nuclei; oöspore wall has taken on its typical contour; periplasm has for most part been resorbed, though occasional periplasmic nuclei still persist, as does fertilization tube. *H.* Mature oöspore; nuclei have not as yet fused.

(Behrens, 1931)

of the oögonium, is cut off from its branch by a cellulin plug (Fig. 68 D, p. 866). It contains about four nuclei. The oögonial wall at the point of application of the antheridium bulges out, papilla-like, possibly because of the slighter resistance of the wall at this point to the internal pressure of the oögonium. This protuberance then springs into a correspondingly formed cavity of the antheridium. Thus the antheridium and the oögonium are brought into intimate contact. Because of the constancy of point of application of the antheridium to the oögonium, Behrens raises the question as to whether or not the female structure emits material attractive to the antheridial branch. The four antheridial nuclei are like those of the oögonium, but stain more intensely. Soon after mitosis has occurred in the oögonium they too undergo a single mitotic division. Only one of the eight nuclei thus formed persists; the remainder degenerate. Soon after this nuclear division the wall of the oögonium dissolves at the point of application of the antheridium, and the antheridium produces a fertilization tube (Fig. 68 E). At the time of entrance of the fertilization tube into the oöplasm there occurs a progressive resorption of the periplasm and an increase in the amount of the deep-staining peripheral oöplasmic material. A delicate membrane is laid down between the vacuolated periplasm with its supernumerary nuclei and the oöplasm. The egg nucleus at this time is as yet unfused with the male nucleus. It possesses a perceptible beak with centrosome-like granules at the tip (Fig. 68 E). Delicate polar rays which extend beyond a darker-stained coenocentrum are clearly visible. Upon the dissolution of the tip of the fertilization tube a single male nucleus is discharged, and this apparently moves fairly quickly to the vicinity of the somewhat larger egg nucleus (Fig. 68 F). The tenuous membrane delimiting the periplasm now becomes continuous, completely separates the oöplasm from the dwindling periplasm, and gradually thickens and becomes doubly contoured, the accretion evidently being derived from the previously mentioned deeper-stained outer layer of the oöplasm. As the wall thickens, this outer layer slowly decreases. The double contour of the wall is visible even before the rays have vanished from the female nucleus. The residue of periplasm and the supernumerary nuclei then disappear. At the same time the oöspore wall thickens and assumes by unequal accretions, aided no doubt by outside material, its characteristic irregular contour. The irregularities of the oöspore wall are not, however, Behrens says, related to the honeycomb-like original disposition of the periplasm, as Minden and others have asserted. That is, the thin primary wall does not form around both periplasm and oöplasm, but originates as an outgrowth from the smooth wall which has been described as lying between the two. During maturation of the oöspore the gamete nuclei remain in close proximity and assume equal size (Fig. 68 G). Not even in the fully mature oöspore was fusion observed (Fig. 68 H). Judging from this, Behrens supposes that karyogamy occurs shortly before germination. Neither of these two processes was observed, however.

In *Araiospora pulchra* the sexual process and the accompanying nuclear phenomena (as described by King, 1903) appear similar to those of *Rhipidium interruptum*, although differences in interpretation are apparent. Cytoplasm and from thirty to thirty-five nuclei migrate into the developing oögonium, which is eventually cut off by a plug from its hypha. The nuclei pass out along radii of the oögonium and become regularly disposed in a peripheral position. The contents at this time are an undifferentiated cytoplasmic meshwork surrounding large irregular vacuoles. As development proceeds, these vacuoles disappear, and the central region becomes more uniformly vacuolate. Near the periphery other regularly placed vacuoles increase in size until the cytoplasm in this region is coarse-meshed. The nuclei, in the interval, have come to rest in the cytoplasmic strands between the vacuoles. In the central region prominent isolated fine-meshed patches appear. King presumes that these eventually fuse to form the coenocentrum, a structure which possibly helps draw the sex nuclei into proximity with one another. Meanwhile differentiation into oöplasm and periplasm has taken place, and at some time a mitotic division of the nuclei has occurred, although the evidence for this is admittedly scanty. The origin of the nucleus of the female gamete was not observed. To judge from the figures given, it is probable that, as in *Rhipidium*, this nucleus assumes at once a central position in the oögonium. As the oöplasm is cut off from the periplasm, a radial division of the intervacuolar strands of the latter gives rise to a large number of cells. Cell walls are then laid down between adjacent peripheral cells, as well as between these and the central oöplasm.

A receptive papilla is formed from a differentiated portion of the egg, just within the oögonial wall at the point of application of the antheridium. A fertilization tube is produced which King considers to be laid down by periplasmic material, not by the antheridium. This point is contrary to Thaxter's observations on living plants of *Araiospora pulchra* and Kevorkian's (1934) with respect to a congeneric form, *A. streptandra*. Behrens, too, concludes from his cytological study of *Rhipidium interruptum* that King was in error, and shows that the fertilization tube in *Rhipidium*, after its tip has deliquesced, gives the appearance of being a canal of oögonial origin. The antheridium contains from five to seven nuclei. From the fact that the older antheridia contained twice this number, it was presumed that here, as in the oögonial nuclei, a mitotic division had occurred. At fertilization a single nucleus is introduced into the egg; the remainder degenerate. While the two sexual nuclei approach the center of the egg (and each other) they become beaked, as though a mutual attraction existed between them. No nuclear fusion was found, and wholly mature oöspores were always binucleate. Like Behrens, King suggests that karyogamy probably occurs at the close of the rest period undergone by the oöspore.

During the maturation of the oöspore the nuclei increase in size. If, as is usual, a large central reserve globule is formed, they are displaced laterally. Although the point is not clearly brought out by King there is much evidence in the figures given to indicate that in *Araiospora pulchra* the wall of the oöspore proper is formed in much the same manner as was described by Behrens for *Rhipidium*. The cellular envelope, so characteristic of *Araiospora* (Fig. 70 D, F–G, p. 890) but not found in *Rhipidium*, appears to be formed directly from the periplasm.

PHYSIOLOGY

Precise knowledge of the metabolic processes and conditions necessary for growth in members of the order is confined chiefly to two genera of the Leptomitaceae, *Leptomitus* and *Apodachlya*. Schade (1940) and Schade and Thimann (1940) made comparative physiological investigations of *L. lacteus* and *A. brachynema*. The more extensive literature pertinent to the physiology of *Leptomitus* is cited in their papers. Findings by Gilpin (1954) on the carbon and nitrogen requirements for growth in *Apodachlya brachynema* do not completely agree with previous reports on nutrition in this species. Those interested should consult his paper. With respect to the Rhipidiaceae, Minden (1916) earlier described the growing in culture of species of *Rhipidium* and *Araiospora* in various natural and synthetic media. Subsequently, Bishop (1940) pointed out something of the nutritional requirements of *Sapromyces elongatus* ("*S. reinschii*"), but neither of these workers attempted a comprehensive study nor presented an extensive analysis of his results. Emerson (1950) isolated *Rhipidium americanum* in pure artificial culture by streaking zoospores, produced at 15° C., on agar plates of glucose-yeast media. Similarly, he also brought *Sapromyces androgynus* into pure culture and, very recently (comm.), *Mindeniella spinospora*. Webster (1943) mentioned that *Araiospora streptandra* had been brought into pure culture and that the formation of spiny sporangia was aided by favorable conditions of nutrition, smooth ones by reduction of nutrition. He also said that smooth-walled sporangia discharge their zoospores "in a shorter time" than do the spiny ones, and that they are the chief means of dispersal of the species.

SYSTEMATIC ACCOUNT

LEPTOMITALES

MICROSCOPIC saprophytic fresh-water fungi, the thallus with or without a well-defined basal cell and holdfasts, the hyphae divided into constricted pseudocells by pseudosepta of cellulin, walls giving a cellulose reaction; reproductive organs consisting of segments of the hyphae or specialized pedicellate structures cut off by cross walls and constrictions from the attendant mycelium; zoosporangia forming mono- or diplanetic biflagellate zoospores; oögonia with or without periplasm, forming (except in *Apodachlyella*) a single egg; antheridium either a single segment or borne on specialized branches of mono- or diclinous origin, with or without a fertilization tube; oöspores single (except in *Apodachlyella*), thick-walled, upon germination forming hyphae.

The order differs from the Saprolegniales primarily in the division of the thallus into pseudocells by pseudosepta, the pedicellate reproductive organs, and the formation of a single (except in *Apodachlyella*) egg in the oögonium.

KEY TO THE FAMILIES OF THE LEPTOMITALES

Thallus filamentous throughout, not differentiated into a basal cell and
   hyphal branches; zoospores diplanetic; oögonial contents not
   differentiated into oöplasm and periplasm..... LEPTOMITACEAE, p. 872
Thallus more or less well differentiated into holdfasts, basal cell, and
   hyphal branches; zoospores only of the secondary type; oögonial
   contents differentiated into oöplasm and periplasm
                                                        RHIPIDIACEAE, p. 882

LEPTOMITACEAE

Thallus filamentous throughout, conspicuously jointed and pseudo-septate, of unlimited growth, contents bearing refractive granules of cellulin; zoosporangia either undifferentiated hyphal segments or specialized pedicellate smooth-walled structures; zoospores diplanetic, the primary swarmers apically biflagellate, the secondary laterally biflagellate; oögonium forming one or several oöspheres the contents of which are homogeneous and not differentiated into oöplasm and periplasm, oöspore smooth-walled, at germination forming several germ tubes which reëstablish the thallus; antheridium a relatively unspecialized segment of the thallus which subtends the oögonium, not forming a fertilization tube.

Saprophytic on various types of submerged debris, frequently fruits and twigs, in fresh water.

KEY TO THE GENERA OF THE LEPTOMITACEAE

Sex organs never formed; plant coarse, the zoosporangia being undifferentiated segments of the mycelium .... LEPTOMITUS, p. 873
Sex organs formed under ordinary conditions of culture; plant more
   delicate, the zoosporangia (if formed) being well-defined pedicellate structures
   Oögonium forming a single oöspore .... APODACHLYA, p. 874
   Oögonium forming more than one oöspore .... APODACHLYELLA, p. 881

LEPTOMITUS Agardh

Systema algarum, p. 47. 1824

(Fig. 69 A–B, p. 875)

Apodya Cornu, Ann. Sci. Nat. Bot., V, 15: 14. 1872.

Thallus stout at the base, filamentous throughout, monopodial, dichotomously branched near the base, the hyphae constricted and pseudoseptate at intervals, the branches arising at the constrictions, apparently without specialized holdfasts, each segment containing one or more cellulin discs; sporangia formed from unspecialized or lateral segments of the mycelium, terminal or developed in basipetal succession; zoospores formed in the sporangia in one row (occasionally irregularly disposed), diplanetic, the primary spores apically biflagellate, emerging through a terminal or lateral pore, encysting after a period of swarming, secondary spores laterally (?) biflagellate; sexual organs not observed.

Saprophytic on debris, often in heavily polluted fresh waters.

The secondary zoospore is described only as being biflagellate.

Leptomitus lacteus (Roth) Agardh

Systema algarum, p. 47. 1824

Conferva lactea Roth, Catalecta botanica, 2: 216. 1800.
Leptomitus libertiae Agardh, *loc. cit.*, p. 49. 1824.
Saprolegnia lactea Pringsheim, Jahrb. wiss. Bot., 2: 228, pl. 23, figs. 6–10, pl. 25, figs. 1–6. 1860.
Apodya lactea Cornu, Ann. Sci. Nat. Bot., V, 15: 14. 1872.
Saprolegnia corcagiensis Hartog, Quart. J. Micro. Sci. (N. S.), 27: 429. 1886–87.

Basal segment stout, up to 48 μ in diameter, branches 8–16 μ in diameter, the segments up to 400 μ in length; zoosporangia cylindrical, formed from slightly swollen segments of the mycelium, primary zoospores pyriform, 10.5–11 μ in diameter, secondary zoospores biflagellate.

Forming large turflike masses often of great extent on organic debris, particularly in waters with a high organic content, rarely in purer waters. Roth (*loc. cit.*), Agardh (*loc. cit.*), Braun (1851: 287), Pringsheim (1860: 228, pl. 23, figs. 6–10, pl. 25, figs. 1–6; 1883a: 288, pl. 7, figs. 1–9), Büsgen (1882: 266, pl. 12, figs. 9–15), Schroeter (1885: 255), Kolkwitz

(1901; 1903), Minden (1915: 582, fig. 14b [p. 580]), GERMANY; Dillwyn (1809: pl. 79), GREAT BRITAIN; Dangeard (1890–91b: 118, pl. 6, figs. 24–31), Radais (1898: 144), Guilliermond (1922), FRANCE; Humphrey (1893: 135, pl. 14, fig. 6), Coker (1923: 170, pl. 58), Kevorkian (1935: pl. 19, figs. 10 a–b), UNITED STATES; Tulloch (1934), ALASKA.

Numerous references are found in the older literature to "*Leptomitus*," one of the earliest-studied members of the water fungi, and exsiccati are quoted by Minden (1915: 582). Fischer (1892: 371) has discussed these older records. A careful morphological study of this species is greatly needed. Kolkwitz (1903: 34), Schade (1940), and Schade and Thimann (1940) have made investigations of the physiology of the organism.

APODACHLYA Pringsheim

Berichte Deutsch. Bot. Gesell., 1: 289. 1883

(Fig. 69 C–E, G–K, p. 875)

Thallus filamentous throughout, the hyphae constricted and pseudo-septate at intervals, monopodial, often richly branched, the branches arising at the constrictions, apparently without specialized holdfasts, contents faintly refractive, bearing from one to three cellulin discs in each segment; zoosporangia terminal or sympodially arranged along the hyphae, rarely in basipetal succession, pedicellate, ovoid, pyriform, or occasionally cylindrical, zoospores few, diplanetic, primary spores apically biflagellate, formed in the sporangium, encysting at once at the orifice after discharge or swimming directly away, secondary spores laterally (?) biflagellate, emerging from the cysts after a period of quiescence; oögonia borne singly, terminally or laterally, subtended by a linklike antheridial cell, fertilization tube lacking; oöspore thick-walled, with one or more large globules, borne singly in the oögonium, which it nearly or entirely fills, upon germination forming from one to two germ tubes.

The five known species are primarily inhabitants of twigs and submerged fruits.

The slender slightly refractive or gray lustrous filaments are readily distinguishable from the coarser ones of *Achlya*, with which they often occur.

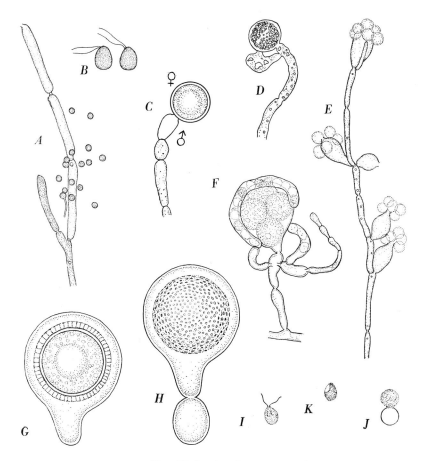

FIG. 69. Leptomitaceae

A–B. Leptomitus lacteus (Roth) Agardh: *A*, portion of plant three of whose segments have discharged their zoospores; latter have encysted; *B*, zoospores after treatment with iodine. *C*. Sex organs of *Apodachlya brachynema* (Hildebrand) Pringsheim. *D*. Sex organs of *Apodachlya minima* Coker and Leitner. *E. Apodachlya pyrifera* Zopf, portion of plant with encysted zoospores at orifices of sporangia. *F. Apodachlyella completa* (Humphrey) Indoh, sex organs. *G–H.* Oöspore of *Apodachlya punctata* Minden: *G*, optical section, showing structure of wall; *H*, surface view, showing punctations (drawn from a photomicrograph). *I–K. Apodachlya brachynema* (Hildebrand) Pringsheim: *I*, primary, apically biflagellate zoospore; *J*, secondary zoospore

Coker (1923) and Kevorkian (1935) describe the oögonium as lacking periplasm. In the development of the sex organs of *Apodachlya brachynema* Coker observed that the future antheridial cell reached its mature size before the oögonium appeared. The latter was then formed by the enlargement of a small globular outgrowth produced at the apex of the antheridium (see "Sexual Reproduction," p. 856).

KEY TO THE SPECIES OF APODACHLYA

Oöspore smooth-walled, not punctate
  Sporangia, if formed, developed singly or in clusters, not in basipetal
    succession
    Oögonia borne at the tips of short moniliform segments; zoo-
      spores, if present, rarely encysting at the orifice of the spo-
      rangium
      Antheridium the suboögonial cell; sporangia formed in abun-
        dance .... *A. brachynema*, p. 876
      Antheridium borne on a short lateral outgrowth beneath the
        oögonium; sporangia rarely formed .... *A. minima*, p. 878
    Oögonia borne at the tips of the main axes, occasionally laterally,
      subtended by an antheridial cell; zoospores generally encyst-
      ing at the orifice of the sporangium .... *A. pyrifera*, p. 879
  Sporangia developed in basipetal succession or singly.. *A. seriata*, p. 880
Oöspore wall minutely punctate .... *A. punctata*, p. 880

APODACHLYA BRACHYNEMA (Hildebrand) Pringsheim

Berichte Deutsch. Bot. Gesell., 1: 289. 1883

(Fig. 69 C, I–K, p. 875)

Leptomitus brachynema Hildebrand, Jahrb. wiss. Bot., 6: 261, pl. 16, figs.
  12–23. 1867–68.
Apodya brachynema (Hildebrand) Cornu, Ann. Sci. Nat. Bot., V, 15: 14.
  1872.

Mycelium branched, the segments 20–185 μ long by 4–23 μ in diameter, generally becoming shorter near the sporangia, the lateral branches mostly distal, often moniliform; sporangia terminal, single

of same fungus emerging from cyst; *K*, secondary zoospore; flagella are not shown, but are laterally inserted.
  (*A–B*, Pringsheim, 1860; *C*, *I–K*, Coker, 1923; *D*, Coker and Leitner, 1938; *E*, Zopf, 1888; *F*, Indoh, 1939)

or several, sympodially arranged or in clusters, subspherical, ovoid, ellipsoidal, or pyriform, with an apical, subapical, or lateral somewhat prolonged discharge papilla, 23–76 μ long by 23–44 μ in diameter; zoospores from six to twenty, primary spores broadly ovoid, 12–14 μ (long?), apically biflagellate, swimming directly from the sporangium before encysting, cysts spherical, 8.5–10 μ in diameter, secondary zoospores biflagellate; oögonia spherical or broadly pyriform, 23.5–29 μ in diameter, terminal, borne singly at the tips of short lateral moniliform segments, the subapical segment functioning as the antheridium; oöspore single, 20–40 μ in diameter, filling the oögonium, wall smooth, about 1.8 μ thick, contents finely granular, with small regularly disposed globules, a vacuole, and from one to two large eccentric globules, upon germination producing a germ tube (?).

On twigs, Hildebrand (*loc. cit.*), Höhnk (1938: 491, figs. 1,2), GER-MANY; Thaxter (1896b: 325), termite, Coker (1923: 173, pl. 59), fruits of apple and *Crataegus*, Kanouse (1927: 338), Harvey (1930: 327), apples and twigs, Sparrow (1932b: 296; 1933c: 532), Wolf (1944: 44), UNITED STATES; twigs of *Prunus yedoensis*, *P. grayana*, *Quercus sp.*, Indoh (1953: 26, figs. 13, 14), JAPAN; decaying culm, Shen and Siang (1948: 198), CHINA; various twigs, Barbier (1950: 28, figs. 1–12), FRANCE.

Kevorkian (1935: 279) mentions that the oöspores of *Apodachlya brachynema* germinate, presumably by a germ tube, but no details of the process are given. The cytological details of fertilization and the role played by the subterminal antheridium have been described (Kevorkian, *loc. cit.*).

APODACHLYA BRACHYNEMA f. MAJOR, stat. nov.

Apodachlya brachynema var. *major* Tiesenhausen, Arch. f. Hydrobiol. u. Planktonk., 7(2): 297, fig. 20. 1912.

Mycelium little branched, hyphae 6–13 μ in diameter, segments 15–537 μ long; sporangia spherical, rarely elongate, 40–52 μ (long?), discharge tube large, 10–20 μ long by 6–10 μ in diameter; zoospores not observed; oöspore spherical, 25–30 μ in diameter.

On twigs, SWITZERLAND.

Differing from *Apodachlya brachynema* principally in having longer sporangia and larger hyphae. As Coker (1923) suggests, this is probably only a form rather than a variety.

APODACHLYA MINIMA Coker and Leitner

J. Elisha Mitchell Sci. Soc., 54: 313, pl. 39. 1938

(Fig. 69 D, p. 875)

"Mycelium flaccid and flocculent, reaching a diameter of 2.5–3 cm. on hemp seed; main hyphae slender and segmented, branching from any point on the segment, mainly from the middle; protoplasm thin except in the oögonial branches, with small round refractive bodies present; segments $3.4–8.5 \times 47.6–170$ μ on hemp seed, but $6–12.2 \times 44–250$ μ on 2 % corn meal agar, becoming shorter at the tips. Sporangia unknown... [Various experiments to produce them were unsuccessful.] Oögonia numerous, borne on the tips of short, moniliform, often recurved, lateral branches, mainly spherical, occasionally short-pyriform or oval or club-shaped or dumbbell-shaped, $12–16$ μ thick; wall unpitted, smooth, about 0.45 μ thick. Egg single, completely filling the oogonium, excentric, the cytoplasm rounded up into a hyaline ball closely appressed to the smaller hyaline oil droplet. Antheridium originating from the suboogonial cell as a lateral branch which grows out and applies itself to the oogonial wall, variable in shape, usually becoming completely empty before the maturation of the egg" (Coker and Leitner, *loc. cit.*).

In a stream slightly contaminated with sewage, substratum (?), UNITED STATES.

Johnson (1955c) observed the zoosporangial stage of this species. Whereas the sizes of the sporangia ($17.6–26.2$ by $12.8–17.6$ μ) suggest those of *Apodachlya pyrifera*, their arrangement is quite different. In most instances they are produced in glomerules and only rarely singly. Very few zoospores were found. These encysted at once upon emergence, the cysts being $6.5–8.0$ μ in diameter.

APODACHLYA PYRIFERA Zopf

Nova Acta Acad. Leop.-Carol., 52: 367, pl. 21, figs. 1–21. 1888
(Fig. 69 E, p. 875)

Leptomitus piriferus Zopf, in Schenk, Handbuch d. Bot.......,4: 299. 1890.

Mycelium extensive, matted, sympodially branched, the segments
long or short, somewhat clavate distally, contents with one or two cellulin bodies in each segment, especially near the constrictions; sporangia terminal, single or in pairs, broadly obpyriform, citriform, fusiform, ovoid, or ellipsoidal, 12–24 μ long by 12–20 μ in diameter, papilla
usually terminal or somewhat lateral, with or without a short discharge
tube; primary zoospores from six to twenty, encysting at the orifice or
swimming directly away, laterally biflagellate (secondary?) spores;
oögonium spherical, generally terminal, or lateral on a short segment
near a constriction, rarely intercalary, the antheridium suboögonial or
lateral; oöspore spherical, filling the oögonium, with a thick smooth
double wall, contents with a large oil globule, germination not observed.

On decaying Characeae, Zopf (*loc. cit.*), twigs, Höhnk (1935: 218),
substratum (?), Richter (1937), Cejp[1] (1932b: 1, pl. 1, figs. 6–9, pl. 2
figs. 4–6), GERMANY; twigs, H. E. Petersen (1909: 388; 1910: 526), Lund
(1934: 33), DENMARK; Thaxter (1896b: 325), birch twigs, Sparrow
(1933c: 532), UNITED STATES; in soil, Wolf (1939: 384), MEXICO; twigs
of *Pyrus pashia*, Shen and Siang (1948: 197, fig. 9), CHINA.

The species name was spelled "*piriferus*" by Zopf in 1890 and
"*pyrifera*" in 1888.

APODACHLYA PYRIFERA f. MACROSPORANGIA, stat. nov.

Apodachlya pyrifera var. *macrosporangia* Tiesenhausen, Arch. f. Hydrobiol.
u. Planktonk., 7(2):295, fig. 19a–c. 1912.

Mycelium sparingly branched, hyphae 5–15 μ in diameter, segments
70–430 μ long, mostly over 100 μ long; sporangia generally single,
terminal or on short lateral branches, pyriform or ellipsoidal, 35–63 μ
long by 14–36 μ in diameter, with a short apical or subapical discharge
tube, often collapsing after discharge; zoospores from four to twenty-
four, primary spores encysting at the orifice, the cysts 11 μ in diameter,
secondary spores spherical, 10–11 μ in diameter; oögonium spherical

[1] Czechoslovakia.

27–31.5 μ in diameter, borne at the tip of a short, two-linked lateral branch arising from the middle of a segment, the antheridium being a lateral link of the same hypha or apparently arising laterally from the same main axis; oöspore spherical, filling the oögonium, 25–33 μ in diameter, with a smooth thick colorless wall and two or more globules, germination not observed.

On twigs of *Picea excelsa*, Tiesenhausen (*loc. cit.*), SWITZERLAND; *Fraxinus* twigs, Sparrow (1932b: 295), UNITED STATES; twigs, Lund (1934: 33), DENMARK.

Although the form, so far as now known, differs primarily in the larger size of the sporangia, a more careful study of the sex organs may reveal other features of divergence. Deviation in size of sporangia alone hardly warrants varietal rank in this group of fungi.

APODACHLYA SERIATA Lund

Kgl. Danske Vidensk. Selsk. Skrift., Naturv. Math., Afd. IX, 6 (1): 34, fig. 14. 1934

"Hyphae branched, constricted into segments, which are 42.5–100 × 5–10 μ, mostly 70–80 × 5–8 μ. Sporangia pyriform, oval, or subcylindrical 35–97 × 15–25 μ, generally 50–60 × 20 μ, terminal on main hyphae, more rarely on lateral branches, or in rows up to four. Zoospores 10–12 μ in diameter, about 26 in a sporangium; escaping through a short apical exit tube, encysting in a hollow sphere at the mouth of the sporangium. Resting spores (oögonia?) spherical, 27–32.5 μ in diameter, generally borne on short side branches, composed of one to few short segments. 1 oospore (?). Antheridia possibly present" (Lund, *loc. cit.*).

On twigs of *Alnus*, DENMARK.

Characterized by long sporangia, which are often in basipetal series.

APODACHLYA PUNCTATA Minden

Kryptogamenfl. Mark Brandenburg, 5: 586, fig. 15 b–d (p. 580). 1912 (1915)

(Fig. 69 G–H, p. 875)

Mycelium like that of *Apodachlya pyrifera*, forming a whitish turf; sporangia spherical, subspherical, ovoid to pyriform, terminal or sympodially arranged, numerous, discharge tube usually lateral or even basal; zoospores ordinarily swimming directly away, rarely encysting at the orifice; oögonium either terminal on the main axis or on a short linklike lateral branch, antheridium basal; oöspore nearly filling the oögonium, thick-walled, golden, the wall minutely and distinctly punctate, germination not observed.

On twigs, Minden (*loc. cit.*), Höhnk (1935: 218), GERMANY; twigs of *Fraxinus*, Sparrow (1933c: 532), UNITED STATES.

Certain investigators (Coker, 1923: 174; Coker and Leitner, 1938: 313) consider the punctations of the egg to be due to the arrangement of oil globules, but in this they are mistaken. Photomicrographs of plasmolyzed oöspores show unquestionably that the wall is punctate.

APODACHLYELLA INDOH

Science Rep. Tokyo Bunrika Daigaku, Sect. B, 4: 45–46. 1939

(Fig. 69 F, p. 875)

"Mycelium filamentous, branched, segmented by numerous constrictions, without basal body. Hyphal segments cylindrical with cellulin grains. Hyphal membrane stainable faintly blue with zinc chloride-iodine.

"Zoosporangium not observed.

"Oogonia multisporous. Oospores without periplasmic membrane. Antheridia with several antheridial cells. Fertilization by a tube from each cell.

"Other characters as in *Apodachlya*.

"Single species" (Indoh, *loc. cit.*).

Saprophytic in fresh water or soil.

For description of the sex organs, see the introduction to the Leptomitales (p. 858).

APODACHLYELLA COMPLETA (Humphrey) Indoh

Science Rep. Tokyo Bunrika Daigaku, Sect. B, 4: 46, pl. 7, figs. 1–11. 1939

Apodachlya (?) *completa* Humphrey, Trans. Amer. Phil. Soc., 17: 137, pl. 20, figs. 119–121. 1893.

"Mycelium slender, filamentous, irregularly branched. Basal segments of hyphae long, cylindrical, 9 to 12 μ in diam., 130 to 200 μ in length; upper segments rather short, 2.5 to 6 μ in diam., 40 to 100 μ in length. Hyphal membrane smooth, hyaline.

"Zoosporangium unknown.

"Oogonia single, terminal, spherical, 23 to 48 μ in diam., rarely pyriform to broad cylindrical, containing 2 to 12 (usually 4 to 7) oospores; membrane thin, smooth, hyaline. Oospores spherical to subspherical, 16 to 24 μ in diam., with a large eccentric oil drop; membrane 1.5 to 1.8 μ in thickness, punctated when matured. Antheridia terminal, single on from 2 to 3 segmented filamentous antheridial branches arising from segment just below oogonia; long, cylindrical, curved, containing 4 to 10 antheridial cells. Antheridial cells spherical, hyaline, smooth, 4.4 to 4.9 μ in diam., arranged in a single row" (Indoh, *loc. cit.*).

Indoh's observations confirm the fact that the multisporous condition of the oogonium is not due to an extraneous organism.

In fresh water and soil on flies and hemp seeds used as bait. Humphrey (*loc. cit.*), UNITED STATES; Indoh (*loc. cit.*), JAPAN.

KEY TO THE GENERA OF THE RHIPIDIACEAE

Basal cell usually giving rise to hyphal branches bearing the reproductive organs; oöspores formed (except in *Rhipidium parthenosporum*)
    Basal cell slender, usually poorly defined; sporangia smooth-walled;
        oöspore with undulate outer wall . . . . SAPROMYCES, p. 883
    Basal cell usually stout and well defined; sporangia smooth-walled
        or spiny or both; oöspore with reticulate or cellular outer wall
        Oöspore wall cellular; sporangia smooth and spiny-walled
                ARAIOSPORA, p. 887
        Oöspore wall reticulate; sporangia smooth-walled   RHIPIDIUM, p. 893
Basal cell never giving rise to hyphal branches, the reproductive organs
    arising directly from it; parthenospores formed . . . MINDENIELLA, p. 901

RHIPIDIACEAE

Thallus always more or less well differentiated into a basal cell, holdfasts, and jointed hyphal branches on which are borne well-defined pedicellate reproductive organs; zoosporangia smooth- or spiny-walled;

zoospores laterally biflagellate, sometimes containing prominent refractive globules; antheridium single, cut off from its concomitant branch by a cross wall, forming a conspicuous fertilization tube; oögonium forming a single oösphere which is differentiated into oöplasm and periplasm; oöspore with a smooth endospore wall surrounded either by a thick undulate or reticulate exospore wall or a cellular layer, germination not observed.

Primarily saprophytic on submerged twigs and fleshy fruits.

SAPROMYCES K. FRITSCH

Österr. botan. Zeitschr., 43: 420. 1893

(Fig. 70 A–B, p. 890)

Naegelia Reinsch, Jahrb. wiss. Bot., 11: 298. 1878. Non Rabenhorst, 1844; Lindley, 1845; Moritzi, 1846; Regel, 1848.
Naegeliella Schroeter, in Engler and Prantl, Natürlichen Pflanzenfam., 1(1): 103. 1893. Non Correns, 1892.

Thallus differentiated into a poorly defined slender or somewhat distorted epibiotic basal cell and, arising from this, a few repeatedly umbellately branched segmented and constricted cylindrical filaments on which are borne the reproductive organs, segments delimited by pseudosepta, the whole anchored to the substratum by a complex of endobiotic branched holdfasts; zoosporangia smooth-walled, either formed in whorls or umbels at the tips of the segments, from which they are separated by septate constrictions, or appearing lateral; zoospores somewhat reniform, laterally biflagellate, emerging upon the deliquescence of an apical papilla, often surrounded by a more or less evanescent vesicle; antheridium either diclinous or androgynous, borne at the tip of a long or short distal prolongation of the segments, apically applied, with a conspicuous fertilization tube; oögonia monandrous, spherical or pyriform, borne in whorls or umbels or on short constricted segments, the contents at maturity differentiated into oöplasm and periplasm; oöspore borne singly and loosely in the oögonium, wall thick, rough, germination not observed.

The two known species are saprophytic on decaying plant materials, especially twigs, in cool pure waters.

Sapromyces differs from *Araiospora* in the less pronounced, more slender basal cell, in forming only smooth sporangia, and in the fact that the oöspore lacks a cellular envelope of periplasmic origin.

KEY TO THE SPECIES OF SAPROMYCES

Antheridia diclinous .... *S. elongatus*, p. 884
Antheridia androgynous .... *S. androgynus*, p. 886

SAPROMYCES ELONGATUS (Cornu) Coker
N. A. Flora, 2 (1): 62. 1937
(Fig. 70 B, p. 890)

Rhipidium elongatum Cornu, Ann. Sci. Nat. Bot., V, 15: 15.1872.
Naegelia sp., "I" (and "II"?) Reinsch, Jahrb. wiss. Bot., 11: 298, pl. 15, figs. 1–6. 1878.
Naegeliella reinschii Schroeter, in Engler and Prantl, Natürlichen Pflanzenfam., 1(1): 103. 1893.
Sapromyces reinschii (Schroeter) K. Fritsch, Österr. botan. Zeitschr., 43: 421. 1893.

Basal cell slender or somewhat distorted, 300–1200 μ long, including the branched holdfasts, by 15–30 μ in diameter, the apical cylindrical or narrowly clavate secondary axes more slender, constricted and septate at their point of origin, 8–25 μ in diameter and up to 620 μ in length, giving rise distally to from one to several successively narrower segments which may further branch at their apices; sporangia pedicellate, borne singly or in whorls of from two to six at the tips of the branches or at the constrictions, subcylindrical, subclavate, ovoid or ellipsoidal, 35–200 μ long by 10–30 μ in diameter; zoospores reniform, 8–10 μ in diameter, laterally biflagellate; antheridium swollen and irregularly clavate, appressed along its whole length or only by its apex to the upper part of the oögonium, borne on a slender often tortuous branched or unbranched long hypha of diclinous origin, 8–12 by 40–65 μ; oögonium spherical, subspherical, or pyriform, 32–63 μ high by 26–40 μ in diameter, pedicellate, borne terminally or laterally, the outer wall with age often exhibiting a brownish transversely disposed incrustation; oöspore not filling the oögonium, spherical, 20–34 μ in diameter, yellowish to brownish, the thick wall with a slightly uneven outer surface, germination not observed.

On decaying stems of *Viscum*, Reinsch (1875, 1878), substratum (?), coll. Claussen, Minden (1915: 591), pine twigs, Minden (*op. cit.*, p. 590, fig. 11; 1916: pl. 7, fig. 73), apple, twigs, and cones of *Picea*, Cejp[1] (1932c; 1936: 370, text fig. D, pl. 10), Richter (1937), GERMANY; cones and twigs of *Pinus sp.*, Thaxter (1894: 49, pl. 5), substratum (?), coll. Couch, Coker (1923: 176, pl. 60) (sterile), twigs of *Pseudotsuga mucronata*, Graff (1928: 170), twigs of *Chamaecyparis*, coll. P. N. Jordan, Sparrow (1932b), twigs, Sparrow (*op. cit.*, p. 294, pl. 7 J), Kevorkian (1935: 279), Bishop (1940: 505, figs. 1–6), Matthews (1935) (sterile), UNITED STATES; twigs of *Picea excelsa*, Tiesenhausen (1912: 298, figs. 21–22), SWITZERLAND; twigs of fir and spruce fir, H. E. Petersen (1910: 527), apples, twigs, Lund (1934: 35, fig. 15), DENMARK; Moore (1908–1909: 234, figs. 23–24), CANADA; twigs of *Quercus*, coll. Barnes, Sparrow (1936a), Sparrow (1936a: 460, pl. 20, fig. 11), Gwynne-Vaughan and Barnes (1937: fig. 42), GREAT BRITAIN; rose fruits and apples, Crooks (1937: 216, pl. 10, fig. 4), AUSTRALIA; twigs of *Pinus*, Apinis (1930: 233), LATVIA; twigs, fruits of *Macrocarpium officinale*, Indoh (1953: 28, figs. 15, 16), JAPAN.

It is difficult to decide whether or not Reinsch's *Naegelia sp.* "II," earlier (1875) called *Hyphomycetarum*, n. gen., belongs here, but, as Minden suggests, it may be a depauperate form of *Sapromyces elongatus*. Since no sex organs were found in Reinsch's material, his fungus may have been the less common *S. androgynus*, and the same is true also of Couch's and Matthews' records. However, from Reinsch's figures (pl. 15, figs. 7–11) it appears more likely his species was actually based on fragments of a *Rhipidium*.

Coker and Matthews (1937: 62) adopted the binomial *Sapromyces elongatus* (Cornu) Coker for this species. There is much to be said for the change, since the oöspore described by Cornu for his *Rhipidium elongatum* possessed an undulate wall. Two things, however, might be noted against the adoption of Cornu's name: (*a*) the absence in this species of a well-developed basal cell, the presence of which in Cornu's fungus is implied by his placing it in *Rhipidium*, (*b*) the lack of a figure by Cornu and his identification of the figures of Reinsch with those of his own *R. interruptum* (not *R. elongatum*). The facts do not seem to be conclusive for either name.

[1] See p. 879 n.

SAPROMYCES ANDROGYNUS Thaxter

Bot. Gaz., 21: 329, pl. 22, figs. 16–19. 1896

(Fig. 70 A, p. 890)

Basal cell slender, 115–247 µ long by 16–23 µ in diameter, holdfasts few, the apical cylindrical or narrowly clavate secondary axes constricted and septate at their point of origin, about 8–16 µ in diameter, up to 180 µ long, whole plant 500–2600 µ long; sporangia pedicellate, borne singly or in whorls, subcylindrical, ovoid, or ellipsoidal, 49–109 µ long by 16–30 µ in diameter; zoospores laterally biflagellate; antheridium androgynous, applied at the apex of the oögonium, consisting of a distally swollen and irregularly clavate slender unbranched sometimes twisted segment which arises laterally just beneath the oögonium; oögonium terminal or lateral, pedicellate, spherical or broadly pyriform, colorless and smooth or with a dark scaly wall, 35–50 by 27–30 µ; oöspore spherical, 20–26 µ in diameter, with a thick colorless or faintly golden wall raised in a series of low uneven prominences, germination not observed.

A species of infrequent occurrence, forming dense pustules often unmixed with other Phycomycetes. On submerged sticks, Thaxter (*loc. cit.*), *Fraxinus* and other twigs, Sparrow (1932b: 295, pl. 7, figs. B, I), twigs, Kevorkian (1935: 279), Johns (comm.), (NORTH CAROLINA) UNITED STATES; cones and twigs of *Picea*, Cejp (1936:text figs. A–C, pl. 11), CZECHOSLOVAKIA; Weston (1938: 246), NEWFOUNDLAND; Weston (*loc. cit.*), PANAMA.

The species has been reported as grown in pure culture by Emerson (1950).

RECENTLY DESCRIBED TAXON [1]

SAPROMYCES INDICUS Iyengar, Ramakrishnan, and Subramanian

J. Indian Bot. Soc., 34: 144, figs. 1–19. 1955

"Basal pseudo-cell relative to the branch system small, obpyriform, 56 × 42 (42–80 × 28–63) µ. Vegetative hyphal system arising from the top of the basal pseudo-cell; hyphae branched and divided into seg-

---

[1] Not included in the key.

ments by constrictions (pseudosepta). Sporangia formed singly or in clusters terminally or sub-terminally, pedicellate, hyaline, obpyriform when young, elongate-clavate when mature, thin and smooth-walled, 80 × 23, (21–144 × 14–30) μ. Oogonia and antheridia borne on separate thalli; oogonia obovate or spherical, pedicellate; antheridia pedicellate, irregularly clavate, 19 × 9.5 μ; oospore one in each oogonium, spherical with a thick reticulately sculptured wall, 28–32 μ in diameter" (Iyengar, Ramakrishnan, and Subramanian, *loc. cit.*).

On dead leaves, INDIA.

EXCLUDED SPECIES OF SAPROMYCES

* SAPROMYCES DUBIUS K. Fritsch

Österr. botan. Zeitschr., 43: 421. 1893

See page 885. Based upon a fragment of a *Rhipidium* (Reinsch, 1878; pl. 15, figs. 7–11).

ARAIOSPORA THAXTER

Bot. Gaz., 21: 326. 1896

(Fig. 70 C–H, p. 890)

Rhipidium Cornu, pro parte, Bull. Soc. Bot. France, 18: 59. 1871.

Thallus differentiated into a well-defined epibiotic basal cell and, arising from this, numerous repeatedly umbellately branched more or less segmented and constricted cylindrical filaments on which are borne the reproductive organs, the whole anchored to the substratum by a complex of endobiotic branched holdfasts; zoosporangia formed in whorls or umbels at the tips of the segments, from which they are separated by a constriction, wall smooth or spiny; zoospores reniform, laterally biflagellate, contents finely granular, fully formed within the sporangium, emerging upon the deliquescence of an apical papilla, often surrounded by a quickly evanescent vesicle; antheridium borne at the tip of a branched or unbranched specialized segment; oögonia spherical, monandrous, borne in whorls or umbels on short lateral constricted segments, the contents at maturity differentiated into oöplasm and periplasm; oöspore borne singly in the oögonium, thick-walled, with a cellular envelope of periplasmic origin which fills the oögonium or lies loosely in it, contents granular, with a large oil globule, germination not observed.

The species are all saprophytes on plant materials, particularly floating twigs, and occur most commonly in late spring or early summer.

Araiospora differs from *Sapromyces* and *Rhipidium* not only in the curious production of spiny-walled and smooth-walled sporangia (Fig. 70 E–F, H) but also in the formation of a cellular envelope around the oöspore. King (1903) concluded after a morphological and cytological study of *A. pulchra* that it shows definite affinities with the Peronosporales and stands between *Pythium* and the Saprolegniaceae. Kevorkian (1934) stated that in *A. streptandra* the fertilization tube is of antheridial origin rather than formed by the oöplasm as King asserted (see also under "Cytology," p. 865).

Because of their symmetrical arborescent habit and exquisitely reticulated often golden oöspores these apparently rare fungi are one of the most exciting "finds" among the water molds, and their delicate beauty never fails to elicit the admiration of the collector fortunate enough to secure them.

KEY TO THE SPECIES OF ARAIOSPORA

Spiny sporangia bearing numerous long slender spines either apically
  or over entire surface
  Oöspore not filling the oögonium, antheridium diclinous   *A. spinosa*, p. 889
  Oöspore filling the oögonium, antheridium monoclinous
    Antheridial hypha often branched, not twisted around the base of
      the oögonium .... *A. pulchra*, p. 891
    Antheridial hypha unbranched, twisted around the base of the
      oögonium
      Echinulate sporangia oval to pyriform; spines 10–15 μ long
                              A. streptandra var. *streptandra*, p. 892
      Echinulate sporangia spherical or nearly so; spines rarely less
          than 30 μ long ..... *A. streptandra* var. *echinulosphaera*, p. 892
Spiny sporangia bearing a crown of from four to six short or slightly
  curved digitate apical spines .... *A. coronata*, p. 893

Araiospora spinosa (Cornu) Thaxter

Bot. Gaz., 21: 326. 1896

(Fig. 70 F, p. 890)

Rhipidium spinosum Cornu, Bull. Soc. Bot. France, 18: 59. 1871.

Basal cell broadly cylindrical, with rounded apex, in large plants up to 800 μ long by 160 μ in diameter, thick-walled, primary axes 780 μ long by 76–96 μ in diameter, coarse, umbellate, unbranched, or giving rise distally to secondary umbels, constricted and segmented only at the place of origin or beneath the reproductive organs, rarely along the filaments; sporangia usually borne in clusters or whorls of from two to eight at the tips of the branches (rarely singly), occasionally directly on the basal cell, smooth sporangia more or less narrowly ellipsoidal, 90–150 μ long by 45–60 μ broad, spiny type ovoid or broadly ellipsoidal, 100–150 μ long by 40–80 μ broad, with an apical crown of solid rigid straight or recurved spines 60–70 μ long by 9 μ broad, of variable number, often occurring in two whorls (the outer having up to eight spines, the inner up to four) around the discharge papilla; zoospores reniform, the two flagella attached in a lateral fold, contents granular; antheridium relatively large, curved-cylindrical, appressed to the oögonium along its whole length, borne at the tip of a long slender often twisted and encircling branch usually of diclinous origin; oögonia clustered on short segments, spherical, with a smooth brownish wall; oöspore spherical, not filling the oögonium, with a thick cellular wall, germination not observed.

On twigs, Cornu (*loc. cit.*), France; twigs of *Quercus*, *Alnus*, rhizomes of water lily, Minden (1902: 822; 1915: 593, fig. 10 [p. 590]; 1916: 151, pl. 1, figs. 1–8), Germany.

Aside from a brief statement by Cornu that certain sporangia possessed long straight or recurved spines, our whole knowledge of this species is due to the investigations of Minden. He not only studied the plant in its natural habitat but obtained pure bacteria-free cultures on plum gelatin decoction and liquid media. This has never been successfully achieved by the few subsequent observers of this species of *Araiospora*.

Minden's descriptions and figures indicate that the inner oöspore wall is very thin and appears to form the inner face of the peripheral cells.

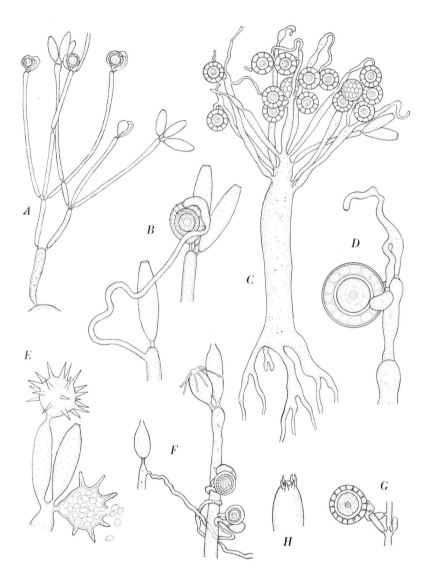

FIG. 70. Rhipidiaceae

A. Sapromyces androgynus Thaxter, habit of plant showing sporangia and sex organs. *B. Sapromyces elongatus* (Cornu) Coker, dioecious sex organs and discharged sporangia. *C–E. Araiospora pulchra* Thaxter: *C*, plant bearing

ARAIOSPORA PULCHRA Thaxter

Bot. Gaz., 21: 328, pl. 23, figs. 20–25. 1896

(Fig. 70 C–E, p. 890)

Basal cell predominantly large, thick-walled, 800–1500 μ long by 25–50 μ in diameter, the apex subcylindrical or subconical, bearing numerous secondary axes 275–2750 μ long which are constricted and septate at the base and repeatedly and umbellately branched distally, the segments of the branches subcylindrical and becoming successively longer and more slender, holdfasts coarse, much branched; sporangia borne in whorls or umbels, smooth sporangia subcylindrical or broadly clavate, 120–175 by 30–35 μ, spiny sporangia broadly ovoid to pyriform, 60–70 by 45–48 μ, the spines coarse, 10–35 μ long, radiating from the whole surface of the sporangium; zoospores emerging singly or in a mass; antheridium terminal, monoclinous, somewhat clavate, applied at the base of the oögonium, borne on a recurved branched or unbranched segment; oögonia borne like the sporangia, pedicellate, terminal, spherical, smooth-walled, 30–60 μ in diameter; oöspore spherical, thick-walled, golden, 35–45 μ in diameter, the contents with a single globule, peripheral cells polygonal, about 7 by 10 μ, the whole completely filling the oögonium, germination not observed.

On twigs, particularly *Fraxinus*, Thaxter (F.) (*loc. cit.*), King (1903: 211, pl. 11–15), Sparrow (S., B.M.) (1932b: 296, pl. 8 f–g), UNITED STATES.

The species occurs in association with *Sapromyces* and *Monoblepharis* in late spring. It may form pustules, but more commonly occurs as single plants. The cytology of the species has been investigated by King (see p. 865).

---

sex organs and discharged smooth-walled sporangia; *D*, detail of sex organs; *E*, spiny and smooth-walled zoosporangia, one sporangium in process of discharging its zoospores. *F. Araiospora spinosa* (Cornu) Thaxter, spiny and smooth sporangia and sex organs. *G. Araiospora streptandra* Kevorkian, sex organs. *H. Araiospora coronata* Linder, tip of sporangium showing crown of spines around discharge orifice.

(*A–D*, Sparrow, 1932b; *E*, Thaxter, 1896b; *F*, Minden, 1916; *G*, Kevorkian, 1934; *H*, Linder, 1926)

ARAIOSPORA STREPTANDRA var. STREPTANDRA Kevorkian

Mycologia, 26: 151. 1934

(Fig. 70 G, p. 890)

"Large sub-cylindrical basal cell with many branches arising from the sub-conical apex. Branches separated by constrictions and repeatedly and umbellately branched, each successive segment becoming more elongate and slender than its predecessor. Sporangia borne singly or in whorls of two to six of two types (1) sub-cylindric or broadly clavate and smooth, 79–111 × 29–49 μ, (2) oval or pyriform and spiny, 60–78 × 46–63 μ. Spines numerous, 15 to 30 μ in length, elongate conical in shape. Antheridia borne singly on short, stout lateral branches, usually originating near the distal ends of the segments, twisted about the base of the oögonia, irregular in outline. Oögonia spherical, 52–68 μ (av. 60–64 μ), arising similarly to and usually near the antheridia. Oöspore spherical, 39 to 46 μ (av. 44 to 46 μ), surrounded by a single layer of hexagonal-appearing peripheral cells derived from the periplasm. Germination of the oöspore not observed" (Kevorkian, *loc. cit.*).

On submerged twigs of *Prunus* and *Salix* (F.), Webster (1943: 31), UNITED STATES.

Distinguished from *Araiospora pulchra*, which it most closely resembles, by the twisted unbranched irregular antheridium, which arises as a short lateral branch near the tip of a segment.

ARAIOSPORA STREPTANDRA var. ECHINULOSPHAERA Shanor and Olive

Mycologia, 34: 540, figs. 1–11. 1942

Echinulate sporangia spherical, 29.8–48.7 μ in diameter, the spines many, for the most part 30 to 50 in number, 3.1–20.4 μ long.

Twigs of birch, UNITED STATES.

The antheridia of this variety were larger and more toruloid than Kevorkian's, a feature not included in its diagnosis.

Some young spinose sporangia were destroyed by an unnamed species of *Rhizophydium*.

ARAIOSPORA CORONATA Linder

Mycologia, 18: 176, pl. 21, figs. 1–14. 1926

(Fig. 70 H, p. 890)

"Basal cell subcylindrical, 826–846 × 45–48 μ, with well developed branched rhizoidal system at the base, and giving rise to few or many sporangiophores at the rounded apex. Sporangiophores with constrictions and repeatedly and umbellately branched, the segments successively more elongate and slender. Zoosporangia elongate-elliptical to subcylindrical, occurring singly or in whorls of two to six, terminating the branches or at the distal ends of the segments which make up the branches. Sporangia of two types: simple sporangia smooth, 63–85 × 11.5–16.2 μ; spinose sporangia with 4–6 short (7–9 μ), straight or slightly curved finger-like spines in a circle around the apical papilla of discharge, 68–130 × 12–26 μ. The entire plant 5 mm. in length. Oöspores not observed" (Linder, *loc. cit.*).

On submerged fruit and twigs (F., L. 258), SOUTH AMERICA (BRITISH GUIANA).

Although no sexual organs were found in this species, the crown of from four to six short straight or slightly curved spines on the spiny sporangia distinguishes it from *Araiospora pulchra*, *A. streptandra*, and *A. spinosa*.

RHIPIDIUM CORNU

Bull. Soc. Bot. France, 18: 58. 1871. Non *Rhipidium* Bernhardi, in Schrader, Journ. für die Botanik, 2: 127. 1800 (1801); non *Rhipidium* Wallroth, Flora cryptogamica Germaniae, 2: 742. 1833

(Fig. 71, p. 894)

Thallus differentiated into a well-defined more or less epibiotic basal cell and hyphal branches, basal cell consisting of a proximal cylindrical main axis surmounted by an expanded peltate, lobed, contorted, or branched thick-walled distal platform (the axis or the platform sometimes lacking); reproductive organs pedicellate on constricted septa, arising singly or in umbellate clusters from branches of the axis, or, more commonly, directly from the edges of the platform, or terminally on long upright cylindrical branches which are constricted and pseudoseptate at their point of origin on the edge of the platform, or appearing lateral by sympodial branching of the supporting filaments, the whole thallus anchored in the substratum by a branched system of filamentous holdfasts; zoosporangia borne singly or in umbellate clusters, with a single discharge papilla; zoospores reniform, laterally biflagellate, contents with numerous coarse refractive granules, formed within the sporangium, emerging in a cylindrical group upon the

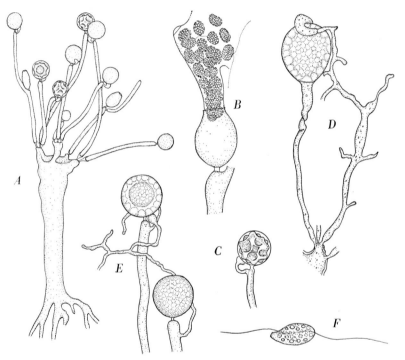

FIG. 71. *Rhipidium*

A–C. Rhipidium americanum Thaxter: *A*, habit of plant with zoosporangia and sex organs; *B*, discharge of zoospores; vesicle surrounding emerged spores has just split; *C*, sex organs, showing androgynous antheridium and oöspore in surface view. *D. Rhipidium thaxteri* Minden, habit of sex organs, showing oögonium with apically applied antheridium. *E. Rhipidium interruptum* Cornu, habit of diclinous sex organs. *F. Rhipidium sp.*, zoospore (freehand drawing).

(*A, C,* Sparrow, 1932b; *B*, after Thaxter, 1896b; *D–E*, after Minden, 1916)

deliquescence of the apical papilla, generally surrounded by an evanescent vesicle; antheridium single, androgynous, monoclinous or diclinous; oögonia borne like the zoosporangia; oöspore borne singly and loosely in the oögonium, thick-walled, areolate or stellate, germination not observed.

The plants form white gummy pustules, primarily on twigs and rosaceous fruits.

The habit of the thallus even in a single species is extremely variable and identification of the species is impossible unless the sex organs are present. One species (*Rhipidium parthenosporum*) forms thin-walled parthenospores rather than oöspores.

Lütjeharms (1937) has presented the arguments for conserving "*Rhipidium*" against several earlier homonyms.

KEY TO THE SPECIES OF RHIPIDIUM

Antheridium present; oöspore stellate, not filling the oögonium
  Antheridium diclinous, monoecious, or dioecious

RHIPIDIUM INTERRUPTUM Cornu

Bull. Soc. Bot. France, 18: 58. 1871; van Tieghem, Traité de Botanique, p. 1024, fig. 617. 1884. Paris

(Fig. 71 E, p. 894)

Rhipidium continuum Cornu, Bull. Soc. Bot. France, 18: 58. 1871.
Rhipidium europaeum Minden, Kryptogamenfl. Mark Brandenburg, 5: 597, fig. 9 (p. 590). 1912 (1915); Falck, Mykolog. Untersuch. Berichte, 2 (2): 187, figs. 3, 5–14, pl. 2, figs. 12–19. 1916.
Rhipidium europaeum var. *interruptum* Minden, in Falck, Mykolog. Untersuch. Berichte, 2: 172. 1916.
Rhipidium europaeum var. *compactum* Forbes, Trans. Brit. Mycol. Soc., 19: 234, pl. 10, fig. 11. 1935.

Basal cell with or without a cylindrical axis, 400–900 μ long by 30–90 μ in diameter, the platform extremely variable in size and shape, either swollen, contorted, gnarled, divided into broad branchlike lobes or appressed and peltate, up to 800 μ broad, the lobes attaining a breadth of 150 μ or more, the wall variable, often 20 μ thick, sometimes roughened; cylindrical branches numerous, generally arising from the apices of the lobes of the platform, constricted and pseudoseptate at the base, more or less constricted and often pseudoseptate along their length, 7–14 μ in diameter by 100–500 μ long, rarely branching, holdfasts extensive, branched; sporangia generally single, terminal, borne on short subspherical segments or sympodially arranged on long cylindrical branches, ovoid to ellipsoidal, sometimes nearly spherical, 40–78 μ long by 18.5–47 μ in diameter, papilla apical, wall smooth, very thin and collapsing after discharge or stout; zoospores reniform, 12–13 μ, biflagellate, contents with numerous refractive granules; antheridium small, 19 μ long by 15 μ wide, somewhat clavate or spherical and appressed distally to the lower part of the oögonium, borne at the tip of a long slender branched or unbranched often tortuous hypha of diclinous, monoecious, or dioecious origin; oögonia borne like the sporangia on the same plant, pedicellate, spherical or pyriform, 40–60 μ in diameter, wall stout, smooth, colorless; oöspore spherical or ellipsoidal, 27–50 μ in diameter, colorless or slightly golden, not filling the oögonium, the inner wall thin, smooth, the outer very thick (up to 17 μ) and raised in an irregular series of broad ridges and protuberances, stellate in section view, germination not observed.

Forming dense pustules, sometimes mats, on fruits and twigs. On twigs, Cornu (*loc. cit.*), FRANCE; fruits and twigs, Minden (*loc. cit.*), Laibach (1927: 599), Behrens (1931: 745, figs. 1–33), plum twigs, Höhnk (1935: 218), GERMANY; twigs of alder, birch, fir, H. E. Petersen (1909: 389; 1910: 526, fig. 4a, e), twigs, apples, Lund (1934: 36, fig. 16), DENMARK; fruits, Boedjin (1923: fig. 1), HOLLAND; fruits, Kanouse (1926: 113, pl. 1, fig. 2; 1927: 341, pl. 48, figs. 27–33, 39), twigs (MICHIGAN) UNITED STATES; apples, Valkanov (1931a: 366), BULGARIA; rose fruits, Forbes (1935a: 234, fig. 1; 1935b: 3), fruits, twigs of *Fraxinus*, Sparrow (1936a: 459, pl. 20, figs. 6, 10), fruits, Waterhouse (1942: 321), GREAT BRITAIN; twigs of *Prunus grayana*, Indoh (1953: 31, figs. 17–18), JAPAN.

The cytology of the species (see p. 865) has been studied by Behrens (1931).

Probably synonymous with this species is *Rhipidium compactum* Matthews (1936: 292, pl. 25), which differs significantly from *R. interruptum* only in having the oögonia minutely papillate in many instances. *R. compactum* is not mentioned in Coker and Matthews' 1937 paper. Matthews' (1936) description of it follows:

Plants appearing on the substratum as small whitish pustules about 0.5–1 mm. in diameter. Individual plants composed of a main trunk, which may or may not be branched, a large number of short secondary branches on which the reproductive organs are borne, and a well developed system of large branched often lobed rhizoids, which may extend into the substratum up to a distance of about 725 μ. Main trunk unbranched or with as many as 8 large branches, 60–83 μ in diameter by 99–214 μ long, constricted slightly at the base where the rhizoids originate. Short secondary branches 9–42 μ (majority about 20 μ) long, from the large trunk, constricted at their point of origin bear the sporangia and oogonia, usually singly, occasionally two, very rarely three. Sporangia 2–10 on a main branch, very variable in shape on the same plant, globose to pyriform ones 33–36 × 42 μ, cylindrical ones 20–29 × 49–70 μ. Zoospores (rarely produced in the laboratory) reniform, biciliate, 6.4–8 × 11.2–12.8 μ, monoplanetic. Oogonia borne on same plant as sporangia and mixed with them, at times even arising from same short branch that bears a sporangium, spherical, 26–40 μ in diameter, wall thin, smooth or usually with minute papillae. Oospores one to an oogonium, 29–33 μ in diameter, wall at maturity sculptured and about 6.6 μ thick. Antheridia one to each oogonium forming a tube to the oosphere and borne on a long antheridial stalk arising from same plant but not from branch bearing the oogonium or in some cases perhaps from a separate plant.

On huckleberry and *Amelanchier* fruits, in Mountain Lake at Mountain Lake, Giles County, Virginia, July and August 1936.

The following variety and form were described by Forbes and Kanouse, respectively. Variations in the species are so common, however—far more striking than any formal diagnosis can depict—that at the moment the character of the sex organs alone seems of important taxonomic value. Although the variety and form are recorded here for reference, they are not recognized.

RHIPIDIUM EUROPAEUM (INTERRUPTUM) var. COMPACTUM Forbes
Trans. Brit. Mycol. Soc., 19: 234, pl. 10, fig. 11. 1935

"Thallus of a very short, broadly cylindrical basal cell bearing a large number of broad, subdivided lobes, which spread out and around the short stalk in a compact bunch; these lobes bear the narrow branches which are rather shorter than in the normal form. Rhizoidal system relatively well developed, rhizoids stout with rounded tips. Sporangia as in the species, 50–60 × 25–35 μ. Oogonia pear-shaped, smaller than in the species, 40–45 μ diameter. Oospores smaller than in the species, 28–36 μ diameter. Antheridia as in the species" (Forbes, *loc. cit.*).

Substratum (?), GREAT BRITAIN.

This variety is probably based on the peltate form commonly found in both this species and *Rhipidium americanum*.

RHIPIDIUM INTERRUPTUM f. ATTENUATA (Kanouse) Coker

N. A. Flora, 2 (1): 67. 1937

Rhipidium europaeum f. *attenuata* Kanouse, Amer. J. Bot., 14: 342, pl. 48, figs. 27–33. 1927.

"Vegetative plant very slender, attached by long, slender penetrating rhizoids. Basal portion very long and narrowly subcylindrical, simple or sometimes once forked, 2000–3200 × 20–50 μ, wall relatively thick, 7–10 μ, protoplasm hyaline, including numerous oil globules upward. Branches scanty, arising from the apex of the main portion, differentiated at point of origin by pedicel-like constrictions which are provided with perforated cellulin deposits, very slender and flexible, 200–500 × 6–9 μ. Asexual reproduction typical" (Kanouse, *loc. cit.*).

On *Crataegus* and apple fruits, UNITED STATES.

Differing chiefly in having a slender, sometimes once-branched, basal cell.

RHIPIDIUM THAXTERI Minden

Kryptogamenfl. Mark Brandenburg, 5:600. 1912 (1915); Falck, Mykolog. Untersuch. Berichte, 2(2):188, pl. 3, figs. 22–24. 1916

(Fig. 71 D, p. 894)

Basal cell as in *Rhipidium interruptum*, often monstrous and discoid, over 800 μ in diameter with lobes up to 200 μ broad, or occasionally more cylindrical, upright filaments constricted only at the base, 7–11 μ in diameter, free-floating, holdfasts branched; sporangia borne as in the other species or in whorls, narrowly ellipsoidal, 50–89 μ long by 20–38 μ in diameter; zoospores as in other species, 13–14 by 10–11 μ; antheridium irregularly spherical, strikingly large, curved around and adnate to the oögonium at the apex, 27–70 μ long by 7–11 μ broad, arising from a narrow tortuous short branched diclinous filament produced from the basal cell; plant monoecious; oögonium somewhat pyriform, 45–57 μ broad by 57–62 μ long with a broad rounded top and a narrow stalklike unconstricted attenuated base, wall moderately thick, somewhat wrinkled at maturity, arising from a short somewhat spirally twisted basally constricted stalk produced from the basal cell; oöspore large, spherical, 33–43 μ in diameter, very thick walled, the outer wall sculptured as in the other species.

On fruits and twigs, occurring with *Blastocladia spp.* and *Rhipidium interruptum*, GERMANY; submerged fruits, tomato fruits, Shen and Siang (1948: 198, fig. 10), CHINA.

This truly remarkable species has been seen only once since Minden's time. He regarded it as a connecting link between *Rhipidium* and *Sapromyces*, its habit and oöspore resembling the former genus, its oögonia and whorled sporangia, the latter.

RHIPIDIUM AMERICANUM Thaxter

Bot. Gaz., 21: 327, pl. 21, figs. 1–15. 1896

(Fig. 71 A–C, p. 894)

Thallus and arrangement of reproductive organs (except the antheridia) as in *Rhipidium interruptum*, not significantly different in size; sporangia 30–90 μ long by 20–46 μ in diameter; zoospores laterally biflagellate, reniform, 10–12 μ long, contents with numerous refractive granules; antheridium broadly clavate, 11–14 μ wide, androgynous, borne on a short arched branch which arises immediately below the oögonium; oögonium 33–55 μ in diameter; oöspore 28–46 μ in diameter, the heavy wall colorless or pale golden and ornamented as in *Rhipidium interruptum*, germination not observed.

In dense gummy pustules or mats. On various vegetable materials, Thaxter (*loc. cit.*), fruits of *Crataegus*, rose, apple, Kanouse (1927: 343, pl. 48, fig. 38 a–c), apples, *Crataegus*, Sparrow (1932b: 297, pl. 8 a–b; 1933c: 532), twigs, Sparrow and Barr (1955: 555), UNITED STATES;

fruits and twigs, Minden (1915: 599; 1916: 188, pl. 3, fig. 21), GERMANY; Cejp (1932b: 1, pl. 1, figs. 1–5, pl. 2, figs. 1–3), CZECHOSLOVAKIA; apples, twigs of *Alnus*, Lund (1934: 37, fig. 17 a–b), DENMARK; rose fruits, Forbes (1935a: 235, fig. 2; 1935b: 3), twigs of *Quercus*, Sparrow (1936a: 460, pl. 20, fig. 2), (?) tomato fruits, Waterhouse (1942: 321), crabapple, GREAT BRITAIN; Beverwijk (1948: 245, fig. 8), HOLLAND; fruits of *Macrocarpium officinale*, Indoh (1953: 33, figs. 19–21), JAPAN.

The record of Crooks (1937: 218, pl. 10, fig. 5) from Australia is open to question, since no sex organs were observed. This species cannot be distinguished from *Rhipidium interruptum* except in the sexual stage.

The isolation and cultivation of this species is recorded by Emerson (1950).

RHIPIDIUM PARTHENOSPORUM Kanouse

Amer. J. Bot., 14: 344, pl. 48, figs. 34–37. 1927

Basal cell slender and elongate, once or twice forked, 800–1000 μ long by 25–30 μ wide, wall smooth, colorless, 7–10 μ thick, branches very short, ellipsoid or globose, umbellate, constricted at the point of origin and beneath the reproductive organs, constrictions with cellulin deposits, holdfasts few; sporangia ellipsoidal, thin-walled, 32–60 μ long by 25–50 μ wide, borne in umbellate clusters on short branches; zoospores not observed; antheridia lacking; oögonia spherical, thin-walled, 52–54 μ in diameter, pedicellate, borne in umbellate clusters on the short branches, the contents during development differentiated into oöplasm and periplasm, the latter with strongly marked radiating periplasmic strands and appearing cellular; mature parthenospore not observed. (Modified from Kanouse.)

In dense mats or loose tufts. On apple, Kanouse (*loc. cit.*), UNITED STATES; apples, Lund (1934: 38, fig. 17c), DENMARK; twigs, Sparrow (1936a: 460), GREAT BRITAIN.

Sparrow (*loc. cit.*) observed that spherical smooth somewhat thick-walled bodies formed in and completely filled the oögonia. These may be the mature parthenospores.

MINDENIELLA KANOUSE

Amer. J. Bot., 14: 301. 1927

(Fig. 72 A–F, p. 902)

Thallus consisting of a narrowly clavate occasionally cylindrical basal cell anchored to the substratum by a system of branched holdfasts; zoosporangia smooth-walled or spiny, borne on short narrow thick-walled pedicels which arise directly from the surface of the basal cell; zoospores of the secondary, biflagellate type, completely formed in the sporangium, contents bearing numerous globules, emerging through an apical pore; resting spore apogamously developed, thick-walled, entirely filling its spiny-walled container, germination not observed.

On decaying rosaceous fruits in fresh water.

Observations on *Mindeniella* by Sparrow and Cutter (1941) showed that the zoospores (Fig. 72 C) of this fungus are biflagellate and, hence, that the genus should be placed in the Leptomitales.

KEY TO THE SPECIES OF MINDENIELLA

Basal cell clavate or cylindrical; zoospores 8–15 by 6–10 μ

M. spinospora, p. 901

Basal cell consistently bent-clavate, or inverted boot-shaped; zoospores 5–9 by 3–7 μ .... *M. asymmetria*, p. 903

MINDENIELLA SPINOSPORA Kanouse

Amer. J. Bot., 14:301, pl. 34, 1927

(Fig. 72 A-F, p. 902)

Basal cell narrowly clavate, rarely cylindrical, predominantly unbranched but occasionally divided apically into two blunt lobes, 200–850 μ long by 100–200 μ in greatest diameter, about 30–40 μ in diameter at the base, from which emerges a system of branched holdfasts, wall thick, occasionally with exfoliated material on its outer surface, contents coarsely granular; zoosporangia arising in most cases from the upper, expanded part of the basal cell, occasionally lower down, borne on short, narrow, thick-walled pedicels from which they are separated by a cellulin plug, predominantly narrowly and symmetrically clavate or ovate, occasionally slightly constricted in the mid-region, somewhat variable in size, 70–250 μ long by 33–75 μ in greatest diameter, smooth-walled or with 1–8 slender spines irregularly disposed around the conspicuous apical discharge papilla; zoospores of the secondary, biflagellate type, 8–15 μ long by 6–10 μ wide, contents bearing numerous small refractive globules, the spores first emerged surrounded by a delicate quickly evanescent vesicle; resting spores brownish, borne like the sporangia, the outer wall of the container either wholly or in its upper part beset with numerous delicate spines 14–30 μ long, germination not observed.

Saprophytic on decaying rosaceous fruits, Kanouse (*loc. cit.*), Sparrow and Cutter (1941: figs. A–H), coll. E. A. Bessey (S.), and M.

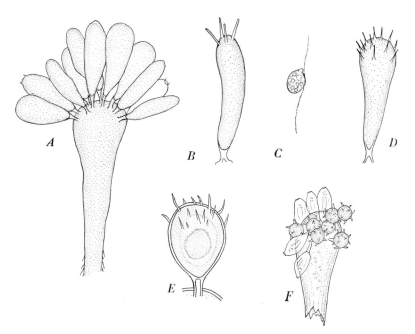

Fig. 72. *Mindeniella spinospora* Kanouse

A. Tip of plant showing enlarged apex of basal cell from which pedicellate zoosporangia arise directly. *B*. Spiny sporangium. *C*. Zoospore. *D*. Another type of spiny sporangium. *E*. Immature resting spore (?). *F*. Tip of plant bearing zoosporangia and resting spores.

(*A–C*, *E*, after Sparrow and Cutter, 1941; *F*, Kanouse, 1927)

Springer (S.), Sparrow (1943: 590), fruits of *Amelanchier*, Sparrow and Barr (1955: 555), R. M. Johns (comm.), Emerson (comm.), (PENNSYL-VANIA), UNITED STATES; twigs, Höhnk (1938: 499), GERMANY.

See Emerson's findings concerning formation of spiny sporangia (p. 855).

MINDENIELLA ASYMMETRIA Johnson

Amer. J. Bot., 38: 74, figs. 1–25. 1951

"Basal cell bent-clavate, slightly irregular in outline, often once-branched in the lower portion; 175–515 μ long in the longitudinal axis, 181–290 μ long in the horizontal axis, 91–143 μ in diameter across the bent portion, predominantly 400 × 250 × 125 μ; attached to the substratum by much-branched, sharply pointed rhizoids; wall variable in thickness in the same thallus, apparently laminate. Zoosporangia 1–14, borne at or near the distal end of the horizontal portion of the basal cell on slender, variable-length pedicels closed with cellulin plugs; predominantly short-ovoid or short-pyriform, rarely long-clavate, and then usually once-branched at the base; 47–88 μ in length by 32–65 μ in diameter, predominantly 60–70 μ × 40–50 μ; clavate zoosporangia averaging about 115 × 25 μ; wall moderately thick, predominantly smooth, but occasionally with 20–30 or more solid, sharp-pointed spines in the upper one-fourth of the sporangium wall. Zoospores reniform, biflagellate, escaping from the zoosporangium through an apical exit papilla, and swimming away at once; 5–9 μ long by 3–7 μ in diameter, predominantly 6–8 μ × 4–6 μ, and averaging 7 × 5 μ. Resting spores intermingled with the zoosporangia or on separate thalli; pedicellate, with a thick wall, and with prominent, solid, sharp-pointed spines in the upper one-third or one-half of the spore wall; spherical; 38–87 μ in diameter, predominantly 56–70 μ; spines 11–36 μ in length. Sexual reproduction unknown" (Johnson, *loc. cit.*).

On apples, UNITED STATES.

Distinguishable from *Mindeniella spinospora* by its distinctly smaller zoospores, smaller sporangia, and consistently bent. "chicken-leg"-like, basal cell.

LAGENIDIALES

THE order Lagenidiales comprises a group of microscopic endobiotic primarily parasitic fungi that are found in fresh and, less
often, marine waters. In the past the genera *Myzocytium*, *Lagenidium*,
Resticularia, and *Ancylistes*, together with *Achlyogeton*, were included
in an old order, Ancylistales, primarily on the basis of their having
segmented thalli. Investigation, however, has proved, as it has for the
chytrids, the fallibility of grouping fungi on similarity of body structure
alone. For example, Butler (1928) pointed out that *Achlyogeton* could
scarcely be allied to *Myzocytium* and *Lagenidium*, since it possessed
posteriorly uniflagellate zoospores. Furthermore, the work of Berdan
(1938) showed clearly that *Ancylistes* itself, in which nonsexual reproduction had not, prior to her work, been observed, was in fact a conidial
phycomycete closely allied to the Entomophthorales, to which order it
is now assigned (see p. 1065).

The genus *Olpidiopsis*, long regarded as belonging in the Chytridiales, is considered to be allied to *Myzocytium*. Although Zopf (1884:
173) pointed out the similarity between these two groups of fungi, it was
Scherffel (1925a) who showed the many resemblances that exist between
them and who furnished abundant evidence that *Olpidiopsis* could not
be a chytrid. The relationship to *Lagenidium* of the little-known marine
genera *Sirolpidium* and *Pontisma* was stressed by H. E. Petersen (1905:
482) and has been substantiated by subsequent morphological studies
(Sparrow, 1934c, 1936b). As a result of these changes the order Lagenidiales (the name proposed by Karling [1939b: 518] on the basis of
Berdan's work) now bears little resemblance to the Ancylistales of
Fischer (1892), Schroeter (1893), and Minden (1915).

Members of the order are known primarily as parasites of algae and
filamentous aquatic Phycomycetes, although a few are parasitic in
fresh-water microscopic animals and in seaweeds. One, *Lagena* (Vanterpool and Ledingham, 1930), has been found parasitic in the roots of

904

certain cereals and wild grasses; another, *Olpidiopsis riccieae* (du Plessis, 1933), occurs in liverworts. A few species are probably saprophytic or attack only moribund organisms. The majority, however, are true parasites, many apparently restricted to a few hosts. Members of the order are alike in being endobiotic, having walls which generally give a cellulose reaction, forming zoospores with two oppositely directed flagella, and possessing a type of sexuality involving the fusion of the contents of two thalloid bodies, with the consequent production in one of a thick-walled resting spore. In the Olpidiopsidaceae and certain Lagenidiaceae the thallus is always one-celled. In other species it is one-celled or multicellular and monophagous, and in the most highly developed species it is multicellular, somewhat filamentous and hypha-like, and may extend through many cells of the host.

DEVELOPMENT AND MORPHOLOGY

THE THALLUS

Infection is accomplished by means of the free-swimming zoospore, which comes to rest on the surface of the substratum and retracts its flagella. In some forms it may move amoeboidly before surrounding itself with a rigid wall and producing an infection tube (Fig. 73 A–E, p. 906). This needle-like structure penetrates the host wall and conveys the contents of the cyst through the wall into the interior of the substratum (Fig. 73 F–G). The development and type of thallus subsequently formed varies with the group.

In the Olpidiopsidaceae, the members of which are primarily parasitic on filamentous water molds, the thallus, unlike that of the Lagenidiaceae and possibly of the Sirolpidiaceae, is ordinarily never attached to the tip of the penetration tube, but is, as Scherffel (1925a) pointed out, almost wholly monad-like and undergoes its development free in the host. Differences in the success of infection by the zoospores have been noted by Butler (1907), who concludes that they are due possibly to variations in the infective powers of the zoospores, but more likely to the age of the hyphae attacked. The younger parts of the vegetative system of the host are most readily penetrated, owing, perhaps, to the unmodified condition of the walls. Since the young

thallus in the Olpidiopsidaceae is free in the host cell it may be carried,
perhaps at first by its own action (Diehl, 1935), but more likely by the
cytoplasmic currents of the host (Diehl, *op. cit.*; McLarty, 1941a), for
varying distances away from the original point of infection (Fig. 73 D–H,
below). Often it tends to develop in the more distal regions of the hypha,
though in other instances it remains intercalary. Wherever the thallus
develops, a marked hypertrophy of the host occurs (Fig. 73 I). The
stimulation to swell, or to produce lateral outgrowths, may possibly be

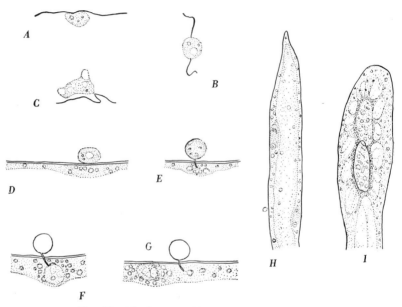

FIG. 73. *Olpidiopsis achlyae* McLarty on *Achlya*

A. Free-swimming zoospore. *B–C.* Two quiescent zoospores showing changes
in shape of body. *D.* Zoospore quiescent on outer surface of wall of host hypha,
other boundary of which is not shown. *E.* Encysted spore, which has now
produced penetration tube that has pierced host wall. *F.* Encysted parasite after contents have been discharged into host. *G.* Very young thallus of parasite
being swept away (to left) from tip of penetration tube by streaming host
protoplasm. *H.* Two young thalli of parasite suspended in peripheral cytoplasmic layer of host. *I.* Two more mature thalli which have assumed a central
position in now distinctly swollen tip of host filament.

(McLarty, 1941a)

due to the intake of water, since vacuoles are common, or to the accumulation of host protoplasm.

In species of *Olpidiopsis* parasitic in water molds, the development and cytology of which are well known from the work of several investigators (particularly Barrett, 1912b; Diehl, 1935; McLarty, 1941b; and Shanor, 1939b, 1940), the very young thallus is uninucleate, slightly granular, and surrounded by a delicate membrane (McLarty, *op. cit.*). As it enlarges, according to Barrett, the refractive apparently fatty granules increase in number and size and a cellulose wall is secreted by the thallus, which has by now assumed a spherical or ellipsoidal shape. The contents then become more dense and are augmented by many small granules and an increased number of refractive fat bodies. The host cytoplasm at this stage forms a dense layer around the parasite, and protoplasmic streamers, between which are large vacuoles, are produced. These protoplasmic strands radiate from the region of the parasite to the peripheral cytoplasmic layer of the hypha of the host. This radiate disposition of the host contents is less extensive as development proceeds. The thallus of the parasite then becomes vacuolate, the fat bodies within it disappear, and its protoplasm assumes a densely granular texture. It may rest in this stage for several weeks, or its contents may cleave into zoospores at once.

The cytological investigations of *Olpidiopsis vexans* by Barrett (1912b) (see also McLarty, 1941b) show that the young uninucleate vacuolated thallus (Fig. 74 A, p. 908), after about doubling its original size, becomes binucleate (Fig. 74 B). The nuclei thus formed are large and have a well-defined nucleolus. Division is mitotic, the spindles being intranuclear (Fig. 74 C–D). As the rather evenly contoured thallus increases in size it is continually more vacuolate, and the nuclei are augmented in number by simultaneous divisions. In an advanced, but as yet unwalled, stage the protoplasm and nuclei line the periphery of a large irregular central vacuole (Fig. 74 E). At about this time a distinct granulation of the outside margin of the thallus is detected, which probably marks the initial stages in wall formation. There then ensues a gradual inward growth of the protoplasm, a decrease of vacuolization with continued rapid nuclear division, and an increase in size. A well-defined wall has now been formed. After the last division of the nuclei (Fig. 74 F) the

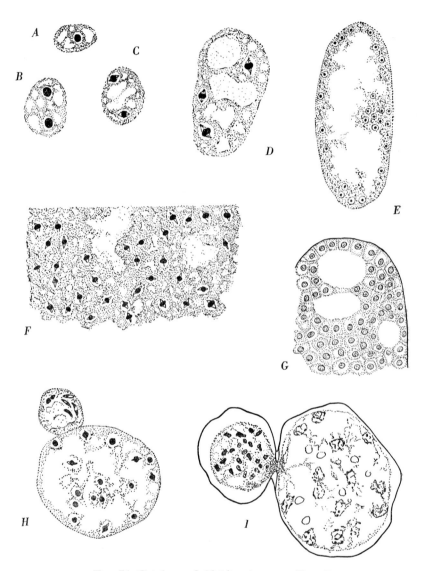

FIG. 74. Cytology of *Olpidiopsis vexans* Barrett

A. Very young uninucleate thallus soon after establishment in host hypha.
B. Binucleate stage. *C.* Binucleated thallus with nuclei dividing, spindles
intranuclear. *D.* Somewhat older thallus, showing vacuolate cytoplasm and

remaining vacuoles become regular in outline, and the nuclei themselves, regularly spaced in the cytoplasm, go into the resting state (Fig. 74 G). No evidences of amoeboid movement or of the fusion of thalli to form a plasmodium were observed by Barrett or McLarty.

The thallus of the Sirolpidiaceae (Petersen, 1905; Sparrow, 1934c, 1936b; Aleem, 1953; Kobayasi and Ookubo, 1953) is tubular, septate, and branched or unbranched. In *Sirolpidium* two main types of vegetative structures are formed. The first is somewhat spherical or elliptical, distinctly olpidioid, and occurs singly or in dense linearly arranged groups (Fig. 77 B, D, p. 967). These bodies are the thalli which were considered by de Bruyne (1890) to be typical of *Sirolpidium* (*Olpidium*) *bryopsidis*. At maturity each is provided with a single discharge tube, of varying length, which usually penetrates the wall of the host. The precise method of formation of such groups has not been ascertained. It has been suggested by Petersen (1905) that they have been produced from zoospores discharged inside the alga. The second type of thallus formed in *Sirolpidium* is an exceedingly interesting one. In very early stages the body of the fungus is a somewhat irregular curved cylindrical tube, often lying near the periphery of the central cavity of the host cell (Fig. 77 A). The thallus, after a period of growth, characterized mainly by elongation, becomes separated by constrictions into a linear series of spherical or cylindrical segments of varying size, each of which at maturity is disarticulated and becomes an independent, walled unit (Fig. 77 C, E, G). These fragments then for a time undergo individual growth. Each one soon loses its original orientation with respect to the parent thallus and ultimately becomes a single sporangium equipped with a discharge tube.

The thallus of *Pontisma* (Petersen, 1905; Sparrow, 1934c; Aleem,

---

nuclei in division. *E*. Young sporangium, showing peripheral arrangement of cytoplasm. *F*. Portion of developing sporangium in which large vacuoles are forming and nuclei are undergoing final division. *G*. Portion of sporangium after segmentation of zoospores has occurred. *H*. Vacuolate receptive (large) and contributing (small) thalli containing irregularly distributed dividing nuclei. *I*. Connection between the two thalli established, nuclei of smaller thallus dividing, those of larger, resting.

(Barrett, 1912b)

1953), though resembling to a degree that of *Sirolpidium*, is more irregularly cylindrical and usually forms short branches (Fig. 78 A, p. 969). At maturity thin cross walls are laid down which delimit irregular, constricted segments. Rarely, what appears to be a rudimentary type of fragmentation may be found. The typical mature thallus consists of a series of somewhat variously shaped connected segments.Occasionally it may be an unsegmented cylindrical structure which curves around the periphery of the utricle of the host cell (Fig. 78 B). The contents of the thallus, though varying in aspect from time to time, generally contain during the period of vegetative activity a large number of regularly placed vacuoles. In more mature plants the protoplasm consists of a mass of closely packed refractive granules.

Each of the segments of the thallus is ultimately transformed into a sporangium having a single discharge tube (Fig. 78 E). Tubes not oriented so as to secure egress from the host cell may ramify extensively within the substratum, frequently simulating to an astonishing degree the hyphae of filamentous Phycomycetes. Unusual powers of growth have also been observed in the discharge tubes of *Sirolpidium* (Fig. 77 F, p. 967) (Sparrow, 1934c, 1936b).

The development and morphology of the thallus of aquatic genera of the Lagenidiaceae are well known from the excellent researches of Zopf (1884), Scherffel (1925a), and others. In both *Lagenidium* and *Myzocytium* the zoospore accomplishes infection of the host in the same manner as in the Olpidiopsidaceae. Zopf noted, however, that the cyst and the infection tube of *L. rabenhorstii* persisted throughout the life of the thallus, whereas those of *Myzocytium* soon disintegrated. A similar situation has been found by Scherffel (*op. cit.*) in several other species of *Lagenidium*. In *L. rabenhorstii* the minute sphere of protoplasm, once established within the alga, elongates to form a relatively thick tube. As this increases in length, irregular swellings, which originate as papilla-like or clavate protrusions from the main body, are formed on it. These outgrowths arise at varying intervals and may develop into long, sometimes curved, branches which curl around the inner face of the host-cell wall. After from twenty-four to seventy-six hours of purely vegetative growth this one-celled, usually branched, tube, which ordinarily never penetrates into adjoining host cells, becomes segmented by the formation at irregular intervals of narrow cross walls. In some instances as many as seven segments are produced from a single thallus. These are transformed into reproductive organs.

In *Myzocytium* (Zopf, 1884) the young one-celled thallus early becomes torulose, as if it were being proliferated by a yeastlike budding. Here, however, in contrast to the development in *Lagenidium*, no branches are formed. At from twelve to twenty-four hours after infection the vegetative stage is superseded by the reproductive phase. There are now laid down at the constrictions between the successive swellings very thick two-layered refractive cross walls which divide the thallus into a chainlike series of links. All of the segments thus formed become reproductive organs (Fig. 79 A–B, p. 977).

In *Lagenidium*, *Myzocytium*, *Pontisma*, and *Sirolpidium* single-celled thalli which resemble those of *Olpidiopsis* are occasionally observed.

Nonsexual Reproduction

The zoospores of the Olpidiopsidaceae and the Sirolpidiaceae are fully formed in the zoosporangium.

In *Olpidiopsis* (Barrett, 1912b) the maturing sporangium is at first strongly vacuolate. Changes in the contour of the spherical vacuoles occur at the same time that the discharge tube forms. Further stages involve the sudden disappearance of the large vacuoles, with the protoplasm assuming a finely granular, lighter, more homogeneous aspect, and the appearance in some instances of small vacuoles. These vacuoles ultimately vanish, the protoplasm becomes more coarsely granular, and the spore origins appear. The zoospores become more definitely outlined and initiate movement. The discharge tube then opens and the zoospores escape. The exit tube, Barrett believes, secretes an enzyme which aids in penetration, although evidences for mechanical action were also observed. A similar sequence has been described by Butler (1907) in *O. aphanomycis*, except that in his fungus a heaping of the protoplasm followed the change in contour of the large vacuoles of the resting sporangium. At this stage Butler supposed that the contents became cleaved into relatively large multinucleate masses. Barrett's cytological preparations of sporangia in the resting, vacuolate, condition showed very definitely, however, that in his material the spore centers were already formed and that some fragmentation had been initiated. He considers the heaping described by Butler simply a phenomenon accompanying final stages in the maturation of the spores. According to Barrett, the zoospores are produced simultaneously by division of the protoplasm, and upon the gelatinization and dissolution of the tip of the discharge tube the swarmers emerge from the sporangium as vacuolated uninucleate biflagellate structures. Schwartze (1922), on the other hand, from observations only of living material of *O. saprolegniae*, described the cleavage as progressing rapidly outward from a central vacuole. When the furrows pierced the thin peripheral layer of cytoplasm the vacuole vanished and the outline of the zoospores became distinguishable. Subsequent development involved the appearance of definite polygonal segments followed by contraction of the whole mass. A further contraction resulted in the rounding off and rocking of the individual spores, which escaped after two minutes. This report agrees, in the main, with the classic account of Rothert (1888) of cleavage in *Saprolegnia* and with the observations of McLarty (1941a, 1941b) on *Olpidiopsis*.

The zoospores of *Olpidiopsis* are relatively small and numerous. The body, in general, is somewhat ovoid, or reniform with a narrower anterior end. The contents are rather granular. From the forward end two oppositely directed flagella of approximately the same length emerge (Fig. 73 A, p. 906).

In the primarily marine *Petersenia* the thallus may extend through one or more cells (Fig. 76 D, p. 960). Its contents are refractive and bear numerous large spherical vacuoles. A homogeneous condition ensues, which is followed by the cleavage of the zoospores. This process has not been observed in its initial phases. The zoospores in their later stages of maturation within the sporangium undergo a rocking and twisting movement very much like that found in *Pythium*. They are minute, grape-seed-like, and laterally biflagellate (Fig. 76 H) (Sparrow, 1934c).

As yet there are not available any precise details concerning the sequence of protoplasmic changes in the developing sporangia of members of the Sirolpidiaceae.[1] Both Petersen (1905) and Sparrow (1934c) state that the zoospores assume motility within the sporangium, emerge by their own efforts, and swim away at once. In *Sirolpidium* (Sparrow, *op. cit.*) the zoospores are minute, narrowly pyriform, somewhat arched or bent and bear two long oppositely directed anteriorly attached flagella (Fig. 77 I, p. 967). [2] A strongly refractive granule is visible in the front part of the body. In *Pontisma* (Sparrow, *op. cit.*), also, the zoospores are relatively small, narrowly pyriform, and bear a refractive granule at either end. The two oppositely directed flagella arise near the center of the body, or possibly at the fore end (Fig. 78 D, p. 969)

In the Lagenidiaceae the process of zoospore formation strongly resembles that in *Pythium*. The relatively large zoospores either are partly formed in the sporangium, as in *Myzocytium* (Zopf, 1884), and complete their maturation in a delicate more or less evanescent vesicle produced at the tip of the discharge tube, or, as in *Lagenidium rabenhorstii* (Zopf, *op. cit.*), undergo their entire development within the extramatrical vesicle. In the sporangia of *M. proliferum*, a parasite of algae, Zopf noted that, coincidently with the formation of the discharge tube, the protoplasm became separated by small vacuoles into approximately like-sized portions. With the gelatinization of the tip of the tube, these segments of protoplasm emerged to form a globular homogeneous motionless mass at the orifice. No divisions of the protoplasm could be observed at this time. Shortly, however, a slight motion of the whole mass was discernible, accompanied by a contraction away from the wall of the delicate surrounding vesicle. The protoplasm was then cleaved into the same number of parts as was previously observed within the sporangium. As separation continued, the spore origins showed individual motion, and underwent amoeboid changes of shape. Delicate flagella became visible around the periphery (Fig. 79 A, p. 977). For a short period after separation the zoospores exhibited a lively swarming within the vesicle, whose delicate membrane eventually deliquesced, releasing the zoospores, which swam away. In *L. rabenhorstii* (Zopf, *op.*

---

[1] See, however, Vishniac (1955b).

[2] Vishniac (*op. cit.*) found the zoospores of *Sirolpidium zoophthorum* to be heterocont, with the shorter flagellum of the tinsel type.

cit.) no separation of the contents of the sporangium could be observed prior to discharge. At maturity the protoplasm flowed out in a continuous stream into a constantly expanding vesicle. There the mass quickly began to rotate and, after a few seconds, was cleaved into parts, each of which in turn assumed individual somewhat amoeboid motion. The zoospores, after forming their flagella and taking on their mature beanlike shape, are liberated upon the disappearance of the vesicle.

Variations from the types of zoospore discharge described by Zopf in *Myzocytium* and *Lagenidium* have been reported by a number of investigators. In *Myzocytium* (Dangeard, 1903b; Thompson, 1934) the zoospores have been observed to form within the sporangium and to initiate motility there. The vesicle was completely absent in the material studied by Thompson, whereas it was quickly evanescent in Dangeard's fungus. In *M. zoophthorum* (Sparrow, 1936a) the zoospores were more or less fully formed in the sporangium and completed their maturation without a surrounding vesicle at the tip of the discharge tube. In *Lagenidium* even more marked departures have been noted. In *L. cyclotellae*, for example, Scherffel (1925a) has observed the zoospores to be completely formed and moving within the sporangium before discharge. He regards these bodies as primary zoospores. Scherffel (*op. cit.*) also states that in *L. oedogonii* the zoospores are sometimes formed as in *Pythium*, but that at other times they divide and move within the sporangium, and at discharge form, as in *Achlya*, a clump of cysts at the orifice of the discharge tube. From each of these cysts a secondary zoospore emerges. Couch (1935b) noted only the *Pythium* type of discharge in *L. oedogonii*. In *L. marchalianum* the zoospores may be delimited within the sporangium and complete their maturation in the extramatrical vesicle, after discharge. A somewhat similar condition has been noted in *L. oophilum* (Sparrow, 1939c). Here, however, the vesicle is apparently completely lacking.

Striking examples of variation in zoospore discharge are provided by three lagenidiaceous parasites of rotifers described by Karling (1944g). In *Myzocytium* (*Lagenidium*) *microsporum* the zoospores become fully delimited within the sporangium, are liberated, and form a mass at the orifice of the discharge tube, where they undergo final maturation and develop their flagella. In *Lagenidium parthenosporum*, although again the zoospore segments are delimited endogenously, they emerge and encyst at once at the tube orifice, later giving rise (from the cysts) to flagellated zoospores. Finally, in *L. distylae* they are entirely delimited and matured outside the sporangium within a vesicle, as in *L. rabenhorstii* and in *Pythium*. Still another example of variation might be cited. In *L. destruens* Sparrow (1950) zoospores are matured as in *L. distylae* but no vesicle is formed.

The functional zoospore in both *Myzocytium* and *Lagenidium* is of the secondary, beanlike, kidney-like, or grape-seed-like, type, with a shallow sinus from which arise two oppositely directed flagella of approximately equal length. The contents frequently bear numerous refractive granules and a centrally disposed vacuole. The movement is an even gliding, sometimes accompanied by a gentle lateral rocking of the whole body. Couch (1935b) noted in an unnamed species of *Lagenidium* occurring in *Oedogonium*, as did Karling (1944g) in *L. distylae*, that the zoospores after coming to rest and encysting may emerge from the cysts again as secondary zoospores and undergo a second swarm period ("repeated emergence"), a further point in which these fungi resemble *Pythium*.

Dangeard (1903b) gave an account of the cytology of the thallus and of zoospore formation in *Myzocytium vermicola*, a parasite of nematodes. The young thallus contains numerous nuclei dispersed in a reticulate cytoplasm. After formation of the cross walls the number of nuclei is augmented, but no division figures were observed. As the sporangia thus delimited approach maturity, the cytoplasm and nuclei become disposed around a large central vacuole, formed probably by the coalescence of several smaller ones, which were previously visible. Lines of granules then delimit irregular polyhedral areas. The central vacuole disappears and the protoplasm fragments into uninucleate zoospores which are discharged through a tube to the outside.

Sexual Reproduction

Sexual reproduction is known in the Olpidiopsidaceae and the Lagenidiaceae. No well-authenticated occurrence of resting spores of either sexual or asexual origin has been reported in the Sirolpidiaceae.

In both the Olpidiopsidaceae and the Lagenidiaceae the resting structure may also be asexually developed (Zopf, 1884; Scherffel, 1925a;
McLarty, 1941a; Karling, 1944g; Sparrow, 1950).

The process that precedes resting-spore formation in *Olpidiopsis* has
been studied by many observers (Cornu, 1872a; Reinsch, 1878; Fischer,
1880, 1882; Butler, 1907; Barrett, 1912b; Shanor, 1939a, 1939b; Mc-
Larty, 1941a, 1941b; etc.). In hypertrophied portions of fungous hyphae
in which several parasites are developing, certain thalli of unequal size
may become associated, usually in pairs. The larger continues to increase
in size and its contents become characterized by the production of
numerous fat bodies. The two unequal-sized thalli then secrete cellulose
walls and are fused together at one point. A pore develops in the wall of
contact, through which the contents of the smaller thallus pass into the
larger, receptive, body. After the contents have fused, an endospore
wall of cellulose forms around the larger thallus. At maturity the outer
surface of the wall of the receptive thallus bears on it a considerable
amount of material, derived, according to McLarty (*op. cit.*), from
localized deposits of host protoplasm during maturation. This material
is usually laid down unevenly and, as a consequence, produces an
exospore layer of spiny, tuberculate, fibrillose, or irregular character.
The numerous variations found by McLarty in the character of the
exospore occurring in cultures of *O. achlyae* derived from single zoospores have rightly brought into question the value of using the exospore
wall as a character in distinguishing species.

The sexual process in *Olpidiopsis* has been examined cytologically by
Barrett (1912b) and McLarty (1941b). Both the contributing and the
receptive thalli are at first uninucleate, but by repeated simultaneous
mitotic divisions they become multinucleate (Fig. 74 H–I, p. 908). The
spindles are intranuclear and the number of chromosomes, according
to Barrett, is six. Barrett believes that fusion of the nuclei in pairs occurs
after the contents of the smaller thallus have passed into the larger one.
This is denied by McLarty, who states that, though plasmogamy does
unquestionably take place, there are no nuclear fusions. At germination
the resting spore becomes converted into a sporangium (Shanor, 1939a;
McLarty, 1941b). No evidences of meiosis could be found by McLarty,
and this, together with the absence of karyogamy and the frequent

maturation of resting spores without previous conjugation, has led him to conclude that sex, at least in *O. achlyae*, is phenotypically, not genotypically, determined.

Sexual reproduction in the Lagenidiaceae is well known, although cytological details concerning it are for the most part lacking. Zopf (1884) showed that adjacent cells of the linklike thallus of *Myzocytium* conjugated. One cell, the antheridium, produced a tube which pierced the walls separating it from the oögonium. The contents of the female structure contracted, moved toward the tip of the tube, and exhibited relatively lively amoeboid motion. With the passage of the protoplasm into the oögonium the female gamete became rounded and nearly quiescent. After fusion the zygote was surrounded by a thick double wall, and a large central globule was formed in the contents. In Zopf's material the oöspore always remained attached to the fertilization tube. Karling (1944g) noted a somewhat similar sexual process in *Myzocytium* (*Lagenidium*) *microsporum*. In this species, however, the male and female gametangia occur in single pairs and only a fertilization pore is formed, not a tube.

Dangeard (1903b) studied cytologically the sexual stage of *Myzocytium vermicola*. The gametangia are multinucleate, the somewhat cylindrical male bearing two nuclei, the more rotund female, about eight. The antheridial cell penetrates the female gametangium by means of a tube and discharges its contents. By this time the protoplasm of the female gametangium has contracted and become vacuolate. One male and one female nucleus persist, but the others degenerate. No coenocentrum is visible. After plasmogamy the zygote rounds off in the gametangium, a thin smooth surrounding wall is formed, and the nuclei approach one another. Later, karyogamy occurs and a reticulate exospore is formed. At germination the single large fusion nucleus is replaced by several smaller ones. Meiosis was not observed, although it presumably took place at this time.

Sexual reproduction in *Lagenidium humanum* Karling (1947c) is quite like that in *Myzocytium microsporum*. In no instance was there significant morphological differentiation of the gametangia or a specialized fertilization tube. In *Lagenidium rabenhorstii* (Zopf, 1884), the thalli, in contrast to those of *Myzocytium*, are ordinarily dioecious, the two plants usually lying parallel in the host. The segment of the thallus which will become the oögonium swells, forming a spherical, ovoid, or fusiform structure. The antheridia are unspecialized segments of the thallus and each forms a tube which makes contact with the oögonium and pierces its wall. The contents of the receptive segment then undergo movement and contract, concentrating at the place of entrance of the fertilization tube. This contraction continues during passage of antheridial material, after which the granular matter in the zygote collects at first into two large refractive masses and then into one. A two-layered smooth colorless wall is now laid down around the zygote. Zopf points out that in *L. rabenhorstii*, in contrast to higher Phycomycetes, the female gamete is still an amorphous mass at the time of fertilization and does not round off until later. *Lagenidium distylae* Karling (1944g) is essentially similar in the character of its sex organs to Zopf's species save that the thallus is monoecious and no fertilization tube is formed.

Some species have parthenogenetically formed resting spores. For example, in *Lagenidium parthenosporum* Karling (1944g) the whole contents of a thallus segment will contract and become surrounded by a thick wall. In *L. destruens* Sparrow (1950), however, the contents of the digitate thallus divide into as many as six segments, each of which becomes a thick-walled resting spore.

The resting spore in both *Myzocytium* and *Lagenidium* lies loosely within the wall of the receptive cell, and closely resembles the oöspore of *Pythium*. The early stages of germination have been observed by Dangeard (1903b) in *M. vermicola*. After resting a few months the oöspore becomes multinucleate and produces a tube through which zoospores may possibly be discharged.

PARASITISM

A few general remarks on the parasitism of this group are pertinent. Specific information is inserted in the discussions of the various species.

The Lagenidiales are primarily a group of parasitic fungi, although a few, little-known, chiefly marine, forms are reported to be capable of living saprophytically in nature. *Lagenidium giganteum* (Couch, 1935b),

L. humanum (Karling, 1947c), and *Sirolpidium zoophthorum* Vishniac (1955b) have been grown on artificial media. Diehl (1935) reported the cultivation to maturity of some immature thalli of *Olpidiopsis* which had been removed from their saprolegniaceous host to artificial media. Species of *Olpidiopsis* and *Rozellopsis* are, with the exception just noted, obligate parasites of aquatic Phycomycetes and of a few fresh-water and marine algae. An experimental study of certain species of *Olpidiopsis* (Shanor, 1940) indicates that they are restricted to relatively few host species (see discussion under *Olpidiopsis*, p. 928). *Pseudolpidium*, *Rozellopsis*, and *Pseudosphaerita* also are, so far as is known, obligate parasites of particular hosts. Species of *Petersenia*, a marine genus, may possibly at times be weakly parasitic on certain marine red algae and initiate the destruction of the alga, but after the death of the host they can maintain themselves as saprophytes (Sparrow, 1934c, 1936b).

Sirolpidium and *Pontisma*, inhabitants of marine algae, perhaps act as parasites in early stages of infection, but for the major part of their development they live as saprophytes (Sparrow, 1934c, 1936b; Aleem, 1953).

Myzocytium and *Lagenidium* (with the exception of *L. giganteum* and *L. humanum*) are at present thought to be obligate parasites of their hosts. They occur primarily as parasites of the Conjugatae, attacking both vegetative and reproductive cells. Other species are found in eel-worms, the eggs, embryos, and adults of rotifers, and so forth, and on pollen grains. As is true of the chytrids, practically no significant exper-imental work has been thus far attempted to ascertain the range of hosts which a single fungus will attack, and claims of host specificity rest for the most part on observations of findings in nature.

SYSTEMATIC ACCOUNT

LAGENIDIALES

MICROSCOPIC, primarily parasitic aquatic fungi of simple body plan or with a septate mycelial development of slight extent, the thallus endo-biotic, holocarpic, forming one or more reproductive organs, without a specialized vegetative system, at first unwalled ("plasmodial") or walled, the walls generally giving a cellulose reaction, infection tube persistent or evanescent, contents in the vegetative stage often having a pale gleaming luster, bearing irregular refractive granules and scattered oil droplets, strongly vacuolate during maturation; zoosporangia forming one or more discharge tubes; the zoospores of the laterally biflagellate type, mono- or diplanetic, produced by successive division within the sporangium or at the orifice of the discharge tube, where they are generally surrounded by a vesicle, capable of repeated emergence; resting spore apparently asexually formed, or sexually after conjugation of the receptive thallus with one or more contributing gametangia, fertilization tube and periplasm present or absent, plants monoecious or dioecious.

Members of the order are most frequently parasites of fresh-water algae, other Phycomycetes, and microscopic aquatic animals. A few are parasitic or saprophytic in seaweeds. Several have been cultivated on artificial media.

The inclusion of the Olpidiopsidaceae in this order seems increasingly justified as more simplified species of *Lagenidium* and *Myzocytium* with endogenously formed zoospores are discovered (see, for example, *L. pythii*, p. 991; *M. microsporum*, p. 980). As Whiffen (1946) pointed out, if the oöspore of *L. pythii* filled its container, it would be indistinguishable from a species of *Olpidiopsis*. Members of the family certainly appear more closely allied to the Lagenidiaceae than to the chytrids.

KEY TO THE FAMILIES OF THE LAGENIDIALES

Thallus always one-celled, infection tube evanescent; zoospores formed
 within the zoosporangium; resting spore lying free in the host, not
 formed in a gametangium .... Olpidiopsidaceae, p. 921
Thallus predominantly multicellular, occasionally one-celled, infection
 tube frequently persistent; zoospores formed inside the zoosporangium or in a vesicle at the tip of the discharge tube; resting
 spore formed in a gametangium
Zoospores formed within the zoosporangium, small, numerous;
 marine fungi .... Sirolpidiaceae, p. 965
Zoospores formed or completing their maturation in a vesicle at the
 orifice of the discharge tube............... Lagenidiaceae, p. 972

OLPIDIOPSIDACEAE

Thallus endobiotic, holocarpic, without a specialized vegetative system, sometimes appearing naked at first ("plasmodial") and somewhat amoeboid, later definitely walled, infection tube not persisting, the walls generally giving a cellulose reaction, usually forming a single reproductive structure, contents with refractive globules, often strongly vacuolate; sporangium liberating its spores by bursting the wall or forming one or more discharge tubes; zoospores formed in the sporangium, mono- or diplanetic (dimorphic), biflagellate; resting spores endobiotic, thick-walled, apparently asexually formed from the thallus or produced after conjugation of the receptive thallus with one or more small contributing thalli, with or without periplasm and fertilization tubes, upon germination forming zoospores.

Parasites of other water fungi and parasitic or saprophytic in algae.

The family includes all endobiotic holocarpic species which form a single sporangium or, rarely, a linear series of sporangia, from the thallus and produce, endogenously, biflagellate zoospores. When more is known about the sexual process, if any, in *Pseudosphaerita* and *Pseudolpidium* it may seem better to place these genera elsewhere.

Scherffel (1925a) called attention to the resemblance of *Olpidiopsis* to *Lagenidium*, first noted by Zopf (1884). This is found not only in the similarity in flagellation of the spore, the composition of the walls, and the behavior and structure of the contents, but also in the tendency toward diplanetism (dimorphism) of the zoospores and the likeness of sexual reproduction.

The thallus in *Olpidiopsis* bears at first sight little resemblance to that in *Lagenidium* and *Myzocytium*. In their body form, however, *Lagena* and *Lagenidium oophilum* approximate a species of *Olpidiopsis*, and *Pontisma* and *Sirolpidium* closely approach *Lagenidium*. The essential differences between the two groups appear to rest in the *Pythium* type of diplanetism of a relatively small number of large zoospores in the Lagenidiaceae and the *Saprolegnia* or *Achlya* type of diplanetism of a large number of small zoospores in the Olpidiopsidaceae. These do not seem of sufficient import when compared with the similarities to maintain the groups as distinct orders.

KEY TO THE GENERA OF THE OLPIDIOPSIDACEAE [1]

Parasitic in aquatic Phycomycetes or in fresh-water or marine algae
   Thallus completely filling the host cell, the sporangia at maturity
      single or in linear series .... ROZELLOPSIS, p. 922
   Thallus not completely filling the host cell
     Sporangia unlobed, not tubular; with one (rarely more) discharge
      tube
       Resting spore sexually formed after conjugation of thalli, or
         parthenogenetically developed; sporangia predominantly
         spherical or ellipsoidal .... OLPIDIOPSIS, p. 926
       Resting spore lacking; sporangia as above ... PSEUDOLPIDIUM, p. 955
     Sporangia predominantly irregularly lobed or tubular, with more
      than one discharge tube .... PETERSENIA, p. 957
Parasitic in Euglenophyceae or Cryptophyceae .... PSEUDOSPHAERITA, p. 961

ROZELLOPSIS KARLING

Mycologia, 34: 205. 1942

(Fig. 75 G, I, p. 939)

"Thallus intramatrical, holocarpic, more or less indistinguishable
from but apparently immiscible with the host protoplasm; becoming
invested with a wall at maturity and forming one sporangium, or cleaving
(?) into several segments which become separated by host walls, mature
in basipetal succession, and develop into sporangia or resting spores.
Sporangia terminal or intercalary, variable in size and shape, with one
to several exit papillae which extend through the host wall; usually
filling the host sporangia or the hypertrophied portions of the hyphae
completely; sporangium wall tightly pressed against, seemingly fused
with, and usually indistinguishable from that of the host. Zoospores
slightly variable in size and shape, with one to several minute globules,
biflagellate and heterocont, shorter flagellum usually extending forward
and the longer one backward in swimming; zoospores swirling in the
sporangium before emerging fully formed and swimming away; contents flowing into host cell through an infection tube in germination,
leaving the empty zoospore case on the outside. Resting spores unknown
in monosporangiate species; solitary in septigenous species, lying free
within host cell and separate from host wall, variable in size, brown,

[1] See also recently described taxa, p. 953.

and spiny; protoplasm coarsely granular, including a large vacuole or globule of hyaline material; germination unknown" (Karling, *loc. cit.*).

The genus was at first merely named by Karling (1942a: 33), without accompanying diagnosis. It was described by him several months later (1942b: 205) but as yet has not been validated by a Latin description. *Rozellopsis* was erected for the *Rozella*-like fungi with biflagellate rather than uniflagellate zoospores. At present both monosporangiate and septigenous species are included. However, Karling considers (1942e: 14) the septigenous ones will be atypical of *Rozellopsis*, if their linear series of sporangia are shown to have arisen by thallus segmentation rather than by multiple infection.

Karling placed the genus, with misgivings, in the Woroninaceae of older authors. He did this primarily on the basis of its plasmodial thallus and the anterior unequally biflagellate zoospores described by Tokunaga (1933a: 25) for *Rozellopsis simulans*. Prowse (1951: 404), who does not regard the latter feature of any great significance in view of the difficulty of observing details in moving spores, noted that in *R. septigena* they were of the laterally biflagellate type, with the posterior flagellum twice as long as the anterior. Waterhouse (1940: 11) described the zoospores in *R. waterhouseii* Karling as somewhat similar but with the anterior flagellum longer than the posterior one. Perhaps, if the biflagellate "*Rozellas*," both monosporangiate and septigenous, had been more thoroughly studied before a new genus was erected for their disposition, questions as to the interrelationship of the species and the relationship of *Rozellopsis* to other genera might be more easily answered. Prowse (1954b) came to the conclusion that the genus cannot satisfactorily be included either in the Plasmodiophorales, the Woroninaceae, or in the Olpidiopsidaceae and he believes that it might better be regarded as a distinct family within the Phycomycetes. For the present, until information is forthcoming on the resting spores of monosporangiate species, it is probably best to retain it in the Olpidiopsidaceae.

KEY TO THE SPECIES OF ROZELLOPSIS

Sporangia septigenate (in linear series); parasitic in Saprolegniaceae
  Parasitic in *Saprolegnia* .... *R. septigena*, p. 924
  Parasitic in *Achlya* .... *R. simulans*, p. 925

Sporangia monosporangiate; parasitic in Pythiaceae

ROZELLOPSIS SEPTIGENA Karling

Mycologia, 34: 206. 1942

(Fig. 75 G, p. 939)

Sporangia in linear series, somewhat inflated or cylindrical, with one or two exit papillae; zoospores narrowly ovoid or pyriform, laterally biflagellate, the posterior flagellum twice the length of the anterior one, 5–8 μ long by 3–4 μ broad; resting spores in swollen lateral branches of host, spherical, 20 μ in diameter, wall brown, covered by tenuous spines 2 μ long, contents with a large oil globule, germination not observed.

Parasitic in hyphae of *Saprolegnia sp.*, not capable of infecting *Achlya*, Fischer (1882), Minden (1915: 272), GERMANY; *Saprolegnia sp.*, Prowse (1951: 400, fig. 1-2; pl. 18), GREAT BRITAIN; *Saprolegnia sp.*, Sparrow (1952d: 759), UNITED STATES.

The septate plasmodium is known to arise from a single zoospore infection.

Karling (1942a: 34; 1942b: 206) treats the fungus Fischer misidentified with Cornu's *Rozella septigena* as though it were a new species described by Fischer. In the interests of clarity a new species name could well have been applied to Fischer's fungus, but since Cornu's name was carried over to a new genus it is valid. *Rozella septigena* Fischer, however, does not exist, hence, cannot be a synonym.

Prowse (1951) investigated the method of infection, development of the sporangia and liberation of the spores in *Rozellopsis septigena*. He offers no evidence as to whether or not the basipetalously developed sporangia arise from a single infection but indicates that the cross walls appear to be laid down by the host and not by the parasite. The zoospores are described as pyriform, hyaline, with two or sometimes four refractive granules, 3 by 5–6 μ, with a long (10 μ) posterior flagellum and a short (5 μ) anterior one. It is also clear that the species is restricted in its parasitism to certain members of *Saprolegnia* and will not attack

Achlya spp. Prowse suggests that *R. septigena* and *R. simulans* are really physiological strains of a single species, differing only in their host range.

Prowse (1954b) also made a careful study of *Rozellopsis inflata* as it occurs on *Zoophagus insidians* and on certain other pythiaceous fungi. His account of the zoospore behavior, infection, and development in this species is the best that has yet been given for a member of the group.

ROZELLOPSIS SIMULANS (Fischer) Karling

Amer. J. Bot., 29: 34. 1942

Rozella simulans Fischer, Jahrb. wiss. Bot., 13: 365. 1882.

Sporangia 60–250 μ long by 25–90 μ in diameter; zoospores narrowly ellipsoidal or cylindrical, 6 by 2.4 μ, with two anterior unequal flagella; resting spore spiny; germination not observed.

In *Achlya polyandra*, *A. racemosa*, Fischer (*loc. cit.*), Minden (1915: 273) (including resting spores), GERMANY; *Achlya*, Maurizio (according to Minden, 1915: 273), ITALY; *Achlya flagellata*, Tokunaga (1933a: 25), JAPAN.

The species is like *Rozellopsis septigena* but is said to be confined to *Achlya*.

ROZELLOPSIS INFLATA (Butler) Karling

Amer. J. Bot., 29: 34. 1942

(Fig. 75 I, p. 939)

Pleolpidium inflatum Butler, Mem. Dept. Agr. India, Bot. Ser., 1: 126, pl. 7, figs. 17–21. 1907.

"Sporangia spherical, oval or pyriform, formed in the spores of the host which, with the supporting hyphae, are greatly swollen, up to 85 μ in diameter, with one or more papillae; zoospores very numerous, elongated, unequilateral, with two cilia, one in front and the other lateral near the back; durable spores not seen" (Butler, *loc. cit.*).

Parasitic in *Pythium intermedium*, Butler (*loc. cit.*), *Pythium sp.*, Sparrow (1943: 125), FRANCE; host?, Remy (1948: 214), GERMANY; *Zoophagus insidians*, *Pythium spp.*, Prowse (1954b), GREAT BRITAIN.

ROZELLOPSIS WATERHOUSEII Karling

Mycologia, 34: 206. 1942

"Sporangia terminal, spherical, up to 74 μ in diam., clavate, oval, or obpyriform with 1-3 apical or lateral exit papillae. Zoospores pyriform, 5–8 μ long with a few small refringent granules in the center or near the posterior end; flagella apparently laterally inserted (?); zoospores active for 24 hours or more, or rounding up and encysting" (Karling, *loc. cit.*).

Parasitic in sporangia of *Phytophthora cryptogea* and *P. megasperma*, occasionally causing slight hypertrophy, Waterhouse (1940: 7, figs. 1–8), GREAT BRITAIN.

The species (named in Karling, 1942a: 34) is based on a fungus which Waterhouse (*loc. cit.*) described as close to "*Pleolpidium inflatum.*" She recognized, however, that, because of the biflagellate zoospores, some other disposition of it might eventually be necessary.

OLPIDIOPSIS CORNU

Ann. Sci. Nat. Bot., V, 15: 114. 1872

(Fig. 75 A-F, p. 939)

Olpidiopsis (Cornu) Fischer, Jahrb. wiss. Bot., 13: 363. 1882; Rabenhorst. Kryptogamen-Fl., 1 (4): 37. 1892.
Pleocystidium Fisch, Sitzungsber. Phys.-Med. Soc. Erlangen, 16: 66. 1884.
Diplophysa Schroeter, in Cohn, Kryptogamenfl. Schlesien, 3 (1): 195. 1885.
Pseudolpidium Fischer, pro parte, Rabenhorst. Kryptogamen-Fl., 1 (4): 33. 1892.
Pleotrachelus Zopf, sectio *integri* H. E. Petersen, Oversigt Kgl. Danske Vidensk. Selskabs. Forhandl., 1905 (5): 448.
Bicilium H. E. Petersen, Bot. Tidsskrift., 29 (4):357. 1909; Ann. Mycologici, 8: 503. 1910.
Pseudolpidiopsis Minden, Kryptogamenfl. Mark Brandenburg, 5: 255. 1911 (1915).

Thallus at first naked, later surrounded by a membrane, endobiotic, holocarpic, forming the rudiment of the sporangium, the receptive thallus, or the contributing thallus (companion cell); sporangium spherical or ellipsoidal, smooth-walled or spiny, nontubular and unlobed, with from one to several discharge tubes; zoospores formed within the sporangium, biflagellate, without well-defined diplanetism; resting spore thick-walled, smooth or spiny, formed asexually or after conjugation of the receptive thallus with from one to several smaller contributing thalli, upon germination functioning as a sporangium.

Primarily parasites of fresh-water fungi, but also occurring in fresh-water and marine algae.

The zoospore was said by Cornu to be posteriorly uniflagellate. Fischer (1882) described it as biflagellate in the species studied by him. His generic description (1892) allows for both types. Schroeter's generic description (1893) mentions only the biflagellate type, as does that of Minden (1915).

Work by Shanor (1939a, 1939b) and McLarty (1939, 1941a) with single-spore cultures of various species of *Olpidiopsis* and forms which would ordinarily be placed in Fischer's genus *Pseudolpidium*, showed that all the fungi parasitic on Phycomycetes studied by them were species of *Olpidiopsis*. Fischer's genus is maintained tentatively (p. 955) for the three algal parasites which lack resting spores. Their true affinities cannot be determined at this time.

As here understood, *Olpidiopsis* includes all forms with unlobed or nontubular endobiotic holocarpic thalli, with biflagellate zoospores, with sporangia bearing one to several discharge tubes, and with resting spores produced either asexually or after conjugation of thalli. In the past the marine forms have been referred both to *Pleotrachelus* (Petersen, 1905) and to *Petersenia* (Sparrow, 1936b), but they differ from the first in having biflagellate zoospores and from the second in having unlobed nontubular sporangia. *Peronium aciculare* Cohn (1853) may possibly have been a species of this genus, but it is too imperfectly known to be considered here.

Butler (1907), Barrett (1912b), Scherffel (1925a), and Diehl (1935) all describe what might be considered a poorly defined type of diplanetism of the zoospores. After the zoospores escape from the sporangium there is a short period of motility, which, in *Olpidiopsis saprolegniae* and *O. schenkiana*, may include slight amoeboid motion; this is followed by a period of quiescence accompanied by retraction of the flagella. During the rest period contractile vacuoles may appear in the plasma. At its conclusion the flagella initiate movement and elongate, and the spore, after rocking for a while, once more assumes motility. No encystment occurs, and the primary zoospore is interpreted as having been directly transformed into the secondary swarmer. Whether such significance should be accorded what is after all only an interval of rest unaccompanied by encystment or change of shape of the zoospore is problematic. Scherffel considers *Olpidiopsis* to exhibit a partial suppression of the primary swarm stage, which reaches its end point in the *Pythium* type, where only secondary zoospores appear. As supporting evidence he cites the behavior of the zoospores of *O. oedogoniarum*, which emerge sometimes as in *Achlya*, sometimes as in *Pythium*. It is important, however, that unquestionable proof be presented that only one species of fungus is involved in such occurrences.

Scherffel also called attention to the close resemblance of *Olpidiopsis* to *Myzocytium*; he regards *Olpidiopsis* as providing a connecting link between the Ectrogellaceae and the Lagenidiales. Indeed, in *O. oedogoniarum*, where, in contrast to other species, the resting spore lies loosely in the receptive thallus, this resemblance is extremely close. A constant difference between the two groups is to be found, according to Scherffel, in the persistence of the infection tube on the thallus of the lagenidiaceous fungus, whereas in *Olpidiopsis* the thallus is established in monad-like fashion and lies wholly free in the host cell.

Whether or not host specialization actually exists in all species of *Olpidiopsis* is not known with certainty. Experimental work here, as in other fungi, is hampered by imperfect knowledge of optimum conditions for resistance of the host plants. Shanor (1940) summarizes an extensive study of the host range of certain species thus:

A study of the host range of certain species of *Olpidiopsis* which occur as parasites of the water molds has been made in which twenty-five species representing eight genera of the Saprolegniaceae were used as possible hosts. In all, two hundred and sixty-four single host exposures have been made. Two species, *Olpidiopsis varians* and *O. fusiformis*, confine their parasitism to species of *Achlya*. *Olpidiopsis varians* parasitizes *Achlya flagellata* and *A. proliferoides* very vigorously and *A. racemosa* and *A. colorata* only to a very slight degree. *Olpidiopsis fusiformis* parasitizes *A. imperfecta* and *A. klebsiana* vigorously and *A. racemosa* only slightly. Two other species, *Olpidiopsis saprolegniae* and *O. incrassata* were found to parasitize all species of *Saprolegnia* exposed to them. *Olpidiopsis saprolegniae* is also capable of parasitizing *Isoachlya anisospora*, *I. unispora* and *I. eccentrica* while *O. incrassata* has parasitized only *I. anisospora* and *I. unispora*. *Olpidiopsis incrassata* is considered a natural parasite of *Saprolegnia* .... The host range of *Olpidiopsis luxurians* appears to be confined to a single species, *Aphanomyces laevis*.

KEY TO THE SPECIES OF OLPIDIOPSIS [1]

In the hyphae of fresh-water Phycomycetes
  Parasitic in *Saprolegnia*; resting spore predominantly spherical
    Resting spore spiny ... *O. saprolegniae* var. *saprolegniae*, p. 930
    Resting spore smooth .... *O. saprolegniae* var. *levis*, p. 933
  Parasitic in other Phycomycetes; resting spore spherical or ellipsoidal
    Parasitic in *Achlya* and *Isoachlya*; resting spore predominantly
      spherical, wall either spiny, tuberculate, fibrillar, undulate, or
      smooth
    Companion cell smooth-walled
      Resting-spore wall smooth .... *O. braziliensis*, p. 933
      Resting-spore wall variously ornamented
        Resting-spore wall spiny; companion cell always present
                     O. fusiformis, p. 934
        Resting-spore wall spiny, tuberculate, fibrillar, or undulate;
          companion cell present or absent .... *O. achlyae*, p. 935
    Companion cell spiny
      Spines short
        Spines tenuous, the outer wall not continuous with that of
          the resting spore .... *O. index*, p. 936
        Spines coarse, the outer wall continuous in most cases with
          that of the resting spore .... *O. varians*, p. 937
        Spines very long and rodlike .... *O. spinosa*, p. 937
    Parasitic in *Achlya* (and *Saprolegnia?*); resting spores predomi-
      nantly ellipsoidal, the walls tuberculate or undulate, never
      spiny .... *O. incrassata*, p. 938
                        (*O. major*, p. 940)
                        (*O. vexans*, p. 940)
  Parasitic in *Aphanomyces*; resting spore spiny
    Resting spore with a smooth-walled companion cell; in *A. laevis*
                        O. luxurians, p. 941
    Resting spore lacking a companion cell; not confined to *A.*
      laevis .... *O. aphanomycis*, p. 942
  Parasitic in *Pythium*
    Resting spore without companion cell
      Resting spore predominantly spherical, the yellowish wall
        covered with long tenuous spines .... *O. gracile*, p. 943

[1] Note that the key is not strictly dichotomous.

OLPIDIOPSIS SAPROLEGNIAE var. SAPROLEGNIAE (Braun) Cornu

Ann. Sci. Nat. Bot., V, 15: 145, pl. 3, fig. 10. 1872

(Fig. 75 A–B, p. 939)

Chytridium saprolegniae Braun, Monatsber. Berlin Akad., 1855: 384;
　Abhandl. Berlin Akad., 1855: 61, pl. 5, fig. 23. 1856.

Diplophysa saprolegniae (Cornu) Schroeter, in Cohn, Kryptogamenfl.
　Schlesien, 3 (1): 195. 1885.

Pseudolpidium saprolegniae Fischer, in Rabenhorst, Kryptogamen- Fl., 1(4):
　35, fig. 3 a–b. 1892.

Olpidiopsis echinata H. E. Petersen, Bot. Tidsskrift, 29 (4): 405, fig. 28a. 1909; Ann. Mycologici, 8: 540, fig. 28a. 1910.

Sporangium predominantly spherical, subspherical, ovoid, or ellipsoidal, up to 150 μ in diameter (45–50 by 3–36 μ when ellipsoidal), generally terminal, occasionally intercalary in the hypertrophied host filaments, wall thin, smooth or spiny, colorless, discharge tubes from one to three, narrowly cylindrical, of variable length; zoospores ovoid or ellipsoidal, 2–4 μ in length, with two apical or subapical oppositely directed flagella; resting spore spherical, 47–107 μ in diameter, colorless or somewhat brownish, with a fairly thick wall, the outer surface densely covered with slender sharp spines about 5–10 μ in length, contents with globules, germination not observed; companion cells from one to two, ovoid or nearly spherical, 18–28 μ in diameter, wall thin, smooth, colorless.

Parasitic in filaments of *Saprolegnia ferax*, Nägeli (1846), Braun (*loc. cit.*), Pringsheim (1860: 205, pl. 24, fig. 15), GERMANY; *Saprolegnia sp.*, Cornu (*loc. cit.*), Dangeard (1890–91b: 88, pl. 4, figs. 5–8), "Saprolegniaceae," Arnaud (1952: 182, fig. 1A), FRANCE; *Saprolegnia sp.*, Sorokin (1883: 27, fig. 27), EUROPEAN RUSSIA, ASIATIC RUSSIA; *S. dioica, S. monoica*, Petersen (*loc. cit.*), DENMARK; *Saprolegnia sp.*, Barrett (1912b: 232, pl. 23, figs. 2, 8–9, 21A, pl. 24), *Achlya imperfecta, A. flagellata*, Coker (1923: 184, pl. 62, figs. 7–10), *Achlya sp.*, Sparrow (1932b: 270, fig. 1c; 1933c: 515), Shanor (1940), *Saprolegnia ferax*, Wolf and Wolf (1941: 271), UNITED STATES; *Saprolegnia monilifera*, Tokunaga (1933a: 24, pl. 2, fig. 9), JAPAN; *Saprolegnia sp.*, Cejp (1934: 228, fig. 3), CZECHOSLOVAKIA; host (?), Forbes (1935b: 3), GREAT BRITAIN; *Saprolegnia ferax*, Shen and Siang (1948: 199), CHINA; *Achlya colorata, Saprolegnia diclina*, Beverwijk (1948: 229, fig. 1), HOLLAND.

For convenience the records of *Pseudolpidium saprolegniae* are listed separately:

Parasitic in hyphae of *Saprolegnia monoica, S. thureti, S. asterophora*, Fischer (*loc. cit.*), *Saprolegnia sp.*, Pringsheim (1860: 205, pl. 24, fig. 14), *Saprolegnia sp.*, Schroeter (1885: 195), Minden (1915: 267), GERMANY; *Achlya (Saprolegnia ?) prolifera*, Cienkowski (1885: 801, pl. 12, fig. 8 and others?), RUSSIA; *Saprolegnia sp.*, Sorokin (1883: 27, fig. 28), ASIATIC RUSSIA; *Saprolegnia sp.*, Constantineanu (1901: 372), RUMANIA; *Achlya racemosa*, H. E. Petersen (1909: 406; 1910: 541, fig. 18d), DENMARK; *Saprolegnia sp.*, Valkanov (1931a: 361), BULGARIA; (?) *Saprolegnia thureti*, Tokunaga (1933a: 22, pl. 2, fig. 5), JAPAN.

Butler (1907: 131), Sawada (1912), and Domján (1936: 52) record the fungus from the sporangial stage alone.

Constantineanu's record can be accepted only with reservation, since the ornamentation of the resting spore is not described.

Marked hypertrophy of the host filament has been noted by all observers of the species. Diehl (1935) reported that the form assumed by the infected hyphae depended upon the size and abundance of protoplasm in the host hypha and the number of parasites infecting it. Considerable increase in diameter and cessation of apical growth occurred in regions harboring the parasite. These "galls" assumed various configurations in agar cultures. Under the conditions of culture the discharge tubes of the sporangia reached great lengths. In the later stages of development isolated parasites on agar reached maturity and discharged their zoospores.

Coker (*loc. cit.*) noted in a single sporangium that the contents were discharged before cleavage of the spores had been completed. The protoplasm remained at the orifice, and after fifteen minutes the spore initials assumed a rocking movement. Eventually, they became separate entities and swam away. This may not be typical of zoospore discharge, but if it is, it affords additional evidence of the diplanetic nature of the zoospores in the genus. His material also possessed resting spores in which the wall sculpturing varied from low warts to definite spines.

Cornu has retained Braun's specific name even though it is now impossible to tell to what species the German fungus belonged.

Tokunaga's collection is queried above because of the unusually coarse spines on the "resting spore" (sporangium). The sporangia are ellipsoidal, 34–120 μ in longer diameter, the zoospores ovoid, 4 by 2 μ, apically and laterally flagellate, and the resting spores spherical or ellipsoidal, 64–87 μ in diameter, with the wall covered by scattered spines. These spines are described as "fine" in the text, but are far coarser and longer than those figured by Fischer for his fungus.

In view of the extensive cross-inoculation studies by Shanor (1940) indicating that this species is confined to *Saprolegnia* and *Isoachlya*, the records of *Olpidiopsis saprolegniae* on *Achlya* are open to question. In fact, Karling (1942e) has gone so far as to suggest that if these cross-inoculation studies are confirmed, it might be expedient, because of the lack of constancy in morphological characters, to lump all the *Olpidiopsis* parasites of *Saprolegnia*, with the possible exception of *O. irregularis*, under *O. saprolegniae*.

OLPIDIOPSIS SAPROLEGNIAE var. LEVIS Coker

The Saprolegniaceae, p. 185, pl. 62, figs. 1–6. 1923

"Sporangia spherical to elliptic, smooth, very variable in size and number, usually occupying the swollen ends of hyphae but not rarely also in intercalary swellings; emptying by one or two tubes which penetrate the host's wall but go little beyond and are usually short, at times however as long or longer than the diameter of the sporangium; spores very minute and numerous, probably with two cilia, swimming rapidly, emerging at first through internal pressure and probably showing the same sequence as described in preceding species but not all stages observed. Oogonia elliptic to nearly spherical, with the wall rather thick and quite smooth and even; antheridial cells smaller than the oogonia, smooth, thin-walled, one or two attached to each oogonium, their contents usually disappearing entirely by the time the oogonia are mature" (Coker, *loc. cit.*).

Parasitic in *Saprolegnia ferax*, *S. monoica*, UNITED STATES.

OLPIDIOPSIS BRAZILIENSIS, nom. nov.

Pseudolpidiopsis achlyae Viégas and Teixeira, Bragantia, 3: 225, pl. 2. 1943.

Sporangium spherical or elliptical, rarely cylindrical, 20-70 by 16–60 μ, with a thin, smooth wall, with one or two cylindrical or conical exit tubes 8–28 by 6 μ; zoospores 4–8 μ in diameter, immediately after discharge spherical and remaining quiescent at orifice of discharge tube, monoplanetic, biflagellate, reniform when actively swimming; resting spore spherical, hyaline, 40–44 μ in diameter, with granular contents and central globule, wall smooth, 2 μ thick; companion cell single, globose or ellipsoidal, 20–30 μ in diameter, hyaline, smooth-walled, germination not observed.

Parasitic in the hyphae, sporangia, and so on, of *Achlya sp.*, BRAZIL. Related to *Olpidiopsis saprolegniae* var. *levis* Coker by reason of the smooth-walled resting spore and the possession of a companion cell. In view of Shanor's (1940) demonstration that *O. saprolegniae* is confined to *Saprolegnia* and *Isoachlya*, the present fungus on *Achlya* is maintained as a distinct entity.

OLPIDIOPSIS FUSIFORMIS Cornu

Ann. Sci. Nat. Bot., V, 15: 147, pl. 4, figs. 1–4. 1872

Pseudolpidium fusiforme Fischer, Rabenhorst. Kryptogamen-Fl., 1(4): 35. 1892.
Olpidiopsis minor Fischer, *ibid.*, p. 39. 1892.
Pseudolpidium stellatum Sawada, Special Bull. Agr. Exp. Sta. Formosa, 3: 70, pl. 8, figs. 11–16. 1912.

Sporangium causing swelling of the host hypha, usually fusiform, also ellipsoidal or cylindrical, 45–350 μ long by 18–78 μ in diameter, with a thin, smooth or spiny, colorless wall, variable in size; zoospores ovoid, 4 μ long by 2 μ wide, biflagellate; resting spore frequently ellipsoidal, or spherical, colorless, thick-walled, the outer surface sparingly covered with broad subulate spines which are joined at their bases to form a reticulum, contents with globules, germination not observed; companion cell spherical, smooth-walled, smaller than the resting spore.

Parasitic in hyphae of *Achlya leucosperma*, *A. racemosa*, *Achlya sp.*, Cornu (*loc. cit.*), FRANCE; *Achlya racemosa*, Reinsch (1878: 304, pl. 17, figs. 1–4), *Achlya sp.*, Fischer (*loc. cit.*), Minden (1915: 265), GERMANY; *Achlya polyandra*, E. J. Butler (1907: 134, pl. 9, figs. 8–11), INDIA; *Achlya sp.*, H. E. Petersen (1909: 406; 1910: 541, fig. 18g), DENMARK; *Achlya sp.*, Sparrow (1932b: 270, fig. 1 f–g), *A. imperfecta*, *Achlya spp.*, Shanor (1939b: text fig. 2, pl. 25, fig. 2; 1940), UNITED STATES; *Achlya flagellata*, *A. flagellata* var. *yezoensis*, *A. racemosa*, Tokunaga (1933a: 23, pl. 2, figs. 6–8), JAPAN; *Achlya racemosa*, *Achlya sp.*, Cejp (1934: 228, figs. 1–2), CZECHOSLOVAKIA; *Achlya sp.*, Shen and Siang (1948: 199), CHINA.

For convenience the records of *Pseudolpidium fusiforme* are listed separately:
Parasitic in hyphae (not confined to the apex) of *Achlya polyandra*,

A. prolifera, Fischer (*loc. cit.*), host (?), Minden (1915: 267), GERMANY; *Achlya flagellata, A. flagellata* var. *yezoensis, A. racemosa*, Tokunaga (1933a: 21, pl. 2, figs. 1–2), JAPAN; *Achlya prolifera, Achlya sp.*, Sawada (see Tokunaga, *op. cit.*, p. 22), FORMOSA; *Achlya sp.*, Sparrow (1936a: 425), GREAT BRITAIN.

Sorokin (1883: 27, fig. 27) assigns oblong sporangia found in *Achlya* and *Saprolegnia* in European and Asiatic Russia to this species.

Because of the great differences in the shape and the size of the sporangia and in the size of the resting spore as described by various investigators, all their data were not included in the diagnosis. Briefly, according to these observers, they are as follows:

Reinsch (1878): Sporangia oblong, irregularly cylindrical or ellipsoidal, 22.4–39.3 μ (in diameter?); resting spore colorless, 22.4–39.3 μ; companion cells from one to three, ellipsoidal, 16.8–22.4 μ in diameter.

Butler (1907): Sporangia spherical, up to 80–120 μ in diameter, resting spore yellowish brown, 40–60 μ in diameter, with a single globule; companion cell smaller.

Sparrow (1932b): Sporangia ovoid or ellipsoidal, occasionally with small spines, 21.7 μ long by 10.4 μ wide; resting spore colorless, 34.5–52.6 μ in diameter, spines 10.5 μ long; companion cell 18.5 μ in diameter.

Tokunaga (1933a): Sporangia spherical or ellipsoidal, sometimes elongate, 45–97 μ long, 25–50 μ wide, with from one to two discharge tubes; resting spore spherical, 32–52 μ in diameter, yellowish brown; companion cells from one to two, 16–24 μ in diameter.

Sawada (see Tokunaga, 1933a: 22): Sporangia not observed; resting spore ovoid to globose, hyaline or yellowish, 24–100 μ in diameter, the wall covered with conical sharp-pointed spines 9–24 μ long.

OLPIDIOPSIS ACHLYAE McLarty

Bull. Torrey Bot. Club, 68: 62, figs. 1–26. 1941

"Zoosporangia solitary or numerous, usually localized in a terminal or intercalary swelling of the host filament, slightly brown and granular, enclosed at maturity by a cellulose wall, smooth or covered with fine or coarse non-cellulose bristles; spherical, oval, ellipsoidal or elongate, variable in size, 13.2–112.4 μ diam. × 115.0–666.4 μ; one to three exit tubes which may extend considerably beyond the surface of the host filament. Zoospores hyaline with numerous small granules, oval, spherical, or somewhat reniform, 2.3–5.7 μ × 2.9–4.3 μ, usually about 4.2 × 3.1 μ, with two approximately equal flagella attached laterally near the anterior end. Resting spores sexual and asexual or parthenogenetic, spherical or oval, 22.8–122.4 μ (usually about 50.0 × 41.0 μ), brown, with several or commonly one, large refringent globule. Endospore composed of cellulose, smooth, 1.0–1.5 μ in thickness. Exospore not composed of cellulose, varying from 1.0–11.4 μ in thickness, with warty protuberances, small or large, narrow or broad-based spines, hair-like fibrillae or with an entire, undulant or slightly serrate margin. Male cells, when present, may or may not discharge contents into female thallus, similar in appearance to zoosporangia, one to three attached to one female thallus, spherical or oval, thin-walled, smooth, sometimes embedded in the exospore. Resting spore in germination transformed into a sporangium liberating zoospores by means of an exit tube" (McLarty, *loc. cit.*).

Parasitic in *Achlya flagellata*, McLarty (*loc. cit.*), CANADA; *Achlya flagellata*, Karling (1949a: 275), UNITED STATES; *Achlya sp.*, Das-Gupta and John (1953: 169, figs. 8–12), INDIA.

Possibly, as McLarty suggests, this fungus is referable to *Olpidiopsis fusiformis*.

OLPIDIOPSIS INDEX Cornu

Ann. Sci. Nat. Bot., V, 15: 145, pl. 3, fig. 11. 1872

Sporangium narrowly ellipsoidal, with a thin smooth colorless wall and a single discharge tube; zoospores not observed; resting spore spherical, with a somewhat thickened wall densely covered with short slender spines; companion cell spherical, sparingly covered with short slender spines.

Parasitic in *Achlya sp.* (preparations), FRANCE; *Saprolegnia*, Sorokin (1883: 29, fig. 30), ASIATIC RUSSIA.

Differing from *Olpidiopsis saprolegniae* in the spiny wall of the companion cell and, to a lesser degree, in the more narrowly ellipsoidal sporangium.

OLPIDIOPSIS VARIANS Shanor

J. Elisha Mitchell Sci. Soc., 55: 171, text figs. A–E, pl. 24, figs. 1–13.
1939

(Fig. 75 D–F, p. 939)

"Zoosporangia single to many, formed either in terminal or inter-calary swellings of the host hypha, elliptical, oval, or spherical, extreme-ly variable in size from 60 by 40 μ up to 350 by 140 μ, frequently about 200 by 80 μ, walls giving cellulose reaction with chloroiodide of zinc, smooth to very spiny, spines slender and somewhat conical, up to 7 μ long, not giving the cellulose reaction; exit tubes commonly one to three (as many as five have been observed). Zoospores oval to elongated, 3.8–4.6 μ long by 2.3–3.0 μ in diameter, usually about 4.2 by 2.8 μ, biciliate, cilia of about equal length, measuring from about 4.2 to 4.6 μ. Oogonia yellowish-brown and very variable in size, spherical, with usually one but sometimes two antheridia attached, 26 to 83 μ in diameter (not including spines), averaging between 52 and 61 μ; exospore wall colorless to yellowish, about 1.2 μ thick, bearing usually coarse abruptly tapering spines which measure up to 8.6 μ long and have a reticulum connecting them, not giving the cellulose reaction; endospore wall yellowish-brown, about 1.7 μ thick, smooth, and giving the cellulose reaction. Antheridia (companion cells) usually spherical, 17 to 30 μ in diameter, commonly about 26 μ, wall occasionally smooth but typically covered by scattered spines similar to those on the oogonia but much shorter, 1.7 μ at the longest, outer part of wall bearing spines usually colorless, inner wall having a slightly yellowish cast. Contents of anther-idia pass into oogonia and antheridia on mature oogonia are empty. Germination takes place in this species by means of a germination tube which usually penetrates the companion cell. Biciliate zoospores are produced when the resting spore germinates" (Shanor, *loc. cit.*).

On *Achlya flagellata* Coker, UNITED STATES.

OLPIDIOPSIS SPINOSA Tokunaga

Trans. Sapporo Nat. Hist. Soc., 13 (1): 25, pl. 2, figs. 10–11. 1933

Sporangium ellipsoidal or cylindrical, mostly 92–198 μ long by 34–61 μ broad, with from one to two discharge tubes; host hypha distended;

zoospores ellipsoidal or somewhat elongate, provided with an anterior and a lateral flagellum; resting spore spherical, 51–73 µ in diameter (without the spines), with a thickened dark or silvery wall, the outer surface covered with numerous hyaline rodlike sharp-pointed spines 9.6 µ long, germination not observed; companion cell spherical, 25.2–32.4 µ in diameter, with a thin wall, the outer surface densely covered with long rodlike sharp spines.

Parasitic in hyphae of *Achlya flagellata*, sometimes occurring with *"Pseudolpidium fusiforme"* and *"Olpidiopsis minor,"* JAPAN.

OLPIDIOPSIS INCRASSATA Cornu

Ann. Sci. Nat. Bot., V, 15: 146, pl. 4, fig. 12. 1872

Pseudolpidium incrassata (Cornu) Fischer, Rabenhorst. Kryptogamen-Fl., 1(4): 37. 1892.

(?) *Olpidiopsis major* Maurizio, Jahresbericht Naturforsch. Gesell. Graubündens, Chur, 38: 15, pl. 1, figs. 4–9. 1895.

(?) *Olpidiopsis vexans* Barrett, Ann. Bot. London, 26: 231, pl. 23, figs. 15, 19–21, pl. 24, figs. 26–27, 32–39, pl. 25, figs. 40–42, 44, 47–71, pl. 26, fig. 75. 1912.

Sporangium ellipsoidal or subspherical, wall thin, smooth, colorless, discharge tube single, stout or narrowly cylindrical; zoospores not observed; resting spore ellipsoidal, yellowish brown, with a thick strongly undulating wall, germination not observed.

Parasitic in *Achlya racemosa*, Cornu (*loc. cit.*), FRANCE; *Achlya sp.*, Sparrow (1933c: 515), UNITED STATES.

Sorokin's fungus (1883: 29, fig. 29) referred to this species is not identifiable.

Only one doubtful instance of a companion cell on a resting spore was noted by Cornu. His fungus, consequently, was referred to *Pseudolpidium* by Fischer. The resting spores observed by Sparrow were nearly colorless.

Shanor (1940) indicated that he would present evidence to prove that *Olpidiopsis major* Maurizio and *O. vexans* Barrett are synonymous with Cornu's species. His experimental work shows, however, that the material on which he based his study is confined to *Saprolegnia*. This agrees with the findings of Maurizio and Barrett, but is contrary to the

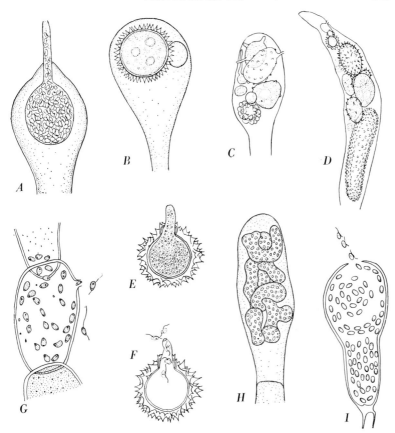

FIG. 75. Olpidiopsidaceae

A-B. Olpidiopsis saprolegniae var. *saprolegniae* (Braun) Cornu in *Saprolegnia sp.: A*, sporangium in swollen tip of hypha; *B*, spiny resting spore with companion cell. *C. Olpidiopsis vexans* Barrett, tip of hypha of *Saprolegnia litoralis* containing smooth- and rough-walled sporangia and a rough-walled resting spore with its companion cell. *D–F. Olpidiopsis varians* Shanor: *D*, tip of hypha of *Achlya flagellata* bearing smooth-, spiny-, and rough-walled zoosporangia and a resting spore with its companion cell; *E–F*, germination of resting spore. *G. Rozellopsis septigena* Karling in *Saprolegnia sp.*, showing emergence of zoospores. *H. Petersenia irregulare* (Constantineanu) Sparrow, thallus in tip of *Achlya* hypha. *I. Rozellopsis inflata* (Butler) Karling, in *Phytophthora sp.*, showing discharge of zoospores.

(*A*, Sparrow, 1943; *B*, Sparrow, 1932b; *C–D*, Shanor, 1939b; *E–F*, Shanor, 1939a; *G*, Prowse, 1951; *H*, Sparrow, 1943; *I*, Waterhouse, 1940)

observations of Cornu and Sparrow. The latter investigators have found *O. incrassata* on *Achlya*. There can be little doubt that Shanor studied his material far more extensively. In view of the host specificity clearly demonstrated by Shanor in his own material and in other species of the genus, it is possible that different physiological strains or even different species are involved. Because of the lack of a specific description by Shanor of his fungus the descriptions of *O. major* and *O. vexans* are appended and their names included in the key to the species (below that of *O. incrassata*).

Olpidiopsis major Maurizio

Jahresbericht Naturforsch. Gesell. Graubündens, Chur, 38: 15, pl. 1, figs. 4–9.
1895

Sporangium spherical and 23.5–80 µ in diameter or ovoid and 22–62 µ wide by 70–124 µ long, wall smooth, thin, colorless, generally in the swollen apical part of the host hypha, with from one to four (mostly two) narrowly cylindrical discharge tubes of variable length; zoospores ovoid, biflagellate, emerging simultaneously through the discharge tubes; resting spore ellipsoidal, 74.5–105 µ long by 30–50 µ broad, thick-walled, the outer wall light yellow and strongly undulate, germination not observed; companion cells from one to four (mostly two), spherical and 18.5 µ in diameter or somewhat ellipsoidal and 15.5–21.5 µ wide by 28–31 µ long, wall smooth, thin, colorless.

Parasitic in *Saprolegnia thureti*, *S. hypogena* var. V, SWITZERLAND.

Placed in synonymy with *Olpidiopsis incrassata* by Karling (1942e), see remarks under that species, above.

Olpidiopsis vexans Barrett

Ann. Bot. London, 26: 231, pl. 23, figs. 15, 19–21, pl. 24, figs. 26–27, 32–39, pl. 25, figs. 40–42, 44, 47–71, pl. 26, fig. 75. 1912

(Fig. 75 C, p. 939)

"Sporangia single or multiple, formed in terminal or intercalary swellings of the host hyphae, elliptical, oval, or spherical, very variable in size, up to 176 µ in diameter, with smooth, colorless membrane, colorless contents, and one to several unbranched exit tubes; zoospores elongated, slightly inequilateral, with two cilia attached at or near the anterior end. Oospores dark grey, with one, sometimes two, antheridial cells; oospores surrounded by a thick endospore and a thin warty exospore, spherical to oval, sometimes elliptical, up to $116 \times 84 \mu$, average 50μ in diameter; antheridia spherical, less commonly oval, average diameter 20μ, with a smooth, colorless wall. Germination of oospores not observed" (Barrett, *loc. cit.*).

In hyphae of *Saprolegnia ferax*, Barrett (*loc. cit.*), *S. monoica*, Graff (1928: 159), UNITED STATES; *Saprolegnia sp.*, Fischer (as *Olpidiopsis saprolegniae*, 1892: 38), Minden (1915: 263), GERMANY; *Saprolegnia sp.*, *Achlya sp.*, Petersen (as *Olpidiopsis saprolegniae*, 1909: 404; 1910: 539, fig. 28b), DENMARK.

Placed in synonymy with *Olpidiopsis incrassata* by Karling (1942e), see remarks under that species (above).

OLPIDIOPSIS LUXURIANS Barrett

Ann. Bot. London, 26: 231, pl. 23, figs. 1, 5–7, 10–14, 17, 21b, 22; pl. 24 figs. 24–25, 28–30; pl. 25, figs. 43, 45; pl. 26, figs. 74, 76–90. 1912

"Sporangia single or multiple, formed in terminal or intercalary swellings of the host hyphae, oval to spherical, very variable in size, with one to three exit tubes extending considerably beyond the wall of the host; zoospores rather small, elongated, with two cilia attached at or near the anterior end. Oospores spherical, with one or two, rarely three, antheridia, with a thick endospore and a thin exospore provided with numerous conical spines up to 2.5μ in length; oospores $25–50 \mu$ in diameter, contain one or more large oil globules; antheridia spherical, frequently oval to elliptical, $10–25 \mu$ in diameter, with a smooth colorless wall. Germination of oospores not observed" (Barrett, *loc. cit.*).

Parasitic in *Aphanomyces laevis*, Barrett (*loc. cit.*), UNITED STATES; in hyphae of *Aphanomyces sp.*, Sparrow (1952c: 105), CUBA.

From the coarseness of the spines on the resting spore, the species appears to be intermediate between *Olpidiopsis fusiformis* ("*O. minor*") and *O. saprolegniae*. Barrett states it could not be transferred to hosts on which *O. fusiformis* ("*O. minor*") had been reported. This has been verified by Shanor (1940).

Listed as a synonym of *Olpidiopsis aphanomycis* by Karling (1942e).

OLPIDIOPSIS APHANOMYCIS Cornu

Ann. Sci. Nat. Bot., V, 15: 148, pl. 4, figs. 5–11. 1872

Pseudolpidium aphanomycis (Cornu) Fischer, Rabenhorst. Kryptogamen-Fl., 1(4): 37. 1892.

Sporangia spherical, solitary or in groups of three or more in terminal or intercalary swellings of the host hypha, with a single fairly broad discharge tube; zoospores and resting spore not observed.

Parasitic in *Aphanomyces sp.*, FRANCE.

Fungi with various types of resting spores have been assigned by later investigators to *Olpidiopsis aphanomycis*. Dangeard (1890-91b: 90, pl. 4, figs. 9–11) figured a spiny spore without a companion cell in *Pythium* and *Aphanomyces*, as did Butler also, in the latter genus. Petersen (1910: 539, fig. 27) showed one in *Aphanomyces* with a warty surface (like that in *O. vexans*) and bearing a companion cell. What kind of resting spore occurred in Cornu's species is, of course, not known. Of the spores reported, Petersen's unquestionably belongs to a species of *Olpidiopsis*. He himself suggests that it may be identical with *O. vexans* and that the smaller size he reports may result from poor nutritional conditions within the host.

When more information concerning the sporangial stage is available, Cornu's species can be redefined. Meanwhile, the present writer has compiled a fuller diagnosis, [1] from the observations since that earlier time. The diagnosis and the occurrences involved are cited below.

Sporangia spherical or ellipsoidal, from one to six, lying loosely in intercalary and terminal swellings of the host hypha, wall thin, smooth, colorless, with from one to two discharge tubes; zoospores somewhat ovoid, flattened, with two laterally attached flagella, upon escape soon coming to rest in a group, assuming motility after from four to five minutes, and dispersing; resting spore spherical, with a thin or somewhat thickened (brownish?) wall covered with short spines or warts, with or without a companion cell.

---

[1] Karling (1942e) also supplies a composite description. He believes the species includes *Olpidiopsis luxurians* Barrett.

Parasitic in hyphae of *Aphanomyces sp.*, Dangeard (*loc. cit.*), FRANCE; Butler (*loc. cit.*), INDIA; Minden (1915: 267), GERMANY; Petersen (*loc. cit.*), DENMARK; *Aphanomyces laevis*, Karling (1949a: 275), UNITED STATES; *Aphanomyces laevis*, Shen and Siang (1948: 200), CHINA.

Another interpretation of this species has been supplied by Whiffen (1942b: 609). It is based on a parasite of *Aphanomyces cladogamous* which could not be induced to infect *A. laevis*. Her diagnosis is given below. The interested investigator can decide which fungus he wishes to call *O. aphanomycis*. Our impression is that Whiffen's species should probably be segregated as new, rather than any attempt be made to identify it with Cornu's poorly known form.

––––––––

Olpidiopsis aphanomycis Cornu, sensu Whiffen

Amer. J. Bot., 29: 609, figs. 4, 10, 24–26. 1942

"Zoosporangia 34.2 to 94.05 µ, one or two, sometimes more in swellings of the host hyphae which are usually unilateral. Zoospores biflagellate. Resting bodies oval, 24.6 × 28.7 µ to 36.9 × 43.05 µ, or spherical, 13.2 to 44.46 µ, covered with broad-based spines, 2.1 to 4.1 µ in length; exospore wall 4.1 µ thick, endospore wall 2.3 µ thick; companion cell lacking" (Whiffen, *loc. cit.*).

Parasitic in *Aphanomyces cladogamous*, not capable of infecting *A. laevis*, UNITED STATES.

––––––––

OLPIDIOPSIS GRACILE (Butler) Karling

Simple Holocarpic Biflagellate Phycomycetes, p. 47. 1942

(Fig. 76 B, p. 960)

Pseudolpidium gracile Butler, Mem. Dept. Agr. India, Bot. Ser., 1: 131, pl. 7, figs. 1–8. 1907.

"Zoosporangia solitary or numerous, up to 40 in a single swelling, hyaline, smooth or spiny, spherical, 4–52 µ, with 1 to 5 contorted and swollen exit tubes of varying lengths which may project considerably beyond the surface of the host cell. Zoospores, isocont (?), hyaline, obclavate, elongate, and somewhat curved with one to several minute refractive granules, size unknown; one flagellum inserted near the anterior end, the other laterally; swimming motion smooth, body of spore often revolving on its long axis. Resting spores parthenogenetic, single or numerous, occurring in association with the zoosporangia, spherical to oval, 12–27 μ exclusive of spines, yellowish, containing a large refractive globule surrounded by a peripheral layer of vacuolate protoplasm; endospore .7 to 1.2 μ thick, exospore 1.7 to 2.5 μ thick and covered with long, 4 μ, tapering, thick, crowded spines; germination unknown; companion or male cells lacking" (Karling, *loc. cit.*).

Parasitic in *Pythium intermedium*, Butler (*loc. cit.*), FRANCE; *Pythium rostratum*, Whiffen (1942b: 607, figs. 7, 8), UNITED STATES; ? host, soil, Remy (1948: 214), GERMANY; from soil, substrate?, Gaertner (1954b: 22), EQUATORIAL EAST AFRICA.

"Causing terminal enlargements and lateral, oval- or balloon-shaped diverticula in the host hyphae which may be 80–90 μ in their greatest diameter" (Karling, *op. cit.*, p. 47).

OLPIDIOPSIS PYTHII (Butler) Karling

Simple Holocarpic Biflagellate Phycomycetes, p. 47. 1942

Pseudolpidium pythii Butler, Mem. Dept. Agr. India, Bot. Ser., 1: 129, pl. 7, figs. 9–16. 1907.

"Zoosporangia solitary or numerous, hyaline, smooth, oval, and ellipsoid, up to 35 μ in the greatest diameter, with a single exit tube of varying length which extends for a short distance beyond the surface of the host. Zoospores isocont, hyaline, uniequilateral, somewhat kidney-shaped with one to several small refractive granules; flagella laterally inserted; swarming in the vicinity of the exit canal for a brief period, then coming to rest for a few minutes in a dense cluster; finally swimming away slowly. Resting spores parthenogenetic, solitary or numerous, often in association with zoosporangia, oval or spherical, 19.2–30 μ, brown, comparatively thin-walled and covered with fine, thread-like, short, evenly spaced spines; germination unknown; companion or male cells lacking" (Karling, *loc. cit.*).

Parasitic in *Pythium monospermum*, *P. rostratum*, *P. vexans*, and *P. intermedium*, Butler (*loc. cit.*), FRANCE; *Pythium sp.*, Minden (1915:

268), soil, Remy (1948: 214), GERMANY; *P. oryzae*, Tokunaga (1933a), JAPAN; *Pythium sp.*, Sparrow (1936a: 425), GREAT BRITAIN; *Pythium sp.*, Karling (1949a: 275), UNITED STATES.

"Causing oval, spherical, obpyriform or balloon-shaped enlargements at the end of the host hyphae or in lateral diverticula, and occasionally leading to septation of the hyphae" (Karling, *op. cit.*, p. 47).

Neither Minden nor Sparrow was certain of their identifications. The fungus occurring on *Pythium* but included by Dangeard (1890-91b: 90) under *Olpidiopsis aphanomycis* may be referable to this species.

OLPIDIOPSIS CURVISPINOSA Whiffen

Amer. J. Bot., 29: 610, figs. 1, 5–6, 21. 1942

"Zoosporangia one to many in terminal or intercalary swellings of the host hyphae, spherical to oval in shape, 12 to 68 µ in longest diameter, cellulose wall smooth or with short bristles, one to three exit tubes. Zoospores with numerous small oil globules, elongate and somewhat reniform, biflagellate, flagellae of about equal length, attached near anterior end of spore. Resting spores, consistently with a companion cell, spherical to oval, 17 to 24 µ in longest diameter, containing one large oil globule surrounded by vacuolate protoplasm. Exospore wall with curved spines up to 5 µ in length. Companion cell spherical or oval, 14 to 20 µ, smooth or with short, closely set spines" (Whiffen, *loc. cit.*).

Parasitic on *Pythium sp.*, UNITED STATES.

Characterized by the bent, flexuous-appearing, intertwining spines on the resting spore.

Found capable of parasitizing *Pythium torulosum* by Whiffen (*op. cit.*, p. 611).

OLPIDIOPSIS BREVISPINOSA Whiffen

Amer. J. Bot., 29: 610, figs. 2, 14, 22, 27. 1942

"Zoosporangia one to many in terminal or intercalary swellings of the host hyphae, swellings up to 125 µ in diameter. Zoosporangia 10.68 to 68.40 µ in longest diameter, wall smooth or with short bristles, with one to three exit tubes. Zoospores with numerous oil globules, elongate and somewhat reniform, biflagellate, the flagellae of about equal length, attached near anterior end of the spore. Resting spore consistently with a companion cell, dark brown, spherical to oval, 10.68 to 45.1 μ in longest diameter, spines on exospore wall up to 3.56 μ in length, endospore wall 0.75 to 1.32 μ thick, exospore wall 1.78 to 2.50 μ thick" (Whiffen, *loc. cit.*).

Parasitic on *Pythium sp.*, coll. P. Couch, UNITED STATES.

Characterized by somewhat short, straight spines.

Not found capable of infecting other species of *Pythium* by Whiffen (*op. cit.*, p. 611).

OLPIDIOPSIS KARLINGIAE Karling

Mycologia, 41: 271, figs. 1–17. 1949

"Sporangia hyaline, smooth, spherical, 8–120 μ, oval, 15–84 × 20–98 μ, oblong and slightly curved, 6–10 × 12–28 μ, pyriform, obpyriform or slightly angular when pressed together, with one simple, rarely two and branched, short and broad, 6–12 by 14–18 μ, or long, 7 × 110 μ, discharge tubes which protrude directly through the host cell wall or the exit papillae. Zoospores reniform, 6–6.5 × 10–10.8 μ, and containing 30 to 50 minute granules which are not particularly refractive; heterocont, anterior and posterior flagella 6.5–7 μ and 11.6–13 μ long, respectively. Resting spores spherical, 8–22 μ, oval, 9–17 × 15–23 μ, oblong, 7–9 × 12–20 μ or angular when pressed together, with a hyaline, smooth, 1.8–2.2 μ, thick wall, evenly but coarsely granular protoplasm and one or more vacuoles; germination unknown" (Karling, *loc. cit.*).

Parasitic in *Rhizophlyctis rosea*, UNITED STATES.

Attempts to infect other chytrids with this species were unsuccessful.

OLPIDIOPSIS GILLII (de Wild.) Friedmann

Österr. Bot. Zeitschr., 99: 209, fig. 6. 1952

Olpidium gillii de Wildeman. Ann. Soc. Belge Micro. (Mém.), 20: 42. 1896.

Sporangia one or two in a host cell, tubular, 4–20 μ in diameter and 5–120 μ long, more or less slightly constricted in the middle, pushing apart the valves of the host, discharge tube apical or subapical, up to 70 μ long by 4–5 μ in diameter, with a broad 8–20 μ in diameter base, the distal end slightly constricted subterminally; zoospores numerous, escaping at the dissolution of the tip of the discharge tube, exhibiting imperfect diplanetism, with two apically inserted flagella, one 7.5–9 μ the other 5.5–7 μ long, with a spherical droplet, during the first swarming period 4.5–5 μ long by 2–3 μ broad, after undergoing a period of rest and halting motion, in the second swarming period 4–4.5 μ long by 3–3.5 μ broad, resting spore not observed.

On *Pleurosigma attenuatum, Cocconema lanceolatum, Nitzschia sp., N. sigmoidea,* coll. Gill, de Wildeman (1896b: 42), GREAT BRITAIN; parasitic in *Gyrosigma attenuatum* and *G. acuminatum,* Friedmann (*loc. cit.*), AUSTRIA.

Unless host specificity is proven in the future, there can be little doubt but that Gill's and Friedmann's fungi are the same. Friedmann states that van Heurck's (1899) Figure 2 is based on Gill's material.

OLPIDIOPSIS SCHENKIANA Zopf

Nova Acta Acad. Leop.-Carol., 47: 168, pl. 15, figs. 1–32. 1884

Pleocystidium parasiticum Fisch, Sitzungsber. Phys.-Med. Soc. Erlangen, 16: 67, pl. 1, figs. 24–39. 1884.

Olpidiopsis parasitica (Fisch) Fischer, Rabenhorst, Kryptogamen-Flora, 1 (4): 40. 1892.

Diplophysa schenkiana (Zopf) Schroeter, Engler und Prantl, Die Nat. Pflanzenf., I, 1: 85, fig. 68, A–D. 1892 (1897).

Pseudolpidiopsis schenkiana (Zopf) Minden, Kryptogamenfl. Mark Brandenburg, 5: 257. 1911 (1915).

Pseudolpidiopsis parasitica (Fisch) Minden, *loc. cit.,* p. 258.

Sporangium broadly or narrowly ellipsoidal, rarely spherical, often somewhat curved, 32–41 by 17 μ, wall thin, smooth, colorless, discharge tube usually single, fairly broad, variable in length, often long and tortuous, arising laterally on ellipsoidal sporangia, occasionally causing swelling of the infected cell; zoospores from eight to fifty, grape-seed-like, biflagellate, with refractive colorless globules in the plasma, 8 by 7 μ, formed in the sporangium and either emerging through the tube and swimming directly away or first undergoing amoeboid motion at the orifice and without encystment being directly transformed into the secondary zoospore, which swims away; resting spore spherical or ellipsoidal, 19–24 µ long, with a smooth, thickened brownish or color-less wall and a large globule in the contents, upon germination producing a discharge tube and functioning as a sporangium; companion cells from one to four, sessile or attached by a short beak, spherical, 10–16.6 µ in diameter, smaller than the resting spore, thin-walled, smooth, colorless.

Often in company with other parasites in vegetative cells, gametangia, and, rarely, zygospores of *Mougeotia sp.*, *Spirogyra sp.*, Zopf (*loc. cit.*), Fisch (*loc. cit.*), Minden (*loc. cit.*), GERMANY; *Spirogyra sp.*, de Wilde-man (1890: 24; 1896b: 31, pl. 2, figs. 1–12, 15–17), coll. Marchal, de Wildeman (1890, 1896b [LUXEMBOURG]), BELGIUM; *Spirogyra sp.*, Con-stantineanu (1901: 375), RUMANIA;*Spirogyra sp.*, E. J. Butler (1907: 135, pl. 10, figs. 11–13), INDIA; *Spirogyra sp.*, *Mougeotia sp.*, Scherffel (1925a: 104, pl. 4, figs. 191–198), Krenner (1935), Domján (1936: 52, pl.1, figs. 172–173, 182–184), *Spirogyra sp.*, Bérczi (1940: 80), HUNGARY; *Spi-rogyra sp.*, Karling (1942e: 50), *Spirogyra sp.*, Sparrow and Ellison (1949: 31, figs. A–G), UNITED STATES; *Spirogyra sp.*, Shen and Siang (1948: 200, fig. 11), CHINA.

On the basis of the reports of Fisch, de Wildeman, and Scherffel, the fungus is strongly nucleophagous.

Zopf's seemingly incorrect observations on the flagellation of the zoospore led Minden to erect the genus *Pseudolpidiopsis* (now in synon-ymy) for the disposition of this species. The affinities of Tokunaga's (1933b: 82, pl. 5, fig. 13) fungus from Japan are doubtful, since the zoospores are said to be uniflagellate.The American material examined by Sparrow and Ellison (*loc. cit.*) was parasitized by a species of *Pythiella* (p. 814).

OLPIDIOPSIS OEDOGONIARUM (de Wild.) Scherffel

Arch. Protistenk., 52: 103, pl. 4, figs. 199–207c, pl. 5, figs. 207d–208. 1925

> *Olpidiopsis fusiformis* var. *oedogoniarum* Sorokin, Arch. Bot. Nord France,
> 2: 30, fig. 31. 1883 (separate).[1]
> *Olpidium oedogoniarum* (Sorok.) de Wildeman, Ann. Soc. Belge Micro.
> (Mém.), 18: 154, pl. 6, figs. 9–10. 1894.

Sporangium lying free in the host cell, elongate, ovoid, saclike, broadly

---

[1] See also Sorokin, *Revue Mycologique*, 11: 84, pl. 80, fig. 99. 1889.

fusiform or reniform, with broad rounded ends, 15–50 μ long by 5–8 μ
in diameter, the long axis parallel with that of the algal cell, with a
single lateral median (rarely otherwise placed) tapering discharge tube
4–6 μ long by 3–4 μ wide which, funnel-like, projects slightly extramatrically, wall thin, colorless, smooth; zoospores oval in outline, dorsally
arched, with hyaline plasma containing refractive granules and a bright
spot, 5 μ long, with two equal, opposed flagella arising from the flattened
ventral surface, generally emerging from the sporangium as partly
formed bodies which undergo their final maturation at the tip of the
discharge tube, escaping rarely as distinct attenuated biflagellate motile
spores which encyst at the mouth of the discharge tube and after a period
of rest emerge from the cysts (3 μ in diameter) as biflagellate zoospores
with a single globule, (shape?), 5 μ long, movement "dancing" or an
even swimming; resting spore spherical or subspherical, 13 μ by 10 μ,
lying loosely within a saclike smooth oögonium, with a thick smooth
colorless wall, the contents with numerous small refractive globules and
a single large eccentric lustrous fat body, without periplasm, germination not observed; companion cell elongate, saclike, or subspherical,
10 μ in diameter, smooth-walled, attached to the wall of the oögonium
by a beaklike projection or sessile on it.

In *Oedogonium sp.*, Sorokin (*loc. cit.*), ASIATIC RUSSIA; *Oedogonium
sp.*, de Wildeman (*loc. cit.*), FRANCE; *Oedogonium sp.*, Scherffel (*loc.
cit.*) Bérczi (1940: 80, pl. 2, figs. 2–3), HUNGARY; *Oedogonium sp.*,
Sparrow (1933c: 516, text fig. I, 9–10), UNITED STATES.

According to Scherffel, the infecting zoospore after coming to rest
on the host wall forms a hemispherical appressorium, from the base
of which a delicate penetration tube is produced. After discharge of
the contents into the host the external parts of the infecting zoospore
disappear and the naked fungous plasma, free from the infection tube,
passively moves, no doubt carried by the host contents, to the vicinity
of the nucleus. Here it becomes surrounded by a membrane, increases in size, and assumes an ovoid shape. In the early stages of
development the host cell is not appreciably altered, but, from the
figures given, presumably all or nearly all of the algal contents are
eventually consumed. Details of the changes undergone by the fungous
contents, which include strong vacuolization and the formation of a

large central vacuole, are given by Scherffel. His account of the degrees of diplanetism exhibited by the zoospores has been mentioned in the discussion of the genus (see p. 928).

Olpidiopsis fibrillosa de Wildeman

La Notarisia, 10 (3): 34. 1895; Ann. Soc. Belge Micro. (Mém.), 20: 28, pl. 2, figs. 13–14, 18–19. 1896

(?) *Pseudolpidiopsis fibrillosa* (de Wild.) Minden, Kryptogamenfl. Mark Brandenburg, 5: 259. 1911 (1915).

Sporangium spherical or ellipsoidal; zoospores not observed; resting spore spherical or ellipsoidal, 20–25 µ in diameter (?), wall thick, densely covered with long delicate radiating fibrils, germination not observed; companion cells one or several, spherical, 12 µ in diameter, with a thin smooth colorless wall.

In *Spirogyra sp.*, coll. Massart, de Wildeman (*loc. cit.*), Belgium (Luxembourg); *Spirogyra longata*, Domján (1936: 41, pl. 1, figs. 1–2, 24, 36), Hungary.

The resting spores figured by Domján have much larger fibrils than those shown by de Wildeman, and one appears to lack a companion cell.

Olpidiopsis appendiculata de Wildeman

La Notarisia, 10 (3): 34. 1895; Ann. Soc. Belge Micro. (Mém.), 20: 30, pl. 1, figs. 4, 8–12. 1896

(?) *Pseudolpidiopsis appendiculata* (de Wild.) Minden, Kryptogamenfl. Mark Brandenburg, 5: 259. 1911 (1915).

Sporangium spherical or ellipsoidal, with a smooth thin colorless wall and a single short discharge tube, causing swelling of the infected cell; zoospores not observed; resting spore spherical, 9–15 µ in diameter, thick-walled, the outer surface moderately covered with sharp spines 3–10 µ long, germination not observed; companion cell vermiform, 20 µ long, with a thin smooth colorless wall, proximal part expanded.

In *Mougeotia sp.*, France (?) ("Beloeil").

OLPIDIOPSIS ZOPFII de Wildeman

La Notarisia, 10 (3): 34. 1895; Ann. Soc. Belge Micro. (Mém.), 20: 26, pl. 1,
figs. 1–3, 5–7. 1896

(?) *Pseudolpidiopsis zopfii* (de Wild.) Minden, Kryptogamenfl. Mark Brandenburg, 5: 259. 1911 (1915).

Sporangium spherical or ovoid, with a single discharge tube, wall
thin, smooth, colorless, causing swelling of the infected cell; zoospores
not observed; resting spore spherical, thick-walled, 16–22 μ in diameter,
covered with numerous coarse sharp spines, germination not observed;
companion cells from one to three, spherical, 12 μ in diameter, with a
thin smooth colorless wall.

In *Spirogyra sp.*, coll. Massart, BELGIUM (LUXEMBOURG).

OLPIDIOPSIS ANDREEI (Lagerheim) Sparrow

Biol. Bulletin, 70: 245, text figs. 1–8, 12. 1936

Pleotrachelus andreei Lagerheim, in Ymer, Tidskr. Svenska Sällskap.
Antropol. Geogr., 19 (4): 436, fig. 1. 1899.
Bicilium andreei (Lagerheim) H. E. Petersen, Oversigt Kgl. Danske Vidensk.
Selskabs. Forhandl., 1905 (5): 448, fig. I, 3–6.
Pleotrachelus ectocarpi Jokl. Österr, botan. Zeitschr., 66: 267, pls. 4–5.
1916.
Petersenia andreei (Lagerheim) Sparrow, *loc. cit.*

Sporangia from one to twenty-three in a cell, predominantly spherical, 5–39 μ in diameter, or ellipsoidal and 8–15 by 15–25 μ, wall thin,
smooth, colorless, with from one to seven cylindrical radiating discharge tubes up to 78 μ in length by 3–5 μ in diameter; zoospores
irregularly pyriform, 4–5 μ long by 3 μ wide, with a refractive area at
either end, anteriorly biflagellate, the flagella equal and oppositely
directed, initiating movement within the sporangium and escaping by
flagellar action through the open end of the discharge tubes, movement
erratic; resting spore spherical or ellipsoidal, 12–23 μ in diameter, with
a thick smooth brownish wall and contents with globules; companion
cell thin-walled, colorless, 4–8 μ in diameter, sometimes nearly as large
as the receptive thallus.

In *Spongomorpha sp.*, coll. André, Lagerheim (*loc. cit.*), KING
CHARLES LAND (ARCTIC); *Acrosiphonia incurva, Acrosiphonia sp., A.*

hystrix, coll. A. Jessen, Petersen (*loc. cit.*), GREENLAND; *Acrosiphonia sp.,* coll. K. Rosenvinge, *A. incurva,* Petersen (*loc. cit.*), *Ectocarpus sp., Striaria attenuata,* Sparrow (1934c: 17, pl. 4, figs. O–S), DENMARK; *Ectocarpus granulosus,* Jokl (*loc. cit.*), "ADRIATIC"; *Ectocarpus siliculosus,* Sparrow (1936b), UNITED STATES; *Ectocarpus simplex, E. siliculosus, Ectocarpus sp., Ceramium diaphanum,* Aleem (1950d: 428, figs. 11–12), FRANCE; *Spongomorpha sp.,* Aleem (1953: 8, figs. 13–16), SWEDEN.

Further observations are needed to confirm the sexual process preceding the formation of the resting spores. Companion cells were found in both the Danish and the American material. The great variation in the size of the companion cells in the American material particularly needs further explanation.

Aleem's (1953) material from Sweden differed in having a less rounded sporangium, which bore only a single discharge tube.

Fragmentary observations on other "*Pleotrachelus*"-like marine forms have been reported by Sparrow (1934c, 1936b); some of these forms approximate *Olpidiopsis andreei.* One, found in *Ceramium diaphanum,* had spherical sporangia up to 96 μ or more in diameter with ten or more radiating discharge tubes. Another completely filled the egg of a microscopic animal and formed from one to three broad discharge tubes, through which biflagellate zoospores emerged.

OLPIDIOPSIS FELDMANNI Aleem

C. R. Acad. Sci. Paris, 235: 1250, figs. a–e. 1952

Sporangium when in the apical cell of the host spherical, 15–30 (35) μ in diameter, when in older parts subspherical or oblong and 30–45 (52) μ long by 20–25 μ wide, with a smooth wall and one (rarely 2–3), short, conical, discharge tube 5–10 μ long by 2–4.5 μ wide; zoospores rounded or slightly pyriform with a refractive droplet 2–2.5 μ long by 1.5–2 μ wide with two equal, oppositely directed flagella, emerging directly from the sporangium and swimming away; resting spore not observed.

Parasitic in the marine algae *Falkenbergia rufolanosa, Tra_illiella intricata*, FRANCE; *Trailliella intricata, Falkenbergia rufolanosa*, Aleem (1953: 10, figs. 17–18), SWEDEN.

This species is here retained in *Olpidiopsis* rather than placing it in *Pseudolpidium* with the other *Olpidiopsis*-like forms which lack resting spores. A new combination seems unnecessary.

RECENTLY DESCRIBED TAXA [1]

OLPIDIOPSIS MAGNUSII J. and G. Feldmann

Rev. Mycologique, 20: 243, fig. 4. 1955

Sporangia spherical, up to 45 µ in diameter, singly or up to five in the inflated rhizoid of the host; zoospores numerous, reniform, 5 µ long, with two lateral flagella, escaping and swimming away through a single cylindrical tapering discharge tube which penetrates the host wall.

In terminal cells of rhizoids of *Ceramium flabelligerum*, J. and G. Feldmann (*loc.cit.*), FRANCE; *Ceramium spp.* Magnus (1875).

J. and G. Feldmann identify their fungus with the one Magnus (1872, 1875) figured in the rhizoids of *Ceramium spp.* The Feldmanns believe that it is a different form from the one Magnus found in the cortical cells and axillary cells, which they consider belongs in *Eurychasmidium* (see p. 822).

OLPIDIOPSIS MYZOCYTIA Rieth

Die Kulturpflanze, 2: 180, fig. 10. 1954

Sporangia mostly one, sometimes up to four in a segment of the host; primary zoospores five to six, encysting at the orifice of a short, isodiametric discharge tube, secondary zoospores with two nearly equal flagella and pulsating vacuole; resting spore sexually formed, the male gamete passing through a pore into the receptive thallus in which a smooth, thick-walled plerotic oöspore (7)–9, 5–(12) µ, is formed whose germination is not known.

Parasitic in segments of the thallus of *Myzocytium proliferum*, GERMANY.

Strongly resembling a *Pythiella* allied to *P. besseyi* (p. 814).

---

[1] Not included in the key.

OLPIDIOPSIS VERRUCOSA Johnson

J. Elisha Mitchell Sci. Soc., 71: 60, figs. 1–24. 1955

"Zoösporangia terminal in the host hyphae, infrequently in short lateral branches; oval or spherical, very rarely pyramidal; 28 × 40 μ –84 × 103 μ, spherical ones 42–92 μ in diameter; smooth; commonly with one or two exit tubes. Zoöspores laterally biflagellate, isocont; oval or ellipsoid, rarely irregular; 3.6–4.8 μ in length by 2.4–3.0 μ in diameter. Resting spores (oögonia) oval, occasionally spherical, never ellipsoid; 22 × 26 μ–63 × 67 μ, predominantly 42–50 × 49–56 μ, inclusive of exospore. Exospore verrucose, crenulate, squarrose, or rugulose, infrequently irregular or bullate, rarely smooth, never echinulate; 1.4–8.4 μ thick. Companion cells (antheridia) 1–5 on a resting spore; spherical, occasionally ellipsoid or oval; smooth; 11–28 μ, predominantly 14–22 μ in diameter. Resting spore germinating by a single germ tube penetrating through the companion cell, the contents forming laterally biflagellate, isocont planonts" (Johnson, *loc. cit.*).

Parasitic in *Achlya glomerata*, from soil, UNITED STATES.

The species differs from *Olpidiopsis vexans* and *O. incrassata* primarily in configuration of the exospore of the resting spore and in the host range.

IMPERFECTLY KNOWN SPECIES OF OLPIDIOPSIS

? OLPIDIOPSIS ELLIPTICA (Schroeter)   Fischer

Rabenhorst. Kryptogamen-Fl., 1(4): 41. 1892

Diplophysa elliptica Schroeter, in Cohn, Kryptogamenfl. Schlesien, 3 (1): 196. 1885.

Resting spore transversely ellipsoidal, occupying nearly the whole breadth of the host cell, with light-brown wall covered with delicate spines; companion cell slightly smaller than the resting spore, with a smooth brown wall; sporangium and zoospores not observed.

In *Mougeotia sp.*, GERMANY.

? OLPIDIOPSIS VUILLEMINIAE Arnaud

Bull. Soc. Mycol. France, 68: 182, fig. 1C. 1952

An incompletely described form having ovoid sporangia (?), sometimes with protuberances, occurring in the sterile hypertrophied basidia of *Corticium comedens*, FRANCE.

? OLPIDIOPSIS SOROKINEI de Wildeman

Ann. Soc. Belge Micro. (Mém.), 14:22, fig. 7. 1890

Olpidium sorokinei de Wildeman, Bull. Soc. Roy. Bot. Belg. (Mém.,) 35:16. 1896.

Empty sporangia, only.

In *Tribonema bombycina*, BELGIUM.

EXCLUDED SPECIES OF OLPIDIOPSIS

*OLPIDIOPSIS LONGICOLLIS Zopf, nom. nudem

Schenk, Handbuch d. Bot.....; 4: 508. 1890

This name was applied to an incompletely observed parasite in the zoocyst of *Vampyrella spirogyrae* figured by Zopf (1888: 351, pl. 19, fig. 14).

GENUS OF THE OLPIDIOPSIDACEAE OF DOUBTFUL STATUS

? PSEUDOLPIDIUM A. FISCHER

Rabenhorst Kryptogamen-Fl., 1(4): 33. 1892

Olpidiopsis sensu Fischer, Jahrb. wiss. Bot., 13: 363. 1882. Non Cornu.

Thallus endobiotic, holocarpic, without a specialized vegetative system, at first naked and somewhat amoeboid, later walled, predominantly spherical or ellipsoidal, forming the rudiment of the sporangium; sporangium smooth-walled, with from one to several discharge tubes, zoospores laterally biflagellate, produced in the sporangium; resting spore unknown.

Parasitic in algae.

The present status of this genus has been discussed above (see p. 927). As it now stands the genus is simply a dumping ground for three incompletely known species. Karling (1942e: 54) suggests that *Pseudolpidium deformans* may be referable to *Rozellopsis* or *Woronina*. McLarty (1941a) and Shanor (1939b) believe the other two will eventually be recognized as species of *Olpidiopsis*.

KEY TO THE SPECIES OF PSEUDOLPIDIUM

Thallus fragmenting; parasitic in *Draparnaldia* .... *P. deformans*, p. 956
Thallus not fragmenting
    Parasitic in *Glenodinium* .... *P. glenodinianum*, p. 956
    Parasitic in *Sphaerita* .... *P. sphaeritae*, p. 956

? PSEUDOLPIDIUM DEFORMANS Serbinow

Scripta Bot. Horti Univ. Imper. Petro., 24: 154, pl. 1, figs. 1–12, pl. 4, fig. 16–28. 1907

Thallus at first naked, amoeboid, dividing into several parts; sporangium spherical, up to 35 μ in diameter, or long-ovoid, 30.5–47.5 μ long by 14.5–27 μ wide, from one to eleven in the swollen host cell, discharge tube cylindrical, up to 15.8 μ long by 8 μ in diameter; zoospores spherical or ovoid, 3.2–4.8 μ in diameter, with two laterally attached flagella, strongly metabolic (amoeboid?), without (?) an oil droplet, swimming away immediately after discharge.

Parasitic in lateral branch cells of *Draparnaldia glomerata*, RUSSIA.

Although strongly resembling a species of *Olpidiopsis* this fungus differs in the fragmentation of the thallus. It is possible that Serbinow confused multiple infection with fragmentation. The figures given afford evidence for both interpretations. The zoospores are said to be without an oil droplet, but this structure is clearly shown in the figures.

? PSEUDOLPIDIUM GLENODINIANUM (Dang.) Fischer

Rabenhorst. Kryptogamen-Fl., 1 (4): 36. 1892

Olpidium glenodinianum Dangeard, Journ. de Botanique, 2: 131, pl. 5, figs. 6–10. 1888.

Sporangium spherical or ellipsoidal, wall thin, smooth, colorless, discharge tube a more or less elongate papilla which pierces the host wall; zoospores about one hundred, spherical, sometimes elongate, laterally biflagellate, with a single globule, discharged in a mass imbedded in mucus and forming for a few seconds a group at the orifice; resting spore not observed.

Parasitic in *Glenodinium cinctum*, FRANCE.

? PSEUDOLPIDIUM SPHAERITAE (Dang.) Fischer

Rabenhorst. Kryptogamen-Fl., 1(4): 36. 1892

Olpidium sphaeritae Dangeard, Le Botaniste, 1: 51, pl. 3, figs. 3–7. 1889.

Sporangium ovoid to somewhat pyriform, wall thin, smooth, colorless, with a long discharge tube which pierces the wall of the cyst; zoospores ellipsoidal, laterally biflagellate; resting spore not observed. In spiny and smooth resting spores of *Sphaerita endogena*, Dangeard (*loc. cit.*), FRANCE.

PETERSENIA SPARROW

Dansk Bot. Ark., 8 (6): 13. 1934

(Figs. 75 H, p. 939; 76 C–I, p. 960)

Pleotrachelus sectio *lobati* H. E. Petersen, Oversigt Kgl. Danske Vidensk. Selskabs. Forhandl., 1905: 460.

Thallus appearing at first somewhat plasmodial, at maturity lobed, contorted, or tubular, rarely ellipsoidal and unlobed, holocarpic, without a specialized vegetative system; sporangium with from two to several discharge tubes (rarely one); zoospores laterally biflagellate, formed within the sporangium, where they assume motility, escaping individually through pores at the apex of the discharge tubes; resting spore not observed.

Primarily parasitic or saprophytic in marine algae; one species (*Petersenia irregulare*) parasitic in the hyphae of fresh-water aquatic Phycomycetes.

In the method of formation of the zoospores, as well as in their shape and flagellation, *Petersenia* strongly resembles *Olpidiopsis*. The irregular lobed or tubular character of the mature thallus, however, and, to a lesser degree, the formation typically of more than one discharge tube distinguish it.

As understood here, *Petersenia* includes only forms with irregular tubular or lobed thalli. The species with more regular spherical or ellipsoidal sporangia also found in marine algae (*Pleotrachelus* sectio *integri* H. E. Petersen, *op. cit.*, p. 448) are considered too closely allied to *Olpidiopsis* to be segregated generically. They differ so far as is known from members of *Olpidiopsis* only in their marine habitat and in being generally provided with more than one discharge tube. Further work may reveal that they have distinguishing characters of more significant taxonomic worth.

In both marine species the thalli are predominantly lobed under optimum conditions for development. When the plant is crowded or when nutriment is not readily available lobation may be less pronounced or even absent, in which case an "olpidioid" type of thallus and sporangium may be formed.

KEY TO THE SPECIES OF PETERSENIA

In marine algae; thallus elongate and lobed or consisting of a complex of lobulations
Thallus predominantly elongate, strongly lobed .... *P. lobata*, p. 958
Thallus consisting of a complex of strongly inflated broadly pyriform
closely interlocked lobes .... *P. pollagaster*, p. 959
In hyphae of fresh-water filamentous Phycomycetes; thallus tubular,
branched .... *P. irregulare*, p. 961

PETERSENIA LOBATA (H. E. Petersen) Sparrow

Dansk Bot. Ark., 8 (6): 13, pl. 2, figs. I–N. 1934

(Fig. 76 D–I, p. 960)

Pleotrachelus lobatus H. E. Petersen, Oversigt Kgl. Danske Vidensk. Selskabs. Forhandl., 1905: 460, fig. V,1–7.

Sporangium elongate, somewhat cylindrical, with lobes of various sizes, particularly near the extremities, sometimes subspherical, ellipsoidal, and lobed or unlobed, 30–192 μ long by 15–30 μ in width, at times extending through several cells of the alga, with from one to three discharge tubes of varying length; zoospores pyriform, 4.5 μ long by 3 μ in width, with a refractive anterior globule and two anteriorly attached oppositely directed flagella; resting spore not observed.

Weakly parasitic or saprophytic in *Callithamnion corymbosum*, coll. K. Rosenvinge, *C. hookeri, Spermothamnion turneri* Petersen (*loc. cit.*), *S. repens* var. *turneri*, Sparrow (*loc. cit.*), DENMARK; *Callithamnion roseum*, Sparrow (1936b: 245, pl. 2, figs. 1–2), UNITED STATES; *Seirospora interrupta*, J. and G. Feldmann (1940: 72, fig. 1), *Callithamnion sp., Aglaothamnion sp., Herposiphonia tenella, Seirospora interrupta*, probably also on tetraspores of *Ceramium*, Aleem (1950d: 427, fig. 10), *Spermothamnion repens, Seirospora griffithsiana*, J. Feldmann (1954: 134), FRANCE; *Ceramium rubrum, C. pedicellatum, C. corticat-*

ulum, Polysiphonia urceolata, Pylaiella littoralis, Aleem (1953:11, figs. 22–26, pl. 1, figs. 2–3), SWEDEN.

Observations on zoospore production in this species (Sparrow, 1934c) showed that the swarmers were fully formed within the sporangium by a process of cleavage, which resembled in its later stages that found within the vesicle of *Pythium*. The spore initials gradually assumed an individual rocking movement, which became more pronounced as separation and fashioning of the spores proceeded. Around the periphery of the spore mass, which at this stage did not completely fill the sporangium, traces of flagellar movement became visible. In later stages the flagella became very apparent, being laterally attached to the shallow-grooved zoospores. These escaped individually, by their own motility, through the discharge tubes.

PETERSENIA POLLAGASTER (H. E. Petersen) Sparrow

Dansk Bot. Ark., 8 (6) :15, pl. 3, figs. I–K. 1934

(Fig. 76 C, p. 960)

Pleotrachelus pollagaster H. E. Petersen, Oversigt Kgl. Danske Vidensk. Selskabs. Forhandl., 1905: 462, fig. VI, 1–5.

Sporangium consisting of a complex of strongly inflated broadly pyriform lobulations, rarely only slightly lobed, large specimens 112 by 104 μ, small ones 35 by 43 μ, with from one to four cylindrical discharge tubes of variable length (10–100 μ); zoospores biflagellate, presumably issuing through the discharge tubes; resting spore not (?) observed.

In *Ceramium rubrum*, H. E. Petersen (*loc. cit.*), *Ceramium sp.*, Sparrow (*loc. cit.*), DENMARK.

The characteristic complex of lobulations in well-developed specimens is striking, and cannot be confused with the more open type found in *Petersenia lobata*.

Thick-walled resting structures occupying all or part of the lobed thallus have been found by Petersen (see Sparrow, *op. cit.*, pl. 3, figs. I, K). Whether they belong to the fungus or are cysts of extraneous parasitic organisms has not been determined.

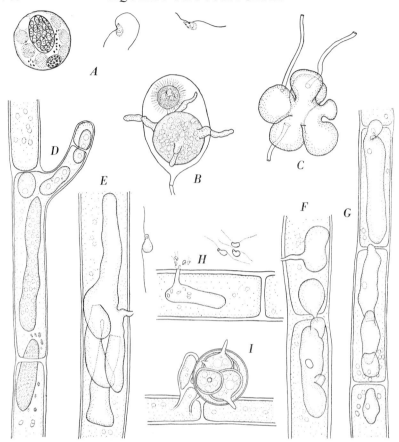

FIG. 76. Olpidiopsidaceae

A. Pseudosphaerita euglenae Dangeard in *Euglena*, parasitized host containing mature sporangium; to the right are two zoospores, enlarged, showing their biflagellate nature. *B. Olpidiopsis gracile* (Butler) Karling on *Pythium intermedium*, mature sporangium, with four discharge tubes and a resting spore, within hypertrophied part of host. *C. Petersenia pollagaster* (Petersen) Sparrow, empty sporangium with three discharge tubes. *D–I. Petersenia lobata* (Petersen) Sparrow in the red seaweed *Spermothamnion: D*, portion of frond of host showing thalli of fungus in various stages of development; *E–G*, empty sporangia within host showing various types of lobulations; *H*, discharging zoosporangium (zoospore at left is a free-hand enlargement); *I*, tetraspores of host containing nearly mature sporangia of parasite.

(*A*, Dangeard, 1933; *B*, Butler, 1907; *C–I*, Sparrow, 1934c)

PETERSENIA IRREGULARE (Constantineanu) Sparrow

Aquatic Phycomycetes, p. 634. 1943

(Fig. 75 H, p. 939)

Olpidiopsis irregularis Constantineanu, Revue Gén. Bot., 13: 373, figs. 76 A–K, 77. 1901.

Sporangium predominantly irregularly tubular, with short contorted branches or lobes of varying length, occasionally ellipsoidal or narrowly reniform, the whole complex 40–90 μ long, causing pronounced swelling of the infected part (generally the apex) of the hypha, with a single short sessile or slightly protruding discharge tube; zoospores somewhat reniform, 4.5–5 μ long by 3–4.5 μ wide, with a few granulations or a small droplet and two unequal oppositely directed flagella, the anterior one shorter than the posterior, emerging quickly in a group or individually through the orifice of the discharge tube, movement slow and even; resting spore not observed.

Parasitic in hyphae of *Saprolegnia sp.*, Constantineanu (*loc. cit.*), RUMANIA; *Achlya sp.*, Sparrow (1934c: 15), DENMARK; *Achlya sp.* (MICHIGAN) UNITED STATES.

Minden (1915: 264) considered the species a doubtful member of *Olpidiopsis*, since no resting stage was observed. Observations on this phase of the present species as well as on *Petersenia lobata* and *P. pollagaster* may result in its segregation from *Petersenia* as well.

IMPERFECTLY KNOWN SPECIES OF PETERSENIA

? PETERSENIA SP. Aleem

Vie et Milieu (Bull. Lab. Arago), 1: 429, figs. 13–16. 1950

Parasitic on *Acrochaetium codii*, FRANCE.

PSEUDOSPHAERITA DANGEARD

Le Botaniste, 4: 242. 1894–95

(Fig. 76 A, p. 960)

Thallus endobiotic, holocarpic, contents vacuolate during maturity; sporangium without a discharge tube; zoospores biflagellate,the flagella attached subapically, the shorter directed anteriorly, the longer posteriorly, formed by successive divisions of the contents, escaping by fracturing of the wall.

Parasitic in the cytoplasm of *Euglena, Cryptomonas.*

Pseudosphaerita Dangeard is apparently most closely related to *Olpidiopsis.* Observations on the method of formation of the resting spore will be necessary, however, to determine its precise affinities.

The genus was founded by Dangeard to include *Sphaerita*-like forms with biflagellate zoospores. Although the thallus superficially resembles that of *Sphaerita,* Dangeard (1933) has pointed out that the two fungi may be distinguished by the different methods of zoospore formation. In *Sphaerita* this is simultaneous. In *Pseudosphaerita* each division of the nucleus of the thallus is followed by a division of the cytoplasm. No mitotic figures were observed. At maturity the contents are cleaved into from 64 to 128 polygonal uninucleated segments. These become flagellate zoospores and may swarm a long time within the sporangium before being liberated. Occasionally, they are discharged within the host and undergo germination *in situ.* The nucleus of these zoospores is larger (2.5 μ) than that formed in the swarmer of *Sphaerita* and possesses a more or less central nucleolus. Although the method of zoospore formation in *Pseudosphaerita* is unusual and led Dangeard (*loc. cit.*) to suggest the erection of a separate family for the inclusion of similar forms with a successive type of spore maturation, it is not unique and has also been observed in the true chytrids.

The parasite may develop and sporulate within the moving host or may attack resting individuals. Puymaly (1927), however, observed that *Euglena viridis* when attacked by a fungus called by him *Sphaerita,* but having biflagellate zoospores and hence probably *Pseudosphaerita,* quickly ceased its flagellar action after infection. It continued to show signs of life until sporulation of the fungus occurred. He also noted that the zoospores of the fungus were strongly attracted to the *Euglena.* The method of infection, however, was not determined. Puymaly, although recalling the conjecture of sexuality in *Sphaerita* proposed by Chatton and Brodsky (1909) and based on observations of conjugation in a *Sphaerita*-like organism by Doflein (1907), was certain that in his fungus the biflagellate swarmers were zoospores and not zygotes.

PSEUDOSPHAERITA EUGLENAE Dangeard

Le Botaniste, 4: 242, fig. 9. 1894–95; *ibid.*, 25: 36, pl. 4, figs. 3–15. 1933

(Fig. 76 A, p. 960)

Sporangium somewhat ellipsoidal, oblong, or tubular; zoospores elongate-pyriform with attenuated apex, 6 μ long by 2.5–3 μ wide, with a small granule at the point of insertion of the flagella, initiating movement within the sporangium, swimming motion accompanied by a trembling of the body.

Parasitic in the cytoplasm of *Euglena*, sometimes accompanying *Sphaerita*, Dangeard (*loc. cit.*), FRANCE; *Euglena caudata*, (?), Mitchell (1928: 29, pls. 4–6), UNITED STATES.

The parasite of *Euglena caudata* so carefully described by Mitchell (1928) has been included here by Karling (1942e). However, since no zoospores were seen its actual relationships are in doubt.

PSEUDOSPHAERITA RADIATA (Dang.) Sparrow

Aquatic Phycomycetes, p. 640. 1943

Sphaerita radiata Dangeard, Le Botaniste, 2: 54, pl. 2, fig. 20. 1890–91.

From one to three parasites in the host, variable in position, if one, occurring at the rear of the body, near the nucleus of the host, the host cell becoming completely deformed and its contents being disorganized as the parasite matures; at maturity the globules of the zoospores showing a distinct radiate arrangement in the sporangium, the latter upon the rupture of the host wall being projected from the host cell, the freed biflagellate zoospores becoming narrow at their two extremities and taking the form of a small rod with a globule in the center; resting spore not observed.

In *Cryptomonas*, FRANCE.

IMPERFECTLY KNOWN GENUS OF THE OLPIDIOPSIDACEAE

? BLASTULIDIOPSIS Sigot

C. R. Soc. Biol. (Strasbourg), 108: 34, 3 figs. 1931

? Blastulidiopsis chattoni Sigot

Loc. cit.

Zoospore upon coming to rest on the host cell losing its flagella and producing a tube that penetrates the host wall and forms within the host a short filament, which enlarges, expands, and branches, the branches forming broad lobes of varying size, the whole thallus transformed at maturity into a single sporangium; zoospores 6–8 μ (long?) with two laterally attached opposed flagella, 15–20 μ in length, and an anterior globule, formed within the sporangium, where individual movement is initiated, and escaping through a pore at the tip of a short discharge tube; resting spore not observed.

Parasitic in eggs of *Cyclops* (fresh-water crustacean), FRANCE.

The thallus is said to be plasmodial and unwalled until just before formation of the zoospores. In the course of development several large vacuoles appear in the cytoplasm, which fuse to form a single large one. The nuclei at maturity are distributed regularly in the cytoplasm surrounding the central vacuole; the spores are cleaved out simultaneously around each of the nuclei.

In the method of formation of the zoospores, their activity within the sporangium, their manner of discharge, and their structure *Blastulidiopsis* resembles *Olpidiopsis*. Its zoospores are, however, much larger. The lobed nature of the sporangium constitutes a strong resemblance to *Petersenia*.

The method whereby the zoospore reaches the eggs of the host, which are still within the egg sac of the animal, is not given by Sigot. He noted that the period of time necessary from infection to sporulation of the parasite was about equal to the time between fertilization and the occurrence of the *Nauplius* stage of the crustacean. The disease appeared in late February or early March and disappeared during May.

The form is difficult to typify because the observations have in the main been derived from sectioned and stained material. Further work of a purely morphological nature is necessary in order clearly to characterize and properly place the genus.

SIROLPIDIACEAE

Thallus endobiotic, holocarpic, without a specialized vegetative system, unbranched or with rudimentary branches, at maturity typically forming a linear series of sporangia, walls giving a cellulose reaction, contents undergoing strong vacuolization; sporangia with a single discharge tube (occasionally several); zoospores biflagellate, monoplanetic, formed in the sporangium; resting stage unknown.

So far as is known, an exclusively marine group, parasitic and saprophytic in green and red algae, and in mollusk larvae.

The thallus, although more highly developed than that of the Olpidiopsidaceae, is, under natural conditions, very rudimentary in character. In both *Sirolpidium* and *Pontisma* the mature thallus may consist of no more than a single cell and it then strongly resembles *Olpidiopsis*. Typically, however, a linear septate type is formed which parallels that found in the chytrid *Septolpidium*.

KEY TO THE GENERA OF THE SIROLPIDIACEAE

Thallus typically narrowly tubular, at maturity becoming septate, the
    fragments disarticulating .... Sirolpidium[1], p. 965
Thallus broadly tubular, often with short, irregular branches, not disarticulating .... Pontisma, p. 970

SIROLPIDIUM H. E. Petersen

Oversigt Kgl. Danske Vidensk. Selskabs. Forhandl. 1905 (5): 480

(Fig. 77, p. 967)

Thallus endobiotic, holocarpic, without specialized vegetative structures, consisting either of a simple saclike body formed directly from an expanded endobiotic zoospore or more commonly of an unbranched or occasionally branched hypha-like tube, contents at first vacuolate, later with numerous refractive granules; sporangium formed from the saclike body or from fragments of the linearly septate progressively

[1] See recently described taxon, p. 968.

disassociated tube, provided with a single discharge tube, the tip of which at least is ordinarily extramatrical; zoospores fully formed within the sporangium, where movement is initiated, grape-seed-like, with a small refractive anterior granule and two anteriorly attached oppositely directed flagella, swimming individually through a pore formed at the tip of the discharge tube; resting stage not observed.

The genus, so far as is known, is confined to marine hosts.

The fungus on which the genus is based is distinct, as Petersen pointed out, from all other related forms in the peculiar septation and subsequent disassociation of the tubular thallus. In very early stages the thallus is a somewhat irregular, curved cylindrical structure just within the host wall (Fig. 77 A).[1] As it matures it elongates and becomes progressively separated by cross walls into a linear series of spherical or cylindrical segments of varying size, each of which becomes an independent walled unit (Fig. 77 E, G). In many such chains the wall of the original thallus can be detected between the segments (Fig. 77 G). Each of the fragments assumes individual growth, soon loses its original orientation with respect to the "parent" thallus, and ultimately becomes a single sporangium with a discharge tube (Fig. 77 B–D, H). Often when the latter structures are not orientated so as to pierce the algal wall they attain great lengths and bear a striking resemblance to the hypha of a filamentous phycomycete (Fig. 77 F). In this connection it has been observed (Sparrow, 1936b: 254) that fragments of the thallus permitted to develop in close contact with the atmosphere, by allowing sea water to drip over them rather than by submerging them, for example, underwent a remarkable transformation in body structure. Instead of being somewhat olpidioid or moniliform they became extensive isodiametric tubular structures which simulated in every respect, as did the discharge tubes, the hyphae of higher Phycomycetes. Because of these facts it is obvious that *Sirolpidium* is of very definite interest in the problem of the origin of the mycelium in the biflagellate series of Phycomycetes. The zoospores are grape-seed-like and biflagellate (Fig. 77 I).

Recent observations by Vishniac (1955b) on *Sirolpidium zoophthorum* (p. 968), which infects clam and oyster larvae, suggest that the fragmentation of the thallus may be due to partial anaerobiosis. When she

---

[1] According to Kobayashi and Ookubo (1953), it is somewhat amoeboid.

grew her isolate on agar in petri dishes the cells did not separate, but if later the plate became slightly dry the cytoplasm dissociated into several olpidioid sporangia. Vishniac points out that the widespread occurrence of this phenomenon among fungi and the ease with which it can be manipulated makes its use as a generic character rather dubious.

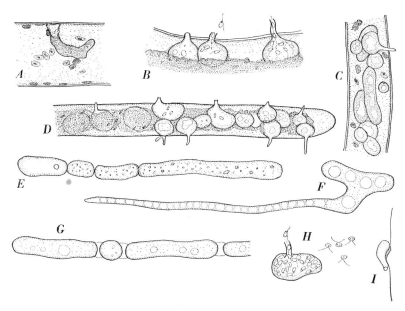

FIG. 77. *Sirolpidium bryopsidis* (de Bruyne) H. E. Petersen

A. Portion of filament of *Bryopsis* showing an early stage in development of fragmenting type of thallus. *B.* Olpidioid sporangia discharging their zoospores. *C.* Fragmenting thallus each part of which becomes a single sporangium. *D.* Tip of filament of *Bryopsis* showing a group of olpidioid sporangia. *E.* Thallus fragmenting; cell at extreme left has already discharged its zoospores. *F.* Long discharge tube produced by thallus. *G.* Thallus fragmenting; traces of original thallus wall are seen connecting the parts. *H.* An olpidioid sporangium discharging its zoospores, and, at right, zoospores which were killed with osmic acid and stained with fuchsin to show flagella. *I.* Interpretation of zoospore (enlarged, freehand drawing).

(Sparrow, 1934c)

SIROLPIDIUM BRYOPSIDIS (de Bruyne) H. E. Petersen

Oversigt Kgl. Danske Vidensk. Selskabs. Forhandl,. 1905(5): 480, fig. 9

Olpidium bryopsidis de Bruyne, Arch. de Biol., 10: 85, pl. 5, figs. 1–15. 1890.

Disarticulated sporangia, 8–90 μ long by 7–16 μ in diameter, olpidioid types 18–38 μ in height by 12–17 μ in diameter, wall thin, smooth, colorless, discharge tube narrowly cylindrical, up to 165 μ or more in length, extending for variable distances outside the alga; zoospores narrowly pyriform, somewhat arched, about 4–6 μ long by 2–3 μ wide, the narrow anterior end bearing a refractive granule and two oppositely directed flagella; resting spore not observed with certainty.

Parasitic or saprophytic in *Bryopsis plumosa*, de Bruyne (*loc. cit.*), ITALY; Petersen (*loc. cit.*), Sparrow (1934c: 11, pl. 2, figs. A–H), DENMARK; *Bryopsis plumosa, Cladophora sp.*, Sparrow (1936b: 252, pl. 1, figs. 4, 7, pl. 3, fig. 1), UNITED STATES; *Bryopsis plumosa, Pseudobryopsis myuria*, Aleem (1950d: 432, figs. 20–22), FRANCE; *Bryopsis plumosa*, Aleem (1953: 16, pl. 2, figs. 1, 2), SWEDEN; *Bryopsis plumosa, Cladophora japonica*, Kobayashi and Ookubo (1953: 61, fig. 7), JAPAN.

In the American material infected plants of *Bryopsis* were recognizable macroscopically by the presence of blackened areas along the fronds. The fungus was cultivated to a small extent in dextrose solutions. In 0.5 and 1.0 per cent solutions in sea water extramatrical hyphae up to 112 μ in length were obtained in forty-eight hours. Attempts to grow the fungus on solid media, however, were uniformly unsuccessful.

Resting spores have not as yet been convincingly demonstrated, although de Bruyne figures spherical or ellipsoidal "cysts de conservation" and Petersen has found thick-walled bodies associated with the sporangia. Zoospores of the Japanese material were described as nephroid with two laterally attached flagella.

RECENTLY DESCRIBED TAXON

SIROLPIDIUM ZOOPHTHORUM Vishniac

Mycologia, 47: 641, figs. 1–8. 1955

Thallus branched, becoming septate; cells containing a large spherical vacuole, 10–15 μ in diameter when young, at maturity up to 82 μ in diameter, irregularly crescent; when old with branched rhizoids; sporangia formed from the swollen terminal cells, with a discharge tube 15–142 μ long and 5 μ in diameter; zoospores monoplanetic, more or less pear-shaped in motion, at rest ovoid to fusiform to irregularly triangular, biflagellate, 5 by 2 μ, swarming within the sporangium and swimming out through the discharge tube; resistant spores about 45–90 by 40–80 μ, light golden-brown, with dense cytoplasm and relatively thick walls; gemmae also formed.

Parasitic in larvae of the clams *Venus mercenaria* and *Venus mortoni* (and of hybrids between them) and of the oyster *Crassotrea virginica*, UNITED STATES.

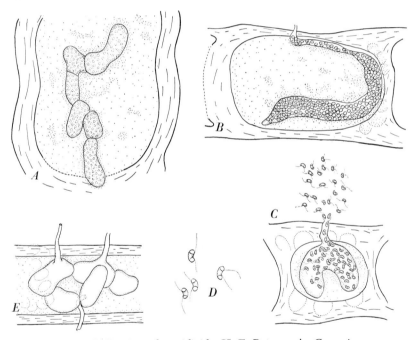

FIG. 78. *Pontisma lagenidioides* H. E. Petersen in *Ceramium*

A. Typical segmented thallus. *B.* Curved unsegmented sporangium within which zoospores have become quiescent. *C.* Discharge of zoospores from an unsegmented sporangium. *D.* Zoospores. *E.* Group of empty sporangia, all segmented portions of single thallus.

(Sparrow, 1934c)

This is the fungus described by Davis, Loosanoff, Weston, and Martin (1954) as the cause of a serious epidemic of clam and oyster larvae in culture.

Ganaros (1957) has reported a fungus, allied either to this species or to *Plectospira dubia*, as the cause of the destruction of eggs of the oyster drill, *Urosalpinx cinerea*, in Connecticut.

PONTISMA H. E. Petersen

Oversigt Kgl. Danske Vidensk. Selskabs. Forhandl., 1905(5): 482

(Fig. 78, p. 969)

Thallus endobiotic, holocarpic, without specialized vegetative structures, consisting of an unbranched or irregularly branched tube of small extent, which at maturity becomes segmented, the segments few in number, occasionally olpidioid or tubular and nonseptate, contents at first vacuolate, later with numerous refractive granules, walls giving a cellulose reaction; sporangia formed from the segments, each bearing a single discharge tube (sometimes several), the tip of which, at least, is extramatrical; zoospores minute, pyriform, with a refractive body at either end and two oppositely directed flagella, completely formed within the sporangium, where motility is initiated, swimming individually through a pore at the tip of the discharge tube; resting spore spherical and thick-walled with several refractive oil drops.

In *Ceramium spp.*

The genus resembles *Sirolpidium* in the segmentation of the thallus, but differs in being branched and in not exhibiting fragmentation.

Pontisma, so far as is known, occurs primarily, if not exclusively, in the marine alga *Ceramium*. The thallus is difficult to characterize precisely because of its "generalized" aspect. Penetration of the zoospore and the very early stages in the establishment of the thallus have not been observed.

Contrary to Karling's (1942e: 63) belief that *Pontisma* should be merged with *Sirolpidium*, actual observers of the fungus (Petersen, Sparrow, Aleem, Höhnk, and Kobayashi and Ookubo) regard it as distinct from that unbranched, fragmenting form. Until the resting stage of *Sirolpidium* can be surely identified and compared with that of *Pontisma*, there is still good reason to keep the two separate.

PONTISMA LAGENIDIOIDES H. E. Petersen

Oversigt Kgl. Danske Vidensk. Selskabs. Forhandl., 1905(5): 482, fig. X, 1–3

Sirolpidium lagenidioides (Petersen) Karling, Simple Holocarpic Biflagellate Phycomycetes, p. 66. 1942.

Thallus at maturity ordinarily composed of a linear series of somewhat irregularly cylindrical simple or short-branched segments 20–60 μ or more long by 11–30 μ in diameter, slightly constricted or sometimes almost disarticulated at the narrow cross walls, olpidioid thalli 14–16 μ long by 13–15 μ high and tubular nonseptate thalli 130–200 μ long occasionally produced; sporangia generally forming a single narrowly cylindrical slightly tapering discharge tube (sometimes several) of variable length (up to 145 μ), the tip of which, at least, is extramatrical; zoospores numerous, somewhat bent, rod-shaped, reniform, or pyriform, 2.5–3 μ in diameter by 4.5–7 μ in length, with a strongly refractive region at either end and two short laterally attached oppositely directed flagella, swarming within the sporangium before emerging by flagellar action through the discharge tube, movement erratic, tumbling; resting spore spherical, somewhat thick-walled, 27 μ in diameter, with several refractive oil drops.

Weakly parasitic or saprophytic in *Ceramium rubrum*, *C. strictum*, *C. fruticulosum*, Petersen (*loc. cit.*), Sparrow (1934c: 11, pl. 3, figs. A–H), DENMARK; saprophytic in *Ceramium diaphanum*, Sparrow (1936b: 252, pl. 1, fig. 5), UNITED STATES; *Ceramium sp.*, Höhnk (1939: 340, fig. 2, a–g), GERMANY; *Ceramium diaphanum*, Aleem (1950c: 714, figs. 3–4; 1950d: 431, figs. 17–19), *Ceramium tenuissimum*, J. Feldmann (1954: 134), J. and G. Feldmann (1955: 246, fig. 5), FRANCE: *Ceramium rubrum*, *C. pedicellatum*, *C. corticatulum*, Aleem (1953: 16, figs. 32–33), SWEDEN; ? *Cladophora japonica*, Kobayashi and Ookubo (1953: 63, fig. 8), JAPAN.

Zoospores of this species closely resemble those figured by Butler (1907) for "*Pleolpidium inflatum* Butler," a parasite of *Pythium*. According to Höhnk (1939), they have only one refractive region—at the forward end.

Kobayashi and Ookubo's fungus reported from *Cladophora japonica* bears a strong resemblance to *Sirolpidium*. They described spherical, thick-walled resting spores in their material.

Pontisma lagenidioides, which appears to occur most commonly in the more delicate species of *Ceramium*, thrives best when the alga is kept under unfavorable conditions or when the host plant is dead.

LAGENIDIACEAE

Thallus endobiotic, holocarpic, occupying one cell or sometimes extending through several cells of host, uni- or multicellular, branched, or unbranched, the contents usually with a lustrous matrix within which are irregularly shaped refractive clods and globules, walls giving a cellulose reaction, the cyst of the zoospore and the infection tube frequently persistent, converted at maturity into reproductive organs; method of zoospore formation and behavior variable; zoospores formed wholly within the sporangium or partly within it and maturing at the orifice of the discharge tube, where they may or may not be surrounded by a temporary vesicle, or formed completely outside the sporangium in a vesicle at the orifice of the discharge tube, when mature swimming away (save in *Myzocytium microsporum* where they immediately encyst and later emerge from the cysts), (always?) of the secondary laterally biflagellate type, usually with a single swarm period; plants monoecious or dioecious, sexual organs consisting of undifferentiated or somewhat specialized vegetative cells, periplasm apparently lacking, fertilization tube sometimes produced; oöspore thick-walled, with a large reserve globule, formed singly in the female gametangium, which it almost always nearly fills; in some species one or more resting spores (apogamous?) formed in a thallus or thallus segment.

Parasites of fresh-water algae, primarily Conjugatae, of other Phycomycetes, liverworts, pollen, microscopic animals, crab eggs, and, in one genus (*Lagena*), of the roots of cultivated cereals and wild grasses.

KEY TO THE GENERA OF THE LAGENIDIACEAE

[Thallus one-celled, attached to the inner host wall by a thick collar of callus; parasitic in roots of cereals . . . . LAGENA [1]]

[1] Not considered in this text, see Vanterpool and Ledingham, *Can. J. Res.*, 2: 192. 1930.

Thallus uni- or multicellular, lying free in the host cell or adherent to
the persistent penetration tube; parasites of algae, microscopic
animals, etc.

Thallus unbranched, occupying one cell of host, strongly constricted
at the cross walls, segments regular, appearing linklike; antheridial cell poorly differentiated .... MYZOCYTIUM, p. 973

Thallus unbranched or branched, occupying one or more cells of host,
little or not at all constricted at the cross walls, segments often
irregular; antheridial cell usually well differentiated

LAGENIDIUM, p. 982

MYZOCYTIUM SCHENK

Über das Vorkommen contractiler Zellen im Pflanzenreiche, p. 10. Würzburg,
1858

(Fig. 79 A–C, F–H, p. 977)

Thallus endobiotic, tubular, unbranched, holocarpic, at maturity one-
celled or more commonly divided by transverse septa into a linear series
of linklike sporangia or gametangia; zoosporangium with a single
discharge tube; zoospores grape-seed-like, laterally biflagellate, incompletely cleaved within the sporangium and undergoing final maturation
often in an evanescent vesicle at the tip of the discharge tube or occasionally emerging completely formed; female gametangium without periplasm, the contents after fusion with the male gamete forming a thick-
walled resting spore, germination not observed; male gametangium like
the female, conveying its contents to the female by a pore or tube formed
in the cross wall.

Parasites of fresh-water algae and microscopic animals.

KEY TO THE SPECIES OF MYZOCYTIUM

Sporangia in regular beadlike chains, extramatrical part of the discharge
tube narrowly cylindrical; in algae

Discharge tube narrowly cylindrical throughout. ... *M. proliferum*, p. 974

Discharge tube with a more or less well defined swelling beneath the
inner face of the host wall .... *M. megastomum*, p. 978

Sporangia in somewhat irregular chains or forming an intricate complex, extramatrical part of the discharge tube broadly conical; in
microscopic animals or their eggs

Sporangia in chains, broadly pyriform, oblong or more or less spherical; fertilization tube formed; in eel worms ... *M. vermicola*, p. 979

Sporangia forming an intricate complex, irregularly saclike, often
  lobulate; fertilization pore formed; in rotifers
                                                    M. zoophthorum, p. 979
Sporangia separate; in rotifers .... *M. microsporum*, p. 980

MYZOCYTIUM PROLIFERUM Schenk

Über das Vorkommen contractiler Zellen im Pflanzenreiche, p. 10.
Würzburg, 1858

(Fig. 79 A–C, p. 977)

Pythium proliferum Schenk, Verhandl. Phys.-Med. Gesell. Würzburg, A. F.,
  9: 27, pl. 1, figs. 30–41. 1859. Non de Bary, Jahrb. wiss. Bot., 2: 182.
  1860.
Pythium globosum Schenk, *op. cit.*, 9: 27, pl. 1, figs. 42–47. 1859.
Pythium globosum Walz, pro parte, Bot. Zeitung, 28: 553, pl. 9, figs. 13–15.
  1870.
Lagenidium globosum Lindstedt, Synopsis der Saprolegnieen, p. 54. Berlin,
  1872.
Myzocytium globosum (Schenk) Cornu, Ann. Sci. Nat. Bot., V, 15: 21. 1872.

Sporangia from one to twenty, in beadlike chains, broadly fusiform,
broadly ellipsoidal and 15.7–26 μ long by 13–16 μ wide, or spherical
and 14.4–25 μ in diameter, separated by two-layered refractive walls up
to 2.4 μ thick, each forming a single narrowly cylindrical predominantly
equatorial discharge tube about 2–3 μ in diameter, which extends for a
variable distance beyond the host wall; zoospores from four to twenty,
bean-shaped, laterally biflagellate, 5.4–10 μ long by 3.6–6 μ wide, undergoing their final maturation in an evanescent vesicle formed at the
orifice; female and male gametangia generally similar to the sporangia
in size and shape or the female sometimes more spherical; oöspore
spherical, 10–25 μ in diameter, lying loosely in the gametangium, with
a smooth colorless double wall and a large eccentric globule, generally
attached to the persistent fertilization tube, germination not observed.

Parasitic in *Spirogyra sp.*, *Zygnema sp.*, "*Conferva*," Schenk (*loc.
cit.*), *Closterium didymotocum*, *C. acerosum*, *Cosmarium connatum*,
Reinsch (1878: 299, pl. 17, figs. 6, 9), *Zygnema sp.*, *Spirogyra sp.*, *Mougeotia sp.*, *Cladophora sp.*, *Oedogonium sp.*, Zopf (1884: 159, pl. 14, figs.
6–34), *Cladophora sp.*, *Spirogyra sp.*, *Zygnema sp.*, Walz (*loc. cit.*),
host (?), *Mougeotia pleurocarpus*, Schroeter (1885: 227), Minden (1915:

430), *Closterium sp.*, Cejp (1932a: 5, pl. 1, figs. 11–13, pl. 2, fig. 5) (CZECHOSLOVAKIA), *Closterium sp.*, *Pleurotaenium trabecula*, *Mougeotia robusta*, Rieth (1954: 172, fig. 7), GERMANY; various algae, Cornu (1869a: 222), host (?), de Wildeman (1896b: 46), *Spirogyra sp.*, Arnaud (1952: 182, fig. 1 D), FRANCE; *Spirogyra sp.*, coll. Marchal, de Wildeman (1893b: 53, pl. 6, figs. 11–12), *Spirogyra sp.*, *Zygnema sp.*, de Wildeman (1895a: 76, pl. 2, figs. 10–12), BELGIUM; host (?), coll. Massart, de Wildeman (*loc. cit.*), NORWAY; *Mougeotia sp.*, *Spirogyra sp.*, Scherffel (1902b: 109), *Mougeotia sp.*, *S. mirabilis*, Domján (1936: 51, pl. 1, figs. 95, 107, 125, 160–164), *Spirogyra sp.*, Bérczi (1940: 87), HUNGARY; *Mougeotia sp.*, H. E. Petersen (1909: 402; 1910: 537, fig. 16e), DENMARK; *Closterium acerosum*, *Closterium sp.*, *Cosmarium didymochondrum*, *Cosmarium sp.*, *Spirogyra maxima*, *Spirogyra sp.*, Voronichin (1920: 11), RUSSIA; *Spirogyra sp.*, Skvortzow (1927: 206, fig. 10), CHINA; *Closterium angustatum*, W. G. Farlow (F. 586), *Cladophora kuetzingiana*, *Zygnema cruciatum*, Graff (1928: 168), *Mougeotia sp.*, (?) *Closterium acerosum*, Sparrow (1932b: 288, fig. 4 a–c), *Mougeotia sp.*, *Spirogyra sp.*, Sparrow (1933c: 532), *Spirogyra sp.*, Thompson (1934: 118, fig. 1 a–d), *Spirogyra crassa*, Wolf (1944: 14), *Closterium sp.*, Sparrow and Barr (1955: 556), UNITED STATES; *Spirogyra sp.*, Valkanov (1931a: 365), BULGARIA; *Spirogyra affinis*, Chaudhuri (1931: 472, figs. 1–7), *Spirogyra affinis*, Mundkur (1938), *Spirogyra sp.*, Das-Gupta and John (1953: 169, figs. 13–15), Lacy (1955: 209), INDIA; *Spirogyra jürgensii*, *Spirogyra sp.*, *Cladophora sp.*, Tokunaga (1934a: 228, fig. 2), JAPAN; *Spirogyra sp.*, Sparrow (1952c: 105), CUBA.

Although Constantineanu (1901: 377, figs. 78–79) reported *Myzocytium proliferum* from Rumania in *Cladophora* and *Spirogyra*, from his figures (all except 78b and 79a) of the sporangia and the one-globuled nature of the emerged zoospores, he probably had a mixture of *Achlyogeton* and *Myzocytium*.

A fungus termed *Myzocytium proliferum* by Martin (1927: 188) is unusual in that the discharge tube is expanded just beneath the host wall. A *Myzocytium* in *Closterium costatum* in the Farlow Herbarium (No. 642) likewise shows a similar enlargement. Canter (1947a) believes this swelling indicates relationship to *M. megastomum* and places Martin's fungus there. Forms occurring in desmids (see *M. megastomum*,

M. irregulare) characteristically exhibit this expansion. The fungus in *Closterium* reported by Sparrow (1932b) is doubtfully *M. proliferum*.

Although *Myzocytium proliferum* has been reported many times and is well known (from the excellent illustrations of Zopf, 1884), more data on the size range of parts are needed. The zoospores described by Tokunaga, for example, are twice as large (10 by 6 μ) as those described by Sparrow (5.4 by 3.6 μ).

The sexual stage (Fig. 79 C) was first observed by Cornu (1869a).

As Zopf pointed out (*op. cit.*), the species is most frequent in shallow, stagnant, brightly lit water. It may occur in epidemic proportions from spring to fall.

In some instances of zoospore discharge the vesicle is so tenuous as to be nearly invisible, and in certain specimens it may be entirely lacking (Thompson, 1934). Chaudhuri (1931) stated that a fertilization tube was not produced by the male gametangium. Since his observations apparently refer to material fixed in formalin, the tube may have been present but had soon been dissolved by the preservative.

MYZOCYTIUM PROLIFERUM Schenk f. MARINUM Kobayasi and Ookubo

Bull. Nat. Sci. Mus. (Tokyo), 33: 64, fig. 9. 1953

"Thallus endobiotic, elongated, unbranched, forming monilioid chain, after maturity segmented in 3–6 or more zoosporangia and gametangia. Zoosporangia in beadlike chains connected by thin outer membrane, globose, ellipsoid or more longer, 10–20 μ in diameter, somewhat thick-walled, colourless, each with a lateral discharge tube; tubes protruding through the wall of host-cell, cylindric, contorted, 50–60 μ long, attaining 280 μ, 5–6 μ in diameter. Zoospores forming a vesicle at the orifice of discharge tube, nephroid, 6 × 3 μ, with lateral two flagella. Male and female gametangia commonly globose, intercalar. Oospore loosely and singly formed within female gametangium, globose or ellipsoid, commonly 15 μ in diameter, smooth, thick–walled, containing an eccentric large oil drop" (Kobayasi and Ookubo, *loc. cit.*).

Parasitic in *Cladophora japonica*, JAPAN.

In *Cladophora* that had been cultivated in artificial sea water. Probably

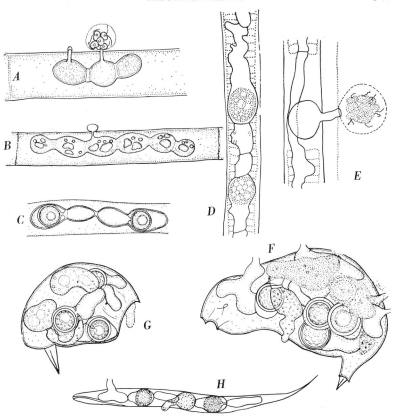

FIG. 79. Lagenidiaceae

A–C. Myzocytium proliferum Schenk in Conjugatae: *A*, three-celled thallus, one cell of which has become converted into a zoosporangium whose recently discharged zoospores are maturing at orifice of discharge tube; *B*, one-celled thallus about to become segmented, cyst of zoospore and penetration tube still persistent; *C*, thallus in *Mougeotia* which has become converted into sex organs; the two outer cells are oögonia, each bearing an oöspore; the two inner cells are antheridia. *D–E. Lagenidium nodosum* (Dangeard) Ingold in *Lyngbya: D*, endobiotic sexually formed resting spores developing on thallus; *E*, protoplasm discharged and forming zoospores in a vesicle at orifice of discharge tube. *F–G. Myzocytium zoophthorum* Sparrow in rotifers, thalli bearing zoosporangia and sex organs. *H. Myzocytium vermicola* (Zopf) Fischer in eelworm, zoosporangia and sex organs in cadaver.

(*A–B*, Sparrow, 1932b; *C*, after Zopf, 1884; *D–E*, Ingold, 1949; *F–G*, Sparrow, 1936a; *H*, Zopf, 1884)

referable to this form is the fungus reported in *Spirogyra* from France by Aleem (1952a: 2650).

MYZOCYTIUM MEGASTOMUM de Wildeman

Ann. Soc. Belge Micro. (Mém.), 17: 53, pl. 6, figs. 6–10, pl. 7, figs. 19–20. 1893

Ancylistes miurii Skvortzow, Arch. Protistenk., 51: 432, figs. 7–10. 1925.

Sporangia ovoid, ellipsoidal, spherical, or sometimes pyriform or cylindrical, 9–32 by 12–50 μ (wide?), variable in number, occurring in beadlike linear series, separated by narrow cross walls, discharge tube frequently equatorial, narrowly or irregularly cylindrical, 2.6 μ wide, distinctly expanded (4–6 μ) just beneath the host wall, prolonged extramatrically for a variable distance, up to 150 μ; zoospores somewhat bean-shaped, 4.5–5 μ long by 5.6–7 μ in diameter, with granular protoplasm bearing several refractive globules and two lateral, oppositely directed flagella of about equal length; gametangia like the sporangia and often occurring with them; oöspore spherical, 11–15 μ in diameter, with a thick smooth double wall and oily contents, lying loosely in the gametangium, germination not observed.

In *Spirotaenia sp.*, *Closterium sp.*, *C. attenuatum*, de Wildeman (*loc. cit.*), BELGIUM; *Closterium sp.*, de Wildeman (1895a: 77), SWITZERLAND; desmid, coll. Massart, de Wildeman (1896b: 47, pl. 3, figs. 22–26), NORWAY; *Closterium acerosum*, Scherffel (1914: 17), HUNGARY; *Closterium sp.*, Skvortzow (1925: 431), MANCHURIA; *Cladophora sp.*, Martin (1927: 188, fig. 1 a–b), *Closterium areolatum* (?), Berdan (1938: 408, fig. 14), *Closterium sp.*, Sparrow and Barr (1955: 556), UNITED STATES; *Cosmarium pericymatium*, Rieth (1954: 171, fig. 6), GERMANY.

Certain inhabitants of *Euastrum* referred tentatively by de Wildeman (1895a: 76, pl. 2, figs. 7–9) to *Myzocytium proliferum*, as well as others called *Olpidium immersum* by this same investigator (*ibid.*, p. 65, pl. 2, figs. 1–6), all from Switzerland, may be simplified forms of *M. megastomum*. The same might be said of the plant shown in Figure 16d, cited as *M. irregulare* by Petersen (1909: 402, fig. 16d; 1910: 538). Rieth (1954: 171) indicates that the zoospores emerge as in *Aphanomyces*.

MYZOCYTIUM VERMICOLA (Zopf) Fischer

Rabenhorst. Kryptogamen-Fl., 1(4): 75. 1892

(Fig. 79 H, p. 977)

Myzocytium proliferum var. *vermicolum* Zopf, Nova Acta Acad. Leop.-Carol., 47: 167, pl. 14, figs. 35–37. 1884.

Sporangia up to twelve in the host, somewhat broadly pyriform, oblong, or more or less spherical, the septa narrow, with one, occasionally two, short broadly conical discharge tubes protruding for a short distance beyond the host wall; zoospores discharged in a quickly evanescent vesicle at the tip of the discharge tube; oögonia pyriform or ellipsoidal; oöspore ellipsoidal or spherical, colorless, not filling the oögonium; antheridium smaller than the oögonium, narrow, somewhat oblong, with a delicate cylindrical penetration tube.

Parasitic in *Anguillula*, Zopf (*loc. cit.*), GERMANY; Dangeard (1903b: 207, pls. 2–5), FRANCE; Valkanov (1931a: 365), BULGARIA.

One-celled thalli were occasionally produced which became transformed into a single sporangium. Fischer (*loc. cit.*) believes, as does Karling (1942e), that *Bicricium lethale* Sorokin is a two-celled form of this species. See, however, the remarks concerning *Bicricium* (p. 188).

Dangeard (*loc. cit.*) described certain cytological details (see p. 917) in this species and has observed the partial germination of the oöspores. The resting bodies, after several months, became multinucleate, vacuolate, and formed a germ tube. They probably then produced zoospores, although this was not observed. The species is considered rare, but Dangeard found that it occurred frequently in his laboratory cultures of eelworms.

MYZOCYTIUM ZOOPHTHORUM Sparrow

J. Linn. Soc. London (Bot.), 50: 461, pl. 19, figs. 1–8, 10–14. 1936

(Fig. 79 F–G, p. 977)

Sporangia variable in number, irregular, saclike, often lobulate, 5–17 μ in diameter, of variable length, separated by narrow inconspicuous septa, discharge tube generally short and broad; zoospores laterally biflagellate, 10–11 μ long by 6–7 μ wide, partly or wholly delimited within the sporangium, at discharge the first few zoospores forming an amorphous subspherical mass in a vesicle at the tip of the broadly conical evacuation tube, quickly becoming separated and undergoing their final maturation at the orifice, the vesicle almost at once disappearing; gametangia similar to the zoosporangia; oöspore spherical, colorless, 12–15 µ in diameter, with a thick smooth wall and a large eccentric globule, lying loosely in the gametangium, germination not observed; male gametangium conveying its contents into the female through a pore formed in the cross wall.

Parasitic on adults and eggs of rotifers, Sparrow (*loc. cit.*), GREAT BRITAIN, DENMARK; on rotifers, soil, Sparrow (1952c: 105), CUBA.

It is possible that the tubular branched thallus shown by Sparrow (1936a: pl. 19, fig. 9) belongs to a species of *Lagenidium* rather than to *Myzocytium zoophthorum*. The lobed thallus observed in adult rotifers recalls the imperfectly known *M. lineare* and, when these lobes are very pronounced, a species of *Lagenidium*, to which genus the fungus may possibly be referable. No specialized antheridial branch, outgrowth, or fertilization tube is ever formed, however, as is generally true of *Lagenidium*.

The zoospores are predaceous and attack moving adult rotifers, possibly attaching themselves by a mucilaginous secretion to the carapace of the host. The animal continues its activities until the thallus is well developed, when death ensues.

MYZOCYTIUM MICROSPORUM (Karling), comb. nov.

Lagenidium microsporum Karling, Lloydia, 7: 328, figs. 1–34. 1944.

"Thalli usually unicellular, up to 40 in a host, oval, 5–15 × 6–25 µ, spherical, 6–20 µ, pyriform or oblong and uniseptate. Sporangia usually of same size and shape as thalli with one broad, 4 × 5 µ, or long, 6 × 20 µ, exit tube. Zoospores fully delimited in sporangium, forming a globular mass at exit orifice but soon swimming away without encysting; oval, 2.5 × 3.5 µ, slightly flattened and bean-shaped, coming to rest intermittently and rounding up but apparently not withdrawing flagella and encysting; diplanetism doubtful. Oogonia oval and spherical, 12–18 µ in diam., slightly utriform and pyriform; antheridia predominantly oval,

5–7 × 7–9 µ, and broadly fusiform, 5–6 × 9–10 µ. Oospores spherical, 7–14 µ, oval, 7–9 × 10–11 µ; content hyaline and granular with a large vacuole; wall hyaline and smooth, 1.5–2 µ thick; germination unknown" (Karling, *loc. cit.*).

Parasitic in the bodies of rotifers, *Distyla sp.*, BRAZIL.

The perfectly globose, thick-walled sporangia and the simplicity of the sex organs make it quite evident that this species belongs in *Myzocytium*.

Since no encysted zoospores were found on the outside of the rotifer, it was considered probable that the zoospores had been engulfed and the animal thus infected.

IMPERFECTLY KNOWN SPECIES OF MYZOCYTIUM

? MYZOCYTIUM IRREGULARE H. E. Petersen

Bot. Tidsskrift, 29:403, fig.xvi a, d, 1909; Ann. Mycologici, 8:538, fig. xvi a,d. 1910

Sporangia short-cylindrical, globose, or irregular in shape, articulation variable, most frequently in pairs, often forming short branches when more than two, discharge tube of variable length, usually expanded beneath the host wall; zoospores and sex organs not observed.

In *Cosmarium sp.*, *Micrasterias sp.*, H. E. Petersen (*loc. cit.*), Sparrow, DENMARK; *Cosmarium sp.*, Scherffel (1914: 17), HUNGARY; *Micrasterias rotata*, Cejp[1] (1933a: 8, pl. 1, fig. 16), (?) Type III on *M. denticula*, Reinsch (1878: 300, pl. 17, figs. 8, 13), GERMANY; *Micrasterias sp.*, W. G. Farlow (F. 384), UNITED STATES.

As Petersen states, the inclusion of this fungus in *Myzocytium* rather than in *Lagenidium* is questionable. In the branched or lobed nature of its thallus it is closer to *Lagenidium*. A similar situation is found in *M. lineare* and *M. zoophthorum*. In the latter, however, the absence of a specialized antheridium appears to relate the species to *Myzocytium* rather than to *Lagenidium*. Since, apparently, no sex organs (or even zoospores) have as yet been described in the present fungus, the antheridial character cannot be used in this instance to determine the genus. Figure XVI d (Petersen, *loc. cit.*) is believed by Canter (1947a) to represent *Myzocytium megastomum*.

[1] Czechoslovakia.

Schulz (1922: 149, fig. 87) has figured in *Micrasterias rotata*, from Danzig, the empty sporangia and resting spores of a fungus which is very similar to *Myzocytium irregulare*.

The two-celled forms of this species resemble *Bicricium* (see p. 188).

? MYZOCYTIUM LINEARE CORNU

Ann. Sci. Nat. Bot., V, 15: 21. 1872

Sporangia tubular, simple or branched, never ovoid, disposed in rows; oögonia very tubular, swollen, and irregular.

In desmids, FRANCE.

Cornu (1877b) identified with his incompletely described species certain fungi found by Reinsch (1878: 300, pl. 17, figs. 5, 14) only in *Cosmarium spp.* (Type II). It is not clear from Reinsch's figure whether the twisted complex of tubes (*op. cit.*, fig. 5) consists of one or more cells. De Wildeman (1895a: 57) doubts that the fungus belongs in *Myzocytium*. Cejp(1933a: 8) considers it disputable whether the form belongs to *Lagenidium* or to *Myzocytium*, although he favors the latter. Since the zoospores were not observed by either Cornu or Reinsch the fungus may belong in the Chytridiales.

LAGENIDIUM SCHENK

Verhandl. Phy.-Med. Gesell. Würzburg, A. F., 9: 27. 1859

(Figs. 79 D–E, p. 977; 80–82, pp. 987, 1002, 1004)

Resticularia Dangeard, Le Botaniste, 2: 96. 1890–91.

Thallus endobiotic, occupying one cell or extending through several cells of host, holocarpic, without specialized vegetative structures, either a one-celled and saccate body or a more or less extensive, irregularly branched or unbranched tube which at maturity becomes transversely segmented to form the rudiments of the zoosporangia or gametangia or both, contents at first having a dull clear lustrous matrix within which are imbedded more refractive, irregularly shaped large clods and fat droplets, later becoming evenly and coarsely granular and vacuolate, walls giving a cellulose reaction, zoospore cyst and infection tube frequently persistent; each of the zoosporangia bearing a single discharge tube, at least the tip of which is extramatrical; zoospores reniform, broadly fusiform or grape-seed-like, laterally biflagellate, fully formed in the sporangium or in an evanescent vesicle at the orifice of the discharge tube, or cleaved out within the sporangium and completing their development naked or in a more or less quickly evanescent vesicle, or, rarely (the primary spores?), moving within the sporangium and encysting at the orifice, movement after discharge generally an even swimming, rarely hopping; plants monoecious or dioecious, the gametangia shaped like the sporangia or the female often more rotund, monandrous, in rare instances lacking an antheridium, the male gametangium forming a fertilization tube, periplasm apparently lacking; oöspore borne singly and loosely (except in one species) in the female gametangium, with a thick wall, more or less coarsely granular parietal plasma, a large oil globule, and often a lateral bright spot, germination not (?) observed; in some species one or more resting spores (apogamous?) formed in a thallus or thallus segment.

Parasitic in fresh-water algae, particularly in the vegetative filaments, gametangia, and zygotes of the Conjugatae, in pollen grains; on eggs and newly hatched young of the blue crab (*Callinectes*); in mosquito larvae, copepods, *Daphne,* and rotifer eggs. Some species have been cultivated on artificial media. One is saprophytic on human skin.

One-celled thalli which are transformed at maturity into either zoosporangia or gametangia are occasionally developed by the multicellular species (for example, *Lagenidium rabenhorstii, L. humanum*). Some species, however, are typically one-celled (Fig. 80, p. 987). It is a question whether these should be retained in *Lagenidium* or segregated in a distinct genus. [1]

In almost half the species of *Lagenidium* the zoospores are developed more or less completely within the sporangium, as in *Olpidiopsis*; in the remainder the process takes place exogenously, with or without a surrounding vesicle. Although the primary zoospores had been thought to be completely suppressed as in *Pythium*, Scherffel (1925a) and Karling

[1] Since no zoospores have been reported in *Lagenidiopsis*, that imperfectly known genus, erected by de Wildeman to include a one-celled dioecious fungus found only in the sexual stage, will not serve the purpose. Karling (1942e) has made the genus synonymous with *Lagenidium*.

(1944g) both have observed their encystment at the orifice as in *Achlya*.

Certain species resemble in complexity of thallus development and sexual reproduction an *Aphragmium* type of *Pythium*. Thus, in *Lagenidium giganteum* (Couch, 1935b) the branched threads may extend as much as 1–2 mm. from the host and the segments which will form the zoosporangia may be 50–200 μ long; similar sizes are found in *L. humanum*. Although in *L. marchalianum* these sizes are not attained, in this species, too, the thallus is extensive and ramifies throughout the algal host in a strikingly *Pythium*-like manner (Fig. 81 B, p. 1002). Further resemblance to *Pythium* is evident in the sexual organs, which are more differentiated in *Lagenidium* than in *Myzocytium*. The antheridium in particular is often more specialized and generally produces a fertilization tube rather than a simple pore. It is still ordinarily not separated, however, from the antheridial branch by a cross wall as in the more highly developed species of *Pythium*. The assumption that the female gametangium lacks periplasm appears to rest entirely on morphological observations.

KEY TO THE SPECIES OF LAGENIDIUM [1,2]

Thallus never septate, forming a single gametangium or zoosporangium
In fresh-water algae
In diatoms
Sporangium rounded or more or less flask–shaped, discharge tube short, blunt, thin-walled throughout .. *L. cyclotellae*, p. 986
Sporangium tubular, unbranched, or occasionally with finger-like branches
Discharge tube very short, with a thick-walled "forcing apparatus"; resting spore lying loosely in the gametangium
L. brachystomum, p. 988
Discharge tube prolonged somewhat extramatrically; resting spore filling the gametangium .... *L. enecans*, p. 989
In   *Oedogonium* .... *L. oedogonii*, p. 990
In other Phycomycetes
Sporangium spherical or pyriform; resting spores single, sexually formed; in *Pythium* .... *L. pythii*, p. 991

---

[1] See also *Lagenidium muenscheri* Cutter (1943), parasitic in root hairs of *Potamogeton spirillus*, a vascular plant.

[2] Note that key is not strictly dichotomous.

LAGENIDIUM CYCLOTELLAE Scherffel

Arch. Protistenk., 52: 18, pl. 2, figs. 49–59. 1925

(Fig. 80 F, p. 987)

Thallus rounded, or by the formation of short lobes more or less irregularly saccate, one-celled, pushing apart the valves of the host, attached to the cyst of the infecting zoospore by the persistent infection tube, forming a single more or less flask-shaped sporangium with a short blunt discharge tube 3 μ long by 3 μ in diameter which protrudes between the separated valves of the host; zoospores from five to six, fully formed in the sporangium, within which motility is initiated, emerging individually from the discharge tube, (primary?) zoospores ovoid, about 6 μ long by 3.5 μ broad, with two oppositely directed flagella, about 6 μ long, which arise subapically from the concave side of the body, contents bearing a posterior parietal refractive fat body, secondary zoospores not observed; plants dioecious, the gametangia like (?) the sporangia, wall of the male gametangium collapsing after fertilization; female gametangium completely filled by the resting spore; resting spore spherical, 10 μ in diameter, or broadly ovoid or occasionally somewhat angular or irregular, 10–12 μ long by 8–10 μ wide, with a smooth thick colorless wall, dense glittering parietal contents, a large eccentric lustrous globule, and a lateral bright spot, germination not observed.

In *Cyclotella kutzingiana*, HUNGARY.

Scherffel justly emphasizes the close similarity of the zoospore discharge in this remarkable species to that in both *Olpidiopsis* and *Ectrogella*. (The fungus also resembles most species of *Olpidiopsis* in

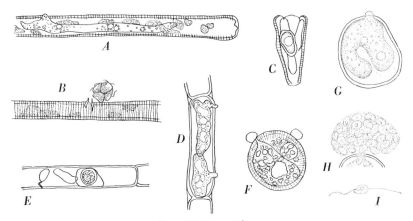

FIG. 80. *Lagenidium*

A–C. Lagenidium brachystomum Scherffel in diatoms: *A*, vacuolate sporangium showing at the left the outgrowth which will become the discharge tube; place of attachment of infection tube was at extreme left tip of thallus; *B*, portion of frustule of *Synedra* from which protrudes the short discharge tube; zoospores are undergoing final maturation at orifice; *C*, mature oöspore in *Gomphonema. D–E. Lagenidium oedogonii* Scherffel: *D*, two vacuolate sporangia with discharge tubes; *E*, oöspore lying loosely within its container, the empty tubular contributing thallus attached to it; a small empty thallus with persistent infection tube is also shown. *F. Lagenidium cyclotellae* Scherffel in *Cyclotella*, host with a large and a small thallus in it, empty epibiotic cysts of infecting zoospores persistent. *G–I. Lagenidium oophilum* Sparrow in rotifer eggs: *G*, nearly mature lobed sporangium with discharge tube protruding through wall of egg; *H*, tip of sporangium with zoospores almost completely discharged; flagella are beginning to form on emerged spores; *I*, single zoospore.

(*A–F*, Scherffel, 1925a; *G–I*, Sparrow, 1939c)

that the resting spore completely fills the female gametangium.) But he considers the persistence of the cyst and the infection tube to be a fundamental character, marking the plant as a species of *Lagenidium*. Evidently no fertilization tube was formed by the male gametangium.

In the early stages of thallus development the content is typically lagenidiaceous, the hyaline smooth plasma bearing refractive irregularly shaped fat clods. Later, a large irregular vacuole always appears (Fig. 80 F). The zoospores are segregated in the parietal layer of cytoplasm lining a large central vacuole. Upon its disappearance the spore initials swell and fill the sporangium, though the cleavage lines remain sharply defined. No special forcing apparatus is formed, the valves merely being pushed apart by the expanding thallus. The zoospores resembled the primary type found in *Ectrogella bacillariacearum*. Secondary zoospores were not observed.

LAGENIDIUM BRACHYSTOMUM Scherffel

Arch. Protistenk., 52: 21, pl. 2, figs. 70–85. 1925

(Fig. 80 A–C, p. 987)

Thallus tubular, very thin-walled, predominantly unbranched and 150–250 μ long by 4–7.5 μ in diameter, or with short or, rarely, somewhat elongate finger-like branches running parallel with the main axis, infection tube occasionally persistent, forming a single sporangium with a very short thick-walled cylindrical discharge tube which functions also as a forcing apparatus between the girdle bands of the host; zoospores few (from two to four) or numerous, grape-seed-like, laterally biflagellate, 6–8 μ long by 4 μ wide, formed in a vesicle at the orifice of the discharge tube; plants dioecious, gametangia resembling the sporangia; resting spore lying loosely in the female gametangium, spherical or broadly ovoid to oblong, 11–24 μ long by 6–10 μ broad, colorless, with a moderately thick smooth wall and with one or two large globules in the dense contents, germination not known.

Parasitic in *Synedra ulna, Cymbella cymbiformis* var. *parva, Gomphonema constrictum, Nitzschia linearis*, Scherffel (*loc. cit.*), HUNGARY; *Synedra sp.*, Couch (1935b: 385, figs. 20–21), UNITED STATES.

The species, according to Scherffel, differs from *Lagenidium enecans* in forming typically an unbranched sporangium (Fig. 80 A) and a very short discharge tube which is not prolonged extramatrically (Fig. 80 B). Further, the valves of the diatom are not split apart but forced.

Mixed infections of this species, with *Ectrogella bacillariacearum* and *E. monostoma*, may occur in *Synedra ulna*. When this happens the type of zoospore discharge, the character of the contents, and the method of exit of the discharge tube are used in differentiating the members of the complex.

The fungus found by Couch apparently lacks the thick-walled forcing apparatus.

LAGENIDIUM ENECANS Zopf

Nova Acta Acad. Leop.-Carol., 47: 154. 1884

Thallus completely tubular, 6–12 μ in diameter by 37–156 μ long, or with a few short broad finger-like branches, sometimes somewhat contorted and saccate, the infection tube persistent, transformed into a single sporangium, the discharge tube cylindrical, 3–6 μ in diameter by 9–36 μ long, prolonged only slightly extramatrically, forming a thick-walled forcing apparatus between the girdle plates; zoospores grape-seed-like, biflagellate, 8–12.5 μ long by 5.7 μ broad, produced in a vesicle at the orifice of the discharge tube, movement rapid, irregular; plants dioecious, gametangia resembling (?) the sporangia; resting spore probably formed after fusion of the contents of a female gametangium with those of an adjacent irregularly spherical male gametangium, filling (?) the receptive gametangium, spherical, 18 μ in diameter, broadly ovoid or irregular and with strongly indented contour, 15–22 by 20–24 μ, with a smooth thick wall, a large central lustrous fat globule, and from one to several bright spots in the finely granular contents, germination not observed.

In *Stauroneis phoenicentron, Cocconema lanceolatum, Pinnularia spp.*, Zopf (*loc. cit.*), GERMANY; (?) diatom, de Wildeman (1893a: 9; 1893b: 44, pl. 4, fig. 32), BELGIUM; *Cymbella gastroides, Pinnularia viridis, Amphora ovalis, Cymatopleura solea, Stauroneis phoenicentron*, Scherffel (1902a: [106]; 1925a: 20, pl. 2, figs. 60–69), HUNGARY; *Navicula cuspidata, N. cuspidata* var. *ambigua, Stauroneis phoenicentron*, Skvortzow (1925: 433), MANCHURIA; *Cymbella cistula*, Friedmann (1952: 209, fig. 7), AUSTRIA.

The species was only briefly described by Zopf, and not figured. Most of our knowledge of it rests on the investigations of Scherffel. Cook (1935: 78) states that the sexual organs were observed by de Wildeman (*loc. cit.*), but the latter merely mentioned having found an organism possibly referable to this species and gave one figure of an empty sporangium. In what he considered this species, Friedmann (1952) observed in one instance the formation of primary anteriorly biflagellate "drop-like" zoospores (6 μ long by 12 μ broad) which encyst.

LAGENIDIUM OEDOGONII Scherffel

Hedwigia, 41: (105). 1902; Arch. Protistenk., 52: 109, pl. 5, figs. 209–219. 1925

(Fig. 80 D–E, p. 987)

Thallus irregularly saccate or ovoid, sometimes with broad finger-like prominent lobes or short branches, occasionally tubular and simple or coiled, variable in size, 20–25 by 35–52 μ, infection tube and zoospore case often persistent, forming a single sporangium with one, generally short, discharge tube, which is slightly constricted when passing through the host wall (rarely two discharge tubes); zoospores grape-seed-like, 6 μ long, furrowed, with a prominent bright spot (vacuole?), predominantly formed in a vesicle at the orifice of the discharge tube, capable of repeated emergence, rarely assuming motility within the sporangium, emerging individually and encysting at the orifice, cysts 4 μ in diameter, escaping as secondary laterally biflagellate zoospores; plants dioecious, female gametangium resembling the sporangium, male gametangium smaller, often somewhat tubular; resting spore spherical, 12–14 μ in diameter, lying loosely in the gametangium, with a smooth colorless wall 2 μ thick, contents with a parietal layer of coarse granules and a large eccentric lustrous fat globule, germination not observed.

Parasitic in *Oedogonium sp.*, Scherffel (*loc. cit.*), Domján (1936: 52, pl. 1, figs. 170, 180–181), Bérczi (1940: 86), HUNGARY; *Oedogonium sp.*, Couch (1935b: 386, figs. 22–31), *Oedogonium sp.*, Sparrow (1943: 663), UNITED STATES; *O. boscii*, Rieth (1954: 164, fig. 1), GERMANY.

The *Achlya*-like behavior of the zoospores in rare instances might perhaps be interpreted as repeated emergence or dicystism in the sense of Coker and Matthews (1937: 15), but not as diplanetism (dimorphism). Emergence of the spores in *Pythium*-like fashion, followed by repeated emergence has been noted by Couch (1935b: figs. 32–34) in what may be a small form of this species.

Scherffel points out that in sexual reproduction there is definite distinction between the male and the female gametangia, the former being smaller and often more tubular than the latter (Fig. 80 E). This is of particular interest since it appears to indicate that here degree of thallus development is not correlated with degree of differentiation of the sexual organs. However, further observations are needed on this phase of the species.

Careful studies of the development have been made by both Scherffel and Couch. Each of these investigators noted the production of a small appressorium by the infecting zoospore and the formation of a protective layer of callus by the host. The parasite reduces the chloroplasts to a brownish residue, the cytoplasm and starch being almost completely consumed.

LAGENIDIUM PYTHII Whiffen

J. Elisha Mitchell Sci. Soc., 62: 54, pl. 7, figs. 6–14. 1946

"Thallus intramatrical, causing hypertrophy of the hypha of the host. Zoosporangial thallus hyaline, smooth-walled, spherical to pyriform, 16–25 μ in shortest diameter. Zoospore [cleaved out within the sporangium] ovoid, 2.1–2.8 × 3.5–4.2 μ, isocont, encysting on surface of the host hypha and discharging contents into the host through an evanescent penetration tube. Antheridial cell smooth-walled, spherical to ovoid, 8–13 μ in shortest diameter. Oogonium spherical to ovoid, smooth-walled, 12–23 μ in shortest diameter. Oospore spherical, smooth-walled, 7–15 μ in diameter." (Whiffen, *loc. cit.*).

Parasitic on *Pythium sp.*, CUBA.

Whiffen was impressed by the great similarity of *Lagenidium pythii* to a species of *Olpidiopsis*, specifically in its possession of a simple thallus, endogenously formed zoospores, and lack of fertilization tube in the antheridial cell. She says (*op. cit.*, p. 56), "If the oogonium of this species were to be filled completely by its oospore, then the resting body in its form and simplicity would be indistinguishable from the typical resting body of *Olpidiopsis*. One is thus led to believe that *L. pythii* may be a transitional form connecting *Olpidiopsis* and *Lagenidium*."

LAGENIDIUM DESTRUENS Sparrow

J. Wash. Acad. Sci., 40: 54, figs. 15–24. 1950

(Fig. 82 A–E, p. 1004)

Thallus consisting of a complex of short, finger-like, irregular and contorted branches of variable size which may fill the strongly hypertrophied host parts; forming a single zoosporangium; zoospores variable in number, reniform, 12 by 8 μ, laterally biflagellate, ejected in an amorphous mass from the discharge tube to the outside of the host where maturation is completed; resting spores asexually formed in a series in branches of the thallus, rectangular or somewhat ellipsoidal, 10–15 by 8–12 μ, bearing numerous oil globules, wall thickened, germination not observed.

Parasitic in hyphae and reproductive organs of *Achlya sp.*, in soil, CUBA.

This species is remarkable for its virulence as a parasite. All parts of the host are invaded and destroyed within a few days. Both zoosporangia and resting spores are formed almost simultaneously. In early stages of thallus development pronounced hypertrophy of the host is evident, even though the parasite itself may be wholly or partly masked by the dense contents of the infected area. Cross walls may or may not be laid down by the host to wall off infection. The thalli converted into zoosporangia discharge their contents through a short tube to the outside, where the mass, apparently without an enveloping vesicle, rapidly becomes converted into biflagellate zoospores. Other thalli by cleavage of their protoplasm into uniform-sized irregular blocks produce asexually the thick-walled resting spores which undoubtedly survive during periods of drought.

LAGENIDIUM OOPHILUM Sparrow

Mycologia, 31: 532, figs. 1–15. 1939

(Fig. 80 G–I, p. 987)

Thallus when occurring singly somewhat irregularly saccate or ellipsoidal, with broad lobes of varying length, when several, more regularly ellipsoidal and often unlobed, converted holocarpically into a single thin-walled colorless sporangium 20–40 μ long by 12–25 μ wide with a short sessile or slightly prolonged discharge papilla 4–5 μ in diameter; zoospores grape-seed-like, laterally biflagellate, 8 μ long by 6 μ wide, discharged individually and undergoing a period of maturation in a group at the orifice of the discharge tube, apparently not surrounded by a vesicle; cystospore 5–6 μ in diameter; sexual reproduction not observed.

Parasitic in eggs and embryos of rotifers, UNITED STATES.

LAGENIDIUM PYGMAEUM Zopf

Abhandl. Naturforsch. Gesell. Halle, 17: 96, pl. 1, figs. 29–31, pl. 2, figs. 1–12. 1887

Thallus tubular, contorted, with irregular lobulations, or spherical, ovoid, ellipsoid, or reniform, frequently single, occasionally from two to four in the host cell, forming a single sporangium provided with a broad short somewhat irregular occasionally basally branched discharge tube; zoospores broadly fusiform, 5 × 8 μ, laterally biflagellate, segmented in the sporangium, completing their development in a vesicle at the orifice; plants monoecious, rarely dioecious, gametangia resembling the sporangia but somewhat stouter, formed by the septation of a single thallus, occasionally a second septum delimiting a sporangium, female gametangium strongly expanded, sometimes with papilla-like outgrowths, male gametangium irregular, forming a fertilization tube; resting spore spherical, lying loosely in the gametangium, 18–29 μ in diameter, with a smooth double wall, contents with a large globule, germination not observed.

Parasitic in pollen grains of *Pinus sylvestris, P. austriaca, P. laricio, P. pallasiana,* Zopf (*loc. cit.*), GERMANY; coniferous pollen grains, Maurizio (1895), de Wildeman (1895a: 74), SWITZERLAND; pollen grains of different plants, H. E. Petersen (1909: 401; 1910: 537), DENMARK; (?) pollen, Voronichin (1920: 12), RUSSIA; pollen of *Pinus spp.,* Karling (1941b: 108; 1941c: 357), Sparrow (1943: 665), apple pollen, Karling (1949a: 275), UNITED STATES; pine-pollen bait, Sparrow (1952c: 106), CUBA; from soil, pollen, Gaertner (1954b: 22), EGYPT, SOUTH AFRICA.

Schulz (1923: 181, figs. 4–7) reported this species from Danzig in *Cosmarium pyramidatum* as well as in pine pollen. With the exception of the organism in pine pollen (his Figure 7), those illustrated are hardly identifiable with *Lagenidium pygmaeum.*

Since the plants are predominantly monoecious and sex organs are formed by the septation of a single thallus, the species is probably capable of multicellular development under less restricted environmental conditions and, hence, is not comparable with truly one-celled, dioecious forms.

Zopf observed that, because of the many zoospores, widespread infection of new pollen could be induced under laboratory conditions within twenty-three hours.

LAGENIDIUM RABENHORSTII Zopf

Sitzungsber. Bot. Vereins Prov. Brandenburg, 20: 77. 1878; Nova Acta
    Acad. Leop.-Carol., 47: 145, pl. 12, figs. 1–28, pl. 13, figs. 1–9. 1884

(Fig. 81 D, p. 1002)

Thallus of small extent, occupying a single cell of host, cylindrical or with frequent irregularities and with short or long often clavate, straight, crooked, or irregular branches 2.5–8 μ in diameter, occasionally somewhat irregularly saccate; sporangia from one to ten, generally from five to seven, delimited by narrow sometimes slightly constricted septations, variable in shape, with a cylindrical or slightly conical discharge tube which is rarely locally constricted when passing through the host wall and which projects only slightly extramatrically; zoospores reniform, 8.5 μ long by 6 μ wide, laterally biflagellate, formed in a vesicle at the orifice of the discharge tube; plants dioecious or, less frequently, monoecious, female gametangium intercalary, lateral or terminal, expanded, spherical, ovoid, fusiform, or irregular, 15–16 μ wide; male gametangium resembling the sporangium or occasionally somewhat crook-necked, laterally applied, with a fertilization tube; oöspore spherical, with a smooth colorless double wall, lying loosely in the gametangium, 10.4–20 μ in diameter, with a fairly large nearly centric globule, germination not (?) observed.

Parasitic in vegetative cells of *Spirogyra sp.*, *Mougeotia sp.*, etc., Zopf (*loc. cit.*), Schroeter (1885: 227), Minden (1915: 434), GERMANY; (?) *Spirogyra sp.*, de Wildeman (1895b: 98, figs. 1–2), FRANCE; *Spirogyra sp.*, Constantineanu (1901: 379), RUMANIA; *Spirogyra sp.*, Scherffel (1914: 17), *Spirogyra sp.*, *Zygnema sp.*, Domján (1936: 51, pl. 1, figs. 56, 94, 174), *Spirogyra sp.*, Bérczi (1940: 86), HUNGARY; *Spirogyra sp.*, Atkinson (1909a: 329, fig. 5 A–B), *S. orthospira*, *Oedogonium plusio-*

sporum, Graff (1928: 169), *Spirogyra sp.*, Sparrow (1932b: 289, fig. 4d), *Mougeotia sp.*, *Spirogyra sp.*, *Oedogonium sp.*, Karling (1942e: 77), Sparrow (1943: 666), UNITED STATES; *Spirogyra sp.*, Cook (1932a: 142, figs. 39–45; 1935: 75, pl. 1, figs. 1–14, pl. 4, figs. 1–8), GREAT BRITAIN; *Zygnema sp.*, Linder (F. 2704) (1947: 244, pl. 13, figs. A–B), CANADIAN EASTERN ARCTIC; *Spirogyra sp.*, Shen and Siang (1948: 201, fig. 12), CHINA.

This species, well known from the excellent researches of Zopf, has, with two exceptions, been reported only in Conjugatae. In early spring, it occurs usually in the sporangial stage. By midsummer, according to Zopf, the thalli are mostly converted into gametangia.

Both Atkinson and Cook have noted the lack of a vesicle during zoospore formation, and it is probable that under certain conditions this structure deliquesces soon after the emergence of the protoplasm. The antheridium, particularly on monoecious individuals, may be strikingly differentiated from the ordinary segment of the thallus and may assume, as Zopf (1884: pl. 12, fig. 26) and Sparrow (1932b: fig. 4d) have shown, a shape reminiscent of the crooknecked type found in *Pythium*.

One-celled thalli, transformed either into sporangia or gametangia, have been described by Zopf, but are atypical.

Germination of the oöspore in this species (the only instance known in the genus) has been reported by Cook (1935) to be as follows: Soon (twenty-four hours) after formation of the resting-spore wall it breaks down and a single nearly spherical biflagellate zoospore 8 μ in diameter is liberated, which after a short period of activity comes to rest on a healthy host cell and infects it. This spore gains access to the outside medium by the breaking down of the algal wall, presumed by Cook to be achieved by natural agencies such as wind and water currents. Although the quick germination of resting structures is recorded in other fungi, the breaking down of the wall and, in particular, the highly inefficient process of liberating only a single zoospore from a sexually formed structure are rare, if not unknown, among these plants and need confirmation.

Very often, *Lagenidium rabenhorstii* will wipe out a population of *Spirogyra* in the vegetative stage, particularly in hot, sunny localities.

LAGENIDIUM PAPILLOSUM Cocconi

R. Accad. Sci. Istituto Bologna, Mem. Ser. V, 4: 362, figs. 1–3. 1894

Thallus resembling that of *Lagenidium rabenhorstii*; plants monoecious, oögonia and antheridia like those of *L. rabenhorstii*; oöspore lying very loosely and centrically in the oögonium, with a thick smooth inner wall and a densely bullate outer wall.

In *Spirogyra sp.*, Cocconi (*loc. cit.*), ITALY; *Spirogyra sp.*, Voronichin (1920: 12), RUSSIA.

The mature oöspore was observed in some specimens to be surrounded by residual protoplasm, termed "periplasm" by Cocconi.

The sporangial stage, from the figures, is somewhat anomalous. Zoospores are pyriform and biflagellate, the flagella appearing apically attached.

LAGENIDIUM DISTYLAE Karling

Lloydia, 7: 330, figs. 69–107. 1944

"Thalli usually elongate, tubular, curved, irregular, lobed and occasionally branched, 6–10 μ in diam., consisting of 2–8 segments, 6–9 × 30–40 μ. Sporangia of same size and shape as segments with one short 4 × 7 μ, or long, 3 × 25 μ, exit tube; content of sporangium emerging as a naked mass, becoming enveloped by a vesicular membrane, and undergoing cleavage [into] zoospores. Zoospores reniform, 6 × 8 μ, diplanetic; cystospores, 6.6–7 μ. Oogonia and antheridia borne on same thallus; oogonia oval, broadly spindle-shaped and locally paunchy, up to 20 μ in diam., and 30 μ in length. Antheridium elongate, tubular, 5–8 × 20–30 μ. Oospores hyaline, smooth, spherical, 12–18 μ, oval, 8–10 × 12–15 μ; content granular with a large vacuole; germination unknown" (Karling, *loc. cit.*).

Parasitic in the eggs of *Distyla sp.*, BRAZIL.

The vesicle surrounding the protoplasm ejected from the sporangium is said by Karling to be developed in this species *after*, not coincident with, emergence. The antheridium is a well-defined structure, as in *Lagenidium rabenhorstii*.

LAGENIDIUM PARTHENOSPORUM Karling

Lloydia, 7: 329, figs. 35–68. 1944

"Thallus consisting of 1 to 5 segments, larger thalli septate, elongate,

8–12 × 20–90 μ, lobed, curved, occasionally branched, and usually constricted at septa; reduced thalli continuous, oval, 9–18 × 12–25 μ, oblong, 6–15 × 13–50 μ, and slightly irregular. Sporangia of same size and shape as segments and reduced thalli with one or two, 3–5 μ broad by 5–18 μ long exit tubes which extend beyond the surface of the host. Zoospore segments delimited completely in the sporangium, rounding up immediately upon emerging and forming a mass of cystospores near the exit orifice; cystospores spherical, 4.5–6 μ, giving rise to slightly reniform, 4–5 × 5.5–6.5 μ, diplanetic zoospores. Oospores or resting spores formed parthenogenetically by contraction and encystment of protoplasm in thallus segments; usually solitary, rarely double in segments; shape spherical, 8–16 μ, oval, 6–10 × 9–14 μ, elongate, 5–8 × 12–20 μ, occasionally curved, irregular, lobed and dumbbell-shaped; wall 2.5–3 μ thick, smooth at first, later becoming deeply wrinkled so as to make spores pointed or somewhat stellate in appearance; content hyaline and finely granular with a large central or eccentric vacuole; germination unknown" (Karling, *loc. cit.*).

Parasitic in the eggs and bodies of *Distyla sp.* and *Philodina sp.*, eggs of *Chaetonotus larus* and bodies of *Heterodera sp.*, from soil, BRAZIL.

Unlike *Lagenidium oedogonii*, the zoospores typically are discharged in *Achlya*-like fashion. Furthermore, they may undergo several repeated emergences. It is possible that future studies may make it advisable to remove this and species with similar zoospore discharge from *Lagenidium*.

LAGENIDIUM INTERMEDIUM de Wildeman

Ann. Soc. Belge Micro. (Mém.), 19: 97, pl. 4, figs. 10–13. 1895

Thallus tubular, complex, more or less isodiametric, rarely torulose, with short or long irregular branches; sporangia relatively few, each composed of a cylindrical element or of a complex of branches, discharge tube very narrowly cylindrical, sometimes slightly expanded beneath the host wall and locally constricted when passing through the wall, frequently prolonged extramatrically; zoospores not observed; (?) resting spore intercalary, spherical, with a thick smooth wall, germination not observed; antheridium not observed.

In *Closterium ehrenbergii*, FRANCE.

A resting structure was observed in only one instance and was tentatively considered to be the resting spore of this species.

The thallus resembles superficially *Lagenidium entophytum*, but in its regularly cylindrical elements approaches *L. rabenhorstii*. In spite of the lack of observations on the zoospores, the fungus is probably correctly referred to *Lagenidium*.

LAGENIDIUM ENTOPHYTUM (Pringsheim) Zopf

Nova Acta Acad. Leop.-Carol., 47: 154, pl. 13, figs. 10–18, pl. 14, figs. 1–5. 1884

(Fig. 81 A, p. 1002)

Pythium entophytum Pringsheim, Jahrb. wiss. Bot., 1: 289, pl. 21, fig. 1. 1858.
Myzocytium entophytum (Pringsheim) Cornu, Ann. Sci. Nat. Bot., V, 15: 21. 1872.
Lagenidium americanum Atkinson, Bot. Gaz., 48: 336, fig. 6. 1909.

Thallus consisting of an irregularly contorted bent relatively thick tube bearing numerous short lateral variously oriented lobulations or short branches; sporangia few, consisting of irregularly tubular lobulate segments of varying length, delimited by thick refractive septate constrictions, the single discharge tube of each segment cylindrical or somewhat irregular, 2 μ in diameter, of variable length, often swollen at the point of contact with the inner wall of the host and locally constricted where it passes through the wall; zoospores reniform, laterally biflagellate, 5–7 μ long by 4–6 μ wide, formed at the orifice of the discharge tube, possibly surrounded by a vesicle; oöspore lying singly and loosely in a tabular segment of the thallus, spherical, 13–16.5 μ in diameter, with a thick, golden, slightly dentate outer wall, parthenogenetically formed, germination not observed.

Parasitic in the zygote of *Spirogyra sp.*, Pringsheim (*loc. cit.*), zygote and zygospores of *Spirogyra sp.*, Zopf (*loc. cit.*), Minden (1915: 436), (?) *Euastrum humerosum*, *Micrasterias mahabuleshwarensis* var. *wallichii*, Schulz (1923: 181, figs. 8–9), GERMANY; *Spirogyra sp.*, de Wildeman (1895b: 100, pl. 3, figs. 24–25), coll. Lemaire, de Wildeman (1896b: 47), *Spirogyra sp.*, Aleem (1952a: 2650, fig. 4), FRANCE; host (?), Scherffel

(1904: 117), HUNGARY; *Spirogyra varians, S. insignis, S. calospora,* Atkinson (1909a), zygospores of *Spirogyra sp.*, Wolf (1944: 15), UNITED STATES; *Spirogyra maxima,* Voronichin (1920: 12), RUSSIA; zygote of *Spirogyra sp.*, Shen and Siang (1948: 202, fig. 13), CHINA; *Spirogyra sp.*, Lacy (1949: 134, fig. 1, A), INDIA; zygospores of *Spirogyra sp.*, Sparrow (1952c: 105), CUBA.

Lagenidium americanum Atk. is said to differ in the lack of a swelling on the discharge tube, but the figures do not seem to bear out this statement. From Zopf's description and figures this swelling is apparently not a constant feature.

The fungus described by Cook (1935: 77, pl. 2, figs. 15–25, pl. 3, figs. 33–35) from Great Britain, though occasionally branched, does not possess the distinctly tubular, contorted, and lobulate appearance characteristic of Zopf's fungus. The sporangia are 12–15 μ long by 4–6 μ in diameter, the zoospores 8 μ long by 4 μ in diameter, and the parthenogenetically developed oöspores spherical and 12 μ in diameter. Further study may show this to be a new species.

Fischer (1892: 82) states that Carter (1856) confused this fungus with the developmental stage of an *Astasia*-like flagellate.

All of the abundant material observed by Sparrow (1952c) formed oöspores bearing a network of low dentations on the outer wall, as was figured by Zopf. This, we believe, to be typical for the species. The Cuban fungus caused a devastating epidemic in zygospores of the host.

LAGENIDIUM GRACILE Zopf

Nova Acta Acad. Leop.-Carol., 47:158. 1884

Thallus tubular, somewhat irregular, coiled, branched, slender, 4.5 μ in diameter, forming a series of cylindrical or spherical sporangia, each provided with a very narrowly cylindrical discharge tube which is expanded beneath the wall of the host gametangium (but not the zygospore) and extends for a short distance extramatrically; zoospores bean-shaped, 7.5 μ long by 4 μ wide, with two equal flagella, formed in a vesicle (?) at the tip of the discharge tube; female gametangium intercalary; rarely terminal, spherical or nearly so; resting spore parthenogenetically formed, lying loosely in the gametangium, spherical, 13–

14 μ in diameter, with a thick smooth wall, germination not observed.

In the gametangia of *Spirogyra sp.*, Zopf (*loc. cit.*), GERMANY; gametangia and zygospores of *Spirogyra sp.*, *S. grevilleana*, coll. Lemaire, de Wildeman (1895b: 102, fig. 3,) FRANCE; zygospores of *Spirogyra sp.*, Cook (1932a: 140, figs. 32–38; 1935: 77, pl. 3, figs. 26–32), GREAT BRITAIN.

Differing from *Lagenidium entophytum* in its more slender, more regularly branched thallus, very slender discharge tube, and smooth-walled resting spore. Zopf stated that the thallus may extend from one host cell to another, but it is possible that this refers to the discharge tube.

LAGENIDIUM NODOSUM (Dangeard) Ingold

Ann. Bot. London, 13 (N.S.): 442, figs. 1–4. 1949

(Fig. 79 D–E, p. 977)

Resticularia nodosa Dangeard, Le Botaniste, 2: 96, pl. 4, figs. 24–31. 1890–91.

Thallus somewhat moniliform because of passing through the cross walls of the host, with poorly developed diverticula and occasional cross walls; zoosporangium either a simple segment of the thallus bearing a short discharge tube which extends beyond the sheath of the host, or a strongly inflated diverticulum and external discharge tube; zoospores seven to ten, formed in a vesicle at the orifice of the discharge tube, bean-shaped with two lateral flagella; plants monoecious, the female gametangium an irregular, unmodified segment of the thallus, the male an adjacent segment, fertilization probably accomplished through a simple pore; oospore spherical, smooth-walled, with a large oil globule, germination not observed.

Parasitic in *Lyngbya aestuarii*, Dangeard (*loc. cit.*), FRANCE; *Lyngbya sp.*, Ingold (*loc. cit.*), GREAT BRITAIN.

The foregoing description is based upon Ingold's observations. He (*loc. cit.*) was certainly dealing with the same fungus as Dangeard and his observations have clarified its relationships. The one observed by Fritsch and ascribed to this species (1903) and ? *Resticularia boodlei* Fritsch, as previously suggested (Sparrow, 1943: 678), are probably mixtures involving Fungi Imperfecti.

The following two were described as species of *Resticularia*.

? Resticularia boodlei F. E. Fritsch

Ann. Bot. London, 17: 661, pl. 29, figs. 1–18. 1903

"Endophytic mycelium (diam. 5–8 μ) with occasional septa; ectophytic mycelium relatively broad (diam. 1.5–5 μ), much branched, forming numerous large thin-walled spores (diam. 12–15 μ), generally in a chain on lateral branches. Infecting hyphae abundant. Endophytic mycelium rarely branched. Zoospores not observed" (Fritsch, *loc. cit.*). In filaments of *Tolypothrix sp.*, GREAT BRITAIN.

? Resticularia oedogonii Skvortzow

Arch. Protistenk., 51: 432, fig. 14. 1924

Endobiotic thallus branched, 1–1.7 μ in diameter, several in a host cell, extramatrical thallus very delicate; resting spores from one to two in a host cell, 11.5–18.5 μ long by 7.4–11.1 μ broad, with a thick smooth colorless wall and a large oil globule nearly filling the lumen. In filaments of *Oedogonium*, MANCHURIA (northern part).

LAGENIDIUM CLOSTERII de Wildeman

Ann. Soc. Belge Micro. (Mém.), 17: 43, pl. 6, figs. 1–5. 1893

(Fig. 81 C, p. 1002)

Thallus extensive, branched, more or less isodiametric or somewhat expanded and irregular, straight or twisted, about 1.8–2.8 μ in diameter; sporangia of variable length, delimited by narrow septa, discharge tube produced as a lateral outgrowth, which forms a large spherical or subspherical structure just beneath the host wall, constricted locally when passing through the wall, more or less prolonged extramatrically, up to 20–30 μ, cylindrical; zoospores bean-shaped, laterally biflagellate, 5.6–6.3 μ long by 3.8 μ wide, formed in a vesicle at the orifice of the discharge tube, movement hopping or describing a smooth spiral path; plants dioecious, female gametangium much expanded; male gametangium cylindrical, with a prolongation which makes contact with the female gametangium; resting spore spherical, not filling the oögonium, 10–12 μ in diameter, with a thick double wall, the outer surface irregularly papillate, contents with a large globule, germination not observed.

In *Closterium rostratum* (and *C. striolatum?*), de Wildeman (*loc. cit.*), BELGIUM; parasitic in *Closterium sp.*, Cejp (1933a: 7, pl. 1, figs. 17–18, pl. 2, fig. 4), CZECHOSLOVAKIA; *Closterium sp.*, Couch (1935b: 381, figs. 35–38), *Closterium setiferum* Karling (1949a: 275), *Closterium sp.*, Sparrow and Barr (1955: 556), UNITED STATES; *Closterium sp.*, H. E. Petersen (1909: 402; 1910: 537), DENMARK.

As Couch has pointed out, before the sporangia are delimited the

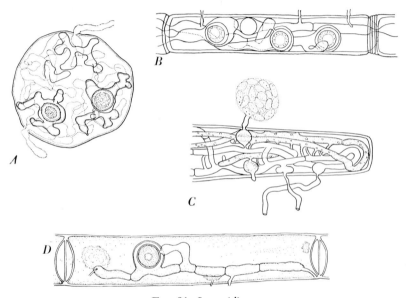

FIG. 81. *Lagenidium*

A. Lagenidium entophytum (Pringsheim) Zopf in zygospore of *Spirogyra*, zygospore cleared to show contorted thallus; extramatrical discharge tubes and two resting spores may be seen. *B. Lagenidium marchalianum* de Wildeman in *Oedogonium*, portion of filament showing sex organs, and empty cylindrical zoosporangia each with discharge tube. *C. Lagenidium closterii* de Wildeman in *Closterium*, portion of host cell showing cylindrical empty sporangia and one sporangium forming its zoospores in a vesicle at orifice of discharge tube. *D. Lagenidium rabenhorstii* Zopf in *Spirogyra*, empty sporangia and monoecious sex organs.

(*A, D*, Zopf, 1884; *B–C*, Couch, 1935b)

well-developed mycelial thallus of this species strongly resembles that of an *Aphragmium* type of *Pythium*. Whether a fertilization tube is formed, as seems probable, is not clear from de Wildeman's description.

LAGENIDIUM MARCHALIANUM de Wildeman

Ann. Soc. Belge Micro. (Mém.), 21: 10, pl. 1, figs. 1–9. 1897

(Fig. 81 B, p. 1002)

Thallus predominantly narrowly cylindrical, 2.2–9 μ in diameter, with occasional irregularly expanded parts up to 13 μ in diameter, especially near the point of infection, sparingly branched, ramifying through many cells of the host, strongly constricted and only 1 μ in diameter when passing through the cross walls, cyst and infection tube persistent; sporangia delimited by narrow cross walls, generally unaccompanied by constrictions, 30–90 μ long by 5–9 μ in diameter, each with a single lateral cylindrical discharge tube 1.5–3 μ in diameter and up to 30 μ long extending for varying distances extramatrically; zoospores few (often only four), grape-seed-like, with a shallow furrow, a vacuole, and a few refractive globules in the clear plasma, delimited within the sporangium and completing their maturation at the orifice of the discharge tube, the vesicle quickly disappearing at discharge; plants monoecious or dioecious, female gametangium monandrous, rarely parthenogenetic, intercalary, rarely terminal, formed from an expanded segment, up to 20 μ in diameter; resting spore lying loosely in the gametangium, spherical, 8–18 μ in diameter, contents with a large eccentric globule, wall smooth, thick (3 μ), germination not observed; male gametangium a somewhat expanded segment either adjacent to the female gametangium or arising as a short lateral subtending branch of the adjacent cell or as a short lateral branch of another thallus, forming a fertilization tube.

Parasitic in vegetative cells of *Oedogonium sp.*, de Wildeman (*loc. cit.*), BELGIUM; *Oedogonium sp.*, Couch (1935b: 384, figs. 39–40), Sparrow (1943: 672), UNITED STATES.

This species, like the following ones, closely resembles an *Aphragmium* type of *Pythium*, not only in its predominantly cylindrical hypha-like thallus, but in its strongly polyphagous habit and sex organs. The antheridium, however, still remains an undifferentiated segment of the thallus, and this, together with the lagenidiaceous aspect of the cytoplasm, marks the fungus as belonging to *Lagenidium*.

It appears to be a true parasite; efforts to propagate it on dead cells were unsuccessful.

Occasionally the filament of the parasite as it emerges from the cross wall is covered for a short distance with a rough layer of wall material laid down by the living host in a futile effort to stop further invasion. A similar formation has been noted by Scherffel and Couch on the infection tube of *Lagenidium oedogonii*.

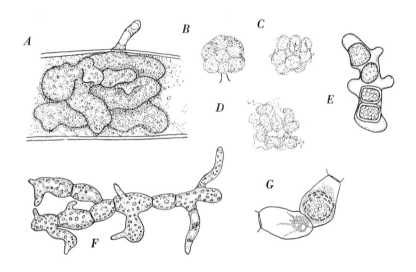

FIG. 82. *Lagenidium*

A–E. Lagenidium destruens Sparrow parasitic in *Achlya sp.: A*, mature sporangium with discharge tube penetrating wall of host hypha; *B–D*, stages in formation of zoospores at mouth of discharge tube; *E*, small thallus bearing resting spores in varying stages of maturity. *F–G. Lagenidium humanum* Karling saprophytic on human skin: *F*, thallus; *G*, sexually formed resting spore.

(*A–E*, Sparrow, 1950; *F–G*, Karling, 1947c)

LAGENIDIUM HUMANUM Karling

Mycologia, 39: 225, figs. 1–39. 1947

(Fig. 82 F–G, p. 1004)

Thallus coarse, extensive, richly branched, at maturity septate and slightly constricted at the septations, rarely one-celled, 4–20 μ in diameter; sporangia elongate (4–7 by 15–200 μ), subspherical (15–30 μ), oval (10–15 by 18–30 μ), oblong, lobate, or irregular, with a single discharge tube; zoospores reniform, 3.5–4.5 by 7.5–8 μ, biflagellate, typically formed at the orifice of the discharge tube in a vesicle, cystospores spherical, 6–7.5 μ in diameter; gametangia poorly differentiated, the receptive and contributing segments of variable size and shape, elongate (5–7 by 15–22 μ), oval (10–15 by 18–25 μ), subspherical (10–25 μ), narrow, fusiform or lobed, the contents of the male gametangium passing through a simple pore into the receptive segment; oöspore hyaline, smooth-walled, spherical (10–18 μ), oval (8–12 by 14–17 μ), or oblong, germination not observed.

Saprophytic on human skin used as bait, Karling (*loc. cit.*); Karling (1949a: 275), UNITED STATES; from soil, substrate?, Gaertner (1954b: 22), NORTHWEST AFRICA.

Although the thallus of this species is elaborately developed, the sex organs are of a primitive type and resemble those of *Myzocytium.*

Karling cultivated the species on a peptone-dextrose-yeast-extract medium on which it grew well. He concluded, therefore, that it was not strictly keratinophilic.

LAGENIDIUM GIGANTEUM Couch

Mycologia, 27: 376, figs. 1–19. 1935

"The main hyphae are segmented, being constricted or not constricted at the septum, the segments sometimes separating from each other; branched. When growing on a copepod, *Daphne*, or mosquito larva, the large segmented hyphae are within the host, but numerous delicate hyphae extend from the host for a distance of one or two millimeters to form a fringe which has much the appearance of a delicate species of *Aphanomyces*. Hyphae 6–40 μ thick, the segments 50–300 μ long. The hyphal walls contain cellulose giving a purplish reaction with chlor-iodide of zinc. The protoplasm has the pale whitish gleam as in the *Ancylistales* [Entomophthorales—Ancylistaceae]. Any segment may become a sporangium. The sporangium empties its content in an undifferentiated, naked mass (or sometimes several masses) through a tube, the dimensions of which are 6–10 × 50–300 μ. This mass becomes differentiated into a variable number of laterally biciliate zoöspores. Zoöspores 8–9 × 9–10 μ, their movement as in *Achlya* but rather sluggish. Monoplanetic. Sexual reproduction not observed.

"Weakly parasitic on mosquito larvae, copepods and *Daphne*. Also culturable as a saprophyte" (Couch, *loc. cit.*).

The species is of exceptional interest, as Couch has indicated, in the hypha-like nature of the thallus—resembling strongly in this an *Aphragmium* type of *Pythium*—and in being readily cultured an a variety of artificial media. He suggests that, from the character of the thallus development, it is intermediate between the filamentous and nonfilamentous Phycomycetes. Observations on the sexual organs, thus far not reported, will probably determine to which group it is more nearly related. A highly opganized sexual apparatus—for example, an oögonium containing periplasm and a well-defined antheridium—might indicate that the species is closer to *Pythium*, perhaps to *P. daphnidarum* (Petersen, 1909, 1910), than to *Lagenidium*.

Infection experiments on living mosquito larvae were inconclusive in demonstrating the parasitic ability of the species.

In the course of cultural studies a mycelial sector appeared which was composed of irregularly branched hyphae mostly 12 μ in diameter and which formed an open ramose rather than a compact type of growth. Further transfers indicated the stability of this mutant.

The fungus termed *Pythium dictyosporum* by Rieth (1954: 176, fig. 8) on *Oedogonium* more closely resembles a species of *Lagenidium* allied to *L. giganteum* than a *Pythium*.

LAGENIDIUM CALLINECTES Couch

J. Elisha Mitchell Sci. Soc., 58: 158, pl. 18, 19. 1942

"Mycelium developing entirely within the egg and eventually pretty well filling the egg, or body of the young crab, consisting of branched

irregular hyphae which are sparingly septate, 5.4–12.6 μ thick. Protoplasm with a pale whitish gleam and numerous oil bodies, becoming
coarsely granular just before spore formation. In the process of spore
formation and discharge the end of a thread becomes applied to the
inner egg wall and swells to form a clavate structure up to 30 μ thick.
The part in contact with the wall forms a narrow tube which grows
through the wall and immediately thickens and elongates to form a large
tube 11–29 × 25–70 μ. The tip of the tube gelatinizes and protoplasm
flows out from the mycelium to collect into a spherical or subspherical
undifferentiated mass surrounded by a thick gelatinous envelope.
Protoplasmic mass up to 100 μ thick. Spores formed as in *Pythium* from
this mass of protoplasm, and becoming very active within the gelatinous
layer before discharge. When mature breaking through the outer gelatinous membrane or vesicle and swimming sluggishly away. Vesicle
persistent. Spores pointed at the front end and rounded behind with a
diagonal groove which arises near the front end and extends backward
over the rounded end. Cilia arising from this groove and one extending
forward, the other backward while swimming. Zoospores about 9.6 ×
12.6 μ, with several oil globules one of which is distinctly larger than
the others. Encysted spores oblong or subglobose, 10 × 11.3 μ; monoplanetic. Resting bodies formed only after the crab eggs begin to disintegrate, apparently formed asexually in the threads, spherical, subspherical or oval, 18–30 μ thick, usually about 25 μ thick, wall up to 3 μ
thick, containing pale whitish protoplasm and an eccentric mass of oil
bodies; germination not observed" (Couch, *loc. cit.*).

Parasitic on eggs and newly hatched young of the blue crab *Callinectes*, UNITED STATES.

The disease caused by this unique marine species has been the subject
of a comprehensive study by Rogers-Talbert (1948). The fungus is a
peripheral parasite of the egg masses of the blue crab, and the eggs are
susceptible to infection in all stages of their development. The infected
areas are brown or gray, depending upon the age of the eggs. While the
fungus spread rapidly over the egg mass, it appeared to penetrate it
slowly, usually going no deeper than 3 mm. This peripheral infection
did not retard the development of the eggs in the interior of the sponge.
Approximately 25 per cent of the eggs of a heavily diseased mass were

infected, but only about 14 per cent of the crabs were actually so affected. Up to 80 or 90 per cent of the crabs in a sample had some degree of infection. The fungus developed abnormally in fresh pond water, whereas in salinities varying from 5 to 30 p. p. t. development proceeded rapidly, indicating a strong tolerance to changes in salt concentration. Under laboratory conditions favoring very rapid transmission of infection, the eggs of the oyster and of mud crabs were also attacked.

IMPERFECTLY KNOWN SPECIES OF LAGENIDIUM

? LAGENIDIUM ELLIPTICUM de Wildeman [1]

Ann. Soc. Belge Micro. (Mém.), 17: 8, pl. 1, figs. 1–11. 1893

Thallus consisting of a single irregularly swollen contorted lobulate tube with filamentous prolongations; zoospores not observed; resting spores ellipsoidal, 20–30 μ long by 10–14 μ wide, with a thick wall provided with irregularly placed blunt protuberances, contents refractive and granular, without a large globule.

In rhizoids of mosses, BELGIUM.

In de Wildeman's Figure 2 what appear to be two short cylindrical discharge tubes are shown. A thorough investigation of the fungi occurring in this peculiar habitat will probably result in the refinding of this well-marked species. Obviously, further data on the reproductive organs are necessary to place the fungus generically.

? LAGENIDIUM SACCULOIDES Serbinow

Défense des Plantes, 2(2): 84. 1925

"Thallus short, unicellular, sac-like with lobes or short branches, or narrowly elongate, 3.5–7.6 μ in diameter, with occasional septa. Zoospores apparently completing their development in an extramatrical vesicle; spherical, 3.5 μ, in fixed and stained preparations; position and relative lengths of flagella and presence of diplanetism unknown. Sexual reproduction isogamous; contents of two adjacent cells flowing together and forming a zygospore (?) in the space between them.

[1] Not strictly aquatic.

Zygospores hyaline, spherical, 13.3 μ, oval, elongate, 7.6 μ × 15.2 μ, with a sculptured outer and a smooth inner wall; containing a large refractive globule; germination unknown" (Karling, 1942e).

Parasitic and saprophytic in *Closterium ralfsii* var. *hybridum*, RUSSIA.

The description (Karling, 1942e: 81) is based upon preserved material. A figure in Jaczewski (1931: 67) shows the antheridial cell to be narrowly ellipsoidal and the oöspores (?) spherical or ellipsoidal, with a papillate outer wall. Until the zoospores have been studied, relationships of the species will be in doubt.

? LAGENIDIUM SYNCYTIORUM Klebahn

Jahrb. wiss. Bot., 24:265, pl. 3, figs. 22–24. 1892

Thallus a straight or irregularly curved filament 3–5 μ in diameter, becoming expanded in beadlike fashion and producing more or less irregular lateral outgrowths, which, by bending under, may form several layers and fill the host cell; sporangia numerous, of different shapes, spherical and 8–10 μ in diameter or oblong, curved or with blunt outgrowths, less often in beadlike chains, separated by narrow cross walls, discharge tube lateral, short, slightly prolonged extra-matrically; zoospores and gametangia unknown.

Parasitic in sexual filaments of *Oedogonium boscii*, GERMANY.

Known only from preserved material. Attacked *Oedogonium* cells were at first little affected by the parasite; nuclear division was not hindered. Cross walls were not, however, laid down by the alga. Up to four cells of normal size and nearly normal shape, lacking cross walls, could be found in which the fungus had been living.

De Wildeman (1895c: 218) has tentatively identified a sterile *Lagenidium* in single cells of *Oedogonium* with this species. He suggests that the still questioned species *Aphanistis pellucida* Sorokin may be referable to this fungus.

? LAGENIDIUM ZOPFII de Wildeman

Bull. Soc. Belge Micro., 16: 139. 1889–90

Thallus tubular, with irregular cylindrical or inflated branches, extending through several cells of the host; zoospores not observed;

parthenogenetic (?) female gametangia expanded; resting spore spherical, about 14 μ in diameter, with a roughened wall.

In *Oedogonium*, BELGIUM.

? LAGENIDIUM SP. Deckenbach

Flora, 92:253. 1903

(The fungus is merely mentioned by Deckenbach, no description being given.)

In *Chaetomorpha aerea*, RUSSIA (BALACLAVA, BLACK SEA).

The binomial *Lagenidium chaetomorphae* Jacz. has been given the plant by Jaczewski (1931: 67).

? LAGENIDIUM SP. Scherffel

Arch. Protistenk., 52: 23, pl. 2, fig. 86. 1925

Thallus tubular, somewhat irregular, with short lateral saccate outgrowths, infection tube persistent; sporangia several, delimited by narrow cross walls, discharge tube cylindrical, forming a thick-walled hourglass-like forcing apparatus which pushes apart the valves of the host, not extended appreciably extramatrically; zoospores not observed, possibly formed as in *Pythium*; plants dioecious (?), female gametangium irregularly expanded; resting spore spherical, not filling the gametangium; male gametangium like the sporangium, with a lateral outgrowth.

In *Pinnularia sp.*, HUNGARY.

? LAGENIDIUM SP. Ookubo

Nagaoa, 2: 125, fig. 79. 1952

On *Aegagropila sp.*, JAPAN.

"This seems near *Lagenidium rabenhorstii*, *L. marchalianum* and *L. closterii*, differing, however, in respect of host-relationship and several morphological characteristics" (Ookubo, *op. cit.*).

IMPERFECTLY KNOWN GENUS OF THE LAGENIDIALES

? LAGENIDIOPSIS DE WILDEMAN

Ann. Soc. Belge Micro. (Mém.), 20: 115. 1896

Thallus endobiotic, tubular, with occasional short branches, holocarpic, without a specialized vegetative system, forming the rudiment of a single male or female gametangium, cyst and infection tube of zoospore persistent; zoosporangia and zoospores not observed; plants dioecious (?), the female gametangium swollen locally and, after fertilization, bearing in it the thick-walled resting spore, germination not observed; male gametangium smaller than the female, broadly expanded distally where it is applied to the female gametangium, separated from the concomitant thallus by a cross wall, forming a fertilization tube.

In oögonia of Characeae.

Until the zoospores can be described, the systematic position of this genus must remain uncertain. The persistence of the cyst and infection tube does lend weight to its being correctly placed in the Lagenidiaceae. De Wildeman was not certain whether the organism is always dioecious. In some specimens the male gametangium appeared to form by septation of the thallus into two gametangia.

The genus has been merged with *Lagenidium* by Karling (1942e).

? LAGENIDIOPSIS REDUCTA de Wildeman

Ann. Soc. Belge Micro. (Mém.), 20: 115, pls. 6–7. 1896

Lagenidium reductum (de Wild.) Karling, Simple Holocarpic Biflagellate Phycomycetes, p. 80. 1942.

Characters of the genus; resting spore spherical or ellipsoidal, 13–19 μ in diameter, lying loosely in the gametangium, with a thick rough wall, contents granular, with one or several large globules, after fertilization the gametangium collapsing somewhat and soon disintegrating.

In oögonia of Characeae, SWITZERLAND.

PERONOSPORALES

THE Peronosporales comprise primarily terrestrial microscopic fungi parasitic for the most part on flowering plants. However, one family, the Pythiaceae, is transitional so far as habitat is concerned, some of the species are distinctly aquatic, others amphibious, and still others terrestrial. Probably all of its parasitic members are able to lead a saprophytic existence. Although certain monographers, notably Schroeter (1893), placed the Pythiaceae in the Saprolegniales, it unquestionably belongs in the Peronosporales (Fischer, 1892). The discussion is restricted to this family, since it contains the only aquatic species of the order.

All genera of the Pythiaceae have aquatic representatives. The species of *Pythiomorpha*, maintained separate in the first edition, are now placed under *Phytophthora*, since Buisman (1927), Drechsler (1930, 1932), and especially Blackwell, Waterhouse, and Thompson (1941) showed that Petersen (1909, 1910) based his genus upon a saprophytic species of *Phytophthora* with proliferous zoosporangia. Matthews (1931) and Middleton (1943) have brought together the material on the aquatic as well as the terrestrial species of *Pythium*; hence, the reader is referred to their monographs as well as to the older classic by Butler (1907). Here it is deemed sufficient to provide a comprehensive key to the valid aquatic and soil-inhabiting species of *Pythium*. The key given (p. 1033), however, contains more than the usual amount of data and is based on and includes descriptive matter taken from Middleton (*op. cit.*).

Species of *Pythium* live as parasites and saprophytes of algae and microscopic animals and are found on bits of debris of plant and animal origin. Although the genus has been regarded as confined to fresh-water hosts, soils, and vascular plants, one species, *P. marinum*, has been isolated on decaying marine red algae (Sparrow, 1934c), another, *P. maritimum*, obtained from living *Ceramium* (Höhnk, 1939), and an unnamed one reported as the cause of rotting of *Porphyra* (Arasaki, 1947). Doubtless, there are others that live in salt water. Höhnk (1953a) records ten species of *Pythium*, several considered new taxa, from brackish habitats. *Pythiogeton* is, morphologically speaking, closely related to *Pythium*, and occurs chiefly on submerged twigs and fruits, often in very foul water. It has been investigated physiologically by Cantino (1949b; 1951b). The species of *Phytophthora* [1] that were formerly placed in *Pythiomorpha* occupy similar substrata to those of *Pythiogeton* but usually live under cleaner conditions offering a better oxygen supply. *Zoophagus* is frequently found ramifying between filaments of algae and between plants of *Chara* or *Nitella*. Its members are of unusual interest because of their predaceous habit of capturing and parasitizing actively moving microscopic animals. Most of the Pythiaceae have been successfully cultivated on artificial media, a recent instance being that of *Zoophagus insidians* (Prowse, 1954b). The monotypic genus *Diasporangium* (Höhnk, 1936), although recovered as free-living in the soil, is evidently a facultative parasite, since it is capable of causing root rot in various phanerogams.

DEVELOPMENT AND MORPHOLOGY

THE THALLUS

The vegetative body in the Pythiaceae is a well-developed, usually much-branched, slender mycelium, which in actively growing parts is nonseptate except where reproductive organs are delimited. With age, however, occasional septations may separate empty from viable parts of the hyphae. Demonstration of a cellulose reaction in the walls of the hyphae is difficult to achieve (Butler, 1907). In aquatic forms the mycelium runs from cell to cell in the host; in terrestrial parasitic ones, such as certain species of *Phytophthora*, it is also intercellular as well, haustoria being formed which absorb materials from the host cells. Gemmae are produced in some species of *Pythium* (Butler, 1907: 20), in *Zoophagus* (Arnaudow, 1921, 1925; Karling, 1936c), and in *Phytophthora* (Ito and Nagai, 1931; Höhnk, 1936). Ward (1883), Butler (*op. cit.*) and later investigators found irregular toruloid swellings or

[1] See Blackwell (1956).

budlike processes on the mycelium of *Pythium* under certain environmental conditions. Some workers (see Drechsler, 1925) have considered these to be intimately connected with nonsexual reproduction, but this is not true in all instances (Sparrow, 1931a). Irregularities of the mycelium and twisted complexes of the hyphae are exhibited by a number of species of *Phytophthora* (Petersen, 1910; Kanouse, 1925; Ito and Nagai, *op. cit.*) and by *Zoophagus* (Prowse, 1954b).

Some aquatic species of *Pythium* parasitic on algae (Sparrow, 1931a, 1931b) bear clusters of clavate or sickle-shaped appressoria wherever the tips of the hyphae come into contact with the substratum. These become cemented to the algal wall by concave hyaline adhesion discs; from the face of each of these anchoring organs a tube develops which penetrates the algal wall (Fig. 86 K, p. 1030). Inside, a hypha of typical diameter is produced. Similar appressoria may be formed within the alga. They are also present in at least one species of *Pythiogeton* (Drechsler, 1932). Another type of specialized mycelial structure occurs in *Zoophagus* and is a lateral outgrowth adapted to capturing rotifers. In *Z. insidians* (Sommerstorff, 1911; Mirande, 1920; Arnaudow, 1921, 1925; Gicklhorn, 1922; Sparrow, 1929; Prowse, 1954b) the extensive hyphae bear numerous short upright peglike branches, the tips of which secrete a mucilaginous material (Fig. 85 A, p. 1029). The rotifer coming into contact with these tips becomes stuck and its body eventually is penetrated by a hyphal outgrowth. The trapping organs, as such, do not develop in culture but there, rather, assume the structure of lateral branches. In *Z. tentaclum* (Karling, 1936c) the lateral branch bears an even more specialized capturing device. It consists of from one to five narrow tentacles formed at the apex of the branch. No mucilaginous secretion could be demonstrated in this particular species (Fig. 85 H).

Well-defined thick-walled chlamydospores have been reported in *Pythium* (Dissmann, 1927; Matthews, 1931; Goldie-Smith, 1952).

REPRODUCTION

Nonsexual Reproduction

In the aquatic species of the Pythiaceae zoosporangia and zoospores are produced. The sporangia are of three main types: (*a*) an undifferentiated portion of the mycelium set off by cross walls and bearing an evacuation tube (Fig. 86 B, p. 1030), (*b*) a complex of irregular digitate or lobulate intercommunicating elements set off by cross walls from the rest of the hyphae and having an evacuation tube (Fig. 86 F), and (*c*) a bursiform, utriform, spherical, or somewhat ovoid terminal or intercalary structure set off by septa from the more or less differentiated hyphae, with or without a discharge tube (Fig. 87 C, E, p. 1032). Intergrades between some of these types apparently occur and make difficult identification of an organism on this basis alone. Somewhat specialized sporangiophores characterize *Phytophthora*.

In the aquatic Pythiaceae, with the exception of *Phytophthora* and *Diasporangium*, the zoospores are formed outside the sporangium, from an amorphous mass of protoplasm. In *Pythium* and in *Zoophagus* this process takes place in a delicate somewhat spherical vesicle produced at the tip of the discharge tube (Fig. 83, p. 1016). In *Pythiogeton* (Minden, 1916; Drechsler, 1932), however, the vesicle is elongate and quickly disappears, leaving the protoplasmic mass, previously concentrated in its distal part, to undergo cleavage into zoospores free in the water (Fig. 88 A–C, p. 1045). Under humid conditions and occasionally when submerged (Minden, *op. cit.*; Drechsler, *op. cit.*) the protoplasmic mass may, in *Pythiogeton*, be shot out with explosive force. Sometimes this ejaculation occurs at the beginning of the evacuation of the sporangium, at other times, after the contents have completely emerged into the vesicle.

Zoophagus and many of the aquatic species of *Pythium* exhibit an undifferentiated sporangium resembling that in certain species of *Lagenidium*. The sequence of changes as they occurred prior to and during the formation of zoospores in *P. adhaerens* (Sparrow, 1931b), parasitic on the green alga *Rhizoclonium*, is as follows: Numerous vacuoles appear in the densely granular contents of the mycelium, but after several hours decrease in size and at last disappear. In the finely granular protoplasm narrow cross walls laid down at considerable intervals along the mycelium may be observed. These blocked-off hyphal portions are the initials of the zoosporangia. The tips of certain hyphae (one for each continuous mycelial segment) now show striking modifications, which indicate that the contents will be evacuated through them. Within the apical curvature of these hyphal tips a narrow zone of hyaline very refractive material develops, which seen in optical section looks like a slender crescent (Fig. 83 A, below). This substance is apparently derived from the apical wall. At the same time, and often before the refractive dome becomes visible, there may be detected, in surface view, a vacuole immediately below the hyphal tip; this vacuole increases in size and perceptibility with the enlargement of the apical material. When viewed in optical section the glistening dome appears to have, shortly before the discharge of the contents, a double contour (Fig. 83 B–C). With the expansion of the apical refractive material protoplasmic ejection is initiated. The dilation of the refractive dome keeps pace with the effluent protoplasm, and forms around it an extremely tenuous vesicle. This structure is never exactly spherical because the somewhat flaring tip of the evacuation tube protrudes slightly into its lower portion (Fig. 83 D). The ejected protoplasm appears as a smoothly granular homogeneous mass which completely fills the vesicle. Immediately after discharge a slight surging movement of the minute particles

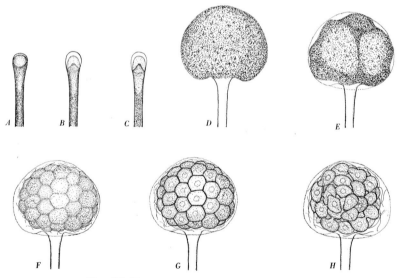

Fig. 83. Formation of zoospores in *Pythium*
(See explanation in text, p. 1015. [Sparrow, 1931b])

of the protoplasm is discernible, and after a few seconds slight contractions in certain regions lend a lumpy irregular appearance to the mass (Fig. 83 E). Faint peripheral lines of cleavage, which demarcate irregularly polygonal areas, soon become visible in the now slightly more contracted contents. About three minutes after discharge a rocking movement of the mass is noticeable. The lines of cleavage have by this time definitely delimited the spore initials (Fig. 83 F), which exhibit a slight individual movement approximately six minutes after the discharge. Short hyaline flagella may now be definitely seen around the periphery. The movement of the spore initials gradually becomes more pronounced, assuming a twisting or writhing character as the spore masses slowly become separated from one another. At about eight minutes after discharge a small vacuole becomes visible in each; the previously short hyaline flagella have increased in length by this time and appear as flexible lashes (Fig. 83 G). Three minutes later the spores have become nearly mature individuals. They still continue, however, to oscillate somewhat until they are perfectly formed (Fig. 83 H). About fourteen minutes after egress this motion is gradually superseded by a frenzied milling around of the zoospores within the confines of the vesicle. Finally the vesicle is ruptured, usually in the upper part, by one or more zoospores, and the mature swarmers escape. The vesicle is ultimately dissolved into the surrounding medium.

In the lobulate and sphaerosporangial species of *Pythium* the sequence of zoospore formation in the vesicle is essentially like that just described.

The zoospores of *Phytophthora* are delimited within the sporangium and upon emergence may or may not be surrounded by a quickly evanescent vesicle. In *Phytophthora*, as in *Pythiogeton* and certain of the sphaerosporangial species of *Pythium*, formation of new sporangia occurs by internal proliferation (Figs. 87 A, p. 1032; 89 A, F, p. 1055; 90 B, D, G, p. 1059).

The zoospore of all members of the Pythiaceae is of the laterally biflagellate secondary type. It is usually capable of repeated emergence (Fig. 86 D, p. 1030). The flagellar structure is like that of the "secondary" zoospore of *Saprolegnia* (p. 10).

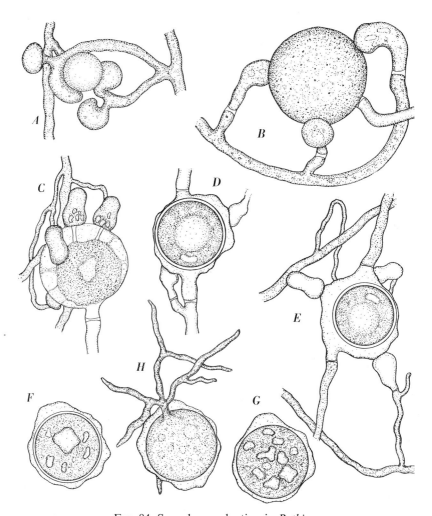

FIG. 84. Sexual reproduction in *Pythium*

A–B. Two stages in development of oögonia and antheridia of *Pythium adhaerens* Sparrow: *A,* antheridial rudiments encircling central oögonial rudiment; *B,* antheridia delimited from their hyphae by cross walls. *C–H.* Sex organs of *Pythium angustatum* Sparrow and germination of oöspore: *C,* terminal oögonium to which is attached a cluster of diclinous antheridia with their fertilization tubes piercing the contracted oöplasm; *D,* mature oöspore with one monoclinous (lower) and one diclinous antheridium persistent on

Sexual Reproduction

Sexual reproduction in the Pythiaceae is oögamous, typically with only a single egg formed in each oögonium. The oögonia and antheridia may be developed on the same hypha, the antheridium originating from the oögonial stalk (monoclinous) (Figs. 86 A, H, p. 1030; 87 B, p. 1032) or on different hyphae and the antheridium not arising from the oögonial stalk (Fig. 86 J) (diclinous).[1] If the relationship of the two is such that the antheridium is surmounted by the oögonium or is formed either within the stalk or at its apex (Fig. 87 D, p. 1032) it is called "hypogyny." If, as in certain species of *Phytophthora*, the antheridium encircles the oögonial stalk, as a consequence of the growth of the oögonial rudiment through that of the antheridium (Fig. 90 I, p. 1059), this peculiar situation is known as "amphigyny." For the most part, however, members of the family have the antheridium applied in lateral association with the oögonium, either near to or distant from the stalk (Fig. 86 A). This last condition is termed "paragyny." The characters of the antheridium (the number, shape, size, place of origin, and so forth) are usually of high taxonomic value in determination of species. Dioecism ("heterothallism") is rare, if not absent, in most genera. According to Arnaudow (1925), it occurs in *Zoophagus insidians*.

The development and structure of the sex organs are best known in *Pythium*. In the aquatic *P. adhaerens* and *P. angustatum*, for example (Sparrow, 1931b), the oögonia originate as terminal or intercalary swellings of the hyphae, which gradually increase in size until they are, when finally mature, spherical bodies cut off by cross walls from the adjacent hyphae. The antheridia in these two species are usually diclinous in origin, occasionally monoclinous, and arise as short lateral expanded hyphal branches, which clasp the oögonium early in its formation. From two to five antheridia are generally in contact with an oögonium, the

---

oögonium; *E*, oöspore to whose oögonium three diclinous antheridia are attached; *F*, oöspore starting to germinate; large globule is broken up and wall is beginning to be resorbed; *G*, oöspore with wall nearly completely resorbed; *H*, branched hyphal system produced by germinating oöspore. (Sparrow, 1931b)

[1] Following usage by Middleton (1943).

single hypha from which they usually arise often surrounding the female gametangium in *P. adhaerens* (Fig. 84 A, p. 1018). When fully mature each antheridium is delimited from the hypha by a cross wall, formed generally at about 15 μ from its tip, which is in contact with the oögonial wall (Fig. 84 B). Fertilization is accomplished in from three to five hours by the gradual transference of all, or nearly all, of the antheridial contents to the oögonium through a cylindrical refractive tube, about 2 μ in diameter, which penetrates the wall of the oögonium and extends an unknown distance into the oöplasm (Fig. 84 C).

Coincidently with the formation of the fertilization tube, the contents of the oögonium become more condensed and contract away from the wall (Fig. 84 C). The oöplasm, connected by hyaline strands of protoplasm to the oögonial wall, generally lies in an eccentric position, in close contact with the part of the wall penetrated by the fertilization tube. During fertilization the contents, instead of having a smooth densely granular consistency, become darker and extremely irregular in contour. As the discharge of antheridial material progresses, the oöplasm continues to contract and the fine droplets of oil which are distributed throughout it combine to form large, irregularly shaped, highly refractive bodies, which finally compose nearly the whole mass.

After fertilization, the contour of the oöspore becomes more even, the refractive bodies rapidly decrease in size, and the protoplasm assumes a coarsely granular aspect. No periplasm could be observed in living material. [1] There is now formed around the oöplasm a thin pellicle which gradually thickens. Finally, during the formation of the wall, the oil droplets dispersed throughout the somewhat mottled oögonial protoplasm fuse into a large centrally disposed refractive globule, whose diameter is usually about one third that of the oöspore (Fig. 84 D–E, p. 1018). Between the inner face of the wall and the oil globule a lenticular structure, probably a nucleus, appears. The mature oöspore in this species lies loosely within the oögonial wall (Fig. 86 I, p. 1030); that is, it is "aplerotic" (in the sense of Middleton, 1943) in contrast to "plerotic" or completely filling the oögonium (Fig. 86 J).

---

[1] According to Patterson (1927), periplasm in *Pythium torulosum* was difficult to demonstrate even by cytological methods. On the other hand, it was relatively conspicuous in living material of *P. dictyosporum* (Sparrow, 1931a).

After a rest period the oöspore germinates. [1] In the course of this process, in *Pythium angustatum* for example, the large oil globule disassociates into a number of refractive parts (Fig. 84 F, p. 1018) that become regularly dispersed throughout the now evenly and finely granular protoplasm. Coincidently with these changes, the oöspore wall steadily decreases in thickness, apparently being absorbed by the protoplasm (Fig. 84 G). The germ hypha, now somewhat constricted as it pierces the spore wall, elongates, branches, and establishes the new mycelium (Fig. 84 H). In water, certain of its branches may be converted into sporangia. Only vegetative development takes place in nutrient solutions.

In *Pythiogeton* sex organs are presumably formed, but absolute proof is as yet lacking. This uncertainty appears largely due to failure of sex organs to develop in pure culture and to the inability of the observer to trace assuredly in gross culture the connection between the sexual and the nonsexual phases. Minden (1916) found two somewhat similar types of sex organs in his material, one of which he associated with *P. utriforme* (Fig. 88 H, p. 1045) and the other with *P. transversum* (Fig. 88 D). The one he assigned to the former species had been previously observed by Thaxter (1895b) growing with *Gonapodya*, which frequently occurs in the same habitat as *Pythiogeton*. It has since been recorded by other investigators, for example, Lund (1934), and Sparrow (1936a). By the two workers mentioned, it was seen, as in Minden's cultures, in conjunction with sporangia of *P. utriforme*. The type which Minden associated with *P. transversum*, has evidently not been reported since his time. The two types of sex organs Minden allied with the sporangial stages of *P. utriforme* and *P. transversum* are here recognized as valid until evidence to the contrary is forthcoming.

According to Minden (1916), in *Pythiogeton utriforme* the rudiments of the antheridia and the oögonia arise as two small vesicles of about equal size, in contact with one another and, at least in some plants, on the same hypha. One of these swellings, the antheridium, which frequently is subterminal on its supporting hypha, fails to grow larger, whereas the other, the oögonial rudiment, expands and becomes packed with spherical or angular refractive structures. During development of the

[1] See Drechsler's (1955) account of this process in *P. butleri*.

oögonium the supporting hypha is drained of its contents. The mature antheridium is hemispherical, with its broad face in contact with the oögonial wall. It forms a blunt fertilization tube which pierces the oögonium and which probably conveys into it the antheridial contents. Minden evidently did not observe the actual process of fertilization. No periplasmic material is discernible, and no contraction of the oögonial contents occurs. After fertilization the droplets in the oögonium gradually disappear, and coincidently a bright refractive "halo" becomes visible on the periphery of the contents. This marks initiation of the oöspore wall. The hyaline material continues to replace the granular contents until finally at maturity only a small spherical central part composed of cytoplasm remains. The mature oöspore consists, then, of a small sphere of living contents, within which a conspicuous reserve globule may frequently be observed, and an extremely thick hyaline, shining, concentrically layered wall, the outer surface of which is in close contact, if not actually fused, with the wall of the oögonium (Fig. 88 H, p. 1045). The mature oöspores are usually formed within or near the surface of the substratum and it is this fact together with the fragility of the slender mycelium on which they are borne which makes it difficult in gross culture to connect them with absolute certainty to the extramatrical mycelium bearing the zoosporangia.

The sex organs associated by Minden (1916) with *Pythiogeton transversum* (Fig. 88 D) were similar in their general configuration to those of *P. utriforme*, but differed in certain respects. The first divergence is in the helical involvement of the supporting hyphae of the sex organs. Whereas there can be seen in Minden's Plate 6, Figure 62, of *P. utriforme* a slight tendency for the oögonial stalk to twist around that of the antheridium, his description and figures of the sex organs of *P. transversum* indicate that the oögonial hypha may make as many as four or five turns around the supporting element of the male organ. Occasionally the reserve situation was found. A second, even more striking, difference concerns the external configuration of the mature oögonia of the two species. This is spherical in *P. utriforme* but in *P. transversum* it is distinctly polygonal, and the spherical oöspore with its strikingly thickened wall lies free within the oögonium.

Stages in the germination of the oöspore of *Pythiogeton utriforme* have been observed (Sparrow, 1936a). In his material the first indication of germination was a slight increase in the amount of the protoplasmic contents and the appearance of faint shadowy areas of indefinite shape in the thick hyaline wall. After twelve hours the large reserve globule in the contents disappeared, the central granular cytoplasm increased in size, and around the periphery of this cytoplasm a large number of short spinelike protuberances appeared Fig. 88 J–L, p. 1045). During the succeeding twenty-four hours the contents continued to expand, at the expense of the refractive wall, and at the same time it became densely granular. The "spines" increased in breadth, until their tips touched the inner wall of the oögonium. In another twenty-four hours the contents almost reached the oögonial wall and the spines again became only short peripheral attenuations. Subsequently, these completely disappeared and the contents occupied the whole oögonium (Fig. 88 M). A discharge tube was then produced, through which, presumably, the contents were ejected (Fig. 88 N). Although the true nature of these curious spines was not determined, it is possible that they simply outline vacuoles. A similar process of germination has been described by Blackwell (1943a) in *Phytophthora cactorum*. There, she interpreted the spines as fine radiating passages in the endospore wall. If this view is correct, it would suggest that the reserves of cellulose, protein, and so forth, are being digested at different rates.

The sex organs and oöspores in *Phytophthora* are so like those in *Pythium* that discussion of them is unnecessary. The production of amphigynous antheridia in *Phytophthora*, however, is unique (see Fig. 90 I), whereas the peculiar method of germination of the oöspore in some species of that genus is a feature shared with *Pythiogeton* (p. 1042). In *Phytophthora fischeriana*, Höhnk (1936) says the oöspore is apogamously developed.

SYSTEMATIC ACCOUNT

PERONOSPORALES

THE aquatic members of the Peronosporales are all species of the Pythiaceae. Their characters are those of that family as given below.

PYTHIACEAE

Microscopic aquatic, amphibious, or terrestrial saprophytic or parasitic fungi; thallus a richly branched hyphal complex, cross walls in vigorously growing parts normally formed only to delimit reproductive organs; thick-walled chlamydospores and gemmae sometimes formed; zoosporangia either undifferentiated portions of the mycelium, or an irregularly expanded complex of lobulate elements and an evacuation tube, or an ovoid, spherical, or bursiform structure with or without a more or less prolonged evacuation tube, formed singly, or in catenulate series, or in whorls, sometimes internally proliferous; zoospores of the reniform laterally biflagellate type, either formed outside the sporangium in a vesicle, or free in the water, or within the sporangium, capable of repeated emergence; oögonia terminal or intercalary, spherical or cylindrical, smooth or spiny-walled, usually containing a single egg which is often differentiated into oöplasm and periplasm; antheridia terminal or intercalary, rarely lacking, monoclinous or diclinous, paragynous, hypogynous or amphigynous, each forming a well-defined fertilization tube; oöspore lying loosely in the oögonium or completely filling it, smooth or rough-walled, upon germination producing a germ tube or zoosporangium.

Parasitic in algae, flowering plants, and microscopic animals; saprophytic on both plant and animal substrata, in water and soil.

KEY TO THE AQUATIC GENERA OF THE PYTHIACEAE

Zoosporangium an undifferentiated portion of the mycelium
    Hyphae bearing short lateral branches adapted to the capturing of
        rotifers .... ZOOPHAGUS, p. 1025
    Hyphae not bearing such branches .... PYTHIUM [1], p. 1031
Zoosporangium differentiated from the mycelium, consisting either
    of a complex of lobulate elements and an evacuation tube or of a

---

[1] Full descriptions and figures of species of *Pythium* may be found in the monographs by Middleton (1943) and Matthews (1931). A comprehensive key (based on Middleton) to the species occurring in soil and water is furnished (p. 1033). Only the ones restricted to higher plants are omitted. Even though the latter doubtless exist in soil, they have not as yet been proven to be "free-living."

somewhat bursiform, spherical, or ovoid enlargement with or without an evacuation tube

Zoospores formed within a vesicle produced at the tip of an evacuation tube; antheridia never amphigynous; oöspores with a moderately thick wall .... PYTHIUM [1], p. 1031

Zoospores either extruded as an undifferentiated mass in an elongate quickly evanescent vesicle or differentiated within the sporangium; antheridia amphigynous in *Phytophthora*; oöspore wall very thick or not unusually so

Zoospores extruded as an undifferentiated mass in an extremely long quickly evanescent vesicle; oöspore wall extremely thick .... PYTHIOGETON, p. 1042

Zoospores differentiated within the sporangium, usually emerging without vesicle formation as separate motile swarmers; oöspore wall not unusually thick

Zoosporangia borne in whorls, their long axes transverse to the short supporting hypha .... DIASPORANGIUM, p. 1050

Zoosporangia not in whorls, their long axes parallel with that of the somewhat specialized sporangiophore of variable length
PHYTOPHTHORA [2], p. 1051

ZOOPHAGUS SOMMERSTORFF

Österr. botan. Zeitschr., 61: 372. 1911

(Fig. 85, p. 1029)

Mycelium delicate, extensive, the main hyphae sparingly branched, bearing numerous short peglike lateral branches modified for the capturing of moving rotifers, septate or nonseptate gemmae sometimes formed; zoosporangium consisting of an undifferentiated portion of the mycelium; zoospores produced at the tip of the discharge tube in a vesicle or, occasionally, with vesicle lacking, laterally biflagellate, capable of repeated emergence; plants dioecious, antheridium clavate, single, oögonium bearing a single egg.

Parasitic on rotifers.

Zoosporangia and sex organs have been recorded thus far only in *Zoophagus insidians*. Sommerstorff (*loc. cit.*) states with respect to nonsexual reproduction that in one instance he found, near the open end of

---

[1] See note 1 page 1024.
[2] See Waterhouse (1956).

a hyphal branch protruding from a rotifer, rounded cysts and a group of about eight bodies of amoeboid shape which were simultaneously twisting and oscillating. The moving bodies soon came to rest and encysted. When next observed they had apparently emerged from their cysts, each through a short germ tube. Arnaudow (1921) describes the zoosporangium as similar to the completely filamentous type found in certain species of *Pythium* and asserts that the zoospores are formed as in that genus. His observations on this process have been confirmed by Prowse (1954b). Middleton (1952) states that a discrete vesicle is sometimes not present. Zoospore formation was not seen by Karling (1936c) in *Z .tentaclum* (see the discussion under *Z. insidians*). Sexual organs have been described, but apparently only by Arnaudow (1925).

Valkanov (1932) considered that the carnivorous aquatic fungi *Synchaetophagus* (Apstein, 1910), *Hydatinophagus*, and *Sommerstorffia* (Arnaudow, 1923a, 1923b) were closely related to *Zoophagus* and that all four should be placed in a special group of the Saprolegniaceae. The reasons he gave were not convincing. From the morphological evidence now at hand, it seems much more likely that this curious carnivorous habit has been separately evolved by members of several distinct groups of aquatic Phycomycetes.

KEY TO THE SPECIES OF ZOOPHAGUS

Capturing organ consisting of an unbranched peglike lateral branch
Z. insidians, p. 1026
Capturing organ consisting of a short lateral branch, from which arise
apically from one to five long slender tentacles ... *Z. tentaclum*, p. 1029

ZOOPHAGUS INSIDIANS Sommerstorff

Österr. botan. Zeitschr., 61: 372, pls. 5–6. 1911

(Fig. 85 A–G, p. 1029)

Mycelium slender, the main hyphae 6–7 μ in diameter, sparingly branched, frequently ramifying between and upon algae, forming numerous lateral unbranched spinelike or peglike apically refractive capturing organs, about 20 μ long by 3 μ in diameter, which arise at right angles from the main hyphae, with which they are continuous, fusiform nonseptate or septate gemmae, 80–100 μ by 8–10 μ, sometimes formed; zoosporangium consisting of an undifferentiated portion of the mycelium and an evacuation tube, 2–3 μ wide, through which the amorphous contents are discharged into a vesicle, within which three to fifteen biflagellate zoospores, 5 by 3 μ, mature; oögonium spherical, terminal on a lateral branch, brownish at maturity; antheridium single, terminal, clavate, diclinous; oöspore single.

A predaceous parasite of fresh-water rotifers. Sommerstorff (*loc. cit.*), Gicklhorn (1922), Austria; Gicklhorn (*op. cit.*), Yugoslavia; Mirande (1920: figs. 1–2), France; Arnaudow (1921: figs. 1–8; 1925: figs. 1–5; 1936), Valkanov (1931b; 1931c; 1932: fig. 10), Bulgaria; Sparrow (1929; 1932b: pl. 8, fig. h; 1933c), Karling (1936c), *Rattulus sp.*, Sparrow (1952d: 771), United States; Barnes and Melville (1932: 94), Sparrow (1936a: 465), *Distyla sp.*, *Monostyla sp.*, *Diplois sp.*, *Diplaxis sp.*, Prowse (1954b: 137, figs. 3–5), Great Britain.

The description of *Zoophagus insidians* above is drawn mainly from Sommerstorff (*loc. cit.*) and Arnaudow (1921, 1925). A comparison of the accounts of zoospore formation in this species as given by Arnaudow (1921) and Gicklhorn (1922) makes it quite evident that two different fungi were involved, one (Arnaudow's) with a filamentous sporangium and the other (Gicklhorn's) with a globular or saccate sporangium. Both produced biflagellate zoospores, it is true, but in Gicklhorn's material the zoospores appeared to be formed in the sporangium before discharge, whereas they were matured outside the sporangium in Arnaudow's fungus. A study of the second account by Arnaudow (1925) of *Z. insidians*, derived from material collected in Germany rather than Bulgaria, and the description of *Z. tentaclum* by Karling (1936c) reveals a striking similarity between their two fungi with respect to the method of formation and the shape of the conidia or "gemmae." Furthermore, Karling states that he was unable to obtain zoospore formation, and Arnaudow reports finding it in only one instance in the German material. From these considerations the interesting possibility arises that Karling and Arnaudow (German material) may have been dealing with conidial Phycomycetes.[1] Gicklhorn's fungus is most certainly distinct from Arnaudow's Bulgarian material. Then, too, Gicklhorn's Plate 2, Figure F, presents structures which he regarded as "conidia," but which most certainly are encysted zoospores, clumped, as in *Sommerstorffia* and *Aphanomyces*, at the tip of a discharge tube projecting from the carapace of the rotifer. It is possible, therefore, that there exist several distinct fungi, alike in their vegetative stage and capturing organs, but differing in their nonsexual reproductive structures. Which character was typical of Sommerstorff's *Z. insidians* cannot now be determined with certainty, although from his few remarks concerning this phase of his fungus it is probable that zoospores were formed as they are in *Pythium.*

Interesting biological observations have been made on *Zoophagus insidians* by Prowse (1954b). He succeeded in growing his material on oatmeal agar, upon the surface of which was an abundance of water of condensation, and discovered that under these circumstances only certain species of rotifers were captured. The fast-moving types escaped, whereas the slow, browsing loricate types, such as *Distyla, Monostyla,* and the like, were held and consumed. Soft-bodied ones like *Rotifer,* however, may crawl over the trapping organs without being snared by the device.

Although zoosporangia were rare in Prowse's field material they were abundant in his water cultures. In the latter the evacuation tubes reached a length of 100 μ and from twenty to fifty zoospores, 10 by 5 μ (that is, significantly larger than those of the wild specimens), were produced. In the cultivated plants the capturing organs were lacking. When living rotifers were introduced into the cultures, some of them were parasitized. Since ingested zoospores, which are capable of infecting the animal, were the only means of parasitism, the extent of predation by the fungus was greatly reduced. All efforts to induce the cultured material to revert to the field form with the peglike capturing organs failed. Further isolations, and studies of a like nature of *Zoophagus* are desirable.

---

[1] The presence of gemmae in Arnaudow's Bulgarian material, in which zoospores were also found, would seem, however, to argue against this.

ZOOPHAGUS TENTACLUM Karling

Mycologia, 28: 308, figs. 1–5. 1936

(Fig. 85 H, p. 1029)

"Mycelium filamentous, greatly extended, 3–6 μ in diameter, hyaline, branched and continuous; possessing numerous relatively short specialized lateral branches, 15–35 μ in length and 3–5 μ in diameter, which

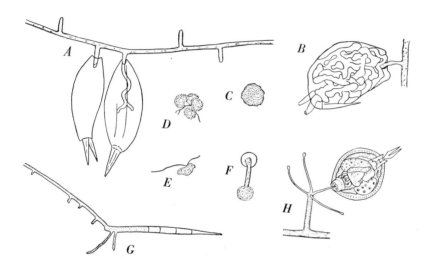

FIG. 85. *Zoophagus*

A–G. Zoophagus insidians Sommerstorff, capturer of rotifers: *A*, portion of mycelium with short peglike lateral branches modified for capture of rotifers; two captured animals are shown in outline form; *B*, dead rotifer within which is a complex of hyphae which have become transformed into zoosporangia and have discharged their zoospores; *C*, discharged mass of protoplasm about to undergo cleavage into zoospores; *D*, zoospores undergoing cleavage; *E*, single zoospore; *F*, encysted zoospore undergoing repeated emergence; *G*, germinating septate gemma from which new mycelia are forming. *H. Zoophagus tentaclum* Karling, lateral branch with three capturing tentacles, to one of which a rotifer is attached.

(*A*, Sparrow, 1932b; *B–F*, Arnaudow, 1921; *G*, after Arnaudow, 1925; *H*, Karling, 1936c)

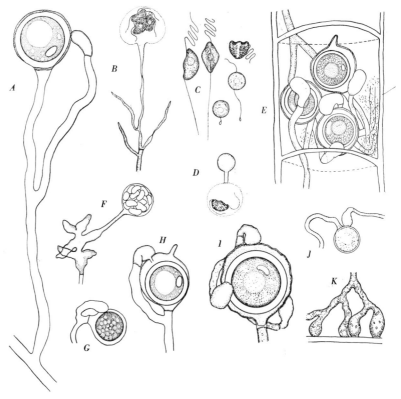

FIG. 86. *Pythium*

A. Pythium monospermum Prings., sexual apparatus showing monoclinous antheridium and plerotic inspissate walled oöspore. *B. Pythium angustatum* Sparrow, showing zoospore formation in an entirely filamentous sporangial type. *C.* Motile and encysting zoospores of *Pythium adhaerens* Sparrow. *D.* Cyst of zoospore of *Pythium adhaerens* undergoing repeated emergence, a smaller zoospore nearly mature within a vesicle. *E. Pythium gracile* Schenk, sex organs in algal cell, showing aplerotic, inspissate walled oöspores. *F.* Lobulate type of sporangium of *Pythium aphanidermatum* (Edson) Fitz., forming zoospores in a vesicle at orifice of slender discharge tube. *G.* Sexual apparatus of *Pythium tenue*, showing monoclinous antheridium alleged to lack a cross wall, and immature oöspore. *H. Pythium dissotocum* Drechsler, sexual apparatus showing monoclinous, crooknecked, inflated antheridium making broad contact with oögonium. *I. Pythium adhaerens* Sparrow, showing polyandrous condition, with aplerotic inspissate oöspore. *J.* Sexual structures bear one to five tenuous, predacious tentacles at the apex. Cytoplasm in the tips of the short lateral hyphae highly refractive; tentacles, 10–17 μ in length and 1.5 to 2 μ in diameter, and terminated by a small knob. Conidia or gemmae produced at the end of the long hyphae in acropetal succession, 40–80 μ in length and 3–6.5 μ in diameter. Growing loosely epiphytic in *Nitella flexilis*; predacious and parasitic on species of *Monostyla, Diostyla*, etc." (Karling, *loc. cit.*).

UNITED STATES.

Prowse (1954b) concurs with the view that since no zoospores were observed, the organism might in fact be a conidial Phycomycete. This is contrary to Middleton's (1952) opinion.

No sexual organs have been found.

PYTHIUM PRINGSHEIM [1]

Jahrb. wiss. Bot., 1: 304. 1858

(Figs. 83, p. 1016; 84, p. 1018; 86, p. 1030; 87, p. 1032)

Mycelium well developed, consisting of much-branched hyphae, occasionally bearing appressoria, sometimes forming tangled complexes, irregular toruloid elements, and chlamydospores; zoosporangium either entirely filamentous and undifferentiated from the vegetative hyphae, simple or branched, acrogenous or intercalary, or consisting of a series of basal complex lobulations and a filamentous discharge tube, or a well-defined sphaeroidal structure sharply distinct from its supporting hypha and acrogenous, intercalary or laterally sessile, with an emission tube of variable length, sometimes internally proliferous; zoospores somewhat reniform, each containing a single vacuole and with two oppositely directed flagella of approximately equal length emerging from a shallow longitudinal groove, expelled from the sporangium as an

---

of *Pythium marinum* Sparrow, showing plerotic oöspore with thin wall and single diclinous antheridium with abruptly tapering apex. *K.* Cluster of appressoria of *Pythium adhaerens* attached to an algal wall.

(*A, F, H*, Middleton, 1943; *B–D, I, K*, Sparrow, 1931b; *E, G*, Matthews, 1931; *J*, Sparrow, 1934c)

[1] See *Phytophthora*, note (p. 1051).

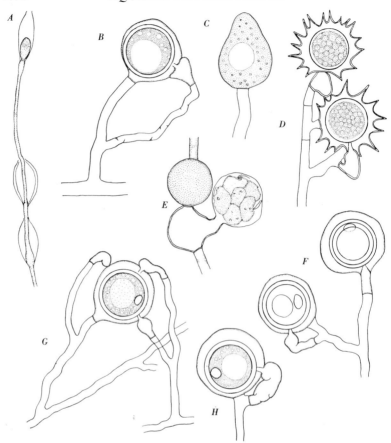

Fɪɢ. 87. *Pythium*

A. Pythium undulatum Petersen; internally proliferous sporangia. *B–C.
Pythium vexans* de Bary: *B*, sexual apparatus, showing aplerotic oöspore and
monoclinous bell-shaped antheridium broadly applied to oögonium; *C*,
sporangium. *D–E. Pythium echinulatum* Matthews: *D*, spiny oögonia with
stalked and sessile (hypogynous) antheridia; *E*, intercalary sporangium forming zoospores in vesicle. *F. Pythium pulchrum* Minden, sexual stage; left
one with monoclinous and right one with hypogynous antheridium. *G. Pythium de baryanum*, sexual stage, showing a monoclinous arched antheridial
stalk and a branched diclinous one bearing two antheridia. *H. Pythium
ultimum* Trow, sexual apparatus, showing single antheridium, which in this
species is typically monoclinous and arises immediately below oögonium.

(*A*, Goldie-Smith, 1952, from photomicrograph; *B, C, F–H*, Middleton,
1943; *D, E*, Matthews, 1931).

undifferentiated mass into a delicate vesicle produced by the tip of the discharge tube where cleavage and maturation takes place, capable of repeated emergence before finally encysting and germinating; plants probably always monoecious; oögonia terminal or intercalary, spherical or subspherical when terminal, ellipsoidal to limoniform when intercalary, smooth-walled, or variously echinulated, for the most part forming a single egg with or without conspicuous periplasm; antheridia none or one to several, hypogynous, monoclinous or diclinous, allantoid, clavate, globose, suborbicular or trumpet-shaped, terminal or intercalary, borne on a short or long stalk, or sessile, usually one to four (may be lacking or if present up to twenty-five) to an oögonium, forming a distinct fertilization tube; oöspores usually borne singly within the oögonium, plerotic or aplerotic, wall smooth or reticulate, thin or inspissate, the granular protoplasm usually bearing a conspicuous reserve globule and a lateral refringent body, upon germination forming one or several germ tubes, or zoospores.

Saprophytic and parasitic on plant and animal material in water and soil.

KEY TO THE SPECIES OF PYTHIUM [1]

Sporangium filamentous
    Sporangium undifferentiated from the vegetative hyphae; without inflations
      Sex organs formed
        Wall of oögonium smooth
          Antheridium delimited by a septum
            Oöspore wall smooth
              Oöspore plerotic (i. e., filling the oögonium)
                Antheridium monoclinous and diclinous; one or two to an oögonium, slightly inflated, clavate, and crooknecked; hyphae with lateral swollen outgrowths; in normal soil (Fig. 86 A)

                            P. monospermum Pringsheim, [2] p. 23 m
              Antheridium either monoclinous or diclinous, one to an oögonium; in marine algae

---

[1] See also the new species *Pythium thalassium* Atkins (1955), parasitic and saprophytic in eggs of the pea crab (*Pinnotheres pisum*).

[2] Page numbers followed by "m" are those of Middleton's (1943) monograph. Note further that these species are not entered in the "List of Substrata" (p. 1073).

Antheridium diclinous, clavate with tapering apex;
zoospores 7.5 by 4 μ; oöspore 13–20 by 15–21 μ
(Fig. 86 J) .... *P. marinum* Sparrow, p. 26m
Antheridium monoclinous, beaked; zoospores 6–9 μ
long; oöspore 16–24 μ in diameter
P. maritimum Höhnk [1]
Oöspore aplerotic (i. e., not filling oögonium)
Oöspore wall noticeably thickened (inspissate)
Antheridium diclinous, never monoclinous
Antheridial cells one or rarely two to an oögonium, each borne on a separate antheridial
branch, inflated-clavate, not greatly curved,
applied narrowly to oögonium; zoospores
6–8 μ by 3–4 μ; oögonia 14–27 μ (mostly 15–
24.2 μ) in diameter; oöspore 11–21.5 μ (mostly 12–21 μ); in fresh-water green algae (Fig.
86 E) .... *P. gracile* Schenk, p. 31m
Antheridial cells one to four to an oögonium,
arising as lateral prolongations of a single
antheridial branch, crooknecked, clavate;
hyphae forming numerous appressoria; zoospores 10 by 5.4–9 μ; oögonia 10–25.2 μ (av.
17.5 μ) in diameter; oöspore 7.2–21.6 μ (av.
14.4 μ), wall 2–2.5 μ thick; in fresh-water
green algae (Fig. 84 A–B; Fig. 86 C, I, K)
P. adhaerens Sparrow, p. 34m
Antheridium usually monoclinous, occasionally diclinous, one to five, arising separately, often sessile when monoclinous, when diclinous usually
arising near the oögonium, arching, antheridial
cell crooknecked, inflated, breviform, 6–16 by
5–8 μ, the apex making broad contact with the
oögonium; oögonium usually terminal, occasionally intercalary, spherical or subspherical,
occasionally with a single papilla, the delimiting
cross wall sometimes inserted beyond the
oögonial contour, 12–33 μ (av. 20.7 μ) in
diameter; oöspore with moderately thickened
wall (.8–1.4 μ), nearly filling oögonium, 11–27 μ
(av. 17.6 μ) in diameter; sporangia sometimes
including slightly swollen elements; zoospores

[1] *Kieler Meeresforsch.*, III (2): 347, fig. 4. 1939.

13 by 8 μ when motile, 8–9 μ in diameter when encysted; in water (Fig. 86 H)

P. dissotocum Drechsler [1], p. 28m

Oöspore wall not appreciably thickened
Antheridium monoclinous or diclinous, one to five
to an oögonium, terminal on lateral distorted
branches, the blunt apex making broad contact
with oögonium; zoospores 8.5 by 5 μ; oögonia
12.6–27.0 μ (av. 19.8 μ) in diameter; oöspore
10.8–25.2 (av. 18 μ) in diameter, wall 1–1.8 μ
thick; in fresh-water green algae (Figs. 84 C–H;
86 B) .... *P. angustatum* Sparrow, p. 35m

Antheridium diclinous, never monoclinous, single;
zoospores 8.4 by 4.8 μ; oögonia 11–20 μ in
diameter; oöspore 9–17 μ in diameter, wall 0.6–
0.8 μ in thickness; in fresh-water green algae

P. apleroticum Tokunaga, p. 36m

Oöspore wall reticulate, sheathed with a gelatinous material, golden; antheridium monoclinous and diclinous,
one to two to an oögonium, clavate, crooknecked,
making narrow contact with oögonium; parasitic in
fresh-water green algae *P. dictyosporum* Raciborski, p. 36m

Antheridium not delimited by a septum, one to two to an
oögonium, mostly monoclinous, clavate, slightly swollen,
terminal; oögonium 7.2–15.6 μ (mean 10.3 μ) diameter;
oöspore thin-walled, aplerotic, 6–12 μ in diameter; parasitic in fresh-water green algae (Fig. 86 G)

P. tenue Gobi, p. 38m

Wall of oögonium papillate, oögonia often catenulate, one to
five, 16.8–26.4 μ in diameter, thin-walled, smooth or with
one to two papillae; oöspore plerotic except for oögonial
neck and papillae, single, occasionally two, moderately thin-
walled; antheridia lacking; zoospores 12 by 7.2 μ; in soil

P. papillatum Matthews, p. 39m

Sex organs lacking; mycelium of irregular width, forming numerous spherical or elliptical swellings 9–27 μ in diameter, delimited by remote septa from the hyphae; zoospores 8–10 μ in
diameter when encysted; on fresh-water green algae

P. afertile Kanouse and Humphrey, p. 39m

Sporangium somewhat differentiated from the vegetative hyphae,
usually consisting of a more or less complex series of lobulate
elements and a discharge tube

[1] Includes *P. perigynosum* Sparrow (1936a).

Wall of oögonium smooth
  Oöspore plerotic
    Catenulate spherical asexual reproductive bodies present,
        terminal or intercalary, single, or three to eight in series,
        10–20 μ (av. 15 μ) in diameter, producing one to three
        germ tubes; sporangium with irregularly swollen budlike
        outgrowths in simple or complex aggregations; zoo-
        spores 8–11 by 6 μ; oögonium smooth-walled, 18–38 μ in
        diameter, terminal or intercalary; antheridia monocli-
        nous or diclinous, one to twelve (usually five to six) to an
        oögonium, clavate, crooknecked, making narrow apical
        contact with oögonium; oöspore with a smooth, thick
        wall, 16–32 μ in diameter .. *P. catenulatum* Matthews, p. 40m
  Catenulate bodies absent
    Antheridia monoclinous, usually one, arising mostly from
        the oögonial stalk, borne on a short, rarely branched
        stalk, antheridial cell allantoid-clavate, the apex con-
        tacting the oögonial wall; oögonia 12–19 μ (mostly 17–
        18 μ) in diameter; oöspore with a moderately thin
        wall; sporangium with a few to numerous, irregularly
        branched, inflated toruloid elements forming simple or
        involved complexes; zoospores 7–8 μ in diameter when
        encysted; in water culture with mosses
                            P. torulosum Coker and Patterson, [1] p. 41m
    Antheridia diclinous, not proximal to oögonium in origin,
        antheridial cells arising from separate simple branches,
        one to two on each of the rarely formed 18–26 μ in
        diameter oögonia; oöspore with a thick wall; spo-
        rangium with irregular to spherical toruloid outgrowths
        8–20 μ in diameter; zoospores not observed; in vege-
        table debris in algal culture... *P. inflatum* Matthews, p. 46m
  Oöspore aplerotic
    Antheridia borne on branched stalks which often wind around
        the oögonial stalk, one to six, monoclinous (androgynous)
        or diclinous; oögonium spherical, 21–35 μ in diameter;
        oöspore 18–28 μ in diameter, wall 1.2–3.3 μ thick; lobes
        of sporangial apparatus moderately broad, not com-
        plicate; zoospores 10–11 by 7.5 μ; on rice bait in water
                            P. helicum T. Ito [2]
    Antheridia not on branched or coiled stalks, one or several,
        monoclinous; oögonia 21.6–27 μ in diameter; oöspore

[1] *P. graminicolum* var. *stagni* Höhnk (1953a) in saline habitats seems to belong here.
[2] *J. Jap. Bot.*, 20: 56, fig. 1. 1944.

16.2–23 μ in diameter, wall 3 μ thick; sporangial appa–
ratus consisting of feebly inflated elements and discharge
tube; zoospores 8.1–10 μ; on animal substrata bait,
saline soil .... *P. aquatile* Höhnk [1]
Wall of oögonium spiny, spines slightly tapering to a blunt apex,
terminal, occasionally intercalary, spherical to subspherical,
body 25–40 μ (mean 33 μ) in diameter; oöspore aplerotic, 20–
34 μ (av. 29.5 μ) in diameter, wall moderately thick; antheridia diclinous, one to three, usually on a single stalk, rarely on
two stalks, the stalks intricately involved with oögonium;
antheridial cell oblong clavate, markedly lobed, making
broad ventral contact with the oögonium; sporangia intercalary, rarely terminal, the basal digitations often aggregated
into massive complexes, in old cultures the contents retract-
ing to form thin-walled resting spores; zoospores 8–11 by
9–10 μ when swimming, 8–10 μ when encysted; in water
P. periplocum var. *coimbatorensis* Balakrishnan [2]
Sporangium spheroidal
Sex organs present
Oögonium wall smooth
Oöspore wall smooth
Oöspore plerotic
Sporangium producing zoospores, not proliferating
Antheridia single, rarely two, monoclinous, originating
in close proximity to the oögonium, crooknecked or
sometimes reduced to a hypogynous cell or short
lateral process, fertilization tube short and stout;
oögonium typically intercalary, 13–29.4 μ (av. 21 μ)
in diameter; oöspore with a moderately thickened
wall, 12–27 μ (av. 20 μ) in diameter; in soil
P. rostratum Butler, p. 71m
Antheridia single or several, monoclinous or diclinous,
arising from the oögonial stalk and from the oögonial hypha, the antheridial branch sometimes encircling oögonium which is smooth, 16–21 μ in diameter; oöspore thin-walled, 14.9–17.6 μ in diameter;
in saline soil ....*P. salinum* Höhnk [3]
Sporangium producing only hyphae, never zoospores, terminal or intercalary, globose, ellipsoidal, or pyriform,
18–41 μ in diameter; antheridia one to four, clavate,

[1] *Veröff. Inst. f. Meeresforsch. Bremerhaven*, 2: 94, fig. 4. 1953.
[2] *Proc. Indian Acad. Sci.*, Sect. B, 28: 31, fig. 3. 1948.
[3] *Veröff. Inst. Meeresforsch. Bremerhaven*, 2: 89, fig. 7. 1953.

monoclinous or diclinous, sometimes borne just beneath the oögonium, short stalked, clavate; oögonium
terminal or intercalary, spherical; oöspore 15–18 μ in
diameter, wall 0.5–0.8 μ thick; on rice bait in water
P. pleroticum T. Ito [1]

Oöspore aplerotic
  Oöspore single in oögonium
    Sporangium proliferating
      Antheridium typically monoclinous, rarely diclinous,
        one to three, usually single and hypogynous, when
        monoclinous or diclinous, either sessile or stalked,
        only slightly inflated, clavate, making moderate
        apical contact with oögonial wall; oögonia spher-
        ical, smooth or with a short apical papilla, ter-
        minal or intercalary, frequently catenulate, 15–28 μ
        in diameter; oöspore thick-walled, 14–24 μ in
        diameter; with a single reserve globule; spo-
        rangium acrogenous, spherical to ovoid, strongly
        proliferous; zoospores 9–16 μ in diameter when
        encysted; in water .. *P. middletonii*, nom. nov. [2] p. 74m
      Antheridium typically diclinous, rarely monoclinous,
        one to four, irregularly expanded, 10–20 by 8–12 μ,
        making broad contact with oögonium; oögonium
        subspherical, 23–39 (30.9 μ av.) in diameter;
        oöspore subspherical, 19–33 μ in diameter, with a
        moderately thick wall (1.95 μ av.) and single
        reserve globule; sporangium subspherical or
        asymmetrically utriform, the long axis generally
        at right angles or less to sporangiophore; zoo-
        spores 9–12 μ in diameter when encysted; in
        decaying water-lily leaves
P. marsipium Drechsler, p. 75m

    Sporangium not proliferating
      Antheridium typically hypogynous, less often monoc-
        linous or diclinous, one to two, when monoclinous
        often sessile or a short lateral protrusion origi-
        nating immediately below the oögonium and de-
        limited by a basal septum, then usually as long as
        broad, sometimes on a somewhat longer branch,

[1] *J. Jap. Bot.*, 20: 59, fig. 3. 1944.
[2] Syn. *Pythium proliferum* de Bary, *Jahrb. wiss. Bot.*, 2: 180, 1860. *Non Pythium proliferum* Schenk, *Verhandl. Phys.-Med. Gesell. Würzburg A. F.*, 9: 27. 1859.

antheridial cell only slightly swollen, clavate, making moderate oögonial contact; oögonium when intercalary sometimes two to five in series, 19.6–37.8 μ (av. 28.3 μ) in diameter; oöspore 13.8–31.1 μ (av. 24.6 μ) in diameter, wall moderately thick, with a single reserve globule; sporangia spherical, elliptical or pyriform, 24–48 μ (av. 38.2 μ) in diameter, terminal or intercalary, occasionally catenulate; encysted zoospores 11–16 μ in diameter; soil and water on plant and animal substrata (Fig. 87 F) . . . . . *P. pulchrum* Minden, p. 83m

Antheridium typically monoclinous or diclinous

    Antheridium one, typically sessile, arising immediately below the oögonium, sharply incurved, or sometimes two, then often of diclinous origin and straight, antheridial cell swollen, making narrow apical contact with base of oögonium; oögonium spherical, terminal, rarely intercalary, 19.6–22.9 μ (av. 20.6 μ) in diameter; oöspore 14.7–18.3 μ (av. 16.3 μ) in diameter, with thick (at least 2 μ) wall and single globule; sporangia chiefly terminal and spherical, 12–28 μ (av. 20 μ) in diameter, or occasionally intercalary and barrel-shaped, 14–17 μ, to 22.9 by 27.8 μ, germinating only by germ tubes (Fig. 87 H) . . . . *P. ultimum* Trow, p. 86m

    Antheridium one to six, typically stalked mono- and diclinous, when monoclinous arising some distance below oögonium not immediately adjacent to it, crooknecked, clavate, the apex obtuse, narrowly applied to the oögonium; oögonium spherical, 15–28 μ (av. 21 μ) in diameter, terminal or intercalary; oöspore 12–20 μ (av. 17 μ) in diameter; sporangia spherical to oval, terminal or intercalary, 15–26 μ (av. 19 μ), germinating by germ tubes or zoospores; in soil (Fig. 87 G)

                      P. debaryanum Hesse, p. 98m

Oöspores typically several in an oögonium, aplerotic, 10.5–29.4 μ (av. 21.6 μ) in diameter, with moderately thick smooth wall; antheridia monoclinous and diclinous, one to several, usually two, stalk of variable length, antheridial cell clavate to swollen, closely to moderately applied terminally to the oögonium; oögonium spherical, ovoid, or irregular, when unisporous 18.9–39.9 μ (av. 30.4 μ) in diameter, when multisporous 26.4–48.4 μ by 39.6–74.8 μ; sporangia spherical, subspherical, occasionally ellipsoidal or pyriform, terminal on lateral branches, 29.5–55 μ (av. 42.8 μ) in diameter, proliferous, secondary sporangia nested within primary; zoospores 8.4–10.5 μ by 10.5–16.8 μ when encysted; in soil .... *P. multisporum* Poitras [1]

Oöspore wall reticulate, oöspore aplerotic; oögonium spherical, terminal or intercalary; antheridia diclinous, one to three, borne terminally on branches of varying length; sporangia spherical; zoospores 8–16 μ long; parasitic in *Lemna spp.* and *Riccia fluitans*

P. cystosiphon (Roze and Cornu) Lindstedt, p. 106m[2]

Oögonium wall echinulate

Oöspore plerotic

Oögonial protuberances 2.7–6.0 μ (av. 4.4 μ) long, conical, oögonium spherical, typically terminal, 13–19.3 μ (av. 16.4 μ) in diameter, exclusive of protuberances; oöspore with moderately thick wall; antheridium usually single, monoclinous, arising in close proximity to oögonium, stalk short, cell clavate with apex moderately applied to oögonium; sporangia spherical, 14.3–20.7 μ (av. 16.3 μ) in diameter, terminal or intercalary; in soil

P. mammillatum Meurs, p. 109m

Oögonial protuberances 5–8 μ long, digitate or blunt, conical, oögonia spherical to subspherical when terminal, sometimes limoniform when intercalary, 13.2–27.4 μ (av. 18.2 μ) excluding spines; oöspore 10.1–25.3 μ (av. 16.7 μ) in diameter, wall moderately thick; antheridia terminal, typically monoclinous, sometimes diclinous, one, rarely two, originating close to oögonium, 12–32 μ by 3–5 μ; sporangia spherical to subspherical when terminal, spherical to spindle-shaped when intercalary, 14–33 μ (av. 22.4 μ), wall usually smooth, occasionally with digitate or blunt conical spines; zoospores rare, germination usually by germ tubes; in soil .... *P. spinosum* Sawada, p. 111m

Oöspore aplerotic

Oöspore 14–24 μ (av. 20 μ) in diameter, one to two in an oögonium; oögonium spherical to cylindrical, terminal

---

[1] *Mycologia*, 41: 171, figs. 1–17. 1949.

[2] According to Miss Waterhouse (comm.), *P. pythioides* (Roze and Cornu) Ramsbottom.

or intercalary, 14–30 μ (av. 24 μ) in diameter exclusive of
numerous 2–8 μ long spines; antheridia monoclinous,
typically hypogynal, one to four (usually one); sporangia
spherical to cylindrical, terminal or intercalary, often
catenulate, three to four in series, 10–30 μ (av. 20 μ) in
diameter; either zoospores or germ tubes produced; in
soil (Fig. 87 D–E) .... *P. echinulatum* Matthews, p. 117m
Oöspore 11.6–21.7 μ, one in an oögonium; oögonium terminal, spheroidal, 16.6–28 μ in diameter, exclusive of the 5–
26.3 μ long by 2-5 μ in diameter, cylindrical, simple, or
bifurcated outgrowths; antheridium androgynous, diclinous, rarely hypogynous, one to four, clavate or oblong;
sporangia terminal, globose, ovoid, or pyriform, 25–35
by 23–30 μ, internally proliferous; hyphae 2.8–8.5 μ in
diameter; on rice bait in water .... *P. polypapillatum* T. Ito [1]
Sex organs absent
Sporangia proliferating
Sporangium papillate
Sporangia on vigorously growing thalli narrowly ellipsoidal
130–170 by 35 μ, under less favorable conditions ovoid
or obpyriform, 50 by 30 μ, typically borne at the tip of an
unbranched, undulating sporangiophore 6–8 μ in diameter, which characteristically widens to 12–15 μ immediately beneath sporangium, proliferous, the secondary
sporangia formed within or more commonly beyond the
primary, sometimes by subsporangial branching as well;
zoospores more or less delimited, sometimes even with
flagella, within the sporangium, completing maturation
outside in a sessile vesicle, encysted zoospores 13–15 μ in
diameter; dark, spherical, rough-walled chlamydospores
sometimes formed; hyphae 3–6 μ in diameter; in water
and soil (Fig. 87 A) ..... *P. undulatum* Petersen, [2] p. 123m
Sporangia spherical to elongate, 20–30 μ (av. 25 μ) in diameter, typically terminal, intercalary, with a well-developed
apical papilla, proliferous, the secondary sporangia formed within or outside the primary; zoospores 8–10 μ long,
completely formed in a stalked vesicle; hyphae 1–4 μ in
diameter; in *Spirogyra*... *P. carolinianum* Matthews, p. 124m
Sporangium not papillate, spherical, terminal, 30 μ in diameter,

[1] *J. Jap. Bot.*, 20: 58, fig. 2. 1944.
[2] Based chiefly on the description by Goldie-Smith (1952) and the present writer's
observations. *P. undulatum* var. *litorale* Höhnk (1953a), from saline habitat, seems
based on abnormal material.

proliferous, often forming a wavy or helicoid discharge
tube several times the length of the sporangium and 2–3 μ
in diameter; zoospores infrequently formed exogenously,
typically within a vesicle; hyphae less than 1.5 μ in diameter; in vegetable debris . . . . *P. diacarpum* Butler, p. 124m
Sporangia not proliferating
    Sporangia catenulate often up to thirteen in a series, spherical,
      18–24 μ in diameter, sessile or separated by short stalks;
      mycelium 2–6 μ in diameter, coenocytic when young, sep-
      tate when mature; in soil . . . . . . *P. intermedium* de Bary, p. 125m
    Sporangia not catenulate, terminal or intercalary, not prolifer-
      ating, spherical, pyriform, cylindrical or curved, when
      spherical measuring 12–50 μ, in diameter, when cylindrical
      up to 65 μ long; zoospores formed in a vesicle at the tip of a
      very long discharge tube, 10–12 μ by 6 μ; sporangia also
      germinating by germ tubes; in soil
                         P. elongatum Matthews, p. 126m

See also the following imperfectly known species of *Pythium* on
aquatic hosts:

    P. akanense Tokunaga, Trans. Sapporo. Nat. Hist. Soc., 12: 119–123. 1932.
    On *Aegagropila sauteri.*
    P. characearum de Wild., Ann. Soc. Belg. Micros. (Mém.), 20: 107–136.
    1896. On oögonia of *Chara sp.*
    P. daphnidarum Petersen, Bot. Tidssk., 29: 345–440. 1909. On *Daphnia*
    and *Bosmina.*
    P. hydrodictyorum de Wild., Ann. Soc. Belg. Micros., 21: 22. 1897. On *Hy-*
    drodictyon.

Note: The fungus from saline habitats, termed *P. echinocarpum* Ito
and Tokunaga by Höhnk (1953a), strongly resembles *P. irregulare* Buisman. Höhnk's (1953a) *P. imperfectum*, a lobulate filamentous sporangial
type lacking sex organs cannot, of course, be compared with other
species.

PYTHIOGETON Minden

Falck, Mykolog. Untersuch. Berichte, 2(2): 241. 1916

(Fig. 88, p. 1045)

Mycelium well developed, consisting of delicate much-branched hyphae, appressoria occasionally formed; zoosporangia terminal or inter-

calary on the ordinary elements of the mycelium or on richly branched
lateral hyphae, spherical or more commonly unsymmetrical and bursiform, the long axis often nearly at right angles to that of the concomitant hypha, forming a more or less prolonged slender evacuation tube,
internally proliferous; zoospores somewhat reniform, each containing a
single vacuole and bearing two oppositely directed flagella of approximately equal length emerging from a shallow longitudinal groove, expelled from the sporangium as an undifferentiated irregularly tubular
mass surrounded by an elongate quickly evanescent vesicle, undergoing
their maturation free in the water, capable of repeated emergence;
hyphae bearing the sex organs often helically involved; oögonium terminal or intercalary, spherical or polygonal, antheridium usually single,
terminal or with a short appendage, arising (always?) from the same
hypha as the oögonium; oöspore spherical, filling the oögonium, with
an enormously thickened refractive often concentrically layered wall
and a large globule, upon germination converted (always?) into a zoosporangium after resorption of the greater part of the wall.

Saprophytic on vegetable debris in fresh water.

Because of the lack of essential data in Minden's descriptions and of
the variations in shape and position of the zoosporangia his species are
difficult to distinguish on the basis of the sporangial stage alone. A study
of Minden's illustrations of his species, which are presumed to represent
typical material, reveals the following qualitative differences between
them. The sporangia of *Pythiogeton utriforme* and *P. ramosum* are predominantly terminal. Those of *P. transversum* are usually (but not always) intercalary, the distal part of the hypha often appearing as a
slender appendage near the orifice of discharged sporangia. The sporangia of *P. utriforme* are somewhat more broadly pouchlike, their discharge tubes are more nearly in line with the mycelial axis, and they
are borne on a more sparingly branched mycelium than are the narrowly
bursiform ones of *P. ramosum*.

Sexual stages have been associated with *Pythiogeton utriforme* and *P.
transversum*.

Species of the genus are as yet poorly defined in the literature, and
further work will be necessary before taxonomic criteria of significant
import can be established. Evaluation of the shape of the sporangium

and of the sizes of the parts as characters of diagnostic importance—the primary bases on which all but two species of the genus are now separated—awaits the results of extensive studies of fungi identifiable with Minden's species as well as of those described since his time.

KEY TO THE SPECIES OF PYTHIOGETON

Sporangia bursiform or irregularly saccate
  Sporangia for the most part terminal
    Sporangia predominantly broadly bursiform, the discharge tube
      nearly parallel with the axis of the attendant hypha; sporangiferous hyphae sparingly branched; oögonia spherical
                    P. utriforme, p. 1044
    Sporangia predominantly narrowly bursiform, the discharge tube
      approximately at right angles to the axis of the attendant hypha; sporangiferous hyphae richly branched; sex organs
      unknown . . . . *P. ramosum*, p. 1046
  Sporangia for the most part intercalary
    Sporangia (four) averaging 154 μ long by 60.5 μ in diameter;
      oögonia polygonal . . . . *P. transversum*, p. 1047
    Sporangia (one hundred) averaging 96 μ long by 42 μ in greatest
      diameter; sex organs unknown . . . . *P. autossytum*, p. 1048
Sporangia spherical or ovoid
  Sporangia 40–56 by 30–40 μ; discharge tube 39–70 μ long
                    P. uniforme, p. 1049
  Sporangia 20–34 by 18–28 μ; discharge tube 4.8–15 μ long
                    P. dichotomum, p. 1049

PYTHIOGETON UTRIFORME Minden

Falck, Mykolog. Untersuch. Berichte, 2(2): 242, pl. 6, figs. 56–65. 1916

(Fig. 88 F–N, p. 1045)

Mycelium composed of slender sparingly branched hyphae 2.5–3.5 μ in diameter; zoosporangium terminal, bursiform or somewhat irregular, the discharge tube slender, more or less prolonged, its long axis frequently nearly parallel with that of the supporting hypha; zoospores reniform, laterally biflagellate; oögonium predominantly spherical, averaging 45 μ in diameter, antheridium single, monoclinous, hemispherical, sometimes bearing a short appendage, applied laterally or near the base of the oögonium, forming a fertilization tube; oöspore spherical, completely

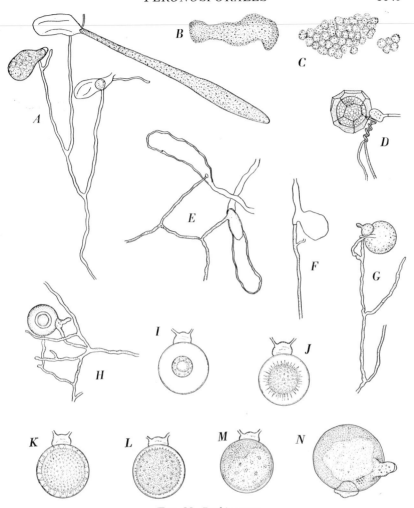

Fig. 88. *Pythiogeton*

A–D. Pythiogeton transversum Minden: *A*, group of sporangia, one of
which is discharging its contents; *B*, ejected contents free in the water; *C*,
contents becoming segregated into zoospores; *D*, sex organs. *E. Pythiogeton
ramosum* Minden, two empty sporangia. *F–N. Pythiogeton utriforme* Minden:
F, empty sporangium; *G*, developing sex organs; *H*, mature oöspore; *I*, mature
oöspore with persistent antheridium; *J*, beginning of germination; *K–M*,
further stages in resorption of oöspore wall; *N*, formation of discharge tube
by germinating oöspore.

(*A–H*, Minden, 1916; *I–N*, Sparrow, 1936a)

filling the oögonium, with a very thick refractive sometimes concentrically layered wall, contents bearing a single large globule surrounded by many small ones, upon germination converted (always?) into a zoosporangium after resorption of the greater part of the wall.

Saprophytic on fruits and twigs, Minden (*loc. cit.*), GERMANY; Thaxter (1895b: pl. 31, fig. 16, oöspore), UNITED STATES; Lund (1934: 53, fig. 27), DENMARK; Sparrow (1936a: 467, fig. 6 c, o–r, fig. 7 a–k), GREAT BRITAIN; decaying grass leaves, Sparrow (1952c: 106), CUBA; from soil, substrate?, Gaertner (1954b: 22), SOUTH AFRICA.

Minden states that this species may well be identical with the imperfectly described *Pythium utriforme* of Cornu (1872a: 13). The resting spore suggested by Thaxter (*loc. cit.*) as belonging to *Gonapodya* is unquestionably that of the present species.

No measurements of the zoosporangia were given by Minden. These have been described by Lund (*loc. cit.*) as 45–97 by 31–67 μ, the discharge tube as 49–63 μ long. In the material studied by Sparrow (*loc. cit.*) the zoosporangia were 32–45 μ long by 17–30 μ in greatest diameter. The oögonia in Lund's material were, when spherical, 28–57 μ in diameter, when subspherical, 34 by 36 μ; the oöspores were 16–39 μ in diameter.

PYTHIOGETON RAMOSUM Minden

Falck, Mykolog. Untersuch. Berichte, 2(2): 238, pl. 8, figs. 74–(?) 75. 1916

(Fig. 88 E, p. 1045)

Mycelium composed of occasionally branched main hyphae bearing numerous secondary branches, on which the zoosporangia are formed; zoosporangium terminal, narrowly bursiform, its long axis at right angles to that of the supporting hypha, the narrow apex usually extended, internally proliferous; zoospores reniform, laterally biflagellate; sex organs unknown.

On decaying beet root, Minden (*loc. cit.*), GERMANY; rice seeds and seedlings, Ito and Nagai (1931: 48), JAPAN; twigs, Sparrow (1932b: 299, pl. 8, fig. I),(?) Wolf (1944: 51), UNITED STATES; Sparrow (*loc. cit.*), CANADA; rice kernels, tomato fruit, Shen and Siang (1948: 202), CHINA.

No dimensions were given by Minden. The species was considered doubtfully distinct from *Pythiogeton transversum*, the complex of branched sporangiferous hyphae being the chief point of difference. The sporangium, however, appears more narrowly bursiform than in typical *P. transversum*. The sporangia in Sparrow's material were about 60 μ long and tapered from 20 μ to 8 μ in diameter. The material studied by Shen and Siang had hyphae 3–4 μ in diameter, the main axes up to 6.6 μ; zoosporangia 28–65 μ long by 24–53 μ wide, with a discharge tube 16–62 μ long by 4–6 μ in diameter. The cysts of the discharged zoospores were 10–11 μ in diameter. No sex organs were seen.

PYTHIOGETON TRANSVERSUM Minden

Falck, Mykolog. Untersuch. Berichte, 2(2): 242, pl. 7, figs. 66–72. 1916

(Fig. 88 A–D, p. 1045)

Mycelium composed of slender moderately branched hyphae; zoosporangium usually intercalary, placed near the tip of the hypha, which appears as a somewhat evanescent short appendage, irregularly bursiform, occasionally somewhat spherical, 70–299 μ long (without including the discharge tube) by 42–79 μ in diameter, the long axis usually nearly at right angles to that of the supporting hypha, to which it is attached near the narrower end, discharge tube more or less prolonged; zoospores reniform, laterally biflagellate; oögonium terminal or intercalary, at maturity polygonal, 37–51 μ in diameter (averaging 50 μ), antheridium single, androgynous (monoclinous), frequently helically involved by or involving the supporting hypha of the oögonium, intercalary, placed near the tip of the hypha, which appears as a somewhat evanescent short appendage, applied near the base of the oögonium; oöspore spherical, nearly filling the oögonium, 33–50 μ in diameter, with a thick refractive somewhat yellowish wall, contents bearing a large oil globule, germination not observed.

On various fruits and on stalks of water hemlock, Minden (*loc. cit.*), GERMANY.

In the globose character of its sporangia a fungus referred to this species by Sparrow (1933c: 533, pl. 49, fig. 24) more nearly resembles *Pythiogeton uniforme* Lund. As may be seen, Minden considered the intercalary forms with somewhat spherical sporangia indistinguishable specifically from the bursiform types.

The material Wolf (1944) doubtfully assigned to this species showed considerable variability with respect to the position of the sporangia. Some of them were terminal and not transversely inserted, others intercalary. They measured 87–128 μ by 20–24 μ.

PYTHIOGETON AUTOSSYTUM Drechsler

J. Wash. Acad. Sci., 22: 447, figs. 1–5. 1932

"Intramatrical mycelium composed of hyphae branching mostly at rather wide angles and at moderate intervals, measuring 1.6 to 7.0 μ in diameter, each element maintaining usually a nearly uniform width from origin to tip, the wider axial hyphae of straightforward course, the shorter branches usually with somewhat abrupt changes in direction, and often bearing appressoria in groups of 5 to 10 or more; the individual appressorium distended clavate, mostly 10 to 13 μ in diameter and 20 to 30 μ in length, after functional frustration often growing out into irregular processes of somewhat crescentic parts. Under aquatic condition extramatrical mycelium rather meager. Aerial mycelium on dry substrata generally meager, arachnoid, yet often spreading rather extensively over surfaces of adjacent bodies.

"Sporangium terminal or intercalary, when intercalary mostly borne only a short distance from the tip of the supporting filament, the distal element mostly 3 to 30 μ in length remaining as an empty appendage; when produced under conditions suitable for zoospore production sometimes subspherical or ellipsoidal, but more often markedly ventricose, utriform, or bursiform, with the expanded part free and its axis directed athwart the axis of supporting hypha, or occasionally bilocular as through fusion of two parts, either of which may be subspherical or bursiform; measuring 16 to 226 μ, mostly 50 to 150 μ (average 96 μ) in length and 13 to 68 μ, mostly 30 to 54 μ (average 42 μ) in greatest diameter; when formed under conditions unsuitable for zoospore formation, mostly subspherical measuring usually 32 to 51 μ (average 40.4 μ) in diameter. Evacuation tube arising often from position opposite attachment of supporting filament and directed in approximate alignment with that filament, but at other times originating from other positions; measuring mostly 3.5 to 7.0 μ (average between 5.5 and 6.0 μ) in diameter, and 5 to 300 μ in length; in cases of frustration often becoming septate, and discharging from a branch. Zoospores formed up to approximately 100 from a single sporangium, broadly reniform, the longitudinal furrow bearing the two cilia well-marked, the forward end more pointed than the rounded rear end, measuring mostly 18 to 20 μ in length and 11 to 13 μ in width in motile state; after rounding up measuring mostly 13 to 17 μ (average 15 μ) in diameter; germinating individually by the production of 1 to 4 delicate germ tubes, or giving rise to a secondary zoospore after proliferating an evacuation tube approximately 2 μ in diameter, and 2 to 27 μ in length" (Drechsler, *loc. cit.*).

On dying and decaying leaves of *Typha latifolia*, UNITED STATES.

PYTHIOGETON UNIFORME Lund

Kgl. Danske Vidensk. Selsk. Skrift., Naturv. Math., Afd. IX, 6 (1): 54, fig. 28 a–c. 1934

"Hyphae about 3–5 μ thick, much branched, sometimes divided by septa. Sporangia subspherical or slightly oval, 40–56 × 30–40 μ, terminating the main hyphae or on side branches, mostly with their long axis at nearly right angles to the hyphae, filled with a granulated plasma. Tube of discharge about 39–70 × 5.6 μ, filled with refractive plasma when young. At maturity the plasma of the sporangium passes through the tube of discharge as a long flowing stream; after some time about 20 biciliate zoospores are differentiated. When the sporangium has emptied, the walls collapse; proliferations frequent. Sexual organs not observed" (Lund, *loc. cit.*).

On hempseed in water, DENMARK.

The sporangial stage of what is probably this species has been reported by Waterhouse (1942: 323) from GREAT BRITAIN.

PYTHIOGETON DICHOTOMUM Tokunaga

Trans. Sapporo Nat. Hist. Soc., 14 (1): 12. 1935

Mycelium intra- and extramatrical, hyphae branched, hyaline, slender,

1.8–3 μ in diameter; zoosporangium terminal on lateral branches, which are unbranched or once or twice dichotomously branched, spherical or ovoid, 20–34 by 18–28 μ, proliferous, with an apical or lateral short exit tube, 4.8–15 μ long by 4–6 μ wide; vesicle oblong-ovoid, with an extremely delicate wall; zoospores reniform, with two lateral flagella; oögonium and oöspore unknown.

In decaying plants of *Oryza sativa*, JAPAN.

EXCLUDED SPECIES OF PYTHIOGETON

* PYTHIOGETON STERILIS Hamid

Proc. Indian Acad. Sci., Sect. B, 15: 212, pl. 3. 1942

From the figures and description, this species appears based upon abnormal sporangial material of *Pythiogeton ramosum*.

Twigs, INDIA.

DIASPORANGIUM Höhnk

Beihefte Bot. Centralbl. 55 (Abt. A): 97. 1936

(Fig. 89 H, p. 1055)

Mycelium composed of main hyphae and narrower branches; zoosporangia regularly ellipsoidal, their long axes transverse to those of the supporting hyphae, sometimes becoming thick-walled and resting; zoospores rarely formed, laterally biflagellate, typically differentiated within the sporangium before escape (no vesicle being formed) or sometimes by division of the extruded naked protoplasm; sporangium occasionally germinating by a germ tube; oögonium globose, with a single oöspore and central reserve globule; antheridia not observed.

In soil.

DIASPORANGIUM JONESIANUM Höhnk

Beihefte Bot. Centralbl., 55 (Abt. A): 97, fig. 3. 1936

Mycelium intra- and extramatrical, the former type more slender than the latter, which is composed of hyphae 4–8 μ in diameter and up to 4 cm. in length, branches arising at somewhat regular intervals as whorls of two to five short slender hyphae, septate with age; zoosporangia ellipsoidal, somewhat angular with age, borne transversely, usually in groups of four, at the tips of short verticellate supporting hyphae, 30–35 μ, germinating by zoospores or a hypha; zoospores laterally biflagellate, swarming briefly before encystment; oögonium spherical, 25 μ in diameter; oöspore nearly completely filling the oögonium, with a large central oil globule.

Saprophytic in soil, capable experimentally of causing root rot of various phanerogams, UNITED STATES; GERMANY.

Evaluation of *Diasporangium jonesianum* is unfortunately hampered by the fragmentary evidence on zoospore development and discharge. Although separation of the protoplasm outside the sporangium into masses, as in *Pythiogeton*, was noted, Höhnk considered it abnormal. In the few cases of zoospore formation that he saw, the process was completed within the sporangium and the zoospores emerged fully formed as in *Phytophthora*. Only scant observations on the sex organs were recorded, but a true peronosporaceous oöspore is figured.

The most impressive distinguishing character, it seems to this writer, is the *Pythiogeton*-like, verticellate sporangia, which typically produce the zoospores endogenously and without a vesicle. New investigations will undoubtedly establish the genus on a firmer basis and make clear generic versus specific differences.

PHYTOPHTHORA DE BARY [1, 2]

J. Roy. Agr. Soc. England (2d ser., 1),12: 240, figs. 1–8. 1876

(Figs. 89 A–G, p. 1055; 90, p. 1059)

Kawakamia Miyabe, Bot. Mag. Tokyo, 17: 306. 1903.
Mycelophagus Mangin, C. R. Acad. Sci. Paris, 136: 472. 1903.
Phloeophthora Klebahn, Centralbl. Bakt. Abt. II, 15: 336. 1906.
Pythiacystis R. E. Smith and E. H. Smith, Bot. Gaz., 42: 221. 1906.
Pythiomorpha H. E. Petersen, Bot. Tidsskrift, 29: 391. 1909.
Nozemia Pethybridge, Sci. Proc. Royal Dublin Soc. (N. S.), 13: 556. 1913.
Blepharospora Petri, R. C. Accad., Lincei , V, 26: 299. 1917.
Pseudopythium Sideris, nom. nud., Phytopath., 20: 953. 1930.

[1] The writer feels strongly his own inadequacy in formulating this generic description. It was made necessary by the total lack of a formal diagnosis (in English) of the genus in Tucker's (1931) monograph. A parallel remark applies to the generic description given for *Pythium* (p. 1031).

[2] See also Waterhouse's (1956) recent account.

Mycelium much branched, the branching frequently monopodial and at nearly right angles, often constricted at the base, sometimes bearing spherical or ellipsoidal or irregular swellings, groups of irregular bud-like outgrowths, or involved torulose complexes, becoming septate with age, when parasitic, intra-and intercellular and often bearing haustoria, protoplasm refractive, pallid, sometimes bearing occasional conspic-uous granules, walls giving a modified cellulose reaction, occasionally forming terminal or intercalary, spherical, ellipsoidal, or irregular chlam-ydospores; zoosporangia borne on more or less well-defined spo-rangiophores which are sometimes slightly swollen near point of origin on hypha, usually ovoid or limoniform, pyriform or bluntly ellipsoidal, occasionally slender, with either a prominent, broad hyaline apical papilla or a blunt nonpapillate apex, persistent on the sporangiophore or abscissing sometimes with an attached, usually short hyphal pedicel, capable of renewed growth by internal proliferation of secondary spo-rangia which may be sessile and "nested" within the primary or borne on a sporangiophore which extends through the discharge orifice, or by the production of compound sympodial sporangiophores, germinating indirectly by zoospores or directly by germ tubes; zoospores completely formed within the sporangium, emerging individually or in a quickly dissociating mass either upon the dissolution of the sessile or slightly elevated apical papilla or by the papilla forming a very quickly evanescent vesicle around the emerging spores, encysting and germinating after a period of swarming or capable of repeated emergences before germinating; plants usually monoecious, antheridia usually amphigy-nous, sometimes paragynous or both; oögonium usually terminal, somewhat spherical, forming a single egg; oöspore single, aplerotic or sometimes plerotic, wall 1–3 μ thick, usually with a large reserve globule, germinating by one or more hyphae or by zoospores.

Parasitic on flowering plants and saprophytic on debris in water.

Blackwell, Waterhouse, and Thompson (1941) confirmed Buisman's (1927) contention that species of *Pythiomorpha* are in reality members of *Phytophthora* and established that *Phytophthora megasperma* and *P. cryptogea* occur in nature living as water molds. The success of Hickman (1940) in growing the strawberry parasite, *P. fragariae*, on hempseed in liquid medium and the ease in general practice of obtaining *Phytoph-*

thora sporangia in water culture are further evidences of its amphibious nature. (This last characteristic is shared by many, probably all, species of *Pythium*.) Whether one can regard all species of *Pythiomorpha* as valid members of *Phytophthora* must await a critical study. Meanwhile, see the discussions of Sparrow (1943) and Middleton (1952)[1]. Note also Blackwell's (1949) very useful clarification of the terminology employed in characterizing species of *Phytophthora*.

KEY TO THE AQUATIC SPECIES OF PHYTOPHTHORA [2]

Sex organs present
  Both oögonia and antheridia formed; sporangia renewed by internal proliferation or cymose branching of sporangiophore or both
    Sporangia papillate; oospore filling the oögonium; without a conspicuous globule .... *P. gonapodyides*, p. 1053
    Sporangia nonpapillate
      Antheridia always amphigynous; oöspore averaging 25 μ in diameter .... *P. cryptogea*, p. 1055
      Antheridia mostly paragynous, occasionally amphigynous; oöspore averaging 41 μ in diameter..... *P. megasperma*, p. 1056
  Only oögonia formed; sporangia renewed only by cymose branching
                                P. fischeriana, p. 1058
Sex organs lacking; sporangia up to 84 μ long (av. *circa* 60 μ)
                                      P. oryzae, p. 1060

PHYTOPHTHORA GONAPODYIDES (H. E. Petersen) Buisman [3]

Meded. phytopath. Lab. Scholten, 11: 7, 1927; also reprinted as Root Rots Caused by Phycomycetes, p. 7. Haarlem, 1927

(Fig. 89 D–G, p. 1055)

Pythiomorpha gonapodyides H. E. Petersen, Bot. Tidsskrift, 29: 391, figs. 6–7. 1909. Ann. Mycologici, 8: 528, figs. 6–7. 1910. Emend. Kanouse, Bot. Gaz., 79: 198, pls. 12–13. 1925.

[1] See Waterhouse (1956, 1958).

[2] *Pythiomorpha undulata* (Petersen) Apinis (1930) is considered to be *Pythium undulatum* Petersen.

[3] Waterhouse's paper (1958), seen too late for interpolation of her conclusions in the body of the text, contains a strict interpretation of this species derived from a study of the type material. It is evident that the fungus had no protruding discharge papilla on the convex apex of the broadly to elongate pyriform sporangium which was 43–70 × 20–32 μ. There were no evidences for repeated emergence of the zoospores and no sexual stage. She rejects all published accounts of sex organs attributed to the species.

Mycelium delicate, profusely branched, with a silvery sheen, the hyphae irregular, 2–8 μ in diameter, bearing budlike projections and knotted complexes, endobiotic and extramatrical, contents with occasional refractive granules; zoosporangium borne on a slender unbranched sporangiophore about 3 μ in diameter, ovoid or pyriform with a broad blunt apex which may disappear just prior to zoospore discharge 26–48 μ long by 16–27 μ in diameter, inner wall distinct, renewed by internal proliferation, the secondarily formed sporangia up to five in number, either sessile and "nested" within the primary sporangia or formed in linear succession by repeated apical growth of the sporangiophore through the base of the sporangium; zoospores formed and initiating movement within the sporangium, somewhat ovoid, 9–15 μ in diameter, the flagella of about equal length, oppositely directed and arising from a shallow groove, capable of repeated emergence, upon germination forming one or more germ tubes; oögonium formed on a short branch, spherical, smooth-walled, 22–36 μ in diameter, antheridium present on about ten per cent of the oögonia, diclinous, somewhat clavate, broadly applied to the oögonium, the antheridial hypha winding around the oögonium; oöspore smooth, thick-walled, filling the oögonium, contents highly refractive, finely granular, without a conspicuous globule, upon germination forming one or more branched hyphae.

Saprophytic on fruits and twigs, Petersen (*loc. cit.*), Lund (1934: 47), DENMARK; (?) fruits and other plant parts, Minden (1916: 219, text fig. 24, pl. 6, figs. 45–48), GERMANY; Cejp (1933b: pl. 1, figs. 1–18, pl. 2), CZECHOSLOVAKIA; fruits, Kanouse (*loc. cit.*), *Fraxinus* twigs, Sparrow (1933c: 533), UNITED STATES; Barnes and Melville (1932), twigs, Sparrow (1936a: 467), (?) Forbes (1935a: pl. 9, fig. 7), GREAT BRITAIN; fruits, Crooks (1937: 220, fig. 6 A–E), AUSTRALIA.

The description above was derived for the most part from Kanouse's (1925) account of her fungus. The fungi described by Cejp (*op. cit.*) and Crooks (*op. cit.*) most nearly approximate it, particularly with respect to the sex organs and the oöspore. The sporangia of the Australian material were, however, somewhat larger, being 40–70 by 20–40 μ. The oögonia were 23–28 μ in diameter, and the oöspores, which lacked a globule and filled the oögonium, were 20–22 μ in diameter. It is possible that larger sporangia were also formed in the material described by Cejp.

Shen and Siang (1948), on the basis of the character of the nonsexual stage, place this species in synonymy with *Phytophthora megasperma.*

PHYTOPHTHORA CRYPTOGEA Pethybridge and Lafferty

Proc. Royal Dublin Soc. (N.S.), 15: 498, pls. 45–47. 1919

(Fig. 90 G–I, p. 1059)

Mycelium intra- and intercellular, composed of branched hyphae which may become septate in empty parts, sometimes bearing lobu-

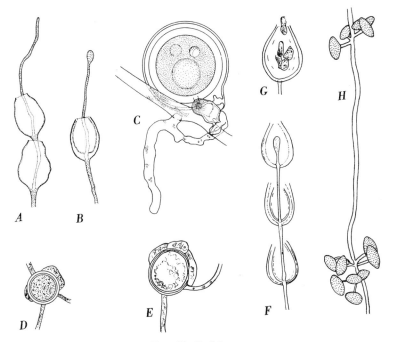

FIG. 89. Pythiaceae

A–C, Phytophthora megasperma Drechsler: *A–B,* proliferous zoosporangia; *C,* sex organs. *D–G, Phytophthora gonapodyides* (H. E. Petersen) Buisman: *D–E,* sex organs; *F,* proliferous zoosporangia; *G,* fully formed zoospores emerging from a zoosporangium. *H. Diasporangium jonesianum* Höhnk, part of plant showing whorls of zoosporangia.

(*A–C,* Drechsler, 1931; *D,* Cejp, 1933b; *E–G,* Kanouse, 1925; *H,* Höhnk, 1936)

ations or swollen complexes; sporangia borne on sympodially branched long straggling uninflated sporangiophores, pyriform, [1] often much elongated and somewhat irregular, the apex blunt and nonpapillate, 24–50 μ long by 17–30 μ broad (av. 40 by 27 μ), when caducous bearing a short pedicel, germinating by zoospores or less often by a germ tube, renewed by internal proliferation; zoospores limoniform, biflagellate, 10–15 μ in diameter when at rest, discharged in a quickly evanescent vesicle; oögonium usually lateral, sometimes terminal, pyriform or spherical, the wall becoming amber-colored and thicker with age, averaging 30 μ in diameter; antheridium terminal or intercalary often borne on a short hypha, variable in size and shape, amphigynous; oöspore lying loosely in the oögonium, straw-colored, averaging 25 μ in diameter, with a smooth, 3 μ thick wall, the contents with a large central oil globule and a small oval, highly refractive, lateral body, germination not observed.

Parasitic in stems and roots of *Lycopersicum esculentum* and *Petunia*, Pethybridge and Lafferty (*loc. cit.*), IRELAND; saprophytic in water, Waterhouse (1940), GREAT BRITAIN.

The excellent growth and abundant production of sporangia by this parasite of phanerogams under aquatic conditions was remarked on by Pethybridge and Lafferty. It strengthens our conviction that it is identical with Waterhouse's fungus.

PHYTOPHTHORA MEGASPERMA Drechsler

J. Wash. Acad. Sci., 21: 524, figs. 1–5. 1931

(Figs. 89 A–C, p. 1055; 90 C–F, p. 1059)

Pythiomorpha miyabeana Ito and Nagai, J. Fac. Agr. Hokkaido Imper. Univ., Sapporo, 32: 50, pl. 8, figs. 1–8. 1931.

"Mycelium intercellular in tissues of host; on artificial substratum of somewhat radiating aspect, composed of freely branching hyphae from 3 to 8 μ in diameter; continuous in actively growing stage, later, on becoming evacuated, developing numerous, rather thick septa; producing aerial growth in small or moderate quantity; under aquatic conditions extramatrical growth meager.

---

[1] Described as "inversely pear-shaped." According to the usage employed throughout this book, the term should be "pyriform," i. e., as the fruit hangs naturally on the tree.

"Sporangium regularly formed terminally on a long, simple or sparingly branched, extramatrical filament measuring mostly 50 μ to 2 mm. in length and 2 to 2.5 μ in diameter, though often expanding in the distal portion to a diameter of 3 to 5 μ; later often coming into a lateral position through continued elongation of the supporting filament from immediately below the delimiting septum; regularly ovoid, but occasionally bearing distally a protuberance or lobe of variable size; measuring 6 to 45 μ in transverse diameter by 15 to 60 μ in length; on dehiscence opening broadly at apex without formation of an outwardly protruding papilla; after evacuation proliferous in moderate measure, both by formation of sessile or nearly sessile secondary or often tertiary sporangia within primary one and by repeated growth of the supporting filament through the orifices of the empty envelope to produce additional sporangia externally. Zoospores produced from 1 to 45 in a sporangium; reniform, longitudinally grooved, biciliated, after rounding up measuring 10 to 13 μ in diameter; individually germinating by germ-tubes usually 1 to 3 in number, or often, whether properly liberated or retained within the sporangial envelope owing to frustrated dehiscence, often giving rise to a secondary zoospore,—the repetitional development taking place either by direct discharge of contents through an evacuation tube 3.5 to 5.5 μ in diameter and 1 to 10 μ in length, or by the production of an elongated miniature sporangium mostly 6 to 10 μ in diameter and 16 to 22 μ in length on a germ sporangiophore mostly 1.5 μ in diameter and 10 to 60 μ in length.

"Oogonium borne terminally on a stalk usually 5 to 15 μ in length; smooth, subspherical, measuring 16 to 61 μ, mostly 42 to 52 μ (average 47.4 μ) in diameter; provided with a wall 0.5 to 1.7 μ (average 1.2 μ) in thickness. Antheridium single; irregularly orbicular or prolate ellipsoidal, sometimes provided with a distal protuberance or lobe; measuring usually 10 to 18 μ in diameter by 14 to 20 μ in length; in some (1 to 35 out of 100) cases amphigynous, but more often paragynous, in latter event usually applied near base of oogonium and often in intimate contact with oogonial stalk; borne laterally or terminally or in intercalary relationship on a branch mostly 5 to 50 μ in length, the branch sometimes arising from a hypha not demonstrably connected with the oogonial hypha, but sometimes having close mycelial connection with the oogonium, the total length of filamentous parts between the septa delimiting the sex organs occasionally not exceeding 40 μ. Oospore colorless or more often distinctly yellowish; smooth, subspherical, measuring 11 to 54 μ, mostly 37 to 47 μ (average 41.4 μ) in diameter; provided with a wall 0.8 to 4.6 μ (average 3.6 μ) in thickness, and containing a reserve globule measuring at early maturity 6.5 to 24.0 μ (average 17.6 μ) in diameter" (Drechsler, *loc. cit.*).

Causing a destructive decay of the stem and roots of *Althaea rosea*, Drechsler (*loc. cit.*), UNITED STATES; rice seeds and seedlings, Ito and Nagai (1931), JAPAN; saprophytic on apple (coll. Hall), Blackwell, Waterhouse, and Thompson (1941), GREAT BRITAIN.

Waterhouse (comm.) believes Ito and Nagai's *Pythiomorpha miyabeana* belongs here and, more specifically, that it is akin to the form described by Tompkins *et al.* in J. Agr. Res., 53: 685. 1936.

"*Pythiomorpha* Sp. III" of Lund (1934: 50, fig. 24 d–e), on twigs of *Alnus*, Denmark, may perhaps be referable to this species.

PHYTOPHTHORA FISCHERIANA (Höhnk), comb. nov.

Pythiomorpha fischeriana Höhnk, Bot. Centralbl., 55 (Abt. A): 92, fig. 2. 1936.

Mycelium intra- and extramatrical, the intramatrical hyphae stout, constricted, and irregular, the extramatrical slender, 2–3 μ in diameter, regular; zoosporangium ovate, 28–46 μ in diameter, renewed by cymose branching of the sporangiophore; zoospores formed within the sporangium, discharged as individuals at the rupturing of its tip, at first irregular in shape but quickly becoming reniform, 10 μ in diameter, with two lateral flagella; gemmae intercalary, ovoid, with thickened walls, rarely terminal and spherical; oögonium apogamous, at maturity bearing loosely within it a single egg with a thickened wall.

On *Alnus* twigs in water, Höhnk (*loc. cit.*; 1939: 351, fig. 6), GERMANY (and the UNITED STATES?).

Waterhouse (comm.) believes this fungus is probably allied to *Phytophthora syringae* (Kleb.) Kleb. She (1958) believes the species should be left as *incertae cedis* and that the binomial be dismissed.

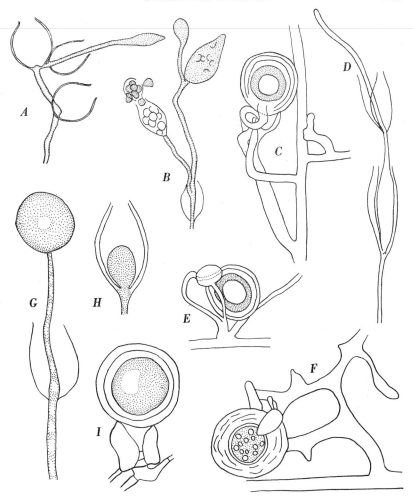

Fig. 90. *Phytophthora*

A–B. Phytophthora oryzae (Ito and Nagai) Waterhouse; *A*, sporangial bearing branch with one proliferous zoosporangium; *B*, sporangial branch with empty, discharging, and immature zoosporangia. *C–F. Phytophthora megasperma* Drechsler: *C*, sexual apparatus; *D*, proliferous, discharge zoosporangia; *E–F.* sexual apparatus. *G–I. Phytophthora cryptogea* Pethybridge and Lafferty: *G–H*, proliferated zoosporangia; *I*, sexual apparatus showing amphigynous antheridium.

(*A–F*, Ito and Nagai, 1931; *G–I*, Pethybridge and Lafferty, 1919)

PHYTOPHTHORA ORYZAE (Ito and Nagai), Waterhouse

Trans. Brit. Mycol. Soc., 41: 200. 1958

(Fig. 90 A–B, p. 1059)

Pythiomorpha oryzae Ito and Nagai, J. Fac. Agr. Hokkaido Imper. Univ., Sapporo, 32: 51, pl. 8, fig. 9, pl. 9, figs. 1–6. 1931.

"Mycelia extra- and intra-matrical; hyphae non-septate, branched monopodially, often swollen in knob-like appearance at irregular intervals, 3.5–11 μ mostly 6–8 μ in width. Sporangia ovoid, ellipsoidal or somewhat elongated, 41–84 × 26–48 μ mostly 60–84 × 29–43 μ in size; later sporangia produced on the hyphae proliferated onwardly through the empty ones, or on the lateral branch from the base of them. Zoospores ellipsoidal or kidney-shaped, about 12 × 7 μ, matured in the sporangium, swarming out directly or discharged being wrapped with the vesicle-membrane which is soon broken off by the self-agitation of the zoospores, and then swarming away. Oogonia and antheridia absent. Gemmae globular or somewhat irregular in shape, intercalary. Hyphal clumps produced on cornmeal agar" (Ito and Nagai, *loc. cit.*).

On rotted rice seeds and on seedlings in rice fields, JAPAN.

"*Pythiomorpha* Sp. I" of Lund (1934: 49, fig. 24 a–b) may possibly be referable to this species. It was found on twigs of *Salix* in Denmark.

ENTOMOPHTHORALES *(ANCYLISTES)*

A LTHOUGH the Entomophthorales are commonly thought of as a group of insect parasites, actually they live in a diversity of habitats and under a variety of biological relationships with their substrata. Of those that are saprophytic some occur on the excrement of frogs and lizards, others on fruiting bodies of higher fungi, on orchid seeds, or on rotten wood, in leaf mold, and so on, and one species, *Completoria complens*, has been found only in fern prothallia.

The discovery by Berdan (1938) that members of the small and hitherto supposedly zoosporic genus *Ancylistes* bore conidia has completely changed our concept of their relationship. From the fact that the thallus consists of a series of multinucleate segments of limited extent and may produce extramatrical conidiophores, from the tips of which conidia are forcibly projected, Berdan rightly concluded that this genus belongs in the Entomophthorales. The new status of these aquatic parasites of desmids separates them from the small number of similar-appearing but zoosporic fungi (*Myzocytium, Lagena,* and *Lagenidium*) which together with *Ancylistes* formed the old order Ancylistales.

All members of the order are characterized by a segmented thallus, the divisions of which are usually multinucleate, and have a rather coarse cytoplasm with numerous large vacuoles. The thallus segments sometimes separate, their parts forming the so-called "hyphal bodies." The conidia are unicellular and usually externally produced at the apex of a modified hypha (conidiophore) from which they are for the most part shot off into the air with considerable force. The resting spores may be asexually formed or sexually after a zygomycetous type of conjugation or one that is reminiscent of an oögamous condition.

Since concern here is only with a single genus of the family Entomophthoraceae, *Ancylistes*, the discussion is confined to it.

DEVELOPMENT AND MORPHOLOGY

THE THALLUS

The vegetative body in *Ancylistes* is a relatively broad tubular structure bearing occasional short lateral branches, the whole crowded within the confines of the host (desmid) cell. Both Dangeard (1886a) and Couch (1949) describe the young hyphae as lacking a definite wall; presumably only a membrane is present. When young, according to both Dangeard (1903b) and Couch (*op. cit.*), the thallus is multinucleate, the nuclei being regularly spaced in linear series. The contents are granular with numerous conspicuous vacuoles. The following somewhat modified account of the establishment and development of the thallus in *A. netrii* is taken from Couch (*loc. cit.*).

Soon after entry, the parasite is carried into contact with the host nucleus where it forms a short tube. The hypha then grows in opposite directions toward the ends of the desmid, usually with one branch in each groove between the plates of the chloroplast. Not infrequently a hypha may encircle the chloroplast, returning on the other side. Mature hyphae are over twice as wide as the young threads and appear to gain this increase after longitudinal growth ceases. Septation then takes place and is progressive from region to region. Each of the segments has several nuclei, as do the conidia, gametangia, and zygotes, thus confirming Dangeard's (1903b) observations. The mature thallus consists of about thirty to fifty multinucleate cells, each of which may effect reproduction in one of three ways: a cell may give rise to an extramatrical hypha, which contacts another desmid, forms a distal appressorium and infects it; after forming an extramatrical hypha this may become a conidiophore bearing a conidium; it may become a gametangium which will either fuse with another within the host to form a zygospore or, without fusion, develop into an azygospore.

REPRODUCTION

Nonsexual Reproduction

In nonsexual reproduction external hyphae from infected host plants which float near the surface function as conidiophores and may arise above the water. Potentially, each cell of the endobiotic mycelium is capable of forming such a structure. A globose conidium develops at the apex of the conidiophore, the tip of which forms a columella that projects into the conidium. After vacuolization phenomena similar to those described for *Conidiobolus* and other members of the family (see Couch, 1939c) take place, the conidium is forcibly shot off into the air, (Fig. 91F, p. 1066), often traveling as far as two millimeters in a horizontal direction. Upon germination, if its germ tube is under water, a hypha forms which may accomplish infection (Fig. 91). If the tube extends through the water film into the air, however, a secondary conidium succeeds, which may either be discharged like the first or germinate directly.

Sexual Reproduction

Because the crowded conditions prevailing in the host cell make observation difficult reports on certain aspects of sexual reproduction in *Ancylistes* are somewhat contradictory. All accounts agree that there is conjugation between the mycelial segments. Pfitzer's (1873) observations on *Ancylistes closterii* clearly indicated that in his material scalariform conjugation took place between segments of two separate thalli, all the segments of one filament being wholly contributory and all those of the other wholly receptive, with the zygotes formed within the latter. Berdan (1938), on the contrary, describes conjugation in this same species as either scalariform or lateral with the gametangia developing simultaneously as outgrowths from the hyphal cells. From continuous study of the development of a single thallus, she presents good evidence to the effect that actually the hyphal strand elongated, doubled back (at the opposite pole of the host) and grew parallel with its original element. Along these parallel strands, after segmentation, instances of both scalariform and lateral conjugation were observed. Couch's (1949) observations on conjugation in *A. netrii* are somewhat inconclusive, due no doubt to the aforementioned crowding within the host. He states, however, that conjugation is scalariform and that the zygotes mature in the conjugation tubes formed between thallus segments (Fig. 91D).

Whether the zygote at maturity is to be called a zygospore or an oöspore is also a matter of dispute. Berdan (*loc. cit.*) reports that in *Ancylistes closterii* conjugation is clearly zygomycetous, but that in *A. berdanii* ("*A. pfeifferi*" Beck) there is a tendency for the protoplast of the zygote to contract away from the wall of its container, thus simulating the egg of the Oömycetes. This suggested to her that here there exists an intermediate condition of sexuality between that group and the Zygomycetes. Couch (1939c), who studied the closely related genus *Conidiobolus,* in which a similar condition exists, points out that actually no egg is differentiated. In both papers (1939c, 1949) however, he carefully avoids the use of the term "zygospore" for the mature zygote. Knowledge concerning nuclear conditions in the gametangia and zygote is still primarily derived from the work of Dangeard (1903b). He stated that the contributory cell at first has two nuclei, whereas the receptive cell has six or eight. A single simultaneous mitotic division in each doubles these numbers. After union of the two gametes, plasmogamy but not karyogamy occurs and the mature resting structure is multinucleate. Germination of the resting zygote is by a hypha.

SYSTEMATIC ACCOUNT

ENTOMOPHTHORALES

The order is usually considered as composed of a single family.

ENTOMOPHTHORACEAE

Mycelium inter- or intracellular, coenocytic at first but usually soon becoming divided by septa into uni- or multinucleate segments which may remain conjoined or separate into hyphal bodies which often multiply, or form asexual reproductive or resting structures; nonsexual reproduction by means of uni- or multinucleate conidia borne on somewhat specialized conidiophores from which they are usually forcibly ejected; conidium giving rise to a mycelium, one or more secondary conidia, or nonmotile endogenously formed spores; resting spores thick-walled, either formed from a single cell ("azygospore") or, more commonly, sexually ("zygospore") after lateral or scalariform conjugation between cells and then borne either within one of the conjugants, or in an outgrowth from one, or at their point of union.

Parasites of insects, desmids, and fern prothallia, and saprophytes in vegetable debris and excrement of frogs and lizards.

The only members of this seemingly omnivorous family which are genuinely aquatic (*Ancylistes spp.*) are parasitic on desmids.

ANCYLISTES Pfitzer

Monatsber. Berlin Akad., 1872: 396. 1873. Emend. Berdan, Mycologia, 30: 400. 1938

(Fig. 91, p. 1066)

"Intramatrical mycelium consisting of one to several septate, tubular hyphae, variable in diameter, straight or slightly wavy, irregularly branching and anastomosing in the isthmus of the host or sparingly in other places by short lateral branches; segments of hyphae somewhat swollen, more or less constricted at the cross septa; cytoplasm with numerous rounded, highly refractive granules and somewhat regularly arranged, conspicuous vacuoles; cell walls giving no cellulose reaction with chlor-iodide of zinc. Each external hypha formed as a lateral outgrowth from an intramatrical segment; passing through the wall of host as a narrow papilla and emerging as a tubular, occasionally branched hypha into which the content of the internal segment flows and is later cut off posteriorly by a septum; growth of external hypha by progressive flow of protoplasm into advancing tip and the successive formation of cross walls. Asexual reproduction by conidia produced at the tips of the external hyphae or conidiophores and forcibly discharged into the air; conidia spherical, hyaline; columella conical, subtended by a vacuole and extending into the mature conidium before it is discharged, collapsing afterwards; conidia forming secondary or tertiary conidia directly or germinating by tube; germ tubes functioning as infection tubes or as conidiophores. Formation of conidia suppressed under water, external hyphae functioning as infection tubes. Sexual reproduction by lateral or scalariform conjugation of the contents of unequal gametangia; zygote formed in a protuberance of the female gametangium and retracted from its wall; wall of this protuberance smooth or with 9–10 truncate warts; zygote oval, spherical, thick-walled with numerous refractive globules; germination unknown" (Berdan, *loc. cit.*).

Parasites of desmids.

The genus *Ancylistes* is a small one. It consists of three valid species,

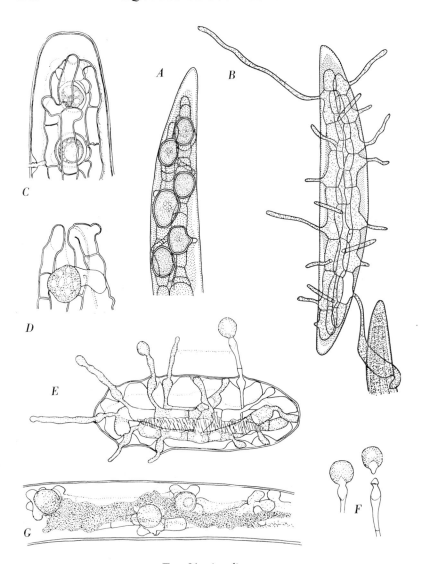

FIG. 91. *Ancylistes*

A–B. Ancylistes closterii Pfitzer in *Closterium sp.: A*, resting spores in portion of *Closterium* cell; *B*, hyphal plant showing extramatrical hyphae one of which has encircled another host cell and formed an appressorium. *C–F. Ancylistes netrii* Couch, in *Netrium sp.: C*, portion of a host cell showing two

all of which are parasites of desmids. They are fairly common in bogs, wet cow pastures, and like situations. Indeed, any collection of *Closterium* or *Netrium* is sure to yield a few cells containing *Ancylistes* in some stage of development. There is definite evidence for host specificity among the species. Thus, while Berdan's material of *A. closterii* was confined to *Closterium striolatum*, *A. berdanii* ("*A. pfeifferi*"), from the same locality and distinct morphologically from *A. closterii*, occurred only on *C. areolatum*. We have frequently encountered *A. netrii* on the saccoderm desmid *Netrium* and, although the host was associated with many other types of desmids, no other alga was attacked.

Both Berdan and Couch noted that infection may either take place by germ tubes from discharged conidia or by extramatrical mycelial elements. Conidia are formed only when infected desmids are floating on or near the surface of the water. They may be shot into the air for as much as two millimeters.

KEY TO THE SPECIES OF ANCYLISTES

Parasitic in *Closterium*; resting spore formed in the gametangium
    Resting-spore container evenly contoured; conidia in water, 15 μ in
        diameter .... *A. closterii*, p. 1067
    Resting-spore container with broad, truncated protuberances; conid-
        ia in water, 22.2–30 μ in diameter .... *A. berdanii*, p. 1069
Parasitic in *Netrium*; resting spore formed in conjugation tube
                                                A. netrii, p. 1070

ANCYLISTES CLOSTERII Pfitzer

Monatsber. Berlin Akad., 1872: 396, figs. 1–15. 1873. Emend. Berdan,
        Mycologia, 30: 401, figs. 1–8. 1938
                (Fig. 91 A–B, p. 1066)

"Intramatrical mycelium irregularly, 7.5–11 μ, wide before septation; cells or segments swollen, more or less constricted at septa, 11–15 μ × 12.5–55 μ, mostly 25–35 μ long, usually with one median and two ter-

nearly mature zygotes; *D*, young zygote apparently formed in conjugation tube; *E*, desmid near surface of water (dotted line) showing conidiophores in various stages of development, each emerging from a hyphal segment; *F*, apices of two conidiophores, one at left with attached conidium, other with just discharged conidium. *G. Ancylistes berdanii*, mature zygotes (redrawn from a photomicrograph).

(*A–B*, Pfitzer, 1873; *C–F*, Couch, 1949; *G*, Berdan, 1938)

minal vacuoles outlined by large, conspicuous, rounded, highly refractive granules, the latter also forming occasional isolated groups in the hyaline cytoplasm. External hyphae one per internal segment, frequently forming at adjacent sides of a cross wall, tubular, occasionally branched, 3–7.5 μ in diameter. Conidia hyaline, spherical, 13.5–17.5 μ, usually 15 μ, in water with a 5 μ long, basal papilla; germinating by a tube, 5 μ in diameter, or forming secondary and tertiary conidia directly. End of conidiophore swollen, 6–7.4 μ, at the base of the conidium and projecting into the undischarged conidium as a conical columella with a minute apical aperture; swollen end cell of germ and infection tube 8–10 μ × 30–60 μ; appressorium barely discernible or lacking. Conjugation lateral or scalariform, gametangia developed simultaneously as lateral outgrowths from cells of the intramatrical hyphae and delimited by 1 or 2 septa depending upon their terminal or median position; male gametangium narrow, 3.5–7.5 μ, straight or slightly curved, female gametangium rounded and enlarged; fusion occurring near base of female gametangium. Zygote developed in smooth-walled protuberance of the female gametangium, separated from the main filament by a short stalk cell; zygote or resting spore smooth, brown, thick-walled, spherical, 14.5–20 μ, usually 18.5 μ, filled with refractive globules, retracted slightly from the enclosing cell, the latter forming an even, hyaline envelope; germination unknown" (Berdan, *loc. cit.*).

Parasitic in *Closterium acerosum*, Pfitzer (*loc. cit.*), GERMANY; *Closterium sp.*, Sorokin (1883: 40, fig. 53), ASIATIC RUSSIA; Dangeard (1886a: 314, pl. 14, figs. 1–10; 1889d: 203; 1890–91b: 93, pl. 4, figs. 19–23; 1903b: 216, pls. 6–8), FRANCE; *Closterium sp.*, de Wildeman (1889–90: 135; 1893b: 62), BELGIUM; *Closterium sp.*, Constantineanu (1901: 379), ROUMANIA; *Closterium spp.*, Petersen (1910: 542, fig. XVI, F), DENMARK; *Closterium delpontii*, Schultz (1923: 178, figs. 1–2), DANZIG; *Closterium ehrenbergii* Valkanov (1931a: 365), BULGARIA; *Closterium sp.*, Couch (in Berdan, *loc. cit.*), *C. striolatum*, Berdan (*loc. cit.*), *Closterium spp.*, Linder (1947: 244) Sparrow (1952d: 771), UNITED STATES; *Closterium lanceolatum*, Bérczi (1940: 86), HUNGARY; *Closterium sp.*, Linder (F. 2597) (1947: 244), CANADIAN EASTERN ARCTIC; *Closterium sp.*, Canter (1949d: 167, fig. 4), GREAT BRITAIN; *Closterium lunula*, Höfler (1950; 381, figs. 1–4), AUSTRIA; *Closterium sp.*, John (1955: 93, figs. 1–12, pls. 5–8), INDIA.

Ancylistes closterii appears to be the commonest species of the genus, although, as Berdan suggests, some of the records based on sterile material may actually refer to *A. berdanii* ("*A. pfeifferi*"). Pfitzer's species is moderately frequent in bogs in Northern Michigan.

Berdan noted a profuse production of external hyphae in *Ancylistes closterii*; she counted as many as 65 radiating to a distance of 1.2 mm. from a single host cell.

ANCYLISTES BERDANII Sparrow

Trans. Brit. Mycol. Soc., 38: 217. 1955

(Fig. 91 G, p. 1066)

Ancylistes pfeifferi Beck, sensu Berdan (1938)

"Intramatrical mycelium irregular, 7.5–14 μ, usually 9.5–11 μ, before septation; enlarged at the free ends and at intervals along the hyphae; segments or cells distinctly femur-shaped, 10.5–11.5 μ in the center, 13–19 μ at the broad ends, 9.5–12.5 μ, usually 10.5–12.5 μ at the septa, and 43–67 μ long; segments with terminal vacuoles and several intermediate ones, and highly granular cytoplasm. Segments of external hyphae 4–7 μ × 44.5–104 μ, average 45–70 μ long. Conidia hyaline, spherical, 21–23.5 μ in air, 22.2–30 μ with papilla in water, germ tube 4.5–5 μ; appressorium at end of infection cell disc-like, 3–4 μ, later appearing as a flat plate with a hyaline, gelatinouslike sheath which extends backward to broader part of infection cell; infection cell 7.5–13 μ × 37–67 μ, usually 11–12 μ × 40–55 μ; penultimate cell often very short and broad, 6–10 μ × 9–26 μ; entrance tube penetrating appressorial plate as a fine papilla. Conjugation lateral or scalariform; gametangia cut off from vegetative cells by 1 or 2 septa depending upon their terminal or median position; male gametangium straight, narrow, sometimes with several blunt branches in cases of lateral conjugation; female gametangium swollen; cell enclosing zygote 30–40 μ, somewhat stellate with the wall extending out at intervals in 9–10 broad, bluntly truncated protuberances and separated from the main filament by a short stalk cell. Zygote or resting spore spherical, 18.5–22 μ, smooth, brown, thick-walled and filled with refractive globules; retracted from wall of enclosing cell and lying free; germination unknown" (Berdan, 1938).

Parasitic in *Closterium sp.*, Berdan (1938: 407, figs. 9–22), CANADA; *Closterium areolatum*, Berdan (*op. cit.*: 397), UNITED STATES; *Closterium sp.*, John (1955: 93, figs. 13–15), INDIA.

Ancylistes berdanii was described by Berdan (1938) and identified with *A. pfeifferi* Beck from Brazil. As she pointed out, however, and as is perfectly clear from his description, Beck (1896) based his species on a mixture of *Ancylistes* and *Myzocytium* (probably *M. megastomum*). The name of a taxonomic group "...must be rejected if the characters of that group were derived from two or more entirely discordant elements, especially if those elements were erroneously supposed to form part of the same individual." [1] Opportunity is therefore afforded to honor one who has contributed so significantly to the genus.

ANCYLISTES NETRII Couch

J. Elisha Mitchell Sci. Soc., 65: 132, pls. 6, 7. 1949

(Fig. 91 C–F)

"Vegetative mycelium within the protoplast of host cell, consisting upon reaching mature size of a branched non-septate thread which usually starts its growth near the isthmus of the desmid in contact with the host nucleus and then elongates in opposite directions toward the ends of the desmid; at first non-segmented and 2.2–4.8 μ thick; when mature consisting of 3–6, usually 4, longitudinal branches which join in the isthmus of the desmid, becoming septate into numerous cells which are usually about 2–3 times as long as thick, measuring 8–15.5 × 15–30 μ; cytoplasm with numerous rounded granules and conspicuous round vacuoles; cells becoming conspicuously swollen just before and during germination. Reproduction by vegetative, asexual and sexual methods; all cells of thallus taking part in reproduction. In vegetative and asexual reproduction exit tubes are formed (one from each cell as a rule) and grow out at right angles or slightly diagonally from the parent cell and after coming in contact with the host wall swell distally to form a club-shaped structure about 2–4 μ thick at the base and 4–9 μ thick at the larger end; if submerged the exit tube, after emerging through the des-

[1] *International Code of Botanical Nomenclature*, Article 66. VIII, Intern. Congress Bot., Paris. Utrecht, 1956.

mid wall, forms an external hypha 3–6.8 μ thick which grows through the water for some distance until it comes in contact with a new susceptible host cell; the protoplasm always in distal part of hypha and closed off from empty part by one or more cross walls. If the desmid is at the surface of the water the exit tubes form conidiophores, each unbranched and with a single apical spherical conidium; conidiophore stalk usually 25–100 μ long, sometimes longer, about 8 μ thick at its thickest point slightly below the conidium; conidia spherical, 16–25 μ thick, with a conical apiculus; forcibly discharged by the sudden outpushing of the apiculus; conidiophore with a distinct cone-shaped columella and quickly disintegrating after discharge of the conidia. Zygotes formed within the host, usually in a row in the center, between the several longitudinal hyphae and apparently by conjugation of two cells of opposite filaments, with the zygote in the conjugation tube; spherical or subspherical from pressure, 19–26 μ thick, the largest seen being 25 × 29.4 μ; wall about 2.5 μ thick, smooth; when mature with one large, slightly eccentric shiny globule embedded in the cytoplasm" (Couch, *loc. cit.*).

In *Netrium digitus*, Couch (*loc. cit.*), (MICHIGAN), UNITED STATES.

"This species is easily distinguished from others by the club-shaped exit hyphae, the position of the zygotes in the center of the host cell and bounded laterally by the empty filaments of the parasite, the larger size of the conidia and zygotes, and finally by its occurrence in *Netrium*" (Couch, *op. cit.*, p. 132).

Ancylistes netrii is very common in certain bogs in Northern Michigan.

IMPERFECTLY KNOWN SPECIES OF ANCYLISTES
? ANCYLISTES SP., Canter
Trans. Brit. Mycol. Soc., 32: 167, figs. 4–6. 1949

"The intramatrical mycelium is unbranched, often extending to the length of the host cell, 98–115 μ long by 10–17 μ broad with rounded ends and containing regularly arranged refractive granules. More than one infection may occur in a single host cell. At maturity, the thallus is cut up into three to twelve segments, 9–25 μ long by 10–17 μ broad. Each segment produces one external hypha which grows rapidly, forming septa posteriorly and contains highly refractive granules collected together in certain regions. Branched external hyphae are commonly seen. One thallus was found which did not become cut up into segments, and produced a single broad external hypha. Infection of new hosts is by the swollen end of an external hypha in contact with the wall. The appressorium is very weakly developed and in many it could not be found" (Canter, *loc. cit.*). In *Tetmemorus sp.*, GREAT BRITAIN.

EXCLUDED SPECIES OF ANCYLISTES

* ANCYLISTES CLADOCERARUM A. Fritsch

Bull. Internat. Acad. Tchèque Sci., 2: 82, fig. 5. 1895

In *Bosmina cornuta, Daphnia sp.*, CZECHOSLOVAKIA.

Considered by Berdan (1938) to be too imperfectly known to be included in the genus. Possibly a species of *Aphanomyces*.

* ANCYLISTES MIURII Skvortzow

Arch. Protistenk., 51: 432, figs. 7–10. 1925

"Intramatrical mycelium at first cylindrical, 7.4–12 μ, with hyaline, granular protoplasm, consisting of 2–5 filaments, 210–245 μ long, in a single host cell; becoming septate and divided up into 11–14 oval, bead-like cells or segments, 17.6–19 μ in length. Exit hyphae swollen, 3.7–4.2 μ, at their base and immediately inside the host wall; external hyphae or infection tubes cylindrical and curved, 2.5–3 μ in diameter. Conidia unknown. Conjugation scalariform; male gametangium cylindrical, female gametangium barrel-shaped, 12–19.5 μ thick by 7.4–12 μ long. Resting spore lying free, spherical, 7.4–9.5 μ, hyaline, smooth, thick-walled with numerous refractive globules in the centre; germination unknown" (Berdan, 1938, p. 409).

Parasitic in *Closterium sp.*, NORTH MANCHURIA, CHINA.

Because of the beadlike nature of the thallus and lack of lateral conjugation, Berdan suggests that this may be a species of *Myzocytium*. A study of the figures indicates beyond a doubt the correctness of her statement. See *M. megastomum* (p. 978), with which it is considered synonymous.

* ANCYLISTES PFEIFFERI Beck

Verhandl. Zoo.-Bot. Gesell. Wien, 46: 233. 1896. Botan. Centralbl., 69: 11 1897

Closterium sp., coll. Löfgren, BRAZIL.

Based upon a mixture of *Ancylistes* and *Myzocytium megastomum* (see p. 1070).

LIST OF SUBSTRATA

PLANTS

THALLOPHYTA

ALGAE

Cyanophyceae[1] (Blue-green Algae)

Anabaena affinis var. *intermedia*
?Rhizosiphon akinetum
  R. anabaenae
  R. crassum
A. circinalis
?Chytridium cornutum
Rhizophydium cornutum
A. flos-aquae
Phlyctidium megastomum
A. macrospora
?Rhizosiphon akinetum
A. spiroides var. *crassa*
Rhizosiphon crassum
Anabaena sp.
Rhizosiphon anabaenae
R. crassum
Aphanizomenon flos-aquae
Phlyctidium globosum
A. gracile?
Rhizophydium subangulosum
Calothrix (Mastigothrix) aeruginea
Rhizophlyctis mastigotrichis
*Rhizophydium microsporum
Calothrix parasitica
Coenomyces consuens
Calothrix sp. (marine)
Coenomyces consuens
Rhizophydium sp.
Chroococcus turgidus
Rhizophydium agile
Dicothrix (Schizosiphon) kerguelenensis
?Rhizophydium caudatum

Filarszkya sp.
Rhizosiphon crassum
Hormotheca sicula
Nowakowskia hormothecae
Lyngbya aestuarii (filaments)
Lagenidium nodosum
Lyngbya sp.
Lagenidium nodosum
Rhizophydium megarrhizum
R. subangulosum
Microcystis aeruginosa
Chytridium microcystidis
M. flos-aquae
Chytridium microcystidis
M. viridis
Chytridium microcystidis
Oscillatoria agardhii?
Rhizophydium subangulosum
O. agardhii var. *isothrix*
Rhizophydium megarrhizum
O. rubescens
Rhizophydium deformans
R. megarrhizum
R. oscillatoriae
R. subangulosum
O. tenuis var. *subfusca*
Rhizophydium subangulosum
Oscillatoria sp.
Phlyctidium anatropum
Rhizophydium megarrhizum
R. subangulosum
"Oscillatoriens"
Rhizophydium megarrhizum
Rivularia atra var. *confluens*
Coenomyces consuens
Stigonema sp.
Phlyctochytrium unispinum

---

[1] Myxophyceae.

1073

Tolypothrix lanata
  Rhizophlyctis tolypotrichis
Tolypothrix sp.
  ?Resticularia boodlei

CHLOROPHYCEAE (GREEN ALGAE)

Aegagropila sauteri
  Olpidium entophytum
Aegagropila sp.
  Lagenidium sp.
Ankistrodesmus sp.
  Zygorhizidium parallelosede
Apiocystis brauniana
  Rhizophydium anomalum
  R. brauni
Bryopsis plumosa
  Sirolpidium bryopsidis
  Thraustochytrium proliferum
Bryopsis sp.
  Chytridium turbinatum
  Eurychasma sp.
  Phlyctidium brevipes var. marinum
  Phlyctochytrium bryopsidis
  Rhizophydium subglobosum
Bulbochaete setigera (setae)
  ?Chytridium minus
Bulbochaete sp. (setae)
  Chytridium chaetophilum
  C. schenkii
  Rhizophydium chaetiferum
Chaetomorpha aerea
  ?Lagenidium sp.
Chaetophora elegans
  Amoebochytrium rhizidioides
  Phlyctidium anatropum
  Phlyctochytrium chaetophorae
  Rhizidium nowakowskii
Chaetophora sp.
  Nowakowskiella elegans
  Rhizidium mycophilum
Characium ancora
  Phlyctidium piriformis
Characium sp.
  ?Chytridium characii
Chlamydococcus pluvialis
  ?Chytridium chlamidococci

Chlamydomonas dillii
  Rhizophydium transversum
C. globulosa
  Rhizidiomyces ichneumon
C. nivalis
  Chytridium neochlamydococci
  Rhizophydium sp.
C. obtusa
  Rhizophydium transversum
C. pluvialis
  Polyphagus nowakowskii
C. pulvisculus
  Entophlyctis apiculata
  Rhizophydium transversum
C. reinhardi
  Polyphagus euglenae
Chlamydomonas sp.
  Entophlyctis apiculata
  Phlyctochytrium proliferum
  P. vernale
  Polyphagus euglenae
  P. laevis
  Rhizophydium acuforme
  Scherffeliomyces appendiculatus
Chlorococcum sp.
  Rhizophydium simplex
Chlorodendron subsalsum
  Ectrogella marina
Chlorogonium elongatum
  Phlyctidium chlorogonii
C. euchlorum
  Phlyctidium chlorogonii
Cladophora fracta
  Chytridium gibbosum
C. glomerata
  Catenaria sphaerocarpa
  Entophlyctis confervae-glomeratae
  ?E. maxima
  Olpidium entophytum
  Rhizophydium globosum
  R. macrosporum
C. (Acrosiphonia) hystrix
  Olpidiopsis andreei
C. (Acrosiphonia) incurva
  Olpidiopsis andreei
  ?Rhizophydium discinctum

C. japonica
  Catenochytridium carolinianum f.
    marinum
  Chytridium lagenaria var. japonense
  Entophlyctis confervae-glomeratae f.
    marina
  Japonochytrium marinum
  Myzocytium proliferum f. marinum
  Phlyctochytrium marinum
  Pontisma lagenidioides
  Sirolpidium bryopsidis

C. kuetzingiana
  Myzocytium proliferum

C. (Acrosiphonia) pallida
  ?Rhizophydium gelatinosum

Cladophora sp.
  Achlyogeton entophytum
  ?Bicricium transversum
  Catenaria sphaerocarpa
  Chytridium aggregatum
  C. inflatum
  C. lagenaria
  C. schenkii
  C. sphaerocarpum
  Diplophlyctis laevis
  Endochytrium ramosum
  Entophlyctis confervae-glomeratae
  Myzocytium megastomum
  M. proliferum
  Olpidium entophytum
  Phlyctidium spinulosum
  ?Phlyctidium sp.
  Phlyctochytrium bullatum
  P. chaetiferum
  P. cladophorae
  P. dentiferum
  P. planicorne
  P. quadricorne
  P. urceolare
  Rhizophydium ampullaceum
  R. chaetiferum
  R. mammillatum
  R. cladophorae
  R. messanense
  ?Saccopodium gracile

Cladophora sp. (marine)
  ?Achlyogeton salinum

?Olpidium aggregatum
  Sirolpidium bryopsidis

Cladophora (Acrosiphonia) sp. (marine)
  Olpidiopsis andreei

Codium fragile
  Rhizoclosmatium marinum

C. mucronatum
  Chytridium codicola
  Rhizophydium codicola

Coleochaete prostrata
  ?Chytridium depressum

C. pulvinata
  Rhizophydium mammillatum

C. pulvinata (oögonia)
  ?Rhizophydium coleochaetes

C. scutata
  Phlyctidium brebissonii

Coleochaete sp.
  Cladochytrium replicatum

Dictyosphaerium pulchellum
  Rhizophydium sphaerocystidis

Draparnaldia glomerata
  Pseudolpidium deformans
  Rhizophydium mammillatum
  Sporophlyctis rostrata

D. nudiuscula
  Rhizophydium mammillatum

D. plumosa
  Canteriomyces stigeoclonii
  Sporophlyctis rostrata

Draparnaldia sp.
  Rhizophydium mammillatum
  Sporophlyctis chinensis

Elaktothrix gelatinosa
  Zygorhizidium parallelosede

Eudorina elegans
  Dangeardia mammillata
  Endocoenobium eudorinae
  Phlyctidium eudorinae
  Rhizophydium eudorinae

E. illinoiensis
  Phlyctidium eudorinae

Eudorina sp.
  Phlyctidium eudorinae

Gemellicystis neglecta
Rhizidium windermerense
Rhizophydium fulgens
R. uniguttulatum
Gloeococcus (Chlamydomonas?) mucosus
Entophlyctis apiculata
Gloeococcus (?) sp.
Entophlyctis apiculata
Gloeocystis bacillus
Olpidium entophytum
Gloeocystis sp.
Entophlyctis apiculata
?Rhizophydium digitatum
Gonium tetras
Rhizophydium transversum
Hormidium flaccidum
?Rhizophydium hormidii
H. penicilliformis
?Olpidium entosphaericum
H. uniflexa
Rhizophydium haynaldii
H. varium
?Chytridium cornutum
Hormiscia sp.
Rhizophydium transversum
Hydrodictyon reticulatum
Catenaria sphaerocarpa
Hyphochytrium hydrodictii
Phlyctochytrium chaetiferum
P. hydrodictyi
H. utriculatum
Phlyctochytrium hydrodictyi
Kirschneriella obesa
Zygorhizidium parvum
Oedogonium apophysatum (oögonia)
Chytridium brevipes
O. boscii
?Lagenidium syncytiorum
L. oedogonii
O. capillare
Chytridium olla
O. cardiacum
?Rhizophydium decipiens
O. crassusculum var. *idiosporum*
Rhizophydium ampullaceum
O. crenulato-costatum
Rhizophydium ampullaceum

O. echinospermum (oögonia)
Chytridium acuminatum
?Rhizophydium decipiens
O. flavescens (oögonia)
Chytridium brevipes
O. obsidionale
?Achlyogeton solatium
O. plagiostomum
Rhizophydium ampullaceum
O. plusiosporum
Lagenidium rabenhorstii
O. rivulare
Phlyctochytrium quadricorne
Rhizophydium globosum
O. rothii (oögonia)
Chytridium acuminatum
O. rufescens
?Rhizophydium decipiens
O. sexangulare
?Rhizophydium decipiens
O. tumidulum
Rhizophydium globosum
O. tumidulum (oögonia)
?Rhizophydium decipiens
O. undulatum
Rhizophydium ampullaceum
O. vaucherii (oögonia)
Chytridium brevipes
?Rhizophydium decipiens
?R. sporoctonum
O. vesicatum
Rhizophydium ampullaceum
Oedogonium sp. (oögonia)
Aphanistis oedogoniorum
Chytridium brevipes
C. olla
C. schenkii
Phlyctochytrium planicorne
?Rhizophydium decipiens
R. mammillatum
?R. v. mindeni
Oedogonium sp. (oöspore)
Chytridium olla
C. schenkii
Rhizophydium ovatum
*R. (?) setigerum

Oedogonium sp. (zygote)
Olpidium entophytum
Rhizophydium parasiticum
Aphanistis oedogoniorum
?A. (?) pellucida
Chytridium aggregatum
C. chaetophilum
C. inflatum
C. lagenaria
?C. minus
*C. oblongum
C. oedogonii
C. olla
C. schenkii
Cladochytrium replicatum
Entophlyctis bulligera
E. confervae-glomeratae
Lagenidium marchalianum
L. oedogonii
L. rabenhorstii
L. zopfii
Micromyces oedogonii
Myzocytium proliferum
Olpidiopsis oedogoniarum
?Olpidium pusillum
*O. indicum
Phlyctidium brevipes var. brevipes
Phlyctochytrium biporosum
P. chaetiferum
P. lagenaria
P. planicorne
P. unispinum
Plasmophagus oedogoniorum
Pleotrachelus petersenii
?Resticularia oedogonii
Rhizophydium ampullaceum
R. canterae
R. chaetiferum
R. constantineani
R. globosum
?R. oedogonii
R. sphaerocarpum
Oocystis lacustris
?Chytridium oocystidis
O. solitaria var. *wittrockiana*
Rhizophydium pseudodistomum
Palmodictyon sp.
Rhizophydium acuforme

Pandorina morum
Dangeardia mammillata
?Phlyctochytrium pandorinae
Pandorina sp.
Rhizophydium simplex
Pithophora sp.
Catenaria sphaerocarpa
Rhizophydium macrosporum
Protoderma sp.
Sporophlyctidium africanum
Pseudobryopsis myuria
Sirolpidium bryopsidis
Rhizoclonium hieroglyphicum
Chytridium lagenaria
Phlyctochytrium hydrodictyi
P. planicorne
Sphaerella lacustris
Chytridium chlamidococcus
S. (Haematococcus) lacustris
Rhizidium vorax
Sphaerella (Haematococcus) sp.
?Chytridium haematococci
Sphaerocystis schroeteri
Polyphagus ramosus
Rhizophydium sphaerocystidis
Zygorhizidium parvum
Sphaeroplea annulina
Olpidium sphaeropleae
Rhizophydium globosum
Spongomorpha vernalis
?Rhizophydium discinctum
Spongomorpha sp.
Olpidiopsis andreei
Stigeoclonium subuligerum
Canteriomyces stigeoclonii
Stigeoclonium sp.
Canteriomyces stigeoclonii
Chytridium curvatum
C. papillatum
C. sphaerocarpum
Phlyctidium anatropum
P. laterale
Rhizophydium mammillatum
R. ovatum
Stylosphaeridium stipitatum
Rhizophydium ephippium

Ulothrix albicans
　?Chytridium minus
U. zonata
　Phlyctidium laterale
　Rhizophydium haynaldii
　R. karlingii
Ulothrix sp.
　Phlyctidium laterale
　Rhizophydium globosum
Ulotrichales
　Thraustochytrium globosum
Volvox carteri
　Loborhiza metzneri
V. globator
　?Chytridium volvocinum

ZYGNEMATALES [1]

Mougeotia genuflexa
　Rhizophydium sphaerocarpum
M. parvula
　Rhizophydium sphaerocarpum
　Zygorhizidium willei
M. pleurocarpa
　Myzocytium proliferum
　?Phlyctidium minimum
M. scalaris
　Micromyces zygogonii
　?Olpidium mougeotia
M. sphaerocarpa
　Rhizophydium sphaerocarpum
M. viridis
　?Rhizophydium hormidii
Mougeotia sp.
　Blyttiomyces spinulosus
　Chytridium acuminatum
　*C. mesocarpi
　C. sphaerocarpum
　Entophlyctis bulligera
　E. pygmaea
　Lagenidium rabenhorstii
　?Micromyces echinocystis
　M. laevis
　M. longispinosus

M. ovalis
M. petersenii
M. zygogonii
?Micromyces sp.
　Myzocytium proliferum
　Olpidiopsis appendiculata
?O. elliptica
O. schenkiana
?Olpidium mesocarpi
　Phlyctidium apophysatum
　Rhizophydium ampullaceum
　R. couchii
?R. digitatum
?R. fallax
　R. sphaerocarpum
　Zygorhizidium willei
Spirogyra affinis
　Myzocytium proliferum
S. areolata
　Rhizophydium couchii
S. calospora
　Lagenidium entophytum
S. communis
　Olpidium entophytum
S. crassa
　Catenaria sphaerocarpa
　Chytridium aggregatum
　Cladochytrium replicatum
　Entophlyctis bulligera
　E. confervae-glomeratae
　Myzocytium proliferum
　Phlyctochytrium lagenaria
　Rhizophydium rostellatum
S. grevilleana
　Lagenidium gracile
S. inflata
　?Micromyces spirogyrae
　?Olpidium spirogyrae
S. insignis
　Lagenidium entophytum
　Phlyctochytrium equale
S. jurgensii
　Myzocytium proliferum
　Olpidium rostriferum

[1] Because many members are important hosts of Phycomycetes, the order Zygnematales is segregated for purposes of this list.

S. longata
 Olpidiopsis fibrillosa
 Zygorhizidium willei
S. majuscula
 Blyttiomyces spinulosus
 Olpidium endogenum
S. maxima
 Lagenidium entophytum
 Myzocytium proliferum
 Rhizophydium haynaldii
 R. sphaerocarpum
S. mirabilis
 Micromyces zygogonii
 Myzocytium proliferum
S. orthospira
 Lagenidium rabenhorstii
 Phlyctochytrium dentatum
S. quadrata
 Micromyces zygogonii
S. spreeiana
 Phlyctochytrium equale
S. varians
 Lagenidium entophytum
 Phlyctidium brevipes var. brevipes
 Phlyctochytrium planicorne
 Rhizophydium minutum
S. weberi
 Blyttiomyces spinulosus
S. (Rhynchonema) sp.
 ?Entophlyctis tetraspora
Spirogyra sp.
 Blyttiomyces spinulosus
 Chytridium kolianum
 C. lagenaria
 C. schenkii
 C. sphaerocarpum
 Endochytrium pseudodistomum
 Entophlyctis bulligera
 E. confervae-glomeratae
 E. vaucheriae
 Lagenidium entophytum
 L. gracile
 L. papillosum
 L. rabenhorstii
 Micromyces cristata var. minor
 M. grandis
 M. longispinosus

M. zygogonii
 Myzocytium proliferum
 Olpidiopsis fibrillosa
 O. schenkiana
 O. zopfii
 Olpidium entophytum
 Phlyctidium brevipes var. brevipes
 P. olla
 Phlyctochytrium biporosum
 P. dentatum
 P. dentiferum
 P. hallii
 P. lagenaria
 P. laterale
 P. planicorne
 ?P. spirogyrae
 P. zygnematis
 *Rhizidium algaecolum
 ?R. variabile
 Rhizophydium ampullaceum
 R. chaetiferum
 R. couchii
 ?R. dubium
 R. gibbosum
 R. globosum
 R. simplex
 R. sphaerocarpum
 Rhizophydium sp.
 ?Rhizophydium sp.

Zygnema cruciatum
 Myzocytium proliferum
 Phlyctochytrium zygnematis

Z. stellina
 Micromyces zygnaemicola
 Phlyctochytrium zygnematis

Zygnema sp.
 Blyttiomyces laevis
 Chytridium kolianum
 C. schenkii
 C. sphaerocarpum
 C. stellatum
 Coralliochytrium scherffelii
 Endochytrium pseudodistomum
 Entophlyctis bulligera
 Lagenidium rabenhorstii
 ?Micromyces echinocystis
 M. intermedia

?M. minimus
M. ovalis var. giganteus
?M. wheldenii
Myzocytium proliferum
Olpidium zygnemicola
Phlyctidium tenue
Phlyctochytrium lagenaria
P. magnum
P. unispinum
?Rhizophydium barkerianum
?R. digitatum
Zygorhizidium willei
Zygogonium sp.
Micromyces fischerii
M. zygogonii
"Conjugatae"
Micromyces zygogonii

DESMIDS (PLACODERM AND SACCODERM)[1]

Arthrodesmus sp.
?Bicricium naso
Rhizophydium difficile
Closterium acerosum
Ancylistes closterii
Myzocytium megastomum
M. proliferum
C. angustatum
Myzocytium proliferum
C. areolatum
Ancylistes berdanii
Myzocytium megastomum
C. attenuatum
Myzocytium megastomum
C. costatum
Micromyces mirabilis
Olpidium utriculiforme
Phlyctochytrium mucronatum
C. delpontii
Ancylistes closterii
C. dianeae
Micromyces mirabilis
Olpidium utriculiforme
C. didymotocum
Myzocytium proliferum
C. ehrenbergii
Ancylistes closterii

Lagenidium intermedium
?Phlyctochytrium desmidiacearum
C. kutzingii
Micromyces mirabilis
C. lanceolatum
Ancylistes closterii
C. lunula
Ancylistes closterii
Micromyces mirabilis
Olpidium endogenum
O. utriculiforme
Rhizophydium globosum
C. pritchardianum
Phlyctochytrium mucronatum
C. ralfsii var. *hybridum*
?Lagenidium sacculoides
Olpidium endogenum
C. rostratum
Chytriomyces closterii
Lagenidium closterii
C. setiferum
Lagenidium closterii
C. striolatum
Ancylistes closterii
Lagenidium closterii
Closterium sp.
Ancylistes berdanii
A. closterii
Chytridium gibbosum
C. schenkii
Lagenidium closterii
Micromyces mirabilis
Myzocytium megastomum
M. proliferum
Olpidium endogenum
O. entophytum
?O. rostratum
Phlyctochytrium closterii
Rhizophydium globosum
?R. septocarpoides
R. verrucosum
Cosmarium botrytis
Olpidium saccatum
O. utriculiforme

[1] An important group of the Zygnematales, hence, placed as a separate head.

C. connatum
Myzocytium proliferum
C. conspersum
Olpidium utriculiforme
C. depressum var. *achondrum*
Olpidium endogenum
C. didymochondrum
Myzocytium proliferum
C. pachydermum
Olpidium endogenum
C. pericymatium
Myzocytium megastomum
C. pyramidatum
Lagenidium pygmaeum
C. undulatum var. *minutum*
Olpidium utriculiforme
Cosmarium sp.
?Myzocytium irregulare
M. proliferum
Olpidium endogenum
?O. immersum
O. saccatum
O. utriculiforme
?Phlyctochytrium autrani
Rhizophydium constantineani
Cylindrocystis brebissonii
Endodesmidium formosum
Zygorhizidium willei
C. crassa
Endodesmidium formosum
Cylindrocystis sp.
Rhizophydium gibbosum
Desmidium swartzii
Olpidium entophytum
Docidium ehrenbergii
Mitochytrium ramosum
Docidium sp.
Mitochytridium ramosum
Euastrum bidentatum
Olpidium utriculiforme
E. humerosum (?)
Lagenidium entophytum
Euastrum sp.
Myzocytium megastomum
Olpidium endogenum

Genicularia sp.
Rhizophydium globosum
Hyalotheca dissiliens
Micromyces cristata var. cristata
Olpidium hyalothecae
?Rhizophydium hyalothecae
H. dubia
Micromyces cristata var. cristata
H. mucosa
Olpidium hyalothecae
Mesotaenium caldariorum
Zygorhizidium verrucosum
Micrasterias denticula
?Myzocytium irregulare
M. mahabuleshwarensis var. *wallichii*
Lagenidium entophytum
M. rotata
?Myzocytium irregulare
M. truncata
Olpidium saccatum
Micrasterias sp.
?Myzocytium irregulare
Olpidium endogenum
Netrium digitus
Ancylistes netrii
Aphanomycopsis desmidiella
?Phlyctochytrium desmidiacearum
N. oblongum
Endodesmidium formosum
Netrium sp.
?Blyttiomyces sp.
Micromyces zygogonii
Rhizophydium conicum
Penium digitus
Rhizophydium globosum
P. margaritaceum
Olpidium endogenum
Penium sp.
Olpidium endogenum
Rhizophydium gibbosum
Phycastrum sp.
Rhizophydium gibbosum
Pleurotaenium trabecula
Aphanomycopsis desmidiella
Myzocytium proliferum
Rhizophydium globosum

Pleurotaenium sp.
  Olpidium endogenum
Sphaerozosma vertebratum
  ?Olpidium algarum var. brevirostrum
Spirotaenia condensata
  Rhizophydium columnaris
  ?R. spirotaeniae
Spirotaenia sp.
  Myzocytium megastomum
  Rhizophydium globosum
Staurastrum dejectum var. *debaryanum*
  ?Chytridium muricatum
S. jaculiferum
  Rhizophydium difficile
Staurastrum sp.
  ?Olpidium immersum
  O. saccatum
  Rhizophydium globosum
Tetmemorus brebissonii
  Micromyces fischerii
Tetmemorus sp.
  Ancylistes sp.
  Olpidium endogenum
"Desmid" (zygote)
  ?Chytridium sp.
"Desmids"
  ?Myzocytium lineare
  Olpidium endogenum
  ?O. immersum
  O. saccatum
  Rhizidium braunii

CHARACEAE

Chara contraria
  Sorodiscus karlingii
C. coronata
  Catenaria sphaerocarpa
  Diplophlyctis intestina
  Endochytrium digitatum
  E. operculatum
  Hyphochytrium catenoides
  Nephrochytrium appendiculatum
  Rhizophydium chaetiferum
  R. macrosporum
C. delicatula
  Diplophlyctis intestina

Nephrochytrium appendiculatum
  Sorodiscus karlingii
C. fragilis
  Diplophlyctis intestina
  D. verrucosa
  Phlyctochytrium hallii
C. polycanthum
  Diplophlyctis intestina
Chara sp.
  Diplophlyctis laevis
  Entophlyctis helioformis
  Nowakowskiella ramosa
Lamprothamnus alopecuroides
  Diplophlyctis intestina
Lychnothamnus barbatus
  Diplophlyctis intestina
Nitella flexilis
  Catenaria sphaerocarpa
  Chytridium lagenaria
  Diplophlyctis intestina
  Endochytrium digitatum
  Hyphochytrium catenoides
  Nephrochytrium appendiculatum
  Rhizophydium macrosporum
N. glomerulifera
  Diplophlyctis intestina
N. gracilis
  Nephrochytrium appendiculatum
N. hyalina
  Nephrochytrium stellatum
N. mucronata
  Diplophlyctis intestina
N. tenuissima
  Diplophlyctis intestina
  Entophlyctis helioformis
  ?Phlyctochytrium catenatum
N. tenuissima (oögonia)
  Chytridium olla
Nitella sp.
  Catenaria anguillulae
  Diplophlyctis intestina
  D. laevis
  Entophlyctis helioformis
"Characeae" (oögonia)
  ?Entophlyctis characearum
  ?Lagenidiopsis reducta

"*Characeae*"
  Apodachlya pyrifera
  Catenaria anguillulae
  Diplophlyctis intestina

XANTHOPHYCEAE [1]

Bumillaria sp.
  Phlyctidium bumilleriae
  Phlyctochytrium biporosum
  ?Rhizophydium sp.
Characiopsis minuta
  Chytridium scherffelii
Chlorobotrys polychloris
  Chytridium chlorobotrytis
  ?Chytridium sp.
Mischococcus confervicola
  Rhizophydium mischococci
Ophiocytium (*Sciadium*) *arbusculum*
  Rhizophydium sciadii
Tribonema bombycina
  Chytridium confervae
  C. lagenula
  ?Olpidium sorokinei
  Plasmophagus oedogoniorum
  Polyphagus parasiticus
  ?Rhizophydium asterosporum
  R. goniosporum
  R. granulosporum
  R. mammillatum
  ?R. persimilis
  ?Rhizophydium sp.
T. bombycina var. *minor*
  Rhizophydium asymmetricum
Tribonema (?) *sp.*
  ?Olpidium algarum
Tribonema sp.
  Phlyctidium anatropum
Vaucheria geminata
  Chytridium cejpii
  C. pyriforme
  C. sexuale
  Entophlyctis rhizina
  ?E. woronichinii
  Olpidium entophytum

V. globifera (*salina*?)
  Olpidium entophytum
V. polysperma
  Phlyctochytrium quadricorne
V. sessilis
  Chytridium cejpii
  C. pyriforme
  Entophlyctis rhizina
  E. vaucheriae
  ?E. woronichinii
  Olpidium entophytum
  Woronina glomerata
V. sessilis (oögonia)
  ?Rhizophydium multiporum
  R. vaucheriae
V. terrestris
  Woronina glomerata
Vaucheria sp.
  Chytridium lagenaria
  Entophlyctis helioformis
  Olpidium entophytum
  Phlyctochytrium biporosum
  P. planicorne
  Rhizophydium constantineani
  Woronina glomerata
Vaucheria sp. (oögonia)
  Phlyctochytrium bullatum
Vaucheria sp. (öospores)
  ?Rhizophydium pyriformis

CHRYSOPHYCEAE

"*Chrysomonad*" (cyst)
  *Rhizophydium utriculus
Chrysopyxis sp.
  ?Rhizophydium chrysopyxidis
Dinobryon divergens
  Rhizophydium oblongum
D. stipitatum
  Rhizophydium oblongum
Dinobryon sp.
  Rhizophydium oblongum
Hyalobryon polymorphum
  Rhizophydium hyalobryonis

[1] Heterokontae.

DINOPHYCEAE[1]

Ceratium hirundinella
  ?Amphicypellus elegans
Glenodinium cinctum
  Pseudolpidium glenodinianum
  Rhizophydium echinatum
Peridinium cinctum
  ?Amphicypellus elegans
Peridinium sp.
  ?Amphicypellus elegans

BACILLARIOPHYCEAE [2]

Achnanthes affinis
  Rhizophydium achnanthis
Amphora ovalis
  Lagenidium enecans
  Physorhizophidium pachydermum
  Podochytrium emmanuelense
Amphora sp.
  Podochytrium clavatum
Asterionella formosa
  Rhizophydium planktonicum
  Zygorhizidium planktonicum
A. gracillima
  Rhizophydium schroeteri
Cocconeis pediculus
  Chytridium cocconeidis
Cocconema lanceolatum
  Lagenidium enecans
  Olpidiopsis gillii
Cyclotella chaetoceras
  Rhizophydium cyclotellae
C. kutzingiana
  Lagenidium cyclotellae
Cyclotella sp.
  Rhizophydium cyclotellae
Cymatopleura elliptica
  Rhizophydium clinopus
C. solea
  Chytridium versatile
  Lagenidium enecans
  Rhizophydium clinopus

Cymbella aspera
  Rhizophydium clinopus
C. cistula
  Lagenidium enecans
C. cymbiformis var. *parva*
  Lagenidium brachystomum
C. gastroides
  Aphanomycopsis bacillariacearum
  Lagenidium enecans
Cymbella sp.
  Chytridium perniciosum
  Rhizophydium clinopus
  R. fusus
Epithemia turgida
  Aphanomycopsis bacillariacearum
E. zebra
  Chytridium epithemiae
  ?Rhizophydium epithemiae
Eunotia amphioxys
  Rhizophydium globosum
E. arcus
  Ectrogella eunotiae
Fragilaria crotonensis
  Chytridium versatile
  Rhizophydium fragilariae
Fragilaria sp.
  Podochytrium clavatum
Gomphonema constrictum
  Lagenidium brachystomum
  Phlyctidium irregulare
  Rhizophydium fusus
G. macropus
  Podochytrium emmanuelense
G. micropus
  Ectrogella gomphonematis
  Podochytrium clavatum
G. navicella
  ?Chytridium minus
Gomphonema sp.
  Ectrogella bacillariacearum
Gyrosigma acuminatum
  Olpidiopsis gillii

---

[1] Dinoflagellates.
[2] Diatoms.

G. attenuatum
  Olpidiopsis gillii

Hantzschia amphioxys
  Olpidium hantzschiae
  Phlyctidium irregulare
  Rhizophydium irregulare

Lauderia borealis
  Ectrogella perforans
  ?Olpidium lauderiae

Licmophora abbreviata
  Ectrogella perforans

L. flagellata
  Ectrogella perforans

L. gracilis
  Ectrogella perforans

L. lyngbyei
  *Ectrogella eurychasmoides

L. lyngbyei (abbreviata?)
  Ectrogella perforans

Licmophora sp.
  Ectrogella licmophorae
  E. perforans

Melosira ambigua
  Chytridium melosireae
  C. versatile
  Rhizophydium fusus

M. italica subsp. *subarctica*
  Zygorhizidium melosirae

M. varians
  Chytridium appressum
  C. nodulosum
  C. versatile
  Podochytrium clavatum
  P. emmanuelense
  P. lanceolatum
  Rhizophydium fusus
  R. globosum
  R. melosirae

Melosira sp.
  Chytridium versatile
  Podochytrium clavatum
  P. emmanuelense
  Rhizophydium fusus

Melosira sp. (marine)
  ?Rhizophydium marinum

Meridion circulare
  Ectrogella bacillariacearum

Navicula cuspidata
  Lagenidium enecans

N. cuspidata var. *ambigua*
  Lagenidium enecans

N. oblonga
  ?Chytridium versatile var. podochytrioides

Navicula sp.
  Chytridium versatile
  Physorhizophidium pachydermum
  Podochytrium clavatum
  Rhizophydium clinopus
  R. gibbosum
  R. globosum

Nitzschia linearis
  Lagenidium brachystomum

N. sigmoidea
  Aphanomycopsis bacillariacearum
  ?Aphanomycopsis sp.
  Chytridium versatile
  Ectrogella bacillariacearum
  Olpidiopsis gillii
  Rhizophydium clinopus

Nitzschia sp.
  Olpidiopsis gillii
  Podochytrium emmanuelense

Pinnularia viridis
  Aphanomycopsis bacillariacearum
  Lagenidium enecans
  Podochytrium emmanuelense
  Rhizophydium globosum

Pinnularia sp.
  Aphanomycopsis bacillariacearum
  Ectrogella bacillariacearum
  E. monostoma
  Lagenidium enecans
  ?Lagenidium sp.
  Podochytrium clavatum
  P. emmanuelense
  Rhizophydium fusus

"Pinnularians"
  Rhizophydium gibbosum

Pleurosigma attenuatum
  Olpidiopsis gillii

Podocystis adriatica
  Ectrogella perforans

Stauroneis phoenicentron
  Lagenidium enecans
Stephanodiscus niagarae
  Podochytrium cornutum
Striatella unipunctata
  Ectrogella perforans
Surirella ovata
  Chytridium surirellae
Surirella sp.
  Rhizophydium fusus
Synedra acus var. *angustissima*
  Zygorhizidium planktonicum
S. capitata
  Ectrogella bacillariacearum
S. lunularis
  Ectrogella bacillariacearum
S. tabulata
  Ectrogella perforans
S. ulna
  Ectrogella bacillariacearum
  E. monostoma
  E. perforans
  Lagenidium brachystomum
Synedra sp.
  Aphanomycopsis bacillariacearum
  Chytridium versatile
  Ectrogella bacillariacearum
  E. monostoma
  Lagenidium brachystomum
  Rhizophydium fusus
  Septolpidium lineare
  Zygorhizidium planktonicum
Tabellaria fenestrata
  Chytriomyces tabellariae
T. flocculosa
  Chytriomyces tabellariae
  Podochytrium clavatum
  P. emmanuelense
T. flocculosa var. *asterionelloides*
  Chytridium versatile
Tabellaria sp.
  Chytridium nodulosum
  C. versatile
Thalassionema nitzschioides (?)
  Ectrogella perforans

"Diatoms"
  Aphanomycopsis bacillariacearum
  Chytridium acuminatum
  Ectrogella bacillariacearum
  Lagenidium enecans
  Phlyctidium irregulare
  Podochytrium clavatum
  Rhizidium braunii
  Rhizophlyctis borneensis
  Rhizophydium clinopus
  R. fusus
  R. globosum

CRYPTOPHYCEAE

Chilomonas sp. (cysts)
  Rhizidium vorax
Cryptomonas sp.
  Pseudosphaerita radiata
Cryptomonas sp. (cysts)
  Rhizophydium simplex

EUGLENOPHYCEAE

Euglena caudata
  Pseudosphaerita euglenae
E. sanguinia
  Polyphagus euglenae
E. viridis
  ?Chytridium euglenae
  Polyphagus euglenae
  P. laevis
  Saccomyces endogenus
  Sphaerita dangeardii
Euglena sp.
  Olpidium euglenae
  Phlyctochytrium longicollum
  Polyphagus euglenae
  P. laevis
  Pseudosphaerita euglenae
  Saccomyces endogenus
  Sphaerita dangeardii
  Sphaerita sp.
Euglena sp. (cysts)
  ?Chytridium euglenae
  *Phlyctochytrium euglenae
  Scherffeliomyces parasitans
Euglena sp. (*Gloeocystis* stage)
  ?Phlyctidium sp.

PHAEOPHYCEAE (BROWN ALGAE)

Akinetospora sp.
   Eurychasma dicksonii
   ?Pleotrachelus olpidium
Chaetopteris plumosa
   Anisolpidium sphacellarum
Chorda filum (hairs)
   ?Pleotrachelus minutus
Cladostephus spongiosus
   Anisolpidium sphacellarum
Ectocarpus confervoides
   Eurychasma dicksonii
   ?Pleotrachelus olpidium
E. constanciae
   Eurychasma dicksonii
E. crinitus
   Eurychasma dicksonii
E. granulosus
   Eurychasma dicksonii
   Olpidiopsis andreei
E. mitchellae
   Anisolpidium ectocarpi
E. penicilliatus
   ?Pleotrachelus olpidium
E. pusillus
   Eurychasma dicksonii
E. sandrianus
   Eurychasma dicksonii
E. siliculosus
   Anisolpidium ectocarpi
   Eurychasma dicksonii
   Olpidiopsis andreei
E. simplex
   Olpidiopsis andreei
Ectocarpus sp.
   Eurychasma dicksonii
   Olpidiopsis andreei
   ?Pleotrachelus olpidium
Litosiphon pusillus
   Pleotrachelus minutus
Punctaria sp.
   Eurychasma dicksonii
Pylaiella littoralis
   Anisolpidium rosenvingii
   Chytridium polysiphoniae

   Eurychasma dicksonii
   Petersenia lobata
   ?Pleotrachelus olpidium
Spermatochnus paradoxus
   Pleotrachelus olpidium
Sphacelaria cirrhosa
   Anisolpidium sphacellarum
S. tribuloides
   Anisolpidium sphacellarum
Sphacelaria sp.
   Anisolpidium sphacellarum
Stictyosiphon soriferus
   Eurychasma dicksonii
S. tortilis
   Eurychasma dicksonii
Striaria attenuata
   Chytridium megastomum
   Eurychasma dicksonii
   Olpidiopsis andreei

RHODOPHYCEAE (RED ALGAE)

Acrochaetium codii
   Petersenia sp.
Aglaothamnion sp.
   Petersenia lobata
Antithamnion plumulae
   ?Olpidium plumulae
Bangia fusco-purpurea
   ?Olpidium entosphaericum
Callithamnion corymbosum
   Petersenia lobata
C. hookeri
   Petersenia lobata
C. plumulae
   ?Olpidium plumulae
C. roseum
   Petersenia lobata
Callithamnion sp.
   Chytridium polysiphoniae
   Petersenia lobata
Ceramium acanthonotum
   Eurychasmidium tumefaciens
C. corticatulum
   Petersenia lobata
   Pontisma lagenidioides

C. diaphanum
Chytridium megastomum
Eurychasmidium tumefaciens
Olpidiopsis andreei
Pontisma lagenidioides
?Rhizophydium discinctum
Thraustochytrium proliferum

C. flabelligerum
Eurychasmidium tumefaciens
Olpidiopsis magnusii

C. fruticulosum
Chytridium polysiphoniae
Pontisma lagenidioides

C. pedicellatum
Petersenia lobata
Pontisma lagenidioides

C. rubrum
Chytridium polysiphoniae
Eurychasmidium tumefaciens
Petersenia lobata
P. pollagaster
Pontisma lagenidioides
?Pyrrhosorus marinus

C. spiniferum
Eurychasmidium tumefaciens

C. strictum
Chytridium polysiphoniae
Pontisma lagenidiodes

C. tenuissimum
Pontisma lagenidioides

Ceramium sp.
Chytridium polysiphoniae
Olpidiopsis magnusii
Petersenia lobata
P. pollagaster
Pontisma lagenidioides

Chondria tenuissima
Chytridium polysiphoniae

Cystoclonium purpurascens
?Pyrrhosorus marinus

Delessaria sanguinea
Chytridium polysiphoniae

Dumontia filiformis
?Olpidium laguncula

D. incrassata
?Olpidium laguncula

Falkenbergia rufolanosa
Olpidiopsis feldmanni

"Floridées"
Eurychasmidium tumefaciens

Furcellaria sp.
Pleotrachelus olpidium

Gracilaria confervoides (verrucosa)
Japonochytrium marinum
Phlyctochytrium japonicum

Gymnothamnion elegans
Petersenia lobata

Halosaccion ramentaceum
?Eurychasma sacculus

Herposiphonia tenella
Chytridium polysiphoniae
Petersenia lobata

Polysiphonia elongata
Pleotrachelus inhabilis

P. fibrillosa
Chytridium polysiphoniae

P. urceolata
Chytridium polysiphoniae
Petersenia lobata

P. violacea
Chytridium polysiphoniae

Polysiphonia sp.
Chytridium polysiphoniae
?Pleotrachelus inhabilis
?P. olpidium
?Rhizophydium discinctum

Rhodymenia palmata
?Eurychasma sacculus

Seirospora apiculata
Petersenia lobata

S. griffithsiana
Petersenia lobata

S. interrupta
Petersenia lobata

Spermothamnion repens
Petersenia lobata

S. repens var. turneri
Petersenia lobata

S. turneri
Petersenia lobata

Trailliella intricata
Olpidiopsis feldmanni

UNIDENTIFIED ALGAE

"CONFERVAE"

"*Conferva*"
Myzocytium proliferum
Rhizophydium mammillatum
Conferva abbreviata
Rhizophydium mammillatum
"*Conferva rhynophila*"
?Chytridium minus
"*Confervacées*"
Achlyogeton entophytum
?A. rostratum
Olpidium algarum
?O. tuba
"*Palmellaceans*"
?Rhizophlyctis palmellacearum
Rhizophydium gibbosum
Various Species
Catenaria anguillulae
Endochytrium digitatum
E. operculatum
Entophlyctis vaucheriae
Myzocytium proliferum

FUNGI

PHYCOMYCETES

Achlya americana
Woronina asterina
W. polycystis
A. apiculata (oögonia)
Rhizidiomyces apophysatus
A. colorata
Olpidiopsis saprolegniae
A. conspicua (oögonia)
Rhizidiomyces apophysatus
A. dioica
Pringsheimiella dioica
A. flagellata
Olpidiopsis achlyae
O. fusiformis
O. saprolegniae
O. spinosa
O. varians
Phlyctidium mycetophagum
Pringsheimiella dioica

Rozella achlyae
Rozellopsis simulans
A. flagellata (oögonia)
Rhizidiomyces apophysatus
A. flagellata var. *yezoensis*
Olpidiopsis fusiformis
A. glomerata
Octomyxa achlyae
Olpidiopsis verrucosa
A. imperfecta
Olpidiopsis fusiformis
O. saprolegniae
A. klebsiana (oögonia)
Rhizidiomyces apophysatus
A. leucosperma
Olpidiopsis fusiformis
A. polyandra
Olpidiopsis fusiformis
Rozella septigena
Rozellopsis simulans
Woronina polycystis
A. polyandra (oögonia)
Rhizidiomyces apophysatus
A. prolifera
Olpidiopsis fusiformis
A. (Saprolegnia?) prolifera
Olpidiopsis saprolegniae
A. proliferoides
Rozella achlyae
A. racemosa
Olpidiopsis fusiformis
O. incrassata
O. saprolegniae
Rozella septigena
Rozellopsis simulans
Woronina polycystis
A. racemosa (oögonia)
Rhizophydium carpophilum
Achlya sp.
Chytridium sphaerocarpum
Lagenidium destruens
Olpidiopsis braziliensis
O. fusiformis
O. incrassata
O. index
O. saprolegniae

O. vexans
Petersenia irregulare
Pringsheimiella dioica
Rozellopsis simulans
Woronina polycystis
Achlya sp. (oögonia)
?Phlyctochytrium sp.
  Rhizidiomyces apophysatus
  Rhizophydium carpophilum
Allomyces anomalus
  Catenaria allomycis
  Olpidium allomycetos
A. arbuscula
  Catenaria allomycis
  Olpidium allomycetos
  Rozella allomycis
A. cystogenes
  Olpidium allomycetos
A. javanicus
  Catenaria allomycis
  Olpidium allomycetos
  Rozella allomycis
A. moniliformis
  Catenaria allomycis
  Olpidium allomycetos
Allomyces sp.
  Rozella allomycis
Aphanomyces cladogamous
  Olpidiopsis aphanomycis
A. laevis
  Chytriomyces parasiticus
  Olpidiopsis aphanomycis
  O. luxurians
Aphanomyces sp.
  Olpidiopsis aphanomycis
  O. luxurians
  Phlyctidium mycetophagum
Aplanes sp. (oögonia)
  Rhizidiomycopsis japonicus
Apodachlya brachynema (sporangia)
  Rozella apodyae-brachynematis
Araiospora spinosa
  Rozella rhipidii-spinosi
Asterophlyctis sarcoptoides
  Phlyctidium mycetophagum

Blastocladia gracilis
  Rozella blastocladiae
B. pringsheimii
  Rozella blastocladiae
Blastocladiella simplex
  Catenaria allomycis
Brevilegnia sp.
  Octomyxa brevilegniae
Choanephora sp.
  Rhizophydium mycetophagum
Chytridium oedogonii
  Rozella canterae
C. polysiphoniae
  Rozella marina
C. urceolatum
  Chytridium parasiticum
Chytriomyces appendiculatus
  Phlyctidium mycetophagum
C. aureus
  Phlyctidium mycetophagum
  Rhizophydium chytriomycetis
C. fructicosus
  Rhizophydium sp.
C. hyalinus
  Phlyctidium mycetophagum
  Rhizophydium chytriomycetis
  Rozella chytriomycetis
C. tabellariae
  Septosperma anomala
Cladochytrium crassum
  Rozella cladochytrii
C. hyalinum
  Rozella cladochytrii
C. replicatum
  Rozella cladochytrii
Dictyuchus anomalus
  Rozella achlyae
D. monosporus
  Rhizophydium carpophilum
  Rozella achlyae
Endochytrium operculatum (sporangia)
  Rozella endochytrii
Entophlyctis sp.
  Chytridium parasiticum
Geolegnia inflata
  Octomyxa brevilegniae

Karlingiomyces granulatus
  Rhizophydium hyperparasiticum
Lagenidium rabenhorstii
  Rozella pseudomorpha
Micromyces sp.
  Septosperma anomala
Monoblepharis macrandra (oöspores)
  Rhizophydium carpophilum
M. polymorpha
  Rozella monoblepharidis-polymor-
    phae
Nowakowskiella elegans
  Rozella cladochytrii
N. profusum
  Rozella cladochytrii
N. ramosum
  Rozella cladochytrii
Olpidiopsis saprolegniae (sporangia)
  Rhizophydium carpophilum
O. schenkiana
  Pythiella besseyi
Phlyctidium bumilleriae
  Septosperma anomala
Phlyctochytrium aureliae
  Rhizophydium chytriophagum
Phytophthora cactorum
  ?Rozella barrettii
P. cryptogea
  Rozellopsis waterhouseii
P. megasperma
  Rozellopsis waterhouseii
Pilobolus crystallinus var. *areolata*
  Pleotrachelus fulgens
P. kleinii
  Pleotrachelus fulgens
P. pirottianus
  Pleotrachelus zopfianus
Polychytrium aggregatum
  Phlyctidium mycetophagum
Polyphagus laevis
  Rozella polyphagi
Pythium dictyosporum
  Pythiella vernalis
P. gracile
  Pythiella vernalis
  Rozella laevis

P. intermedium
  Olpidiopsis gracile
  O. pythii
  Rozella cuculus
  Rozellopsis inflata
P. monospermum
  Olpidiopsis pythii
  Rhizophydium pythii
  Rozella cuculus
P. oryzae
  Olpidiopsis pythii
P. proliferum
  Sorodiscus cokeri
P. rostratum
  Olpidiopsis gracile
  O. pythii
P. vexans
  Olpidiopsis pythii
  Rozella irregularis
Pythium sp.
  Lagenidium pythii
  Olpidiopsis brevispinosa
  O. curvispinosa
  O. pythii
  Rozella laevis
  R. irregularis
  Rozellopsis inflata
  Solutoparies pythii
Rhizidiomyces hirsutus
  Phlyctidium mycetophagum
Rhizidium richmondense
  Chytridium parasiticum
  C. suburceolatum
  Septosperma rhizophidii
Rhizophlyctis petersenii
  Rozella rhizophlyctii
R. rosea
  Olpidium allomycetos
  Olpidiopsis karlingiae
  Phlyctidium mycetophagum
  Rhizophydium hyperparasiticum
  Rozella rhizophlyctii
Rhizophlyctis sp.
  Chytridium parasiticum
  Olpidium rhizophlyctidis
  Rhizophydium marshallense
  Septosperma rhizophidii

Rhizophydium coronum
Phlyctidium mycetophagum

R. discinctum
?Pleotrachelus paradoxus

R. globosum
Rozella rhizophydii

R. goniosporum (sporangia)
?Rhizophydium parasitans

R. keratinophilum
Phlyctidium mycetophagum

R. macrosporum
Septosperma rhizophidii

R. nodulosum
Chytridium rhizophydii

R. planktonicum
Septosperma anomala

Rhizophydium spp.
Septosperma rhizophidii

Saccomyces sp.
?Phlyctidium dangeardii

Saprolegnia asterophora
Olpidiopsis saprolegniae

S. asterophora (oögonia)
Rhizidiomyces apophysatus

S. diclina
Olpidiopsis saprolegniae

S. dioica
Olpidiopsis saprolegniae
Rozella septigena

S. ferax
Olpidiopsis saprolegniae
O. saprolegniae var. levis
O. vexans
Rhizophydium carpophilum
Woronina polycystis

S. ferax (oögonia)
Rhizidiomyces apophysatus

S. hypogena "var. *V.*"
Olpidiopsis major

S. monilifera
Olpidiopsis saprolegniae

S. monoica
Olpidiopsis saprolegniae
O. saprolegniae var. levis

O. vexans
Woronina polycystis

S. spiralis
Rozella septigena
Woronina polycystis

S. thureti
Olpidiopsis major
O. saprolegniae

Saprolegnia sp.
Olpidiopsis index
O. saprolegniae
O. vexans
Petersenia irregulare
Rozella septigena
Rozellopsis septigena
Woronina polycystis

Saprolegnia sp. (oögonia)
Rhizidiomyces apophysatus
Rhizophydium carpophilum

"Saprolegniaceae"
Olpidiopsis saprolegniae

"Saprolegnian"
Rhizidiomyces apophysatus

Septochytrium macrosporum
Rhizophydium hyperparasiticum
Rozella cladochytrii

S. plurilobulum
Rhizophydium hyperparasiticum

S. variabile
Phlyctidium mycetophagum

Septosperma rhizophidii
Chytridium parasiticum

Siphonaria variabilis
Phyctidium mycetophagum

Sphaerita endogena
Pseudolpidium sphaeritae

Synchytrium endobioticum
Phlyctochytrium synchytrii

Thraustotheca clavata
Phlyctidium mycetophagum

Zoophagus insidians
Phlyctidium mycetophagum
Rozellopsis inflata

Zygorhizidium willei
Septosperma anomala

ASCOMYCETES

Ascobolus immersus
  Phlyctochytrium lippsii
A. leveillei
  Phlyctochytrium lippsii
A. stercorarius
  Phlyctochytrium lippsii
Ascophanus holmskjoldii
  Phlyctochytrium lippsii
Helotium sp.
  Hyphochytrium infestans
Lasiobolus equinus
  Phlyctochytrium lippsii
Sordaria coronifera
  Phlyctochytrium lippsii

BASIDIOMYCETES

Corticium comedens
  *Olpidiopsis vuilleminiae
Puccinia airae
  Olpidium uredinis
P. rhamni
  Olpidium uredinis
P. violae
  Olpidium uredinis

FUNGI IMPERFECTI

  Phlyctidium mycetophagum

BRYOPHYTA

HEPATICAE

"*Liverworts*"
  Catenaria anguillulae

MUSCI

Funaria hygrometrica
  Pleotrachelus wildemani
"*Moss rhizoids*"
  ?Lagenidium ellipticum

PTERIDOPHYTA

LYCOPODINEAE

Isoetes echinospora (microspores)
  Rhizophydium sphaerotheca
I. lacustris
  Ligniera isoetes

I. lacustris (microspores)
  Rhizophydium sphaerotheca

EQUISETINEAE

Equisetum (spores)
  Rhizophlyctis rosea

FILICINEAE

Aspidium (spores)
  Rhizophydium subangulosum
"*Fern spores*"
  Rhizophydium pollinis-pini
  R. sphaerotheca
Marsilea mucronata
  Physoderma marsiliae

SPERMATOPHYTA

GYMNOSPERMAE

GYMNOSPERM POLLEN

Abies sp.
  Rhizophydium pollinis-pini
Keteleeria sp.
  Rhizophydium pollinis-pini
Picea excelsa
  Olpidium luxurians
Pinus austriaca
  Lagenidium pygmaeum
P. caribaea
  Chytridium citriforme
P. koraiensis
  Olpidium luxurians
P. laricio
  Lagenidium pygmaeum
P. montana
  Olpidium luxurians
  O. pendulum
  Phlyctochytrium africanum
  P. biporosum
  P. kniepii
  P. palustre
  Rhizophydium ampullaceum
  R. carpophilum
  R. globosum
  R. hyperparasiticum
  R. keratinophilum

R. minutum
R. racemosum
R. sphaerocarpum
R. sphaerotheca
R. subangulosum
R. transversum
P. pallasiana
  Lagenidium pygmaeum
P. ponderosa
  Olpidium pendulum
P. sylvestris
  Lagenidium pygmaeum
  Rhizophydium pollinis-pini
  R. sphaerotheca
Pinus sp.
  Blyttiomyces helicus
  Lagenidium pygmaeum
  Olpidium longicollum
  O. luxurians
  O. pendulum
  ?Phlyctidium pollinis-pini
  Phlyctochytrium papillatum
  P. semiglobiferum
  P. spectabile
  Rhizophydium bullatum
  R. halophilum
  *R. monoporum
  R. pollinis-pini
  R. sphaerotheca
  R. utriculare
Pseudotsuga mucronata
  Rhizophydium sphaerotheca
Taxus sp.
  Olpidium luxurians
"Coniferous pollen grains"
  Lagenidium pygmaeum
"Gymnospermous pollen"
  Rhizophydium sphaerotheca

ANGIOSPERMAE

ANGIOSPERM POLLEN

Cannabis sp.
  Olpidium luxurians

Cucurbita sp.
  Rhizidiomyces hirsutus
Helianthus sp.
  Rhizophydium pollinis-pini
Lilium sp.
  Olpidium luxurians
Liquidambar sp.
  Rhizidiomyces apophysatus
Phlox sp.
  Rhizophydium pollinis-pini
Populus sp.
  Rhizophydium pollinis-pini
Pyrus malus (apple)
  Lagenidium pygmaeum
Tropaeolum sp.
  Rhizophydium pollinis-pini
Typha sp.
  ?Achlyella flahaultii
  Chytridium chaetophilum
  Olpidium luxurians
  Rhizophydium sphaerotheca
Ulmus sp.
  Rhizophydium sp.
"Angiosperms"
  Rhizophydium pollinis-pini
  Rhizophydium sp.
"Barrträd"
  Rhizophydium pollinis-pini
"Pollen"
  Lagenidium pygmaeum
  Olpidium luxurians
  O. maritimum
  O. pendulum

MATURE PLANTS[1]

Aeschynomene indica
  Physoderma aeschynomenis
Althaea rosea
  Phytophthora megasperma
Aponogeton undulatus
  Physoderma aponogetonis
Callitriche spp.
  Sorodiscus callitrichis

[1] Certain terrestrial forms, such as *Althaea rosea*, are included simply because they are hosts of type species mentioned in this book.

Catabrosa aquatica
  Sorosphaera radicalis
Diplanthera wrightii
  Plasmodiophora diplantherae
Dulichium arundinaceum
  Physoderma dulichii
Elodea canadensis
  Catenaria sphaerocarpa
  ?Chytridium elodeae
  Cladochytrium replicatum
  Entophlyctis texana
  Megachytrium westonii
Elodea sp.
  Nowakowskiella elegans
Eriocaulon septangulare
  Entophlyctis texana
Halophila ovalis
  Plasmodiophora halophilae
Heteranthera dubia
  Sorodiscus heterantherae
Juncus spp.
  Ligniera junci
Lemna minor
  Reessia amoeboides
  R. lemnae
L. polyrhiza
  Reessia amoeboides
  R. lemnae
L. trisulca
  Reessia lemnae
Lycopersicum esculentum
  Phytophthora cryptogea
Lycopus americana
  Physoderma lycopi
Oryza sativa
  Pythiogeton dichotomum
Petunia sp.
  Phytophthora cryptogea
Potomogeton panormitanus
  Tetramyxa parasitica
Ruppia spp.
  Tetramyxa parasitica
Triaena sp.
  ?Cladochytrium polystomum

Veronica spp.
  Sorosphaera veronicae
Zannichellia spp.
  Tetramyxa parasitica
Zostera nana
  Plasmodiophora bicaudata

PLANT PARTS [1]

WOODY TWIGS

Abies sp.
  Gonapodya polymorpha
  Macrochytrium botrydioides
  Rhipidium interruptum
  Sapromyces elongatus
Aesculus sp.
  Blastocladia glomerata
  B. rostrata
  Macrochytrium botrydioides
  Monoblepharis laevis
  ?Rhizidium lignicola
Alnus sp.
  Apodachlya seriata
  Araiospora spinosa
  Macrochytrium botrydioides
  Phytophthora fischeriana
  Rhipidium americanum
  R. interruptum
Betula sp.
  Apodachlya pyrifera
  Monoblepharis polymorpha
  Rhipidium interruptum
Chamaecyparis sp.
  Sapromyces elongatus
Corylus avellana
  ?Chytridium xylophilum
Fraxinus excelsior
  Monoblepharis bullata
  M. insignis var. minor
  M. laevis
  M. macrandra
  M. polymorpha
Fraxinus sp.
  Apodachlya punctata
  A. pyrifera var. macrosporangia
  Araiospora pulchra

[1] Including vegetable debris and baits of like origin.

Blastocladia pringsheimii
B. sparrowii
Macrochytrium botrydioides
Monoblepharis laevis
Phytophthora gonapodyides
Rhipidium interruptum
Sapromyces androgynus
Morus sp.
  ?Blastocladia sp.
Picea excelsa
  Apodachlya pyrifera f. macrospo-
    rangia
  Sapromyces elongatus
Picea sp.
  Sapromyces androgynus
  S. elongatus
Populus trichocarpa
  Blastocladia ramosa
Prunus grayana
  Apodachlya brachynema
  Rhipidium interruptum
P. yedoensis
  Apodachlya brachynema
Prunus sp.
  Araiospora streptandra
  Rhipidium interruptum
Pseudotsuga mucronata
  Sapromyces elongatus
Pyrus pashia
  Apodachlya pyrifera
  Gonapodya prolifera
  Monoblepharis polymorpha
Quercus robur
  Monoblepharis bullata
  M. fasciculata var. fasciculata
  M. fasciculata var. magna
  M. hypogyna
  M. insignis var. insignis
  M. insignis var. minor
  M. macrandra
  M. laevis
  M. polymorpha
  M. sphaerica
Quercus sp.
  Apodachlya brachynema
  Araiospora spinosa

Gonapodya polymorpha
G. prolifera
Macrochytrium botrydioides
Rhipidium americanum
Sapromyces elongatus
Salix sp.
  Araiospora streptandra
Tilia sp.
  ?Chytridium xylophilum
Ulmus sp.
  Monoblepharis macrandra
"Twigs"
  Apodachlya brachynema
  A. brachynema f. major
  A. punctata
  A. pyrifera
  A. pyrifera f. macrosporangia
  Araiospora coronata
  A. pulchra
  A. spinosa
  Blastocladia pringsheimii
  B. ramosa
  Gonapodya polymorpha
  G. prolifera
  ?Hamidia indica
  Macrochytrium botrydioides
  Monoblepharis fasciculata var. fasci-
    culata
  M. insignis var. insignis
  M. macrandra
  M. ovigera
  M. polymorpha
  M. regignens
  M. sphaerica
  Phytophthora gonapodyides
  Pythiogeton ramosum
  *P. sterilis
  Rhipidium americanum
  R. interruptum
  R. parthenosporum
  R. thaxteri
  Sapromyces androgynus
  S. elongatus
"Spruce fir"
  Sapromyces elongatus
"Spruce mucilage"
  Gonapodya polymorpha

"Wood"
?Haplocystis mirabilis
Tetrachytrium triceps

CONES

Picea sp.
Sapromyces androgynus
S. elongatus
Pinus sp.
Sapromyces elongatus
Pinus sp. (carpellate)
Sapromyces elongatus
Pinus sp. (staminate)
Physocladia obscura

FRUITS

Amelanchier sp.
Mindeniella spinospora
Apple (Malus sp.)
Apodachlya brachynema
Blastocladia angusta
B. aspergilloides
B. globosa
B. gracilis
B. pringsheimii
B. prolifera
B. ramosa
B. truncata
Gonapodya polymorpha
G. prolifera
Macrochytrium botrydioides
Mindeniella asymmetrica
Phytophthora megasperma
Rhipidium americanum
R. interruptum
R. interruptum f. attenuata
R. parthenosporum
Sapromyces elongatus
Banana (Musa sapientum)
Blastocladia pringsheimii
B. ramosa
Cornus officinalis
Blastocladia globosa
B. incrassata
B. prolifera
Cotoneaster sp.
Blastocladia pringsheimii

Crabapple
Blastocladia globosa
B. pringsheimii
Crataegus sp.
Apodachlya brachynema
Blastocladia globosa
B. pringsheimii
B. tenuis
Rhipidium americanum
R. interruptum f. attenuata
Japonica sp.
Blastocladia pringsheimii
B. prolifera
Macrocarpium officinale
Rhipidium americanum
Sapromyces elongatus
"Medlar"
Rhipidium americanum
Pears (Pyrus sp.)
Blastocladia pringsheimii
B. ramosa
Macrochytrium botrydioides
Rose
Blastocladia angusta
B. aspergilloides
B. gracilis
B. pringsheimii
B. tenuis
Monoblepharis laevis
Rhipidium americanum
R. interruptum
Sapromyces elongatus
Solanum pseudo-capsicum
Blastocladia globosa
Tomato
Blastocladia glomerata
B. gracilis
B. pringsheimii
Gonapodya prolifera
Pythiogeton ramosum
Rhipidium americanum
R. thaxteri
Winter cherry
Blastocladia pringsheimii
"Rosaceous fruits"
Mindeniella spinospora

"Fruits"

Araiospora coronata
Blastocladia pringsheimii
B. ramosa
B. rostrata
Gonapodya polymorpha
G. prolifera
Macrochytrium botrydioides
Phytophthora gonapodyides
P. megasperma
Pythiogeton transversum
P. utriforme
Rhipidium americanum
R. interruptum
R. thaxteri

SOFT TISSUES AND SEEDS [1]

Allomyces javanicus
A. javanicus var. allomorphus
A. macrogynus
A. moniliformis
A. neo-moniliformis
Amoebochytrium rhizidioides
Apodachlya brachynema
Apodachlyella completa
Araiospora spinosa
Blastocladia prolifera
Blastocladiella asperosperma
B. cystogena
B. laevisperma
B. microcystogena
B. simplex
B. stomophilum
Blastocladiopsis parva
Catenaria anguillulae
C. sphaerocarpa
Catenochytridium carolinianum
C. laterale
Catenomyces persicinus
?Chytridium xylophilum
Chytriomyces aureus
C. hyalinus
C. spinosus
Cladochytrium aurantiacum
C. aureum
?C. cornutum

C. crassum
C. granulatum
C. hyalinum
?C. irregulare
C. replicatum
C. taianum
C. tenue
Cylindrochytridium johnstonii
Diasporangium jonesianum
Diplophlyctis amazonense
D. laevis
D. sexualis
Endochytrium operculatum
E. ramosum
Entophlyctis aurea
E. texana
Hyphochytrium catenoides
Karlingiomyces granulatus
Leptomitus lacteus
Ligniera junci
Macrochytrium botrydioides
Monoblepharella elongata
M. endogena
M. laruei
M. mexicana
M. taylori
Monoblepharis sphaerica
?Myceliochytrium fulgens
Nephrochytrium aurantium
Nowakowskiella crassa
N. delica
N. elegans
N. elongata
N. macrospora
N. profusa
N. ramosa
Phlyctochytrium aureliae
P. planicorne
P. stipitatum
Phytophthora oryzae
?Pleotrachelus radicis f. intermedia
?P. radicis f. major
?P. radicis f. minor
Polychytrium aggregatum
Pythiogeton autossytum
P. ramosum

---

[1] Mostly baits.

P. transversum
P. uniforme
P. utriforme
Rhipidium americanum
Rhizidiomyces hansonii
R. hirsutus
Rhizidium nowakowskii
R. richmondense
R. verrucosum
Rhizophlyctis hyalina
R. petersenii
R. rosea
R. spinosa

Rhizophydium coronum
R. macrosporum
Sapromyces androgynus
S. elongatus
Septochytrium macrosporum
S. marilandicum
S. plurilobulum
S. variabile
Tetrachytrium triceps

VEGETABLE DEBRIS

Karlingiomyces granulatus
Oedogoniomyces lymnaeae

ANIMALS

PROTOZOA

Amoeba limax
  ?Sphaerita endogena
A. terricola
  Rhizophydium amoebae
A. verrucosa
  Nucleophaga amoebae
Arcella sp.
  ?Olpidium arcellae
Chilomonas sp.
  Rhizidium vorax
Difflugia sp.
  ?Olpidium difflugiae
Gonyostomum semen
  Sphaerita sp.
Heterophrys dispersa
  ?Sphaerita endogena
Lecythium hyalinum
  Chytridium lecythii
Leptophrys vorax (zoocyst)
  ?Olpidium leptophrydis
  ?Rhizophydium leptophrydis
Nuclearia simplex
  ?Sphaerita endogena
Pseudospora leptoderma (cysts)
  Olpidiomorpha pseudosporae
P. parasitica ? (zoocysts)
  Olpidium pseudosporearum
Pseudosporopsis bacillariacearum? (zoo-
  cysts)
  Olpidium pseudosporearum

Trachelomonas teres var. *glabra*
  (lorica)
  ?Sphaerita trachelomonadis
T. swirenkoi
  ?Sphaerita trachelomonadis
Vampyrella pendula (zoocyst)
  Chytridium lateoperculatum
V. spirogyrae (zoocyst)
  *Olpidiopsis longicollis
Vampyrella sp. (zoocyst)
  Olpidium vampyrellae
  Rhizophydium vampyrellae
"Infusoria"
  Catenaria anguillulae
"Monadineae" (cysts)
  Endochytrium operculatum
"Rhizopods"
  ?Sphaerita endogena
"Protozoan"
  Rhizophydium apiculatum
  Rhizophydium sp.

PLATYHELMINTHES

TREMATODA (Eggs)

Fasciola hepatica
  Catenaria anguillulae
"Helminth"
  Catenaria anguillulae
"Liver-fluke"
  Catenaria anguillulae
  Rhizophydium zoophthorum

NEMATHELMINTHES

NEMATODA

Anguillula sp.
 ?Achlyogeton (?) rostratum
 Myzocytium megastomum
 ?Olpidium zootocum
 Rhizophydium vermicola
Gordius sp.
 Catenaria anguillulae
Heterodera schacti
 Olpidium nematodeae
Heterodera sp. (bodies)
 Lagenidium parthenosporum
"Anguillulae"
 Catenaria anguillulae
"Eelworms"
 Bicricium lethale
"Nematodes"
 Catenaria anguillulae
 Endochytrium operculatum
 Olpidium nematodeae
 Phlyctochytrium nematodeae
 Rhizophydium gibbosum

TROCHELMINTHES

ROTIFERA

Anuraea cochlearis
 ?Pleotrachelus rotatoriorum
Brachionus sp.
 Olpidium gregarium
Diplais sp.
 Zoophagus insidians
Diplaxis sp.
 Zoophagus insidians
Distyla sp.
 Myzocytium microsporum
 Zoophagus insidians
 Z. tentaclum
Distyla sp. (eggs)
 Lagenidium distylae
 L. parthenosporum
Euchlanis sp.
 Olpidium gregarium

Monostyla sp.
 Zoophagus insidians
 Z. tentaclum
Philodina roseola (adults and eggs)
 ?Woronina elegans
Philodina sp. (adults and eggs)
 Lagenidium parthenosporum
Rattulus sp.
 Zoophagus insidians
"Rotifers"
 Catenaria anguillulae
 Myzocytium zoophthorum
 Olpidium rotiferum
 Rhizophydium gibbosum
 R. zoophthorum
 Zoophagus insidians
"Rotifers" (eggs)
 Catenaria anguillulae
 ?Endochytrium oophilum
 E. operculatum
 Lagenidium oophilum
 Myzocytium zoophthorum
 Olpidium allomycetos
 O. entophytum var. intermedium
 O. granulatum
 O. gregarium
 ?O. macrosporum
 O. rotiferum
 Rhizophydium gibbosum
 R. zoophthorum

GASTROTRICHA

Chaetonotus larus (eggs)
 Lagenidium parthenosporum

ARTHROPODA

CRUSTACEA

Acroperus leucocephalus
 ?Chytridhaema cladocerarum
Bosmina cornuta
 *Ancylistes cladocerarum
Callinectes sp. (eggs and young)
 Lagenidium callinectes
Chydorus sphaericus
 ?Blastulidium paedophthorum
Crangon vulgaris (eggs)
 Plectospira dubia

Cyclops sp. (eggs)
?Blastulidiopsis chattoni
Daphnia obtusa
?Blastulidium paedophthorum
Daphnia sp.
*Ancylistes cladocerarum
"Daphne"
Lagenidium giganteum
Gonoplax rhomboides (eggs)
Plectospira dubia
Leander serratus (eggs)
Plectospira dubia
Lynceus sp.
?Blastulidium paedophthorum
Macropodia sp. (eggs)
Plectospira dubia
Pinnotheres pisum (eggs and adults)
Leptolegnia marina
Plectospira dubia
Pythium thalassium (eggs)
Portunus depurator (eggs)
Plectospira dubia
Simocephalus retulus
?Blastulidium paedophthorum
?Chytridhaema cladocerarum
Typton spongicola (eggs)
Plectospira dubia
"Cladocerans"
*Ancylistes cladocerarum
"Copepods"
Lagenidium giganteum
"Crustacea" (eggs and embryos)
?Blastulidium paedophthorum
?Chytridhaema cladocerarum

INSECTA (living: bodies and larvae)

Diptera[1]

Aëdes aegypti
Coelomomyces quadrangulatus
  var. lamborni
C. stegomyiae
A. vexans
Coelomomyces psorophorae

Anopheles aconitus
Coelomomyces indiana
A. annularis
Coelomomyces anophelesica
C. indiana
A. barbirostris
Coelomomyces indiana
A. crucians
Coelomomyces bisymmetricus
C. cribrosus
C. dodgei
C. keilini
C. lativittatus
C. sculptosporus
Coelomomyces sp.
A. gambiae
Coelomomyces africanus
A. jamesi
Coelomomyces indiana
A. nigerrimus
Coelomomyces indiana
A. punctipennis
Coelomomyces cribrosus
C. quadrangulatus var. irregularis
C. sculptosporus
A. quadrimaculatus
Coelomomyces punctatus
A. ramsayi
Coelomomyces indiana
A. subpictus
Coelomomyces anophelesica
C. indiana
A. vagus
Coelomomyces anophelesica
A. varuna
Coelomomyces anophelesica
C. indiana
Anopheles sp. (larvae)
Coelomomyces quadrangulatus var.
  quadrangulatus
Corethra sp. (larvae)
?Blastulidium paedophthorum
Culex erraticus
Coelomomyces pentangulatus

[1] Mosquitoes only, here. Checked by Dr. H. K. Townes.

Culiseta inornata
  Coelomomyces psorophorae
Psorophora ciliata
  Coelomomyces psorophorae
P. howardii
  Coelomomyces psorophorae
Uranotaenia sapphirina
  Coelomomyces uranotaeniae
"Mosquitoes"
  Lagenidium giganteum

HEMIPTERA

BACK SWIMMERS

Notonecta sp. (adults)
  ?Coelomomyces notonectae

INSECT EXUVIAE AND BAITS

ORTHOPTERA

"Cockroach"
  Rhizidium nowakowskii

ISOPTERA

"Termite"
  Apodachlya brachynema

ODONATA

"Dragonflies"
  Phlyctorhiza endogena
  Rhizoclosmatium aurantiacum
  R. globosum
  Rhizophlyctis petersenii
  Siphonaria variabilis

EPHEMERIDA

"Mayflies"
  Asterophlyctis sarcoptoides
  Chytriomyces aureus
  C. hyalinus
  Phlyctorhiza endogena
  Rhizidium chitinophilum
  R. ramosum
  Rhizoclosmatium aurantiacum
  R. globosum
  Rhopalophlyctis sarcoptoides
  Siphonaria petersenii
  S. sparrowii
  S. variabilis

TRICHOPTERA

Phryganeidae (caddis flies)
  Asterophlyctis sarcoptoides
  Obelidium mucronatum
  Rhizidium ramosum
  Rhizoclosmatium aurantiacum
  R. globosum
  Siphonaria variabilis

DIPTERA

Chironomidae (midges)
  Asterophlyctis sarcoptoides
  Obelidium mucronatum
  Rhizidium ramosum
  R. chitinophilum
  Rhizoclosmatium aurantiacum
  R. globosum
  Rhizophlyctis petersenii
"Flies"
  Apodachlyella completa
  Blastocladiella simplex
  Obelidium mucronatum
  Rhizidiomyces bivellatus
"Gnats"
  Phlyctorhiza endogena
"Mosquitoes"
  Phlyctorhiza endogena

COLEOPTERA

"Beetles"
  Tetrachytrium triceps
"INSECTS"
  Allomyces arbuscula
  Asterophlyctis sarcoptoides
  Catenaria anguillulae
  Phlyctochytrium aureliae
  Rhizidiomyces bivellatus
  Rhizidium braziliensis
  R. laevis
  R. verrucosum
  Rhizoclosmatium aurantiacum
  R. globosum
  Rhizophydium amoebae
  Siphonaria variabilis
  Zygochytrium aurantiacum

ARACHNIDA

"Mite" (eggs)
  Catenaria anguillulae

MOLLUSCA

LAMELLIBRANCHIATA

Barnea candida (body, eggs, and embryo)
  Leptolegnia marina
Cardium echinatum (body, eggs, and embryo)
  Leptolegnia marina
Crassotrea virginica
Venus mercenaria
V. mortonii
  Sirolpidium zoophthorum

GASTROPODA

Lymnaea ollula
  Oedogoniomyces lymnaeae
L. reticulata
  Oedogoniomyces lymnaeae
Urosalpinx cinerea
  ?Sirolpidium

CHORDATA

ASCIDIANS

Anurella roscovitana
  Nephromyces roscovitanus

Anurella sp.
  ?Nephromyces roscovitanus
Ctenicella appendiculata
  Nephromyces sp.
Listhonephrya sp.
  ?Nephromyces sorokini
Molgula socialis
  ?Nephromyces molgularum

BATRACHIAN

  *Allomyces monspeliensis

ANIMAL PARTS

  Blastocladiella simplex
  B. stubenii
  B. variabilis
  Catenaria anguillulae
  Cladochytrium replicatum
  "Cladochytria" (fossil)
  Lagenidium giganteum
  Monoblepharis polymorpha
  M. sphaerica
  Rhizophydium macrosporum
  Septosperma rhizophidii

ORGANIC SUBSTANCES[1]

CELLULOSE

  Catenochytridium kevorkianii
  C. laterale
  Catenomyces persicinus
  Chytriomyces lucidus
  C. spinosus
  Cladochytrium crassum
  C. setigerum
  Cylindrochytridium johnstonii
  Diplophlyctis amazonensis
  D. sexualis
  Entophlyctis aurea
  Karlingiomyces lobatus
  K. marilandicus
  Leptomitus lacteus
  ?Myceliochytrium fulgens

  Nowakowskiella atkinsii
  N. elegans
  N. elongata
  N. hemisphaerospora
  N. macrospora
  N. profusa
  N. ramosa
  Rhizidium richmondense
  R. varians
  Rhizophlyctis petersenii
  R. rosea
  Rhizophydium coronum

CHITIN

  Asterophlyctis sarcoptoides
  Chytriomyces appendiculatus
  C. aureus

[1] Chiefly baits.

C. fructicosus
C. hyalinus
C. stellatus
Karlingiomyces asterocystis
K. curvispinosus
K. dubius
?Myceliochytrium fulgens
Obelidium mucronatum
Phlyctochytrium aureliae
Polychytrium aggregatum
Rhizidium elongatum
R. nowakowskii
Rhizidiomyces hansonii
Rhizophlyctis chitinophila
R. petersenii
Rhizophydium chitinophilum

KERATIN

Aphanodictyon papillatum
Blastocladiopsis parva
Catenaria anguillulae
C. sphaerocarpa
Lagenidium humanum
?Myceliochytrium fulgens
Phlyctidium keratinophilum
?Phlyctorhiza peltata
?P. variabilis
Rhizophydium apiculatum
R. keratinophilum
R. nodulosum
R. piligenum

BIBLIOGRAPHY

ADAIR, E. J., AND VISHNIAC, H. S. 1958. Marine fungus requiring vitamin B_{12}. Science, 127: 147-148.

AGARDH, C. A. 1824. Systema algarum, Vol. 1. Lund.

AJELLO, L. 1942. *Polychytrium*: a new cladochytriaceous genus. Mycologia, 34: 442-451, 16 figs.

—— 1945. *Phlyctochytrium aureliae* parasitized by *Rhizophydium chytriophagum*. *Ibid.*, 37: 109-119, 28 figs.

—— 1948a. A cytological and nutritional study of *Polychytrium aggregatum*. I. Cytology. Amer. J. Bot., 35: 1-12, 49 figs.

—— 1948b. A cytological and nutritional study of *Polychytrium aggregatum*. II. Nutrition. *Ibid.*, 35: 135-140, 1 fig.

ALEEM, A. A. 1950a. The occurrence of *Eurychasma dicksonii* (Wright) Magnus in England and Sweden. Meddel. från Göteborgs Botaniska Trädgård, 18: 239-245, 9 figs.

—— 1950b. A fungus in *Ectocarpus granulosus* C. Agardh near Plymouth. Nature, 165: 119, 1 fig.

—— 1950c. Phycomycètes marins parasites de Diatomées et d'Algues. C. R. Acad. Sci. Paris, 231: 713-715, 4 figs.

—— 1950d. Phycomycètes marins parasites de Diatomées et d'Algues dans la région de Banyuls-sur-mer (Pyrénées-Orientales). Vie et Milieu, 1: 421-440, 26 figs. Paris. (Bull. Lab. Arago.)

—— 1952a. Sur l'autécologie d'une Spirogyre d'eau saumâtre. C. R. Acad. Sci. Paris, 234: 2648-2650, 4 figs.

—— 1952b. *Olpidiopsis feldmanni* sp. nov., Champignon marin parasite d'Algues de la famille des Bonnemaisoniacées. *Ibid.*, 235: 1250-1252, figs. a-e.

—— 1953. Marine fungi from the West-Coast of Sweden. Arkiv för Botanik, 3 (1): 1-33, 51 figs., 2 pls.

ANTIKAJIAN, G. 1947. *Rhizophydium chitinophilum*. Mycologia, 39: 612-616, 20 figs.

—— 1949. A developmental, morphological, and cytological study of *Asterophlyctis* with special reference to its sexuality, taxonomy, and relationships. Amer. J. Bot., 36: 245-262, 79 figs.

APINIS, A. 1930. Untersuchungen über die in Lettland gefundenen Saprolegniaceen nebst Bemerkungen über andere Wasserpilze. Acta Horti Bot. Univ. Latv., 4: 201-246, 4 figs., 4 pls. 1929.

—— 1935. Fertilization of oospheres by planogametes in Saprolegniaceae. *Ibid.*, 8: 103-110, 15 figs., 1 pl. 1933.

APSTEIN, C. 1910. *Synchaetophagus balticus*, ein in *Synchaeta*-lebender Pilz. Wissensch. Meeresunters. Abt. Kiel (N.F.), 12: 163-166.

ARASAKI, S. 1947. Studies on the rot of *Porphyra tenera* by a *Pythium*. J. Jap. Soc. Fisheries (Nihon Suisan Gakkai-Shi), 13 (3): 74-90. (In Japanese.)

ARCHER, WILLIAM. 1860. On the occurrence of zoospores in the family Desmidiaceae. Quart. J. Micro. Sci., 8: 215-239, pl. 11, figs. 1-12.

—— 1867. *Chytridium barkerianum. Ibid.* (N. S.), 7: 89-90.

ARNAUD, G. 1952. Mycologie concrète: Genera. Bull. Soc. Mycol. France, 68: 181-223, 8 figs.

ARNAUDOW, N. 1921. Zur Morphologie und Biologie von *Zoophagus insidians* Sommerstorff. Jahrb. Univ. Sophia, 15-16 : 1-32, 8 figs. (Separate.) 1918-20. (In Bulgarian, with German summary.)

—— 1923a. Untersuchungen über *Sommerstorffia spinosa*, nov. gen., nov. spec. *Ibid.*, 19, Heft 2, Abt. 1a: 161-196, 4 figs. 1922-23.

—— 1923b. Ein neuer Rädertiere (*Rotatoria*)-fangender Pilz. (*Sommerstorffia spinosa*, nov. gen., nov. sp.). Flora, 116: 109-113, 5 figs.

—— 1925. Untersuchung über den Tiere-fangenden Pilz *Zoophagus insidians* Som. *Ibid.*, 118-119: 1-16, 5 figs.

—— 1936. Belezhki vurkhu *Aphanomyces* i *Zoophagus* (Notizen über *Aphanomyces* und *Zoophagus*). Izv. Bŭlg. Bot. Druzh. (Bull. Soc. Bot. Bulgaria), 7: 91-99.

ATKINS, D. 1929. On a fungus allied to the Saprolegniaceae, found in the pea-crab *Pinnotheres*. J. Mar. Biol. Ass. U.K. (N.S.), 16: 203-219, figs. 1-13.

—— 1954a. Further notes on a marine member of the Saprolegniaceae, *Leptolegnia marina* n. sp., infecting certain invertebrates. *Ibid.*, 33: 613-625, figs. 1-5.

—— 1954b. A marine fungus *Plectospira dubia* n. sp. (Saprolegniaceae), infecting crustacean eggs and small crustacea. *Ibid.*, 33: 721-732, figs. 1-5.

—— 1955. *Pythium thalassium*, sp. nov. infecting the egg-mass of the pea-crab, *Pinnotheres pisum*. Trans. Brit. Mycol. Soc., 38: 31-46, 9 figs.

ATKINSON, G. F. 1894. Intelligence manifested by the swarm spores of *Rhizophidium globosum*. Bot. Gaz., 19: 503-504.

—— 1909a. Some fungus parasites of algae. *Ibid.*, 48: 321-338, figs. 1-8.

—— 1909b. Some problems in the evolution of the lower fungi. Ann. Mycologici, 7: 441-472, figs. 1-20.

—— 1910. A new genus of chytrids. Bot. Gaz., 49: 311-312.

—— 1915. Phylogeny and relationships in the Ascomycetes. Ann. Missouri Bot. Gard., 2: 315-376.

BAIL, T. 1855. Mykologische Berichte. Bot. Zeitung, 13: 673-682.

BALAKRISHNAN, M. S. 1948. South Indian Phycomycetes. II. Some little known species of *Pythium* occurring in South India. Proc. Indian Acad. Sci., Sect. B, 28: 27-34, 4 figs.

BALLY, W. 1911. Cytologische Studien an Chytridineen. Jahrb. wiss. Bot., 50: 95-156, pls. 1-5. 1912.

—— 1913. Die Chytridineen in Lichte der neueren Kernforschung. Mycol. Centralbl., 2: 289-297.

—— 1919. Einige Bemerkungen zu den amitotischen Kernteilung der Chytridineen. Berichte Deutsch. Bot. Gesell., 37: 115-122, figs. 1-2.

BARBIER, J. 1950. Contribution à l'étude de la biologie des Phycomycètes aquatiques. Rev. Gén. Bot., 57: 23-47, 20 figs.

BARLOW, C. H. 1925. The life cycle of the human intestinal fluke *Fasciolopsis buski* (Lankester). Amer. J. Hyg. (Monogr. Ser), 4: 1-98, pls. 1-10.

BARNER, H. D., AND CANTINO, E. C. 1952. Nutritional relationships in a new species of *Blastocladiella*. Amer. J. Bot., 39: 746-751, 4 figs.

BARNES, B., AND MELVILLE, R. 1932. Notes on British aquatic fungi. Trans. Brit. Mycol. Soc., 17: 82-96, 6 figs.

BARRETT, J. T. 1912a. The development of *Blastocladia strangulata*, n. sp. Bot. Gaz., 54: 353-371, pls. 18-20.

—— 1912b. Development and sexuality of some species of *Olpidiopsis* (Cornu) Fischer. Ann. Bot. London, 26: 209-238, pls. 23-26.

—— 1934. A chytridiaceous parasite of *Phytophthora*. Phytopathology, 24: 1138.

BARTSCH, A. F. 1939. Reclassification of *Chytridium spinulosum* with additional observations on its life history. Mycologia, 31: 558-571, figs. 1-24.

—— 1945. The significance of zygospore character in *Polyphagus euglenae*. *Ibid.*, 37: 553-570, figs. 1-18.

—— AND WOLF, F. T. 1938. Two new saprolegniaceous fungi. Amer. J. Bot., 25: 392-395, 11 figs.

BARY, A. DE. 1858. Untersuchungen über die Familie der Konjugaten (Zygnemeen und Desmidieen). 91 pp., pls. 1-8. Leipzig.

—— 1860. Einige neue Saprolegnieen. Jahrb. wiss. Bot., 2: 169-192, pls. 19-21.

—— 1863. Recherches sur le développement de quelques champignons parasites. Ann. Sci. Nat. Bot., IV, 20: 5-148, pls. 1-13.

—— 1864. Beiträge zur Morphologie und Physiologie der Pilze. Erste Reihe. *Protomyces* und *Physoderma*. Abhandl. Senck. Naturforsch. Gesell., 5: 137-232, pls. 26-31.

—— 1866. Morphologie und Physiologie der Pilze, Flechten und Myxomyceten. xii + 316 pp. Text figs., 1 pl. Leipzig.

—— 1876. Researches into the nature of the potato-fungus—*Phytophthora infestans*. J. Roy. Agr. Soc. England (2d ser.), 12: 239-269, 8 figs.

—— 1881a. Zur Systematik der Thallophyten. Bot. Zeitung, 39: 1-17, 33-36.

—— 1881b. Zur Kenntniss der Peronosporeen. *Ibid.*, 39: 617-625, pl. 5.

—— 1881c. Untersuchungen über die Peronosporeen und Saprolegineen und die Grundlagen eines natürlichen Systems der Pilze. Vierte Reihe. Abhandl. Senck. Naturforsch. Gesell., 12: 225-369, pls. 1-6.

—— 1883. Zu Pringsheim's neuen Beobachtungen über den Befruchtungsact der Gattungen *Achlya* und *Saprolegnia*. Bot. Zeitung, 41: 38-46, 54-60.

—— 1884. Vergleichende Morphologie und Biologie der Pilze, Mycetozoen und Bacterien. xvi + 558 pp. 198 figs. Leipzig.

BARY, A. DE. 1887. Comparative morphology and biology of the fungi, Mycetozoa and bacteria. 525 pp., 198 figs. Oxford.

—— 1888. Species der Saprolegnieen. Bot. Zeitung, 46: 597-610, 613-621, 629-636, 645-653, pls. 9-10.

—— AND WORONIN, M. 1865a. Beitrag zur Kenntnis der Chytridieen. Berichte Verhandl. Naturforsch. Gesell. Freiburg, 3 (2): 22-61, pls. 1-2.

—— 1865b. Supplement à l'histoire des Chytridinées. Ann. Sci. Nat. Bot., V, 3: 239-269, pls. 9-10.

BECK, G. R. 1896. *Ancylistes pfeifferi*, n. sp. Verhandl. Zoo.-Bot. Gesell. Wien, 46: 232-233.

—— 1897. *Ancylistes pfeifferi*, n. sp. Bot. Centralbl., 69: 11-12.

BECKER, E. R. 1926. *Endamoeba citelli*, sp. nov., from the striped ground squirrel *Citellus tridecemlineatus*, and the life history of its parasite, *Sphaerita endamoebae*, sp. nov. Biol. Bull., 50: 444-454, 1 pl.

BEHRENS, A. 1931. Zytologische Untersuchungen an *Rhipidium europaeum* (Cornu) v. Minden. "Planta," Archiv wiss. Bot., 13 (4): 745-777, 33 figs.

BENEKE, E. S. 1948. The *Monoblepharidaceae* as represented in Illinois. Trans. Illinois Acad. Sci., 41: 27-31, pl. 1.

—— 1948. A new species of *Achlya* and of *Dictyuchus*. J. Elisha Mitchell Sci. Soc., 64: 261-265, pls. 29-30.

—— AND WILSON, G. B. 1950. Treatment of *Allomyces javanicus* var. *japonensis* Indoh with colchicine and sodium nucleate. Mycologia, 42: 519-522.

BENISCH, J. 1940. Künstlich hervorgerufener *Aphanomyces* Befall bei Wollhandkrabben. Zeitschr. Fisch. u. Hilfsw., 38: 71-80.

BÉRCZI, L. 1940. Adatok Magyarország vízigomba vegetációjához. Vízigombákkal végzett mesterséges fertözési kísérletek (Angaben zur Wasserpilzvegetation ungarns nebst mich Wasserpilzen durchgeführten Ansteckungsversuchen). Acta Geobot. Hung., 3: 79-99, [pl. 1] figs. 1-11; [pl. 2] figs. 1-47.

BERDAN, H. B. 1938. Revision of the genus *Ancylistes*. Mycologia, 30: 396-415, 22 figs.

—— 1939. Two new genera of operculate chytrids. Amer. J. Bot., 26: 459-463, figs. 1-2.

—— 1941a. A developmental study of three saprophytic chytrids. I. *Cladochytrium hyalinum* sp. nov. *Ibid.*, 28: 422-438, figs. 1-84.

—— 1941b. A developmental study of three saprophytic chytrids. II. *Catenochytridium carolinianum* Berdan. *Ibid.*, 28: 901-911, figs. 1-72.

—— 1942. A developmental study of three saprophytic chytrids. III. *Septochytrium variabile* Berdan. *Ibid.*, 29: 260-270, figs. 1-52.

BERKELEY, M. J. 1864. Egg parasites and their relatives. Intellectual Observer, 5: 147.

BERLESE, A. N., AND TONI, G. B. DE. 1888. *In* Saccardo, Sylloge fungorum, Vol. 7. xxx + 498 pp. Padua.

BESSEY, C. E. 1903. The structure and classification of the Phycomycetes. Trans. Amer. Micro. Soc., 24: 27-54.

—— 1907. Synopsis of plant phyla. Univ. Nebraska Studies, 7: 275-373.

—— 1914. Revisions of some plant phyla. *Ibid.*, 14: 37-73.

BESSEY, ERNST A. 1939. Isoplanogametes in *Blastocladia.* Mycologia, 31: 308-309.

—— 1942. Some problems in fungus phylogeny. *Ibid.*, 34: 355-379, 5 figs. (portrait).

—— 1950. Morphology and taxonomy of fungi. xiii + 791 pp. Blakiston, Philadelphia.

BEVERWIJK, A. L. VAN. 1948. Observations on submerged water moulds in the Netherlands. A. v. Leeuwenhoek, 14: 223-250, figs. 1-9.

BHARGAVA, K. S. 1943. Physiological studies on some members of the family Saprolegniaceae. I. Enzyme action. J. Indian Bot. Soc., 22: 85-99.

—— 1945. Physiological studies on some members of the family Saprolegniaceae. III. Nitrogen requirements. *Ibid.*, 24: 67-72.

BIGELOW, H. B. 1931. Oceanography. 263 pp. Houghton Mifflin, Boston.

BISHOP, H. 1940. A study of sexuality in *Sapromyces reinschii.* Mycologia, 32: 505-529, 6 figs.

BISHOP, M. W. H. 1950. Fungoid infection in *Ectocarpus granulosus.* Nature, 165: 937.

BLACKWELL, E. M. 1937. Germination of the resistant spores of *Blastocladia pringsheimii.* Nature, 140: 933.

—— 1939. The problem of gamete production in *Blastocladia.* Mycologia, 31: 627-628.

—— 1940. A life cycle of *Blastocladia pringsheimii* Reinsch. Trans. Brit. Mycol. Soc., 24: 68-86, 9 figs.

—— 1943a. The life history of *Phytophthora cactorum* (Leb. & Cohn) Schroet. *Ibid.*, 26: 71-89, figs. 1-7.

—— 1943b. On germinating the oospores of *Phytophthora cactorum.* *Ibid.*, 26: 93-103.

—— 1944. Species of *Phytophthora* as water moulds. Nature, 153: 496, 1 fig.

—— 1949. Terminology in *Phytophthora.* Mycological Papers, No. 30, Commonwealth Mycol. Inst., pp. 1-23, figs. 1-30, 1 pl.

—— 1956. The genus *Phytophthora.* Diagnoses (or descriptions) and figures from the original papers. Misc. Publ. Commonwealth Mycol. Inst., 12: 120 pp., 66 pl., 10 figs.

—— AND WATERHOUSE, G. M. 1941. Water moulds as a source of infection by pathogenic species of *Phytophthora.* Mycologia, 33: 449.

—— —— AND THOMPSON, M. V. 1941. The invalidity of the genus *Pythiomorpha.* Trans. Brit. Mycol. Soc., 25: 148-165, 2 figs.

BLAKESLEE, A. F. 1904. Sexual reproduction in the Mucoraceae. Proc. Amer. Acad. Arts and Sci., 40: 205-319, pls. 1-4.

BLYTT, A. 1882. Bidrag til Kundskaben om Norges Soparter. Vidensk. Selsk. Skr. Christiana (Mat.-Nat. Kl.), 1882 (5): 1-29.

Bock, K. J. 1956. Zur Ökologie und Systematik saprophytischer Wasserpilze aus dem Silbersee bei Bremerhaven. Veröff. Inst. f. Meeresforsch. Bremerhaven, 4: 25-44, 4 pls.

Boedjin, K. 1923. Nieuwe Nederlandsche Saprolegniineae II. (Hortus Botanicus Amsterdam). Mededeelingen van de Nederlandsche Mycologische Vereeniging, 13: 84-90. Illust.

Bogoyavlensky, N. 1922. *Zografia notonectae*, n.g., n. sp. Russkii arkhiv protistologii (Arch. Soc. Russe Protist.), 1: 113-119, pl. 10. (In Russian, with German summary, p. 118).

Borzi, A. 1884. *Protochytrium spirogyrae.* Nuovo Giornale Bot. Ital., 16: 1-32, pl. 1.

—— 1885. *Nowakowskia*, eine neue Chytridiee. Bot. Centralbl., 22 (1): 23-26, pl. 1, figs. 1-10.

Braun, A. 1851. Betrachtungen über die Erscheinung der Verjüngung in der Natur, insbesondere in der Lebens- und Bildungsgeschichte der Pflanze. 363 pp., pls. 1-3. Leipzig.

—— 1853. Reflections on the phenomenon of rejuvenescence in nature, especially in the life and development of plants. Ray Society, Botanical and Physiological Memoirs. 341 pp., pls. 1-5. London.

—— 1855a. Ueber *Chytridium*, eine Gattung einzelner Schmarotzergewächse auf Algen und Infusorien. Monatsber. Berlin Akad., 1855: 378-384.

—— 1855b. Algarum unicellularium genera nova et minus cognita, etc. 111 pp., 6 pls. Leipzig.

—— 1856a. Über *Chytridium*, eine Gattung einzelliger Schmarotzergewächse auf Algen und Infusorien. Abhandl. Berlin Akad., 1855: 21-83, pls. 1-5.

—— 1856b. Über einige neue Arten der Gattung *Chytridium* und die damit verwandte Gattung *Rhizidium.* Monatsber. Berlin Akad., 1856: 587-592.

—— 1856c. Untersuchungen über einige mikroskopische Schmarotzergewächse . . . . Flora (N.S.), 14: 599-600.

Brébisson, L. A. de. 1856. Liste des Desmidiacées observées en Basse-Normandie. Mém. Soc. Sci. Nat. Cherbourg, 4: 113-166, pls. 1-2.

Brewster, M. S. 1952. A new species of *Physoderma.* Mycologia, 44: 97-100, 1 fig.

Brown, D. H., and Cantino, E. C. 1955. The oxidation of malate by *Blastocladiella emersonii.* Amer. J. Bot., 42: 337-341, figs. 1-7.

Brumpt, E., and Lavier, G. 1935. Sur une *Nucleophaga* parasite d'*Endolimax nana.* Ann. Parasitologie, 13: 439-444, pl. 11.

Bruyne, C. de. 1890. Monadines et Chytriacées, parasites des algues du Golfe de Naples. Arch. de Biol., 10: 43-104, pls. 3-5.

Buckley, J. J. C., and Clapham, P. A. 1929. The invasion of Helminth eggs by chytridiacean fungi. J. Helminth., 7: 1-14, text figs. 1-21, pl. 1.

Buell. C. B., and Weston, W. H. 1947. Application of the mineral oil conservation method to maintaining collections of fungous cultures. Amer. J. Bot., 34: 555-561, 2 figs.

BUISMAN, C. J. 1927. Root rots caused by Phycomycetes. viii + 51 pp.. 12 figs. Haarlem.

BÜSGEN, M. 1882. Die Entwickelung der Phycomycetensporangien. Jahrb. wiss. Bot., 13: 253-285, pl. 12.

—— 1887. Beitrag zur Kenntniss der *Cladochytrien*. *In* Cohn, Beitr. Biol. Pflanzen, 4: 269-283, pl. 15.

BUTLER, EDWIN J. 1907. An account of the genus *Pythium* and some Chytridiaceae. Mem. Dept. Agr. India, Bot. Ser., 1: 1-160, pls. 1-10.

—— 1911. On *Allomyces*, a new aquatic fungus. Ann. Bot. London, 25:1023-1035, figs. 1-18.

—— 1928. Morphology of the chytridiacean fungus *Catenaria anguillulae*, in liver fluke eggs. *Ibid.*, 42: 813-821, figs. 1-19.

BUTLER, J. BAYLEY, AND BUCKLEY, J. J. C. 1927. *Catenaria anguillulae* as a parasite of the ova of *Fasciola hepatica*. Sci. Proc. R. Dublin Soc. (N. S.), 18 (45): 497-512, pls. 23-26.

—— AND HUMPHRIES, A. 1932. On the cultivation in artificial media of *Catenaria anguillulae*, a chytridiacean parasite of the ova of the liver fluke, *Fasciola hepatica*. *Ibid.*, 20 (25): 301-324, pls. 13-18.

BÜTSCHLI, O. 1888. Protozoa. Einleitung. *In* Broun, Klassen u. Ordnungen Thierreichs, 1 (1): 1-616, 38 pls. Leipzig u. Heidelberg.

CANTER, H. M. 1946. Studies on British chytrids. I. *Dangeardia mammillata* Schröder. Trans. Brit. Mycol. Soc., 29: 128-134, 5 figs., 1 pl.

—— 1947a. On *Myzocytium megastomum* de Wildeman. *Ibid.*, 31: 80-85, 3 figs., 1 pl.

—— 1947b. Studies on British chytrids. II. Some new monocentric chytrids. *Ibid.*, 31: 94-105, 8 figs., 2 pls.

—— 1947c. Studies on British chytrids. III. *Zygorhizidium willei* Löwenthal and *Rhizophydium columnaris* n. sp. *Ibid.*, 31: 128-135, 4 figs., 1 pl.

—— 1949a. Studies on British chytrids. IV. *Chytriomyces tabellariae* (Schröter) n. comb., parasitized by *Septosperma anomalum* (Couch) Whiffen. *Ibid.*, 32: 16-21, 3 figs.

—— 1949b. Studies on British chytrids. V. On *Olpidium hyalothecae* Scherffel and *Olpidium utriculiforme* Scherffel. *Ibid.*, 32: 22-29, 5 figs., 1 pl.

—— 1949c. Studies on British chytrids. VI. Aquatic Synchytriaceae. *Ibid.*, 32: 69-94, 13 figs., 5 pls.

—— 1949d. On *Aphanomycopsis bacillariacearum* Scherffel, A. *desmidiella* n. sp., and *Ancylistes* spp. in Great Britain. *Ibid.*, 32: 162-170, 6 figs.

—— 1949e. Studies on British 'chytrids. VII. On *Phlyctochytrium mucronatum* n. sp. *Ibid.*, 32: 236-240, 2 figs.

—— 1950a. Studies on British chytrids. VIII. On *Rhizophidium anomalum* n. sp. New Phytologist, 49: 98-102, 2 figs.

—— 1950b. Studies on British chytrids. IX. *Anisolpidium stigeoclonii* (de Wildeman) n. comb. Trans. Brit. Mycol. Soc., 33: 335-343, 6 figs., 3 pls.

CANTER, H. M. 1950c. Studies on British chytrids. X. Fungal parasites of the phytoplankton. I. Ann. Bot. London (N.S.), 14: 263-289, 16 figs., 1 pl.

—— 1950d. Studies on British chytrids. XI. *Chytridium oedogonii* Couch. Trans. Brit. Mycol. Soc., 33: 354-358, 3 figs., 2 pls.

—— 1951. Studies on British chytrids. XII. Fungal parasites of the phytopklankton, II. Ann. Bot. London (N.S.), 15: 129-156, 14 figs., 4 pls.

—— 1953. Annotated list of British aquatic chytrids. Trans. Brit. Mycol. Soc., 36: 278-303.

—— 1954. Studies on British chytrids. XIII. Fungal parasites of the phytoplankton, III. *Ibid.*, 37: 111-133, 9 figs., 3 pls.

—— 1955. Annotated list of British aquatic chytrids. Supplement I. *Ibid.*, 38: 425-430.

—— AND LUND, J. W. G. 1948. Studies on plankton parasites. I. Fluctuations in the numbers of *Asterionella formosa* Hass. in relation to fungal epidemics. New Phytologist, 47: 238-261, 11 figs.

—— —— 1951. Studies on plankton parasites. III. Examples of the interaction between parasitism and other factors determining the growth of diatoms. Ann. Bot. London (N.S.), 15: 359-371, 4 figs., 2 pls.

—— —— 1953. Studies on plankton parasites. II. The parasitism of diatoms with special reference to lakes in the English Lake district. Trans. Brit. Mycol. Soc., 36: 13-37, 6 figs.

CANTINO, E. C. 1948. The vitamin nutrition of an isolate of *Blastocladia pringsheimii*. Amer. J. Bot., 35: 238-242, 5 figs.

—— 1949a. The physiology of the aquatic phycomycete, *Blastocladia pringsheimii*, with emphasis on its nutrition and metabolism. *Ibid.*, 36: 95-112, 13 figs.

—— 1949b. The growth and nutrition of *Pythiogeton*. *Ibid.*, 36: 747-756, 14 figs.

—— 1950. Nutrition and phylogeny in the water molds. Quart. Rev. Biol., 25: 269-277, 2 figs.

—— 1951a. Metabolism and morphogenesis in a new *Blastocladiella*. A. v. Leeuwenhoek, 17: 325-362, 21 figs.

—— 1951b. Evidence for an accessory factor involved in fructose utilization by the aquatic fungus, *Pythiogeton*. Amer. J. Bot., 38: 579-585, 9 figs.

—— 1952. The biochemical nature of morphogenetic patterns in *Blastocladiella*. Amer. Naturalist, 86: 399-404, 4 figs.

—— 1955. Physiology and phylogeny in the water molds — a reevaluation. Quart. Rev. Biol., 30: 138-149, 1 fig.

—— 1956. The relation between cellular metabolism and morphogenesis in *Blastocladiella*. Mycologia, 48: 225-240, 4 figs.

—— AND HORENSTEIN, E. A. 1954. Cytoplasmic exchange without gametic copulation in the water mold *Blastocladiella emersonii*. Amer. Naturalist, 88: 143-154, 3 figs.

—— —— 1955. The role of ketoglutarate and polyphenol oxidase in the synthesis of melanin during morphogenesis in *Blastocladiella emersonii*. Physiologia plantarum, 8: 189-221, 20 figs.

CANTINO, E. C., AND HORENSTEIN, E. A. 1956a. Gamma and the cytoplasmic control of differentiation in *Blastocladiella*. Mycologia, 48: 443-446, 2 figs.

—— —— 1956b. The stimulatory effect of light upon growth and CO_2 fixation in *Blastocladiella*. I. The S.K.I. cycle. *Ibid.*, 48: 777-799, 3 figs.

—— AND HYATT, M. T. 1953a. Phenotypic "sex" determination in the life history of a new species of *Blastocladiella*, *B. emersonii*. A. v. Leeuwenhoek, 19: 25-70, 14 figs.

—— —— 1953b. Carotenoids and oxidative enzymes in the aquatic Phycomycetes *Blastocladiella* and *Rhizophlyctis*. Amer. J. Bot., 40: 688-694, 3 figs.

—— —— 1953c. Further evidence for the role of the tricarboxylic acid cycle in morphogenesis in *Blastocladiella emersonii*. J. Bact., 66: 712-720, 3 figs.

—— LOVETT, JAMES, AND HORENSTEIN, E. A. 1957. Chitin synthesis and nitrogen metabolism during differentiation in *Blastocladiella emersonii*. Amer. J. Bot., 44: 498-505, 7 figs.

CARPENTER, C. W. 1940. A chytrid in relation to chlorotic streak disease of sugar cane. Hawaiian Plant. Rec., 44: 19-33, 12 figs.

CARTER, H. J. 1856. Further observations on the development of gonidia (?).... Ann. and Mag. Nat. Hist., II, 17: 101-127, pls. 8-9.

—— 1858. On the spermatology of a n. sp. of *Nais*. *Ibid.*, III, 2: 90-104, pls. 2-4.

CAVERS, F. 1915. The inter-relationships of *Protista* and primitive fungi. New Phytologist, 14: 94-104, 164-168, 223-227, 275-280, 302-304. figs. 1-6.

CEJP, KAREL. 1932a. Some remarks to the knowledge of the parasitic Phycomycetes of conjugates in Bohemia. Bull. Internat. Acad. Sci. Bohême, 42 (3): 1-6, 2 pls. (Separate.) 1933.

—— 1932b. *Rhipidium americanum* Thaxter a *Apodachlya pirifera* Zopf v Československu. Rozpravyl II Třídy České Akad. Ročník, 42 (20): 1–11, pls. 1–2. (Separate.) 1933.

—— 1932c. První Príspěvek k poznání českych Saprolegnií (Contribution to the knowledge of Saprolegniales of Bohemia. I). Zvláštní Otisk Časopisu Mykologia, 8: 95–100.

—— 1933a. Further studies on the parasites of conjugates in Bohemia. Bull. Internat. Acad. Sci. Bohême, 42 (3): 1–11, 2 pls. (Separate.)

—— 1933b. Studies on the genus *Pythiomorpha* Petersen, with phylogenetic considerations of some orders of Macro-Oomycetes. Z. Věstníku Král. čes. Spol. Nauk. Tř. II. Roč. 1932: 1–22, pls. 1–2. (Separate.)

—— 1934. Nejnižší houby jako parasiti parasitů. Věda Přírodní, 15: 225–228, 4 figs.

—— 1936. *Sapromyces androgynus* Thaxter en Europe et étude de l'espèce *Sapromyces reinschii* (Schroeter) Fritsch. Bull. Soc. Mycol. France, 52: 370–376, figs. A–D, pls. 10–11.

—— 1946. Sur les affinités des Blastocladiaceae. Revision du genre *Gonapodya*, sa position systématique. Bull. Soc. Mycol. France, 62 (3–4): 1–12. (Separate.)

—— 1947. Monografiká studie řádu Blastocladiales (Phycomycetes). Z. Věstníku Král. čes. Spol. Nauk. Tř. mat.-přírod. Roč., 1946: 1–55, pls. 1–2. (Separate.)

CEJP, KAREL, 1957. Houby. I. (Fungi) Československá Akad. Věd, Sekce biologická. 495 pp., 114 figs., 8 [pls.]. Prague.

CHATTON, E. 1908. Sur la reproduction et les affinités du *Blastulidium paedoph-thorum* Ch. Pérez. C. R. Soc. Biol., 64: 34–36.

—— AND BRODSKY, A. 1909. Le Parasitisme d'une Chytridinée du genre *Sphaerita* Dang., chez *Amoeba limax* Dryard. Arch. Protistenk., 17: 1–18, figs. 1–6.

CHAUDHURI, H. 1931. On a *Myzocitium* parasitic on *Spirogyra affinis*. Arch. Protistenk., 75: 472–475, 7 figs.

—— 1942. Indian water moulds. V. A new genus of the Saprolegniaceae: *Hamidia* gen. nov. Proc. Indian Acad. Sci., Sect. B, 15: 225–227, pl. 1., figs. 1–21.

—— AND BANERJEE, M. L. 1942. Indian water moulds. IV. Proc. Indian Acad. Sci., Sect. B, 15: 216–224, 3 pls.

—— *et al.* 1947. A handbook of Indian water moulds. Pt. I. 70 pp. Univ. Punjab.

—— AND KOCHHAR, P. L. 1935. Indian water moulds. I. Proc. Indian Acad. Sci., Sect. B, 2: 137–154, pls. 5–12.

—— AND LOTUS, S. S. 1936. Indian water moulds. II. *Ibid.*, 3: 328–333.

CIENKOWSKI, L. 1855. Algologische Studien, I. Bot. Zeitung, 13: 801–806, pl. 12.

—— 1857. *Rhizidium confervae glomeratae*. *Ibid.*, 15: 233–237, pl. 5 A, figs. 1–6.

—— 1867. Ueber den Bau und der Entwickelung der Labyrinthuleen. *In* Schultze, Archiv micro. Anat., 3: 274–310, pls. 15–17.

CLAUSSEN, P. 1912. Zur Entwicklungsgeschichte der Ascomyceten. *Pyronema confluens*. Zeitschr. Bot., 4: 1–64, 13 figs., pls. 1–6.

CLINTON, G. P. 1902. *Cladochytrium alismatis*. Bot. Gaz., 33: 49–61, pls. 2–4.

COCCONI, GIROLAMO. 1894. Ricerche sullo sviluppo evolutivo di due specie nuove di funghi *Lagenidium papillosum* ed *Exoascus flavoraureus* e sul parassitismo della *Phoma uncinulae* sull' *Uncinula aduncalév*. R. Accad. Sci. Istituto Bologna, Mem. Ser. V, 4: 361–372, 7 figs.

CODREANU, R. 1931. Sur l'évolution des *Endoblastidium*, nouveau genre de pro-tiste parasite coelomique des larves d'éphémères. C. R. Acad. Sci. Paris, 192: 772–775, 7 figs.

COHN, F. 1853. Untersuchungen über die Entwicklungsgeschichte der mikros-kopischen Algen und Pilze. Nova Acta Acad. Leop.-Carol., 24: 101–256, pls. 15–20.

—— 1865. Chytridii species novae marinae. Hedwigia, 4: 169–170, 2 pls.

—— 1867. Beiträge sur Physiologie der Phycochromaceen und Florideen. *In* Schultze, Archiv micro. Anat., 3: 1–60, 2 pls.

—— 1872. Conspectus familiarum cryptogamarum secundum methodum natu-ralem dispositarum auctore F. Cohn. Hedwigia, 11: 17–20.

—— 1879. Ueber sein Thallophytensystem. Jahres-bericht. Schles. Gesell. Vater-land. Cultur., 57: 279–289.

COKER, W. C. 1923. The Saprolegniaceae, with notes on other water molds. 201 pp., 63 pls. Univ. North Carolina Press, Chapel Hill.

—— 1927. Other water molds from the soil. J. Elisha Mitchell Sci. Soc., 42: 207–226, pls. 27–36.

—— 1930. Notes on fungi, with a description of a new species of *Ditiola*. *Ibid.*, 46: 117–120, pls. 8–9.

—— AND BRAXTON, H. H. 1926. New water molds from the soil. J. Elisha Mitchell Sci. Soc., 42: 139–147, pls. 10–15.

—— AND COUCH, J. N. 1923. A new species of *Thraustotheca*. J. Elisha Mitchell Sci. Soc., 37: 112–115, pl. 8.

—— AND GRANT, F. A. 1922. A new genus of water mold related to *Blastocladia*. J. Elisha Mitchell Sci. Soc., 37: 180–182, pl. 32.

—— AND LEITNER, J. 1938. New species of *Achlya* and *Apodachlya*. J. Elisha Mitchell Sci. Soc., 54: 311–318, pls. 38–39.

—— AND MATTHEWS, V. D. 1937. Blastocladiales, Monoblepharidales, Saprolegniales. N. A. Flora, 2 (1): 1–76. (Bibliography by W. C. Coker and J. H. Barnhart.)

CONSTANTINEANU, M. J. C. 1901. Contributions à la flore mycologique de la Roumanie. Revue Gén. Bot., 13: 369–389, figs. 75–84.

COOK, M. T. 1935. Root diseases of sugar cane in Puerto Rico. Part I. Normal structures of roots. Part II. A new parasitic fungus in the roots of sugar cane. J. Agric. Univ. P. R., 19 (2): 121–128, 8 pls.

COOK, W. R. I. 1926. The genus *Ligniera* Maire and Tison. Trans. Brit. Mycol. Soc., 11: 196–213, pls. 8–9.

—— 1928. The inter-relationships of the Archimycetes. New Phytologist, 27: 230–260, 298–320, 111 figs., 8 diagrams, 9 pls.

—— 1932a. An account of some uncommon British species of the Chytridiales found in algae. New Phytologist, 31: 133–144, 45 figs.

—— 1932b. The parasitic slime-moulds. Hong Kong Naturalist (Suppl.), No. 1: 29–39, 1 fig., pls. 13–17.

—— 1933a. The water-moulds. Watson's Microscope Record, 28: 3–7, figs. 1–4; 29: 12–13.

—— 1933b. A monograph of the Plasmodiophorales. Arch. Protistenk., 80: 179–254, 14 figs., pls. 5–11.

—— 1935. The genus *Lagenidium* Schenk, with special reference to *L. rabenhorstii* Zopf and *L. entophytum* Zopf. *Ibid.*, 86: 58–89, pls. 1–4.

—— AND FORBES, E. J. 1933. Investigations on aquatic fungi. Nature, 132: 641.

—— AND MORGAN, E. 1934. Some observations on the Saprolegniaceae of the soils of Wales. Journal of Botany, 72: 345–349.

—— AND NICHOLSON, W. H. 1933. A contribution to our knowledge of *Woronina polycystis* Cornu. Ann. Bot. London, 47: 851–859, 16 figs.

COOK, W. R. I., AND SCHWARTZ, E. J. 1930. The life history, cytology and method of infection of *Plasmodiophora....* Phil. Trans. Roy. Soc. London, Ser. B, 218: 283–314, pls. 19–21.

COOKE, M. C. 1882–84. British freshwater algae, 1: 1–329; 2: 130 pls. London, Williams and Norgate.

COOKSON, I. 1937. On *Saprolegnia terrestris*, sp. nov., with some preliminary observations on Victorian soil Saprolegniales. Proc. Roy. Soc. Victoria (N. S.), 49 (2): 235–243, figs. 1–2, pl. 11.

CORNU, M. 1869a. Note sur l'oospore du *Myzocytium.* Bull. Soc. Bot. France, 16: 222–223.

—— 1869b. Note sur le *Chytridium roseum* de B. et Woro. *Ibid.,* 16: 223–224.

—— 1870. Note sur une Saprolégniée, parasite d'une nouvelle espèce d'*Oedogonium.* Bull. Soc. Bot. France, 17: 297–299.

—— 1871. Note sur deux genres nouveaux de la famille des Saprolégniées. *Ibid.,* 18: 58–59.

—— 1872a. Monographie des Saprolégniées; étude physiologique et systématique. Ann. Sci. Nat. Bot., V, 15: 1–198, pls. 1–7.

—— 1872b. Affinité des Myxomycètes et des Chytridinées. Bull. Soc. Bot. France, 19: 70–71.

—— 1877a. Causes qui déterminent la mice en liberté des corps agiles (zoospores, anthérozoïdes) chez les végétaux inférieurs. C. R. Acad. Sci. Paris, 85: 860–862.

—— 1877b. Remarques sur quelques Saprolégniées nouvelles. Bull. Soc. Bot. France, 24: 226–228.

COTNER, F. B. 1930a. Cytological study of the zoospores of *Blastocladia.* Bot. Gaz., 89: 295–309, 10 figs.

—— 1930b. The development of the zoöspores in the Oömycetes at optimum temperatures and the cytology of their active stages. Amer. J. Bot., 17: 511–546, 1 fig., pls. 30–32.

COUCH, J. N. 1924. Some observations on spore formation and discharge in *Leptolegnia, Achlya* and *Aphanomyces.* J. Elisha Mitchell Sci. Soc., 40: 27–42, pls. 4–5.

—— 1926a. Notes on the genus *Aphanomyces*, with a description of a new semi-parasitic species. *Ibid.,* 41: 213–226, pls. 26–33.

—— 1926b. Heterothallism in *Dictyuchus*, a genus of the water moulds. Ann. Bot. London, 40: 849–881, 3 figs., pls. 35–38.

—— 1927. Some new water fungi from the soil, with observations on spore formation. J. Elisha Mitchell Sci. Soc., 42: 227–242, pls. 37–43.

—— 1931. *Micromyces zygogonii* Dang., parasitic on *Spirogyra. Ibid.,* 46: 231–239, pls. 16–18.

—— 1932. *Rhizophidium, Phlyctochytrium,* and *Phlyctidium* in the United States. *Ibid.,* 47: 245–260, pls. 14–17.

—— 1935a. New or little known Chytridiales. Mycologia, 27: 160–175, figs. 1–64.

—— 1935b. A new saprophytic species of *Lagenidium*, with notes on other forms. *Ibid.*, 27: 376–387, figs. 1–40.

—— 1935c. An incompletely known chytrid: *Mitochytridium ramosum*. J. Elisha Mitchell Sci. Soc., 51: 293–296, pl. 62.

—— 1937. Notes on the genus *Micromyces*. Mycologia, 29: 592–596, figs. 1–14.

—— 1938a. A new chytrid on *Nitella*: *Nephrochytrium stellatum*. Amer. J. Bot., 25: 507–511, figs. 1–34.

—— 1938b. A new species of *Chytridium* from Mountain Lake, Virginia. J. Elisha Mitchell Sci. Soc., 54: 256–259, pl. 24.

—— 1938c. Observations on cilia of aquatic Phycomycetes. Science, 88: 476.

—— 1939a. Technic for collection, isolation, and culture of chytrids. J. Elisha Mitchell Sci. Soc., 55: 208–214.

—— 1939b. Heterothallism in the Chytridiales. *Ibid.*, 55: 409–414, pl. 49.

—— 1939c. A new *Conidiobolus* with sexual reproduction. Amer. J. Bot., 26: 119–130, 52 figs.

—— 1941. The structure and action of the cilia in some aquatic Phycomycetes. *Ibid.*, 28: 704–713, figs. 1–58.

—— 1942. A new fungus on crab eggs. J. Elisha Mitchell Sci. Soc., 58: 158–162, pls. 18–19.

—— 1945a. Observations on the genus *Catenaria*. Mycologia, 37: 163–193, 78 figs.

—— 1945b. Revision of the genus *Coelomomyces*, parasitic in insect larvae. J. Elisha Mitchell Sci. Soc., 61: 124–136, pls. 1–2.

—— 1949. A new species of *Ancylistes* on a saccoderm desmid. *Ibid.*, 65: 131–136, pls. 6–7.

—— 1953. The occurrence of thin-walled sporangia in *Physoderma zeae-maydis* on corn in the field. J. Elisha Mitchell Sci. Soc., 69: 182–184, 8 figs.

—— AND DODGE, H. R. 1947. Further observations on *Coelomomyces*, parasitic on mosquito larvae. J. Elisha Mitchell Sci. Soc., 63: 69–79, pls. 15–20.

—— LEITNER, J., AND WHIFFEN, A. 1939. A new genus of the Plasmodiophoraceae. J. Elisha Mitchell Sci. Soc., 55: 399–408, pls. 47–48.

—— AND WHIFFEN, A. J. 1942. Observations on the genus *Blastocladiella*. Amer. J. Bot., 29: 582–591, 66 figs.

COX, H. T. 1939. A new genus of the Rhizidiaceae. J. Elisha Mitchell Sci. Soc., 55: 389–397, fig. 1, pls. 45–46.

CRASEMANN, J. M. 1954. The nutrition of *Chytridium* and *Macrochytrium*. Amer. J. Bot., 41: 302–310, 5 figs.

—— 1957. Comparative nutrition of two species of *Blastocladia*. *Ibid.*, 44: 218–224, 8 figs.

CROOKS, KATHLEEN M. 1937. Studies on Australian aquatic Phycomycetes. Proc. Roy. Soc. Victoria (N. S.), 49 (2): 206–232, figs. 1–11, pl. 10.

CURTIS, K. M. 1921. The life history and cytology of *Synchytrium endobioticum* (Schilb.) Perc., the cause of wart disease in potato. Phil. Trans. Roy. Soc. London, Ser. B, 210: 409–478, pls. 12–16.

CUTTER, V. M., JR. 1941. Observations on certain species of *Aphanomyces*. Mycologia, 33: 220–240, 15 figs.

—— 1943. An undescribed *Lagenidium* parasitic on *Potamogeton*. Mycologia, 35: 2–12, 21 figs.

DANGEARD, P. A. 1884–85a. Note sur le *Chytridium subangulosum* A. Braun. Bull. Soc. Linn. Normandie, III, 9: 88–91.

—— 1884–85b. Note sur le *Catenaria anguillulae* Sorok., *Chytridium zootocum* A. Br. *Ibid.*, III, 9: 126–136.

—— 1886a. Recherches sur les organismes inférieurs. Ann. Sci. Nat. Bot., VII, 4: 241–341, pls. 11–14.

—— 1886b. Sur un nouveau genre de Chytridinées, parasite des Rhizopodes et des Flagellates. Bull. Soc. Bot. France, 33: 240–242.

—— 1886c. Note sur un *Chytridium* endogène. *Ibid.*, 33: 356.

—— 1887a. Notes mycologiques. *Ibid.*, 34: xxi–xxv.

—— 1887b. Sur l'importance du mode de nutrition au point de vue de la distinction des animaux et des végétaux. C. R. Acad. Sci. Paris, 105: 1076–1077.

—— 1888a. Les Péridiniens et leurs parasites. Journ. de Botanique, 2: 126–132.

—— 1888b. Sur un nouveau genre de Chytridinées parasite des algues. C. R. Acad. Sci. Paris, 107: 50–51.

—— 1888c. Les Péridiniens et leurs parasites. Journ. de Botanique, 2: 141–146, pl. 5. (See 1888a.)

—— 1888d. Sur deux espèces nouvelles de *Chytridium*. Bull. Soc. Linn. Normandie, IV, 2: 152–153.

—— 1889a. Recherches sur les Cryptomonadinae et les Euglenae. Le Botaniste, 1: 1–38, pl. 1.

—— 1889b. Mémoire sur les Chytridinées. *Ibid.*, 1: 39–74, pls. 2–3.

—— 1889c. Étude du noyau dans quelques groupes inférieurs de végétaux. *Ibid.*, 1: 208–210.

—— 1889d. Étude du noyau dans quelques groupes inférieurs de végétaux. C. R. Acad. Sci. Paris, 109: 202–204.

—— 1890–91a. Contribution à l'étude des organismes inférieurs. Le Botaniste, 2: 1–58, pls. 1–2.

—— 1890–91b. Recherches histologiques sur les champignons. *Ibid.*, 2: 63–149, pls. 3–7.

—— 1890–91c. Mémoire sur quelques maladies des algues et des animaux. *Ibid.*, 2: 231–268, pls. 16–19.

—— 1891. Note sur la délimitation des genres *Chytridium* et *Rhizidium*. Revue Mycologique, 13: 134–135.

—— 1892. Recherches sur la reproduction sexuelle des champignons. Le Botaniste, 3: 221–281, pls. 20–23.

—— 1894–95a. A propos d'un travail du Dr. C. J. Minot sur la distinction des animaux et des végétaux. *Ibid.*, 4: 188–189.

—— 1894–95b. Mémoire sur les parasites du noyau et du protoplasma. *Ibid.*, 4: 199–248, 10 figs.

—— 1896–97. Note sur une nouvelle espèce de Chytridinées. *Ibid.*, 5: 21–26, 1 fig.

—— 1898. L'Influence de mode de nutrition dans l'évolution de la plante. *Ibid.*, 6: 1–63.

—— 1900–1901a. Note sur un nouveau parasite des amibes. *Ibid.*, 7: 85–87.

—— 1900–1901b. La Reproduction sexuelle des champignons. Étude critique, *Ibid.*, 7: 89–130.

—— 1900–1901c. Recherches sur la structure du *Polyphagus euglenae* Nowak. et sa reproduction sexuelle. *Ibid.*, 7: 213–257, 3 figs., pls. 6–7.

—— 1900–1901d. Étude comparative de la zoospore et du spermatozoïde. *Ibid.*, 7: 269–272, 3 figs.

—— 1900–1901e. Le *Chytridium transversum* A. Braun. *Ibid.*, 7: 282–284, 1 fig.

—— 1901a. Étude comparative de la zoospore et du spermatozoïde. C. R. Acad. Sci. Paris, 132: 859–861.

—— 1901b. Du rôle des noyaux dans la fécondation nucléaire chez les Oomycètes. Revue Mycologique, 13: 53–55.

—— 1903a. Sur le nouveau genre *Protascus*. C. R. Acad. Sci. Paris, 136: 627–628.

—— 1903b. Recherches sur le développement du périthèce chez les Ascomycètes Le Botaniste, 9: 1–303, pls. 1–18.

—— 1911. Un nouveau genre de Chytridiacées. Bull. Soc. Mycologique France, 27: 200–203, fig. 1.

—— 1912. Recherches sur quelques algues nouvelle ou peu connues. Le Botaniste, 12: I–XXI, 2 pls. (1911)

—— 1932. Observations sur la famille des Labyrinthulées et sur quelques autres parasites des *Cladophora*. *Ibid.*, 24: 217–258, pls. 22–24.

—— 1933. Nouvelles observations sur les parasites des Eugléniens. *Ibid.*, 25: 3–46, pls. 1–4.

—— 1937. Sur un nouveau moyen de défense très curieux de certaines Desmidiées contra les parasites de la famille des Chytridiacées. *Ibid.*, 28: 187–200, pl. 19.

DANGEARD, PIERRE. 1934. Sur la présence a Roscoff d'une Chytridiale des Ectocarpées, l'*Eurychasma dicksonii* (Wright) Magnus. Ann. Protistol. (Paris), 4: 69–73, pl. 8, figs. A–E.

DAS-GUPTA, S. N., AND JOHN, RACHEL. 1953. Studies in the Indian aquatic fungi. I. Some water moulds of Lucknow. Proc. Indian Acad. Sci., 38: 165–170, 15 figs.

DAUGHERTY, L. H. 1941. The upper Triassic flora of Arizona. Contrib. Paleontol. Carnegie Inst. Washington, No. 526. iii + 108 pp., pls. 1–34.

DAVIS, H. C., LOOSANOFF, V. L., WESTON, W. H., AND MARTIN, C. 1954. A fungus disease in clam and oyster larvae. Science, 120: 36–38, fig. 1.

DEBAISIEUX, P. 1920. *Coelomycidium simulii*, nov. gen., nov. spec., et remarques sur l'*Amoebidium* des larves de *Simulium*. La Cellule, 30 (2): 249–276, pls. 1–2.

DECKENBACH, C. VON. 1902–3. *Coenomyces consuens*, n.g., n. sp. Scripta Bot. Horti Univ. Petropol., 19: 1–42, 2 pls. (In Russian, with German summary.)

—— 1903. *Coenomyces consuens*, n. g., n. sp. (ein Beitrag zur Phylogenie der Pilze). Flora, 92: 253–283, pls. 6–7.

DENIS, M. 1926. La Castration des Spirogyres par des champignons parasites. Revue Algologique, 3: 14–21, figs. 1–3. 1926–28.

DERBÈS, A., AND SOLIER, A. J. J. 1853. Mémoire sur quelques points de la physiologie des algues. C. R. Acad. Sci. Paris (Supplement), 1: 1–120, pls. 1–23.

DESIKACHARY, T. V. 1945. Note on the reactions of *Gloeotrichia raciborskii* Wolosz. to a parasitic attack. Current Science, 14: 207–208, 11 figs.

DESOR, E. 1844. Excursions et séjour dans les glaciers et hautes régions des Alpes. (Cited in Braun, 1856a.)

DIEDICKE, H. 1911. Note. Mitteilungen des Thüringischen botanischen vereins (N. F.), 28: 83.

DIEHL, H. 1935. Beiträge zur Biologie von *Olpidiopsis saprolegniae* Barrett. Centralbl. f. Bakteriol., Parasitenk. u. Infektionskrankh., Abt. 2, 92: 229–249, 23 figs.

DILLWYN, L. W. 1809. British Confervae.... 87 pp., pls. 1–109, Supplement, pls. A–G. London.

DISSMANN, E. 1924. Einige Beobachtungen zur Gattung *Apodachlya* Pringsheim. Schriften f. Süsswasser. und Meereskunde, 4: 93–97, 20 figs. Büsum, Holstein.

—— 1927. Vergleichende Studien zur Biologie und Systematik zweier *Pythium*-Arten. Arch. Protistenk., 60: 142–192, 36 figs.

—— 1931. Zur Kenntnis einer neuen *Isoachlya*-Art aus dem Erdboden. Beihefte Bot. Centralbl., II, 48: 103–111, 7 figs.

DOFLEIN, F. 1907. Fortpflanzungserscheinungen bei Amöben und verwandten Organismen. Sitzungsber. Gesell. Morph. Physiol. München, 23 (1): 10–18, 2 figs.

DOMJÁN, A. 1936. "Vízigombás"-Adatok Szeged és Tihany Vidékéröl ("Wasserpilz"-daten aus der Umgebung von Szeged und Tihany). Folia cryptogam., 2 (1): 8–59, pl. 1.

DRECHSLER, C. 1925. The cottony leak of cucumbers caused by *Pythium aphanidermatum*. J. Agr. Res., 30: 1035–1042, 1 fig., 2 pls.

—— 1927. Two water molds causing tomato rootlet injury. J. Agr. Res., 34: 287–296, 2 figs.

—— 1930. Some new species of *Pythium*. J. Wash. Acad. Sci., 20: 398–418.

—— 1931. A crown rot of hollyhocks caused by *Phytophthora megasperma*. *Ibid.*, 21: 513–526, 5 figs.

—— 1932. A species of *Pythiogeton* isolated from decaying leaf-sheaths of the common cat-tail. *Ibid.*, 22: 421–449, 5 figs.

—— 1945. Several additional Phycomycetes subsisting on nematodes and amoebae. Mycologia, 37: 1–31, 4 figs.

—— 1946. Several species of *Pythium* peculiar in their sexual development. Phytopathology, 36: 781–864, figs. 1–29.

—— 1955. Production of zoospores from germinating oospores of *Pythium butleri.* Sydowia, 9: 451–463, 8 pl.

DURAND, E. J. 1894. The development of *Olpidium sp.*, one of the Chytridiaceae. Bull. Torrey Bot. Club, 21: 410.

EHRENBERG, C. G. 1840. Berichte (Monatsber. Berlin Akad.), 1840: 150.

ELLIOT, E. W. 1949. The swarm-cells of myxomycetes. Mycologia, 41: 141–170, 25 figs.

ELLISON, B. R. 1945. Flagellar studies on zoospores of some members of the Mycetozoa, Plasmodiophorales, and Chytridiales. Mycologia, 37: 444–459, figs. 1–4.

EMERSON, R. 1938a. A new life cycle involving cyst-formation in *Allomyces*. Mycologia, 30: 120–132, 11 figs.

—— 1938b. Correction on Ralph Emerson's paper. *Ibid.*, 30: 479.

—— 1939. Life cycles in the Blastocladiales. Trans. Brit. Mycol. Soc., 23: 123.

—— 1941. An experimental study of the life cycles and taxonomy of *Allomyces*. Lloydia, 4: 77–144, 16 figs.

—— 1950. Current trends of experimental research on the aquatic Phycomycetes. Ann. Rev. Microbiol., 4: 169–200.

—— 1954. The biology of water molds. Chap. 8 *in* Aspects of synthesis and order in growth, D. Rudnick, ed. vii + 274 pp. Princeton Univ. Press, Princeton. Pp. 171–208, 5 figs., 8 pls.

—— AND CANTINO, E. C. 1948. The isolation, growth, and metabolism of *Blastocladia* in pure culture. Amer. J. Bot., 35: 157–171, 9 figs.

—— AND FOX, D. L. 1940. Gamma-carotene in the sexual phase of the aquatic fungus *Allomyces*. Proc. Royal Soc. London, Ser. B, 128 (852): 275–293, pl. 16.

—— AND WILSON, C. M. 1949. The significance of meiosis in *Allomyces*. Science, 110: 86–88, 2 figs.

—— —— 1954. Interspecific hybrids and the cytogenetics and cytotaxonomy of *Euallomyces*. Mycologia, 46: 393–434, 15 figs.

ENTZ, G., SR. 1873. *Rhizidium euglenae* Alex. Braun. Adalék a *Chytridium* félék ismeretéhez. M. Tud. Akadémia. Értekezések a Természettudományok köréböl., 3 (13): 1–20, 2 pls.

ENTZ, G., JR. 1930. Über schnelles Wachstum und rasche Entwicklung eines Phycomycetenprotisten *Oovorus copepodorum* (n.gen., n.sp.). Arch. Protistenk., 69: 175–194, pl. 13, figs. 1–18.

―――― 1931. Miért pusztulnak ki véglénytenyészeteink—A Szt. Istv. Akadémia felolvasásai, 2: köt. 9 sz. (Not seen, quoted in Domján, 1936.)

FAY, D. J. 1947. *Chytriomyces spinosus* nov. sp. Mycologia, 39: 152–157, 39 figs.

FELDMANN, G. 1956. Développement d'une plasmodiophorale marine: *Plasmodiophora bicaudata* J. Feldm., parasite du *Zostera nana* Roth. Rev. Gén. Botanique, 63: 390–421, 9 figs, pls. 20–24.

FELDMANN, J. 1941. Une nouvelle espèce de *Plasmodiophora* (*P. bicaudata*) parasite du *Zostera nana* Roth. Bull. Soc. d'Hist. Nat. Afrique du Nord, 31: 171–177, 2 figs.

―――― 1954. Inventaire de la flore marine de Roscoff. Suppl. 6, Travaux Sta. Biol. de Roscoff, pp. 1–152.

FELDMANN, J. AND G. 1940. Note sur une Chytridiale parasite des spores de Céramiacées. Bull. Soc. d'Hist. Nat. Afrique du Nord, 31: 72–75, 1 fig.

―――― ―――― 1955. Observations sur quelques Phycomycètes marins nouveaux ou peu connus. Rev. Mycologique, 20 (3): 231–251, 6 figs.

FERDINANDSEN, C., AND WINGE, Ö. 1914. *Ostenfeldiella*, a new genus of Plasmodiophoraceae. Ann. Bot. London, 28: 643–649, 4 figs., pl. 45.

FERRIS, V. R. 1954. A note on the flagellation of *Phytophthora infestans* (Mont.) de Bary. Science, 120: 71–72, figs. 1–2.

FISCH, CARL. 1884a. Beiträge zur Kenntniss der Chytridiaceen. Sitzungsber. Phys.–Med. Soc. Erlangen, 16: 29–72, pl. 1, 39 figs.

―――― 1884b. Ueber zwei neue Chytridiaceen. *Ibid.*, 16: 101–103.

FISCHER, A. 1880. Ueber die Stachelkugeln in Saprolegniaschläuchen. Bot. Zeitung, 38: 689–696, 705–711, 721–726.

―――― 1882. Untersuchungen über die Parasiten der Saprolegnieen. Jahrb. wiss. Bot., 13: 286–371, pls. 13–15.

―――― 1892. Phycomycetes. Die Pilze Deutschlands, Oesterreichs und der Schweiz. Rabenhorst. Kryptogamen-Fl., 1 (4): 1–490. Leipzig.

FISCHER, G.W. 1953. Manual of the North American smut fungi. xii + 343 pp., Ronald Press, New York.

FITZPATRICK, H. M. 1923. Generic concepts in the Pythiaceae and Blastocladiaceae. Mycologia, 15: 166–173.

―――― 1930. The lower fungi. Phycomycetes. xi + 331 pp. McGraw-Hill, New York.

FJERDINGSTAD, E. 1955. *Rhizophidium deformans*. En algeparasit i *Oscillatoria*-arter fra Mølleåen. Bot. Tiddsk., 52: 171–172, 1 fig.

FORBES, E. J. 1935a. Observations on some British water moulds (Saprolegniales and Blastocladiales). Trans. Brit. Mycol. Soc., 19: 221–239, 2 figs., pls. 8–10.

—— 1935b. Water moulds of the Manchester district. Mem. and Proc. Manchester Lit. and Phil. Soc., 79: 1–11. (Separate.)

FOTT, B. 1942. Über eine auf den Protococcalenzellen parasitierende *Chytridiacee*. Studia Bot. Čechica, 5 (3–4): 167–170, 5 figs.

—— 1950. New chytrids parasiting on algae. Z. Věstník Král. čes. Spol. Nauk. Tř. Matem.-Přivo. Roč., 4: 1–10, 20 figs., 1 pl. (Separate.) (1951)

—— 1952. Mikroflora oravských rašelin. Preslia, 24: 189–209, 4 figs.

—— 1957. Taxonomie drobnohledné flory našich vod. Preslia, 29: 278–319, 11 figs., pl. 19.

FOUST, FRANCES K. 1937. A new species of *Rozella* parasitic on *Allomyces*. J. Elisha Mitchell Sci. Soc., 53: 197–204, pls. 22–23.

FRAGOSA, R. G. 1925. *De-Tonisia*, gen. nov., de hongo parasito en una *Spirogyra*. Nuova Notaris, 36 : 141–143, figs. 1–5.

FREY, R. 1950. Chitin und Zellulose in Pilzzellwänden. Ber. Schweiz. Botan. Gesell., 60: 198–230, pl. 3.

FRIEDMANN, I. 1952. Über neue und wenig bekannte auf Diatomeen parasitierende Phycomyceten. Österr. Bot. Zeitschr., 99 (2–3): 173–219, 8 figs.

—— 1953. Eine neue Chytridiale, *Chytridium surirellae* n.sp. *Ibid.*, 100 (1–2): 5–7, 1 fig.

FRITSCH, A. 1895. Über Parasiten bei Crustaceen und Raederthieren der süssen Gewässer. Bull. Internat. Acad. Tchèque Sci., 2: 79–85, figs. 1–9.

FRITSCH, F. E. 1903. Two fungi, parasitic on species of *Tolypothrix*.... Ann. Bot. London, 17: 649–664, pl. 29.

FRITSCH, K. 1892. Nomenclatorische Bemerkungen. IV. Der Gattungsname *Naegelia*. Österr. botan. Zeitschr., 42: 333–334.

—— 1893. Nomenclatorische Bemerkungen. VI. *Naegeliella* Schröt. *Ibid.*, 43: 420–421.

GAERTNER, A. 1954a. Beobachtungen über die Bewegungsweise von Chytridineenzoosporen. Archiv für Mikrobiologie, 20: 423–426, 1 fig.

—— 1954b. Über das Vorkommen niederer Erdphycomyceten in Afrika, Schweden und an einigen mitteleuropäischen Standorten. *Ibid.*, 21: 4–56, 7 figs.

—— 1954c. Beschreibung dreier neuer Phlyctochytrien und eines *Rhizophidium* (Chytridiales) aus Erdboden. *Ibid.*, 21: 112–126, 7 figs.

—— 1954d. Einige physiologische und morphologische Beobachtungen an Kulturen niederer Phycomyceten (*Rhizophidium, Phlyctochytrium*). *Ibid.*, 21: 167–177, 4 figs.

GANAROS, A. E. 1957. Marine fungus infecting eggs and embryos of *Urosalpinx cinerea*. Science, 125: 1194, 1 fig. 1957.

GAUMANN, ERNST A. 1926. Vergleichende Morphologie der Pilze. 626 pp., 398 figs. Jena.

GAUMANN, ERNST A., AND DODGE, C. W. 1928. Comparative morphology of fungi. 701 pp., 406 figs. McGraw-Hill, New York.

GEITLER, L. 1942. Eine neue Chytridiale, *Zygorhizidium verrucosum* n. sp. und ihre Wirkung auf die Wirtszellen. Arch. Protistenk., 96: 109–118, 2 figs.

GIARD, A. 1888. Sur les *Nephromyces*, genre nouveau de champignons parasites du rein des Molgulidées. C. R. Acad. Sci. Paris, 106: 1180–1181.

GICKLHORN, J. 1922. Studien an *Zoophagus insidians* Som., einem Tiere fangenden Pilz. Glasn. hrv. Prirodosl. Dr., 34 (2): 198–227, pls. 1–2. 1922–25.

—— 1923. *Aphanomyces ovidestruens* nov. spec.—ein Parasit in den Eiern von Diaptomus. Lotos, 71: 143–156, 8 figs.

GILL, C. H. 1893. On an endophytic parasite of diatoms. J. Roy. Microscopical Soc. London, 1893 (1): 1–4, pl. 1, figs. 1–9.

GILPIN, R. H. 1954. Concerning the nutrition of *Apodachlya brachynema*. Mycologia, 46: 702–707.

GIMESI, NÁNDOR. 1924. Hydrobiologiai Tanulmányok (Hydrobiologische Studien) II. *Phlyctidium eudorinae* Gim., n. sp. (Adatok A Phycomycesék Ismeretehez). Növénytani Szakosztályának, 1924: 1–5. Németül 6–8 (1 tábla, 1 rajz). (Separate.)

GOBI, C. 1884. Ueber die Gruppe der Amoeboideae. Arbeiten St. Petersburger Naturf.-Ges., 15 (1): 1–36. (German abstract by Borodin *in* Bot. Centralbl., 21: 35–38. 1885.)

—— 1900. O nouom parazitnom gribkie (Ueber einen neuen parasitischen Pilz...) *Rhizidiomyces ichneumon*, nov. sp. Scripta Bot. Horti Univ. Imper. Petro., 15: 227–272, pls. 6–7.

GOEBEL, K. 1884. *Tetramyxa parasitica*. Flora, 67: 517–521, pl. 7.

GOLDIE-SMITH, E. K. 1946. *Chytridium lecythii* (Ingold) n. comb. Trans. Brit. Mycol. Soc., 29: 68–69, 1 fig.

—— 1951. A new species of *Sorodiscus* on *Pythium*. J. Elisha Mitchell Sci. Soc., 67: 108–121, 2 pls., 39 figs.

—— 1952. The sporangial phase of *Pythium undulatum* Petersen. *Ibid.*, 68: 273–292, 2 figs., pls. 24–26.

—— 1954. The position of *Woronina polycystis* in the Plasmodiophoraceae. Amer. J. Bot., 41: 441–448, 29 figs.

—— 1956a. A new species of *Woronina*, and *Sorodiscus cokeri* emended. J. Elisha Mitchell Sci. Soc., 72: 348–356, 35 figs.

—— 1956b. Maintenance of stock cultures of aquatic fungi. *Ibid.*, 72: 158–166.

GRAFF, P. 1928. Contributions to our knowledge of western Montana fungi. II. Phycomycetes. Mycologia, 20: 158–179.

GRAN, H. H. 1900. Bemerkungen über einige Plankton-diatomeen. Nyt Mag. Naturvid., 38 (2): 105–128, figs. 8–9, pl. 9.

GRENFELL, J. G. 1894. Note on fungi parasitic on diatoms. J. Quekett Micros. Club, 5 (2d Ser.): 371.

GRIFFITHS, B. M. 1925. Studies in the phytoplankton of the lowland waters of Great Britain. No. III. The phytoplankton of Shropshire, Cheshire, and Staffordshire. J. Linn. Soc. London. Bot., 47: 75–98, pl. 1.

GRIGGS, R. F. 1908. On the cytology of *Synchytrium.* Ohio Naturalist, 8 (5): 277–286, pls. 19–20.

——— 1909a. Some aspects of amitosis in *Synchytrium.* Bot. Gaz., 47: 127-138, pls. 3–4.

——— 1909b. Mitosis in *Synchytrium. Ibid.,* 48: 339–358, pls. 16–18.

——— 1909c. A note on amitosis by constriction in *Synchytrium.* Ohio Naturalist, 9 (7): 513–515, 4 figs.

GROSS, G. 1851. De l'embryogénie ascendante des espèces.... Moskovskoe obschchestro linbitelei prirody. (Bull. Soc. Impér. Naturalistes de Moscou), 24: 283–340, 429–502, pls. A–C, C′, D–F.

GROVE, W. B. 1917. *Rhizophidium acuforme* Fisch. New Phytologist, 16: 177–180, fig. 1.

GUILLIERMOND, A. 1922. Nouvelles observations cytologiques sur les Saprolegniacé. La Cellule, 32: 429.

GWYNNE-VAUGHAN, H., AND BARNES, B. 1937. The structure and development of the fungi. 2d ed. xvi + 449 pp. Cambridge, England.

[HAMID, ABDUL. 1942. Indian water moulds. III. Proc. Indian Acad. Sci., Sect. B, 15: 206–215, 3 pls.

HANSON, A. M. 1944a. A new chytrid parasitizing *Volvox: Loborhiza metzneri* gen. nov., sp. nov. Amer. J. Bot., 31: 166–171, 31 figs.

——— 1944b. Three new saprophytic chytrids. Torreya, 44: 30–33.

——— 1945a. A morphological, developmental, and cytological study of four saprophytic chytrids. I. *Catenomyces persicinus* Hanson. Amer. J. Bot., 32: 431–438, 52 figs.,

——— 1945b. A morphological, developmental, and cytological study of four saprophytic chytrids. II. *Rhizophydium coronum* Hanson. *Ibid.,* 32: 479–487, 61 figs.

——— 1946a. A morphological, developmental, and cytological study of four saprophytic chytrids. III. *Catenochytridium laterale* Hanson. *Ibid.,* 33: 389–393, 31 figs.

——— 1946b. A morphological, developmental, and cytological study of four saprophytic chytrids. IV. *Phlyctorhiza endogena* gen. nov., sp. nov. *Ibid.,* 33: 732–739, 49 figs.

HARANT, H. 1931. Contribution à l'histoire naturelle des ascides et de leurs parasites. Ann. Inst. Océanograph. (Monaco), 8 (4): 231–389, 61 figs.

HARDER, R. 1937. Über das Vorkommen von Chitin und Zellulose und seine Bedeutung für die phylogenetische und systematische Beurteilung der Pilze. Nachrichten Gesell. Wiss. Göttingen, Math.–Physik. Kl., Fachgruppe VI (Biol.) (N. F.), 3 (1): 1–7.

HARDER, R. 1939a. Über die Bedeutung von Chitin und Cellulose für die Phylogenie der P'lze. Abstracts of Communications, Third Internat. Congress for Microbiology, New York, Sect. VI, p. 239.

—— 1939b. Untersuchungen an mikroskopischen Erdpilzen der dominikanischen Republik. I. Über das Vorkommen von Chitin und Zellulose und seine Bedeutung für die phylogenetische und systematische Beurteilung der Pilze. Publ. Inst. Científico Dominico-Alemán, 1 (1): 108–117.

—— 1939c. *See* Strasburger, Lehrbuch der Botanik für Hochschulen. 20th ed. Jena.

—— 1948. Über das Vorkommen niederer Phycomyceten in deutschen Böden. Nachrichten Akad. Wiss. Göttingen, Math.-Physik. Kl., 1948: 5–7.

—— 1954. Über die arktische Vegetation niederer Phycomyceten. *Ibid.*, 1954: 1–9.

—— AND SÖRGEL, G. 1938. Über einen neuen plano-isogamen Phycomyceten mit Generationswechsel und seine phylogenetische Bedeutung. Nachrichten Gesell. Wiss. Göttingen, Math.-Physik Kl., Fachgruppe VI (Biol.) (N.F.), 3 (5): 119–127, 4 figs.

—— —— 1939. Same title. Veröffentlich. Deutsch-Dominikanischen Tropenforschungsinstituts, 1: 118–127.

—— AND UEBELMESSER, E. 1955. Über marine saprophytische Chytridiales und einige andere Pilze vom Meeresboden und Meeresstrand. Archiv für Mikrobiol., 22: 87 114, 1 fig.

HARIOT, P. 1889. Champignons. Mission Scientifique du Cap Horn, V, Bot., pp. 173–200. Paris.

HARTMANN, M. 1925. Untersuchungen über relative Sexualität. Biol. Centralbl., 45: 449–467.

HARTOG, M. M. 1887. On the formation and liberation of the zoospores in the Saprolegniae. Quart. J. Micro. Sci. (N.S.), 27: 427–438.

HARVEY, J. V. 1925. A study of the water molds and pythiums occurring in the soils of Chapel Hill. J. Elisha Mitchell Sci. Soc., 41: 151–164, pls. 12–19.

—— 1927. A survey of the water molds occurring in the soils of Wisconsin, as studied during the summer of 1926. Trans. Wisc. Acad. Sci. Arts, Lett., 23: 551-562, pls. 4-7.

—— 1928. A survey of the water molds occurring in the soils of North Carolina, Wisconsin and Oklahoma. Proc. Okla. Acad. Sci., 7: 135.

—— 1930. A taxonomic and morphological study of some members of the Saprolegniaceae. J. Elisha Mitchell Sci. Soc., 45: 319–332, pls. 32–33.

—— 1942. A study of western watermolds. J. Elisha Mitchell Sci. Soc., 58: 16–42, pls. 1–8.

—— 1952. Relationship of aquatic fungi to water pollution. Sewage and Industrial Wate s, 24: 1159–1164.

HASKINS, R. H. 1939. Cellulose as a substratum for saprophytic chytrids. Amer. J. Bot., 26: 635–639, figs. 1–14.

—— 1946. New chytridiaceous fungi from Cambridge. Trans. Brit. Mycol. Soc., 29: 135–140, figs. 1–21.

—— 1948. Studies in the lower Chytridiales. Thesis, Harvard University.

—— 1950. Studies in the lower Chytridiales. II. Endo-operculation and sexuality in the genus *Diplophlyctis*. Mycologia, 42: 772–778, 10 figs.

—— AND WESTON, W. H., JR. 1950. Studies in the lower Chytridiales. I. Factors affecting pigmentation, growth, and metabolism of a strain of *Karlingia* (*Rhizophlyctis*) *rosea*. Amer. J. Bot., 37: 739–750, 11 figs.

HATCH, WINSLOW R. 1933. Sexuality of *Allomyces arbuscula* Butler. J. Elisha Mitchell Sci. Soc., 49 (1): 163–170, pl. 12.

—— 1935. Gametogenesis in *Allomyces arbuscula*. Ann. Bot. London, 49: 623–649, 33 figs.

—— 1936. Zonation in *Allomyces arbuscula*. Mycologia, 28: 439–444, figs. 1–5.

—— 1938. Conjugation and zygote germination in *Allomyces arbuscula*. Ann. Bot. London (N.S.), 2: 583–614, pls. 18–22.

—— 1944. Zoösporogenesis in the resistant sporangia of *Allomyces*. Mycologia, 36: 650–663, 2 figs.

—— AND JONES, R. C. 1944. An experimental study of alternation of generations in *Allomyces arbusculus*. Mycologia, 36: 369–381.

HAUCK, F. 1878. Notiz über *Rhizophydium dicksonii* Wright. Österr. bot. Zeitschr., 28: 321.

HÄYRÉN, E. 1930. Ein für Finland neuer Wasserpilze. Mem. Soc. pro Fauna et Flora Fennica, 5: 97. 1928–29.

—— 1943. Über das Zusammenballen der Schwarmer des zweiten Schwarmstadiums von *Saprolegnia dioica*. Ibid., 18: 89–93, 2 figs.

HEIDT, K. 1937. Beitrag zur Kenntnis der Gattung *Micromyces*. Berichte Deutsch. Bot. Gesell., 55: 204–217, 8 figs.

HENFREY, A. 1859. On *Chlorosphaera*, a new genus of unicellular freshwater algae. Trans. Micro. Soc. London (N. S.), 7: 25–29, pl. 3, figs. 1–18.

HENNINGS, P. 1892. Beiträge zur Pilzflora von Schleswig-Holstein. Schrift. Nat. Ver. Schleswig-Holstein, 9: 229–258.

HEURCK, H. VAN. 1899. Traité des Diatomées. 572 pp. Anvers.

HICKMAN, C. J. 1940. The red core root disease of the strawberry caused by *Phytophthora fragariae*, n. sp. J. Pomology, 18 (2): 89–118, figs. 9–10, 2 pls.

HILDEBRAND, F. 1867–68. Mykologische Beiträge. I. Ueber einige neue Saprolegnieen. Jahrb. wiss. Bot., 6: 249–269, pls. 15–16.

HILLEGAS, A. B. 1940. The cytology of *Endochytrium operculatum* (de Wildeman) Karling in relation to its development and organization. Bull. Torrey Bot. Club, 67: 1–32, pls. 1–7.

—— 1941. Observations on a new species of *Cladochytrium*. Mycologia, 33: 618–632, 40 figs.

Hine, F. B. 1878–79. Observations on several forms of Saprolegnieae. Amer. Quart. Micro. Journ., 1: 18–28, 136–146, pls. 5–7.

Höfler, K. 1950. Einige Beobachtungen an *Ancylistes closterii* Pfitzer. Sydowia, Ann. Mycol., II, 4: 381–388, figs. 1–4.

Höhnk, Willy. 1933. Polyplanetism and zoospore-germination in Saprolegniaceae and *Pythium*. Amer. J. Bot., 20: 45–62, 6 figs., pl. 1.

—— 1935. Saprolegniales und Monoblepharidales aus der Umgebung Bremens, mit besonderer Berücksichtigung der Oekologie der Saprolegniaceae. Abhandl. Naturwiss. Vereins Bremen, 29 (3): 207–237, 7 figs.

—— 1936. On three pythiaceous Oomycetes. Beihefte Bot. Centralbl., 55 (Abt. A): 89–99, 4 figs.

—— 1938. Über heimische Phycomyceten. I. Abhandl. Naturwiss. Vereins Bremen, 31: 491–501, fig. 1, pl. 1.

—— 1939. Ein Beitrag zur Kenntnis der Phycomyceten des Brackwassers. Kieler Meeresforsch., 3 (2): 337–361, 8 figs.

—— 1952a. Die in Nordwestdeutschland gefundenen ufer- und bodenbewohnenden Saprolegniaceae. Veröff. Inst. f. Meeresforsch. Bremerhaven, 1: 52–90, 15 pls. (Nachtrag, pp. 126–128.)

—— 1952b. Studien zur Brack- und Seewassermykologie. I. *Ibid.*, 1: 115–125.

—— 1952c. Studien zur Brack- und Seewassermykologie. II. Oomycetes, 1. *Ibid.*, 1: 247–278, 3 figs., 1 pl.

—— 1953a. Studien zur Brack- und Seewassermykologie. III. Oomycetes, 2. *Ibid.*, 2: 52–108, 4 figs., 9 pls.

—— 1953b. Eine neue uferbewohnende Saprolegniazee *Calyptralegnia ripariensis* nov. spec. *Ibid.*, 2: 230–235, 7 figs.

—— 1953c. Mykologische Studien im Brack- und Seewasser. *In* Abstracts of Communications, Sixth Int. Congress for Microbiology, Rome, 7 (22): 374–378.

—— 1954. Von den Mikropilzen in Watt und Meer. Abh. naturw. Verein Bremen, 33 (3): 407–429, 1 pl.

—— 1955. Niedere Pilze vom Watt und Meeresgrund (Chytridiales und Thraustochytriaceae). Naturwissenschaft., 11: 348–349.

—— 1956a. Mykologische Abwasser-studie. I. Veröff. Inst. f. Meeresforsch. Bremerhaven, 4: 67–110.

—— 1956b. Studien zur Breckund Seewassermykologie. VI. Über die pilzliche Besiedlung verschieden salziger submerser Standorte. *Ibid.*, 4: 195–213.

—— 1957a. Über Wuchsformen bei den Saprolegniaceen. *Ibid.*, 5: 124–134, 3 figs.

—— 1957b. Fortschritte der marinen Mykologie in jüngster Zeit. Naturwiss. Rundschau, 2: 39–44.

—— 1958. Mykologische Notizen: I. Micropilze im Eis. Veröff. Inst. f. Meeresforsch. Bremerhaven, 5: 193–194.

—— and Aleem, A. A. 1953. Ein Brackwasserpilz: *Olpidium maritimum* nov. spec. Veröff. Inst. f. Meeresforsch. Bremerhaven, 2: 224–229, 1 pl., 7 figs.

—— AND BOCK, K. J. 1954. Ein Beitrage zur Ökologie der saprophytischen Wasserpilze. Veröff. Inst. f. Meeresforsch. Bremerhaven, 3: 9–26.

—— AND VALLIN, ST. 1953. Epidemisches absterben von *Eurytemora* im Bottnischen Meerbusen, verursacht durch *Leptolegnia baltica* nov. spec. Veröff. Inst. f. Meeresforsch. Bremerhaven, 3: 215–223, 3 figs., 1 pl.

HOOD, O. 1910. On *Rhizophidium eudorinae*, a new chytridiaceous fungus. Proc. Birmingham Nat. Hist. and Phil. Soc., 12: 38–45, 5 figs.

HORNE, A. S. 1930. Nuclear divisions in the Plasmodiophorales. Ann. Bot. London, 44: 199–231, 1 fig., pls. 15–16.

HOVASSE, R. 1936. *Rhizophidium beauchampi*, sp. nov., Chytridinée parasite de la Volvocinée *Eudorina* (*Pleodorina*) *illinoisensis* (Kofoid). Ann. Protistol., 5: 73–81, 4 figs.

HUBER-PESTALOZZI, G. 1931. Infektion einer *Mougeotia*-Population durch *Micromyces zygogonii* Dangeard an einem alpinen Standort. Hedwigia, 71: 88–93, pl. 3.

—— 1944. *Chytridium oocystidis* (spec. nova), ein Parasit auf *Oocystis lacustris* Chodat. Zeitschr. f. Hydrobiologie, 10 (1): 117–120, 8 figs.

—— 1946. Der Walensee und sein Plankton. *Ibid.*, 10 (2–3): 1–123, 7 figs.

HUMPHREY, J. E. 1893. The Saprolegniaceae of the United States, with notes on other species. Trans. Amer. Phil. Soc., (N.S.), 17: 63–148, pls. 14–20.

HUNEYCUTT, M. B. 1948. Keratinophilic Phycomycetes. I. A new genus of the Saprolegniaceae. J. Elisha Mitchell Sci. Soc., 64: 277–285, pls. 35–36.

—— 1952. A new water mold on keratinized materials. *Ibid.*, 68: 109–112.

INDOH, HIROHARO. 1935. *Monoblepharis* found in Japan. Bot. Mag. Tokyo, 49: 471–473, 3 figs. (In Japanese, with English summary.)

—— 1937. Aquatic fungi in Senshunyen. Hakubutsugaku Zasshi (Mag. Nat. Hist.), 35 (60): 295–301, pls. 14–16.

—— 1939. Studies on the Japanese aquatic fungi. I. On *Apodachlyella completa*, sp. nov., with revision of the Leptomitaceae. Science Rept. Tokyo Bunrika Daigaku, Sect. B, 4: 43–50, pl. 7, figs. 1–11.

—— 1940. Studies on Japanese aquatic fungi. II. The Blastocladiaceae. *Ibid.*, 4: 237–284, 34 figs.

—— 1941. Observations on some aquatic molds collected from Micronesia. (Preliminary note.) Hakubutsugaku Zasshi, Tokyo (Mag. Nat. Hist.), 38 (72): 86–91, 5 figs. (In Japanese.)

—— 1952. A new variety of *Allomyces javanicus* Kniep. Nagaoa, 2: 24–29, figs. 1–4.

—— 1953. Observations on Japanese aquatic fungi. I. *Apodachlya, Sapromyces,* and *Rhipidium*. *Ibid.*, 3: 26–35, figs. 13–21.

INGOLD, C. T. 1940. *Endocoenobium eudorinae*, gen. et sp. nov., a chytridiaceous fungus parasitizing *Eudorina elegans* Ehrenb. New Phytologist, 39: 97–103, 4 figs., pl. 2.

INGOLD, C. T. 1941. Studies on British chytrids. I. *Phlyctochytrium proliferum* sp. nov. and *Rhizophidium lecythii* sp. nov. Trans. Brit. Mycol. Soc., 25: 41–48, 3 figs., pl. 4.

—— 1944. Studies on British chytrids. II. A new chytrid on *Ceratium* and *Peridinium*. *Ibid.*, 27: 93–96, 3 figs., pl. 9.

—— 1949. On the genus *Resticularia*. Ann. Bot. London (N. S.), 13: 435–443, 4 figs.

—— 1951. Aquatic Ascomycetes: *Ceriospora caudae-suis* n. sp. and *Ophiobolus typhae*. Trans. Brit. Mycol. Soc., 34: 210–215, 3 figs., pl. 7.

—— 1952. *Funaria* rhizoids infected with *Pleotrachelus wildemani*. Trans. Brit. Bryol. Soc., 2: 53–54, 1 fig.

—— 1954. Aquatic Ascomycetes: Discomycetes from lakes. Trans. Brit. Mycol. Soc., 37: 1–18, 15 figs.

—— 1955. Aquatic Ascomycetes: Further species from the English Lake District. *Ibid.*, 38: 157–168, 9 figs.

INGRAHAM, J. L., AND EMERSON, R. 1954. Studies of the nutrition and metabolism of the aquatic Phycomycete, *Allomyces*. Amer. J. Bot., 41: 146–152, 4 figs.

ITO, SEIYA. 1936. Mycological flora of Japan. I. Phycomycetes. 340 pp., 125 figs. Tokyo.

—— AND NAGAI, M. 1931. On the rot-disease of the seeds and seedlings of rice-plant caused by some aquatic fungi. J. Fac. Agr. Hokkaido Imper. Univ., Sapporo, 32: 45–69, pls. 8–11. 1931–33.

—— AND TOKUNAGA. Y. 1935. Notae mycologicae, Asiae Orientalis. I. Trans. Sapporo Nat. Hist. Soc., 14 (1): 11–33.

ITO, TAKESI. 1944. Some aquatic species of Phycomycetes found in Kyoto. Contrib. Lab. Phytopathol. and Mycol. Kyoto Imper. Univ., No. 187 [J. Jap. Bot. XX–1], pp. 51–60, figs. 1–3.

IYENGAR, M. O. P. 1935. Two new fungi of the genus *Coelomomyces* parasitic in larvae of *Anopheles*. Parasitology, 27: 440–449, 5 figs.

—— RAMAKRISHNAN, K., AND SUBRAMANIAN, C. V. 1955. A new species of *Sapromyces* from South India. J. Indian Bot. Soc., 34: 140–145, 31 figs.

JAAG, O., AND NIPKOW, F. 1951. Neue und wenig bekannte parasitische Pilze auf Planktonorganismen schweizerischer Gewässer. I. Berichte Schweiz. Bot. Gesell., 61: 478–498, pls. 11–16.

JACZEWSKI, A. A. 1898. Série de matériaux pour la flore mycologique du gouvernement de Smolensk, III: 65–94; IV: 1–16. Moscow.

—— 1931. Opredelitel gribov. Sovershennye griby (diploidnye stadii) (Determination of fungi. Perfect fungi, diploid species). Moskva, Leningrad, Gosudarstvennoe izdatel'stvo sel' skokhoziaistevennoi i kolkhoznokooperativnoi literaury. I. Fikomitsety (Phycomycetes). 294 pp., 329 figs.

JAHN, T. L. 1933. On certain parasites of *Phacus* and *Euglena*; *Sphaerita phaci*, sp. nov. Arch. Protistenk., 79: 349–355, pls. 16–17.

JANE, F. W. 1946. Revision of the genus *Harpochytrium*. J. Linn. Soc. London, Bot., 53: 28–40, 28 figs.

JOHANNES, H. 1950. Zwei neue Arten der Saprolegniaceen. Archiv für Mikrobiologie, 14: 594–601, 2 figs.

—— 1955. Die Gattung *Cladolegnia* Joh. gen. nov. (*Isoachlya* Kauffman) der Saprolegniaceae Nees. Repert. spec. nov. reg. veg.: 209–220.

JOHANSON, A. E. 1943. *Septochytrium plurilobulum* sp. nov. Amer. J. Bot., 30: 619–622, fig. 1.

—— 1944. An endo-operculate chytridiaceous fungus: *Karlingia rosea* gen. nov. *Ibid.*, 31: 397–404, 37 figs.

—— 1945. A new mycelioid chytrid: *Myceliochytrium fulgens* gen. nov. et sp. nov. Torreya, 45: 104–105.

JOHN, RACHEL. 1955. Studies in the Indian aquatic fungi. II. On the occurrence of two species of *Ancylistes* in *Closterium*. Proc. Indian Acad. Sci., Sect. B, 41: 86–95, 15 figs., pl. 5–8.

JOHNS, R. M. 1956. Additions to the Phycomycete flora of the Douglas Lake region. III. A new species of *Scherffeliomyces*. Mycologia, 48: 433–438, 12 figs.

—— 1957. A new species of Physoderma on *Dulichium*. Mycologia, 49: 298–299.

—— AND BENJAMIN, R. K. 1954. Sexual reproduction in *Gonapodya*. Mycologia, 46: 201–208, 17 figs.

JOHNSON, T. W., JR. 1950. A study of an isolate of *Brevilegnia* from New Caledonia. Mycologia, 42: 242–252, 1 fig.

—— 1951a. An isolate of *Dictyuchus* connecting the false-net and true-net species. *Ibid.*, 43: 365–372, 14 figs.

—— 1951b. A new *Mindeniella* from submerged, rosaceous fruits. Amer. J. Bot., 38: 74–78, 26 figs.

—— 1955a. Inoculation studies with a polysporangiate *Rozella* parasitic in *Dictyuchus anomalus*. *Ibid.*, 42: 119–123, 7 figs.

—— 1955b. A species of *Olpidiopsis* parasitic in *Achlya glomerata*. J. Elisha Mitchell Sci. Soc., 71: 58–64, 24 figs.

—— 1955c. The asexual stage of *Apodachlya minima*. Trans. Brit. Mycol. Soc., 38: 415–418, 1 fig.

—— 1956. The genus *Achlya*: morphology and taxonomy. xv + 180 pp., 22 pls. Univ. Michigan Press, Ann Arbor, Michigan.

—— 1957a. Resting spore development in the marine Phycomycete *Anisolpidium ectocarpii*. Amer. J. Bot., 44: 875–878, figs. 1–26.

—— 1957b. Marine fungi. III. Phycomycetes. Mycologia, 49: 392–400, 1 fig.

—— 1957c. On the marine Phycomycete *Thraustochytrium proliferum*. Trans. Brit. Mycol. Soc., 40: 292–294, 1 fig.

—— AND MEYERS, S. P. 1957. Literature on halophilous and halolimnic fungi. Bull. Marine Sci. Gulf and Caribbean, 7: 330–359.

—— AND SURRATT, J. 1955. Taxonomy of the species of *Isoachlya* possessing single oospores. Mycologia, 47: 122–129, 34 figs.

JOHNSON, T. W., JR., ZIEGLER, A. W., AND LINTHICUM, B. 1951. A note on *Dictyuchus pseudodictyon*. Mycologia, 43: 728–729.

JOKL, M. 1916. Eine neue Meereschytridinee: *Pleotrachelus ectocarpii.* nov. spec. Österr. botan. Zeitschr., 66: 267–272, pls. 4–5.

JONES, F. R., AND DRECHSLER. C. 1920. Crownwart of alfalfa caused by *Urophlyctis alfalfae.* J. Agr. Res., 20 : 295-331, pl. 47-56.

JONES, P. M. 1928. Morphology and cultural life history of *Plasmodiophora brassicae*. Arch. Protistenk., 62: 313–327, pls. 15–21.

JONES, R. C. 1946. Factors affecting the production of resistant sporangia of *Allomyces arbuscula*. Mycologia, 38: 91–102, 1 fig.

JUEL, H. O. 1901. *Pyrrhosorus,* eine neue marine Pilzgattung. Bih. Kgl. Svensk. Vetensk.-Ak. Handl., 26, Afd. 3, No. 14: 1–16, 1 pl., figs. 1–29.

KANOUSE, B. B. 1925. Physiology and morphology of *Pythiomorpha gonapodioides*. Bot. Gaz., 79: 196–206, pls. 12–13.

—— 1926. On the distribution of the water molds, with notes on the occurrence in Michigan of members of the Leptomitaceae and Blastocladiaceae. Papers Mich. Acad. Sci., Arts, Letters, 5: 105–114, pl. 1. 1925.

—— 1927. A monographic study of special groups of the water molds. I. Blastocladiaceae. II. Leptomitaceae and Pythiomorphaceae. Amer. J. Bot., 14: 287–306, 335–357, pls. 32–34, 48.

—— 1932. A physiological and morphological study of *Saprolegnia parasitica*. Mycologia, 24: 431–452, pls. 12–13.

KARLING, J. S. 1928a. Studies in the Chytridiales. I. The life history and occurrence of *Entophlyctis heliomorpha* (Dang.) Fischer. Amer. J. Bot., 15: 32–42, pl. 1.

—— 1928b. Studies in the Chytridiales. II. Contribution to the life history and occurrence of *Diplophlyctis intestina* (Schenk) Schroeter in cells of American Characeae. *Ibid.,* 15: 204–214, 2 figs., pl. 14.

—— 1928c. Studies in the Chytridiales. III. A parasitic chytrid causing cell hypertrophy in *Chara*. *Ibid.,* 15: 485–496, 9 figs., pl. 32.

—— 1930. Studies in the Chytridiales. IV. A further study of *Diplophlyctis intestina* (Schenk) Schroeter. *Ibid.,* 17: 770–778, 2 figs., pls. 46–49.

—— 1931a. Studies in the Chytridiales. V. A further study of species of the genus *Entophlyctis. Ibid.,* 18: 443–464, pls. 35–38.

—— 1931b. Studies in the Chytridiales. VI. The occurrence and life history of a new species of *Cladochytrium* in cells of *Eriocaulon septangulare. Ibid.,* 18: 526–557, pls. 42–44.

—— 1932. Studies in the Chytridiales. VII. The organization of the chytrid thallus. *Ibid.,* 19: 41–74, 138 figs.

—— 1934a. A saprophytic species of *Catenaria* isolated from roots of *Panicum variegatum*. Mycologia, 26: 528–543, figs. 1–3, pls. 57–58.

—— 1934b. Resting sporangia of *Cladochytrium*. Science (N. S.), 79: 390.

—— 1934c. New stations for *Physoderma* and *Ligniera*. Torreya, 34: 13–14.

—— 1935. A further study of *Cladochytrium replicatum* with special reference to its distribution, host range and culture on artificial media. Amer. J. Bot., 22: 439–452, figs. 1–29.

—— 1936a. The endo-exogenous method of growth and development of *Chytridium lagenaria*. *Ibid.*, 23: 619–627, 2 figs.

—— 1936b. Germination of the resting spores of *Diplophlyctis intestina*. Bull. Torrey Bot. Club, 63: 467–471, 8 figs.

—— 1936c. A new predaceous fungus. Mycologia, 28: 307–320, 5 figs.

—— 1937a. The structure, development, identity, and relationship of *Endochytrium*. Amer. J. Bot., 24: 352–364, 53 figs.

—— 1937b. The cytology of the Chytridiales with special reference to *Cladochytrium replicatum*. Mem. Torrey Bot. Club, 19 (1): 3–92, 2 text figs., 6 pls.

—— 1937c. A new species of *Phlyctochytrium* on *Hydrodictyon reticulatum*. Mycologia, 29: 178–186, 3 figs.

—— 1937d. Pascher and the genus *Asterocystis* of de Wildeman. *Ibid.*, 29: 291–294.

—— 1938a. A new chytrid genus: *Nephrochytrium*. Amer. J. Bot., 25: 211–215, figs. 1–2.

—— 1938b. A further study of *Catenaria*. *Ibid.*, 25: 328–335, 34 figs.

—— 1938c. Two new operculate chytrids. Mycologia, 30: 302–312, 37 figs.

—— 1938d. A large species of *Rhizophidium* from cooked beef. Bull. Torrey Bot. Club, 65: 439–452, figs. 1–39, pls. 20–21.

—— 1938e. Studies on *Rhizophidium*. II. *Rhizophidium laterale*. *Ibid.*, 65: 615–624, pl. 31, figs. 1–19.

—— 1939a. A note on *Phlyctidium*. Mycologia, 31: 286–288.

—— 1939b. A new fungus with anteriorly uniciliate zoospores: *Hyphochytrium catenoides*. Amer. J. Bot., 26: 512–519, figs. 1–18.

—— 1939c. Studies on *Rhizophidium*. III. Germination of the resting spores. Bull. Torrey Bot. Club, 66: 281–286, pl. 6.

—— 1941a. *Cylindrochytridium johnstonii* gen. nov. et sp. nov., and *Nowakowskiella profusum* sp. nov. *Ibid.*, 68: 381–387, 16 figs.

—— 1941b. Texas chytrids. Torreya, 41: 105–108.

—— 1941c. Notes on *Endochytrium* du Plessis. Mycologia, 33: 356–359.

—— 1942a. Parasitism among the chytrids. Amer. J. Bot., 29: 24–35, 47 figs.

—— 1942b. A synopsis of *Rozella* and *Rozellopsis*. Mycologia, 34: 193–208.

—— 1942c. A new chytrid with giant zoospores: *Septochytrium macrosporum* sp. nov. Amer. J. Bot., 29: 616–622, 15 figs.

—— 1942d. The Plasmodiophorales. ix + 144 pp., 17 pls. New York.

—— 1942e. The simple holocarpic biflagellate Phycomycetes. x + 123 pp., 25 pls. New York.

—— 1943. The life history of *Anisolpidium ectocarpii* gen. nov. et sp. nov., and a synopsis and classification of other fungi with anteriorly uniflagellate zoospores. Amer. J. Bot., 30: 637–648, 21 figs.

KARLING, J. S. 1944a. *Phagomyxa algarum* n. gen., n. sp., an unusual parasite with plasmodiophoralean and proteomyxean characteristics. *Ibid.*, 31: 38–52, 74 figs.

—— 1944b. Brazilian chytrids. I. Species of *Nowakowskiella*. Bull. Torrey Bot. Club, 71: 374–389, 69 figs.

—— 1944c. Brazilian chytrids. II. New species of *Rhizidium*. Amer. J. Bot., 31: 254–261, 72 figs.

—— 1944d. Brazilian ansiochytrids. *Ibid.*, 31: 391–397, 64 figs.

—— 1944e. Brazilian chytrids. III. *Nephrochytrium amazonensis*. Mycologia, 36: 351–357, 28 figs.

—— 1944f. Brazilian chytrids. IV. Species of *Rozella*. *Ibid.*, 36: 638–647, 28 figs.

—— 1944g. New lagenidiaceous parasites of rotifers from Brazil. Lloydia, 7: 328–342, 107 figs.

—— 1945a. Brazilian chytrids. V. *Nowakowskiella macrospora* n. sp., and other polycentric species. Amer. J. Bot., 32: 29–35, 51 figs.

—— 1945b. *Rhizidiomyces hirsutus* sp. nov., a hairy anisochytrid from Brazil. Bull. Torrey Bot. Club, 72: 47–51, 19 figs.

—— 1945c. Brazilian chytrids. VI. *Rhopalophlyctis* and *Chytriomyces*, two new chitinophyllic operculate genera. Amer. J. Bot., 32: 362–369, 61 figs.

—— 1945d. Brazilian chytrids. VII. Observations relative to sexuality in two new species of *Siphonaria*. *Ibid.*, 32: 580–587, 53 figs.

—— 1946a. Two new chytrid parasites of *Chytriomyces*. Mycologia, 38: 103–109, 19 figs.

—— 1946b. Brazilian chytrids. VIII. Additional parasites of rotifers and nematodes. Lloydia, 9: 1–12, 53 figs.

—— 1946c. Brazilian chytrids. IX. Species of *Rhizophydium*. Amer. J. Bot., 33: 328–334, 37 figs.

—— 1946d. Keratinophilic chytrids. I. *Rhizophydium keratinophilum* n. sp., a saprophyte isolated on human hair, and its parasite, *Phlyctidium mycetophagum* n. sp. *Ibid.*, 33: 751–757, 60 figs.

—— 1946e. Keratinophilic chytrids. *Ibid.*, 33, Suppl. No. 3, p. 219.

—— 1947a. Keratinophilic chytrids. II. *Phlyctorhiza variabilis* n. sp. *Ibid.*, 34: 27–32, 48 figs.

—— 1947b. Brazilian chytrids. X. New species with sunken opercula. Mycologia, 39: 56–70, 56 figs.

—— 1947c. *Lagenidium humanum*, a saprophyte isolated on dead human skin. *Ibid.*, 39: 224–230, 39 figs.

—— 1947d. New species of *Chytriomyces*. Bull. Torrey Bot. Club, 74: 334–344, 48 figs.

—— 1948a. Chytridiosis of scale insects. Amer. J. Bot., 35: 246–254, 49 figs.

—— 1948b. Keratinophilic chytrids. III. *Rhizophydium nodulosum* sp. nov. Mycologia, 40: 328–335, 20 figs.

—— 1948c. An *Olpidium* parasite of *Allomyces*. Amer. J. Bot., 35: 503–510, 32 figs.

—— 1949a. A new *Olpidiopsis* parasite of *Karlingia rosea* from Maryland. Mycologia, 41: 270–276, 17 figs.

—— 1949b. *Truittella setifera* gen. nov. et sp. nov., a new chytrid from Maryland. Amer. J. Bot., 36: 454–460, 44 figs.

—— 1949c. *Nowakowskiella crassa* sp. nov., *Cladochytrium aureum* sp. nov., and other polycentric chytrids from Maryland. Bull. Torrey Bot. Club, 76: 294–301, 17 figs.

—— 1949d. Three new species of *Chytriomyces* from Maryland. *Ibid.*, 76: 352–363, 59 figs.

—— 1949e. New monocentric eucarpic operculate chytrids from Maryland. Mycologia, 41: 505–522, 78 figs.

—— 1949f. Two new eucarpic inoperculate chytrids from Maryland. Amer. J. Bot., 36: 681–687, 48 figs.

—— 1950. The genus *Physoderma* (Chytridiales). Lloydia, 13: 29–71.

—— 1951a. *Cladochytrium setigerum* sp. nov. and *Septochytrium marilandicum* sp. nov. from Maryland. Bull. Torrey Bot. Club, 78: 38–43, 30 figs.

—— 1951b. Polycentric strains of *Phlyctorhiza variabilis*. Amer. J. Bot., 38: 772–777, 3 figs.

—— 1952. *Sommerstorffia spinosa* Arnaudow. Mycologia, 44: 387–412, 76 figs.

—— 1953. *Micromyces* and *Synchytrium*. *Ibid.*, 45: 276–287.

—— 1954a. Possible relationships and phylogeny of *Synchytrium*. Bull. Torrey Bot. Club, 81: 353–362, 1 fig.

—— 1954b. An unusual keratinophilic microorganism. Proc. Indiana Acad. Sci., 63: 83–86, 10 figs. (Separate.)

KAUFFMAN, C. H. 1908. A contribution to the physiology of the Saprolegniaceae, with special reference to variations of the sexual organs. Ann. Bot. London, 22: 361–387, pl. 23.

—— 1921. *Isoachlya*, a new genus of the Saprolegniaceae. Amer. J. Bot., 8: 231–237, pls. 13–14.

KEILIN, D. 1921. On a new type of fungus: *Coelomomyces stegomyiae* n. g., n. sp., parasitic in the body-cavity of the larva of *Stegomyia scutellaris* Walker (Diptera, Nematocera, Culicidae). Parasitology, 13: 225–234, 7 figs.

—— 1927. On *Coelomomyces stegomyiae* and *Zografia notonectae*, fungi parasitic in insects. *Ibid.*, 19: 365–367.

KEVORKIAN, ARTHUR G. 1934. The structure and development of a new aquatic phycomycete. Mycologia, 26: 145–152, 11 figs.

—— 1935. Studies in the Leptomitaceae. II. Cytology of *Apodachlya brachynema* and *Sapromyces reinschii*. *Ibid.*, 27: 274–285, pls. 19–20.

KIBBE, ALICE L. 1916. *Chytridium alarium* on *Alaria fistulosa*. Publ. Puget Sound Biol. Sta., 1: 221–226, pls. 39–40.

KING, C. A. 1903. Observations on the cytology of *Araiospora pulchra* Thaxter. Proc. Boston Soc. Nat. Hist., 31 (5): 211–245, pls. 11–15.

KLEBAHN, H. 1892. Studien über Zygoten. II.... Jahrb. wiss. Bot., 24: 235–267, pls. 1–3.

KLEBS, G. 1896. Die Bedingungen der Fortpflanzung bei einigen Algen und Pilzen. xviii + 543 pp., 3 tables, 15 figs. Jena.

—— 1898. Zur Physiologie der Fortpflanzung einiger Pilze. I.   Jahrb. wiss. Bot., 32: 1–70, 2 figs.

—— 1899. Zur Physiologie der Fortpflanzung einiger Pilze. II.   *Ibid.*, 33: 71–151, 1 fig.

—— 1900. Zur Physiologie der Fortpflanzung einiger Pilze. III.   *Ibid.*, 35: 80–203. For reviews of the four items above, see Bot. Gaz., 23: 214; 28: 441; 36: 311.

KLEIN, J. 1882. *Vampyrella* Cnk., ihre Entwicklung und systematische Stellung. Bot. Centralbl., 11: 187–215, 247–264, pls. 1–4.

KLOSS, H. 1856a. Monatsber. Berlin Akad., 1856. (Cited in Schenk, 1858a.)

—— 1856b. Parasitismus.   Frankfurter Museum, 1856 (28): 218. (Cited in Braun, 1856a.)

KNIEP, H. 1928. Die Sexualität der niederen Pflanzen. iv + 544 pp. Illust. Jena.

—— 1929. *Allomyces javanicus*, n. sp., ein anisogamer Phycomycet mit Plano-gameten.   Berichte Deutsch. Bot. Gesell., 47: 199–212, 7 figs.

—— 1930. Über den Generationswechsel von *Allomyces*.   Zeitschr. Bot., 22: 433–441, 2 figs.

KNY, L. 1871a. *Chytridium olla*.   Sitzungsber. Gesell. Naturforsch. Freunde zu Berlin, 1871: 55; *also in* Bot. Zeitung, 1871: 870–871.

—— 1871b. *Chytridium (Olpidium) sphacellarum*.   Sitzungsber. Gesell. Natur-forsch. Freunde zu Berlin, 1871: 93–97; *also in* Hedwigia, 11: 81–87. 1872.

KOBAYAS[H]I, Y., AND OOKUBO, M. 1952a. Studies on the aquatic fungi of the Oze-gahara moor. (1).   J. Jap. Bot., 27 (4): 101–110, figs. 1–7. (In Japanese.)

—— 1952b. Studies on the aquatic fungi of Ozegahara moor. (2).   *Ibid.*, 27 (6): 181–188, figs. 8–13.   (In Japanese, with résumé in English.)

—— 1953. Studies on the marine Phycomycetes. [I.]   Bull. Nat. Sci. Mus. (Tokyo), 33: 53–65, 9 figs.

—— —— 1954a. On a new genus *Oedogoniomyces* of the Blastocladiaceae. *Ibid.*, (N. S.), 1, No. 1 (34): 59–66, 6 figs., pl. 21–22.

—— —— 1954b. Studies on the aquatic fungi of the Ozegahara moor. (3). Rept. Osegahara Gen. Sci. Surv. Comm., 1954: 561–575, 18 figs. (In Japanese.)

—— —— 1954c. Studies on the marine Phycomycetes. II.   Bull. Nat. Sci. Mus. (Tokyo), (N. S.), 1, No. 2 (35): 62–71, 9 figs.

KOCH, W. J. 1951. Studies in the genus *Chytridium*, with observations on a sexu-ally reproducing species.   J. Elisha Mitchell Sci. Soc., 67: 267–278, 2 figs., pls. 19–21.

—— 1956. Studies of the motile cells of chytrids. I. Electron microscope observations of the flagellum, blepharoplast and rhizoplast. Amer. J. Bot., 43: 811–819, 27 figs.

—— 1957. Two new chytrids in pure culture, *Phlyctochytrium punctatum* and *Phlyctochytrium irregvlare*. J. Elisha Mitchell Sci. Soc., 73: 108–122, 24 figs.

—— 1958. Studies of the motile cells of chytrids. II. Internal structure of the body observed with light microscopy. Amer. J. Bot., 45 : 59–72, 143 figs.

KOHLER, ERICH. 1924. *Phlyctochytrium synchytrii*, n. spec., ein die Dauersporangien von *Synchytrium endobioticum* (Schilb.) Perc. tötender Parasit. Arb. biol. Abt. (Anst.-Reichsanst.) Berlin, 13: 382–384, pls. 1–2.

KOL, E. 1942. The snow and ice algae of Alaska. Smithsonian Miscl. Coll., 101, No. 16: 1–36. 5 figs., 6 pls.

KOLE, A. P. 1954. A contribution to the knowledge of *Spongospora subterranea* (Wallr.) Lagerh., the cause of powdery scab of potatoes. Tijdschrift over Plantenziekten, 60: 1–65, 1 fig., pls. 1–8.

KOLKWITZ, R. 1901. Zur Biologie von *Leptomitus lacteus*. Berichte Deutsch. Bot. Gesell., 19: 288–291.

—— 1903. Über Bau und Leben des Abwasserpilzes *Leptomitus lacteus*. *Ibid.*, 21: 147–150.

KÖLLIKER, A. 1860a. Über das ausgebreitete Vorkommen von pflanzen Parasiten in den Hartgebilden niederer Thiere. Zeitschr. f. wissensch. Zool., 10: 215–232. Leipzig.

—— 1860b. On the frequent occurrence of vegetable parasites in the hard tissues of the lower animals. Quart. J. Micro. Sci., 8: 171–187, pl. 8, figs. 1–9.

KRENNER, J. A. 1935. Néhány adat hazánk gombaflórájához (Ein. Beiträge zur Pilzflora Ungarns). Bot. Közl., 32: 201. (Cited in Domján, 1936.)

—— 1943. Tanulmányok az alsóbbrendü gombák köréböl. I. Egy félreismert *Pythium*-fajról. (Studien aus dem Gebiete der mikroskopischen Pilze. I. Über eine verkannte *Pythium*-Art.) *Ibid.*, 40: 58–81, 3 pls.

KUSANO, S. 1907. On the cytology of *Synchytrium*. Centralbl. f. Bakteriol., Parasitenk. u. Infektionskrankh., Abt. 2, 19: 538–543, 1 pl.

—— 1909. A contribution to the cytology of *Synchytrium* and its hosts. Bull. Coll. Agr. Tokyo, 8: 79–147, pls. 8–11.

—— 1912. On the life history and cytology of a new *Olpidium* with special reference to the copulation of motile isogametes. J. Coll. Agric. Imp. Univ. Tokyo, 4: 141–199, pls. 15–17. 1911–14.

—— 1928. The relative sexuality in *Synchytrium*. Proc. Imp. Acad. Japan, 4: 497–499.

—— 1929. Observations on *Olpidium trifolii* Schroet. J. Coll. Agr. Imp. Univ. Tokyo, 10: 83–99, 7 figs.

—— 1930a. The life history and physiology of *Synchytrium fulgens* Schroet. with special reference to its sexuality. Japanese J. Bot., 5: 35–132, 19 figs.

—— 1930b. Cytology of *Synchytrium fulgens* Schroet. J. Coll. Agr. Imp. Univ. Tokyo, 30: 347–388, pls. 17–19. 1928–30.

KUSANO, S. 1932. The host-parasitic relationship in *Olpidium*. *Ibid.*, 11: 359–426, 10 figs.

—— 1936. On the parasitism of *Olpidium*. Japanese J. Bot., 8: 155–187, 8 figs.

LACOSTE, C. M. V. D. SANDE, AND SURINGAR, W. F. R. 1861. Nieuw Beschrevene en Voor Onze Flora Nieuwe Zoetwater-Wieren, Verzameld in Drenthe, 9–20 Julij 1859. Nederl. Kruidk. Arch., 5 (2): 262–290, pl. A.

LACY, R. C. 1949. Studies in aquatic Phycomycetes. Indian Phytopathology, 2: 134–141, 3 figs.

—— 1955. Studies in aquatic Phycomycetes, II. *Ibid.*, 8: 208–209.

LAGERHEIM, G. 1884. Algologiska och mykologiska anteckningar från en botanisk resa i Luleå Lappmark. Öfversigt af K. Vetensk.-Akad. Förhandl., 1884 (1): 91–119.

—— 1888. Sur un genre nouveau de Chytridiacées parasite des urédospores de certaines Uredinées. Journ. de Botanique, 2: 432–440, pl. 10, figs. 1–15.

—— 1890. *Harpochytrium* und *Achlyella*, zwei neue Chytridiaceen Gattungen. Hedwigia, 29: 142–145, pl. 2.

—— 1892. *Mastigochytrium*, eine neue Gattung der Chytridiaceen. *Ibid.*, 31: 185–189, pl. 18.

—— 1899. Om växt-och djurlämningarna i Andrées polarboj. *In* Ymer, Tidskr. Svenska Sällskap. Antropol. Geogr., 19 (4): 425–443, fig. 1. 1900.

—— 1900. Mykologische Studien. II. Untersuchungen über die Monoblepharideen. Bih. Kgl. Svensk. Vetensk.-Ak. Handl., 25, Afd. 3, No. 8: 1–42, pls. 1–2.

LAIBACH, F. 1926. Zur Zytologie von *Monoblepharis*. Berichte Deutsch. Bot. Gesell., 44 (1): 59–64, 3 figs.

—— 1927. Zytologische Untersuchungen über die Monoblepharideen. Jahrb. wiss. Bot., 66: 596–628, 12 figs., pls. 12–13.

LEDINGHAM, G. A. 1934. Zoospore ciliation in the Plasmodiophorales. Nature, 133: 534, 4 figs.

—— 1935. Occurrence of zoosporangia in *Spongospora subterranea* (Wallroth) Lagerheim. *Ibid.*, 135: 394, 4 figs.

—— 1936. *Rhizophidium graminis*, n. sp., a parasite of wheat roots. Canadian J. Research (C), 14: 117–121, 15 figs.

—— 1939. Studies on *Polymyxa graminis*, n. gen., n. sp., a plasmodiophoraceous root parasite of wheat. *Ibid.*, 17: 38–51, pls. 1–5.

LÉGER, L., AND DUBOSCQ, O. 1909. Sur les Chytridiopsis et leur évolution. Arch. Zool. Expér. Gén., V, 1: ix–xiii, 2 figs.

LEITGEB, H. 1868. Zwei neue Saprolegnieen. Bot. Zeitung, 26: 502–503. 1868.

LEMMERMAN, E. 1901. Die parasitischen und saprophytischen Pilze der Algen. Abhandl. Naturwiss. Vereins Bremen, 17 (1): 185–201.

LIND, J. 1905. Ueber einige neue und bekannte Pilze. Ann. Mycologici, 3: 427–432, 4 figs.

LINDAU, G. 1900. *Rhizidium lignicola*, nov. spec., eine holzbewohnende Chytridiacee. Verhandl. Bot. Vereins Prov. Brandenburg, 41: xxvii–xxxiii, 12 figs.

LINDER, D. H. 1926. A new species of *Araiospora* from British Guiana. Mycologia, 18: 172–178, pl. 21.

—— 1947. Fungi. *In* Botany of the Canadian Eastern Arctic. II. Thallophyta and Bryophyta. v + 573 pp. Nat. Mus. Canada. Bull. No. 97, Biol. Ser. No. 26. Pp. 234–297, 5 figs., pls. 12–18.

LINDSTEDT, K. 1872. Synopsis der Saprolegnieen und Beobachtungen über einige Arten. 69 pp., 4 pls. Berlin.

LINE, J. 1921. A note on the biology of the crown-gall fungus of Lucerne. Proc. Cambridge Phil. Soc., 20: 360–365, 7 figs.

LITVINOW, M. A. 1953. Data on studying the Chytridiales of fresh waters of Latvia. Akad. Nauk. SSSR Bot. Inst., Trudy 2, Sporovye Rost., 8: 73–84. (Plantae Cryptogamae.) (In Russian.)

LLOYD, DAPHNE. 1938. A record of two years' continuous observations on *Blastocladia pringsheimii* Reinsch. Trans. Brit. Mycol. Soc., 21: 152–166, figs. 1–3.

LOHMAN, M. A. 1942. A new fungous parasite on dung-inhabiting Ascomycetes. Mycologia, 34: 104–111, 15 figs.

LOHWAG, H. 1926. Ueber die Homologie der Sporangien, Oogonien, und Antheridien bei den Oomyceten. Arch. Protistenk., 55: 1–62, figs. A–X.

LOTSY, J. P. 1907. Algen und Pilze. Vorträge über botanische Stammesgeschichte, 1: 1–828, 430 figs. Jena.

LÖWENTHAL, W. 1905. Weitere Untersuchungen an Chytridiaceen. Arch. Protistenk., 5: 221–239, pls. 7–8.

LUDERS, J. E. 1860. Einige Bemerkungen über Diatomeen-Cysten und Diatomeen-Schwärmsporen. Bot. Zeitung, 18: 377–380, 1 fig.

LUGG, J. H. 1929. Some notes on *Allomyces arbuscula* Butler. Trans. Wisc. Acad. Sci., 24: 343–355.

LUND, A. 1930. A new species of *Pleotrachelus* with remarks on this genus. Bot. Tidsskrift., 41: 240–243, 1 fig.

—— 1934. Studies on Danish freshwater Phycomycetes and notes on their occurrence particularly relative to the hydrogen ion concentration of the water. Kgl. Danske Vidensk. Selsk. Skrift., Naturv. Math., Afd. IX, 6 (1): 1–97, 39 figs.

LUTHER, HANS. 1950. Beobachtungen über *Tetramyxa parasitica* Goebel. Mem. Soc. pro Fauna et Flora Fennica, 25: 88–96. 1948–49.

LÜTJEHARMS, W. J. 1937. Conservation of later generic homonyms: *Rhipidium* Cornu versus *Rhipidium* Auct. Blumea, 2 (4): 327–328.

McCRANIE, J. 1942. Sexuality in *Allomyces cystogenus*. Mycologia, 34: 209–213, 1 fig.

McLARTY, D. A. 1939. Observations on the genus *Pseudolpidium*. Amer. J. Bot., 26: 194–195, figs. 1–17.

—— 1941a. Studies in the family Woroninaceae. I. Discussion of a new species including a consideration of the genera *Pseudolpidium* and *Olpidiopsis*. Bull. Torrey Bot. Club. 68: 49–66, figs. 1–26.

—— 1941b. Studies in the Woroninaceae. II. The cytology of *Olpidiopsis achlyae*, sp. nov. (ad. int.). *Ibid.*, 68: 75–99, figs. 1–80.

MACHLIS, L. 1953a. Growth and nutrition of water molds in the subgenus *Euallomyces*. I. Growth factor requirements. Amer. J. Bot., 40: 189–195, 5 figs.

—— 1953b. Growth and nutrition of water molds in the subgenus *Euallomyces*. II. Optimal composition of the minimal medium. *Ibid.*, 40: 450–460, 12 figs.

—— 1953c. Growth and nutrition of water molds in the subgenus *Euallomyces*. III. Carbon sources. *Ibid.*, 40: 460–464, 2 figs.

—— 1957. Factors affecting the lag phase of growth of the filamentous fungus, *Allomyces macrogynus*. Amer. J. Bot., 44: 113–119, 7 figs.

—— AND CRASEMANN, J. M. 1956. Physiological variation between the generations and among the strains of watermolds in the subgenus *Euallomyces*. Amer. J. Bot., 43: 601–611, 7 figs.

—— AND OSSIA, E. 1953a. Maturation of the meiosporangia of *Euallomyces*. I. The effect of cultural conditions. Amer. J. Bot., 40: 358–365, 2 figs.

—— —— 1953b. Maturation of the meiosporangia of *Euallomyces*. II. Preliminary observations on the effect of auxins. *Ibid.*, 40: 465–468, 3 figs.

MAGNUS, P. 1872. ...Ueber ein *Chytridium*.... Sitzungsber. Gesell. Naturforsch. Freunde Berlin, 1872: 87–90.

—— 1875. Die botanischen Ergebnisse der Nordseefahrt von 21. Juli bis 9. Sept. 1872. Wissensch. Meeresunters. Abt. Kiel, 2–3: 59–80, pls. 1–2.

—— 1885. Botanische Mitteilungen. Verhandl. Bot. Vereins Prov. Brandenburg, 26: 69–81.

—— 1897. On some species of the genus *Urophlyctis*. Ann. Bot. London, 11: 87–96, pls. 7–8.

—— 1902a. Ueber eine neue untererdischlebende Art der Gattung *Urophlyctis*. Berichte Deutsch. Bot. Gesell., 19 (Gen. Versam.-Hefte): 145–153.

—— 1902b. Ueber die in den Knolligen Wurzelauswüchsen der Luzerne lebende *Urophlyctis*. *Ibid.*, 20 (5): 291–296, pl. 15.

—— 1905. Über die Gattung, zu der *Rhizophydium dicksonii* Wright gehört. Hedwigia, 44: 347–349, 3 figs.

MAIRE, R. 1910. ...Chytridinée nouvelle observée sur des grains de pollen.... Bull. Soc. Linn. Normandie, VI, 2: 68.

—— AND TISON, A. 1909. La cytologie des Plasmodiophoracées et la classe des Phytomyxinae. Ann. Mycol., 7: 226–253, figs. A–B, pls. 4–6.

—— —— 1911a. Recherches sur quelques Cladochytriacées. C. R. Acad. Sci. Paris, 152: 106–107.

—— —— 1911b. Sur quelques Plasmodiophoracées non hypertrophiantes. *Ibid.*, 152: 206.

—— —— 1911c. Nouvelles recherches sur les Plasmodiophoracées. Ann. Mycol., 9: 226–246, fig. 72, pls. 10–14.

MANTON, I., CLARKE, B., AND GREENWOOD, A. D. 1951. Observations with the electron microscope on a species of *Saprolegnia*. J. Exper. Bot., 2: 321–331, 8 pls.

—— —— —— AND FLINT, E. A. 1952. Further observations on the structure of plant cilia, by a combination of visual and electron microscopy. *Ibid.*, 3: 204–215, 11 pls.

MARTIN, G. W. 1922. *Rhizophidium polysiphoniae* in the United States. Bot. Gaz., 73: 236–238, 10 figs.

—— 1927. Two unusual water molds belonging to the family Lagenidiaceae. Mycologia, 19: 188–190, 1 fig.

—— 1932. Systematic position of the slime molds and its bearing on the classification of the fungi. Bot. Gaz., 93 (4): 421–435.

—— 1940. The Myxomycetes. Bot. Rev., 6: 356–388.

MASSEE, G. 1891. British fungi. Phycomycetes and Ustilagineae. xv + 232 pp., 8 pls. London.

MATTHEWS, V. D. 1928. *Nowakowskiella* and a new species of *Pythium*. J. Elisha Mitchell Sci. Soc., 43: 229–232, pls. 34–35.

—— 1931. Studies on the genus *Pythium*. 136 pp. Illust. Univ. North Carolina Press, Chapel Hill.

—— 1935. Notes on some Oomycetes from the vicinity of Mountain Lake, Giles County, Virginia. J. Elisha Mitchell Sci. Soc., 51: 306–310, pl. 63.

—— 1936. A new species of *Rhipidium* from Mountain Lake, Virginia. *Ibid.*, 52: 291–293, pl. 25.

—— 1937. A new genus of the Blastocladiaceae. *Ibid.*, 53: 191–195, 1 fig., pls. 20–21.

MAURIZIO, A. 1895. Zur Kenntniss der schweizerischen Wasserpilze nebst Angaben über eine neue Chytridinee. Jahresbericht Naturforsch. Gesell. Graubündens, Chur, 38: 9–38, 1 pl.

MEIER, H., AND WEBSTER, J. 1954. An electron microscope study of cysts in the Saprolegniaceae. J. Exper. Bot., 5: 401–409, pls. 1–4.

MEILLON, DE B., AND MUSPRATT, J. 1943. Germination of the sporangia of *Coelomomyces* Keilin. Nature, 152: 507, 5 figs.

MELHUS, I. E. 1914. A species of *Rhizophidium* parasitic on the oospores of various Peronosporaceae. Phytopathology, 4: 55–62, pl. 4, figs. 1–5.

MEREDITH, C. H. 1940. A quick method of isolating certain phycomycetous fungi from soil. Phytopathology, 30: 1055–1056.

MHATRE, J. R., AND MUNDKUR, B. B. 1945. The *Synchytria* of India. Lloydia, 8: 131–138.

MIDDLETON, J. T. 1943. The taxonomy, host range and geographic distribution of the genus *Pythium*. Mem. Torrey Bot. Club. 20: 1–171, 17 figs.

—— 1952. Generic concepts in the *Pythiaceae*. Tijdschrift over Plantenziekten, 58: 226–235.

MIGULA, W. 1903. Myxomycetes, Phycomycetes, Basidiomycetes.... *In* Thomé, Flora Deutschl., Österr. u. d. Schweiz, Pilze, 3 (1): 1–510. Berlin.

MILLER, C. E. 1955. *Micromyces grandis*, a new member of the aquatic Synchytriaceae. J. Elisha Mitchell Sci. Soc., 71: 247–255, 29 figs.

MILOVTZOVA, M. 1935. Aquatic Phycomycetes from Kharkov and its environs. Trans. Inst. Bot. Charkov, 1: 28–37, figs. A–L.

MINDEN, M. VON. 1902. Ueber Saprolegniineen. Centralbl. f. Bakteriol., Parasitenk. u. Infektionskrankh., Abt. 2, 8: 805–810, 821–825.

—— 1915. Chytridiineae, Ancylistineae, Monoblepharidineae, Saprolegniineae. Kryptogamenfl. Mark Brandenburg, 5: Pt. 2, pp. 193–352, 1911; Pt. 3, pp. 353–496, 1911; Pt. 4, pp. 497–608, 1912; Pt. 5, 609–630, 1915.

—— 1916. Beiträge zur Biologie und Systematik einheimischer submerser Phycomyceten. *In* Falck, Mykolog. Untersuch. Berichte, 2 (2): 146–255, 24 figs., pls. 1–8.

MIRANDE, R. 1920. *Zoophagus insidians* Sommerstorff, capteur de rotifères vivants. Bull. Soc. Mycol. France, 36: 47–53, 2 figs.

MITCHELL, J. B., JR. 1928. Studies on the life history of a parasite of the Euglenidae. Trans. Amer. Micro. Soc., 47: 29–41, pls. 4–6.

MOESZ, G. 1938. Fungi Hungariae II. Archimycetes et Phycomycetes. Annales Hist.-Nat. Mus. Nat. Hungarici, 31 (Bot.): 58–109.

MONIEZ, R. 1887. Sur des parasites nouveaux des Daphnies. C. R. Acad. Sci. Paris, 104: 183–185.

MOORE, C. L. 1908–9. Some Nova Scotian aquatic fungi. Proc. and Trans. Nova Scotia Inst. Sci., 12: 217–235, figs. 23–24.

MOREAU, F. AND F. 1948. Contribution à l'étude de la microflore fongique des eaux douces de Normandie. Bull. Soc. Mycol. France, 64: 223–237, 4 figs.

MORGAN, E. 1938. The phycomycete flora of Glamorgan; the Saprolegniales, especially the terrestrial forms. J. Brit. A. A. Sci., 1938: 109–110.

MORINI, F. 1896. Note Micologiche. Malpighia, 10: 72–99, pl. 3.

—— 1913. Osservazioni Micologiche. Mem. R. Accad. Sci. Istituto Bologna, Ser. VI, 10: 297–308, 1 pl. 1912–13.

MÜLLER, FRITZ. 1911. Untersuchungen über die chemotaktische Reizbarkeit der Zoosporen von Chytridiaceen und Saprolegniaceen. Jahrb. wiss. Bot., 49: 421–521.

MUNDKUR, B. B. 1938. Fungi of India. Supplement I. Sci. Monogr. No. 12, Imper. Council Agr. Res., Delhi.

MURRAY, G. 1893. Parasites on algae. Grevillea, 21: 103–104.

NABEL, KURT. 1939. Über die Membran niederer Pilze, besonders von *Rhizidiomyces bivellatus*, nov. spez. Archiv f. Mikrobiol., 10 (4): 515–541, 7 figs.

NAGAI, M. 1931. Studies on the Japanese Saprolegniaceae. J. Fac. Agr., Hokkaido Imp. Univ., 32: 1–43, 7 pls.

NÄGELI, C. 1846. Zeitschr. wiss. Bot. (Zurich), Vol. 1, Hefte 3–4. (Cited in Braun, 1856a.)

NÄGLER, KURT. 1911. Studien über Protozoen aus einen Almtümpel. II. Parasitische Chytridiaceen in *Euglena sanguinea*. Arch. Protistenk., 23: 262–268.

NAWASCHIN, S. 1899. Beobachtungen über den feineren Bau und Umwandlungen von *Plasmodiophora brassicae* Woron. im Laufe ihres intracellularen Lebens. Flora, 86: 404–427, pl. 20.

NĚMEC, B. 1912. Zur Kenntnis der niederen Pilze. IV. *Olpidium brassicae* Wor., und zwei *Entoplyctis*-Arten. Bull. Internat. Acad. Sci. Bohême, 17: 16–25. Illust.

NEWCOMBE, C. L., AND ROGERS, M. R. 1947. Studies of a fungus parasite that infects blue crab eggs. Turtox News, 25: 180–186, 6 figs.

NOWAKOWSKI, L. 1876a. Beitrag zur Kenntniss der Chytridiaceen. *In* Cohn, Beitr. Biol. Pflanzen, 2: 73–100, pls. 4–6. 1877.

—— 1876b. Beitrag zur Kenntniss der Chytridiaceen. II. *Polyphagus euglenae*. *Ibid.*, 2: 201–219, pls. 8–9. 1877.

—— 1878. Przyczynek do morfologii i systematyki Skoczków (Chytridiaceae). Akad. umiejetnošci Krakowie. Wydzíat mat.-przyród., Pamietník, 4: 174–198, pls. 7–10.

OBEL, P. 1910. Researches on the conditions of the forming of oogonia in *Achlya*. Ann. Mycologici, 8: 421–443, 4 figs.

OOKUBO, M. 1952. *Lagenidium* sp. on *Aegagropila*. Nagaoa, 2: 124–126, fig. 79.

—— 1954. Studies on the aquatic fungi collected in the moor and ponds of Hakkôda. *Ibid.*, 4: 48–60, figs. 38–48. (In Japanese.)

—— AND KOBAYASI, Y. 1955. Studies on the water moulds on keratinized materials. *Ibid.*, 5: 1–10, 6 figs. (In English.)

OSTENFELD, C. H., AND PETERSEN, H. E. 1930. On a new Plasmodiophoracea found in Canada. Zeitschr. Bot., 23: 13–18, 6 figs.

PALM, B. T. 1908. Till kännedomen om Stockholmstraktens svampflora. Svensk. Bot. Tidsskrift, 2: 38–48.

—— 1918. Sur un Plasmodiophoracée nouvelle *Ligniera isoetes*. *Ibid.*, 12: 228–232.

—— AND BURKE, M. 1933. The taxonomy of the Plasmodiophoraceae. Arch. Protistenk., 79: 263–276, 15 figs.

PATERSON, R. A. 1956. Additions to the phycomycete flora of the Douglas Lake region. II. New chytridiaceous fungi. Mycologia, 48: 270–277, 2 figs.

PATTERSON, P. M. 1927. Oogenesis in *Pythium torulosum*. J. Elisha Mitchell Sci. Soc., 43: 124–128, pl. 11.

PAVILLARD, J. 1910. État actuel de la protistologie végétale. Progressus Rei Bot., 3 (3): 474–544.

PENDERGRASS, W. R. 1948. A new member of the *Plasmodiophoraceae.* J. Elisha Mitchell Sci. Soc., 64: 132–134, pl. 15.

—— 1950. Studies on a plasmodiophoraceous parasite, *Octomyxa brevilegniae.* Mycologia, 42: 279–289, 29 figs.

PÉREZ, CH. 1903. Sur un organisme nouveau, *Blastulidium paedophthorum,* parasite des embryons de Daphnies. C. R. Soc. Biol., 55: 715–716, figs. A–E.

—— 1905. Nouvelles observations sur le *Blastulidium paedophthorum. Ibid.,* 58: 1027–1029, 2 figs.

PERRONCITO, E. 1888. *Chytridium elegans,* n. sp., eine parasitäre Chytridinee aus der Classe der Räderthiere. Centralbl. f. Bakteriol., Parasitenk. u. Infektionskrankh., 4: 295.

PERROTT, P. E. [THOMAS]. 1955. The genus *Monoblepharis.* Trans. Brit. Mycol. Soc., 38: 247–282, 17 figs, pls. 9–13.

PETERSEN, H. E. 1903. Note sur les Phycomycètes observés dans les téguments vides des nymphes de Phryganées avec description de trois espèces nouvelles de Chytridinées. Journ. de Botanique, 17: 214–222, 17 figs.

—— 1905. Contributions à la connaissance des Phycomycètes marins (Chytridineae Fischer). Oversigt Kgl. Danske Vidensk. Selskabs. Forhandl., 1905 (5): 439–488, 11 figs.

— 1906. Om Forekomsten af *Coenomyces consuens* i Danmark. Bot. Tidsskrift, 27: xxii–xxiii.

— 1909. Studier over Ferskvands-Phycomyceter. Bidrag til Kundskaben om de submerse Phykomyceters Biologi og Systematik, samt om deres Udbredelse i Danmark. *Ibid.,* 29 (4): 345–440, 27 figs. (English abstract.)

—— 1910. An account of Danish freshwater Phycomycetes, with biological and systematical remarks. Ann. Mycologici, 8: 494–560, figs. I–XXVII.

PETHYBRIDGE, G. H. 1913. On the rotting of potato tubers by a new species of *Phytophthora* having a mode of sexual reproduction hitherto undescribed. Sci. Proc. Roy. Dublin Soc. (N. S.), 13: 529–565, pls. 42–44.

—— AND LAFFERTY, H. A. 1919. A disease of tomato and other plants caused by a new species of *Phytophthora.* Sci. Proc. Roy. Dublin Soc. (N. S.), 15: 487–505, pls. 45–47.

PFITZER, E. 1870. Über weitere Beobachtungen…auf Diatomaceen parasitischen Pilze aus der Familie der Chytridieen. Sitzungsber. Niederrhein. Gesell. Natur- und Heilkunde (für 1869) (*in* Verhandl. Naturhist. Vereins Preuss. Rheinl. u. Westphalens.), 27: 62. 1870.

—— 1873. *Ancylistes closterii.* Monatsber. Berlin Akad., 1872: 379–398, 15 figs.

PIETERS, A. J. 1915. The relation between vegetative vigor and reproduction in some Saprolegniaceae. Amer. J. Bot., 2: 529–576, 2 figs. 1916.

PLESSIS, S. J. DU. 1933. The life history and morphology of *Olpidiopsis ricciae*, nov. sp., infecting *Riccia* species in South Africa. Ann. Bot. London, 47: 755–762, 12 figs.

POISSON, R. 1929–30. Recherches sur quelques Eccrinides. Arch. Zool. Expér. et Gén., 69: 179–216, 23 figs.; 74: 53–68, 7 figs.

POITRAS, A. W. 1949. A new aquatic species of *Pythium*. Mycologia, 41: 171–176, 17 figs.

——— 1955. A preliminary report on the aquatic Phycomycetes for the Pittsburgh region of Western Pennsylvania. Proc. Pennsylvania Acad. Sci., 29: 127–129.

PORTER, C. L., AND ZEBROWSKI, G. 1937. Lime-loving molds from Australian sands. Mycologia, 29: 252–257, 1 fig.

PRINGSHEIM, N. 1855. Über die Befruchtung der Algen.... Monatsber. Berlin Akad., 1855: 133–165, 33 figs.

——— 1858. Beiträge zur Morphologie und Systematik der Algen. II. Die Saprolegnieen. Jahrb. wiss. Bot., 1: 284–304, pls. 19–21.

——— 1860. Beiträge zur Morphologie und Systematik der Algen. IV. Nachträge zur Morphologie der Saprolegnieen. *Ibid.*, 2: 205–236, pls. 22–25.

——— 1873–74. Weitere Nachträge zur Morphologie und Systematik der Saprolegnieen. *Ibid.*, 9 (2): 191–234, pls. 17–22.

——— 1882. Neue Beobachtungen über d. Befruchtungsact der Gattung *Achlya* und *Saprolegnia*. Sitzungsber. Berlin Akad., 1882: 855–890, pl. 15.

——— 1883a. Über Cellulinkörner, eine Modification der Cellulose in Körnerform. Berichte Deutsch. Bot. Gesell., 1: 288–308, pl. 7.

——— 1883b. Ueber die Vermeintlichen Amoeben in den Schlauchen und Oogonien der Saprolegnieen. Bot. Centralbl., 14: 378–382.

——— 1884. Nachträgliche Bemerkungen zu der Befruchtungsact von *Achlya*. Jahrb. wiss. Bot., 14: 111–131.

——— 1895. Ueber die Stachelkörper.... Zur Kritik und Geschichte der Untersuchungen über das Algengeschlecht. Gesammelte Abhandlungen, Vol. 1. vi [2] + 414 pp., 1 por., 28 pls. Jena.

PROWSE, G. A. 1951. On *Rozellopsis septigena*. Trans. Brit. Mycol. Soc., 34: 400–405, 2 figs., pl. 18.

——— 1954a. *Aphanomyces daphniae* sp. nov., parasitic on *Daphnia hyalina*. *Ibid.*, 37: 22–28, 3 figs.

——— 1954b. *Sommerstorffia spinosa* and *Zoophagus insidians* predaceous on rotifers, and *Rozellopsis inflata* the endoparasite of *Zoophagus*. *Ibid.*, 37: 134–150, 8 figs.

PUYMALY, A. DE. 1927. Sur le *Sphaerita endogena* Dangeard, Chytridiacée parasite des Euglènes. Bull. Soc. Bot. France, 74: 472–476.

QUANTZ, L. 1943. Untersuchungen über die Ernährungsphysiologie einiger niederer Phycomyceten (*Allomyces kniepii, Blastocladiella variabilis* und *Rhizophlyctis rosea*). Jahrb. wiss. Bot., 91: 120–168, 15 figs.

Rabenhorst, L. 1868. Flora Europaea algarum..., Vol. 3. xx + 461 pp. Leipzig. 1864–68.

—— 1871. Uebersicht der von Herrn Prof. Dr. Haussknecht im Orient gesammelten Kryptogamen. Hedwigia, 10: 17–27.

Raciborski, M. 1900. Parasitische Algen und Pilze Java's. 1: 1–39. Batavia, Java.

Radais, M. 1898. Sur l'appareil végétatif des Saprolégniées. Bull. Soc. Mycol. France, 14: 144–148.

Raitschenko, A. A. 1902. Ueber eine Chytridiacee: *R. sphaerocarpum* (Zopf) Fischer. Bull. Jardin Impér. Bot. St. Petersb., 2: 124, 8 figs.

Ramsbottom, J. 1913. Some recent work on the cytology of fungus reproduction. II. Mycol. Centralbl., 3 (5): 221–234.

—— 1914. Recent published results on the cytology of fungus reproduction (1913). Trans. Brit. Mycol. Soc., 4: 249–291.

—— 1915a. The generic name *Protascus*. *Ibid.*, 5: 143–144.]

—— 1915b. A list of the British Phycomycetes, with a key to the genera. *Ibid.*, 5: 304–317.

—— 1915c. Notes on the list of British Phycomycetes. *Ibid.*, 5: 318–323.

—— 1916. Some notes on the history of the classification of the Phycomycetes. *Ibid.*, 5: 324–350.

—— 1931. Aquatic fungi. J. Quekett Microscope Club, 16: 151–166.

Raper, J. R. 1936. Heterothallism and sterility in *Achlya* and observations on the cytology of *Achlya bisexualis*. J. Elisha Mitchell Sci. Soc., 52: 274–289, pls. 22–23.

—— 1939a. Rôle of hormones in the sexual reaction of heterothallic achlyas. Science, 89: 321–322.

—— 1939b. Sexual hormones in *Achlya*. I. Indicative evidence for a hormonal co-ordinating mechanism. Amer. J. Bot., 26: 639–650, figs. 1–27.

—— 1940a. Sexual hormones in *Achlya*. II. Distance reactions, conclusive evidence for a hormonal coördinating mechanism. *Ibid.*, 27: 162–173, 14 figs.

—— 1940b. Sexuality in *Achlya ambisexualis*. Mycologia, 32: 710–727, 4 figs.

—— 1942a. Sexual hormones in *Achlya*. III. Hormone A and the initial male reaction. Amer. J. Bot., 29: 159–166, 6 figs.

—— 1942b. Sexual hormones in *Achlya*. V. Hormone A′, a male-secreted augmenter or activator of hormone A. Proc. Nat. Acad. Sci., 28: 509–516, 2 figs.

—— 1949. Recent findings on sexual hormones in *Achlya*. Amer. J. Bot., 36 (Suppl. No. 10): 814. (Abstract.)

—— 1950a. Sexual hormones in *Achlya*. VI. The hormones of the A-complex. Proc. Nat. Acad. Sci., 36: 524–533, 5 figs.

—— 1950b. Sexual hormones in *Achlya*. VII. The hormonal mechanism in homothallic species. Bot. Gaz., 112: 1–24, 11 figs.

—— 1951. Sexual hormones in *Achlya*. Amer. Scientist, 39: 110–120, 130.

—— 1952. Chemical regulation of sexual processes in the Thallophytes. Bot. Rev., 18: 447–545.

—— 1954. Life cycles, sexuality, and sexual mechanisms in the fungi. *In* Sex in microorganisms, D. H. Wenrich, ed. v + 362 pp. Symposium, Amer. Ass. Adv. Sci., Washington, D. C. Pp. 42–81, 8 figs.

—— 1955. Some problems of specificity in the sexuality of plants. *In* Biological specificity and growth, E. G. Butler, ed. Princeton Univ. Press, Princeton. Pp. 119–140, 4 figs.

—— AND HAAGEN-SMIT, A. J. 1942. Sexual hormones in *Achlya*. IV. Properties of hormone A of *Achlya bisexualis*. J. Biol. Chem., 143: 311–320.

RAPER, K. B. 1928. Studies on the frequency of the water molds in the soil. J. Elisha Mitchell Sci. Soc., 44: 133–139.

RATTRAY, JOHN. 1887. Note on *Ectocarpus*. Trans. R. Soc. Edin., 32 (3): 589–600, pls. 147–148. 1885.

REINBOLDT, B. 1951. Über die Verteilung einiger niederer Phycomyceten im Erdboden. Archiv. f. Mikrobiol., 16: 177–200, 9 figs.

REINSCH, P. F. 1875. Contributiones ad algologiam et fungologiam, Vol. 1. vi + 103 pp., 27 pls. Leipzig.

—— 1877. Species ac genera nova algarum aquae dulcis quae sunt inventa in speciminibus in Expeditione Vener. transit. hieme 1874–75 in Insula Kerguelensi a clar. Eaton collectis. J. Linn. Soc. London (Bot.), 15: 205–221. 1876.

—— 1878. Beobachtungen über einige neue Saprolegnieae, über die Parasiten in Desmidienzellen und über die Stachelkugeln in Achlyaschläuchen. Jahrb. wiss. Bot., 11: 283–311, pls. 14–17. 1877.

—— 1879. Beobachtungen über entophyte und entozoische Pflanzenparasiten. Bot. Zeitung, 37: 33–43.

REISCHER, H. S. 1949a. Preservation of *Saprolegniaceae* by the mineral oil method. Mycologia, 41: 177–179.

—— 1949b. A new species of *Achlya*. *Ibid.*, 41: 339–345, 5 figs.

REMY, E. 1948. Über niedere Bodenphycomyceten. Archiv f. Mikrobiol., 14: 212–239, 6 figs.

RENN, C. E. 1936. The wasting disease of *Zostera marina*. I. A phytological investigation of the diseased plant. Biol. Bull., 70: 148–158, pls. 1–2.

REYNOLDS, N. 1940. Seasonal variations in *Staurastrum paradoxum* Meyen. New Phytologist, 39: 86–89, 2 figs.

RICHARDS, M. 1951. The life history of *Diplophlyctis laevis*. Trans. Brit. Mycol. Soc., 34: 483–488, 19 figs., pl. 24.

—— 1956. Some inoperculate chytrids from South Wales. *Ibid.*, 39: 261–266, 5 figs. pls. 6–7.

RICHTER, P. 1897. Süsswasseralgen aus dem Umanakdistrikt. Bibliotheca Botan., 42: 1–12, 6 figs.

RICHTER, W. 1937. Vorarbeiten zu einer Saprolegniaceenflora von Marburg. Flora, 31: 227–262.

RIETH, A. 1950a. Beitrag zur Kenntnis der Gattung *Micromyces* Dangeard. I. *Micromyces ovalis* nov. spec. Österr. bot. Zeitschr., 97: 510–516, 12 figs.

—— 1950b. Beobachtungen zur Biologie und Entwicklungsgeschichte eines selteneren Süsswasseralgenparasiten aus der Verwandtschaft des Kartoffelkrebserregers. Naturwissenschaftliche Rundschau, 6: 264–269, 13 figs.

—— 1951. Zur Phycomycetenflora Württembergs. I. Teil. Naturschutz in Württemberg-Hohenzollern, 1950: 259–271, 14 figs.

—— 1954. Ein weiterer Beitrag zur Kenntniss algenparasitärer Phycomyceten. Die Kulturpflanze, 2: 164–184, 11 figs.

—— 1956a. *Micromyces laevis* Canter in Deutschland nebst einigen Bemerkungen über die wasserlebende, algenparasitäre Gruppe der Synchytriaceae. *Ibid*, 4: 29–45, figs. 1–25, pl. 1.

—— 1956b. Beitrag zur kenntniss der Phycomyceten III. *Ibid*, 4: 181–186, 2 figs., pl. 6.

RITCHIE, D. 1947. The formation and structure of the zoospores in *Allomyces*. J. Elisha Mitchell Sci. Soc., 63: 168–206, pls. 22–26.

ROBERTS, JOHN M. 1948. Developmental studies of two species of *Nowakowskiella* Schroeter: *N. ramosa* Butler and *N. profusa* Karling. Mycologia, 40: 127–157, 2 figs.

ROBERTS, MARJORIE. 1953. *Micromycopsis oedogonii* sp. nov. Trans. Brit. Mycol. Soc., 36: 320–323, 12 figs. 1 pl.

ROGERS-TALBERT, R. 1948. The fungus *Lagenidium callinectes* Couch (1942) on eggs of the blue crab in Chesapeake Bay. Biol. Bull., 95: 214–228, 7 figs.

ROSEN, F. 1887. Ein Beitrag zur Kenntniss der Chytridiaceen. Cohn, Beitr. Biol. Pflanzen, 4 (3): 253–266, pls. 13–14.

ROSSY-VALDERRAMA, C. 1956. Some water molds from Puerto Rico. J. Elisha Mitchell Sci. Soc., 72: 129–137, 29 figs.

ROSTRUP, E. 1894. Mykologiske Meddelelser (V). Bot. Tidsskrift., 19: 201–214, 3 figs. (Résumé in French, pp. 215–218.)

—— 1896. Mykologiske Meddeleser. *Ibid*, 20 (2): 126–129, 2 figs.

—— 1905. Mykologiske Meddeleser (IX). *Ibid*, 26: 305–317, figs. 1–7. (With an English summary.)

ROTH, A. G. 1800. Catalecta botanica, Vol. 2. 258 pp., 10 pls. Leipzig.

ROTHERT, W. 1888. Die Entwickelung der Sporangien bei den Saprolegnieen. Cohn, Beitr. Biol. Pflanzen, 5: 291–349, pl. 10. 1892.

—— 1894. Ueber das Schicksal der Cilien bei den Zoosporen der Phycomyceten. Berichte Deutsch. Bot. Gesell., 12: 268–282, pl. 20.

ROTHWELL, F. M. 1956. Nutritional requirements of *Phlyctorhiza variabilis*. Amer. J. Bot., 43: 28–32, 4 figs.

ROZSYPAL, J. 1934. Pilze in Cysten von *Heteroderas schactii* Schmidt aus mährischen Rübenböden. Věstn. čsl. Akad. Zeměd., 10: 413–422, pl. 2, figs. 72–79.

RYTZ, W. 1907. Beiträge zur Kenntnis der Gattung *Synchytrium*. Centralbl. f. Bakteriol., Parasitenk. u. Infektionskrankh., Abt. 2, 18: 799–825, 10 figs., 1 pl.

SACCARDO, D. AND P. A. 1905. Sylloge fungorum, Vol. 17. 991 pp. Padua.

SACCARDO, P. A., BERLESE, N., AND DE TONI, G. B. 1888. Sylloge fungorum, Vol. 7, Pt. 1 (Phycomyceteae). xxx + 498 pp. Padua.

—— AND TRAVERSO, J. B. 1911. Sylloge fungorum, Vol. 20. 1158 pp. Padua.

SAKSENA, R. K., AND BHARGAVA, K. S. 1941. A physiological study of *Saprolegnia delica* Coker. Proc. Nat. Acad. Sci. India (Sec. B), 11: 27–40.

—— —— 1944. A new variety of *Isoachlya anisospora* (de Bary) Coker. Current Science, 13: 79.

—— —— 1946. Some cytological observations on spore formation in *Thraustotheca clavata*. Mycologia, 38: 554–564, 2 figs.

—— —— AND DAYAL, D. 1943. The structure of the cilia of *Thraustotheca clavata* (de Bary) Humph. J. Indian Bot. Soc., 22: 37–39, 2 figs.

SAKSENA, R. K., AND BOSE, S. K. 1944. The enzymes of two water molds. J. Indian Bot. Soc., 23: 108–112.

SALVIN, S. B. 1940. The occurrence of five successive swarming stages in a nonsexual *Achlya*. Mycologia, 32: 148–154, 1 fig.

—— 1941. Comparative studies on the primary and secondary zoospores of the Saprolegniaceae. I. Influence of temperature. Mycologia, 33: 592–600, 2 figs.

—— 1942. Variations of specific and varietal character induced in an isolate of *Brevilegnia*. Mycologia, 34: 38–51, 4 figs.

SAMPSON, K. M. 1932. Observations on a new species of *Olpidium* occurring in the root hairs of *Agrostis*. Trans. Brit. Mycol. Soc., 17: 182–194, 5 figs., pls. 10–12.

—— 1933. Note on the occurrence of a new species of *Olpidium* in the root hairs of *Agrostis*. J. Bd. Greenkeep. Res. Brit. Golf. Unions, 3: 32–33.

SANDOZ, M. D., ROGERS, M. R., AND NEWCOMBE, C. L. 1944. Fungus infection of eggs of the blue crab *Callinectes sapidus* Rathbun. Science (N. S.), 99: 124–125.

SASSUCHIN, D. N. 1934. Hyperparasitism in Protozoa. Quart. Rev. Biol., 9: 215–224, 11 figs.

SAWADA, K. 1912. Studies in the rot-disease of rice seedlings. Spec. Bull. Agr. Exp. Sta. Formosa, III (cited in Tokunaga, 1933a).

—— 1922. Materials for the mycological study of Formosa. No. 24. Trans. Nat. Hist. Soc. Formosa, 62: 77–84. (In Japanese.)

SCHAARSCHMIDT, J. 1883. *Phlyctidium haynaldii*, n. sp. Magyar Növénytani Lapok. Kolozsvár, 1883 (7): 58–63, pl. 2; Hedwigia, 22: 125.

SCHADE, A. L. 1940. The nutrition of *Leptomitus*. Amer. J. Bot., 27: 376–384, 5 figs.

—— AND THIMANN, K. V. 1940. The metabolism of the water-mold, *Leptomitus lacteus*. Amer. J. Bot., 27: 659–670, 9 figs.

SCHENK, A. 1858a. Algologische Mittheilungen. Verhandl. Phys.-Med. Gesell. Würzburg, A. F., 8: 235–259, pl. 5.

—— 1858b. Ueber das Vorkommen contractiler Zeller im Pflanzenreiche. 20 pp., 15 figs. Würzburg.

—— 1858c. Fadenpilz in *Conferva* und *Spirogyra*. Verhandl. Phys.-Med. Gesell. Würzburg, A. F., 8 (Sitzungsber.): xxviii–xxx.

—— 1859a. *Achlyogeton*, eine neue Gattung der Mycophyceae. Bot. Zeitung, 17: 398–400, pl. 13, fig. A, 1–8.

—— 1859b. Algologische Mittheilungen. Verhandl. Phys.-Med. Gesell. Würzburg, A. F., 9: 12–31, pl. 1, figs. 1–48.

SCHERFFEL, A. 1902a. Mycologische u. algologische Notizen. Hedwigia, 41: (105)–(106).

—— 1902b. Néhány adat Magyarhon növény-és állatvilágának ismeretéhez. Növénytani Közlemények, 1: 107–111.

—— 1904. Újabb adatok Magyarország alsórendü szervezeteinek ismeretéhez. (Neuere Beiträge zur Kenntnis der niederen Organismen in Ungarn.) *Ibid.*, 3 (3): 116–119, fig. 30.

—— 1914. Kisebb Közlemények a kryptogamok köréböl. (Kryptogamic Miszellen.) Bot. Közl., 13: 12–17.

—— 1925a. Endophytische Phycomyceten-Parasiten der Bacillariaceen und einige neue Monadinen. Ein Beitrag zur Phylogenie der Oomyceten (Schröter). Arch. Protistenk., 52: 1–141, pls. 1–5.

—— 1925b. Zur Sexualität der Chytridineen (Der "Beiträge zur Kenntnis der Chytridineen," Teil I). *Ibid.*, 53: 1–58, pls. 1–2.

—— 1926a. Einiges über neue oder ungenügend bekannte Chytridineen (Der "Beiträge zur Kenntnis der Chytridineen," Teil II). *Ibid.*, 54: 167–260, pls. 9–11.

—— 1926b. Beiträge zur Kenntnis der Chytridineen, Teil III. *Ibid.*, 54: 510–528, pl. 28.

—— 1930a. Néhány érdekesebb alsórendü szervezet a Balatonból és annak Környékéröl. (Einige interessantere niedere Organismen aus dem Balaton n. dessen Umgebung.) A Magy. Biol. Kut. Int. I. oszt. Munkái., 3: 254.

—— 1930b. Abstracts of communications, V. Internat. Bot. Congress, Cambridge. 680 pp. Cambridge Univ. Press.

—— 1931. Über einige Phycomyceten. Arch. Protistenk., 73: 137–146, pl. 9.

SCHIKORA, F. 1903. Über die Krebpest und ihren Erreger. Fischerei-Zeitung, 6: 353–355.

—— 1906. Die Krebpest. *Ibid.*, 9: 529–532; 549–555; 561–566; 581–583.

—— 1922. Über die Krebpest und ihrer Erreger *Aphanomyces magnusii* Schikora. Verhandl. Bot. Vereins Prov. Brandenburg, 63: 87–88.

SCHLÖSSER, L. A. 1929. Geschlechterverteilung und fakultative Parthenogenese bei Saprolegniaceen. "Planta," Archiv. wiss. Bot., 8: 529–570, 14 figs.

SCHRÖDER, B. 1898a. Planktologische Mitteilungen. Biol. Centralbl., 18: 525–535.

—— 1898b. *Dangeardia*, ein neues Chytridineen Genus auf *Pandorina morum* Bory. Berichte Deutsch. Bot. Gesell., 16: 314–321, pl. 20.

SCHROETER, J. 1879. *Protomyces graminicola* Saccardo. Hedwigia, 18: 83–87.

—— 1883. Untersuchungen der Pilzgattung *Physoderma*. Jahres-bericht. Schles. Gesell. Vaterland. Cultur., 60: 198–200. 1882.

—— 1885. Die Pilze Schlesiens. *In* Cohn, Kryptogamenfl. Schlesien, 3 (1): 1–814. 1885–89.

—— 1893. Phycomycetes. *In* Engler and Prantl, Natürlichen Pflanzenfam., 1 (1): 63–141. 1892–93. (Parts issued separately from 1889 on.)

SCHRÖTER, C. 1897. Die Schwebeflora unserer Seen (Das Phytoplankton). Neujahrblatt Naturf. Gesell. Zurich, 99: Anmerk. 1–57, pl. 1. 1896.

SCHULZ, E. 1942. Arbeitsmethoden bei Kultur- und Infektionsversuchen mit *Pythium*-Arten. Centralbl. f. Bakteriol., II, 105: 248–254.

SCHULZ, P. 1922. Desmidiaceen aus dem Gebiete der Freien Stadt Danzig.... Botan. Archiv, 2 (3): 113–173, 101 figs.

—— 1923. Kurze Mitteilungen über Algenparasiten. Schriften f. Süsswasser und Meereskunde, 2 (11): 178–181, 14 figs.

SCHUSSNIG, B. 1949. Stammesgeschichtlicher Formenwandel und Gestaltungstypen im Reich der Pilze. Berichtigung und Nachtrag. Sydowia, 3: 267.

SCHWARTZ, E. J. 1910. Parasitic root diseases of the "Juncaceae." Ann. Bot. London, 24: 236, 511–522, pl. 40, figs. 1–23.

—— 1911. The life-history and cytology of *Sorosphaera graminis*. *Ibid.*, 25: 791–797, pl. 61.

—— 1914. The Plasmodiophoraceae and their relationship to the Mycetozoa and the Chytrideae. *Ibid.*, 28: 227–240, pl. 12.

—— AND COOK, W. R. I. 1928. The life-history and cytology of a new species of *Olpidium*; *Olpidium radicale*, sp. nov. Trans. Brit. Mycol. Soc., 13: 205–221, pls. 13–15.

SCHWARTZE, C. A. 1922. The method of cleavage in the sporangia of certain fungi. Mycologia, 14: 143–172, pls. 15–16.

SCOURFIELD, D. J. 1936. The occurrence of a minute fungus on a free-swimming alga (a chytrid on *Chlorogonium*) in an Epping Forest pond. Essex Naturalist, 25: 120–123, 1 pl.

SERBINOW, I. 1925. Sur la morphologie et la biologie du *Lagenidium sacculoides*, n. sp. Défense des Plantes, 2 (2): 84–87. (In Russian.)

SERBINOW, J. L. 1899. Vorläufiger Bericht über die Morphologie und Biologie des *Olpidium ramosum* spec. nov. Leningradskoe obshchestvo estestvoispy-tateleĭ Trudy (Trav. Société des Naturalistes de Leningrade), 30: 255–256. (In German; pp. 224–226 in Russian.)

SERBINOW, J. L. 1907. Kenntniss der Phycomyceten. Organisation u. Entwicke-lungsgeschichte einiger Chytridineen Pilze (Chytridineae Schröter). Scripta Bot. Horti Univ. Imper. Petro., 24: 1–173, pls. 1–6. (In Russian, with German summary.)

SETCHELL, W. A. 1924. Three new fungi. Mycologia, 16: 240–244, pls. 18–19.

SEURAT, L. G. 1920. Histoire naturelle des Nématodes de la Bérbérie. Trans. Lab. Zool. Gén. Univ. Alger., p. 189. (Not seen.)

SEYMOUR, A. B. 1929. A provisional host index of the fungi of the United States. xiii + 732 pp. Cambridge, Massachusetts.

SHADBOLT, G. 1852. On the sporangia of some filamentous fresh-water algae. Trans. Micro. Soc. London, 3: 168–170, pls. 22.

SHANOR, L. 1939a. Studies in the genus Olpidiopsis. I. Resting spore germina-tion in a new species. J. Elisha Mitchell Sci. Soc., 55: 167–177, figs. A–E; pl. 24, 13 figs.

—— 1939b. Studies in the genus *Olpidiopsis*. II. The relationship of *Pseudol-pidium* Fischer and *Olpidiopsis* (Cornu) Fischer. *Ibid.*, 55 (1): 179–195, 3 figs., pl. 25.

—— 1940. Studies in the genus *Olpidiopsis*. III. Some observations on the host range of certain species. *Ibid.*, 56: 165–176.

—— 1942a. A new *Monoblepharella* from Mexico. Mycologia, 34: 241–247, 20 figs.

—— 1942b. A new fungus belonging to the *Cladochytriaceae*. Amer. J. Bot., 29: 174–179, 38 figs.

—— 1942c. A new *Rozella* of the polysporangiate series. J. Elisha Mitchell Sci. Soc., 58: 99–101, pl. 17.

—— 1944. Additional records of aquatic Phycomycetes isolated from Mexican soils. J. Wash. Acad. Sci., 34: 330–333.

—— AND CONOVER, R. A. 1942. A new *Protoachlya*. Amer. Midl. Nat., 28: 746–751, 27 figs.

—— AND OLIVE, L. S. 1942. Notes on *Araiospora streptandra*. Mycologia, 34: 536–542, 11 figs.

—— AND SASLOW, H. B. 1944. *Aphanomyces* as a fish parasite. Mycologia, 36: 413–415, 1 fig.

SHEN, SAN-CHIUN. 1944. A form of *Sporophlyctis rostrata* with ciliated spores. Amer. J. Bot., 31: 229–233, 21 figs.

—— AND SIANG, W. N. 1948. Studies in the aquatic Phycomycetes of China. Sci. Repts. Nat. Tsing Hua Univ., Ser. B: Biol. and Psychol. Sci., 3: 179–203, 13 figs.

SIANG, W. 1949. Are aquatic Phycomycetes present in the air? Nature, 164: 1010.

SIDERIS, C. P. 1929. *Rhizidiocystis ananasi* Sideris, nov. gen. et sp., a root hair parasite of pineapples. Phytopath., 19 (4): 367–382, 9 figs.

SIGOT, ANDRÉ. 1931. Une chytridiacée nouvelle, parasite des oeufs de *Cyclops*: *Blastulidiopsis chattoni*, N. G., N. Sp. C. R. Soc. Biol. (Strasbourg), 108: 34–37, 3 figs.

SINTO, Y., AND YUASA, A. 1934. Studies in the cytology of reproductive cells. II. Bot. Mag. Tokyo, 48: 720–729, 19 figs.

SKUJA, H. 1948. Taxonomie des Phytoplanktons einiger Seen in Uppland, Schweden. Symbolae Bot. Upsaliensis, 9 (3): 1–399, pls. 1–39.

—— 1956. Taxonomische und biologische Studien über das Phytoplankton Schwedischer Binnengewässer. Nova Acta Reg. Soc. Sci. Upsaliensis, Ser. IV, 16 (3): 1–404, 63 pls.

SKVORTZOW, B. W. 1925. Zur Kenntnis der Phycomyceten aus der Nordmandshurei, China. Arch. Protistenk., 51: 428–433, 12 figs.

—— 1927. Über einige Phycomyceten aus China. *Ibid.*, 57: 204–206, 10 figs.

SMITH, R. L. 1940. Studies on two strains of *Aphanomyces laevis* found occurring as wound parasites on crayfish. Mycologia, 32: 205–213, 1 fig.

SMITH, W. 1853. On the stellate bodies occurring in the cells of freshwater algae. Quart. J. Micro. Sci. (N. S.), 1: 68–72, pl. 9, figs. 1–3, 5.

SOMMERSTORFF, H. 1911. Ein Tiere fangender Pilz (*Zoophagus insidians*, nov. gen., nov. sp.). Österr. botan. Zeitschr., 61: 361–373, pls. 5–6.

SÖRGEL, G. 1936. Über heteroploide Mutanten bei *Allomyces kniepii*. Nachrichten Gesell. Wiss. Göttingen, Math.-Physik. Kl., Fachgruppe VI (Biol.), (N. F.), 2 (10): 155–170, 4 figs.

—— 1937a. Über heteroploide Mutanten bei *Allomyces kniepii*. Zeitschr. Bot. 31: 335–336.

—— 1937b. Untersuchungen über den Generations-wechsel von *Allomyces*. *Ibid.*, 31: 401–446, 15 figs.

—— 1941. Über die Verbreitung einiger niederer Phycomyceten in Erden Westindiens. Beihefte Bot. Centralbl., Abt. B, 61: 1–32, 4 figs.

—— 1952. Über mutmassliche phylogenetische Zusammenhänge bei niederen Pilzen, insbesondere den Blastocladiales. Biol. Zentralbl., 71: 385–397, 13 figs.

SOROKIN, N. W. 1874a. Einige neue Wasserpilze (*Zygochytrium aurantiacum*, *Tetrachytrium triceps*). Bot. Zeitung, 32: 305–315, pl. 6.

—— 1874b. Aperçu systématique du groupe des Siphomycètes. Bull. Soc. Nat. Kazan, 4 (3): 1–26, pls. 1–2. (In Russian.)

—— 1876. Les végétaux parasites des Anguillulae. Ann. Sci. Nat. Bot., VI, 4: 62–71, pl. 3, figs. 1–45.

—— 1877. Vorläufige Mittheilung über zwei neue mikroskopische Pilze—*Prophytroma tubularis* und *Saccopodium gracile*. Hedwigia, 16 (6): 87–88, 2 figs.

—— 1883. Aperçu systématique des Chytridiacées recoltées en Russie et dans l'Asie Centrale. Arch. Bot. Nord France, 2: 1–42, 54 figs. 1884–87. (Issued as a separate, pp. 1–44, 1883.)

SOROKIN, N. W. 1889. Matériaux por la flore cryptogamique de l'Asie Centrale. Rev. Mycologique, 11: 69–85, 136–151, 207–208. 1889; 12: 3–16, 49–61. 1890; pls. 76–111. (Includes almost exact duplication of the account of the chytrids in the 1883 paper.)

SOST, H. 1955. Über die Determination des Generationswechsels von *Allomyces arbuscula* (Butl.). (Polyploidieversuche.) Arch. Protistenk., 100: 541–564, 8 figs., Pl. 17.

SPARROW, F. K., JR. 1927. Occurrence of *Pythium gracile* in the United States. Rhodora, 29: 37–39.

—— 1929. A note on the occurrence of two rotifer-capturing Phycomycetes. Mycologia, 21: 90–96, 1 fig.

—— 1931a. Observations on *Pythium dictyosporum*. *Ibid.*, 23: 191–203, 1 fig., pl. 20.

—— 1931b. Two new species of *Pythium* parasitic in green algae. Ann. Bot. London, 45: 257–277, 2 figs., pl. 9.

—— 1931c. Two new chytridiaceous fungi from Cold Spring Harbor. Amer. J. Bot., 18: 615–623, pl. 45.

—— 1931d. A note on a new chytridiaceous fungus parasitic in *Elodea*. Occ. Papers Boston Soc. Nat. Hist., 8: 9–10.

—— 1932a. Observations on the parasitic ability of certain species of *Pythium*. Phytopathology, 22: 385–390.

—— 1932b. Observations on the aquatic fungi of Cold Spring Harbor. Mycologia, 24: 268–303, 4 figs., pls. 7–8.

—— 1933a. Observations on operculate chytridiaceous fungi collected in the vicinity of Ithaca, N. Y. Amer. J. Bot., 20: 63–77, 2 figs., pls. 2–3.

—— 1933b. The Monoblepharidales. Ann. Bot. London, 47: 517–542, 2 figs., pl. 20.

—— 1933c. Inoperculate chytridiaceous organisms collected in the vicinity of Ithaca, N. Y., with notes on other aquatic fungi. Mycologia, 25: 513–535, 1 fig., pl. 49.

—— 1933d. New chytridiaceous fungi. Trans. Brit. Mycol. Soc., 18: 215–217.

—— 1934a. The occurrence of true sporangia in the *Physoderma* disease of corn. Science (N. S.), 79: 563–564.

—— 1934b. *Scherffeliomyces*. Mycologia, 26: 377.

—— 1934c. Observations on marine Phycomycetes collected in Denmark. Dansk Bot. Ark., 8 (6): 1–24, 4 pls.

—— 1935a. Recent contributions to our knowledge of the aquatic Phycomycetes. Biol. Rev. Cambridge Phil. Soc., 10: 152–186, 2 figs.

—— 1935b. The interrelationships of the Chytridiales. *In* Proc. Zesde Internationaal Bot. Congres Amsterdam, Vol. 2. xiii + 317 pp. Leiden.

—— 1936a. A contribution to our knowledge of the aquatic Phycomycetes of Great Britain. J. Linn. Soc. London (Bot.), 50: 417–478, 7 figs., pls. 14–20.

—— 1936b. Biological observations on the marine fungi of Woods Hole waters, Biol. Bull., 70: 236–263, 35 figs., pls. 1–3.

—— 1936c. Chytridiaceous fungi from two unusual substrata. Mycologia, 28: 87–88.

—— 1936d. Evidences for the possible occurrence of sexuality in *Diplophlyctis*. *Ibid.*, 28: 321–323, 2 figs.

—— 1937a. Some chytridiaceous inhabitants of submerged insect exuviae. Proc. Amer. Phil. Soc., 78 (1): 23–53. 5 figs., 4 pls.

—— 1937b. Some new species of chytrids. Occ. Papers Boston Soc. Nat. Hist. 8: 295–296.

—— 1938a. Some chytridiaceous fungi from North Africa and Borneo. Trans. Brit. Mycol. Soc., 21: 145–151, 2 figs.

—— 1938b. Remarks on the genus *Rozella*. Mycologia, 30: 375–378.

—— 1938c. Chytridiaceous fungi with unusual sporangial ornamentation. Amer. J. Bot., 25: 485–493, 41 figs.

—— 1938d. The morphology and development of *Obelidium mucronatum*. Mycologia, 30: 1–14, 44 figs.

—— 1939a. Unusual chytridiaceous fungi. Papers Mich. Acad. Sci., Arts, Letters, 24, Pt. I: 121–126, pls. 1–2. 1938.

—— 1939b. The entomogenous chytrid *Myrophagus* Thaxter. Mycologia, 31: 439–444, 8 figs.

—— 1939c. A new species of *Lagenidium* parasitic on rotifer eggs. *Ibid.*, 31: 527–532, 15 figs.

—— 1939d. *Monoblepharis taylori*, a remarkable soil fungus from Trinidad. *Ibid.*, 31: 737–738.

—— 1940a. Chytridiaceous fungi in relation to disease in flowering plants, with special reference to *Physoderma*. *In* Abstracts of Communications, Third Internat. Congress for Microbiology, New York. viii + 883 pp. New York. Pp. 514–516.

—— 1940b. Phycomycetes recovered from soil samples collected by W. R. Taylor on the Allan Hancock 1939 Expedition. Allan Hancock Pacific Expeditions, Publ. Univ. So. Calif., 3 (6): 101–112, pls. 16–17.

—— 1942. A classification of aquatic Phycomycetes. Mycologia, 34: 113–116.

—— 1943. The aquatic Phycomycetes, exclusive of the Saprolegniaceae and *Pythium*. xix + 785 pp. 634 figs. Univ. Michigan Press, Ann Arbor.

—— 1946. Observations on chytridiaceous parasites of phanerogams. I. *Physoderma menyanthis* de Bary. Amer. J. Bot., 33: 112–118, 41 figs.

—— 1947a. Observations on chytridiaceous parasites of phanerogams. II. A preliminary study of the occurrence of ephemeral sporangia in the *Physoderma* disease of maize. *Ibid.*, 34: 94–97, 17 figs.

—— 1947b. Observations on chytridiaceous parasites of phanerogams. III. *Physoderma claytoniana* and an associated parasite. *Ibid.*, 34: 325–329, 17 figs.

SPARROW, F. K., JR. 1948. Soil Phycomycetes from Bikini, Eniwetok, Rongerik and Rongelap atolls. Mycologia, 40: 445–453, 19 figs.

—— 1950. Some Cuban Phycomycetes. J. Wash. Acad. Sci., 40: 50–55, 30 figs.

—— 1951. *Podochytrium cornutum* n. sp., the cause of an epidemic on the planktonic diatom *Stephanodiscus*. Trans. Brit. Mycol. Soc., 34: 170–173, 1 fig.

—— 1952a. A contribution to our knowledge of the Phycomycetes of Cuba. Pt. I. Rev. Soc. Cubana Bot., 9: 34–40, 10 figs.

—— 1952b. A contribution to our knowledge of the Phycomycetes of Cuba. Pt. II. *Ibid.*, 9: 68–74, 10 figs.

—— 1952c. A contribution to our knowledge of the Phycomycetes of Cuba. Pt. III. *Ibid.*, 9: 104–108, 3 figs.

—— 1952d. Phycomycetes from the Douglas Lake region of northern Michigan. Mycologia, 44: 759–772, 1 fig.

—— 1953a. A new species of *Monoblepharella*. *Ibid.*, 45: 592–595, 1 fig.

—— 1953b. Cytological observations on the zygote of *Monoblepharella*. *Ibid.*, 45: 723–726, 1 fig.

—— 1953c. Observations on chytridiaceous parasites of phanerogams. IV. *Physoderma aponogetonis* sp. nov. parasitic on *Aponogeton*. Trans. Brit. Mycol. Soc., 36: 347–348, 1 fig.

—— 1955. *Ancylistes pfeifferi* Beck sensu Berdan renamed *A. berdanii* sp. nov. *Ibid.*, 38: 217.

—— 1957a. A further contribution to the Phycomycete flora of Great Britain. Trans. Brit. Mycol. Soc., 40: 523–535, 2 figs.

—— 1957b. Observations on chytridiaceous parasites of phanerogams. VII. A *Physoderma* on *Lycopus americanus*. Amer. J. Bot. 44: 661–665, 26 figs.

—— AND BARR, M. E. 1955. Additions to the Phycomycete flora of the Douglas Lake region. I. New taxa and records. Mycologia, 47: 546–556, 27 figs.

—— AND CUTTER, V. M., JR. 1941. Observations on *Mindeniella spinospora*. Mycologia, 33: 288–293, 1 fig.

—— AND ELLISON, B. 1949. *Olpidiopsis schenkiana* and its hyperparasite *Ectrogella besseyi* n. sp. Mycologia, 41: 28–35, 1 fig.

—— AND PATERSON, R. A. 1955. A note concerning *Rhizidiopsis* and *Podochytrium*. Mycologia, 47: 272–274.

SPRINGER, M. E. 1945a. Two new species of *Monoblepharella*. Mycologia, 37: 205–216, 51 figs.

—— 1945b. A morphologic study of the genus *Monoblepharella*. Amer. J. Bot., 32: 259–269, 46 figs.

STANIER, R. Y. 1942. The cultivation and nutrient requirements of a chytridiaceous fungus, *Rhizophlyctis rosea*. J. Bacteriol., 43: 499–520. Illust.

STOLL, K. 1936. Saprolegniineen aus der Umgebung von Greifswald. Mitteilungen Naturwiss. Verein f. Neuvorpommern u. Rügen i. g. Jg., 63–64: 20–42, 4 figs.

STRASBURGER, E. 1878. Wirkung des Lichtes und der Wärme auf Schwärmsporen. Jenaische Zeitschr. f. Nat., 12: 551–625.

STÜBEN, H. 1939. Über Entwicklungsgeschichte und Ernährungsphysiologie eines neuen niederen Phycomyceten mit Generationswechsel. "Planta," Archiv wiss. Bot., 30 (3): 353–383, 17 figs.

TETER, H. E. 1944. Isogamous sexuality in a new strain of *Allomyces*. Mycologia, 36: 194–210, 3 figs.

THAXTER, R. 1894. Observations on the genus *Naegelia* of Reinsch. Bot. Gaz., 19: 49–55, pl. 5.

—— 1895a. New or peculiar aquatic fungi. 1. *Monoblepharis*. *Ibid.*, 20: 433–440, pl. 29.

—— 1895b. New or peculiar aquatic fungi. 2. *Gonapodya* Fischer and *Myrioblepharis*, nov. gen. *Ibid.*, 20: 477–485, pl. 31.

—— 1896a. New or peculiar aquatic fungi. 3. *Blastocladia*. *Ibid.*, 21: 45–52, pl. 3.

—— 1896b. New or peculiar aquatic fungi. 4. *Rhipidium*, *Sapromyces*, and *Araiospora*, nov. gen. *Ibid.*, 21: 317–330, pls. 21–23.

—— 1903. Mycological notes, 1–2. Rhodora, 5: 97–108, pl. 46.

THIRUMALACHER, M. J. 1947. Some fungal diseases of Bryophytes in Mysore. Trans. Brit. Mycol. Soc., 31: 7–12, 8 figs.

—— AND WHITEHEAD, M. D. 1951. An undescribed species of *Physoderma* on *Aeschynomene indica*. Mycologia, 43: 430–436, 17 figs.

THOMAS [PERROTT], P. E. 1939. Studies of species of *Monoblepharis* occurring in South Wales. Trans. Brit. Mycol. Soc., 23: 124, figs. I–III.

THOMPSON, G. E. 1934. Sporangial germination in the genus *Myzocytium*. Mycologia, 26: 118–121.

THWAITES, G. H. K. 1846–47. On the occurrence of tetraspores in algae. Ann. Nat. Hist., 17: 262–263.

TIEGS, E. 1919. Beiträge zur Oekologie der Wasserpilze. Berichte Deutsch. Bot. Gesell., 37: 496–501.

TIESENHAUSEN, M. VON. 1912. Beiträge zur Kenntnis der Wasserpilze der Schweiz. Arch. f. Hydrobiol. u. Planktonk., 7 (2): 261–308, 24 figs.

TIFFNEY, W. N. 1939a. The host range of *Saprolegnia parasitica*. Mycologia, 31: 310–321, 2 figs.

—— 1939b. The identity of certain species of the Saprolegniaceae parasitic to fish. J. Elisha Mitchell Sci. Soc., 55: 134–151.

—— AND WOLF, F. T. 1937. *Achlya flagellata* as a fish parasite. J. Elisha Mitchell Sci. Soc., 53: 298–300.

TOBLER, GERTRUD. 1913. Die Synchytrien. Arch. Protistenk., 28: 1–98, pls. 1–4.

TOKIDA, J. 1948. Swollen-head disease of *Sphacelaria* and swollen-foot disease of *Spongomorpha*. Bot. Mag. Tokyo, 61, No. 721–726: 113–116, 17 figs.

Токunaga, Y. 1932. A new species of *Pythium* parasitic on *Aegagropila sauteri* (Nees) Kützing. Trans. Sapporo Nat. Hist. Soc., 12 (3): 119–123, 2 figs.

—— 1933a. Studies on the aquatic chytrids of Japan. I. Woroninaceae. *Ibid.*, 13 (1): 20–28, pl. 2.

—— 1933b. Studies on the aquatic chytrids of Japan. II. Olpidiaceae. *Ibid.*, 13: 78–84, pl. 5.

—— 1934a. Notes on the Lagenidiaceae in Japan. *Ibid.*, 13: 227–232, 3 figs.

—— 1934b. Studies on the aquatic chytrids of Japan. III. Rhizidiaceae. *Ibid.*, 13 (4): 388–393, pl. 11.

Tomaschek, A. 1879. Über Binnenzellen in der grossen Zelle (Antheridiumzelle) des Pollens einiger Coniferen. Sitzungsber. Acad. Wiss. Wien (Math.-Nat. Cl.), 78: 197–212, 17 figs. 1878.

Torrey, G. S. 1945. Two orthographic errors in fungous names. Mycologia, 37: 160–162.

Trammsdorf, R. 1917. Über die Wachstumsbedingungen der Abwasserpilze *Leptomitus* und *Sphaerotilus.* Centralbl. f. Bakteriol., Parasitenk. u. Infektionskrankh., Abt. 2, 48: 62–76.

Trégouboff, G. 1913. Sur un Chytriopside nouveau, *Chytridioides schizophylli*, n. g., n. sp., parasite de l'intestin de *Schizophyllum mediterraneum* Latzel. Arch. Zool. Expér. Gén., 52: 25–31, 2 figs.

Trotter, A. 1904. Notulae Mycologicae. Ann. Mycol., 2: 533–538, 4 figs.

—— 1916. Osservazioni e richerche istologiche sopra alcuve morfosi vegetali determinate da funghi. Marcellia, rivista internazionale di cecidologia. Avellino, 15: 58–111, 14 figs.

Truscott, J. H. L. 1933. Observations on *Lagena radicicola.* Mycologia, 25: 263–265, 11 figs.

Tucker, C. M. 1931. The taxonomy of the genus *Phytophthora* de Bary. Missouri Agr. Exper. Sta. Res. Bull., No. 153: 1–208, 30 figs.

Tulloch, J. S. 1934. A new record for *Leptomitus* from Alaska. Torreya, 34: 43–44.

Turian, G. 1952. Caroténoides et différenciation sexuelle chez *Allomyces.* Experimentia, 8: 302.

—— and E. Kellenberger. 1956. Ultrastructure du corps paranucléaire, des mitochondries et de la membrane nucléaire des gamètes d'*Allomyces.* Exp. Cell Research, 11: 417–422.

Turner, W. B. 1892. The fresh-water algae (principally Desmidiae) of the East Indies. Bih. Kgl. Svensk. Vetensk.-Ak. Handl., 25, Afd. 5, No. 10: 1–187, 23 pls.

Uebelmesser, E. R. 1956. Über einige neue Chytridineen aus Erdboden (*Olpidium, Rhizophidium, Phlyctochytrium*, und *Rhizophlyctis*). Arch. f. Mikrobiol., 25: 307–324, 7 figs.

Valkanov, A. 1929a. Protistenstudien. 4. Die Natur und die systematische Stellung der Labyrinthuleen. Arch. Protistenk., 67: 110–121, 10 figs.

—— 1929b. Protistenstudien. 5. *Hyphochytrium hydrodictii*—ein neuer Algenpilz. *Ibid.*, 67: 122–127, 11 figs.

—— 1931a. Protistenstudien. 7. Beitrag zur Kenntnis der Süsswasserphycomyceten Bulgariens. *Ibid.*, 73: 361–366, 8 figs.

—— 1931b. Über Morphologie und Systematik der rotatorienbefallenden Pilze. *Ibid.*, 74: 5–17, 16 figs.

—— 1931c. Über die Morphologie und Systematik der rotatorienbefallenden Oomyceten. Ann. Univ. Sofia, II (Phys.-Math.) (Sci. Nat.), 27: 215–233. 1930–31. (In Bulgarian, with German summary.)

—— 1932. Nachtrag zu meiner Arbeit über rotatorienbefallende Pilze. Arch. Protistenk., 78: 485–496, 10 figs.

VALLIN, S. 1951. Plankton mortality in the Northern Baltic caused by a parasitic water-mould. Ann. Rept. for 1950, Inst. Freshwater Res. Drottringholm. Rept. No. 32, Fishery Board, Sweden, pp. 139–148, 8 figs.

VANTERPOOL, T. C., AND LEDINGHAM, G. A. 1930. Studies on "browning" root rot of cereals. I. The association of *Lagena radicicola*, n. gen., n. sp., with root injury of wheat. Canadian J. Research, 2: 171–194, 7 figs., 2 pls.

VIÉGAS, A. P., AND TEIXEIRA, A. R. 1943. Alguns fungos do Brasil (Phycomycetos). Bragantia, 3: 223–269, 4 figs., 22 pls.

VILLOT, A. 1874. Monographie des Dragonneaux. Arch. Zool. Expér. Gén., 3: 181–238, pls. 6–9.

VISHNIAC, H. S. 1955a. Marine mycology. Trans. New York Acad. Sci., Ser. II, 17: 352–360, 3 figs.

—— 1955b. The morphology and nutrition of a new species of *Sirolpidium*. Mycologia, 47: 633–645, 8 figs.

—— 1956. On the ecology of the lower marine fungi. Biol. Bull., 111: 410–414.

—— 1958. A new marine phycomycete. Mycologia, 50: 66–79, 5 figs.

—— AND R. F. NIGRELLI. 1957. The ability of the Saprolegniaceae to parasitize platyfish. Zoologica, 42: 131–134, pl. 1.

VLADESCU, G. 1892. Archiv. Soc. Scientific si Literare Iasi, Vol. 3. (In Rumanian. Not seen, cited by Constantineanu, 1901.)

VLK, W. 1938. Ueber den bau der Geissel. Arch. Protistenk., 90: 448–488.

—— 1939. Ueber die Geisselstruktur der Saprolegniaceenschwärmer. *Ibid.*, 92: 157–160.

VORONICHIN, N. 1920. K florie Phycomycetes Kavkaza (Contributions à la connaissance de Phycomycètes de la Caucasie). Moniteur Jard. Bot. Tiflis, 50: 8–14. (In Russian, with French résumé.)

VUILLEMIN, P. 1896. Le *Cladochytrium pulposum* parasite de la Betteraves. Bull. Soc. Bot. France, 43: 497–505.

—— 1897. Sur les éléments musculiformes des Chytridinées. Bibliogr. anat., 5: 131.

—— 1907. Les Bases actuelles de la systématique en mycologie. *In* Lotsy, Progressus Rei Botanicae, 2 (1): 1–171. Jena.

VUILLEMIN, P. 1909. Valeur morphologique et biologique des tubercules radicaux des légumineuses. Bull. Soc. Sci. Nancy, 10: 30–45.

WAGER, H. 1899a. The formation of the zygospore in *Polyphagus euglenae*. Rep. Brit. A. A. Sci. Bristol, 1898: 1064–1065.

—— 1899b. The sexuality of the fungi. Ann. Bot. London, 13: 575–597.

—— 1913. Life-history and cytology of *Polyphagus euglenae*. *Ibid.*, 27: 173–202, pls. 16–19.

WALKER, A. J. 1938. Fungal infections of mosquitoes, especially of *Anopheles costalis*. Ann. Trop. Med. and Parasitol., 32: 231–244, pls. 4–5.

WALLROTH, F. G. 1833. Flora crytogamica Germaniae, 2: 1–923. Nüremburg.

WALZ, J. 1870. Beiträge zur Kenntniss der Saprolegnieen. Bot. Zeitung, 28: 537–546, 553–557, pl. 9.

WARD, H. M. 1883. Observations on the genus *Pythium* (Pring.).   Quart.J. Micro. Sci. (N. S.), 23: 485–515, pls. 34–36.

WARD, M. W. 1939. Observations on *Rhizophlyctis rosea*. J. Elisha Mitchell Sci. Soc., 55: 353–360, pls. 32–33.

WATERHOUSE, G. M. 1940. A chytrid allied to *Pleolpidium inflatum* Butler.   Trans. Brit. Mycol. Soc., 24: 7–19, 8 figs.

—— 1942. Some water moulds of the Hogsmill River collected from 1937 to 1939. *Ibid.*, 25: 315–325, 1 fig.

—— 1945. The true nature of *Myrioblepharis* Thaxter. *Ibid.*, 28: 94–100, 4 figs. pl. 5.

—— 1956. The genus *Phytophthora*. Diagnoses (or descriptions) and figures from the original papers.   Misc. Publ. Commonw. Mycol. Inst., 12. 120 pp., 66 pl., 10 figs.

—— 1958. The invalidity of Pythiomorpha.—II. Trans. Brit. Mycol. Soc., 41: 196–202.

WEBB, P. C. R. 1935. The cytology and life history of *Sorosphaera veronicae*. Ann. Bot. London, 49: 41–52, 4 figs.

WEBSTER, R. C. 1943. Influence of nutrition in sporangial formation in *Araiospora streptandra*. Trans. Kentucky Acad. Sci., 11 (2): 31.

WELCH, P. S. 1952. Limnology. xi + 538 pp. Illust. 2d edition. McGraw-Hill, New York.

WERNHAM, C. C. 1935. A species of *Sorodiscus* on *Heteranthera*. Mycologia, 27: 262–273, 2 figs., pls. 17–18.

WEST, W. AND G. S. 1906. A comparative study of the plankton of some Irish lakes. Trans. R. Irish Acad. Dublin, 33 (Sect. B): 77–116, pls. 6–11.

WESTON, W. H., JR. 1919. Repeated zoospore emergence in *Dictyuchus*. Bot. Gaz., 68: 287–296, 1 fig., pl. 23.

—— 1938. Heterothallism in *Sapromyces reinschii*. Preliminary note. Mycologia, 30: 245–253, fig. 1.

—— 1941. The role of aquatic fungi in hydrobiology. *In* A symposium on hydrobiology. ix + 405 pp. Univ. Wisconsin Press, Madison.

WETTSTEIN, F. VON. 1921. Das Vorkommen von Chitin und seine Verwertung als systematisch-phylogenetisches Merkmal in Pflanzenreich. Sitzungsber. Acad. Wiss. Wien. (Math-Nat. Cl.), 130 (1): 1–20.

WHIFFEN, A. J. 1939. Cytology of a new species of Plasmodiophorales. J. Elisha Mitchell Sci. Soc., 55: 243. (Abstract.)

—— 1941a. A new species of *Nephrochytrium*: *Nephrochytrium aurantium*. Amer. J. Bot., 28: 41–44, 26 figs.

—— 1941b. Cellulose decomposition by the saprophytic chytrids. J. Elisha Mitchell Sci. Soc., 57: 321–330, 1 fig., pl. 8.

—— 1942a. Two new chytrid genera. Mycologia, 34: 543–557, 52 figs.

—— 1942b. A discussion of some species of *Olpidiopsis* and *Pseudolpidium*. Amer. J. Bot., 29: 607–611, 27 figs.

—— 1943. New species of *Nowakowskiella* and *Blastocladia*. J. Elisha Mitchell Sci. Soc., 59: 37–43, pls. 2–4.

—— 1944. A discussion of taxonomic criteria in the Chytridiales. Farlowia, 1: 583–597, 2 figs.

—— 1945. Nutritional studies of representatives of five genera of the Saprolegniaceae. J. Elisha Mitchell Sci. Soc., 61: 114–123.

—— 1946. Two new terricolous Phycomycetes belonging to the genera *Lagenidium* and *Blastocladiella*. *Ibid.*, 62: 54–58, pl. 7.

—— 1951. The effect of cycloheximide on the sporophyte of *Allomyces arbuscula*. Mycologia, 43: 635–644, 1 fig.

WILDEMAN, É. DE. 1889–90. Note sur quelques Saprolegniées parasites des algues. Bull. Soc. Belge Micro., 16: 134–139.

—— 1890. Chytridiacées de Belgique. Ann. Soc. Belge Micro. (Mém.), 14: 5–28, 7 figs.

—— 1891. Notes sur quelques organismes inférieurs. C. R. Soc. Roy. Bot. Belg. (Bull.), 30 (2): 169–177, figs. 1–2.

—— 1892. Une Espèce nouvelle du genre *Lagenidium* Schenk. *Ibid.*, 31: 178–181.

—— 1893a. Notes mycologiques I. Ann. Soc. Belge Micro. (Mém.), 17: 5–30, pls. 1–3.

—— 1893b. Notes mycologiques II. *Ibid.*, 17: 35–63, pls. 4–7.

—— 1894. Notes mycologiques III. *Ibid.*, 18: 135–161, pls. 4–6.

—— 1895a. Notes mycologiques IV. *Ibid.*, 19: 59–80, pl. 2.

—— 1895b. Notes mycologiques V. *Ibid.*, 19: 85–114, 3 figs., pls. 3–4.

—— 1895c. Notes mycologiques VI. *Ibid.*, 19: 191–232, pls. 6–9.

—— 1895d. Quelques Chytridiacées nouvelles parasites d'algues. La Notarisia, 10 (3): 33–35.

—— 1896a. Census Chytridinaearum. Bull. Soc. Roy. Bot. Belg. (Mém.)., 35: 7–69.

WILDEMAN, É. DE. 1896b. Notes mycologiques VII. Ann. Soc. Belge Micro. (Mém.), 20: 21–64, 1 fig., pls. 1–3.

—— 1896c. Notes mycologiques VIII. *Ibid.*, 20: 107–136, pls. 6–12.

—— 1897a. Notes mycologiques IX. *Ibid.*, 21: 3–31, 2 pls.

—— 1897b. Notes mycologiques X. *Ibid.*, 22: 113–124, pl. 2, figs. 1–7.

—— 1897c. Index alphabétique des espèces citées dans les fascicules I–X des "Notes mycologiques." *Ibid.*, 22: 125–128.

—— 1900a. Une Nouvelle Chytridinée. Mém. Herb. Boissier, 1900 (3): 1–2.

—— 1900b. Observations sur quelques Chytridinées nouvelles ou peu connues. *Ibid.*, 1900 (15): 1–10, 3 figs.

—— 1931. Sur quelques Chytridinées parasites d'algues. Bull. Acad. Roy. Belg. (Sci.), V, 17: 281–298, 3 figs., 2 pls.

WILLE, N. 1884. Bidrag til Sydamerikas Algflora. I–III. Bih. Kgl. Svensk. Vetensk.-Ak. Handl., 8, Afd. 1, No. 18: 1–64, pls. 1–3.

—— 1899. Om nogle Vandsoppe. Vidensk. Selsk. Skr. Christiana (Mat.-Nat. Kl.), 1899, No. 3: 1–14, 27 figs.

WILLOUGHBY, L. G. 1956. Studies on soil chytrids. I. *Rhizidium richmondense* sp. nov. and its parasites. Trans. Brit. Mycol. Soc., 39: 125–141, 9 figs.

—— 1957. Studies on soil chytrids. II. On *Karlingia dubia* Karling. Trans. Brit. Mycol. Soc., 40: 9–16, 5 figs.

WILSON, C. M. 1952. Meiosis in *Allomyces.* Bull. Torrey Bot. Club. 79: 139–160, 23 figs.

WINGE, Ö. 1913. Cytological studies in the Plasmodiophoraceae. Arch. f. Botanik, 12 (9): 1–39, pls. 1–3.

WOLF, F. T. 1939. A study of some aquatic Phycomycetes isolated from Mexican soils. Mycologia, 31: 376–387, 4 figs.

—— 1940. The genus *Allomyces* in Cuba. Lloydia, 3: 301–303.

—— 1941a. A contribution to the life history and geographic distribution of the genus *Allomyces.* Mycologia, 33: 158–173, 2 figs.

—— 1941b. An addition to the fungus flora of Barro Colorado Island. Trans. Brit. Mycol. Soc., 25: 191–193.

—— 1944. The aquatic Oomycetes of Wisconsin. Part 1. 64 pp., 52 figs. Univ. Wisconsin Press, Madison.

—— AND WOLF, F. A. 1941. Aquatic Phycomycetes from the Everglades of Florida. Lloydia, 4: 270–273.

WOLK, P.C. VAN DER. 1913. *Protascus colorans*, a new genus and a new species of the Protoascineae-group; the source of "yellow-grains" in rice. Mycol. Centralbl. 3: 153–157, pl. 1.

WOLLE, F. 1887. Fresh-water algae of the United States. xix + 364 pp. 210 pls. Bethlehem, Pennsylvania.

WORONIN, M. 1878. *Plasmodiophora brassicae*, Urheber der Kohlpflanzen-Hernie. Jahrb. wiss. Bot., 11: 548–574, pls. 29–34.

—— 1904. Beitrag zur Kenntnis der Monoblepharideen. Mém. Acad. Impér. Sci. St. Péters., Phys.-Math. Cl., VIII, 16: 1–24, pls. 1–3.

WRIGHT, E. P. 1879a. On a new species of parasitic green alga belonging to the genus *Chlorochytrium* of Cohn. Trans. R. Irish Acad. Dublin (Sci.), 26: 355–368, pls. 4–5. 1877.

—— 1879b. On a species of *Rhizophydium* parasitic on species of *Ectocarpus*, with notes on the fructification of the *Ectocarpi*. *Ibid.*, 26: 369–380, pl. 6. 1877.

—— 1879c. On the cell structure of *Griffithsia setacea* (Ellis) and the development of the antheridia and tetraspores. *Ibid.*, 26: 28–44, pls. 4, 5.

YAW, K. E., AND CUTTER, V. M., JR. 1951. Crosses involving biochemically deficient mutants of *Allomyces arbuscula*. Mycologia, 43: 156–160.

YOUNG, E. L., III. 1943. Studies on *Labyrinthula*. The etiologic agent of the wasting disease of eel-grass. Amer. J. Bot., 30: 586–593, 2 figs.

YUASA, A. 1935. Studies in the cytology of reproductive cells. III. The genesis of the flagellum in the planocyte of *Fuligo septica*. Bot. Mag. Tokyo, 49: 538–545, 27 figs.

ZEBROWSKI, G. 1936. New genera of Cladochytriaceae. Ann. Missouri Bot. Gard., 23: 553–564, pl. 27.

ZELLER, S. M. 1918. Fungi found on *Codium mucronatum*. Publ. Puget Sound Biol. Station, 2: 121–125, pl. 20, figs. 1–7.

ZIEGLER, A. W. 1948a. A comparative study of zygote germination in the Saprolegniaceae. Science, 107: 506–507.

—— 1948b. A comparative study of zygote germination in the Saprolegniaceae. J. Elisha Mitchell Sci. Soc., 64: 13–40, pls. 1–6.

—— 1953. Meiosis in the Saprolegniaceae. Amer. J. Bot., 40: 60–66, 52 figs.

—— AND GILPIN, R. H. 1954. A description of a new species of *Achlya* with some observations on its physiology. Mycologia, 46: 647–651, 10 figs.

—— AND LINTHICUM, B. 1957. A note on the occurrence of certain aquatic fungi in Florida. Mycologia, 49: 160–161.

ZIMMERMAN, A. 1902. Ueber einiger an tropischen Kulturpflanzen beobachtete Pilze. II. Centralbl. f. Bakteriol., Parasitenk. u. Infektionskrankh., Abt. 2, 8: 149–151.

ZOPF, W. 1878. Ueber einem neuen parasitischen Phycomyceten.... Sitzungsber. Bot. Vereins Prov. Brandenburg, 20: 77–79.

—— 1882. Ueber Parasiten in den Antheridien, Oogonien und Oosporen von Saprolegnieen. Bot. Centralbl., 12 (10): 356–357.

—— 1883. Erwiderung. *Ibid.*, 15: 156–158.

—— 1884. Zur Kenntniss der Phycomyceten. I. Zur Morphologie und Biologie der Ancylisteen und Chytridiaceen. Nova Acta Acad. Leop.-Carol., 47: 143–236, pls. 12–21.,

Zopf, W. 1885. Die Pilzetiere oder Schleimpilze. Encyklopaedie der Naturwissenschaften. 174 pp., 51 figs. Breslau.

—— 1887. Ueber einige niedere Algenpilze (Phycomyceten) und eine neue Methode ihre Keime aus den Wasser zu isolieren. Abhandl. Naturforsch. Gesell. Halle, 17: 77–107, 2 pls.

—— 1888. Zur Kenntniss der Infections-Krankheiten niederer Thiere und Pflanzen. Nova Acta Acad. Leop.-Carol., 52: 313–376, pls. 17–23.

—— 1890. *See* A. Schenk, Handbuch. d. Bot., Encyclopaedie der Naturwissenschaften, 4: 271–781. Breslau.

—— 1892. Zur Kenntniss der Färbungsursachen niederer Organismen. III. Phycomyceten-Färbungen. Beitr. Physiol. Morph. niederer Organismen, 2: 1–35, pls. 1–2.

—— 1894. Ueber niedere thierische und pflanzliche Organismen, welche als Krankheitserreger in Algen, Pilzen, niederen Thieren und höheren Pflanzen auftreten. *Ibid.*, 4: 43–68, pls. 2–3.

Zukal, H. 1893. Mykologische Mittheilungen. Österr. botan. Zeitschr., 43: 310–314, pl. 11.

INDEX

Words in italics designate synonyms; boldface page numbers refer to technical descriptions

1165